DNA Microarrays

A *Molecular Cloning* Manual

DNA Microarrays

A *Molecular Cloning* Manual

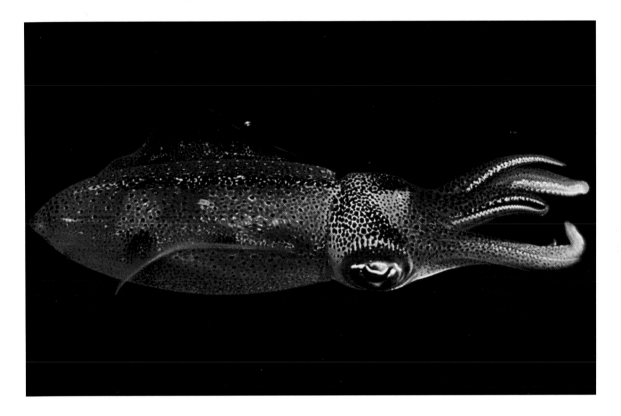

Edited by

David Bowtell and
Joseph Sambrook

Peter MacCallum Cancer Institute
and The University of Melbourne, Australia

COLD SPRING HARBOR LABORATORY PRESS
Cold Spring Harbor, New York

DNA Microarrays
A *Molecular Cloning* Manual

Associate Editor	Kaaren Janssen
Managing Editor	Jan Argentine
Developmental Editor	Kaaren Janssen
Production Manager	Denise Weiss
Project Coordinator	Inez Sialiano
Production Editor	Dotty Brown
Desktop Editor	Susan Schaefer
Cover Designer	Ed Atkeson

Front cover artwork (paperback edition): Photograph of a Caribbean Reef Squid (*Sepioteuthis sepioidea*) at night taken near the wreck of the Balboa in Grand Cayman. The glowing spotted pattern symbolizes the display of microarray data. (Photograph by Mikki Barry, CyberDive www.cyberdive.org [© 2002 all rights reserved].)

Library of Congress Cataloging-in-Publication Data

Bowtell, David.
    DNA microarrays : a molecular cloning manual / David Bowtell, Joseph Sambrook.
        p. cm.
    Includes bibliographical references and index.
    ISBN 0-87969-624-9 (cloth : alk. paper) -- ISBN 0-87969-625-7 (pbk. : alk. paper)
    1. DNA microarrays--Laboratory manuals. I. Sambrook, Joseph. II. Title

QP624.5.D726 B69 2002
572.8'6--dc21

                                                                            2002071255

10 9 8 7 6 5 4 3 2 1

Contents

Section
1

Generation of Probes for Spotted Microarrays, 1
S. Chandrasekharappa, A. Holloway, V. Iyer, D. Monte, M. Murphy, N.J. Nowak

v

Section 4

Membrane-based Spotted cDNA Arrays, 289
K.G. Becker, W.H. Wood III, C. Cheadle

INTRODUCTION, 289

PART 1: PREPARATION AND HYBRIDIZATION OF MEMBRANE ARRAY, 292
PROTOCOLS
1. Printing Membrane Arrays, 293
2. RNA Preparation and Labeling, 297
3. Hybridization of Target to Membrane Arrays, 300
   - Additional Protocol: Target Stripping and Reuse of Membranes, 303

PART 2: DATA ANALYSIS AND INTERPRETATION, 305

Section 7

An Introduction to Microarray Bioinformatics, 509
C.A. Ball, Y. Chen, S. Panavally, G. Sherlock, T. Speed, P.T. Spellman, Y.H. Yang

Section 8

Tissue Microarrays, 603
K. Brand, G. Hostetter, O.-P. Kallioniemi, J. Kononen, G. Sauter, M. Trivett

Appendices

The *DNA Microarrays* Companion Web Site

A COMPANION WEB SITE (www.dna-microarrays.org) to *DNA Microarrays: A Molecular Cloning Manual* provides supplemental information about this fast-moving field of research. The site will include:

- An expansion of the material found in the print edition of Appendix 1: Generation of Full-length Libraries by Piero Carninci.
- References linked to Medline.
- Links to other databases of value to working scientists.
- Selected figures from the book for use in troubleshooting.

Additional information will be added after the book is published. To access the Web Site:

1. Open the home page of the site.
2. Follow the simple registration procedure that begins on that page. No unique access code is required, since the site is open to anyone who completes the registration process.
3. Your e-mail address and password (selected during the registration process) become your log-in information for subsequent visits to the site.

The FAQ section of the site contains answers about the registration procedure. For additional assistance with registration, and for all other inquiries about the dna-microarrays.org Web Site, please e-mail support@dna-microarrays.org or call 1-800-843-4388 (in the continental U.S. and Canada) or 516-422-4100 (all other locations) between 8:00 a.m. and 5:00 p.m. Eastern U.S. time.

Participants in the DNA Microarrays meeting at the Banbury Center of Cold Spring Harbor Laboratory in April 2001. Many of the protocols published in this manual were presented and discussed at this meeting.

Front row (*from left to right*): C. Best, A. Massimi, Y. Chen, G. Hostetter, C. Ball, K. Schütze, D. Bowtell, J. Wei, E. Wang, P. Carninci, J. Lee, E. Tom, A. Holloway, D. Monte, V. Mittal

Back row (*from left to right*): T. Speed, T. Harris, D. Pinkel, D. Albertson, S. Grimmond, J. Pollack, P. Spellman, M. Dietz, C. Heller, G. Sherlock, S. Chandrasekharappa, J. Sambrook, J. DeRisi, V. Iyer, M. Bittner

Preface

THIS MANUAL WAS CONCEIVED WHEN THE MICROARRAY FIELD was approaching consensus about the types of experimental and analytical approaches needed to produce reliable results—a situation reminiscent of the early days of recombinant DNA. Like the first cloners, the early users of spotted microarray technology found that robust protocols were scarce and few reagents were commercially available. In this pioneering setting, the development of the technology was driven, for the most part, by postdoctoral fellows and students working in a small number of academic laboratories, using custom-built equipment and "homemade" reagents. We have been extremely fortunate to have many of the leaders of this young field contribute to this book.

Our goal was to produce a laboratory guide that would allow anyone who is persistent and careful and has a moderate budget to manufacture, use, and analyze microarrays. Assembling the material for this manual began in earnest in April 2001, when Jan Witkowski generously agreed to host a microarray meeting at the Banbury Center of Cold Spring Harbor Laboratory. Participants in the meeting offered and analyzed many of the protocols that now form the core of this manual. Their initial drafts were refined and edited over the following year, often undergoing substantial changes in response to developments in the field. Additional key protocols were added, along with information from a growing number of commercial providers of microarray equipment and reagents.

Modern DNA microarrays used for parallel analysis of gene expression are direct descendants of gridded arrays of bacterial cDNA clones grown on membrane filters. Because gridded filter arrays remain a useful, affordable method of expression analysis, we have included several protocols describing their synthesis and use. The bulk of the manual, however, deals with the two currently dominant technologies: spotted DNA microarrays on glass slides, which were pioneered in Patrick Brown's laboratory at Stanford University, and in situ synthesized oligonucleotide arrays produced by Affymetrix Inc. Spotted microarrays can be produced in academic laboratories, albeit with a fair amount of effort and skill. By contrast, the use of Affymetrix arrays is more "turnkey," sidestepping the production of the arrays themselves and making use of kits to label and hybridize the targets. Because neither technique is free of difficulties, we have included a detailed troubleshooting section that discusses problems frequently encountered with both spotted and Affymetrix arrays. The manual is deliberately weighted toward the use of cDNA microarrays for expression analysis, as this has so far been the dominant application of the technology. There is an increasing desire to apply this type of analysis to very small numbers of purified cells, and we have therefore included protocols describing microdissection and in vitro amplification of small amounts of RNA. As any technology develops, clever minds conceive additional applications of the technology, and this has certainly been a feature of the microarray field. There is growing use of microarrays to detect and analyze genomic variation—both natural and pathogenic—and a major section of the manual deals with applications of this type. Microarrays generate vast amounts of data that must be validated using other methods. We have therefore included protocols describing the use of in situ hybridization and immunohistochemistry for rapid downstream analysis of array data.

A major frontier remains the development of powerful user-friendly bioinformatics tools to manage microarray experiments and to mine and extract data. These tools are in a state of rapid advance. Applications focused on unsupervised methods of clustering data—for example, Mike Eisen's Cluster program and similar programs—remain enormously useful for exploring microarray data where little other information is available to guide analysis. However, methods based on supervised machine learning are increasingly powerful and provide a fertile area for future development. Given the rapid rate of change in the microarray bioinformatics field, no description of this area can remain useful or current for long. In this manual, established techniques, including hierarchical clustering, are described in detail. For the most part, however, the authors of this section have focused on fundamental concepts that should be enduring, such as the capturing of numerical data, experimental design, and database requirements.

Because of the enormous rate of change in the microarray field, it was important to rapidly convert draft protocols into a published text. We express our gratitude to the contributors, who dealt with pressing timelines with extraordinary grace and professionalism. Many of the scientists who provided individual protocols appear in the accompanying photograph, taken at the Banbury meeting. These and many other people provided invaluable continuing technical advice at various stages during the preparation of the book. We thank, in particular, Vivek Mittal, Marcelo Bento Soares, Christoph Heller, Roland Toder, Josh Dabna, and Karin Schütze, and Ed Southern, who in one sense is the father of the field, for providing an elegant Foreword to the manual.

We have been supported in many ways during the production of this text. We thank Beth Nickerson, who became involved toward the later stages of production of the manual and provided many invaluable insights and suggestions. The editorial and production staff at Cold Spring Harbor Laboratory Press were impressively efficient and involved and, despite being half a world away, made each step in the process remarkably painless. In particular, we thank David Crotty, Dorothy Brown, Susan Schaefer, Nora Rice, Mary Cozza, Siân Curtis, Denise Weiss, and Kimberly LaVine. Their efforts were coordinated and enhanced by Inez Sialiano and Jan Argentine, who provided wisdom, calm, and direction when there seemed an endless amount to be accomplished. We are indebted to our colleagues at the Peter MacCallum Cancer Institute, who were patient when meetings were canceled and had the decency to appear convinced when told, for the umpteenth time, that "the book is almost done." Linda Stevens provided wonderful help, rescheduling meetings and generally managing our lives.

We owe a special debt to our Associate Editor Kaaren Janssen, without whom this manual would not have been possible. She has been an active participant from the initial organization of the Banbury meeting to the final editing of last protocol, managing to remain cheerful, enthusiastic, tireless, and uncomplaining through the entire process. We have been extremely fortunate to work with her and to enjoy her friendship. Finally, we express heartfelt thanks to our families who have provided support, encouragement, and understanding during many lost evenings and absent weekends.

D.B.
J.S.

Foreword

THE BRANCH OF BIOLOGY NOW CALLED GENOMICS WAS BORN in the late 1970s when Sanger introduced the notion that the sequence of the entire genome of a genetically defined entity formed a good start to understanding its biology. With his colleagues at the Laboratory of Molecular Biology in Cambridge, he used his methods [1] to sequence the genomes of bacteriophage φX174 [2], the human mitochondrion [3], and bacteriophage λ [4]. Among other discoveries, the φX174 sequence revealed overlapping genes, and the mitochondrial sequence showed that it used alternative codons. This pioneering work inspired much larger projects, culminating in recent years in the sequencing of most of the human genome [5, 6]. The huge quantity of high-quality sequence information in the public databases, a measure of Sanger's legacy, presents us with the challenge of progressing from sequence to function for genomes and organisms of high complexity. Computer-based methods of analysis—also pioneered in Sanger's group [7]—go a long way to extracting biologically relevant information from the sequences, by finding candidate genes, for example. But the computer cannot measure levels of gene expression or analyze sequence variation in DNA samples. For these and other problems, we need experimental methods, as well as methods that can be applied on a scale commensurate with the large size of complex genomes.

There are two ways to carry out experiments on a large scale. Automation of serial processes was the route taken to adapt the Sanger DNA sequencing method to the large scale needed to analyze complex genomes. The other route, parallel processing, exemplified by microarrays, has a number of advantages over serial methods, but it requires a simple process that can be developed into a device that carries multiple discrete test sites. The remarkable ability of nucleic acids to form a duplex from two strands with complementary base sequences is just such a process. The microarray, comprising large sets of probes of known sequences, enables many hybridization reactions to be carried out in parallel in a small device.

There are a number of variants on the basic design, but almost all use impermeable supports as the substrate on which spots of probes are fixed. Impermeable supports have a number of advantages over the membranes used in earlier methods of analysis based on molecular hybridization. Importantly, it is possible to pack many small features on an impermeable surface. Typically, the features of microarrays are approximately 20–200 μm in size, so that several thousand features can fit into the area of the standard microscope slide. In addition, because the solutions of the analyte do not penetrate the surface, the processes of hybridization and washing are much faster than with permeable supports. The most commonly used support is glass [8], which has desirable physical properties. Unlike conventional blotting membranes, glass does not deform when wetted and dried. Dimensional stability is very important for accurate localization of the spots of probe during both manufacture and reading of the arrays.

The printing methods adapted to array fabrication are capable of resolutions of a few microns and can be used either to deliver presynthesized probes, cDNA clones, PCR products, or synthetic oligonucleotides or to deliver reagents to synthesize probes in situ. Spotting presynthesized probes is the only method of fabrication available to most investigators who make their own arrays. In situ methods are used by a few commercial manufacturers, but, for the present, they are expensive and beyond the reach of many users, especially those working in academic laboratories.

Some applications, such as the analysis of gene expression from *Saccharomyces cerevisiae*, require a standard set of probes—a set that will address every gene product, for example. Once an optimized set has been established, there are benefits to adopting it as a standard. Spotting presynthesized probes [9] and the photolithographic method [10] lend themselves well to the production of many arrays of the same design; however, they are not suitable for the fabrication of different arrays from one round to the next as may be needed in some research programs. On the other hand, ink jet in situ synthesis [11] and light-directed fabrication using micromirror arrays [12] are suitable both for production runs of a single design and for the production of arrays of different designs, which can be achieved simply by altering the instruction set sent from the computer to the ink jet printer or the micromirror array.

For all methods of fabrication, quality control is a major problem. There are few methods for checking the sequence and amount of the probe deposited or synthesized in each spot [13, 14]. Propagation of probes by rounds of amplification can lead to overgrowth by contaminating sequences. For this reason, it is likely that probes made by chemical synthesis will replace clones and PCR products. The growing recognition of the importance of alternative splicing as a mechanism for regulating gene function also suggests a need to use oligonucleotides to measure gene expression exon by exon. The quality of probes produced by in situ synthesis depends mainly on the efficiency of the coupling chemistry. Stepwise yields of the photosynthetic method are relatively low [15] and limit the length of oligonucleotide that can be made to 25 mers. However, ink jet fabrication can produce oligonucleotides as long as 60 mers [11], long enough for most applications. The quality of the spots is another factor affecting performance of arrays. For example, quills or capillaries may produce spots of very different shape and size, making the work of finding and integrating the hybridization signal more difficult.

High sensitivity and specificity are desired for all applications of the method. But these present conflicting needs. Short probes, of ~20 mers, give relatively low hybridization signals. Longer probes give greater sensitivity but may have reduced specificity because they may interact with targets that have a low degree of sequence similarity. One thorough study [11] showed the large effect of hybridization conditions on specificity and sensitivity and emphasized the conflict between these two demands—optimum specificity requires conditions of higher stringency than conditions that give optimum hybridization yield. For some applications, it is absolutely necessary to use short probes. For example, to detect a single-base mismatch by hybridization, it is not possible to use probes longer than ~20 bases; longer probes will show too little difference in yield between the perfectly matched duplex and the mismatched duplex.

The massive scale of microarray experiments demands the help of computers. They are needed at the outset to design the array and guide the fabrication process; they are used during capture of the image of the hybridized target; they are needed to convert the image to usable measures of the extent of hybridization; and they are needed to interpret the extent of hybridization into a meaningful measure of the amount of the complementary sequence in the target. Packages are available to handle all aspects of the process. The most demanding computational tasks are in the interpretation of results, and much effort has gone into methods for statistical evaluation of the quality of the results and for finding patterns in the data—the use of clustering algorithms to find common patterns of gene regulation, for example. Some commercial packages are too expensive for academic users, but public domain programs such as those available at the EBI http://www.ebi.ac.uk/microarray should address this need.

The successes of the technology have fueled demand for improvements, such as ever more sensitive detection of mRNAs. In turn, this demand exposes a need for greater understanding of the mechanisms of the underlying processes. In response, we begin to see more published work on the structure of the attached probes and on the mechanism of hybridization, which are fundamental to the performance of the devices. For example, in situ synthesis can produce densities of oligonucleotides so high that the molecules on the surface interact with each other; steric hindrance inhibits close approach of target to probe. The steric effect can be relieved by attaching probes through a long linker [13, 16] or by diluting their density [13], increasing hybridization yields by 6- to 150-fold. High probe density also affects the kinetics of hybridization. Typically, probes are at a density of ~1–10 pmoles per mm^2. Thus, there are 0.01–0.1 pmole (~10^{10}–10^{11} molecules) of probe in a typical spot of 100 μm diameter. The amount of probe in a spot will often be vastly in excess of the amount of its target in solution; in a typical analysis of transcription levels, a total of ~1 μg of RNA (~1 pmole) may be hybridized to an array of 10,000 spots, carrying a total of ~1 nmole probes. The effect is that the solution of target immediately above a spot is rapidly exhausted of target molecules complementary to the probes in the spot, the reaction is diffusion-limited, and stirring has a large effect on overall rate [17]. A practical consequence is that it may be better to apply the target to the array diluted into a large volume that can be stirred effectively than to apply it concentrated in a thin film that cannot be stirred.

The technology has already produced many significant results in quite different areas of application. Analysis of transcripts has been used to discover exons and genes for the annotation of the draft sequence of the human genome [18]. Analysis of genomic DNA detects amplifications and deletions found in tumors [19, 20]. Differential gene expression analysis has uncovered networks of genes within common pathways of regulation [21, 22]; it has revealed differences between cancers that cannot be distinguished by conventional means [23, 24]. None of these important results could have been achieved as simply or speedily by any other means of analysis.

The array platform is a relatively complex technology and is drawing together a vigorous community of interest from several disciplines: engineers, materials scientists, mathematicians, and chemists, in addition to molecular biologists, geneticists, and computer scientists. There will be an outpouring of new methods and applications. Those who already use the technology need to keep abreast of developments; those new to the field need help to get started. The present volume provides up-to-date accounts that will guide the efforts of users and those seeking to advance the method and to develop new applications.

Ed Southern

REFERENCES

1. Sanger F. and Coulson A.R. 1975. A rapid method for determining sequences in DNA by primed synthesis with DNA polymerase. *J. Mol. Biol.* **94:** 441–448.

2. Sanger F., Coulson A.R., Friedmann T., Air G.M., Barrell B.G., Brown N.L., Fiddes J.C., Hutchison C.A., III, Slocombe P.M., and Smith M. 1978. The nucleotide sequence of bacteriophage phiX174. *J. Mol. Biol.* **125:** 225–246.

3. Anderson S., Bankier A.T., Barrell B.G., de Bruijn M.H., Coulson A.R., Drouin J., Eperon I.C., Nierlich D.P., Roe B.A., Sanger F., Schreier P.H., Smith A.J., Staden R., and Young I.G. 1981. Sequence and organization of the human mitochondrial genome. *Nature* **290:** 457–465.

4. Sanger F., Coulson A.R., Hong G.F., Hill D.F., and Petersen G.B. 1982. Nucleotide sequence of bacteriophage lambda DNA. *J. Mol. Biol.* **162:** 729–773.

5. Lander E.S., Linton L.M., Birren B., Nusbaum C., Zody M.C., Baldwin J., Devon K., Dewar K., Doyle M., FitzHugh W., et al. 2001. Initial sequencing and analysis of the human genome. *Nature* **409:** 860–921.

6. Venter J.C., Adams M.D., Myers E.W., Li P.W., Mural R.J., Sutton G.G., Smith H.O., Yandell M., Evans C.A., Holt R.A., et al. 2001. The sequence of the human genome. *Science* **291:** 1304–1351.

7. Staden R. 1977. Sequence data handling by computer. *Nucleic Acids Res.* **4:** 4037–4051.

8. Maskos U. and Southern E.M. 1992. Oligonucleotide hybridizations on glass supports: A novel linker for oligonucleotide synthesis and hybridization properties of oligonucleotides synthesised in situ. *Nucleic Acids Res.* **20:** 1679–1684.

9. Schena M., Shalon D., Davis R.W., and Brown P.O. 1995. Quantitative monitoring of gene expression patterns with a complementary DNA microarray. *Science* **270:** 467–470.

10. Lipshutz R.J., Fodor S.P., Gingeras T.R., and Lockhart D.J. 199. High density synthetic oligonucleotide arrays. *Nat. Genet.* (suppl.) **21:** 20–24.

11. Hughes T.R., Mao M., Jones A.R., Burchard J., Marton M.J., Shannon K.W., Lefkowtiz S.M., Ziman M., Schelter J.M., Meyer M.R., Kobayashi S., Davis C., Dai H., He Y.D., Stephaniants S.B., Cavet G., Walker W.L., West A., Coffey E., Shoemaker D.D., Stoughton R., Blanchard A.P., Friend S.H., and Linsley P.S. 2001. Expression profiling using microarrays fabricated by an ink-jet oligonucleotide synthesizer. *Nat. Biotechnol.* **19:** 342–347.

12. Singh-Gasson S., Green R.D., Yue Y., Nelson C., Blattner F., Sussman M.R., and Cerrina F. 1999. Maskless fabrication of light-directed oligonucleotide microarrays using a digital micromirror array. *Nat. Biotechnol.* **17:** 974–978.

13. Peterson A.W., Heaton R.J., and Georgiadis R.M. 2001. The effect of surface probe density on DNA hybridization. *Nucleic Acids Res.* **29:** 5163–5168.

14. Gray D.E., Case-Green S.C., Fell T.S., Dobson P.J., and Southern E.M. 1997. Ellipsometric and interferometric characterization of DNA probes immobilized on a combinatorial array. *Langmuir* **13:** 2833–2842.

15. McGall G.H., Barone A.D., Diggelmann M., Fodor S.P.A., Gentalen E., and Ngo N. 1997. The efficiency of light directed synthesis of DNA arrays on glass substrates. *J. Am. Chem. Soc.* **119:** 5081–5090.

16. Shchepinov M.S., Case-Green S.C., and Southern E.M. 1997. Steric factors influencing hybridisation of nucleic acids to oligonucleotide arrays. *Nucleic Acids Res.* **25:** 1155–1161.

17. Ramakrishnan R., Dorris D., Lublinsky A., Nguyen A., Domanus M., Prokhorova A., Gieser L., Touma E., Lockner R., Tata M., Zhu X., Patterson M., Shippy R., Sendera T.J., and Mazumder A. 2002. An assessment of Motorola CodeLink microarray performance for gene expression profiling applications. *Nucleic Acids Res.* **30:** e30.

18. Shoemaker D.D., Schadt E.E., Armour C.D., He Y.D., Garrett-Engele P., McDonagh P.D., Loerch P.M., Leonardson A., Lum P.Y., Cavet G., Wu L.F., Altschuler S.J., Edwards S., King J., Tsang J.S., Schimmack G., Schelter J.M., Koch J., Ziman M., Marton M.J., Li B., Cundiff P., Ward T., Castle J., Krolewski M., Meyer M.R., Mao M., Burchard J., Kidd M.J., Dai H., Phillips J.W., Linsley P.S., Stoughton R., Scherer S., and Boguski M.S. 2001. Experimental annotation of the human genome using microarray technology. *Nature* **409:** 922–927.

19. Fritz B., Schubert F., Wrobel G., Schwaenen C., Wessendorf S., Nessling M., Korz C., Rieker R.J., Montgomery K., Kucherlapati R., Mechtersheimer G., Eils R., Joos S., and Lichter P. 2002. Microarray-based copy number and expression profiling in dedifferentiated and pleomorphic liposarcoma. *Cancer Res.* **62:** 2993–2998.

20. Hodgson G., Hager J.H., Volik S., Hariono S., Wernick M., Moore D., Nowak N., Albertson D.G., Pinkel D., Collins C., Hanahan D., and Gray J.W. 2001. Genome scanning with array CGH delineates regional alterations in mouse islet carcinomas. *Nat. Genet.* **29:** 459–464.

21. Miki R., Kadota K., Bono H., Mizuno Y., Tomaru Y., Carninci P., Itoh M., Shibata K., Kawai J., Konno H., Watanabe S., Sato K., Tokusumi Y., Kikuchi N., Ishii Y., Hamaguchi Y., Nishizuka I., Goto H., Nitanda

H., Satomi, S., Yoshiki A., Kusakabe M., DeRisi J.L., Eisen M.B., Iyer V.R., Brown P.O., Muramatsu M., Shimada H., Okazaki Y., and Hayashizaki Y. 2001. Delineating developmental and metabolic pathways in vivo by expression profiling using the RIKEN set of 18,816 full-length enriched mouse cDNA arrays. *Proc. Natl. Acad. Sci.* **98:** 2199–2204.

22. Zhu G., Spellman P.T., Volpe T., Brown P.O., Botstein D., Davis T.N., and Futcher B. 2000. Two yeast forkhead genes regulate the cell cycle and pseudohyphal growth. *Nature* **406:** 90–94.

23. Sorlie T., Perou C.M., Tibshirani R., Aas T., Geisler S., Johnsen H., Hastie T., Eisen M.B., van de Rijn M., Jeffrey S.S., Thorsen T., Quist H., Mmatese J.C., Brown P.O., Bostein D., Eystein Lonning P., and Borresen-Dale A.L. Gene expression patterns of breast carcinomas distinguish tumor subclasses with clinical implications. *Proc. Natl. Acad. Sci.* **98:** 10869–10874.

24. Alizadeh A.A., Eisen M.B., Davis R.E., Ma C., Lossos I.S., Rosenwald A., Boldrick J.C., Sabet H., Tran T., Yu X., Powell J.I., Yang L., Marti G.E., Moore T., Hudson J., Jr., Lu L., Lewis D.B., Tibshirani R., Sherlock G., Chan W.C., Greiner T.C., Weisenburger D.D., Armitage J.O., Warnke R., Staudt L.M., et al. 2000. Distinct types of diffuse large B-cell lymphoma identified by gene expression profiling. *Nature* **403:** 503–511.

Contributors

Donna Albertson *Comprehensive Cancer Center, Cancer Research Institute, and Department of Laboratory Medicine, University of California, San Francisco*

Catherine A. Ball *Stanford University School of Medicine, Stanford, California*

Bernd Becker *Universität Regensburg, Regensburg, Germany*

Kevin G. Becker *DNA Array Unit, National Institute on Aging, National Institutes of Health, Baltimore, Maryland*

Monique Bernsen *Academisch Ziekenhuis Nijmegen, Nijmegen, The Netherlands*

Carolyn J.M. Best *Pathogenetics Unit, Laboratory of Pathology and Urologic Oncology Branch, National Cancer Institute, Bethesda, Maryland*

Tone Björnsen *University Hospital, Department of Pathology, Regionsykehuset Tromso-RiTo, Tromsoe, Norway*

Michael Bittner *National Human Genome Research Institute, National Institutes of Health, Bethesda, Maryland*

Karl Brand *Peter MacCallum Cancer Institute, East Melbourne, Victoria, Australia*

Dieter Brocksch *Business Group Microscopy, Carl Zeiss, Göttingen, Germany*

Renate Burgemeister *P.A.L.M. Microlaser Technologies AG, Bernried, Germany*

Christer Bush *University Hospital, Department of Pathology, Regionsykehuset Tromso-RiTo, Tromsoe, Norway*

Ron Butow *University of Texas Southwestern Medical Center, Dallas*

Piero Carninci *Genome Science Laboratory, Riken Main Campus, Wako, Saitama, Japan*

Settara Chandrasekharappa *National Human Genome Research Institute, National Institutes of Health, Bethesda, Maryland*

Chris Cheadle *DNA Array Unit, National Institute on Aging, National Institutes of Health, Baltimore, Maryland*

Yidong Chen *National Human Genome Research Institute, National Institutes of Health, Bethesda, Maryland*

Geoffrey Childs *Albert Einstein College of Medicine, Bronx, New York*

Rodrigo F. Chuaqui *Pathogenetics Unit, Laboratory of Pathology and Urologic Oncology Branch, National Cancer Institute, Bethesda, Maryland*

Annette Clement-Sengewald *Frauenklinik der Ludwig Maximilians Universität, Munich, Germany*

Suzanne Dee *Affymetrix, Inc., Santa Clara, California*

Joseph DeRisi *University of California, San Francisco*

Maximilian Diehn *Stanford University School of Medicine, Stanford, California*

James Eberwine *University of Pennsylvania Medical Center, Philadelphia*

Michael R. Emmert-Buck *Pathogenetics Unit, Laboratory of Pathology and Urologic Oncology Branch, National Cancer Institute, Bethesda, Maryland*

Charles B. Epstein *Aventis Pharmaceuticals, Cambridge, Massachusetts*

Jian-Bing Fan *Affymetrix, Inc., Santa Clara, California*

Gabriele Friedemann *P.A.L.M. Microlaser Technologies AG, Bernried, Germany*

John W. Gillespie *Pathogenetics Unit, Laboratory of Pathology and Urologic Oncology Branch, National Cancer Institute, Bethesda, Maryland*

Richard Glynne *Eos Biotechnology, South San Francisco, California*

Sean Grimmond *ARC-SRC for Functional and Applied Genomics, Gene Expression Profiling Facility, Institute of Molecular Bioscience, University of Queensland St Lucia, Australia*

Thomas Harris *Albert Einstein College of Medicine, Bronx, New York*

Wolfgang Heckl *Institute of Cristallography, Ludwig Maximilians Universität, Munich, Germany*

Joel N. Hirschhorn *Whitehead Institute/MIT Center for Genome Research, Cambridge, Massachusetts; Harvard Medical School, Boston, Massachusetts; Divisions of Genetics and Endocrinology, Children's Hospital, Boston, Massachusetts*

Andrew Holloway *Peter MacCallum Cancer Institute, East Melbourne, Australia*

Galen Hostetter *Cancer Genetics Branch, National Human Genome Research Institute, National Institutes of Health, Bethesda, Maryland*

Bi-Huei Hou *Carnegie Institute of Washington, Stanford, California*

Xiaohua Huang *Affymetrix, Inc., Santa Clara, California*

Trey Ideker *Whitehead Institute for Biomedical Research, Cambridge, Massachusetts*

Vishwanath Iyer *University of Texas, Austin*

Janet Estee Kacharmina *University of Pennsylvania Medical Center, Philadelphia*

Olli-P. Kallioniemi *Cancer Genetics Branch, National Human Genome Research Institute, National Institutes of Health, Bethesda, Maryland*

Sophie Katsabanis *Peter MacCallum Cancer Research Institute, Melbourne, Australia*

Javed Khan *Advanced Technology Center, Pediatric Oncology Branch, National Cancer Institute, NIH, Gaithersburg, Maryland*

Juha Kononen *Cancer Genetics Branch, National Human Genome Research Institute, National Institutes of Health, Bethesda, Maryland*

Georgia Lahr *Academic-Hospital München-Harlaching, Munich, Germany*

Jerry Lee *Eos Biotechnology, South San Francisco, California*

Isabel M. Leiva *Pathogenetics Unit, Laboratory of Pathology and Urologic Oncology Branch, National Cancer Institute, Bethesda, Maryland*

Yin-Mei Lim *Whitehead Institute/MIT Center for Genome Research, Cambridge, Massachusetts*

Per Lindahl *Göteborg University, Department of Medical Biochemistry, Göteborg, Sweden*

Kerstin Lindblad-Toh *Whitehead Institute/MIT Center for Genome Research, Cambridge, Massachusetts*

Chih Long Liu *Biological and Biomedical Sciences, Division of Biomedical Sciences, Harvard Medical School, Boston, Massachusetts*

Robert Lucito *Cold Spring Harbor Laboratory, Cold Spring Harbor, New York*

Tracy McIntosh *University of Pennsylvania Medical Center, Philadelphia*

Paolo Marciano *University of Pennsylvania Medical Center, Philadelphia*

Francesco M. Marincola *HLA and Immunogenetics Laboratory, National Cancer Institute, National Institutes of Health, Bethesda, Maryland*

Aldo Massimi *Albert Einstein College of Medicine, Bronx, New York*

Hajime Matsuzaki *Affymetrix, Inc., Santa Clara, California*

Annette Mayer *Institute of Anthropology and Human Genetics, Goethe University, Frankfurt/Main, Germany*

Damares Monte *Carnegie Institute of Washington, Stanford, California*

Maria Murphy *Peter MacCallum Cancer Institute, East Melbourne, Australia*

Sven Nilsson *Göteborg University, Department of Medical Biochemistry, Göteborg, Sweden*

Norma J. Nowak *School of Medicine and Biomedical Sciences, State University of New York, Buffalo and Roswell Park Cancer Institute, Buffalo, New York*

Sujatha Panavally *National Human Genome Research Institute, National Institutes of Health, Bethesda, Maryland*

Nila Patil *Affymetrix, Inc., Santa Clara, California*

Daniel Pinkel *Comprehensive Cancer Center and Department of Laboratory Medicine, University of California, San Francisco*

Jonathan R. Pollack *Stanford University School of Medicine, Stanford, California*

Virgil Rhodius *University of California, San Francisco*

Thomas Ryder *Affymetrix, Inc., Santa Clara, California*

Guido Sauter *Institute of Pathology, University of Basel, Switzerland*

Stefan J. Scheidl *Göteborg University, Department of Medical Biochemistry, Göteborg, Sweden*

Karin Schütze *P.A.L.M. Microlaser Technologies AG, Bernried, Germany*

Richard Segraves *Comprehensive Cancer Center, Cancer Research Institute, University of California, San Francisco*

Gavin Sherlock *Stanford University School of Medicine, Stanford, California*

Pamela Sklar *Whitehead Institute/MIT Center for Genome Research, Cambridge, Massachusetts; Harvard Medical School, Boston, Massachusetts; Department of Psychiatry, Massachusetts General Hospital, Boston*

Antoine Snijders *Comprehensive Cancer Center, Cancer Research Institute, University of California, San Francisco*

Shauna Somerville *Carnegie Institute of Washington, Stanford, California*

Terry Speed *University of California, Berkeley*

Paul T. Spellman *University of California, Berkeley*

Monika Stich *Academic-Hospital München-Harlaching, Munich, Germany*

Wilhelm Stolz *Universität Regensburg, Regensburg, Germany*

Minoru Takemoto *Göteborg University, Department of Medical Biochemistry, Göteborg, Sweden*

Stefan Thalhammer *Institute of Cristallography, Ludwig Maximilians Universität, Munich, Germany*

Ed Tom *Eos Biotechnology, South San Francisco, California*

Melanie Trivett *Peter MacCallum Cancer Institute, East Melbourne, Australia*

Marcory C.R.F. van Dijk *Academisch Ziekenhuis Nijmegen, Nijmegen, The Netherlands*

Thomas Vogt *Universität Regensburg, Regensburg, Germany*

Ena Wang *HLA and Immunogenetics Laboratory, National Cancer Institute, National Institutes of Health, Bethesda, Maryland*

Jun S. Wei *Advanced Technology Center, Pediatric Oncology Branch, National Cancer Institute, NIH, Gaithersburg, Maryland*

Michael Wigler *Cold Spring Harbor Laboratory, Cold Spring Harbor, New York*

Dorian Willhite *Eos Biotechnology, South San Francisco, California*

William H. Wood III *DNA Array Unit, National Institute on Aging, National Institutes of Health, Baltimore, Maryland*

Yee Hwa Yang *University of California, Berkeley*

Suzanne Ybarra *Eos Biotechnology, South San Francisco, California*

1 | Generation of Probes for Spotted Microarrays

INTRODUCTION

Probes and Targets

The first step in the production of spotted DNA microarrays is the generation of "array-ready" material, which serves as the feedstock for printing. A slightly vexed issue concerns the nomenclature used to describe the material to be arrayed and, by extension, the material that is hybridized to the microarray. Throughout this manual, we abide, sometimes uneasily, with the convention of describing material on the microarray as the *probe* and the material to be hybridized to the microarray as the *target*. The background and logic to this nomenclature are described in the panel on NOMENCLATURE OF PROBES AND TARGETS at the end of this Introduction.

This section focuses on the production of probes for analysis of gene expression, which has been the dominant application of DNA microarrays to date. Later sections of the manual describe printing of microarrays and the production of probes for other purposes, for example, genomic clones used in microarray-based comparative genomic hybridization.

Probes for microarrays can be constructed using either synthetic oligonucleotides or cDNA fragments. For most investigators, the ideal microarray for expression profiling will be a complex array of sequence-validated probes, where each sequence is unique and displays minimal cross-hybridization to related sequences. Part of the power of microarray experiments lies in taking an unbiased approach to gene discovery (Brown and Botstein 1999). Hence, the probes on a microarray would ideally be a comprehensive representation of the expressed fraction of the genome including splice variants. For complex organisms, however, this goal currently presents significant problems in terms of cost, availability of suitable probes, and the logistics required for production of microarrays containing representations of thousands of exons. Constraints on producing the "perfect" expression array are best understood by considering the various sources of probe material.

Clone Sets

Serious efforts to sequence libraries of cDNAs from a variety of tissues and organisms commenced in the late 1980s and early 1990s. The goal was to characterize transcripts, to identify expressed genes, and, during the course of several years, to map the expressed sequence space of the entire genome. Although these ambitious goals have not yet been fully realized, cDNA sequencing projects nevertheless have provided the physical resources—such as cloned libraries—needed to generate complex collections of probes for use in microarrays. The information panel on CLONE SETS describes the origins of these clone sets for humans and some model species and explains concepts underlying their use; the accompanying table on suppliers of clone sets in the information panel (Table 1-5) provides information on the availability and complexity of some clone sets in current use.

These days, most investigators who array cDNA fragments work with the latest version of an off-the-shelf clone set, supplementing the set with individual expressed sequence tags (ESTs) that are appropriate to their particular needs. Individual ESTs of interest are identified by diligent scanning of databases and are purchased from commercial suppliers. Managing tens of thousands of cDNAs presents special challenges if the clone set is to remain viable, uncontaminated, and ordered. Initial clone sets were compromised by contamination with bacteriophage T1, multiple clones in individual wells, and incorrect sequence assignment (Halgren et al. 2001). Options for dealing with the pesky problem of contamination of clone sets by bacteriophage T1 are provided in the information panel on **PREVENTION AND DETECTION OF BACTERIOPHAGE T1 IN GENOMIC AND cDNA LIBRARIES**.

Between 1% and 5% of clones in well-maintained clone sets are said to be misassigned; i.e., they do not contain the sequence they were supposed to contain, although even this figure has been disputed (Knight 2001). The repurification of single clones and their sequence validation have reduced, although not eliminated, the error rate in available clone sets. The rate at which new errors are introduced depends on the degree of care taken both by the suppliers of clone sets and by the individual laboratories that use them. Protocol 1 describes steps for careful replication and storage of clone sets. However, because errors can be introduced at any of the steps from the replication of clones to the final printing of microarrays, it is dangerous to assume that results of microarray experiments are completely reliable. Validation of microarray findings by an independent method is mandatory.

DNA for arraying is typically prepared from clone sets by high-throughput polymerase chain reaction (PCR), rather than by purification of recombinant constructs, such as plasmids. Because clone sets usually employ a restricted range of cloning vectors, it is usually possible to use universal primers (detailed in Table 1-1) for the amplification of cDNA inserts. The quality of the microarrays produced is critically dependent on efficient, high-yielding, reproducible PCR amplification and on the certainty that the material produced is free from the primers, deoxynucleotides, and enzymes used in its production. Protocol 2 describes the PCR setup; Protocols 3, 4, and 5 detail processes for purification, quantification, and quality control of the amplified products; and Protocol 5 provides details for processing and resuspending array-ready material for printing and storing.

At present, yeast is the only eukaryotic organism for which a complete catalog of genes is available. Protocol 6 describes techniques for the production of novel clone sets from yeast by PCR with gene-specific primer sets. As more genomic sequences become available and the tools used to analyze them grow in sophistication, the sequence complexity of clone sets will increase, as will the proportion of the expressed genomes represented. However, until this process is complete, there remains a need for production of additional clone sets that represent the expressed space of each particular species, tissue, and developmental stage. For information about the processes of normalization and subtraction, common techniques used in the production of clone libraries to enrich for less-abundant mRNA species, please see Appendix 2 and Bonaldo et al. (1996).

Using Genomic Information for Construction of Microarrays

The completion of the DNA sequence of the human genome and of a wide range of model organisms has made possible the in silico design of probes for expression studies. One such approach is to use short oligonucleotide primers to amplify fragments corresponding to expressed regions of the genome, a strategy that was first applied to yeast (Iyer et al. 1999). The production of probes encompassing most of the expressed genome of *Saccharomyces cerevisiae* is described in the information panel on **YEAST PROBES** at the end of this section. Other genomes have been amplified in this way, including bacterial genomes (Wei et al. 2001) and plants (Hegde et al. 2000). Although this is an appealingly systematic approach, it is not without challenges in designing primers for efficient high-throughput PCR amplification. A more direct method is the use of oligonucleotides of 50–70 bases (so-called "longmers"), based on known and predicted open reading frames, for direct printing of spotted arrays. The identification of expressed regions of the genome is achieved by using available cDNA sequence information and sequence prediction programs. The production of complex spotted oligonucleotide microarrays has become progressively more accessible as the cost of oligonucleotide synthesis has dropped from dollars to cents per base and the yield of full-length longmers has improved. Like clone sets, longmer sets that encompass a sizable proportion of expressed sequences in different organisms are available commercially. Various considerations for and approaches to the design of longmers are discussed in the information panel on **SPOTTING OF LONG OLIGONUCLEOTIDES: AN ALTERNATIVE TO cDNA ARRAYS FOR EXPRESSION ANALYSIS**; the accompanying table (Table 1-6) provides information on commercially available libraries of oligonucleotides.

NOMENCLATURE OF PROBES AND TARGETS

For 25 years, northern blotting has been the workhorse technique for analysis of RNA expression and has strongly influenced our understanding of the terms *probe* and *target*. In a northern blot, the probe is the entity that is *labeled*, often radioactively, *free* in solution, and *known*—for example, a single fragment of cloned DNA. The target RNA is *complex*, *tethered* to a solid support, and is the entity that is interrogated. In microarray experiments, the physical locations of the known and interrogated entities are reversed. The known entity, individual cloned fragments of DNA, is arrayed on a solid support, such as a glass slide. The unknown entity—the complex RNA pool—is in solution. The intent of the experiment is not changed, however, namely, to measure the level of expression of individual genes in an RNA sample.

Inversion of the physical locations led to confusion about the meaning of the term "probe" in microarray experiments. Some investigators use "probe" to refer to the material on the solid support, whereas others understand that it means the labeled entity. The editors of a comprehensive review of microarray technology entitled "The Chipping Forecast," published in *Nature Genetics* (1999), encouraged their authors to describe the tethered nucleic acid as "probe" and the free nucleic acid as "target" (Phimister 1999). Although there seems to be something comforting about the old-fashioned northern blot nomenclature, we have nevertheless followed the advice of the editors. In this manual, the probe is always tethered, unlabeled, and known. The target under interrogation is always labeled, in solution, and undefined.

Replication and Storage of cDNA Clone Sets

Andrew Holloway,* Maria Murphy,* and Settara Chandrasekharappa[†]

*Peter MacCallum Cancer Institute, East Melbourne, Australia; [†]National Human Genome Research Institute, National Institutes of Health, Bethesda, Maryland 20892

This protocol describes the propagation of clone sets in bacterial hosts. Repurification and sequence verification of clones have reduced substantially the number of errors present in the early UniGene sets (Halgren et al. 2001). This effort can be undone, and the clone set rendered essentially useless, by cross-contamination of cultures. Contamination of a clone set generally occurs for one of three reasons: as a result of improper replication techniques, spillage of cultures between wells, or condensation dripping from the plate lids into the wells. Another type of contamination resulting from infection with bacteriophage T1, an extremely aggressive phage, can drastically reduce clone growth and is a further hazard that may greatly limit the value of clone sets. T1 infection is to clone sets as mycoplasma contamination is to mammalian cell lines. Methods for detecting and controlling T1 infection of bacterial stocks are discussed in the information panel on **PREVENTION AND DETECTION OF BACTERIOPHAGE T1 IN GENOMIC AND cDNA LIBRARIES.**

When working with a clone set for the first time, it is advisable to verify the aseptic handling of cultures, as described in the initial steps of this protocol. All manipulations of bacterial stocks should be carried out in a laminar flow hood, with extreme care taken to avoid cross-contamination. Other important issues to consider when a new clone set arrives in the lab include the following:

- *How many copies are to be kept?* At a minimum, aim to produce a working copy and a backup set. The original clone set should be kept as an archive, stored in a separate location.

- *Are there adequate –80ºC storage facilities for the original and copies?* A set of 40,000 clones, shipped in a 96-well format, involves almost 400 plates and occupies approximately one third of a standard –80ºC freezer.

- *What hardware is required to replicate stocks* and what precautions should be taken to ensure that it remains ordered and free from cross-contamination?

- *Who is responsible for the storage and use of a clone set?* Having many people accessing the set in an uncontrolled way is a recipe for disaster.

- *Are there restrictions on the distribution* of the set to other investigators? Different conditions may apply to academic and commercial users.

Details of some commonly used clones sets and their derivation are provided in the information panel on **CLONE SETS.**

5

MATERIALS

Buffers and Solutions

Please see Appendix 2 for components of stock solutions, buffers, and reagents.
Dilute stock solutions to the appropriate concentrations.

Carbenicillin (GIBCO)

Carbenicillin stock solution (1 g of carbenicillin in 10 ml of sterile H_2O)
> Sterilize the solution by filtration through a 0.22-μm filter. Store the solution in small aliquots at -20°C.

Ethanol (95% and 70%)
> Some batches of absolute ethanol (100% or 200 proof) have been reported to contain fluorescent contaminants that generate high backgrounds in microarray experiments; 95% ethanol does not have this problem. To avoid difficulties, either use 95% ethanol or identify a brand of absolute ethanol that does not generate high levels of background fluorescence. Absolute ethanol (USP-grade ethyl alcohol, 64-17-5) purchased from Warner-Graham Co. (Cockeysville, Maryland) performs consistently well.

Glycerol (sterile, 45% and 80% w/v) in H_2O
> Prepare 450 g of enzyme-grade glycerol per liter. Sterilize the solution by autoclaving for 20 minutes at 15 psi (1.05 kg/cm^2) on liquid cycle.

Sodium hypochlorite (3%) (bleach)

Media

LB (Biofluids, Rockville, Maryland)

LB containing 100 μg/ml carbenicillin
> Add 1 ml of carbenicillin stock solution to 1 liter of LB medium. Do not store unused antibiotic-containing medium for more than 1 week.

LB containing 100 μg/ml carbenicillin/8% glycerol
> Add 100 ml of 80% autoclaved glycerol that has cooled to <40°C to 900 ml of sterile LB containing 110 μg/ml carbenicillin.

Vectors and Bacterial Strains

Bacterial strain for testing aseptic technique
> Any vigorously growing strain of *Escherichia coli* can be used for this purpose.

Clone sets to be replicated
> These sets are usually provided as master plates of bacterial stocks.

Special Equipment

Adhesive microtiter plate seals (e.g., Sealing Tape, 7742000, ICN)

Freezer rack for microtiter plates (PGC Scientific)
> Consult with the supplier of the –80°C freezer to choose the appropriate racks for storage of microtiter plates.

Heat seals (removable) for microtiter plates (e.g., Easy Peel Film, AB-0559, ABgene, Surrey UK)

Inoculation tools
> Disposable or stainless steel reusable 96-pin tools or 384-pin tools are available (V&P Scientific, Genetix). If using robotics, then a replicator tool with associated drying instruments should be used, for example, an HDRT (high-density replicator tool) designed to fit on a Biomeck Robot (Beckman).

Laminar flow hood

Liquid handling tools
> Multichannel pipettes are ideal for manual replication of clone sets. A variety of multichannel pipettes are available, from simple devices (adjustable for one-time delivery) to sophisticated

programmable machines for repeated delivery of a fixed volume (suppliers such as Matrix, Oxford, Brinkmann). Plate fillers, such as the Q-Fill plate filler (QFIll2, GENETIX) are almost a necessity. Complete robotic liquid handling platforms are available from various companies (please see Table 1-2).

Microtiter plates (96-well, U-bottom; 3799, Corning)

Plate seals (Mylar gas-permeable; T640205, ICN)

Plate seals (sterile, 96-well, e.g., SEAL-THN-STR; Elkay Products, Shrewsbury, Massachusetts)

Reservoirs (50-ml sterile, disposable) for media (4870, Costar)

Thermosealer (Combisealer, AB-0384/240, ABgene, Surrey UK)

METHOD

Verifying Aseptic Technique and Effective Transfer

Before a valuable clone set is replicated, it is important to ensure that daughter plates can be inoculated reproducibly and that the replicator tool is efficiently sterilized as it moves among the source plates. Before replicating the clone set proper, carefully check both parameters by establishing a controlled inoculation matrix, as described in Steps 1–5. This protocol is designed for a 96-well format, but it can be scaled to a 384-well format if desired.

1. Prepare a 10-ml standard overnight bacterial culture in LB.

2. Carefully pipette 150 μl of the overnight culture into alternate wells of a 96-well plate, filling the remaining wells with sterile LB without antibiotics (please see Figure 1-1, Plate A). Repeat the procedure with a second plate but reverse the positions of the wells containing cultures and uninoculated medium (Figure 1-1, Plate B).

3. Add 150 μl of LB without antibiotic to each of the wells of ten 96-well plates.

4. Use the replication method of choice to replicate plate A to one daughter plate (plate #1). Sterilize the replicator tool or change pipette tips and then replicate plate B to a second daughter plate (plate #2). Continue replicating pairs of daughter plates until all ten have been inoculated.

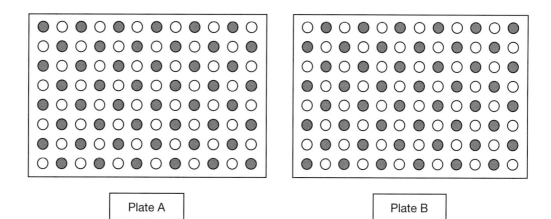

Plate A

Plate B

FIGURE 1-1. Controlled inoculation matrix for a 96-well plate. The pattern of inoculation is reversed in Plate A and Plate B. (*Closed circles*) Wells inoculated with bacterial culture; (*open circles*) wells with sterile inoculation medium.

For robotic replication: Program the robot to dip the tool sequentially in baths containing 3% bleach, sterile H_2O, and 70% ethanol, each for 30 seconds. Dry the replicator tool thoroughly (usually a fan-forced drying apparatus is necessary).

For manual replication: Set up a tray containing 80% ethanol for sterilization of the inoculation pins. Dip the replicating tool in the ethanol. Remove the tool from the alcohol bath and flame the pins. Allow the replicating tool to cool briefly (~10 seconds) before use. Have a flame-resistant lid for the ethanol tray available. 80% ethanol is preferred to absolute ethanol as it reduces the possibility of fire.

> **IMPORTANT:** Never return the replicating tool to the ethanol tray after flaming the pins.

5. Incubate the plates overnight at 37°C without shaking.

6. Inspect the plates by placing them on a light box. Check that all replicas show patterns of bacterial growth identical to those of plate A or plate B.

> If any growth occurs in wells that should be sterile, check the aseptic technique. Most cross-contamination comes from aerosols created during pipetting or from insufficient sterilization of the replicator tools. Avoid these problems by using aerosol barrier tips and by following the protocol described above to sterilize replicator tools.

> Once the aseptic technique and reliable transfer have been established, begin to replicate the clone set(s).

Replication of Clone Sets

7. Incubate the sealed master plates of the clone set(s) overnight at 30°C.

> Bacterial cultures provided by commercial suppliers are sometimes of low density. Replicating directly from these dilute stocks might result in failure of the daughter cultures to grow.

> Growing cultures at 30°C instead of 37°C prevents exhaustion of the antibiotic, which can occur when bacteria carrying multicopy plasmids are grown to saturation. Maintaining an adequate concentration of antibiotic is important to prevent growth of bacteria devoid of plasmids.

8. Label sets of standard 96-well round U-bottom plates and transfer 100 µl of LB containing 100 µg/ml carbenicillin/8% glycerol to each well (50 µl/well for 384-well plates). Label both the tops and bottoms of the plates.

> These plates will be used as working copies. Fill the plates by pouring the medium into sterile disposable reservoirs and delivering it to the wells using either 8- or 12-channel pipettes, a robotic system, or a Q-Fill apparatus fitted with an 8-channel manifold for 96-well plates, or a 16-channel manifold for 384-well plates.

> Check the information supplied with the clone set to ensure that the cloned cDNAs are carried in a vector conferring ampicillin resistance, as is usually the case with human IMAGE clones. Carbenicillin, a semisynthetic carboxypenicillin, is more stable than ampicillin and is therefore the preferred selective agent for plasmid-containing clones.

> Glycerol (8% final concentration), used as a cryoprotectant during freezing of cultures, can be added to media before or after growth of the cultures. However, the former is recommended because it avoids a further handling step and therefore reduces the chance of contamination.

9. Centrifuge the master plates in a horizontal microtiter plate rotor at 1300*g* for 2 minutes at room temperature to remove condensation and water droplets from the seals before opening.

    Bacterial culture fluid on the inner tape surface can be transferred all too easily between wells, cross-contaminating the stocks.

    If starting from frozen plates, there is no need to centrifuge the plate; remove the plate sealers when the contents of the wells are still frozen, and then let the cultures thaw at room temperature (please see the panel on **ADDITIONAL PROTOCOL: ACCESSING FROZEN STOCKS** at the end of this protocol).

10. Place each daughter plate (to be inoculated) next to the appropriate master plate, so that the rows and columns line up in the same order in both of the plates. Dip the replicating tool in the master plate, and then into the daughter plates.

    There is the potential for introduction of errors if the master and daughter plates are not oriented in the same way. When master and daughter plates are still in a stack, run a black felt-tip pen down the plate corner near the A-1 well. When plates are subsequently separated, this marking will facilitate their correct orientation. Number both the plates and lids.

    Choose a 96-pin tool that is flat-tipped rather than sharp-tipped to pick up and deliver a sufficient number of cells. In addition, dip the pin tool so that it touches the bottom of the well. Then stir the cultures gently with the pins to ensure that a good-sized inoculum is transferred. A robot will improve the efficiency of inoculation significantly at this step. Transferring the clones is not only laborious and time-consuming, but also prone to operator error. Using robotics will reduce the risk of incorrect transfer.

    If replicating several copies of the daughter plates, reinoculate the pins between each replication.

11. Seal the inoculated daughter plate with a gas-permeable Mylar plate seal, or replace the lid. Make sure that the inoculation tools are sterilized between each inoculation. As a control, at the end of each run, include a blank plate inoculated with a sterilized replicator, as well as a blank plate that is not inoculated.

    Preferably, the plates should be sealed with a gas-permeable seal that allows sufficient gas exchange to permit growth while reducing the chance of contamination. Simply replacing the lid of the plate increases the chance of cross-contamination. Gas-permeable seals are not appropriate for storage at –80ºC and should be replaced with a suitable cryo-resistant seal after growth and prior to storage.

12. Place the inoculated LB plates either sealed or with the lid on in an incubator and grow them overnight at 30ºC without shaking.

    Turbidity in the cultures (and cells at the bottom) shows the growth of cells. The plates may need to be incubated for 18–20 hours to achieve a reasonable density.

    There is no need to shake the cultures. To avoid the cultures drying out, place the plates in a humidified bag, e.g., a 1-liter "Zip-Lock" bag, containing a moistened paper towel. After growth of the replica plate, it is important to check that the blank plates remain sterile.

13. If no glycerol was included in the media for growing the cultures, then add 50 µl of 45% (w/v) sterile glycerol to each well. Seal the plates with a gas-impermeable seal, replace the lids, and stack them on storage racks. Store the plates at –80ºC.

CLONE ANNOTATION SPREADSHEET						
	Source plate			Destination plate		
Clone ID	plate	row	column	plate	row	column
AA324398	1	H	1	1	A	1
AA755111	2	E	1	1	A	2
AA947096	3	D	3	1	A	3
AA430733	6	G	12	1	A	4
AA229529	7	D	5	1	A	5
AA203631	9	E	6	1	A	6
AA562669	15	A	8	1	A	7
AA972704	22	E	3	1	A	8
AA925652	22	D	11	1	A	9
AA828055	26	B	10	1	A	10
AA937131	40	G	7	1	A	11
AA635869	40	H	8	1	A	12
AA870438	43	C	2	1	B	1
			etc.			

ADDITIONAL PROTOCOL: ACCESSING FROZEN STOCKS

A successful microarray experiment requires that the original frozen stock plates be used to recover cDNA inserts of interest for further analyses. Clones from the stock plates can be expanded into bacterial cultures growing either in the wells of a fresh microtiter plate or in 15-ml tubes. Either way, it is prudent always to reisolate a single bacterial clone for future analysis and sequencing. The following protocol describes manual picking of clones. Several robotic colony-picking devices are available and should be used in accordance with instructions provided by the manufacturer.

1. Prepare a clone annotation spreadsheet (see facing page), listing plate numbers and clone positions in the frozen clone set. Prepare a recipient plate containing 100 μl of appropriate medium in each destination well.

    Alternatively, prepare a set of 15-ml tubes containing 1–2 ml of medium in each tube. Label the tubes clearly with the unique identifier of the clone, and its location (i.e., the plate and the well number) as described in the example below.

    IMPORTANT: Maintain aseptic technique during clone picking. Include controls to check for the sterility of the growth media and picking device.

2. Work with the replicate stock plates, rather than with the master plates. It is useful to place the plates on a light box fitted with a stencil, indicating row and column numbers.

3. Remove the seal from each plate in turn while cultures are still frozen. Use a sterile toothpick or pipette tip to gently scrape the frozen surface of the appropriate clone and inoculate the destination culture. Keep track of the wells that have been accessed by placing a cross on the lid above each well as it is sampled.

    IMPORTANT: *Do not* allow the plate to thaw completely. Repeated thawing and freezing of plates will affect viability. The task of picking colonies is made easier by allowing the plate to warm up until the stock thaws slightly, sufficient to scrape the surface easily.

4. Reseal the donor plate with a cryoresistant seal or an adhesive seal and return it to the freezer.

    Work quickly here; do not allow the heat sealer to warm the media too much.

5. Incubate the replicate cultures overnight. For microtiter cultures, the growth conditions are identical to those used to replicate the original clone set (Step 12 of main protocol). Incubate the cultures in 15-ml tubes at 37°C with vigorous shaking. Once the overnight cultures have grown, streak for single colonies on the surface of LB agar plates containing 100 μg/ml carbenicillin.

6. Pick four to six well-isolated colonies and grow them overnight. Prepare plasmid DNA from them and from the parental culture (Step 5) (please see Protocol 2, Alternative Protocol, or Sambrook and Russell 2001).

    The cDNA inserts in these clones should be excised by restriction digestion and checked by agarose gel electrophoresis to ensure that a single band is present in the parental culture and that the same sized band is present in the subcultures.

7. Sequence the cDNA inserts of the plasmids isolated from the subcultures and verify that the DNA sequences correspond to those provided in the spreadsheet accompanying the clone set.

    Before using a clone set, some investigators resequence a random selection of clones in order to gauge the initial rate of misannotation in the clone set.

    Keep a log of all users of the set and compile their experiences. In this way, information can be accumulated about the level of de novo contamination and/or misannotation in the replicated clone set.

PCR Amplification of Probes from Bacterial Clone Sets

Andrew Holloway,* Maria Murphy,* and Settara Chandrasekharappa[†]

*Peter MacCallum Cancer Institute, East Melbourne, Australia; [†]National Human Genome
Research Institute, National Institutes of Health, Bethesda, Maryland 20892

Perhaps the most laborious aspect of generating spotted cDNA microarrays is the production
of concentrated solutions of array-ready cDNA fragments by high-throughput PCR. The
goals are to amplify inserts from a large percentage of clones, to avoid cross-contamination,
and to purify the fragments from the enzymes, nucleotides, primers, and other components
of the PCR. Although the process is time-consuming, if done correctly, sufficient material can
be produced from each 100-μl PCR to enable the printing of thousands of microarray slides.

Because large numbers of amplified fragments are required, it is highly desirable to incorporate some level of robotic automation into the procedure, for example, a multichannel
pipetting robot such as a Multimek or Biomek FX (Beckman). Robotic instrumentation not
only increases throughput, but also reduces the possibility of errors that may result from
human handling. Amplification of clone sets containing more than a few thousand clones is
challenging without the use of robotics. For a list of instruments for liquid handling, please
see Table 1-2 at the end of this protocol.

Use the guidelines given in the introduction to this section and in the information panel
on **CLONE SETS** when considering clone sets and vector/primer pairs. Most clone sets are supplied with instructions for amplification. However, before using the supplier's protocol for
large-scale amplification, it is advisable to carry out preliminary experiments using a single
plate of clones.

The following protocol is designed for a 96-well format and should be scaled as appropriate for 384-well plates.

MATERIALS

Buffers and Solutions

Please see Appendix 2 for components of stock solutions, buffers, and reagents.
Dilute stock solutions to the appropriate concentrations.

10x Amplification buffer (available from Applied Biosystems, N808-0190).
    Alternatively, 10x amplification buffer made according to the following recipe works well:
        500 mM KCl
        100 mM Tris-HCl (pH 8.3)

    Store the buffer in small aliquots at −20°C

H_2O (sterile)
    Milli-Q water occasionally has a very low pH. An alternative is to use commercially prepared
    water for injection (Baxter Healthcare).

$MgCl_2$ (25 mM)

TABLE 1-1. Primers for Amplification

Vector	Libraries used	Fwd and Reverse primers
pT3-T7Pac	Soares	Fwd: ctgcaaggcgattaagttgggtaac
		Rev: gtgagcggataacaatttcacacaggaaaacagc
pCMV-Sport 6	NCI-GAP	Fwd: ctgcaaggcgattaagttgggtaac
		Rev: gtgagcggataacaatttcacacaggaaaacagc
pBluescriptSK-	NCI-GAP; Stratagene	Fwd: ctgcaaggcgattaagttgggtaac
		Rev: gtgagcggataacaatttcacacaggaaaacagc
LafmBA	Soares 1 NIB	Fwd: ctgcaaggcgattaagttgggtaac
		Rev: gtgagcggataacaatttcacacaggaaaacagc
pCMV-Sport	Beddington embryonic region	Fwd: ggagagagctatgacgtcgc
		Rev: gacactatagaaggtacgcctgc
pCMV-Sport 1	NIA	Fwd: ccagtcacgacgttgtaaaacgac
		Rev: gtgtggaattgtgagcggataacaa
pCMV-Sport 2	Life Tech embryo	Fwd: ggagagagctatgacgtcgc
		Rev: gacactatagaaggtacgcctgc
pOT2A	BDGP *Drosophila* library	Fwd: aatgcaggttaacctggcttatcg
		Rev: aacgcggctacaattaatacataacc
Vectors with M13 priming sites[a]	wide range	Fwd: gttttcccagtcacgacgttg
		Rev: tgagcggataacaatttcacacag

[a]Primers described by Hegde et al. (2000) are recommended so as to avoid point mutations that are present in the universal priming sites of some vectors.

Enzymes and Buffers

Taq DNA polymerase (5 units/µl) (e.g., Amplitaq Gold from Applied Biosystems)
Many laboratories use *Taq* polymerase purified from recombinant *E. coli* expressing the protein. A simple purification strategy is described in Pluthero (1993).

Nucleic Acids and Oligonucleotides

Amplification primers
For a list of primers to amplify the inserts of commonly used clone sets, please see Table 1-1.
Antisense primer (100 µM) in H$_2$O
Store the stocks in small aliquots at –20°C.
dNTP solution, containing all four dNTPs, each at a concentration of 10 mM
The solution is available from, e.g., Amersham Pharmacia, or it may be prepared as described in Appendix 2. Store the stocks in small aliquots at –20°C
Sense primer (100 µM) in H$_2$O
Store the solution in small aliquots at –20°C.

Special Equipment

Barrier tips
Benchtop/clinical centrifuge with adaptors
These centrifuges should be capable of spinning deep and standard-sized 96-well microtiter plates (e.g., Eppendorf 5810R, Allegra 6R from Beckman Coulter or equivalent).
Microseal "A" film (MJ Research)
Microtiter plates (thin-walled, 100 µl)
Multichannel pipette or liquid handling robot
Thermal cycler(s) fitted with a heated lid (e.g., the Tetrad [MJ Research] which can accommodate 4 x 96-well plates or the GeneAmp 9700 [Applied Biosystems])

METHOD

Preparation of Template

1. Prepare fresh overnight cultures of the clones to be amplified by replicating the plates exactly as described in Protocol 1.

   This protocol, for amplification directly from heat-killed bacteria, uses a fresh overnight culture of bacterial cells as template. The yield of PCR product is significantly improved by use of fresh cultures as a source of template DNA. With planning, it is possible to link the protocols of replication and PCR amplification of clone sets. Replicate only as many plates as can be used in PCRs. Use part of each culture to generate PCR templates (see Step 2) and freeze the remainder. The presence of glycerol in the medium does not affect subsequent PCR amplification.

2. Add 90 μl of sterile H_2O to each well of a thin-walled PCR microtiter plate.

3. Mix the overnight cultures (prepared in Step 1) with a multichannel pipette or a liquid-handling robot.

   It is essential that the bacterial cultures be resuspended thoroughly to obtain sufficient template for PCR.

4. Use a multichannel pipette or liquid-handling robot to deliver 10 μl of each fresh overnight culture to wells of the microtiter plate containing H_2O (prepared in Step 2).

   Use barrier tips to reduce the risk of cross-contamination.

5. Seal the microtiter plate with adhesive sealing tape and place it in a thermal cycler for 10 minutes at 100°C.

6. Centrifuge the plate at 1300g for 5 minutes. A small pellet of cellular debris should be visible.

7. Use 1 μl of supernatant as template for each PCR amplification. Store the plate at –80°C. This stock can be thawed and refrozen several times without affecting the yield of PCR product.

   It is possible to use 1 μl of a fresh overnight culture directly as template in a PCR and to lyse the bacteria in situ by increasing the length of the denaturation step in the first cycle of PCR to 5 minutes (please see Yue et al. 2001). This method is somewhat faster, but it may give slightly lower yields and has an increased failure rate.

   Purified PCR product can be used as template for further PCR amplification. The reaction product is resuspended in TE (pH 7.9) or H_2O at a concentration of 100 ng/μl. Use 1 μl of the diluted DNA as template.

   If the failure rate is unacceptably high (>5%) or the yield is variable, consider using purified plasmid as template, instead of a centrifuged lysate (please see the panel on **ALTERNATIVE PROTOCOL: PREPARATION OF PLASMID DNA AS A TEMPLATE FOR AMPLIFICATION** at the end of this protocol).

Amplification of cDNA Clones

Table 1-1 describes primers commonly used for amplification. The following series of steps provides a general guideline that works well for bacterial or plasmid templates using primers based on M13 forward and reverse primers.

8. For each 96-well plate, prepare an amplification reaction mix (PCR mix) by combining the following reagents on ice:

10x amplification buffer	1.1 ml
25 mM MgCl$_2$	1.1 ml
10 mM solution of four dNTPs	220 µl
100 µM sense primer	55 µl
100 µM antisense primer	55 µl
5 units/µl *Taq* polymerase	55 µl
H$_2$O	8.3 ml

   This preparation, sufficient for ~105 PCRs, provides an excess of mix to accommodate slight pipetting errors and other losses.

9. Label and date an appropriate number of sterile thin-walled PCR microtiter plates.

10. Transfer 99 µl of PCR mix into each well.

    Make sure that the donor plate (containing the bacterial templates) and recipient plate (containing the PCR mix) are correctly aligned.

11. Use a multichannel pipette or a liquid-handling robot to deliver 1 µl of bacterial lysate template into each well.

    Change the pipette tips after delivery of template into each row. Double check that the donor plate and recipient plate are correctly aligned.

12. Seal the plates with silicon seals according to the manufacturer's instructions.

13. Transfer the microtiter plate(s) to a thermal cycler, and amplify the DNA templates using the denaturation, annealing, and polymerization times and temperatures listed below:

Number of cycles	Denaturation	Annealing	Polymerization
1	60 seconds at 95ºC		
30	30 seconds at 94ºC	45 seconds at 65ºC	3 minutes, 30 seconds at 72ºC
Last cycle		5 minutes at 72ºC	

    These times are optimal for the specific equipment and reactions described in this protocol, but the conditions may need to be adapted to suit other types of equipment and reactions. For example, the initial denaturation step must be increased to 5 minutes when amplifying directly from (unlysed) bacteria. Thirty cycles is a general recommendation; for some clone sets, longer cycling times may be necessary: For example, the suppliers of the National Institute of Ageing (NIA) mouse 15K set suggest the use of 38 cycles.

14. Once cycling is complete, remove the microtiter plate from the thermal cycler and continue with purification and analysis for spotted microarrays (please see Protocol 3 and Protocol 4).

    Alternatively, plates can be stored for 24–48 hours at 4ºC, or for longer periods at –20ºC. Further purification of PCR products is not required for the production of nylon filter arrays (please see Section 4, Protocol 1).

TABLE 1-2. Liquid Handling

Company	Platform	Comments
Beckman (http://www.beckman.com)	Biomek 2000	Single- and eight-channel liquid handler (single head with eight interchangeable tools for pipetting and diluting); can use nonbarrier or barrier tips.
		Delivers volumes in the range of 1 μl to 1 ml; the deck surface supports four to eight plates. The system is capable of upgrading to higher throughput through the use of one or two Stacker Carousels, with each Stacker Carousel holding up to 120 plates.
	Multimek-96	96-well automated liquid handler with high-throughput reagent addition and transfer.
		Delivers volumes in the range of 1–200 μl. The system is capable of utilizing 96–96 or 96–384 formats on the same work surface.
	Biomek FX	Single or dual bridge systems with pipetting heads including Span 8, 96, or 384 configuration.
		Delivers volumes in the range of 0.5–200 μl, with the capability for bulk dispensing using the Span 8 system.
		The system is capable of upgrading to higher capacity with one or two Stacker Carousels, each Carousel holding 120 plates.
Robbins Scientific (http://www.robsci.com)	Hydra-96	System configured for 96-well pipetting with 100-μl, 290-μl, 580-μl, and 1-ml syringes. Delivers volumes down to 100 nl with 100-μl syringes. Upgradable with automated wash system, plate positioning stage, and plate stacker.
	Hydra-384	System configured for 384-well and other high-density plates with 100-μl, 290-μl, 580-μl, and 1-ml syringes. Delivers volumes down to 100 nl with 100-μl syringes. Upgradable with automated wash system, plate positioning stage, and plate stacker.
	Tango Liquid-Handling System	May be configured with 1-, 8-, 12-, 96-, and 384-channel removable dispensing heads with 100-μl, 290-μl, 580-μl, and 1-ml syringes. Delivers volumes down to 50 nl with 100-μl syringes. Includes 12-position XY stage and stage optional plate stacker with 240-microplate capacity.
Genetix (http://www.genetix.com)	QBot	Available as an option on the QBot.
		96-channel liquid-handling head uses disposable plastic tips. Tips are loaded and ejected automatically.
		The system is capable of aspirating and dispensing volumes in the range of 1–50 μl.
		Compatible with 96- or 384-well plates.
		Plate capacity: source–72 plates, destination–24 plates.
	QPet	Stand alone 96- or 384-channel bench top system capable of aspirating and dispensing.
		The system is compatible with 96- and 384-well plates and is capable of holding either disposable plastic tips or stainless steel needles. Two tip sizes are available with a volume range of 1–30 μl or 10–300 μl. The stainless steel needles have a volume range of 0.5–100 μl.
		Plate capacity: source or destination–100 standard plates or 30 deep-well blocks.
BioRobotics (http://www.biorobotics.com)	MicroGrid II	Multipin tool can transfer up to 384 samples at a time between mother and daughter plates. Transfer is possible between plates of the same density or of different densities in expansion and/or compression modes.
		Delivers volumes in the nl range.
		Plate capacity: up to 48 microtiter plates.
		The system is capable of handling 1536-well plates.

Company	Product	Description
Qiagen (http://www.qiagen.com)	BioRobot 3000	System available as 96 or 384 or 96–384 or 384–96-well format. Delivers volumes in the range of 1 µl to 2.5 ml, using 4 probes (stainless steel or disposable tips or combination). Capable of upgrading to higher throughput through the use of stacker.
	BioRobot 8000	System available as 96 or 384 or 96–384 or 384–96-well format. Delivers volumes in the range of 1 µl to 2.5 ml, using 8 probes (stainless steel or disposable tips or combination). Capable of upgrading to higher throughput through the use of stacker.
	BioRobot Rapid Plate	System available as 96 or 384 or 96–384 or 384–96-well format. Delivers volumes in the range of 1–200 µl, using 96 probes (disposable tips). Capable of upgrading to higher throughput through the use of stacker.
Tecan (http://www.tecan-us.com)	Genesis Robotic Sample Processor	Four- or eight-tip arm for high throughput. Any combination of standard and disposable tips can be used on a single arm. Uses 200-µl or 1000-µl disposable tips, with or without filters, to deliver volumes in the range of 1 µl to 1 ml. Integrates with Genesis workstation to handle medium throughput (200 microplates).
Packard BioScience (http://www.packardbioscience.com)	MiniTrak MPD System (IV, V, VI, VII)	Compact liquid-handling module configured in 4 or 6 module systems for 96/384/1536-well pipetting. The MPD (multiposition dispense module) head includes 96 disposable tips that deliver volumes of 5–235 µl; the dispenser can be positioned for aspirating and dispensing from 96-, 384-, and/or 1536-well labware. Module can be upgraded to a 96-tip P50 dispense head (volume range 0.5–50 µl) or to a 384-tip P30 dispense head (volume range 0.5–30 µl). Capable of upgrading to higher throughput through the use of Universal Stacker Modules; each module accommodates up to 50 SBS standard microplates, 15 deep-well plates, or PCR plates using a plate carrier.
	MultiProbe II	The MultiPROBE II family offers multiple deck sizes. Standard systems offer deck capacity of up to 16 labware tiles (maximum capacity is 16 96-well plates). Expanded systems are designed with a central 16-tile capacity, but they can have two expansion modules added that provide 8-tile capacities each (will hold a maximum of 32 96-well plates). Four independent tips including either disposable or fixed tips (fixed tips are washable, stainless steel sampling probes coated with Teflon). The low-volume tip option delivers volumes in the range from 200 nl to milliliters. Standard tips deliver volumes of 1 µl to 1 ml using 20-µl, 200-µl, or 1-ml tips.
	MultiProbe II HT	Eight independent tips including either disposable or fixed tips (fixed tips are washable, stainless steel sampling probes coated with Teflon). Special low-volume tips are capable of dispensing volume ranges from 500 nl to microliters.
Hamilton (http://www.hamiltoncomp.com)	MicroLab 4000 Series	MicroLab 4000 provides an 18-microplate deck capacity and an active wash station. Deck Capacity MPH-96 34 Microplates in Portrait; 38 Microplates in Landscape MPH-48 16 Microplates in Portrait; 18 Microplates in Landscape

(Continued on following page.)

TABLE 1-2. *Continued.*

Company	Platform	Comments
		The extended deck of the MICROLAB 4200 provides a 38-microplate deck capacity and an active wash station.
		The MPH-96 has a large deck capacity and a 96-tip probe head, whereas the MPH-48 offers a smaller footprint and a 48-tip probe head. Both provide the same performance and standards.
		The probe head can access every part of the deck, including custom labware positions, in either landscape or portrait orientations; can pipette all 96 or 48 channels simultaneously or control groups of eight syringes separately for individual control of rows in portrait deck orientation or columns in landscape deck orientation.
MWG (http://mwgbiotech.com)	RoboSeq 4200	Single- and four-channel liquid handler.
		Washable and/or disposable tips. Volumes down to 1 μl. Can work with 96/384 formats and various tube formats.
		Features Peltier-cooled reagent racks, pipetting stations, and stackers.
		Options: integrated MWG thermal cyclers, microplate readers, vacuum manifolds; DNA sequencing comb loading.
	RoboSeq 2500	Eight- and 16-channel liquid handler.
		Washable and/or disposable tips. Volumes down to 1 μl. Can work with 96/384 formats.
		Features Peltier-cooled reagent racks, pipetting stations, and stackers.
		Options: integrated MWG thermal cyclers, vacuum manifolds.
	RoboSmart	Eight-channel system designed to be perfect companion robot to capillary DNA sequencer. Provides walk-away integration for all aspects of setup: plasmid preps; seq setups; integrated cycling; dye-term removal.
Lawrence Berkeley National Lab Human Genome Center (http://www.jgi.doe.gov/ programs/instrumentation/ preptrack.htm)	Prep Track Robot	The system can be configured with several possible modules.
		The high-volume dispensing station has four 96-channel pipettor modules (each module configured with 96 fixed-tip syringes).
		Capable of dispensing from 5 μl to several milliliters.
		A plate-fetching module at the input and output of the system can transfer microtiter plates to and from conveyor belts for continual processing.

ALTERNATIVE PROTOCOL: PREPARATION OF PLASMID DNA AS A TEMPLATE FOR AMPLIFICATION

Some laboratories find that the yield of the amplification reaction is improved by using purified plasmid as template, instead of a centrifuged lysate. Plasmid DNA can be prepared from 1–1.3-ml bacterial cultures using a commercially available miniprep kit according to the manufacturer's instructions.

Additional Materials

CAUTION: Please see Appendix 3 for appropriate handling of materials marked with <!>.

Agarose gel (1%), cast in 1x TAE, containing 0.5 µg/ml ethidium bromide <!>
Culture block (e.g., Qiagen Flat Bottom block 19579 or Millipore Cell Culture Block with Cover LSKC CB500)
Plasmid miniprep kit (e.g., Millipore Montage Plasmid Miniprep 96 kit LSKP09601 or Qiagen Qiaprep 96 Turbo Miniprep kit 27191)
Replicator (96-pin) or a liquid-handling robot with a 96-pin replicator tool
T0.1E (pH 8.0)
   10 mM Tris-HCl (pH 8.0)
   0.1 mM EDTA
Terrific Broth containing appropriate concentration of antibiotic

Method

1. Deliver 1–1.3 ml of Terrific Broth, containing an appropriate antibiotic, to each well of a 96-deep-well culture block using a multichannel pipette or robot.

2. Inoculate the wells with bacteria using a 96-pin replicator or a liquid handling robot with a 96-pin replicator tool.

   Take care that donor and host plates are in the same orientation, and if using a robot, check that the replicator tool comes into contact with the growth medium in the well. To avoid cross-contamination, it is essential that the replicator tool be thoroughly cleaned between plates.

3. Seal the plates with gas-permeable tape, and culture them with shaking at 200–300 rpm for 16–22 hours at 37°C.

4. Isolate plasmid DNA from the overnight cultures using a commercially available miniprep kit according to the manufacturer's instructions.

   Typically, this procedure involves alkaline lysis of bacteria, followed by a resin-based affinity cleanup system, and elution of the purified plasmid DNA.

5. Estimate the DNA concentration of a representative sample of purified plasmid DNAs by agarose gel electrophoresis, followed by ethidium bromide staining. For quantitation, compare 1 µl of the sample to known concentrations (50 ng, 100 ng, 150 ng) of a supercoiled plasmid DNA standard.

6. Resuspend the plasmid DNAs in T0.1E (pH 8.0) at a final concentration of 100 ng/µl.

   At this stage, the DNA preparations are in the wells of a 96-well plate, supplied as part of the miniprep kit.

   The volume used for resuspension varies according to the plasmid DNA yield, which in turn is dependent on the vector and host strain. For most vector/host combinations, yields in the range of 20 µg/well are standard.

7. Use 1 µl of the plasmid DNA preparations as a template for PCR amplification (Step 12 of the main protocol). Store the remainder of the plasmid DNA at –20°C.

Purification of PCR Products

Andrew Holloway,* Maria Murphy,* and Settara Chandrasekharappa[†]

*Peter MacCallum Cancer Institute, East Melbourne, Australia; [†]National Human Genome
Research Institute, National Institutes of Health, Bethesda, Maryland 20892

The purification of PCR products before the printing of microarrays serves to remove enzymes or other proteins that can clog printing tips, oligonucleotide primers that compete with the product for substrate binding, and salts that can affect binding to the substrate. Two methods for purification are described here: size exclusion and ethanol precipitation. Size-exclusion-based methods are superior but are more expensive.

The size-exclusion method described here uses Millipore Multiscreen plates, although other similar products are available (e.g., CentriSep-96, Princeton separation). Ethanol precipitation is described in the panel on **ALTERNATIVE PROTOCOL: PURIFICATION OF AMPLIFIED PRODUCTS USING ETHANOL PRECIPITATION** at the end of this protocol.

MATERIALS

Buffers and Solutions

Please see Appendix 2 for components of stock solutions, buffers, and reagents.
Dilute stock solutions to the appropriate concentrations.

H_2O (sterile)
Printing buffers (please see Protocol 5)

Nucleic Acids and Oligonucleotides

Amplification products (from Protocol 2)

Special Equipment

Benchtop/clinical centrifuge with adaptors
These centrifuges should be capable of spinning deep and standard 96-well microtiter plates (e.g., Eppendorf 5810R, Allegra 6R from Beckman Coulter or equivalent).
Microtiter plate shaker (MPS1, Ratek Platform Shaker)
Multichannel pipettor
Multiscreen PCR plates (MAN U03010, Millipore)
Mulitiscreen vacuum manifold (MAVM096 OR, Millipore)
Rotary vacuum concentrator with adaptors for microtiter plates

METHOD

1. Use a multichannel pipette to transfer the products of the amplification reaction(s) (Protocol 2) to Multiscreen PCR plates. Place the plates on the vacuum manifold and apply vacuum at 20 inches of Hg for 5–10 minutes, until no liquid remains in the wells.

2. Wash the plate twice with 50 µl of H_2O per well. Apply vacuum to remove the wash, as described in Step 1.

3. Resuspend the samples in 100 µl of sterile H_2O. Place the plate on a vigorously shaking platform for 10 minutes; make sure that the liquid in the wells is swirling.

4. Remove the plates from the shaker and transfer the samples to a fresh 96- or 384-well microtiter plate, using a multichannel pipettor or a robot.

5. Remove 0.5–2 µl of each sample for analysis by gel electrophoresis (please see Protocol 4).

6. Dry the remaining volume in a vacuum concentrator and store the plates sealed at –20°C prior to printing. For advice on resuspending the samples in preparation for print, see Protocol 5.

   It is important to use a rotary vacuum concentrator and a suitable vacuum pressure (15 mBar) so that the DNA is neither freeze-dried nor completely dehydrated. Apply vacuum for the minimum time required to remove all visible traces of the aqueous solvent. After drying, it is desirable to have all the DNA in a minimum area in the bottom of the well. If the sample is freeze-dried, DNA tends to be deposited on the sides of the wells and may not be redissolved when the sample is rehydrated.

ALTERNATIVE PROTOCOL: PURIFICATION OF AMPLIFIED PRODUCTS
USING ETHANOL PRECIPITATION

Products of the amplification reaction may be recovered from the reaction mixtures and purified by precipitation in the presence of ethanol.

Additional Materials

Ethanol (95% and 70%)
> Some batches of absolute ethanol (100% or 200 proof) have been reported to contain fluorescent contaminants that generate high backgrounds in microarray experiments; 95% ethanol does not have this problem. To avoid difficulties, either use 95% ethanol or identify a brand of absolute ethanol that does not generate high levels of background fluorescence. Absolute ethanol (USP-grade ethyl alcohol, 64-17-5) purchased from Warner-Graham Co. (Cockeysville, Maryland) performs consistently well.

Microtiter plate (V-bottom, polystyrene), rated for centrifugation at 1300g (e.g., 3894, Corning)
Sodium acetate (3 M, pH 5.2)

Method

1. Transfer the amplification products to a V-bottom polystyrene microtiter plate. Use a multichannel pipette to add 5 μl of 3 M sodium acetate (pH 5.2) and 150 μl of 95% ethanol to each well.
   > Thin-walled PCR plates may deform during centrifugation. Do not use polypropylene plates because DNA will not stick to the surface.

2. Precipitate the DNAs for 1 hour at –80°C or overnight at –20°C.

3. Recover the DNAs by centrifugation at 1300g for 1 hour at 4°C.

4. Decant the supernatant carefully, and place the inverted plates on a paper towel briefly to drain. Use a multichannel pipette to add 150 μl of 70% ethanol down the side of each well, taking care not to displace the DNA.

5. Recover the DNAs by centrifugation at 1300g for 1 hour at 4°C.

6. Remove the supernatants as described in Step 4. Allow the plates to dry overnight in a laminar flow hood.
   > Overdrying following ethanol precipitation results in DNA that is difficult to resuspend.

7. Store the plates with the lids on, sealed in Saran Wrap, at –20°C. Alternatively, resuspend the DNAs in 100 μl of H_2O for analysis and printing (for advice on resuspending samples to print, please see Protocol 5).

Protocol 4

Visualization and Assessment of PCR Products

Andrew Holloway,* Maria Murphy,* Settara Chandrasekharappa,[†] and Damares Monte[‡]

Peter MacCallum Cancer Institute, East Melbourne, Australia; [†]National Human Genome Research Institute, National Institutes of Health, Bethesda, Maryland 20892; [‡]Carnegie Institute of Washington, Stanford, California 94035

DNA yield, the presence of free primers or primer dimers, and the number of bands in each reaction are important measures of the quality of PCR-amplified material available for printing. Quality control can be performed prior to or after purification of PCR products. Analysis before purification avoids the cost and effort involved in processing failed PCRs. On the other hand, analysis after purification provides a better estimate of final yield. We recommend performing pilot amplification reactions before purification to check the yield and consistency of amplification. Once reliable results are established, it is best to check the quality of the samples following purification.

The quality and the quantity of PCR products can be assessed using a combination of two procedures: agarose gel electrophoresis (described in this protocol) and staining with the fluorescent dye PicoGreen (described in the panel on **ADDITIONAL PROTOCOL: QUANTITATION USING PICOGREEN**). By preparing loading plates as described below, it is possible to perform these two procedures efficiently and in tandem.

Agarose gels of almost any capacity can be constructed easily to analyze large numbers of PCR products. It is highly desirable to use combs with the correct spacing for gel loading with multichannel pipettes. Commercial systems (e.g., ready-to-run or rapid analysis gel electrophoresis) are available that provide rapid efficient analyses; however, they may have limited resolution. A failure rate (multiple bands or no product) of 5% or less should be achieved in the initial round of PCR, with about half of these initial failures being retrieved in a subsequent round of PCR.

MATERIALS

CAUTION: Please see Appendix 3 for appropriate handling of materials marked with <!>.

Buffers and Solutions

Please see Appendix 2 for components of stock solutions, buffers, and reagents.
Dilute stock solutions to the appropriate concentrations.

6x Gel-loading buffer (with bromophenol blue/xylene cyanol tracking dyes) <!>
H_2O (sterile)
TE (pH 7.5)

Nucleic Acids and Oligonucleotides

DNA ladder (1 kb) (15615-016, GIBCO)

Samples to be analyzed (direct products of PCR amplifications [Protocol 2] or purified products [Protocol 3])

Gels

Commercial precast gel system (e.g., Ready-to-Run) (1.2% agarose 96-well gel; 80-6461-33, Amersham)

Electrophoresis system (80-6460-95, Amersham)

Special Equipment

Aluminum tape (3M Scotch)

Microtiter plate (96-well, V-bottom polypropylene; MLP-9601, MJ Research)

Multichannel pipettor

METHOD

Preparation of the Gel Plate

1. Transfer 2 µl of each PCR product or purified product into the wells of a fresh 96-well plate, containing 0.4 µl of 6x gel-loading buffer in each well. Mix the samples by pipetting. Cover the plates with 3M Scotch aluminum tape to prevent evaporation. Store the plate at –20ºC if the gels are not to be run the same day.

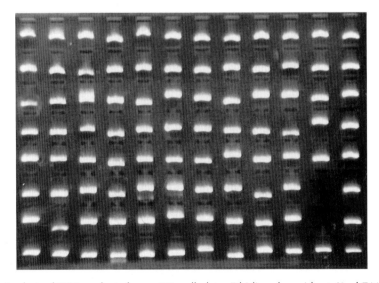

FIGURE 1-2. Analysis of PCR products from a 96-well plate. Ethidium-bromide-stained DNAs are analyzed by electrophoresis through a 1.2% Ready-to-Run gel and visualized under UV illumination. In this example, the amplification reactions have worked well, as there is a consistently high yield of a single DNA species in most lanes, with only two failed reactions.

2. Load 2-μl aliquots of each DNA sample from the gel plate into the wells of a Ready-to-Run gel. Carry out electrophoresis until the bromophenol blue has migrated approximately half the length of the gel.

   250 ng of a 1-kb ladder can be used as a molecular-weight marker and to assist quantitation.

3. Photograph the gel under UV illumination. For an example of a stained gel, please see Figure 1-2.

   Because ethidium bromide is included in the Ready-to-Run gel, there is no need to stain the gel after electrophoresis.

Scoring Gels

4. Score the PCR products for their quality as follows (for an example of each code, please see Figure 1-3):

0	Acceptable	The sample contains only one band of a substantial intensity.
1	Blank	No PCR product is visible on the gel.
2	Double bands	Two bands of roughly equal intensity are visible in the same sample.
3	Multiple bands	Three or more bands of roughly the same intensity are visible in the same sample.
4	Smear	The PCR fails to produce a distinct product, or chemical contaminants in the sample prevented the sample from running properly. Smears are a rare occurrence.
5	Faint bands	The PCR product is of "low" intensity when compared to the DNA marker.
6	Extra band(s)	The PCR product contains two or more bands, but a single dominant PCR product is visible. Extra bands may or may not interfere with array hybridization.

Although some PCR products have multiple deficiencies, only one code can be used per sample. Double bands (2) and Multiple bands (3) have precedence over Faint bands (5). When, for example, a sample contains two faint bands of equal strength, the sample is marked as a Double as opposed to a Faint (5) sample.

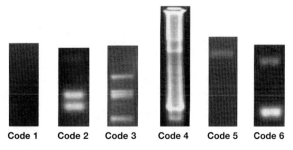

Code 1   Code 2   Code 3   Code 4   Code 5   Code 6

FIGURE 1-3. Examples of different problems encountered in the amplification of PCR products. By converting the images into a numerical code, it is possible to enter this information into the clone annotation spreadsheet. This information is then available when assessing the outcome of a microarray experiment.

Standard	DNA standard solution in assay (µl)	Total DNA per well (ng)
1	100.00	200.00
2	100.00	100.00
3	100.00	50.00
4	100.00	25.00
5	100.00	12.50
6	100.00	6.25
7	100.00	3.12
8	100.00	0.00

ADDITIONAL PROTOCOL: QUANTITATION USING PICOGREEN

A variety of methods can be used to quantify amplified products:

- Estimating the intensity of the bands on agarose gels relative to standards.

- Measuring the absorbance at 260 nm. The disadvantages of this method include its relative insensitivity (between 10% and 20% of the PCR product is used to obtain a result in the linear range), the contribution of nucleotides and single-stranded nucleic acids to the signal, and interference caused by contaminants. The latter two problems can be reduced by appropriate purification of the product following amplification.

- Using a sensitive dye such as PicoGreen that can detect double-stranded DNA in the pg/ml range and has a linear detection range from 25 pg/ml to 1000 ng/ml.

If results such as those shown in Figure 1-2 are obtained consistently, it is probably sufficient to measure the yield by absorbance at 260 nm of a small number of purified samples and estimate an average value for the set. However, when the yields are variable, it may be desirable—and more accurate—to measure the yields of all samples using PicoGreen and adjust the volume of the samples accordingly. Variation among products will make this process tedious, but it may be necessary to produce good-quality microarrays. Even if the sample volumes are not adjusted, it is useful to know when interpreting the outcome of microarray experiments which samples are desired from weak or failed reactions.

Additional Materials

Aluminum foil
DNA standards
    Prepare 10 ng/µl stock solutions of DNA standards. Freeze the samples in 100-µl aliquots at –20°C.
PicoGreen dsDNA Quantitation kit (P-7589, Molecular Probes)
Plates (black 96-well clear bottom) (25096, E&K Scientific)
3x SSC, diluted from 20x SSC (15557-036, GIBCO)
Spectrophotometer fluorescence microtiter plate reader (Tecan Spectra Fluor)
TE (pH 7.5)

Method

1. Prepare DNA standards in duplicate from stock solutions for the assay (see example on facing page).

2. Transfer 1 µl of each PCR product or purified product to the wells of a fresh 96-well plate, containing 50 µl of H_2O or TE (pH 7.5) in each well.
   Cover the plate with aluminum tape and, if the plate is not to be used the same day, freeze it at –20°C. *Do not discard* these temporary plates while performing the following analysis as they may be needed for reexamination.

3. Pipette 5 µl of each DNA sample from the "Temporary Plate" to a black 96-well plate, and add 95 µl of TE (pH 7.5) to each well for a total of 100 µl per well.

4. Prepare the PicoGreen working solution by diluting the PicoGreen dye stock 1:200 in TE (pH 7.5) just before use.

5. Add 100 µl of PicoGreen working solution to each well of the plates and mix thoroughly on a plate shaker for 5 minutes (centrifuge the plate for 1 minute following shaking to recover solution from the walls of the wells) or use the plate-shaking feature of a plate reader to shake the plate just prior to measuring.

6. Cover the plates with aluminum foil to protect the samples from light.

7. Read all plates in the plate reader (e.g., Tecan Spectra Fluor) and export the data to Excel or SigmaPlot.

8. Create a standard curve and calculate the concentration of the DNA solutions.

Resuspending Array-ready DNA for Printing and Storing

Andrew Holloway,* Maria Murphy,* and Settara Chandrasekharappa[†]

*Peter MacCallum Cancer Institute, East Melbourne, Australia; [†]National Human Genome
Research Institute, National Institutes of Health, Bethesda, Maryland 20892

Array-ready material must be resuspended before printing. The optimal solvent for the DNA depends on the geometry of the printing tip or delivery device, the printing substrate being used, the length of time the plates are exposed during printing, and the degree and type of environmental control available in the printing device. With so many variables affecting the outcome, it is wise to experiment to find the solvent and printing conditions best suited to the particular circumstances.

- *Printing solutions.* The most commonly used solutions to print DNA are 3x SSC or 150 mM phosphate buffer (pH 8). Both of these printing solutions may be supplemented as follows:

    DMSO (up to 50% v/v) is used to reduce evaporation during printing, to improve spot morphology, and to facilitate DNA denaturation (Hegde et al. 2000). Betaine (1.5 M) can be added to improve the efficiency of DNA binding, to increase homogeneity of spots, and to reduce background (Diehl et al. 2001).

    Sarkosyl or SDS (0.05% to 0.1%) can be used when spotting with pin and ring machines, to lower surface tension and encourage spreading of the spot. This reduces doughnut formation and gives a more uniform spot morphology. Sarkosyl can also be used with quill-based pens. For example, ArrayIt recommends a concentration of 0.005% Sarkosyl with the ArrayIt Stealth Microspotting Pins.

- *Volume.* The volume of solution in the wells of the printing plates is important. A minimum volume is required to obtain consistent filling of the printing pins and should take evaporation into account during the print run. Conversely, overly full wells can lead to excessive wetting of the exterior surface of pins and poor spot morphology as well as dripping. Volumes of 5 or 6 µl (no more than 1 mm depth) are commonly used for the wells of 384-well printing plates.

- *Concentration of arrayed material.* Probe DNA should be in excess relative to target to ensure good signals and maximum dynamic range of quantification, However, excessively concentrated solutions waste valuable material and can lead to smearing or comet tails (please see Section 3). DNA concentrations in the printing solutions are typically in the range of 100–250 µg/ml. If the DNA concentration is lower than 100 µg/ml, there is a loss of sensitivity and an underestimation of the degree of differential expression between samples (Yue et al. 2001).

- *Storage between printing runs.* Because of variable evaporation of the printing solution during and between print runs, it is advisable to dry the printing material completely in a vacuum concentrator (or overnight in a 37°C incubator) at the end of each run. Store the dried material in sealed plates at –20°C. Reconstitute the material by the addition of distilled H_2O prior to printing, taking into account the volume of the sample removed previously for printing. Typically, the volume removed during printing is 0.25 µl for quill-based pins (e.g., ArrayIt [Stealth Microspotting Pins, SMP3]) or 1 µl for an Affymetrix pin and ring printer. It is possible to use the same printing plates through several cycles of printing, drying, replenishment, and resuspension. Care must be taken, however, that the residual material does not become degraded or cross-contaminated over time, to avoid lowering the quality of the microarrays produced.

This protocol describes the rehydration of purified PCR products (obtained from Protocols 1–3).

MATERIALS

Buffers and Solutions

Please see Appendix 2 for components of stock solutions, buffers, and reagents. Dilute stock solutions to the appropriate concentrations.

Printing buffer of choice (3x SSC or 150 mM phosphate [pH 8])
Microspotting solutions are also available commercially (e.g., by Telechem, www.arrayit. com).

Nucleic Acids and Oligonucleotides

Purified samples from the amplification reaction (from Protocols 1–3)

Special Equipment

Adhesive film for sealing plates (e.g., 7742000, ICN)
Benchtop/clinical centrifuge with adaptors
These centrifuges are capable of spinning deep and standard 96-well microtiter plates (e.g., Eppendorf 5810R, Allegra 6R from Beckman Coulter, or equivalent).

METHOD

1. Add the appropriate volume of printing buffer to the plate of purified probe DNAs. Cover the plates with adhesive sealing film and centrifuge them at 1300*g* for 2 minutes.
   For a discussion of volumes and concentrations, please refer to the Introduction to this protocol.

2. Mix the samples on a microtiter plate shaker for 5 minutes.

3. Recover the DNA samples from the walls of the wells by centrifugation at 1300*g* for 2 minutes.

4. Allow the samples to stand overnight at 4°C.

5. Repeat Steps 2 and 3.

Protocol 6

Isolation and Amplification of Array Material from Yeast

Vishwanath Iyer

University of Texas, Austin, Texas

Yeast genomic DNA is the template for amplifying coding regions and other loci of *S. cerevisiae* by PCR. The yeast genome that was initially sequenced was that of strain S288c (*MATα gal2 mal*). The DNA of this strain is generally used as the source of template for amplification, and the oligonucleotide primer pairs were designed using this sequence. For further information, please see the information panel on **YEAST PROBES**. This protocol is divided into three stages:

- Isolation of Genomic Yeast DNA

- Purification and Analysis of Genomic DNA

- Amplification of the Genomic DNA by PCR

To maximize the yield from a single round of PCR amplifications, it is recommended that PCRs be carried out in a volume of 100 μl for each gene or microarray element; 40 ng of yeast genomic DNA is required as the template for each reaction, and therefore for amplification of the entire set of yeast genes, ~250 μg of template DNA is required. The method described in this protocol yields ~1 mg of genomic DNA from 500 ml of yeast culture grown nearly to saturation in rich media. Genomic DNA may also be isolated using commercial kits (e.g., from Qiagen). Alternatively, S288c genomic DNA can be purchased from a few companies such as Research Genetics (40802) and Novagen (69240-3).

For amplification of yeast genomic elements, genomic primer sets are available in 96-well microtiter plates, and all manipulations are done in this format (please see Table 1-3). PCR amplification of such a large set in a reasonable amount of time depends on the availability of appropriate infrastructure for high-throughput manipulations. Before embarking on this operation, it is advisable to pilot the entire procedure on a small number (e.g., four) of 96-well primer plates, to ensure success of every step. PCR and precipitation plates can be labeled in advance to streamline the process.

Sporadic failures can occur due to vagaries of the amplification reaction, problems in primer synthesis, or thermal cyclers. When using the primer sets described here, the success rate of amplification reactions should exceed 95%.

MATERIALS

CAUTION: Please see Appendix 3 for appropriate handling of materials marked with <!>.

Buffers and Solutions

Please see Appendix 2 for components of stock solutions, buffers, and reagents.
Dilute stock solutions to the appropriate concentrations.

β-mercaptoethanol (0.28 M) <!>

TABLE 1-3. Primer Sets for Amplification of Yeast Genomic Fragments

Description	Quantity	Sufficient for	Catalog number
ORF Genepairs in plates	30 µl of 10 µM mix	3 reactions	40603.1P
ORF Genepairs in tubes	200 µl of 20 µM stocks	50 reactions	40603.1T
Intergenic Genepairs in plates	30 µl of 10 µM mix	3 reactions	40903.1P
Intergenic Genepairs in tubes	200 µl of 20 µM stocks	50 reactions	40903.1T
pORF Genepairs in plates	50 µl of 10 µM mix	5 reactions	40510.1P
pORF Genepairs in tubes	200 µl of 20 µM stocks	50 reactions	40510.1T

Primer sets are available from Research Genetics.

Ethanol (95% and 70%)
   Some batches of absolute ethanol (100% or 200 proof) have been reported to contain fluorescent contaminants that generate high backgrounds in microarray experiments; 95% ethanol does not have this problem. To avoid difficulties, either use 95% ethanol or identify a brand of absolute ethanol that does not generate high levels of background fluorescence. Absolute ethanol (USP-grade ethyl alcohol, 64-17-5) purchased from Warner-Graham Co. (Cockeysville, Maryland) performs consistently well.
Lysis buffer (prepare 100 ml)
   0.9 M sorbitol
   0.1 M Tris-Cl (pH 8.0)
   0.1 M EDTA
$MgCl_2$ (25 mM)
Potassium acetate (5 M)
Resuspension buffer I (prepare 50 ml)
   50 mM Tris-Cl (pH 8.0)
   20 mM EDTA
Resuspension buffer II
   50 mM Tris-Cl (pH 8.0)
   1 mM EDTA
SDS (10%) <!>
Sodium acetate (3 M, pH 5.2)

Enzymes and Buffers

10x Amplification buffer (available from Applied Biosystems N808-0190)
   Alternatively, 10x amplification buffer made according to the following recipe works well:
      500 mM KCl
      100 mM Tris-HCl (pH 8.3)
      $MgCl_2$ is added separately in Step 20. Store the buffer in small aliquots at –20ºC.
RNase A (10 mg/ml) stored in small aliquots at –20°C
Taq DNA polymerase (5 units/µl) (e.g., Amplitaq Gold from Applied Biosystems)
Zymolyase (0.5 mg/ml solution made in lysis buffer)
   Prepare fresh just before use.

Nucleic Acids and Oligonucleotides

dNTP (100 mM solutions of each of the four dNTPs; 27-2035-03 Amersham Pharmacia)
Forward and reverse PCR primer pairs in 96-well plates (Primer plates)
   The primers are supplied at 20 µM in TE and are stored at –20ºC until required.
   For information on selection of appropriate primer pairs, please see the information panel on **YEAST PROBES** and Table 1-3.

Cells

Saccharomyces cerevisiae strain S288c
    This strain can be purchased from ATCC (26108) or Research Genetics (95500).

Media

YPD medium (prepare 500 ml)

Special Equipment

Barrier pipette tips
    For all pipetting steps that do not involve a multichannel pipettor, use barrier pipette tips to avoid carryover contamination.
Benchtop/clinical centrifuge with adaptors capable of spinning deep and standard 96-well microtiter plates (e.g., Eppendorf 5810R, Allegra 6R from Beckman Coulter, or equivalent)
PCR plates (96-well) and sealing mats suitable for heated lids (e.g., Multiplate and Microseal A from MJ Research)
Pipettor tips (disposable in racks of 8 X 12 to fit pipettors) and pipetting basins
Pipettors (adjustable-volume 12-channel 2.5 µl and 200 µl capacities)
Pipettors (adjustable single-channel) and barrier tips
Thermal cycler(s) (96-well plate with a heated lid)
    The Tetrad from MJ Research can accommodate 4 x 96-well plates, permitting high throughput. Another option is the GeneAmp 9700 from Applied Biosystems.
Water bath set at 65ºC

Additional Reagents

This protocol requires the additional reagents and equipment for purification and analysis of PCR products listed in Protocol 3 and Protocol 4.

METHOD

Isolation of Genomic Yeast DNA

1. Inoculate 500 ml of YPD medium with 1 or 2 ml of an overnight culture of *S. cerevisiae* strain S288c. Grow this culture in a shaking incubator overnight at 30ºC. At the end of the growth period, the culture should be near saturation (O.D. at 600 nm ~5.0).

2. Harvest the cells by centrifugation at 2000*g* for 10 minutes at room temperature. Discard the supernatant, and resuspend the cells in 25 ml of lysis buffer, pipetting up and down with a 10-ml serological pipette and/or vortexing to ensure thorough resuspension.

3. To the cell suspension, add 2.5 ml of 0.28 M β-mercaptoethanol and 2.5 ml of a freshly prepared solution of Zymolyase (0.5 mg/ml in lysis buffer). Mix the solutions thoroughly by swirling.

4. Divide the suspension equally into two smaller (30 ml) centrifuge tubes. Incubate the tubes with shaking at 200 rpm for 1 hour at 37ºC.
    This step digests the cell walls to yield spheroplasts.

5. Harvest the spheroplasts by centrifugation at 2000*g* for 5 minutes at room temperature. Discard the supernatant.

6. Resuspend the spheroplasts in each tube in 10 ml of Resuspension buffer I, pipetting up and down and/or vortexing to ensure thorough resuspension.

7. Add 1 ml of 10% SDS to each tube and mix the solution by swirling the tube. Incubate the tubes for 30 minutes in a 65°C water bath.

    This step lyses the spheroplasts.

8. Add 4 ml of 5 M potassium acetate to each of the two tubes. Mix the solution by inverting the tubes a few times. Place the tubes on ice for 30 minutes to 1 hour.

9. Centrifuge the tubes at 5000g for 15 minutes at 4°C to remove precipitated SDS and protein and cell debris. Collect all the supernatants carefully without disturbing the precipitated material. Divide the supernatants equally (~30 ml total) among four centrifuge tubes.

10. To each tube, add 2 volumes (~15 ml) of 95% ethanol. The nucleic acid should precipitate immediately. Allow the tubes to stand for 5 minutes at room temperature.

11. Centrifuge the tubes at 5000g for 30 minutes at 4°C to pellet the DNA. Resuspend each of the pellets in 1 ml of Resuspension buffer I. Consolidate the solutions into one centrifuge tube (~4 ml total). Resuspension might require breaking up the pellet with a 1-ml disposable pipettor tip and pipetting up and down.

Purification and Analysis of Genomic DNA

12. Add 20 µl of RNase A (10 mg/ml), and incubate the tubes for 30 minutes at 37°C.

13. Add 400 µl of 3 M sodium acetate (pH 5.2) and 11 ml of 95% ethanol. Store the tube for 5 minutes at room temperature. The precipitated DNA can also be stored overnight at –20°C at this point (or during Step 10).

14. Centrifuge the tube at 5000g for 30 minutes at 4°C to pellet the DNA.

15. Wash the pellet with an equal volume of 70% ethanol. Remove the ethanolic solution by vacuum suction and stand the open tube on the bench until the pellet of DNA is damp-dry. Resuspend the pellet in 4 ml of Resuspension buffer II.

    The DNA may require several hours to redissolve completely. This process can be accelerated by standing the tube in a water bath set at 60°C.

16. Quantify the DNA by spectrophotometry and resuspend it at a final concentration of 400 ng/µl.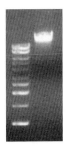

17. Analyze a small amount of the DNA preparation by agarose gel electrophoresis to ensure that the intensity of the DNA band, visualized by ethidium bromide staining, is concordant with the calculated concentration. An image of a typical gel is shown in the figure.

Amplification of Genomic DNA by PCR

18. Remove the plates containing the primers from the freezer and thaw them at room temperature or in a shallow dish containing warm (~45°C) water. After the primers have thawed, centrifuge the plates at 2000g for 2 minutes to collect all of the solution at the bottom.

19. Carefully peel off the coverings from the primer plates. Mix the primers in the stock plate by pipetting up and down two or three times with a multichannel pipettor. Transfer 5 µl each of the forward primers and of the reverse primers into a 96-well PCR plate that is oriented correctly with respect to the primer plates.

    Use a fresh set of tips each time the source plates are visited.

20. For *each* 96-well plate, prepare an amplification reaction mix by combining the following components in a disposable multichannel pipettor basin in the order listed. This reaction mix, sufficient for four 96-well plates, can be mixed in a single basin.

H$_2$O	7.05 ml
10x PCR buffer	1 ml
25 mM magnesium chloride	0.8 ml
100 mM stocks of each of the four dNTPs	25 µl of each
yeast genomic DNA (400 ng/µl stock) (from Step 16)	10 µl

When amplifying the entire genomic set, it is convenient to make a large stock of the master mix including the above components. Freeze 36-ml aliquots of the master mix at –20ºC. Each aliquot is sufficient for four plates. Thaw the frozen aliquots by microwaving the tubes with loosened caps for 20 seconds. Transfer the thawed mix to a pipetting basin and add *Taq* polymerase just before adding the reaction mix to the primers.

21. For each 96-well plate, add 40 µl of *Taq* polymerase (5 units/µl) to the reaction mix. Dispense the viscous enzyme evenly along the width of the basin. Mix the components thoroughly by pipetting the reaction mix up and down several times.

22. Use a multichannel pipettor to transfer 90 µl of the reaction mix containing *Taq* polymerase to each row of the 96-well PCR plate containing the primers. When adding the reaction mix to the PCR plate containing the primers, mix the final solution by pipetting up and down two or three times. Use a fresh set of tips for delivering the components of each reaction.

23. Cover the PCR plate with a sealing mat and place it in the thermal cycler.

24. Amplify the reactions using the denaturation, annealing, and polymerization times and temperatures listed below:

Number of cycles	Denaturation	Annealing	Polymerization
1	30 seconds at 95ºC		
36	30 seconds at 94ºC	45 seconds at 56ºC	3 minutes, 30 seconds at 72ºC
Last cycle		5 minutes at 72ºC	

These times and conditions are optimal for amplifying yeast elements using the Research Genetics primers, and for the specific equipment and reactions described in this protocol; however, the conditions may need to be adapted to suit other types of equipment and reactions. Including an extra 94ºC denaturation step at the beginning and final extension steps at 72ºC and 25ºC does not appear to affect the yield or the rate of success.

For the analysis, quantitation, and purification of the products of the amplification reactions, please see Protocol 3 and Protocol 4.

CLONE SETS

Expressed Sequence Tags

Origins of Expressed Sequence Tags

Traditional approaches to gene discovery, such as the mapping and cloning of recessive or dominant mutations or the isolation of genes corresponding to biochemically characterized proteins, have defined between 10% and 20% of expressed sequences in humans and model organisms. By the year 2001, ~7000 human genes had been defined as "named" and had additional biological information associated with them. However, the rate of gene discovery has been greatly accelerated through the use of large-scale sequencing of cDNAs to generate expressed sequence tags (ESTs). Initially promoted by Craig Venter and associates (Adams et al. 1991), projects to identify and catalog ESTs in a wide range of species are ongoing in both commercial and academic laboratories. By far the largest efforts are focused on human ESTs. In 1991, Merck Inc. and Washington University established a collaboration that led to the deposition of 480,000 human EST sequences into GenBank. By 2001, that number had grown to 3 million, through the efforts of Washington University and members of the IMAGE consortium (Integrated Molecular Analysis of Genomes and their Expression [Lennon et al. 1996], http://image.llnl.gov) and other projects such as the Cancer Genome Anatomy Project (CGAP, http://cgap.nci.nih.gov).

EST Nomenclature

A confusing number of names and other identifiers are associated with EST clones. Table 1-4 helps to clarify these identifiers (courtesy of the American Type Culture Collection [ATCC]). It is important to note that a designation beginning with HG, HT, or THC is not a unique identifier for a clone. These are aggregate identifiers for human genes, human transcripts, or tentative human consensus sequences generated by assembling EST sequences, respectively. The following are specific identifiers: ATCC number, MGC number, clone name, GenBank or dbEST identifier, or GDB probe identifier.

EST Databases as a Tool to Define New Genes

EST sequences from large-scale sequencing projects are deposited in dbEST (http://www.ncbi.nlm.nih.gov/dbEST/index.html), a division of GenBank, where an automated process called UniGene compares ESTs and assembles overlapping sequences into clusters in a manner similar

TABLE 1-4. Names and Other Identifiers Associated with EST Clones

Identifier	Format	Correspondence to clone	Example
ATCC number	5–7 digits	unique	105303
MGC number	4–7 digits	unique	20317
Clone name or alias	Alphanumeric	may be more than one per clone	NIB345
IMAGE Clone ID	5–7 digits	may be more than one per clone	60800
GenBank accession number	capital letter followed by 5 digits *or* 2 letters followed by 6 digits	may be more than one per clone	T12121, AA234567
EST number	EST followed by digits	0 to several per clone	EST149990
Washington University sequence Id	lowercase alphanumeric string followed by a period then r or s, then a digit	0–2 per clone	Yb34g01.s1
Unigene	2 letters followed by 1–6 digits	unique	Hs.1254

to that of shotgun sequencing (http://www.ncbi.nlm.nih.gov/UniGene/index.html). Each time this process is reiterated (referred to as a UniGene *build*; http://www.ncbi.nlm.nih.gov/UniGene/build.html), some of the additional sequences serve to join previously nonoverlapping clusters within a single gene, thereby collapsing some of the clusters and further refining the definition of expressed genes. Information derived from genomic sequencing serves to condense clusters still further. Conversely, the condensed clusters inform and facilitate the annotation of the genomic sequence. Ideally, each cluster would correspond to one gene, but several nonoverlapping clusters may exist for large genes, for genes expressed in low abundance, or for genes with variably spliced transcripts. Additionally, errors in alignment programs can produce false clusters (overclustering). For the foreseeable future, the number of clusters is therefore likely to exceed the number of separate genes from whose sequence they are derived. The IMAGEne Database (http://image.llnl.gov/image/imagene/ current/bin/search) aligns human IMAGE clones with nonredundant records in GenBank and returns a group of related IMAGE clones, ranked by full-length, insert size, and library quality. A Java applet allows users to view actual sequence alignments.

Other databases compile consensus sequences for contiguous regions that form a gene or mRNA transcript. These can generally be searched by gene name or GenBank accession number. The TIGR Database (http://www.tigr.org/tdb/index.shtml) integrates the human ESTs into human transcripts (HTs), described by gene name in EGAD (Expressed Gene Anatomy Database, http://www.tigr.org/tdb/egad/egad.shtml) and TIGR human contigs (THC assemblies) based on contiguous sequence data from ESTs in the Human Gene Index (HGI, http://www.tigr.org/tdb/hgi/index.html). The THC assemblies are valuable as they denote putative gene sequences. Integration by links between the two databases allows searching by gene name, cellular role, sequence data, EST identifier, or GenBank number. HGI includes clones from many sources, and it displays the relative positions of the clones with respect to the human transcript. The EGAD HT descriptor provides the nucleotide range defined as the coding sequence for the transcript.

The allgenes database (www.allgenes.org) was developed with the aim of providing an integrated database of every known and predicted human and mouse gene, using publicly available data. There is an attempt to integrate various types of data including EST sequences, genomic sequence, expression data, and functional information. Allgenes provides a comprehensive index of predicted human and mouse genes. Currently, gene predictions are drawn from transcripts, predicted by clustering and assembling EST and mRNA sequences. These EST and mRNA clusters are from the latest release of the Database of Transcribed Sequences (DoTS), developed at the Computational Biology and Informatics Laboratory (http://www.cbil.upenn.edu/) at the University of Pennsylvania. stackdb (www.sanbi.ac.za/Dbases.html) is a similar attempt to generate a complete database of human transcripts (Miller et al. 1999; Christoffels et al. 2001) from publicly available sequence data, with information on regional distribution of transcript expression. It was developed by the South African National Bioinformatics Institute (SANBI) and National Centre for Genome Resources (NCGR).

The Mammalian Gene Collection (MGC; http://mgc.nci.nih.gov) provides a complete set of full-length (open reading frame or ORF) sequences and cDNA clones of expressed genes for human and mouse. The MGC is an NIH-sponsored initiative that supports the production of cDNA libraries, clones, and sequences. The NIH MGC seeks to identify and sequence a representative full-length ORF clone for each human and mouse gene. Since 2000, the MGC has produced more than 80 cDNA libraries enriched for full-length cDNAs derived from human tissue and cell lines, and mouse tissue. The quality of each library is first assessed by 5′ and 3′ EST analysis of a limited number of clones. An additional 10,000–30,000 5′ EST reads are generated from each library that meets the quality standards set by the project. Several algorithms are used to select putative full-length ORF clones.

As of February 2001, more than 500,000 reads of 5′ EST sequences have been generated, and a nonredundant set of more than 20,000 human and mouse putative full-length ORF clones has been assembled within MGC. The inserts in these clones are fully sequenced at high accuracy and the ESTs are assessed to see if they span a complete open reading frame. At the time of this writing, more than 3000 clones have been fully sequenced and ~75% of the selected clones proved to have full-length ORFs. All of the MGC resources, including EST sequences, full-insert sequences, and clones, are fully accessible by the community. The value of full-length clones for microarray experiments probably lies more in sequence information and their use for functional validation than as a resource for probes per se. Full-length clones can be difficult to amplify efficiently in large numbers, and such probes are more likely to cross-hybridize with related sequences than are clones confined to 3′ UTR (untranslated region) sequences.

Sequencing of the ESTs of other organisms, such as the mouse (http://genome.wustl.edu/est/mouse_esthmpg.html), *Drosophila melanogaster* (http://www.fruitfly.org/sequence/genomic-clones.html), and *Arabidopsis* (http://www.cbc.umn.edu/ResearchProjects/Arabidopsis/index.html), lags behind sequencing of human ESTs in terms of sheer number. Clustering is consequently more restricted in these species, and the quality of the corresponding clone sets is therefore more limited. Interestingly, sequencing of a large number of *Drosophila* testis cDNAs identified many clones that correspond to genomic DNA sequences but have not been previously predicted to be expressed genes (Andrews et al. 2000). This underscores the fragility of current algorithms for analysis of complex genomes.

ESTs as a Resource for Microarrays

Clone sets, comprising a single representative of each cluster, are distributed by licensed vendors for distribution to investigators (http://image.llnl.gov/image/html/idistributors.shtml), with the most comprehensive sets being distributed by Research Genetics and the Resource Center of the German Human Genome Project (RZPD) (please see Table 1-5). Substantial efforts have been taken to reduce the error rate in clone sets through clone purification and resequencing. LION Bioscience (http://www.lionbioscience.com) has developed sets of mouse, rat, and dog clones specifically optimized for use in microarray analysis: They are similar to each other in size (usually between 600 and 200 bp), correspond to the 3′ UTRs of mRNAs, and contain no repetitive elements or poly(A) tracts (please see Table 1-5). These properties should reduce clone-to-clone variation in the intensity of labeling and minimize problems of cross-hybridization. Incyte Genomics, a major provider of validated sets in the past, stopped making their clone sets available in May 2001, but continue to provide array-ready material from these sets for spotting. In addition to the IMAGE consortium, other major contributors of cDNA clone sets include RIKEN (http://genome.rtc.riken.go.jp/home.html), TIGR (http://www.tigr.org), and other individuals (see, e.g., http://www.atcc.org/SearchCatalogs/tasc2.cfm#who). In many of these cases, individual clones or sets of clones are publicly available, although for some, access involves the licensing or sharing of any intellectual property generated with them.

ATCC (www.atcc.org) is also an IMAGE provider and is a valuable site for ordering individual clones. To find clones of interest, it is best to search with more than one clone ID, as some clone IDs are no longer unique; two IDs assure proper selection and speed the ordering process. Clone IDs can be found by a preliminary search of clone information in Genbank. Once the clones of interest have been identified, they should be found easily at the ATCC by searching in the molecular biology section of the ATCC Web Site using one ID and confirming with the other. If a clone is not found by searching a specific subgroup, then a general search through the entire molecular biology collection may yield results.

TABLE 1-5. Clone Sets

	Research Genetics/Invitrogen[a]	Resource Center of the German HGP[b]	LION Biosciences[c]

Currently available	**Human sequence verified**
	Known genes collection: ~7,500
	EST gene cluster collection: ~40,000
	
	The collection includes more than 45,000 sequence-verified clones from the IMAGE Consortium/LLNL Human collection, including the NCI CGAP collection. A cDNA clone is chosen from a UniGene cluster based with preference given to a 3′-end sequence and a NCI-CGAP clone. The sequence is matched to the NCBI UniGene database using BLAST analysis to confirm identity.
	
	Mouse sequence verified
	Gene cluster collection: ~16,000
	
	The collection includes more than 15,000 sequence-verified clones from the IMAGE Consortium/LLNL Mouse collection, including the BMAP collection. The sequence verification process is the same as that for the human clones noted above.
		Human Sets
		RZPD Human Unigene1: 36,425 clones (redundancy >1.8-fold, based on Unigene clustering)
		Available upon request.
		http://www.rzpd.de/cgi-bin/db/showLib.pl.cgi/response?libNo=950
		
		RZPD Human Unigene2: >72,000 clones (redundancy not absolutely known)
		
		The human Unigene2 set is selected for expression profiling (inserts 400–1500 bp, average 800 bp; localization within the genes is strongly biased toward the 3′ end; only one primer pair to amplify all clones).
		
		Based on Unigene clustering. RZPD human Unigene2 is completely resequenced (finished end of 2001) for verification and to remove redundancy.
		
		Cost: 105.000 Euro
		
		RZPD Human Unigene3: 48,000–53,000 clones
		
		Human Unigene3 is a sequence-verified subset of human Unigene2, with no sequence redundancy, optimized for expression profiling (see human Unigene2).
		
		Based on Unigene clustering with major modifications, available early 2002.
		
		Mouse Sets
		RZPD Mouse Unigene1: 24,500 clones (redundancy >2-fold)
		
		Clones may be amplified using two different primer pairs, average insert size ~680 bp.
		Based on clustering performed by Dept. Theoretical Bioinformatics, DKFZ.
		http://www.rzpd.de/cgi-bin/db/showLib.pl.cgi/response?libNo=952
			arrayTAG Mouse A (Status: July 2001)
			Sequence verified cDNA clones: 10,000
			7198 match on NCBI Unigene clusters, among these:
			  2207 show description "EST"
			  141 are referred to as "DNA segments"
			  2354 have a description like "Riken cDNA…"
			  2496 are clearly annotated
			2800 array
			TAGs represent yet unknown transcripts.
			Insert range is 200–600 bp (mean value 303 bp; standard deviation 83 bp).
			Full insert sequence is provided.
			
			arrayTAG Rat A (Status: July 2001)
			Sequence-verified cDNA clones: 10,000
			7027 match on NCBI Unigene clusters, among these:
			  3780 show description "EST"
			  500 are referred to as "EST highly similar"
			  1025 are in the "EST moderate" or "EST weak similar" category
			  1722 are clearly annotated
			2900 array
			TAGs represent yet unknown transcripts.

Insert size range is 200–600 bp (mean 322 bp; standard deviation 60 bp). Full insert sequence is provided.

RZPD Mouse Unigene2: >50,000 clones (redundancy not yet known)

Based on clustering performed by Dept. Theoretical Bioinformatics, DKFZ (Deutsches Krebsforschungzentrum); optimized for expression profiling (see human Unigene2); available end of 2001.

RZPD Mouse Unigene3: >40,000 clones (completely sequence-verified without sequence redundancy)

Mouse Unigene3 is a subset of RZPD mouse Unigene2, based on Unigene clustering with major modifications; optimized for expression profiling (see human Unigene2); available early 2002.

Rat Set

RZPD Rat Unigene1: 28,896 clones (redundancy most likely <2.5-fold)

Based on clustering performed by University of Iowa: Currently available, inquire for cost. http://www.rzpd.de/cgi-bin/db/showLib.pl.cgi/response?libNo=953

Rat sequence verified

Gene cluster collection: ~16,000

Currently, the collection from the University of Iowa (Dr. Bento Soares) includes more than 15,000 sequence-verified clones for *Rattus norvegicus*, composed of normalized and subtracted rat (Sprague-Dawley) cDNA libraries utilized for EST sequencing. The resulting clones have been clustered to create a unique collection of rat genes, derived from both adult and embryonic tissue.

Drosophila melanogaster

EST collection: ~55,000

D. melanogaster ESTs have been constructed by the Berkeley *Drosophila* Genome Project (BDGP). Clones were generated from various tissues utilizing two different vectors. For details, please see http://www.fruitfly.org.

arrayTAG Dog A

Sequence-verified cDNA clones: 10,000

The annotation strategy of canine cDNAs is based on homology searches against human NCBI-Unigene clusters and on annotation data generated with LION's sequence annotation package bioSCOUT. With the given stringency criteria, ~15% of the dog arrayTAG sequences match their corresponding human NCBI-Unigene cluster and ~35% yield to a clear assignment of annotation based on an automated bioSCOUT run.

Insert size range is 400–900 bp (mean 602 bp; standard deviation 60 bp).

—

Arabidopsis Set

RZPD *Arabidopsis* Unigene1: <15,000 clones (no sequence redundancy)

Based on RZPD clustering; available second quarter of 2002.

Continued on following pages.

TABLE 1-5. *Continued from previous pages*

	Research Genetics/ Invitrogen[a]	Resource Center of the German HGP[b]	LION Biosciences[c]
	Saccharomyces cerevisiae ORF-specific primers: ~6,000 The *S. cerevisiae* ORF-specific primers have been designed to amplify, from genomic DNA, the complete coding region including the start and stop codons. The 5′ end of all forward primers has been designed to start with the sequence 5′-GGAATTCCAGCTGACCACC, followed by the start codon ATG and first 25 or so bases of the ORF. The 5′ end of all reverse primers has been designed to start with the sequence 5′-GATCCCGGGAATTGCCATG, followed by the wild-type stop codon and reverse complement of the last 25 or so bases of the ORF. **Xenopus laevis** A variety of collections for *X. laevis* are available. For details, please see www.resgen.com. **TIGR EST Clones** A variety of clones from the TIGR EST collection are available, including viruses, eubacteria (both pathogens and nonpathogens), archaea (the so-called third domain of life), eukaryotes (plants, animals, fungi, and protists such as the malarial parasite). For additional information, please see www.tigr.org.	**Named (Known) Genes of a Species** Subsets of clones from all species are extracted to create sets of clones that represent all known genes from the respective species; available early 2002. **Customized Clone Sets** Clones are provided based on accession number and/or sequences delivered by the customer. The clones delivered are subsets of Unigene sets described above and are therefore sequence-verified. —	— — —
T1 contamination	Sequence-verified clones are transformed into T1-resistant hosts and placed into the sequence-verified clone collection.	All clones are tested for phage infection and for non-*E. coli* contamination and are provided only when successfully cleared by the respective tests.	Random sampling of every replicated collection for contamination with bacteriophages T1, T4, and λ is performed prior to shipment. The arrayTAG clone collections do not have a history of phage contamination.

Supply format	All collections are supplied in 96-well micro-titer plates.	Clone sets are available in various forms and formats: high-density colony arrays on filters, DNA arrays, sets of PCR products, and viable strains in 384-well format as frozen stocks on dry ice.	Deep frozen glycerol stocks in 96-well plates.
Information provided	For each clone set, information is provided on clone identifiers, gene names (if known), vector, antibiotic, and size (if known).	For each clone set, information is provided on clone identifiers, accession numbers, and if available, gene name, gene symbol, Unigene cluster ID (when applicable), including Unigene build, and chromosomal location (if known).	An annual license fee provides access to arrayBASE, a comprehensive annotation database providing in-depth information for every arrayTAG. Clone shipment is accompanied by QC certificates, FASTA sequence file, annotation summary file containing plate coordinates, Genbank and UG IDs, UG, and bioSCOUT descriptions.
General information, plans, etc.	—	The Resource Center is one of five authorized distributors of IMAGE.ESTs, which is, with more than 3 million clones, the greatest public EST collection currently available. In addition, the Resource Center distributes the clones generated by the German cDNA consortium (S. Wiemann, DHGP) and of the Mammalian Gene Collection (R. Strausberg, NIH).	There are currently 10,000 clones in each collection, soon to increase to 20,000 nonredundant cDNA clone sets. cDNAs were cloned de novo in a uniform vector system, to yield homogeneously sized cDNAs derived from the 3′ end of the mRNA. The poly(A) tail is eliminated and every sequence tag is checked for repetitive or low-complexity regions. Sequences are clustered using in-house methods and matched with NCBI Unigene clusters. Representative sequences are used for detailed clone annotations using LION's bioSCOUT sequence annotation system. All annotation data may be accessed through arrayBASE, a comprehensive Web-based annotation database. For more detailed information, please see www.lionbioscience.com/arrayTAG.

[a]Web Site: http://www.resgen.com.
[b]Web Site: http://www.rzpd.de.
[c]Web Site: http://www.lionbioscience.com.

CONTROLS USED IN SPOTTED MICROARRAYS

Andrew Holloway

Peter MacCallum Cancer Institute, East Melbourne, Victoria, Australia

Variations in experiments can occur at any stage of expression analysis, from printing of slides through hybridization to acquisition of data. To quantify these variations, many investigators integrate a series of control DNAs into the elements of the array. Analysis of the data obtained from these controls provides information on the dynamic range, sensitivity, and specificity of the hybridization, and allows statistical analysis of the reproducibility of the observed expression ratios. By spotting a number of control DNAs at different locations in the array, systematic spatial variations and bias in the strength of the Cy3 and Cy5 signals can be measured and corrected.

Types of Controls

Wherever possible, the control DNAs should be prepared by the same methods used for other elements on the array and should be printed in an identical fashion.

Positive Controls

These controls are designed to hybridize to the probe, regardless of its origin, and are used to verify that the target DNAs are labeled to an acceptable specific activity by Cy3 and Cy5. Each population of cDNA (i.e., test and reference) should generate signals of approximately equal intensity after hybridization to a positive control element. A simple series of positive controls can be generated by combining into a single pool an equal volume (~1 µl) of all the elements spotted onto the array. A dilution series can then be generated containing, say, 750, 500, 400, 300, 150, 75, and 10 ng/µl of the pooled DNAs. The entire dilution series should be printed together with the individual elements of the pool. After hybridization, the strength of the signal should be proportional to the amount of DNA present in each of the control spots over a wide range of concentrations, and the expression ratio of the test and reference samples should be close to unity (Yang et al. 2002).

Negative Controls

These controls are used to assess the degree of nonspecific hybridization and thereby to set a value for the threshold signal. Any spot on the array whose signal is not significantly stronger than that of the negative control should be scored as absent from the fluorescently labeled target. Typically, negative controls are segments of coding DNA derived from organisms that have no known (or expected) homologs or paralogs in the species under study. Microarrays used in expression analysis of mammalian genes often include negative controls composed of a combination of plant or bacterial coding sequences (e.g., please see Miki et al. 2001). To prepare negative controls, select a set of genes or coding sequences that are evolutionarily distant from, but have approximately the same content of guanine and cytosine as the species under study. The controls should be printed at the same concentration as the other elements in the array. Additional negative controls include (1) printing buffer containing no added DNA and (2) a solution of poly(dA)$_{18-24}$ at a series of concentrations ranging from 4 to 40 pM in printing buffer. After hybridization and scanning, verify that the signals obtained from these negative controls are not significantly higher than the background level in each channel. A signal emanating from the elements used as negative controls usually indicates non-specific hybridization of the probe to the array and may identify a need for increased stringency during hybridization and washing. Negative controls may be used to estimate background (please see Section 7).

Spiked Controls

To verify the equivalence of labeling with Cy3 and Cy5, known amounts of a polyadenylated mRNA species are added into each labeling reaction. RNAs of this type can be synthesized in vitro by standard techniques using a bacteriophage-encoded RNA polymerase, from a recombinant clone containing a poly(A) sequence at the 3′ end of the coding strand. (There is no requirement, however, for a poly(A) sequence if the mRNA will be labeled by random priming.) Segments of the same DNAs used as templates for in vitro transcription should also be prepared for spotting on the array. However, the 3′ poly(A) sequence should be omitted from the arrayed material.

Spiked controls should be chosen that do not cross-hybridize with any sequences known to be expressed in the organism or cell lines under study. Typically, spiked controls are synthesized from bacterial or plant genes, or yeast intergenic regions. Spiked controls can be added at a range of concentrations to tests and reference samples to provide data on the dynamic range of the system. Array elements corresponding to these controls should hybridize with equal intensity to the Cy3 and Cy5 probes across a range of concentrations. In labeling reactions containing 0.5 μg of mRNA or 50 μg of total RNA, spiked controls are added in quantities (typically 5 pg to 25 ng) that are therefore equivalent in abundance to 0.001% to 5% of the endogenous mRNA.

A complementary method is to vary systematically the amount of spiking target added to the two labeling reactions and then to compare the observed signal ratios in the Cy5:Cy3 channels with those predicted from the stoichiometry. The spiking targets should be added at a 1:10, 1:5: 1:2, 1:1, 2:1, 5:1, and 10:1 ratio in the two labeling reactions. Typically, the spiking targets should be added in concentrations in the middle of the dynamic range of the system.

RNA Integrity/Reverse Transcription Controls

Arrayed control DNAs can also be used to verify the integrity of the mRNA labeled for hybridization and the efficiency of reverse transcription. In the design of these spots, several clones from one gene should be generated that are derived from the 5′, central, and 3′ regions of the target gene. Comparing the hybridization of the samples with each of these spots generates information on the length of the target sequence that was copied into cDNA during each labeling reaction. In addition, if the spots derived from the 3′ region of the target gene hybridize with equal efficiency to, for example, Cy3- and Cy5-labeled targets, whereas the spots derived from the 5′ region consistently display a Cy3:Cy5 ratio greater than 1, then the efficiency of labeling distal sequences with Cy5 may be less efficient than labeling with Cy3. This can be verified by reversing the labels.

Normalization

Controls of this type are commonly used to normalize data, i.e., to eliminate systematic variation in microarray experiments that affect the measured levels of gene expression. Systematic variation can arise, for example, as a result of differences in labeling efficiencies between the two fluorescent dyes. Yang et al. (2002) and the Web Site http://www.stat.Berkeley.EDU/users/terry/zarray/Html/normspie.html describe three types of genes that can be used for normalization.

- ***DNAs included in the arrayed set of genes.*** In many types of microarray experiments, only a small number of genes are expected to be differentially expressed in the samples under comparison. The remaining genes, whose levels of expression are not expected to change, can be used to normalize the intensities of the signals from the two dyes. An advantage of using endogenous DNAs as normalization controls is that nonsystematic differences between the expression levels of the arrayed genes are flattened by averaging the red and green signals across a large number of elements.

- ***Constantly expressed genes.*** Many investigators spot onto microaarrays a small number of housekeeping genes that are thought to be expressed at constant levels in many types of cells. Examples of such genes include cyclophilin, glyceraldehyde-6-phosphate dehydrogenase (G6PD), and β-actin. Unfortunately, there is no guarantee that the housekeeping genes chosen as standards are invariant in their expression from one sample to the next. In fact, data show that the expression levels of genes commonly used for normalization may not be constant from one mammalian tissue to another, from one cell line to another, or from the cells of the same type grown under different conditions (e.g., please see Mansur et al. 1993; Spanakis 1993; Bhatia et al. 1994; Eickhoff et al. 1999).

- ***Spiked controls.*** As described earlier, spiked DNA controls are spotted onto the microarray (usually in duplicate). Usually, the spiked DNA consists of sequences derived from an organism unrelated to the one under study. The corresponding RNA is included in equal amounts in the two RNA preparations prior to labeling. In the absence of sytematic variation, the output from the red and green channels should be equal. Some investigators print a series of spots containing different quantities of spiked controls, which are expected to exhibit equal intensities of red and green fluorescence across the range of concentrations.

Statistical methods to normalize data obtained from exogenous and spiked controls in expression analysis experiments are described by Yang et al. (2002; and http://www.stat.Berkeley.EDU/users/terry/zarray/Html/normspie.html) and in Section 7.

Commercial Sets of Controls

Several companies sell kits containing DNA samples for spotting, together with matched poly(A)$^+$ RNAs (spike mixes), that can be used to validate, normalize, and monitor the performance of microarrays used for expression analysis of mouse and human genes.

- Lucidea Microarray ScoreCard, sold by Amersham Pharmacia Biotech (e.g., human, RPK1161B) uses artificial genes and mRNAs to measure dynamic range. A software system is available to analyze and plot the data. For further details, please see http://www.apbiotech.com/lsn_home/lsn_index.html.

- SpotReport , sold by Stratagene Inc. (252005), uses PCR products and corresponding poly(A)$^+$ RNAs of three *Arabidopsis thaliana* genes to measure dynamic range and to construct ratio controls. For further details, please see Davis et al. (2001) (available on-line at http://www.stratagene.com/vol13_4/p128-130.htm).

Both commercial sets also contain housekeeping genes and a variety of DNAs that can be used as negative controls.

PREVENTION AND DETECTION OF BACTERIOPHAGE T1 IN GENOMIC AND cDNA LIBRARIES

Norma J. Nowak

Director of the Microarray and Genomics Facility
School of Medicine and Biomedical Sciences for the State University of New York, Buffalo
and Roswell Park Cancer Institute, Buffalo, New York 14263

The ability of bacteriophage T1 to contaminate susceptible bacterial stocks is the stuff of legends. As Drexler (1988) points out "...its short latent period and its resistance to drying present challenges to careful workers and nightmares to those whose sterile technique is less than adequate." The valuable genomic and cDNA libraries, developed as part of the Human Genome Project (HGP), were for the most part generated before strains of *E. coli* resistant to bacteriophage T1 became available.

Many of the large-scale mapping and sequencing projects supported by the HGP required the parallel growth of thousands of T1-susceptible cultures. During this process, although most microbial contaminants could be controlled, T1 was able to quickly spread and sometimes, to make it nearly impossible to clone or propagate susceptible bacterial cultures. Often, the initial contamination went unnoticed. The failure of a small percentage of clone cultures to grow in microtiter plates was assumed to be due to a failed inoculation. However, the cause was sometimes more insidious in nature with the apparent lack of growth being the consequence of lytic infection with T1. Once established in a laboratory, the phage spread rapidly by aerosols, infecting adjacent microtiter wells and destroying valuable libraries. Several measures can be implemented to safeguard susceptible clone sets and to monitor for T1 contamination.

Top Agar Assay for Phage Detection

Laboratories involved in high-throughput technologies involving large clone collections should routinely examine clone sets using the top agar assay described below. This assay can be used to monitor individual cultures, as well as to quickly confirm suspected T1 contamination in microtiter plates.

MATERIALS

Buffers and Solutions

Please see Appendix 2 for components of stock solutions, buffers, and reagents.
Dilute stock solutions to the appropriate concentrations.

H_2O (sterile)
Sodium hypochlorite (10% and 20%, bleach) or 10% Tegedyne

Media

LB
LB agar plates (thin, 22 x 22-cm; Nunc), without antibiotic
> The layer of LB agar in thin agar plates is ~2.5 mm in depth, approximately half of the standard thickness. Each 22 x 22-cm plate is poured with ~120 ml of LB agar. The plates may be stored at 4°C, inverted in a plastic sleeve, for up to 2 days.

LB top agar (500 ml of LB + 0.8% agarose in a bottle)

Bacterial Strains

DH10B (Invitrogen)

Special Equipment

Bacterial plates (22–22 cm; Nunc)
Shaking incubator set at 37°C
Water bath set at 42°C

METHOD

1. The evening before phage testing, inoculate 50 ml of LB (without antibiotic) with DH10B cells. Incubate the culture in a shaking incubator overnight at 37°C.

2. Dilute the overnight culture to an OD_{600} of 0.25 using warmed fresh LB (usually 150–200 ml is required). Incubate the culture for 1 hour at 37°C in a shaking incubator until the OD_{600} reaches 0.45. At this stage, the culture is in the mid-log phase of growth.

3. Remove the culture of DH10B from the incubator and store it at room temperature until ready to use.

4. Melt LB top agar in a 50-ml bottle in a microwave oven and place it in a 42°C water bath for at least 2 hours. Swirl the solution every 30 minutes to ensure that the melted agar is evenly mixed and cooled.

   IMPORTANT: 42°C is a crucial temperature. If the agar is too hot, the DH10B will be killed, and if it is too cool, the solution will gel prematurely.

5. Remove the thin LB agar plates from storage at 4°C and store them at 37°C until ready to pour the top agar (minimum storage time = 30 minutes).

6. Thoroughly clean the laminar flow hood before and after use. Disinfect the hood with 10% bleach or 10% Tegedyne followed by sterile H_2O.

7. Arrange the thin agar plates on the bench. Label the bases and lids of the plates and then remove the lids.

8. Remove the 500-ml bottle of melted top agar from the water bath and add 11.25 ml of the mid-log phase culture of DH10B. Mix the cell suspension gently but thoroughly by gently rocking and rolling the bottle, without introducing air bubbles.

9. Pour a layer of seeded top agar (~80 ml) onto the thin LB agar plates. Use a sterile pipette tip to push any air bubbles to the side of the plate.

   IMPORTANT: Do not flame plates as this will kill DH10B cells!

10. Allow the plates to cool. Make sure that the layer of top agar is set thoroughly before replacing the lids on the plates.

    IMPORTANT: Plates must be either used on the day they are made or thrown away.

    Once the phage assay plates are cool and set, they can be used for stamping samples of cultures growing in microtiter plates with 96-pin or 384-pin replicators, or streaking of individual colonies.

11. After the plates have been stamped, incubate them, *NOT INVERTED*, overnight at 37°C, sealed in Saran Wrap and Parafilm.

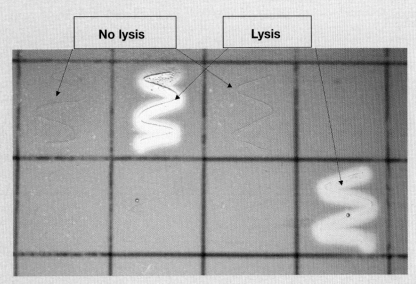

FIGURE 1-4. Assay for T1 contamination. The phage assay plate demonstrates lysis of the top agar bacterial lawn after 18 hours of incubation with phage-infected BAC clone cultures.

The DH10B cells seeded in the top agar will grow overnight causing the agar layer to become opaque. If phage is present in the sample being tested, it will infect the DH10B cells, resulting in a clear plaque in the DH10B lawn. The "clearing" of the lawn is very obvious, and easily recognized (see Figure 1-4). Infection with phage eliminates the lawn of DH10B surrounding the area of the assayed streaked-out clone.

12. Decontaminate leftover cultures of DH10B and bottles containing top agar.

    For leftover cultures of DH10B: Add an equal volume of 20% bleach and mix the solution thoroughly and wait for at least 15 minutes before flushing the solution down the sink with plenty of running water.

    For bottles containing top agar: Fill the bottles with 10% bleach and shake the solution vigorously. Wait for at least 15 minutes before flushing the solution down the sink with plenty of running water.

Prevention of Contamination with Bacteriophage T1

Contamination with T1 can be prevented by vigilant maintenance of impeccable aseptic technique. The spread of infection in clone sets can be controlled by implementing the measures described below.

- ***Construct genomic and cDNA libraries in phage-resistant hosts.*** The best method for prevention of bacteriophage T1 infection is to construct genomic and cDNA libraries in phage-resistant hosts such as MAX Efficiency DH5α cells, Electromax DH10B T1-phage-resistant cells, or "Gene Hogs" (Invitrogen). Resistant cells carry a mutation in the FhuA membrane protein (*tonA*) (Killmann et al. 1996). The FhuA protein, which is normally used for iron uptake, contains a gating loop that serves as a receptor for infecting particles of bacteriophage T1 and its close relative T5 (Killmann et al. 1995). DH10B cells carry a mutation in FhuA that renders them partially resistant to bacteriophage T5 and completely resistant to infection by T1. Contaminated clone sets can be rescued or cured by preparing plasmid DNA individually from each clone by phenol:chloroform extraction, followed by retransformation into a phage-resistant host.

- **Reduce the titer of T1 in infected plates.** The titer of viable bacteriophage T1 in infected microtiter plates can be effectively reduced by culturing the cells in a medium containing 1 μM ferrichrome (F-8014, Sigma). The ferrichrome binds to the FhuA receptor and blocks binding of bacteriophage T1, T5, and φ-80. Although this does not destroy the phage, it will significantly reduce the titer to the point where valuable clone collections can be saved. This method was developed as part of the Berkeley *Drosophila* Genome Project (see http://www.fruitfly.org/DGC/phage.html).

- **Handle clones and libraries in a laminar flow hood.** Clones and libraries must always be handled in a laminar flow hood. This includes picking, streaking to single colony, transferring cultures, arraying clones, phage testing, and other procedures. When using hoods, do not block the meshed air-circulation system.

- **Disinfect the work area.** The work area must be disinfected *before* and *after* using the laminar flow hood. Use 10% bleach or 10% Tegedyne followed by sterile H_2O. Disinfect used pipettes and forceps in 10% bleach.

- **Keep germicidal lamps on in hoods.** Germicidal lamps in laminar flow hoods must be turned on when the hood is not in use. The lights should remain on throughout the evening and weekends. Lamps are turned off in the morning.

  WARNING: Do not look at the germicidal lamps or their reflection. Serious eye damage can occur within seconds.

- **Use a waste beaker.** Any disposable tip or toothpick tip that has been used to transfer clones or that has come in contact with a live culture must be placed in a "waste" beaker lined with a bag containing 10% bleach. These tips must remain in the hood, exposed to the germicidal lamp overnight. The following day, working in the hood, seal the bag and place in an autoclave bag for incineration.

- **Sterilize incubators.** After use, shaking incubators must be wiped down with 10% bleach, followed by sterile H_2O.

- **Use overhead germicidal lamps.** The laboratory should be fitted with overhead germicidal lamps that are switched on by an automatic timer for 3 hours in the middle of the night, when the laboratory is unoccupied. A warning bell should sound before the lights are activated. A warning light at the entrance(s) to the laboratory must be activated when the germicidal lamps are in use.

  WARNING: Do not look at the germicidal lamps or their reflection. Serious eye damage can occur within seconds.

- **Use portable germicidal lamps.** Portable germicidal lamps should be used to sterilize areas where bacterial cultures are handled or processed, including shaking incubators and biohazardous waste containers.

SPOTTING OF LONG OLIGONUCLEOTIDES: AN ALTERNATIVE TO cDNA ARRAYS FOR EXPRESSION ANALYSIS

The disadvantages of using cDNA clone sets for arraying are that the physical handling of large numbers of clones, including replication and amplification, is labor-intensive, and the complexity of the processes involved creates opportunities for errors. Spotted arrays generated with sets of long synthetic oligonucleotides (>50 + bases) represent an attractive alternative to the arraying of cDNA-derived PCR products. The use of commercially available oligonucleotide sets obviates much of the work in the development of array-ready material and takes advantage of the rapid growth in genome sequence information. In addition, sequences can be chosen to represent specific splice variants, regions of cross-homology with related genes can be avoided, and 5′ amine modification can be used to specify the direction of binding of the oligonucleotide to the substrate. In principle, investigators are free to generate oligonucleotide sets to any available sequence, and they are not limited by the availability of physical clones. However, for reasons of cost and ready availability, many investigators opt for the use of commercially available oligonucleotide sets, which encompass large numbers of genes ascertained from the latest build of the relevant genomic sequence (please see Table 1-6). There is, however, the opportunity to supplement commercial sets with additional oligonucleotides that are specific to individual projects. Initial findings indicate a high level of concordance between results obtained with printed arrays of PCR-amplified cDNAs and long oligonucleotide microarrays (Hughes et al. 2001). In fact, the Yeast Genome Oligo Set (Operon) is reported in the trade literature (Ten Bosch et al. 2001) to yield results that are more accurate and reproducible than those obtained in parallel with amplified cDNAs. As analyses of genomic DNA sequences increase in sophistication and accuracy, long oligonucleotides corresponding to individual exons may eventually displace amplified cDNAs from their present position of dominance. However, these are early days. Information on newly developed oligonucleotide sets is often sparse, and investigators should exercise care when migrating from cDNA to long oligonucleotide microarrays.

Careful design of oligonucleotides is key to their performance. Using an ink-jet printer to synthesize large sets of human and yeast oligonucleotides, Hughes et al. (2001) evaluated key features of oligonucleotide design that influenced sensitivity and specificity. Maximal sensitivity and specificity of hybridization were obtained with oligonucleotides of 60 bases, annealed to targets in the presence of 32% formamide at 40°C. Avoidance of high deoxycytidine content and sequence similarity to related genes were important in achieving maximum specificity.

Some commercially available oligonucleotide sets for expression analysis are listed in Table 1-6 at the end of the Information Panels, including background information regarding their design and quality control. Common features in design include:

- *Selecting for correct (antisense) strand with a bias toward sequences mapping at the 3′ regions of mRNA.* Choosing the correct strand is an obvious requirement, which can nevertheless be overlooked, as occurred in an embarrassing case with an Affymetrix mouse oligonucleotide array (Knight 2001). Sequence elements derived from 3′-UTRs of mRNAs are less likely to cross-hybridize among gene family members. In addition, as synthesis of most labeled targets is primed using oligo(dT), the use of probes corresponding to 3′ sequences minimizes problems caused by truncated targets. Truncation may result, for example, from degradation of the mRNA templates, especially templates derived from tissues, or by inefficient reverse transcription caused by steric difficulties in incorporating bulky fluorescent nucleotides.

- *Avoiding sequence errors by selecting consensus sequences identified by analysis of large numbers of ESTs.* Single mismatches caused by sequencing errors are unlikely to affect the hybridization characteristics of oligonucleotides of >50 bases (Hughes et al. 2001). However, the presence of several mismatches between target and probe sequences may reduce both the specificity and kinetics of hybridization. The magnitude of these effects depends on the location of the mismatches within the two sequences.

- *Selecting oligonucleotides that fall into a narrow range of melting temperatures (T_m).* Given that identical hybridization and washing conditions are used for all oligonucleotide probes in the set, it is important that all oligonucleotides have similar melting temperatures. This can be achieved by selecting sequences with a similar G + C content and/or by calculating the theoretical T_m of all oligonucleotides using one of the available algorithms (see Sambrook and Russell 2001).

- *Avoiding sequences that are likely to cross-hybridize or are self-complementary.* Cross-hybridization limits the specificity of the assay. Repetitive or low-complexity sequences can be excluded by screening the oligonucleotide set for known sequence elements. No inverted or self-complementary sequences >3 bp should be present as such sequences, as these can result in hairpin formation that will reduce the efficiency of hybridization to targets. Finally, the use of programs such as BLAST, which are large-scale sequence comparison searches, allows oligonucleotide sets to be screened for fortuitous homology with sequences in the genomes from which the targets were derived.

- *Choosing oligonucleotides that represent individual genes with limited, or at least known, redundancy.* The recognition of transcribed genes makes use both of exon prediction programs, such as ORF finder (http://www.ncbi.nlm.nih.gov/gorf/gorf.html), and of EST information. Most oligonucleotide sets for complex mammalian or plant genomes, where the intronic and repetitive sequences are abundant, are designed using EST data. As described in the information panel on **CLONE SETS**, constant revision of EST data compiled in Unigene and similar databases leads to the collapsing of clusters over time. Thus, the particular Unigene "build" used to inform the synthesis of the set is important and provides some indication of the number of separate genes that are likely to be represented by the set. Hughes et al. (2001) argue that a single carefully selected oligonucleotide is sufficient to represent each gene, although some investigators believe that the use of two or three oligonucleotides per gene provides important internal validation of results. Affymetrix oligonucleotide arrays are an extreme example of this approach, as these incorporate ~20 oligonucleotides per "feature." In this case, however, the oligonucleotides are substantially shorter (20–24 mers) and are thus less specific and more finicky to hybridize than oligonucleotides of >50 bases.

The exact approach used in the design of commercial oligonucleotides is often commercial in confidence. As an example, however, Hughes et al. (2001) describe a step-wise approach to oligonucleotide design:

1. 60-mer sequences were selected that lay within 1 kb or 50–350 bp of the 3′ end of the transcript for yeast and human genes, respectively.

2. Low complexity and repetitive sequences were masked using RepeatMasker (University of Washington Genome Center [http://www.genome.washington.edu/uwgc/analysistools/repeatmask.htm] and Genetic Information Research Institute [http://www.girinst.org]). RepeatMasker does not score self-complementarity, unless palindromic repeats are present in the sequence.

3. Probes with 35–45% G + C (yeast) or both <50% G and 20–70% G + C (human) were selected. Sequences with homopolymeric stretches of more than six bases were rejected. This was very important in providing a narrow range of melting temperatures for the oligonucleotides.

4. Strand orientation of ESTs that have homology with known genes was obtained using database annotation. Other approaches were used based on the kinetics of hybridization of sense versus antisense primers, where correctly oriented oligonucleotides hybridize with slower kinetics characteristic of specific hybridization.

5. Oligonucleotides that passed these steps were tested for sequence similarity to the respective yeast and human databases using BLAST (http://www.ncbi.nlm.nih.gov/BLAST), and the most specific sequence was chosen for synthesis.

Commercial software packages, such as Array Designer (http://www.premierbiosoft.com/dnamicroarray/dnamicroarray.html), allow automated oligonucleotide design for microarray experiments.

YEAST PROBES

Saccharomyces cerevisiae (baker's, brewer's, or budding yeast) was the first eukaryote to have its entire genome completely sequenced (Goffeau et al. 1996), and fittingly, it was the first organism whose entire genome was represented on a DNA microarray (DeRisi et al. 1997). These and many subsequent studies of gene expression in yeast used spotted DNA microarrays constructed from full-length PCR-amplified representations of the entire complement of yeast genes.

In many respects, the design and manufacture of DNA microarrays for gene expression from this model organism represented an "easy" case. Known and predicted protein-coding sequences generated a total of ~6000 genes; the annotation for coding sequences was reasonably robust; and the catalog was completed by addition of a small number of genes identified by profiling techniques such as SAGE (Velculescu et al. 1997). Open reading frames (ORFs) in yeast are fairly small; the median size is 1.1 kbp, and 80% of the ORFs are 2 kbp or less in length. In addition, a very small fraction of the transcripts (~230 of the 6000 genes, or 3.8%) undergo splicing. These properties of the genome greatly influenced the design and manufacture of microarrays from yeast. Soon after the gene catalog had been completed, primer pairs for amplifying the entire sequence between the known or predicted start and stop codons, using yeast genomic DNA as the template, became commercially available (Research Genetics, http://www.resgen.com). These primers typically incorporate restriction enzyme sites to enable cloning of the PCR products into standard plasmid vectors and also have common 5′ ends to permit reamplification with a single pair of flanking primers annealing to the common 5′ ends.

In addition to expression analysis, DNA microarrays have been used in yeast to map identical-by-descent loci using the technique of genomic mismatch scanning (Cheung and Nelson 1998), to directly compare the genomes of related varieties of *S. cerevisiae*, and to map the genome-wide in vivo binding distribution of DNA-binding proteins on promoters (Iyer et al. 2001; Reid et al. 2000; Ren et al. 2000). This is possible because the intergenic region immediately upstream of a yeast gene contains the elements controlling its expression. Segments of intergenic DNA containing these elements can be amplified by PCR and used to construct DNA microarrays.

An alternative strategy for representation of yeast sequences on DNA microarrays involves the use of long oligonucleotides (60–70 mers), which have the advantage of ease of preparation and avoidance of cross-hybridization between conserved coding regions. However, PCR-amplified fragments may be more appropriate for assays involving intergenic regions, where, for example, prior knowledge of protein-binding sites may not be available.

The *S. cerevisiae* genome sequenced was that of the strain S288c (*MATα mal gal2*). Genomic DNA from this strain is typically used as the template for amplification, and coordinates of the genomic sets of PCR primer pairs pertain only to this strain. If microarrays generated from the S288c DNA sequence are used for genomic comparisons among related yeast strains, genomic loci that are present in other strains but deleted in S288c cannot be identified.

Research Genetics synthesized the first set of PCR primer pairs for amplifying all yeast genes, and at the time of writing, the company remains the only commercial source of this primer set. Several options for primer pairs are available from Research Genetics (please see Table 1-3). The primer pairs intended to amplify the entire ORF are called GenePairs, and the entire set is available at two different concentrations. Primer pairs are available to amplify intergenic regions and can also be obtained at two different concentrations. A further set of primer pairs (pORF Primers) are designed to amplify a partial ORF. The advantage of these over the standard ORF primer set is that the resulting PCR products are shorter, with all of the products being just under 1 kbp in length. This is intended to alleviate some of the problems associated with full-length amplification of the longer ORFs by PCR. In addition, the pORFs are targeted to the nonconserved regions of ORFs, to reduce the level of cross-hybridization seen among gene sequences with high sequence similarity. A disadvantage of the pORF set is that the primers do not have common flanking sequences, making it impossible to reamplify the PCR products with a common pair of primers, as can be done with the standard set of ORF primers.

The intergenic primer set, which is available at two different concentrations, is required for genomic mapping and chromatin immunoprecipitation (please see Section 6, Protocols 10 and 11). Together with the ORF set, the intergenic set covers virtually every locus in the yeast genome. Currently, non-ORF features from the nuclear genome, such as rRNAs, tRNAs, snoRNAs, Ty-LTR elements, etc., as well as all mitochondrial genes, are included in the "intergenic" set.

Although the annotation of features in the yeast genomic sequence has progressed substantially, it is still a work in progress. Many ORFs are completely uncharacterized, and it is possible that a number of them may not be transcribed. Although these fragments will be included in the ORF set, they rightfully belong in the intergenic set. Likewise, a seemingly featureless intergenic fragment might harbor a cryptic transcript, perhaps one that encodes a small protein or RNA. Investigators must therefore be prepared to incorporate new elements into the microarray or, if using the complete set, be able to change the annotations of existing elements within the archival database.

TABLE 1-6. Oligo Set Suppliers

	Compugen[a]	Operon[b]	MWG Biotech[c]
OligoLibrary sets[d]	**Human OligoLibrary** Number of oligos: 18,861 LEADS human clusters represented: 18,664 (plus 197 controls) UniGene human clusters represented: 15,223 Public domain human genes not found as well-characterized genes in UniGene database: 3,441 Number of oligos per LEADS cluster: 1 Oligo length: 60 bases (5′-C6 amino modification) Distance from the 3′ end: 95% of oligos are within 61–1309 bases from the 3′ end. The average distance from the 3′ end is 397 bases. Cross-homology: 95% of oligos contain a predicted cross-homology of <66.2%. Average cross-homology is 33.8%. Human UniGene Build #138 was used for mapping oligos to UniGene clusters.	**Human Genome Oligo Set** Total number of of oligos: 21,329 Number of human genes represented: 21,329 (+ 30 controls) Oligo length: 70 bases (5′-C6 amino modification) Distance from the 3′ end: within 750 bases from the 3′ end. All oligonucleotides in the Human Genome Oligo Set were designed from the representative sequences in the UniGene database, Hs build #147.	**Pan Human 10K Oligo Set** Number of oligos: 9,984 UniGene clusters represented: 9,850 Number of oligos per UniGene cluster: 1 Oligo length: 50 bases (5′-C6 amino modification) **Pan Human Cancer Oligo Set** Number of oligos: 1,920 UniGene clusters represented: 1,900 Number of oligos per UniGene cluster: 1 Oligo length: 50 bases (5′-C6 amino modification)
	Mouse OligoLibrary Number of oligos: 7,524 LEADS mouse clusters represented: 7,445 (plus 79 controls) UniGene mouse clusters represented: 6,544 Public domain mouse genes not found as well-characterized genes in UniGene database: 901 Number of oligos per LEADS cluster: 1 Oligo length: 65 bases (5′-C6 amino modification) Distance from the 3′ end: 95% of oligos are within 65–1133 bases from 3′ end. The average distance from the 3′ end is 396 bases. Cross-homology: 95% of oligos contain a predicted cross-homology of <66.5%. Average cross-homology is 30.5%. Mouse UniGene Build #93 was used for mapping oligos to UniGene clusters.	**Mouse Genome Oligo Set** Total number of oligos: 16,463 Number of mouse genes represented: 16,463 (+ 16 controls) Oligo length: 70 bases (5′-C6 amino modification) Distance from the 3′ end: within 750 bases from the 3′ end The oligonucleotides in the Mouse Genome Oligo Set were designed from the representative sequences in the Mouse UniGene database, Mm Build #102.	**Pan Mouse 10K Oligo Set** Number of oligos: 9,984 UniGene clusters represented: 9,850 Number of oligos per UniGene cluster: 1 Oligo length: 50 bases (5′-C6 amino modification) **Pan Rat Liver Oligo Set** Number of oligos: 1,408 UniGene clusters represented: 1,353 Number of oligos per UniGene cluster: 1 Oligo length: 50 bases (5′-C6 amino modification) **Pan Rat 5K Oligo Set** Number of oligos: 5,760 UniGene clusters represented: 5,535 Number of oligos per UniGene cluster: 1 Oligo length: 50 bases (5′-C6 amino modification)

Continued on following pages.

TABLE 1-6. *Continued from previous page.*

Compugen[a]	Operon[b]	MWG Biotech[c]
Rat OligoLibrary Number of oligos: 4,854 LEADS rat clusters represented: 4,803 (plus 51 controls) UniGene rat clusters represented: 3,821 Public domain rat genes not found as well-characterized genes in UniGene database: 982 Number of oligos per LEADS cluster: 1 Oligo length: 65 bases (5'-C6 amino modification) Distance from the 3' end: 95% of oligos are within 65–928 bases from the 3' end. The average distance from the 3' end is 302 bases. Cross-homology: 95% of oligos contain a predicted cross-homology of <66.2%. Average cross-homology is 29.2%. Rat UniGene Build #90 was used for mapping oligos to UniGene clusters.	**Yeast Genome Oligo Set** Total number of oligos: 6,307 Number of *S. cerevisiae* ORFs represented: 6,307 (+10 controls) Oligo length: 70 bases (5'-C6 amino modification) Distance from the 3' end: within 750 bases from the 3' end The oligo set represents the ORFs of *S. cerevisiae* from the *Saccharomyces* Genome Database (SGD) at Stanford University. **Malaria Genome Oligo Set** Total number of oligos: 6,369 Number of *Plasmodium falciparum* genes represented: 6,231 (+ 138 controls) Oligo length: 70 bases Distance from the 3' end: within 750 bases from the 3' end The oligo set represents ORFs from *P. falciparum.* The genomic sequence for *P. falciparum* was obtained from the Sanger Center, TIGR, and Stanford University. From this genomic sequence, ORFs were predicted using the gene prediction software, GLIMMR for malaria, developed at TIGR. **Tuberculosis Genome Oligo Set** Total number of oligos: 4,321 Number of *Mycobacterium tuberculosis* genes represented: 4,269 (+ 26 controls) Oligo length: 70 bases Distance from the 3' end: within 750 bases from the 3' end	**Pan Yeast Oligo Set** Number of oligos: 6,368 UniGene clusters represented: 6,250 Number of oligos per UniGene cluster: 1 Oligo length: 40 bases (5'-C6 amino modification) **Pan *H. pylori* Oligo Set** Number of oligos: 1,920 UniGene clusters represented: 1,877 Number of oligos per UniGene cluster: 1 Oligo length: 50 bases (5'-C6 amino modification) **Pan *E. coli* K12 Oligo Set** Number of oligos: 4,416 UniGene clusters represented: 4,289 Number of oligos per UniGene cluster: 1 Oligo length: 40 bases (5'-C6 amino modification)

Tuberculosis Genome Oligo Set (continued)

A major portion of the oligos were designed from the Sanger Center's set of 3,924 predicted protein-coding gene sequences for the *M. tuberculosis* genome. This set of predicted gene sequences is from the strain H37RV (lab strain), which was entirely sequenced at the Sanger Center. A smaller portion of the oligo set was designed from the strain CDC-1551, sequenced and predicted by TIGR. Note that 371 predicted genes from this strain were found to have <97% homology with H37RV predicted genes, and these are included in the oligo set.

Oligo Design

The production of the OligoLibraries is based on clustering and assembly of GenBank EST and mRNA sequences (GenBank version #121 was used for the design). The clustering algorithms take into account known repetitive elements, low-complexity regions, chimeric sequences, vector contamination, and correct sequence orientation. The oligo sequences are optimized to minimize the distance from the 3' end, cross-hybridization, and secondary structures and to normalize the homogeneity of GC content and T_m across the collection.

Assembly algorithms correct for sequencing errors, predict antisense genes, and use expressed and genomic data to model alternative splicing and predict transcripts for each gene. Using these criteria, each oligo was selected from a sequence segment common to a maximal number of transcripts predicted for a gene.

A proprietary program developed by Operon is used to design oligonucleotides 70 bases in length and to have normalized melting temperature, i.e., having a T_m range of ±2°C. The formula used to calculate the T_m is as follows:

$$T_m = 81.5 + 16.6 \times \log[Na^+] + 41 \times (\#G + \#C)/\text{length} - 500/\text{length}, \text{ where } [Na^+] = 0.1 \text{ M}$$

The oligos are designed to hybridize within 750 bases of the 3' end of the gene (ORF) in order to accommodate incomplete reverse transcription reactions using oligo(dT) priming. The sequences are optimized to have minimal homology (thus, minimal cross-hybridization) with other genes, by using BLAST against a large data set, including the genome database UniGene. The design allows for the differentiation of overlapping or alternatively spliced genes.

Oligos are selected on the basis of 3' bias and on preferential coding sequence. Redundant sequence entries for the same gene are assembled, and the most complete coding sequence is entered into the MWG CodeSeq database. CodeSeq includes alternative splice forms of the same gene. Each species-specific gene index can be searched to find the gene of interest. The same search tells to which family group a given gene belongs and which oligos are needed to detect it, its alternative splice form, or family members. Oligos are checked for cross-hybridization in extensive alignments based on BLAST and global Smith-Waterman searches. Secondary structure is minimized by testing for reverse complementarity. The sequences are optimized using BLAST against EST and genomic databases (the UniGene build used is the current release). The MWG CodeSeq database is used for all checks.

For in silico design, oligos are selected based on physical parameters, including GC content, T_m, secondary structure, primer dimer formation, and unique binding sites.

Continued on following pages.

TABLE 1-6. *Continued from previous pages.*

	Compugen[a]	Operon[b]	MWG Biotech[c]
Oligo synthesis	OligoLibraries are manufactured by Sigma-Genosys using the proprietary Abacus oligo synthesis platform that provides a coupling efficiency of 98.5%. The minimum amount of full-length sequence represented is 41% for human and 38% for mouse and rat.	The Mouse, Human, and Yeast Genome Oligo Sets carry the 5'-C6 amino modification. A coupling efficiency of 99% will give ~50% full-length products, whereas a coupling efficiency of 99.5% provides an expected yield of ~70% of full-length product. The efficiency reached is normally in the upper range at 99.25% or better. The capping efficiency during synthesis is observed to be up to 100%, resulting in almost no internal deletion products. (The mutation rate is reported to be 1/1000.)	All oligos are synthesized with a proprietary HPSF technology, ensuring a high percentage of full-length oligos, and no contaminants (salt, metal, etc.). All oligos are amino(C6)-modified 50 mers (some nonmammalian arrays use 40 mers where appropriate).
Quality control procedures	Quality control includes OD measurements on every oligo. MALDI-TOF mass spectrometry is performed on every batch of synthesized oligos to confirm molecular weight and to ensure correct well location and oligo sequence.	Monitoring is performed for trityl peaks, final trityl peaks, and iodine peaks to assess whether the synthesis process is running correctly. Iodine and trityl peaks are measured for all oligos together, not for the single oligo. The final trityl peaks are measured for every oligo to provide information about the last coupling step. The oligos are routinely assessed by UV spectroscopy. (Mass spectrometry is not possible for 70 mers.) Capillary electrophoresis can be performed with a portion of oligos to assess the yield of full-length oligos. UV spectroscopy is used as a direct assessment to check the coupling efficiency, because the yield will drop drastically if the coupling efficiency is decreased by 1% or more.	Trityl monitoring and MALDI-TOF mass spectrometry analysis are performed on all oligo sets to ensure 90% purity. Bar-coding and tracking ensures 100% identity confirmation of the plated product.
Supply format	OligoLibrary sets are provided as 96-well plates or custom 384-well plates. OligoLibrary subsets are provided as individual 384-well plates or sets of four 96-well plates. Oligos are arranged on the plates according to standard Gene Ontology (GO) assignments for easy selection of oligos derived from genes with similar function. Concentration: 50 μM (in H_2O) or 1 nmole Recommended printing concentration: 20 μM. Recommended printing surface: all major surfaces.	The genome oligo sets are provided in 96-well plates at 2000 pmoles per well, or in 384-well plates at 600 pmoles per well. Oligonucleotides are shipped as lyophilized samples (dried from water). Recommended printing concentration: 40 μM. Recommended printing surface: Poly-L-lysine-coated slides.	The oligo sets are provided in 96-well plates or 384-well plates, 1400 pmoles of oligo per well, supplied frozen in H_2O or at the concentration and in the buffer of the customer's choice. We offer our own optimized buffers for pin & ring and split-pin arrayers, or the customer can supply another buffer for us to use. Recommended printing surface: Epoxy and all major surfaces.

| Information provided | Interactive Web interface with search capabilities. Gene lists, plate and well locations, accession numbers, sequence information, oligo properties, gene annotation and GO assignments, links to NCBI Entrez and UniGene, proprietary LEADS data on mRNA splice variants, homology reports, SAGE expression reports, and more.

For gene lists and more information on the technology, please see http://www. labonweb. com/chips. | The genome oligo sets are accompanied by a user manual and disc containing a gene list with accession numbers and well positions, a T_m distribution graph, a readme file with product information, and a resuspension and printing protocol.

More information on the Array-Ready Oligo Sets is available via the Operon Microarray database (OMAD) on the Web. This database provides links to the corresponding genome databases, the gene sequence, chromosomal location, and the BLAST search results for each corresponding oligo. | Gene lists and more information on the technology are available at http://www.mwg-biotech.com. |

[a]Web Site: http://www.cgen.com.
[b]Web Site: http://www.operon.com.
[c]Web Site: http://www.mwg-biotech.com.
[d]Note that custom synthesis oligo sets are available from Invitrogen, Genosys, Transgenomics, and Illumina.

REFERENCES

Adams M., Kelly J., Gocayne J., Dubnick M., Polymeroppoulos M., Xiao H., Merril C., Wu A., Olde B., Moneno R., Kerlavage A., McCrombie R., and Venter J.C. 1991. Complementary DNA sequencing: Expressed sequence tags and Human Genome Project. *Science* **252**: 1651–1656.

Andrews J., Bouffard G.G., Cheadle C., Lu J., Becker K.G., and Oliver B. 2000. Gene discovery using computational and microarray analysis of transcription in the *Drosophila melanogaster* testis. *Genome Res.* **10**: 2030–2043.

Bhatia P., Taylor W.R., Greenberg A.H., and Wright J.A. 1994. Comparison of glyceraldehyde-3-phosphate dehydrogenase and 28S-ribosomal RNA gene expression as RNA loading controls for northern blot analysis of cell lines of varying malignant potential. *Anal. Biochem.* **216**: 223–226.

Bonaldo M.F., Lennon G., and Soares M.B. 1996. Normalization and subtraction: Two approaches to facilitate gene discovery. *Genome Res.* **6**: 791–806.

Brown P.O. and Botstein D. 1999. Exploring the new world of the genome with DNA microarrays. *Nat. Genet.* **21**: 33–37.

Cheung V.G. and Nelson S.F. 1998. Genomic mismatch scanning identifies human genomic DNA shared identical by descent. *Genomics* **47**: 1–6.

Christoffels A., van Gelder A., Greyling G., Miller R., Hide T., and Hide W. 2001. STACK: Sequence Tag Alignment and Consensus Knowledgebase. *Nucleic Acids Res.* **29**: 234–238.

Davis H.A., Wong D.T., Colbert I., Soares S., Sorge J.A., and Mullinax R.L. 2001. Normalize and validate array systems using exogenous nucleic acid controls. *Strategies Newsl.* **13(4)**: 128–130 (http://www.stratagene.com/vol13_4/p128-130.htm)

DeRisi J.L., Iyer V.R., and Brown P.O. 1997. Exploring the metabolic and genetic control of gene expression on a genomic scale. *Science* **278**: 680–686.

Diehl F., Grahlmann S., Beier M., and Hoheisel J.D. 2001. Manufacturing DNA microarrays of high spot homogeneity and reduced background signal. *Nucleic Acids Res.* **29**: E38.

Drexler H. 1988. Bacteriophage T1. In *The bacteriophages* (ed. R. Calendar), vol. 1, p. 236. Plenum Press, New York.

Eickhoff B., Korn B., Schick M., Poustka A., and van der Bosch J. 1999. Normalization of array hybridization experiments in differntial gene expression analysis. *Nucleic Acids Res.* **27**: e33.

Goffeau A., Barrell B.G., Bussey H., Davis R.W., Dujon B., Feldmann H., Galibert F., Hoheisel J.D., Jacq C., Johnston M., Louis E.J., Mewes H.W., Murakami Y., Philippsen P., Tettelin H., and Oliver S.G. 1996. Life with 6000 genes. *Science* **274**: 546–567.

Halgren R.G., Fielden M.R., Fong C.J., and Zacharewski T.R. 2001. Assessment of clone identity and sequence fidelity for 1189 IMAGE cDNA clones. *Nucleic Acids Res.* **29**: 582–588.

Hegde P., Qi R., Abernathy K., Gay C., Dharap S., Gaspard R., Hughes J.E., Snesrud E., Lee N., and Quackenbush J. 2000. A concise guide to cDNA microarray analysis. *BioTechniques* **29**: 548–556.

Hughes T.R., Mao M., Jones A.R., Burchard J., Marton M.J., Shannon K.W., Lefkowitz S.M., Ziman M., Schelter J.M., Meyer M.R., Kobayashi S., Davis C., Dai H., He Y.D., Stephaniants S.B., Cavet G., Walker W.L., West A., Coffey E., Shoemaker D.D., Stoughton R., Blanchard A.P., Friend S.H., and Linsley P.S. 2001. Expression profiling using microarrays fabricated by an ink-jet oligonucleotide synthesizer. *Nat. Biotechnol.* **19**: 342–347.

Iyer V.R., Horak C.E., Scafe C.S., Botstein D., Snyder M., and Brown P.O. 2001. Genomic binding sites of the yeast cell-cycle transcription factors SBF and MBF. *Nature* **409**: 533–538.

Iyer V.R., Eisen M.B., Ross D.T., Schuler G., Moore T., Lee J.C.F., Trent J.M., Staudt L.M., Hudson J., Jr., Boguski M.S., Lashkari D., Shalon D., Botstein D., and Brown P.O. 1999. The transcriptional program in the response of human fibroblasts to serum (see comments). *Science* **283**: 83–87.

Killmann H., Benz R., and Braun V. 1996. Properties of the FhuA channel in the *Escherichia coli* outer membrane after deletion of FhuA portions within and outside the predicted gating loop. *J. Bacteriol.* **178**: 6913–6920.

Killmann H., Videnov G., Jung G., Schwarz H., and Braun V. 1995. Identification of receptor binding sites by competitive peptide mapping: Phages T1, T5, and φ80 and colicin M bind to the gating loop of FhuA. *J. Bacteriol.* **177**: 694–698.

Knight J. 2001. When the chips are down. *Nature* **410**: 860–861.

Lennon G., Auffray C., Polymeropoulos M., and Soares M.B. 1996. The I.M.A.G.E. Consortium: An integrated molecular analysis of genomes and their expression. *Genomics* **33**: 151–152.

Mansur N.R., Meyer-Siegler K., Wurzer J.C., and Sirover M.A. 1993. Cell cycle regulation of the glyceraldehyde-3-phosphate dehydrogenase/uracil DNA glycosylase gene in normal human cells. *Nucleic Acids Res.* **21**: 993–998.

Miki R., Kadota K., Bono H., Tomaru Y., Carninci P., Itoh M., Shibata K., Kawai J., Konno H., Watanabe S., Sato K., Tokusumi Y., Kikuchi N., Ishii Y., Hamaguchi Y., Nishizuka I., Goto H., Nitanda H., Satomi S., Yoshiki A., Kusakabe M., DeRisi J.L., Eisen M.B., Iyer V.R., Brown P.O., Muramatsu M., Shimada H., Okazaki Y., and Hayashizaki Y. 2001. Delineating developmental and metabolic pathways in vivo by expression profiling using the RIKEN set of 18,816 full-length enriched mouse cDNA arrays. *Proc. Natl. Acad. Sci.* **98:** 2199–2204.

Miller R.T., Christoffels A.G., Gopalakrishnan C., Burke J., Ptitsyn A.A., Broveak T.R., and Hide W.A. 1999. A comprehensive approach to clustering of expressed human gene sequence: The sequence tag alignment and consensus knowledge base. *Genome Res.* **9:** 1143–1155.

Nature Genetics. 1999. The chipping forecast (supplement), vol. 21, no. 1. Nature America Inc., New York, New York.

Phimister B. 1999. Going global. *Nat. Genet.* **21:** 1.

Pluthero F.G. 1993. Rapid purification of high-activity Taq DNA polymerase. *Nucleic Acids Res.* **21:** 4850–4851.

Reid J.L., Iyer V.R., Brown P.O., and Struhl K. 2000. Coordinate regulation of yeast ribosomal protein genes is associated with targeted recruitment of Esa1 histone acetylase. *Mol. Cell* **6:** 1297–1307.

Ren B., Robert F., Wyrick J.J., Aparicio O., Jennings E.G., Simon I., Zeitlinger J., Schreiber J., Hannett N., Kanin E., Volkert T.L., Wilson C.J., Bell S.P., and Young R.A. 2000. Genome-wide location and function of DNA binding proteins. *Science* **290:** 2306–2309.

Sambrook J. and Russell D.W. 2001. *Molecular cloning: A laboratory manual,* 3rd edition. Cold Spring Harbor Laboratory Press, Cold Spring Harbor, New York.

Spanakis E. 1993. Problems related to the interpretation of autoradiographic data on gene expression using common constitutive transcripts as controls. *Nucleic Acids Res.* **21:** 3809–3819.

Ten Bosch J., Seidel C., Batra S., Lam H., Tuason N., Saljoughi S., Zhou H., and Saul R. 2001. Operon® Array-Ready Oligo Sets™ provide sequence-optimized 70 mers for DNA microarrays. *QIAGEN News* issue no. 4 (http://www.qiagen.com/literature/qiagennews).

Velculescu V.E., Zhang L., Zhou W., Vogelstein J., Basrai M.A., Bassett Jr., D.E., Hieter P., Vogelstein B., and Kinzler K.W. 1997. Characterization of the yeast transcriptome. *Cell* **88:** 243–251.

Wei Y., Lee J.M., Richmond C., Blattner F.R., Rafalski J.A., and LaRossa R.A. 2001. High-density microarray-mediated gene expression profiling of *Escherichia coli. J. Bacteriol.* **183:** 545–556.

Yang Y.H., Dudoit S., Luu D., Lin D.M., Peng V., Ngai J., and Speed T.P. 2002. Normalization for cDNA microarray data: A robust composite method addressing single and multiple slide systematic variation. *Nucleic Acids Res.* **30:** e15.

Yue H., Eastman P.S., Wang B.B., Minor J., Doctolero M.H., Nuttall R.L., Stack R., Becker J.W., Montgomery J.R., Vainer M., and Johnston R. 2001. An evaluation of the performance of cDNA microarrays for detecting changes in global mRNA expression. *Nucleic Acids Res.* **29:** E41–41.

WWW RESOURCES

http://cgap.nci.nih.gov The Cancer Genome Anatomy Project (CGAP)

http://genome.rtc.riken.go.jp/home.html RIKEN Genome Exploration Research Group, Genome Science Laboratory

http://genome.wustl.edu/est/mouse_esthmpg.html Washington University Mouse EST Project

http://image.llnl.gov I.M.A.G.E. Consortium (Integrated Molecular Analysis of Genomes and their Expression

http://image.llnl.gov/image/html/idistributors.shtml The I.M.A.G.E. Consortium Distributors

http://image.llnl.gov/image/imagene/current/bin/search IMAGEne Database

http://mgc.nci.nih.gov Mammalian Gene Collection (MGC), National Cancer Institute

http://mwgbiotech.com MWG Biotech Homepage

http://www.allgenes.org All Genes database. Computational Biology and Informatics Laboratory at the University of Pennsylvania.

http://www.apbiotech.com/lsn–home/lsn–index.html Samartzidou H., Turner L., and Houts T. 2001. Lucidea™ Microarray ScoreCard: An integrated tool for validation of microarray gene expression experiments. Amersham Biosciences LSN On-line

http://www.arrayit.com TeleChem International, Inc.

http://www.atcc.org American Type Culture Collection (ATCC)

http://www.atcc.org/SearchCatalogs/tasc2.cfm#who ATCC: Who makes ESTs

http://www.beckman.com Beckman Coulter, Inc. Homepage

http://www.biorobotics.co.uk/Pages/replicat.html BioRobotics Replication Accessories

http://www.cbc.umn.edu/ResearchProjects/Arabidopsis/index.html *Arabidopsis* cDNA Sequence Analysis Project

http://www.cbil.upenn.edu Computational Biology of Informatics Laboratory at the University of Pennsylvania.

http://www.cgen.com Compugen Ltd.Homepage

http://www.fruitfly.org Berkeley *Drosophila* Genome Project (BDGP)

http://www.fruitfly.org/sequence/genomic-clones.html BDGP Release 2.5 Drosophila Genomic Sequence

http://www.genetix.com Genetix Homepage

http://www.genome.washington.edu/uwgc/analysistools/repeatmask.htm RepeatMasker (University of Washington Genome Center

http://www.jgi.doe.gov/programs/instrumentation/preptrack.htm JGI Programs, DOE Joint Genome Institute operated by The University of California for the U.S. Department of Energy Lawrence Berkeley National Lab Human Genome Center (Kaaren Q'd David-see Liq.Handling)

http://www.labonweb.com/chips LabOnWeb Oligolibraries

http://www.lionbioscience.com LION Bioscience

http://www.mwg-biotech.com MWG Biotech AG

http://www.ncbi.nlm.nih.gov/BLAST National Center for Biotechnology Information, BLAST Info

http://www.ncbi.nlm.nih.gov/dbEST/index.html Expressed Sequence Tags Database

http://www.ncbi.nlm.nih.gov/gorf/gorf.html Open Reading Frame (ORF) Finder

http://www.ncbi.nlm.nih.gov/UniGene/index.html UniGene Resources

http://www.operon.com Operon Homepage

http://www.packardbioscience.com Packard BioScience Company Homepage

http://www.premierbiosoft.com/dnamicroarray/dnamicroarray.html Premier Biosoft International

http://www.qiagen.com QIAGEN Homepage

http://www.resgen.com ResGen: An Invitrogen Corporation

http://www.robsci.com Robbins Scientific Homepage

http://www.rzpd.de Resource Center/Primary Database (RZPD)

http://www.sanbi.ac.za/Dbases.html South African National Bioinformatics Institute (SNABI)

http://www.stat.Berkeley.EDU/users/terry/zarray/Html/normspie.html) Yang Y.H., Dudoit S., Luu P., and Speed T. 2001. Normalization for cDNA microarray data. Speed Group Microarray Page.

http://www.stratagene.com/vol13_4/p128-130.htm Stratagene Inc. *Strategies Newsletter.*

http://www.tecan-us.com TECAN U.S.

http://www.tigr.org The Institute for Genomic Research (TIGR)

http://www.tigr.org/tdb/egad/egad.shtml The Expressed Gene Anatomy Database (EGAD)

http://www.tigr.org/tdb/hgi/index.html TIGR Human Gene Index

http://www.tigr.org/tdb/index.shtml TIGR Databases

2

Printing Spotted Glass Microarrays

INTRODUCTION

Placing DNA samples at regular intervals on a solid support is conceptually straightforward, but precise and reliable manufacture of microarrays is not without its challenges. This section focuses on the production of microarrays on glass slides for expression analysis. The production and use of filter microarrays are described in Section 4.

Glass slide microarrays were first produced at Stanford University (Schena et al. 1995). The microarrays were produced by an *XYZ* axis gantry robot that used banks of pins to ferry small volumes of DNA solutions from the wells of 96-well plates to the prepared surfaces of a series of glass slides. Although other approaches seem likely to displace it in the near future, at the time of writing, this process is the workhorse technique for the "in-house" production

61

of microarrays. Initially, the availability of commercially produced microarray robots was very limited, and the early pioneers of the technology made use of detailed specifications provided by Pat Brown's group to build their own arrayers (http://cmgm.stanford.edu/ pbrown/mguide/index.html). Building one's own arrayer remains an effective and affordable option. However, an increasing number of commercial robots are available that can precisely position a print head over a field of glass slides, and many investigators opt to purchase these devices as a fast, relatively painless (but not inexpensive), way of entering into the arraying field. Summaries of some of these machines and the issues affecting their performance are discussed in Table 2-1 and in the information panel on **ARRAYERS AND PINS USED FOR CONTACT PRINTING OF MICROARRAYS** at the end of this section.

Common procedures for printing glass slide microarrays using contact spotting arrayers are described in Protocol 2. The protocol is supported by the information panel on **ARRAYERS AND PINS USED FOR CONTACT PRINTING OF MICROARRAYS**, which discusses some of the issues that determine the quality of the microarrays produced. Key among these are the shape, reproduciblity, and durability of the printing pins (also referred to as tips, pens, and quills). Uneven pins deliver unequal volumes of DNA solution during a print run and tax the abilities of image analysis programs. Problems with pins, which become readily apparent

TABLE 2-1. Arrayers: Specifications

Company	Time to print full platter of 10K slides	Slide capacity/ immobilization	Dimensions in cm (WxDxH)	Wash and sonication	Pins	Pitch, spot size, maximum density
Affymetrix: affymetrix.com						
Affymetrix 417 Arrayer	25 hr (including wash/dry time)	42/spring clips and aligning bars	80x53x49	Fluid stream, vacuum dry	1 or 4 Pin and Ring, 1.5 µl per pickup 50 pl delivered	User-defined, by 10-µm steps 150–200 µm >30,000
Affymetrix 427 Arrayer	12.5 hr (including wash/dry time)	42/spring clips and aligning bars	80x53x49	Fluid stream, Venturi system (compressed air)	8 Pin and Ring, 0.5 µl per pickup 50 pl delivered	User-defined, by 10-µm steps 150–200 µm >30,000
BioRobotics: www.BioRobotics.com						
Microgrid 2	8 hr for 108 slides	108	90x75x76	Vac/wash	Solid pins (BioRobotics) or quill (Telechem) 1–64	10 µm
Microgrid 2 compact	4 hr	48	60x70x74	Vac/wash	Solid pins (BioRobotics) or quill (Telechem) 1–48	10 µm
Microgrid 1	8 hr for 94 slides	84		Wash	Solid pins (BioRobotics) or quill (Telechem) 1–48	200 µm
Cartesian: www.cartesian.com						
MicroSys 5100	3.5 hr	10	60.5x35.5x38	Vac/wash	Quill Telechem 32	150 µm

once the slides are hybridized and scanned, are depicted in the Troubleshooting Guide in Section 3. Some arrayers are supplied with proprietary pins, whereas others make use of pins from one of several specialist manufacturers. Protocol 3 describes processes for the care and cleaning of pins, as well as sources of commercially produced pins.

Another critical element affecting spot morphology is the solution in which the DNA is resuspended. For a discussion of different spotting solutions, please see Section 1, Protocol 5. The generation of array-ready material for spotting is described in Section 1, Protocols 2 and 3. The nature of the spotting material and the choice of slide substrate are tightly linked. The information panel on **SUBSTRATES FOR PRINTING** provides details of some commonly used substrates and their availability. Protocol 1 describes the preparation of slides coated with poly-L-lysine and their treatment prior to printing.

Because of the physics of picoliter spot delivery, the spot quality and array sensitivity are ultimately dependent on an interplay among printer movement, pin performance, the physical and chemical characteristics of the DNA solution, and the printing surface. Given these considerations, there is no substitute for systematically determining the best combination of these factors appropriate to the particular platform for each research facility.

Resolution in microns	Plate stacker Lids on or off Capacity Plate format	Humidity	Air filtration	Other features
Accuracy: ±10 Repeatability: ±2	No 3 microplate slots, manual load	No	No	Consistent spotting (no loss of spots from first to last); integrated system: spotting, scanning, tracking software, analysis software, mining software; dedicated field service and field support
Accuracy: ±10 Repeatability: ±2	No 3 microplate slots, manual load	Yes	No	Consistent spotting (no loss of spots from first to last); integrated system: spotting, scanning, tracking software, analysis software, mining software; dedicated field service and field support
1.5	Integrated stacker; 24 plates lids on 96/384/1536	Yes/extra	Yes/extra	Clonetracking Softtouch Bar code reading Plate cooling Membrane printing
1.5	1–4 plate capacity	Yes/extra	Yes/extra	Clone tracking Softtouch Bar code reading
5	Integrated stacker; 24 plates lid on 96/384	No	Yes/extra	Clone tracking Bar code reading Membrane printing
1.5	No	Yes	–	No

(Continued on following pages.)

TABLE 2-1. *Continued*

Company	Time to print full platter of 10K slides	Slide capacity/ immobilization	Dimensions in cm (WxDxH)	Wash and sonication	Pins	Pitch, spot size, maximum density
PixSys 5500	6 hr	50	76.2x81.2x65.5	Vac/wash	Quill Telechem 32 or 48	150 μm
ProSys 5510	6.5 hr	100	71x74x36.5	Vac/wash/sonic	Quill Telechem 32 or 48	150 μm
GeneMachines: www.genemachines.com						
OmniGrid	10,000 spots for 100 slides in 3.5 hr; with 48 pins, one 384-well plate can be deposited on 100 slides in less than 7.5 min; 28,000 spots in <8.5 hr	100	135x143x153	Customizable combination of sonication water/fluid wash with peristaltic pump and vacuum dry	1–48 Telechem quill or solid, Majer Precision quill; pins available through GeneMachines	User-defined, in 2.5-μm increments, 10-μm minimum 100–200 μm (depending on tip type) 100,000+ features per slide
OmniGrid Accent	10,000 spots for 50 slides in 2.5 hr; 4000 spots per slide on 50 slides with 48 pins in 1 hr	50	104.5x74x53.3 130x130x160	Customizable combination of sonication, water/fluid wash with peristaltic pump, and vacuum dry	1–48 Telechem quill or solid, Majer Precision quill; pins available through GeneMachines	User-defined in 2.5-μm increments, 10-μm minimum 100–200 μm (depending on tip type) 100,000+ features per slide
Genetix: www.genetix.com						
QArray	26 hr for 84x10K slides with 24 Genetix 150-μm diameter tip solid microarray pins; 8.5 hr with 24 multispot (split) pins; time includes pin loading, wash/dry cycles (variable)	84/spring held clips in 6 removable slide holders	143x73x175 including table	3 different washing reagents at high pressure and compressed air drying	Up to 24 Genetix 150-μm diameter tip solid microarray pins; approved for use with other manufacturers; option to have up to 48 pins	280 μm with a spot diameter of 250 μm using Genetix 150-μm pins; pitch depends on array pattern, is user selectable in 1-μm steps
QArray*lite*	Data not available	90/vacuum held with 6 independent rows of 15 slides	143x73x75 QArray Lite unit only	2 different washing reagents at high pressure and compressed air drying; options include 3 bottle, 1 bottle, or sonicator bath	Up to 24 Genetix 150-μm diameter tip solid microarray pins; approved for use with other manufacturers; option to have up to 48 pins	280 μm with a spot diameter of 250 μm using Genetix 150-μm pins; pitch depends on array pattern, is user selectable in 1-μm steps
QArray*mini*	Data not available	54/vacuum held	93x65x52	2 different washing reagents at high pressure and compressed air drying	Up to 24 Genetix 150-μm diameter tip solid microarray pins	280 μm with a spot diameter of 250 μm using Genetix 150-μm pins; pitch depends on array pattern, is user selectable

Resolution in microns	Plate stacker Lids on or off Capacity Plate format	Humidity	Air filtration	Other features
1.5	Optional	Yes	–	Clone tracking
1.5	Optional	Yes	–	Clone tracking, bar code, vision system, ultrasonic wash station
Accuracy: <±2.5 Positional Resolution: 2.5 μm (*x* and *y* axes); 1.25 μm (*z*-axis)	Optional server Arm for handling 72 96- or 384-well plates; long, unattended runs; delidding feature; allows random access of sample plates	Yes Control up to 80% with sensor and controller	Yes HEPA filtration for dust-free printing	Standard enclosure; clear panels in a controlled environment. Flexible software; multiple duplications options; calibration settings, input plates, user-defined print area; substrates, and wash scheme; samples tracking feature integrates OmniGrid's array data with scanner and anallysis software Custom substrate sizes and types; membrane printing; blotting pad Field and in-house applications support Optional: Bar code system Incyte license included
2.5	No 3 96-well or 384-well plates	Optional Control up to 80% with sensor and controller	Yes HEPA filtration for dust-free printing	Laptop computer included; software with multiple array design options, plate calibrations, input plates, user-defined print area; substrates, and wash schemes; sample tracking feature integrates Accent's array data with leading scanner and analysis software Custom substrate sizes and types; membrane printing; blotting pad Comprehensive field and in-house support Incyte license included
1 μm on all axes (*x, y,* and *z*)	Optional plate stacker for up to 70 Genetix low-profile 96- or 384-well plates, with automated lid removal and replacement; plate capacity without stacker is 5 96- or 384-well plates	Yes standard	Yes standard	Flexible pattern set up and use of varying numbers of pins, e.g., 1, 2, 4, 8, 16, and 24; spot pitch can be varied in steps of 1 μm; options to calibrate multispotting pins and vary dip depth in the well plate at the start of the run; linked database for storing well plate information (QSoft Library Manager) used to generate exported data files for spot tracking during data analysis; software can track bar codes on source plates and slides; optional stacker with automated lid lift for source plates
1 μm on all axes (*x, y,* and *z*)	No stacker available; plate capacity is 5 96- or 384-well plates	Optional	Optional	Flexible pattern set up and use of varying numbers of pins, e.g., 1, 2, 4, 8, 16, and 24; spot pitch can be varied in steps of 1 μm; options to calibrate multispotting pins and vary dip depth in the well plate at the start of the run; linked database for storing well plate information (QSoft Library Manager) used to generate exported data files for spot tracking during data analysis; adjustable height source plate holder allows the use of a range of plate types
1 μm (*x* axis), 1 μm (*y* axis), 50 μm (*z* axis)	No stacker available; plate capacity is 5 96/384-well plates	Optional	Optional	Flexible pattern set up and use of varying numbers of pins, e.g., 1, 2, 4, 8, and 16; QSoft Library Manager used to generate exported data files for spot tracking during data analysis; adjustable height source plate holder allows the use of a range of plate types

(Continued on following pages.)

TABLE 2-1. *Continued*

Company	Time to print full platter of 10K slides	Slide capacity/ immobilization	Dimensions in cm (WxDxH)	Wash and sonication	Pins	Pitch, spot size, maximum density
Intelligent Bioinstruments: www.intelligentbio.com						
IBI Microarrayer HT	Adjustable by user	100	75x25	Automated soni-cated wash system, multipin vacuum dry station	12–48 spotting pins	5000 spots/sq. cm 20,000 spots/slide 100–150 μm, 75–100-μm pin optional
Packard BioScience: www.packardbioscience.com						
SpotArray Enterprise	300 samples/hr onto 108 slides; cycle time depends on cleaning desired and material printed	108/vacuum; custom chips and microplates possible (nonslide)	173.4x122.4x130	2 wash stations; custom internal and external sonication	8 Piezo tips	1600 spots/sq. cm Size: 150–200 μm, depends on sub-strate
SpotArray 24	1536 (4x384) duplicate samples on 20 slides in 26 min	24/positioned using precision registration actuators	Instrument module: 66.3x64x41; 60 lbs	4 pressure jets/pin, vacuum drying	1–48 Stealth pins	Up to 81,920 spots/slide, 75–150 μm in diameter
SpotArray 72 (see SpotArray 24)	duplicate samples on 68 slides in 1 hr	72 slides	100x70x43 130 lbs	Same as above	Same as above	Same as above
BioChip Arrayer	100 samples on 20 slides in 1 hr	25/vacuum held; custom chips and microplates possible	135x84x58.6	2 wash stations; custom internal and external sonication	4 Piezo tips	1600 spots/sq. cm Size: 150–200 μm, depends on sub-strate
TeleChem: www.arrayit.com						
SpotBot Personal Microarrayer	30 hr (including sample load, and wash/dry time)	14/spring with aligning bar	30x30x24	Fluid bath, compressed air manifold dry; programable	1, 2, or 4 patented Stealth Micro-spotting Pins; 0.25 μl per pickup; 0.5 nl delivered; 20 designs	User-defined in 1-μm increments 90–300 μm depending on the Stealth pin used ~50,000
Virtek Vision Corp: ww.virtekbiotech.com						
Chipwriter Pro	~8 hr	126 glass slides or 15 membranes	127x97x126	Vacuum; flow-through wash station; sonicator	Up to 48 TeleChem Stealth quill pins or 48 TeleChem solid pins	User-defined by 1.25-μm steps min center to center: 120-μm spot diam-eter: Microspotting pins 75–400 μm; solid pins 75–500 μm; Max. density: 123,333 spots/slide
Chipwriter Compact	~6 hr	24 glass slides or 2 membranes	60x87.5x67.5	Vacuum; 2 wash stations; sonicator; flexible, user-defined protocols for pin cleaning	Up to 48 TeleChem Stealth quill pins or 48 Telechem solid pins	User-defined by 2.5-μm steps min center to center: 150-μm spot diam-eter: Microspotting pins 75–400 μm; solid pins 75–500 μm; Max. density: 78,933 spots/slide

Resolution in microns	Plate stacker Lids on or off Capacity Plate format	Humidity	Air filtration	Other features
0.55 μm (*x* axis) 0.88 μm (*y* axis) 1.63 μm (*z* axis)	Automated plate and lid handling; up to 108 plates 96/384-well plates	Optional	Optional	Chilled storage chamber for plates Programmable spot spacing Blotting station Bar code reader
0.1-μm precision; 8-μm accuracy; 1-μm precision	Up to 50 plates, chilled to 4ºC; 96/384 well plates	Not applicable for Piezo printing	Not available	Noncontact dispensing; can handle custom-size chips; flexible samples (DNA, proteins, cells, beads, peptides); <6% coefficient of variation uniformity of spot size
Repeatability: ±10	1–4 96- or 384-well plates; lid lifter	Controlled between 50–65% RH	0.3-μm HEPA filter	Pin lifter creates more compact arrays; plate bar code reader; lid lifter and sensors to ensure lid is removed; optional flat panel monitor
Same as above	Same as above	Same as above	Same as above	Same as above, with 3 times more spots in twice the time compared to SpotArray 24
Resolution: 2-μm Accuracy: 20-μm Repeatability: ±10	Up to 4 source plates, cooled to 4ºC	Not applicable for Piezo printing	Ionizer to remove static	Noncontact dispensing; can handle custom-size chips; flexible samples (DNA, proteins, cells, beads, peptides); <5% coefficient of variation uniformity of spot size; targeting camera to spot on microstructures
Accuracy: ±10 Repeatability: ±10	No 1 384-well microplates manual load	Coming soon	Coming soon	Equipped with a Mini-Stealth Micro Spotting device (U.S. Patent Number 6101946); lowest cost arrayer on the market; comes calibrated and includes mapping software; easy self-install/setup; completely portable; prints a variety of sample types including DNA, proteins, carbohydrates, lipids, and more
1.25 μm (*x, y* axis) 0.25 μm (*z* axis)	Yes Plate capacity of 18 or 32 for 96- or 384-well plates	Yes	Yes	Clone tracking; liquid handling; colony picking; membrane gridding; up to 250 spots/source well visit Fixed platen; suitable for most genomic and proteomic applications
1.22 μm (*x, y* axis) 0.61 μm (*z* axis)	No stacker available; plate capacity of 1 96- or 384-well plate	Yes	Yes	Built-in sample tracking; ability to spot both slides and membranes Fixed platen; suitable for most genomic and proteomic applications

Preparing Poly-L-lysine Slides for Microarrays

DeRisi Laboratory

University of California, San Francisco, California 94143

Poly-L-lysine is one of the most effective coating agents for glass slides used in microarray analysis; for a discussion of substrates, surfaces, and coating agents, please see the information panel on **SUBSTRATES FOR PRINTING** at the end of this section. This protocol describes the preparation of reagents and a method for coating a batch of 180 glass slides with poly-L-lysine. Note that the use of commercial coated slides is not recommended by the DeRisi laboratory.

- Ensure that the slide racks are bent slightly inward in the middle to hold slides more securely.
- Use nitrile gloves. DO NOT use powdered gloves at any time.
- To avoid dust, keep slides covered or submerged in solution at all times.
- Use calcium- and magnesium-free phosphate-buffered saline (PBS).
- For measuring poly-L-lysine, use only plastic labware.

  WARNING: Wear eye protection, gloves, and laboratory coat.

MATERIALS

CAUTION: Please see Appendix 3 for appropriate handling of materials marked with <!>.

Buffers and Solutions

Please see Appendix 2 for components of stock solutions, buffers, and reagents.
Dilute stock solutions to the appropriate concentrations.

Ethanol (95% and 70%)
> Some batches of absolute ethanol (100% or 200 proof) have been reported to contain fluorescent contaminants that generate high backgrounds in microarray experiments; 95% ethanol does not have this problem. To avoid difficulties, either use 95% ethanol or identify a brand of absolute ethanol that does not generate high levels of background fluorescence. Absolute ethanol (USP grade, 64-17-5) purchased from Warner-Graham Co. (Cockeysville, Maryland) performs consistently well.

H_2O (sterile)

NaOH pellets <!>

1x Phosphate-buffered saline (PBS) (filtered), without Mg^{2+} and Ca^{2+}

Poly-L-lysine solution (0.1% w/v) (P 8920, Sigma)

Special Equipment

Horizontal shaker
Microslides (glass, Gold Seal; 12-518-100A, Fisher)
Slide box (plastic)
Slide chamber (glass; ThermoShandon)
Slide racks (metal; ThermoShandon)
Tabletop centrifuge with plate carriers (e.g., GS-6KR Allegra 6R series, Beckman Instruments)
Vacuum oven (50°C)

METHOD

1. Prepare the slide wash solution.

   a. Dissolve 200 g of NaOH pellets in 800 ml of sterile H_2O.

      WARNING: This is a strongly exothermic reaction! Wear eye protection, gloves, and lab coat.

   b. Add additional NaOH pellets to the solution until it is saturated.

   c. Add 1200 ml of 95% ethanol to the NaOH solution.

   d. Add additional H_2O to the solution until it clears.

2. Rinse the slide dishes thoroughly with H_2O. Place one rack of Gold Seal microslides (30 slides/rack) in each slide dish.

3. Cover the slides with the wash solution prepared in Step 1. Place the slide dishes on a shaking platform and shake the dishes gently for at least 1–6 hours.

   This wash removes residual oil and debris from "precleaned" slides.

4. Rinse each rack of slides individually with distilled H_2O for ~30 seconds, making sure to rinse both surfaces of each slide. After rinsing, submerge the slide racks in a 4-liter beaker filled with H_2O. Stack the racks so that they all fit in the same beaker. It is best to let the slides sit overnight in H_2O to ensure the removal of all NaOH.

   Alternatively, submerge the slide racks in a glass slide dish filled with H_2O, rinse for 30 minutes, and then transfer to another slide dish filled with H_2O. Repeat the wash four times.

5. Prepare the poly-L-lysine solution in individual slide dishes by mixing the following reagents on a stir plate.

H_2O	285 ml
PBS (filtered) Ca^{2+}- and Mg^{2+}-free	35 ml
poly-L-lysine solution	30 ml

6. Remove each rack from the 4-liter beaker of H_2O and allow the excess fluid to drain away. Submerge the slides in the poly-L-lysine solution, and gently agitate the slides in the solution on a horizontal shaker for 30–60 minutes.

7. Rinse each rack individually by removing them one by one from the poly-L-lysine solution, allowing them to drain briefly, and submerging them in a fresh 4-liter beaker of H_2O. Twist each rack gently back and forth to rinse, and then place it into a tabletop centrifuge (GS-6KR or equivalent).

It is possible to reuse the poly-L-lysine solution if several batches of slides are to be prepared. Simply filter the solution after each use and store it in a plastic container at 4ºC. The filtered solution may be used up to four times, but it should be discarded after 2 months.

8. Dry the slides by centrifuging the racks at the lowest speed (540 rpm) for 2 minutes.

    Wipe the inside of the centrifuge before loading the racks to remove any dust that could be transferred onto the slides.

9. Place the slides in a vacuum oven and dry them for 10–30 minutes at 50ºC.

10. Store the slides in a clean plastic box for *at least* 14 days before spotting DNA.

    IMPORTANT: We do *not* recommend using slides that are more than 4 months old. The hydrophobicity of a slide can be tested by watching a drop of water slide down its surface. No beads of water should remain attached to the slide.

IMPORTANT: Before printing the slides:

- Check that the poly-L-lysine coating is not opaque.
- Check the quality of each batch of slides by printing, hybridizing, and scanning a sample set (please see Protocol 4).

Printing on Glass Slides

Aldo Massimi,* Thomas Harris,* Geoffrey Childs,* and Shauna Somerville[†]

*Albert Einstein College of Medicine, Bronx, New York 10461; [†]Carnegie Institution of Washington, Stanford, California 94305

Protocols for printing material onto glass slides in dense arrays vary depending on the features and components of the particular arrayer (for a discussion of various microarray printing robots, please see the information panel on **ARRAYERS AND PINS USED FOR CONTACT PRINTING OF MICROARRAYS** at the end of this section). This protocol provides generic background information required to set up the print run and to process the printed slides in readiness for hybridization. Details of the printing process itself are *not* described here and are best obtained from the advice supplied by the manufacturer of the arrayer. Yue (2001) provides a useful analysis of issues affecting glass microarray performance. The following critical issues should be considered before commencing with any print run:

Array Material

- Check the preparations of amplified DNAs on agarose gels to confirm that only a single band is present. Purify the amplified DNAs from contaminating primers, salts, nucleotides, and proteins (please see Section 1, Protocol 3).

- Resuspend the amplified cDNAs in printing solution at 150–250 µg/ml (please see Section 1, Protocol 5). If the DNA has been dried down at the end of the last print run (which is the best way to store it), resuspend it for several hours or overnight (Section 1, Protocol 5). Centrifuge the plates briefly after resuspension so that the DNA solution is deposited in the base of the wells. Adjust the print head of the gridding robot so that the printing pins dip into the wells to a depth of ~1 mm. This precaution is taken to minimize the amount of printing solution that adheres to the outside of the printing pins. Excess solution on the outside of the printing pins will be distributed disproportionately to the first few spots that are printed, giving rise to large irregular spots.

- Dissolve the material for arraying in a printing buffer appropriate for the slides to be used. Do not use buffers (e.g., Tris) containing free amine groups that inhibit binding of DNA to silanated or silylated slides (please see the information panel on **SUBSTRATES FOR PRINTING**).

- Resuspend long oligonucleotides for printing at a concentration of ~40 pM.

- Establish an appropriate print order, taking into account which controls should be included, where the controls should be placed on the array, how many times per array the controls should be printed, etc. It is advisable to include control DNAs known to give bright spots in the four corners of every sub-grid within the array, as this makes it easier to establish the grids used by various software programs to align with the printed array image. For further considerations, please see the information panel on **CONTROLS USED IN SPOTTED MICROARRAYS** in Section 1.

Printers and Pins

- Examine the pins under a stereomicroscope to verify that the external face and groove (quill pin) is clean and that the pin ends are intact and straight. Rectify any problems if necessary. For methods used to clean pins, please see Protocol 4 and the information panel on **ARRAYERS AND PINS USED FOR CONTACT PRINTING OF MICROARRAYS.**
- Warm up the printer and ensure that it is operating correctly. Check that the humidity is within acceptable limits. A relative humidity within the range of 50–60% is generally recommended.

Arrayer Set Up

- Do not touch the arrayer if you are not sure how to configure it—alignment among the pins, plates, and slides must be correct. Grinding pins into the surface of a misaligned microtiter plate is a very expensive mistake.
- Before using the arrayer to print valuable samples, carry out a test print run with a single test plate to verify that the machine is operating correctly. Confirm that the humidity (50–60%) and temperature (20–24ºC) are within the normal range. Check that each pin is performing correctly and clean those that are not (Protocol 4).
- Make certain that the wash station is operating correctly.
- For a discussion of performance characteristics including dwell time and contact speed, please see the information panel on **ARRAYERS AND PINS USED FOR CONTACT PRINTING OF MICROARRAYS.**

Slides

- Ensure that the slides are of high quality and that their surface properties match the characteristics of the printing buffer (please see the information panel on **SUBSTRATES FOR PRINTING**).
- Some slides are coated only on one side (e.g., ArrayIT Super Amine slides available from http://arrayit.com/Products/Substrates/substrates.html). Take care to ensure that the coated side is facing up.
- Label slides with a diamond pen; do not use ink. Note the orientation of the slides in the arrayer so that the position of the first spot is consistent between batches. Do not allow the slides to be moved during the print run.
- Ensure that there are plenty of slides in stock (note that slides coated with poly-L-lysine should not be more than 4 months old). It is advisable to test print and hybridize a new batch of slides before using them in a large-scale print run.
- Check that the print head remains in register with all of the slides on the platter. Small errors in slide dimensions, when accumulated across an entire platter of slides, can result in a substantial displacement of slide position (please see Figure 2-1).

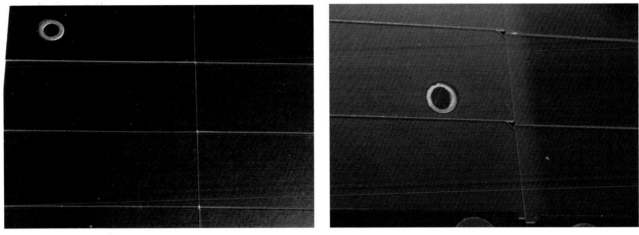

FIGURE 2-1. Layout of slides on a printing platter. (*Left*) Slides of regular dimensions aligned correctly on a printing platter; (*right*) slides of irregular dimensions that do not align properly.

The Print Run

For a well-executed print run:

- Ensure close, continuous monitoring of the machine throughout the run. If the print run will be long, draw up a well-defined schedule for the people involved. Organize a tag-team approach.
- Arrange the slides on the platter and immobilize them.
- Recheck the configuration of the arrayer.
- Once the run is under way, make sure that the plate changes are carried out according to the schedule.
- Stop the print run occasionally and check the spots on the slides using a magnifying glass, looking for evidence of pin clogging or spots that are too large. Irregularities in every spot suggest problems such as humidity, volume of the printing solution, or the printer settings. Problems with individual spots suggest a problem with the corresponding pin, which should be removed and checked carefully.
- If spots are missing from occasional slides, there may be a problem with the Z-axis settings, exacerbated by the table not being completely flat.
- At the end of the print run, allow the slides to dry for ~12 hours, and then carefully remove them for processing as described in the protocol below. Drying for this period may facilitate binding of the printed DNA and the slide coating.
- At the end of the print run, remove the pins and clean them in a sonicating bath. Rinse them with ethanol and store them dry, as described in Protocol 3.
- Avoid handling the slides with latex gloves as these can release fluorescent compounds.

Postprinting Processing

The specific method used for processing of slides after printing is dictated to a large extent by the type of coating on the slide surface (please see the information panel on **SUBSTRATES FOR**

PRINTING). In general, however, postprinting processing includes the following steps.

- Fixing the DNA to the slide surface (baking and/or UV cross-linking).
- Prewashing the slide to remove unbound DNA.
- Denaturing the DNA.
- Blocking remaining unbound sites on the slide.
- Removing blocking reagents by washing.
- Storing homemade poly-L-lysine slides to allow them to mature.

The slides can be analyzed both before and after processing to ensure proper arraying using one of the methods described in Protocol 3.

MATERIALS

CAUTION: Please see Appendix 3 for appropriate handling of materials marked with <!>.

Buffers and Reagents

Please see Appendix 2 for components of stock solutions, buffers, and reagents.
Dilute stock solutions to the appropriate concentrations.

Ethanol (95%)
> Some batches of absolute ethanol (100% or 200 proof) have been reported to contain fluorescent contaminants that generate high backgrounds in microarray experiments; 95% ethanol does not have this problem. To avoid difficulties, either use 95% ethanol or identify a brand of absolute ethanol that does not generate high levels of background fluorescence. Absolute ethanol (USP-grade ethyl alcohol, 64-17-5) purchased from Warner-Graham Co. (Cockeysville, Maryland) performs consistently well.

H_2O (sterile)
$NaBH_4$ (S 9125, Sigma) <!>
Phosphate-buffered saline (PBS), without Mg^{2+} and Ca^{2+} (P 3813, Sigma)
SDS (0.2%) <!>

Nucleic Acids and Oligonucleotides

Printed microarrays

Special Equipment

Diamond pen for marking slides
Hot plate set at 100–140ºC (see Step 3)
Nitrile gloves (powder-free)
Oven set at 80ºC
Slide rack (900234, Wheaton)
Tabletop centrifuge, equipped with slide holders (e.g., Beckman GS-6KR or Allegra 6R)
UV cross-linker (Stratagene 1800 or 2400 Stratalinker)
Water bath (boiling)

METHOD

The following regimen applies primarily to poly-L-lysine- and aldehyde-coated slides. Many of these steps are common to the treatments for different types of slides. Specific requirements for a number of commonly used slides are indicated in the panel **SPECIFIC CONDITIONS FOR PROCESSING PRINTED SLIDES** at the end of this protocol. For procedures appropriate for different commercial slides, also consult the manufacturers' protocols.

Marking the Slides

1. Wear powder-free nitrile gloves to remove the slides from the printing plates and place them in a slide holder.

2. Use a diamond pen to mark the boundaries of the array on the back of the slide with lines above and below the array.

   The array will become invisible when salts are removed during postprinting processing. The markings on the slide will help in correctly placing the target solution and coverslip.

Rehydration

3. (*Optional*) Rehydrate the DNA by lightly moistening the array face of each slide in the vapor of a warm (<37ºC) water bath for 1–5 minutes. To prevent condensation, the slides should be at room temperature before being exposed to the water vapor. The arrayed spots should "glisten" but not run together. Immediately snap-dry the slide by heating it for 1–2 seconds on a hot plate set at 100–140ºC.

   Some investigators swear by this step, whereas others find it unnecessary. Whether it is required depends on the characteristics of the printing solution, slide substrate, and arrayer/pin performance. The purpose of the step is to encourage the DNA to become distributed evenly across the full diameter of the spot and to reduce the appearance of doughnuts. However, if done inappropriately, rehydration can result in smearing of spotted samples. Consider performing this step if slides have many spots with doughnut morphology as shown in the Troubleshooting Guide in Section 3.

Fixation of DNA to the Substrate

The method used to fix the DNA covalently to the slide substrate, usually by either baking or UV cross-linking, depends on the nature of the slide surface. Because covalent attachment of DNA to aldehyde-modified slides occurs by an amine-aldehyde condensation reaction, there is no need to fix DNA printed onto these slide surfaces. The recommended method for fixation of DNA to poly-L-lysine-coated slides is UV cross-linking, whereas baking is preferred for fixation to amine-coated slides. For some surfaces, either method of fixation may be used, either singly or in combination.

4. Fix the DNA to the slide substrate (for general recommendations for conditions, times, and settings, please see Table 2-2 and for specific conditions, please see the panel at the end of this protocol):

TABLE 2-2. Recommended Conditions for Fixing DNA to the Slide Substrate

Type of slide/slide coating	Baking	UV cross-linking
Poly-L-lysine	X	60 mJ
Telechem SuperAmine	1 hour	(optional)
Telechem SuperAldehyde	X	X
Corning MicroTechnology Gamma amino propyl silane (CMT-GAPS II)	2–4 hours	200 mJ

Examples of recommended handling conditions for some commonly used substrates. X signifies that the method is inappropriate, not needed, or not the preferred method for the specified slide coating.

To fix by baking: Place the slides in an oven preset to 80°C for an appropriate period of time.

Baking times vary from 1 to 4 hours. Longer times are required when baking alone, rather than in combination with UV-irradiation, is used to promote cross-linking.

To fix by UV cross-linking: Irradiate the slides by exposure to 60–200 mJ as appropriate.

For slide coatings that require cross-linking to achieve covalent attachment of DNA to the substrate, (e.g., for poly-L-lysine-coated slides), it is critical that cross-linking be performed effectively. Because the degree of cross-linking may affect the strength of the signal, it is worth experimenting to find the optimal time of baking and/or exposure to UV-irradiation when using new types of substrates. Ensure that the UV lamps have not deteriorated over time. Failure to adequately fix DNA to the slides can be a common cause of "comets" (please see Section 3).

5. (*Optional*) Immediately snap-dry the slide by heating it for 20–30 seconds (5 seconds for poly-L-lysine-coated slides) on a hot plate set at 100–140°C.

This treatment is usually recommended for amino-silane, CMT-GAPS II, and poly-L-lysine-coated slides. A 20–30-second snap-heat step after UV cross-linking usually eliminates the comet tail problem with CMT-GAPS II and with amino-silane-coated slides. The slides should then be air cooled to avoid shattering and rinsed in a large volume of distilled H_2O.

Washing and Blocking the Slides

6. Wash the slides in 0.2% SDS in a glass container with vigorous agitation for 1 minute at room temperature. Transfer the slides to a fresh solution of 0.2% SDS and repeat the wash.

7. Rinse the slides twice in a fresh container of ultrapure H_2O for 1 minute at room temperature.

These washes are done to remove free DNA and salt left over at the end of printing. Unless the washing is vigorous, DNA released from the slide may re-adhere locally, resulting in "comet tails" (please see Section 3).

8. Denature the DNA by transferring the slide rack into boiling ultrapure H_2O for 2 minutes. Remove the slide rack to a clean glass container and allow the slides to cool to room temperature in the air.

The purpose of this step is to denature the DNA and make it accessible for hybridization.

9. Prepare the $NaBH_4$ blocking buffer immediately before use:

    a. Dissolve 1 g of $NaBH_4$ in 300 ml of PBS in a glass jar.

    b. After the solute has dissolved, add 90 ml of 95% ethanol and stir the solution.

    c. Place the container with the blocking solution on the shaker. Place the slides in slide rack(s) in the blocking solution and incubate them with gentle agitation for 5 minutes. Monitor the slides for air bubbles once every minute by manually shaking the slides gently to remove any air bubbles that form on the slide surface.

    > Aldehyde- and poly-L-lysine-coated slides are routinely blocked to remove reactive sites that would otherwise bind to labeled target. Blocking of amine-coated slides is optional and dependent on the level of background encountered during slide use.

ALTERNATE BLOCKING WITH SUCCINIC ANHYDRIDE

The addition of 1,2-dichloroethane and *N*-methylimidazole to the succinic anhydride solution has been reported to reduce background by accelerating the blocking procedure and thereby limiting reattachment of unbound DNA released during blocking rinses (Diehl et al. 2001).

1. Prepare succinic anhydride blocking solution:

    a. Prepare the 15 ml of 0.2 M sodium borate in a 50-ml conical tube.

    b. Dissolve 6 g of succinic anhydride in 325–350 ml of 1-methyl-2-pyrrolidinone. Rapid addition of reagent is crucial.

    c. Immediately after the succinic anhydride dissolves, add 15 ml of the sodium borate solution (Step a), and mix well.

2. Immediately pour the blocking solution into an empty slide chamber.

3. Plunge the rack of slides rapidly into the blocking solution. Vigorously shake the slide rack up and down for a few seconds, making sure that the slides never leave the solution.

4. Incubate the slides for 15–20 minutes in the blocking solution on an orbital shaker.

---

10. Wash the slides three times in 0.2% SDS, and once in ultrapure H_2O at room temperature, for 1 minute at each time, with continuous shaking.

    > Some investigators provide a final rinse in 95% ethanol, or heat the slides for several seconds in boiling H_2O, for more effective drying prior to centrifugation and storage.

11. Place the slides in a tabletop centrifuge and remove any residual solution from the slides by centrifuging them at 500*g* for 3 minutes. Store the slides in a light-proof box.

    > Use plastic-only boxes *without* cork liners as cork can contaminate the slide surface. Some investigators choose to "age" poly-L-lysine slides for several days to 1 week before experimental use.

As there are a number of options for varying postprinting processing, the following summaries are provided for some commonly used slides.

SuperAmine Protocol

1. Bake the slides for 60–80 minutes at 80°C.
    > The printed arrays are stored after baking, and then processed immediately before use.
2. (*Optional*) Rehydrate, snap-heat, and UV cross-link at 60 mJ.
    > This series of steps may be unnecessary, as baking for more than 1 hour seems to provide sufficient retention of DNA on the slide surface. There are, however, reports that cross-linking after baking increases retention of DNA on the amine surface. Because cross-linker efficiencies may vary, optimize the exposure to UV to suit the particular lab conditions.
3. Wash for 2 minutes with agitation in the following series of solutions:
    > **IMPORTANT:** Do not use glass slide holders—they shatter in the transition to ice-cold ethanol.
    > 0.1% Sarkosyl
    > 2x SSC at room temperature
    > H_2O at 95°C or boiling
    > Ice-cold ethanol
    > Sarkosyl is used in place of SDS as it is washed from the slides easily. Furthermore, SDS can be highly fluorescent if not completely removed.
4. Dry by centrifugation at 500g for 2 minutes.
5. Use the slides immediately for hybridization.

SuperAldehyde Protocol

No baking or cross-linking is required. The printed arrays are dried and stored after printing, and then processed immediately before use. Note that this protocol omits the blocking step, which, although it may reduce hybridization background, is thought to decrease the strength of the fluorescent signal emitted by the array.

1. Wash the slides for 2 minutes with agitation in the following series of solutions:
    > **IMPORTANT:** Do not use glass slide holders—they shatter in the transition to ice-cold ethanol.
    > 0.1% Sarkosyl
    > 2x SSC at room temperature
    > H_2O at 95°C or boiling
    > Ice-cold ethanol
    > Sarkosyl is used in place of SDS as it is washed from the slides easily. Furthermore, SDS can be highly fluorescent if not completely removed.
2. Dry by centrifugation at 500g for 2 minutes.
3. Use the slides immediately for hybridization.

CMT-GAPS II Protocol

1. Rehydrate the slides and snap-heat.
2. Bake 2–4 hours at 80°C or UV cross-link (200 mJ).
3. Rehydrate and snap-heat for 20–30 seconds.
    > These slides usually produce comet tails without this step, especially if spotting with concentrated solution. In addition, overhydration can cause spot bleeding and distortion of spot morphology.
4. Air cool to room temperature (to avoid shattering the glass substrate).
5. Block in succinic anhydride if experiencing high background.
    > This is an optional step that can usually be omitted for these slides, especially if using a prehybridization step with a solution containing BSA.
6. Wash in 0.2% SDS for 20 seconds at room temperature and then in H_2O for 20 seconds at room temperature.
7. Wash in H_2O for 2 minutes at 95°C and then immerse in 95% ethanol for 1 minute at room temperature.
8   Dry and store the slides.

Poly-L-Lysine Protocol

1. Rehydrate the slides and UV cross-link (60 mJ).
2. Rehydrate and snap-heat for 5 seconds and then cool to room temperature.
3. Block in succinic anhydride.
4. Wash in 0.2% SDS for 20 seconds at room temperature and then in H_2O for 20 seconds at room temperature.
5. Heat in H_2O for 1.5 to 3 minutes at 95°C.
    > Avoid boiling as this can soften slide coating and induce peeling.
6. Immerse in 95% ethanol for 1 minute at room temperature.
7. Dry and store the slides.

Protocol 3

Checking the Quality of the Printed Slides

Bi-Huei Hou,* Shauna Somerville,* Andrew Holloway,† and Maria Murphy†

*Carnegie Institute of Washington, Stanford, California 94305; †Peter MacCallum Cancer Institute, East Melbourne, Victoria, Australia

There are several ways to evaluate the quality of microarrays before hybridizing them to valuable targets. These include staining the array with dimeric cyanine dyes, or hybridizing the array with a labeled primer complementary to a sequence either within the priming site for the clone set or within the vector sequence downstream from the priming site. The most rigorous test of a slide involves hybridization with a set of distinct, labeled RNA samples reflecting differing expression patterns.

Some scanners have more than two lasers. With these scanners, a third laser can be used to assess the quality of a hybridized slide by staining with a general DNA stain appropriate for the wavelength of light emitted by the third laser. Whichever approach is selected, one of these sampling procedures should be performed on every 15–20th slide in a print run to ensure the quality of the printed slides.

Microarrays may also be evaluated before postprocessing (fixing) using Red Reflection scanning by examining the arrays using a scanner with a 633-nm filter, as described in the panel **IMAGING SPOTTED cDNA BEFORE POSTPROCESSING OF ARRAYS** on the following page. A comparison of the various approaches for evaluating microarrays is shown in Figures 2-2 and 2-3 and is described in Yue (2001).

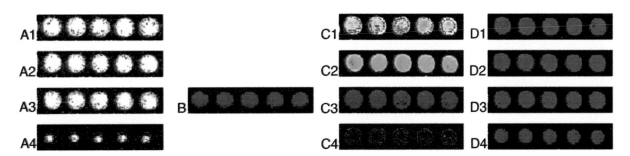

FIGURE 2-2. Examples of good DNA spots on arrays. cDNA samples at 800, 600, 200, and 50 ng/μl were spotted on glass slides as five duplicates and then examined by Red Reflection scanning (A1 to A4), ToTo-3 iodide staining (C1 to C4), or hybridization to *Arabidopsis* Col-0 total RNA, labeled with Cy5 dye (D1 to D4). In panel B, cDNA samples of 200 ng/μl were spotted in a similar manner and examined by PoPo-3 iodide staining. In panels B, C1, C2, C3, and C4, the intensity of each spot is represented by a color. The strength of spot intensity is arbitrarily ordered as white, red, yellow, green, and blue, with white being the strongest. The blue color in panels D1, D2, D3, and D4 are due to hybridization of the Cy5-labeled target and should not be directly compared to the blue color in the other panels for quantitation purposes.

It is advisable to include a well-characterized set of positive, negative, and spiking controls printed at several locations on the arrays (for a discussion of the merits of various controls, please see the information panel on **CONTROLS USED IN SPOTTED MICROARRAYS** in Section 1). The behavior of the controls on each print and with each hybridization provides a useful aid both in identifying problems and in diagnosing the origins of problems.

Evalution of Microarrays Using Fluorescent DNA Dyes

Dimeric cyanine nucleic acid dyes are extremely sensitive fluorescent probes that exhibit a high affinity for nucleic acids. Staining the printed array with DNA-avid dyes such as SYTO 61 (Yue et al. 2001), or PoPo-3 or ToTo-3, provides a measure of evenness of DNA deposition and spot morphology. These cyanine dyes, which may be used to stain either double-stranded DNA or single-stranded DNA and RNA, are essentially nonfluorescent in the absence of DNA and exhibit 100–1000-fold enhancement of fluorescence following DNA binding. ToTo-3 staining is recommended because, for unknown reasons, PoPo-3 can sometimes give high background. Staining with ToTo-3 iodide can be used to estimate roughly the amount of spotted DNA on the basis of the intensity of the spot when the concentrations of DNA solutions spotted on the slide are between 800 ng/μl (Figure 2-2, C1) and 50 ng/μl (Figure 2-2, C4). The size of the spots derived from ToTo-3 iodide staining correlate well with those derived from hybridization, as demonstrated by the comparison between C3 and D3 in Figure 2-2.

This protocol encompasses a series of procedures for assessing the quality of printed arrays: a primary method for staining with fluorescent dyes, an alternative protocol for hybridizing with Cy-labeled primers, and a final panel at the end of the protocol describing hybridization of the array with targets prepared from RNA expressed from different cell lines or tissue sources.

IMAGING SPOTTED CDNA BEFORE POSTPROCESSING OF ARRAYS

The size and shape of the spots on an array can be directly examined by pausing the printing and using a magnifying glass during the print run or under a dissecting microscope after printing. Irregular spots associated with a single pin are suggestive of a pin-specific problem (see Protocol 2). Usually, bigger spots contain more DNA; however, because the size of a spot depends on the coating of the slide, the spots on a slide with one coating should not be compared with those on a slide with a different coating. The size and shape of the spots on an array can also be examined by Red Reflection scanning using a microarray scanner with a 633-nm laser and a 633-nm filter (e.g., Packard BioScience, Scan Array Lite 4000 or 5000). Note that these methods do not work with dimethylsulfoxide (DMSO) or other nonsalt printing buffer, nor when the deposited salt crystals on the spots are washed off.

The technical staff at Packard Biochip (http://www.packardbiochip.com) have developed a protocol called "Reflective Imaging," which allows one to view slides printed with salt-containing DNA solutions in a simple, nondestructive manner using a scanner. The method is based on capturing the laser light that is reflected from the salt crystals that remain in each spot after the DNA solution has dried onto the slide. The reflected light is filtered through a neutral density filter before collection by the PMT. Reflective Imaging does not provide a quantitative estimate of the amount of DNA printed to the slide, although spots that have very small of amounts of DNA can be identified (compare the spots printed at 200 ng/μl presented in Figure 2-2, A3 versus those printed at 50 ng/μl displayed in Figure 2-2, A4). It is the authors' experience that the sizes of the spots derived from Red Reflection scanning cannot be directly compared to those derived from hybridization (compare A4 to D4 in Figure 2-2). Thus, this method is used primarily to make present/absent calls for each printed spot.

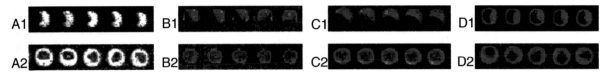

FIGURE 2-3. Examples of imperfect DNA spots on arrays. cDNA samples at 200 ng/µl were spotted on glass slides as five duplicates and then examined by Red Reflection scanning (A1, A4), PoPo-3 iodide staining (B1, B2), ToTo-3 iodide staining (C1, C2), or hybridization to *Arabidopsis* Col-0 total RNA, labeled with Cy5 dye (D1, D2). Imperfect spots can emerge as moon-shaped (A1, B1, C1, D1) or doughnut-shaped (A2, B2, C2, D2). In panels B, C1, and C2, the intensity of each spot is represented by a color. The strength of spot intensity is arbitrarily ordered as white, red, yellow, green, and blue, with white being the strongest in intensity. The blue color in panels D1 and D2 are due to hybridization of the Cy5-labeled target and should not be directly compared to the blue color in other panels for quantitation purposes.

MATERIALS

CAUTION: Please see Appendix 3 for appropriate handling of materials marked with <!>.

Buffers and Solutions

Please see Appendix 2 for components of stock solutions, buffers, and reagents.
Dilute stock solutions to the appropriate concentrations.

Dimeric cyanine nucleic acid stains (Molecular Probes)
> Either PoPo-3 (P-3584, Molecular Probes) or ToTo-3 (T-3604, Molecular Probes) may be used in this protocol. ToTo staining is recommended because, for unknown reasons, PoPo staining can sometimes give high background.
> PoPo-3 (m.w. = 1223) is provided at 1 mM in dimethylformamide <!>; its absorption (Abs) and fluorescence emission (Em) maxima are 534 nm and 570 nm, respectively. ToTo-3 is provided at 1 mM in DMSO; its absorption (Abs) and fluorescence emission (Em) maxima are 642 nm and 660 nm, respectively. Upon receipt, store the dye solution in a desiccator at –20ºC; the solution may be used up to 6–12 months. Before use, allow the solutions to warm to room temperature and mix thoroughly.

10x Phosphate-buffered solution (PBS) (70013-032, GIBCO)
Wash solution
> 10 mM Tris (pH 7.5)
> 1 mM EDTA
> 0.1% SDS <!>

Nucleic Acids and Oligonucleotides

Printed DNA microarray

Special Equipment

Centrifugal vacuum concentrator (e.g., SpeedVac)
Glass jar for washing slides
Microarray scanner
> Some scanners have more than two lasers. With these scanners, a third laser can be used to assess the quality of the slide by staining with a general DNA stain appropriate for the wavelength of light emitted by the third laser.

Plastic surface (e.g., plastic lip that can hold up to 4 slides) (EK26161, E&K)
or
Plastic coverslip (22 x 40 mm) (e.g., Hybrislip; 247456, Research Products)
Slide rack (900234, Wheaton)

METHOD

1. Thaw the frozen ToTo-3 dye and dilute the dye to a final concentration of 1 µM in 1× PBS at room temperature.

2. Apply 50 µl of the diluted dye to a plastic coverslip or plastic surface. Place a slide (array faces down) onto the coverslip. Make sure that the diluted dye immediately covers the whole slide.

   Alternatively, add an appropriate volume of the dye (~15 µl for an array of 1.8 × 1.8 cm) to the center of the array (face up) and immediately cover the array with a plastic coverslip.

   IMPORTANT: It is critical to apply the diluted dye quickly onto the array.

3. Incubate the array with the diluted dye for 30 minutes at room temperature in the dark.

4. During the incubation, place a slide rack in a glass jar filled with 350 ml of 1× PBS.

5. At the end of the 30-minute incubation, use forceps to place the slide into the slide rack in PBS. Plunge the slide rack up and down in the jar containing PBS for 2 minutes to remove the coverslip and unbound dye.

6. Dry the slides by centrifugation in a vacuum concentrator (SpeedVac) at the lowest speed for 5 minutes at room temperature.

7. Scan the DNA using one of the methods below.

   To detect DNA stained with ToTo-3 iodide: Scan the array by using the red laser and Cy5 filter. ToTo-3 exhibits absorption/emission maximum of 642/660 nm when bound to double-stranded DNA.

   To detect DNA stained with PoPo-3 iodide: Scan the slide by using the green laser and Cy3 filter. PoPo-3 iodide exhibits absorption/emission maximum of 534/570 nm when bound to double-stranded DNA.

   Although using the stained slide is not recommended, if necessary, the slides could be used for hybridization when the dye is removed. To remove the dye, incubate the slide in wash solution for 1 hour at room temperature. After drying, the slides can be used for hybridization. For more information, please check the Web Site: https://www.probes.com.

   ToTo-3 iodide staining can be used to roughly estimate the amount of spotted DNA based on the intensity of the spot. ToTo-3 is effective when the concentrations of DNA solution spotted on the slide are between 800 ng/µl (Figure 2-2, C1) and 50 ng/µl (Figure 2-2, C4). Figure 2-2, C3 and D3, shows that the size of the spots derived from ToTo-3 iodide staining correlates well with those derived from hybridization. PoPo-3 iodide staining is basically the same as ToTo-3 iodide staining. However, ToTo-3 iodide staining is preferred because the background is generally lower.

ALTERNATIVE PROTOCOL: HYBRIDIZATION WITH LABELED PRIMERS

Microarrays may be evaluated by hybridization with a Cy-dye-labeled oligonucleotide complementary to the common priming site used with PCR products. This approach provides a better measure of the availability of the probe for target hybridization than does the use of fluorescent dyes such as ToTo-3. Any fluorescent dye, such as Texas Red, can be used to label the primer. The advantage of using Cy3 is that all commercial scanners have the appropriate lasers to detect the fluorescence. The use of an oligonucleotide of 50 bases improves the binding specificity. An example of the results of hybridization with a Cy-dye-labeled oligonucleotide is shown in Figure 2-4.

Additional Materials

Cy3-labeled oligonucleotide, lyophilized (5´ fluorescent dye modified, purchased from a commercial oligonucleotide provider)
> The sequence must match that of the primer used to amplify the clone set or be in a region of the vector downstream from the priming site. The advantage of using a sequence downstream from the priming site is that the oligonucleotide will bind only to amplified material, not to any primer contaminants on the slide. The oligonucleotide (50 mer) below includes the sequence of the reverse primer used for the amplification of the Research Genetics human clone sets.

> 5´-3´ Cy3GT GAG CGG ATA ACA ATT TCA CAC AGG AAA CAG CTA TGA CCA TGA TTA CGC

Glass coverslips (Esco or Menzel Glaser)
Hybridization and washing materials as described in Section 3, Protocol 20, Part 3

Method

1. Resuspend the oligonucleotide at a concentration of 1 µg/µl in filtered sterile H_2O. The solution should be fluorescent pink in color. Divide the solution into 15-µl aliquots and then store at –20°C in a light-proof box.

2. Prepare the solutions required for a hybridization reaction (see Section 3, Protocol 20), replacing the purified labeled sample with 1.5 µg of Cy3-labeled oligonucleotide.

3. Hybridize the microarray with the labeled oligonucleotide for 12 hours and wash it as described for hybridization with cDNA (see Section 3, Protocol 3, Part 3).

4. Scan the microarray using the Cy3 channel.

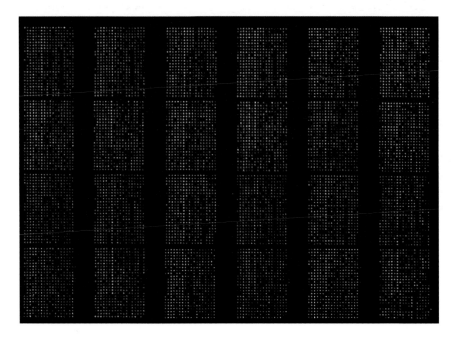

FIGURE 2-4. Example of a slide hybridized with a Cy3-labled primer. Note that regions with little DNA are readily apparent.

ASSESSING THE QUALITY OF SLIDES BY HYBRIDIZATION WITH TARGETS PREPARED FROM RNA

Test RNA samples derived from tissues or cell types whose expression patterns are substantially different, for example, breast and lymphocyte cell lines (please see Figure 2-5), can be hybridized to slides to check the quality of the arrays (please see Section 3, Parts 2 and 3, for labeling and hybridization procedures, respectively). The results can be compared with previous experiments using these test RNAs. This procedure, although more expensive than other protocols, and requiring a stock of appropriate RNA, has several advantages:

- It provides a measure of the quality of the slides for their final purpose. Staining with a DNA-avid dye does not measure *availability* of the DNA to targets.

- If many of the targets are differentially labeled, the distinctive pattern obtained should help to identify any errors in plate assignment that may have occurred during printing. By contrast, such errors are unlikely to be detected if the slide is incubated with fluorescent dye or hybridized with an oligonucleotide.

- Examining the threshold sensitivity of each slide provides a measure of the quality of the slides relative to previous experiments.

Listed below are suggested pairs of cell lines:

Human: MCF-7 and Jurkat

Mouse: Immortalized murine fibroblasts and immortalized murine promyelocytes

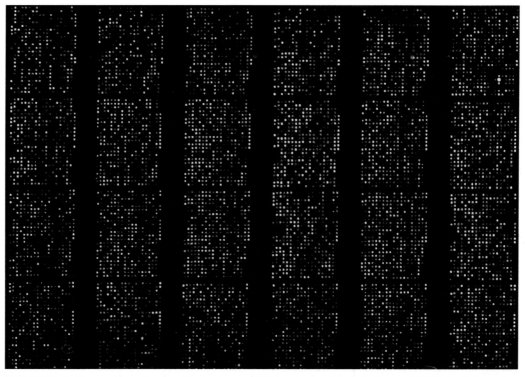

FIGURE 2-5. Comparison of expression patterns of RNAs extracted from Jurkat and MCF-7 cell lines. An overlay false-color image of a human 10K microarray, hybridized with fluorescently labeled cDNA derived from Jurkat (Cy3) and MCF-7 (Cy5) cell lines. The range of signals obtained and the complexity of hybridization pattern can be used to compare the quality of various batches of microarrays.

Protocol 4

Care and Cleaning of Quill Pins

Andrew Holloway,* Maria Murphy,* Aldo Massimi,[†] Thomas Harris,[†] and Geoffrey Childs[†]

*Peter MacCallum Cancer Research Institute, Melbourne, Australia; [†]Albert Einstein College of Medicine, Bronx, New York 10461

Quill pins may be used to print multiple slides before revisiting the source plate. Pins of this type, however, are prone to damage and clogging of the very fine groove cut in the end of the tip. When the external surface becomes coated or the internal groove becomes clogged, the shape and size of spots vary substantially over the course of a print run (e.g., please see Section 3). To minimize problems, it is advisable to use highly purified DNA for printing and to ensure that the wash station is operating correctly during the printing cycle. Pins should be cleaned by sonication at the end of each print run. The following procedure is recommended when the pins are removed for cleaning. It is very important to wear powder-free nitrile gloves while cleaning pins.

MATERIALS

CAUTION: Please see Appendix 3 for appropriate handling of materials marked with <!>.

Buffers and Solutions

Please see Appendix 2 for components of stock solutions, buffers, and reagents.
Dilute stock solutions to the appropriate concentrations.

Cleaning solution

Listed below are the recommended solutions for cleaning pins from different sources in a sonication bath.

- warm water (Majer Precision)
- Loctite 7840 degreaser, diluted 1:100 in H_2O (Genetix)
- 2–5% solution of Micro Cleaning Solution (MCS-1, Telechem)
- 50 mM solution of KOH <!>; pins must be rinsed thoroughly before printing

Telechem warns that deionized H_2O can leach ions from their pins and damage them; its use should be avoided.

Ethanol (95% and 70%)

Some batches of absolute ethanol (100% or 200 proof) have been reported to contain fluorescent contaminants that generate high backgrounds in microarray experiments; 95% ethanol does not have this problem. To avoid difficulties, either use 95% ethanol or identify a brand of absolute ethanol that does not generate high levels of background fluorescence. Absolute ethanol (USP-grade ethyl alcohol, 64-17-5) purchased from Warner-Graham Co. (Cockeysville, Maryland) performs consistently well.

If latex gloves come into contact with ethanol, material leaches out of the gloves and contaminates the solution, producing a green fluorescence.

H$_2$O (distilled)

> The use of deionized H$_2$O with stainless steel pins may cause corrosion. Pins that are not made from stainless steel are susceptible to corrosion if left wet, especially if the solution contains salts.

5x SSC

Special Equipment

Compact Ultrasonic Cleaner (32695K21, McMaster-Carr)

> This sonication bath has only two settings: on or off.

Drying instrument (hair dryer or oil-free compressed air canister)

Ear protection device

Flotation device for holding pins in the sonication bath

Stereoscopic microscope

METHOD

1. Fill the bath of the sonicator with 0.5x SSC or recommended cleaning solution.

2. Place the pins in a suitable holding or flotation device to float them on the surface of the sonication bath (please see Figure 2-6).

   > Be careful when inserting the pins through the holder, as contact even with soft foam materials may damage the ends of the pins. Damage may also occur if the pins contact the sides of the sonicator, especially when it is operating.

3. Rinse the pins in hot tap water for several minutes.

4. Sonicate the pins for 3 minutes in the appropriate cleaning solution, and then perform a final rinse with 95% ethanol.

   > The wash sequence during printing typically consists of two cycles of 3 seconds in the wash bath followed by 8 seconds at the dry station. The most appropriate sonication time and

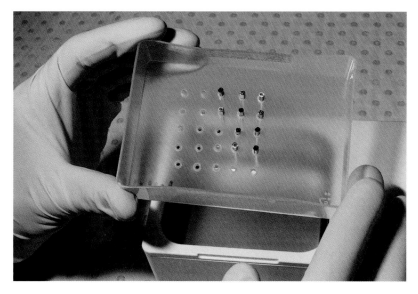

FIGURE 2-6. Flotation device. The support is used to float pins on the surface of the sonication bath.

power setting for cleaning pins, separate from the printing cycle, may be different and should be determined empirically.

5. Dry the pins with a hair dryer or other drying instrument.

6. Examine the pins under a stereoscopic microscope, searching for bridges of material between the prongs.

> When examining the pin under a dissecting microscope, gently touch the end to a droplet of 3x SCC. If the pin is functioning normally, the solution should wick freely up the slot of the pin. If the pins are heavily clogged, clean the tips using steel shims as described in the panel below **CLEANING CLOGGED PINS**. Alternatively, fill the pin slot with solution and then observe under the microscope. If the pin is held at an angle with the tip pointing down, reverse capillary action will be evident as the solution dries (the evaporation rate is increased if a warm lamp is used to provide heat). As the liquid dries, the cavity should empty from the top down. If the liquid level migrates away from the tip before the pin is completely dry, then poor pin operation is likely to occur during printing. This phenomenon usually occurs with pins that have a nonuniform gap.

7. Replace the pins in the print head of the arrayer, taking particular care when the ends are introduced through the holder. The pins should always be stored dry.

CLEANING CLOGGED PINS

For pins that are heavily contaminated, carefully remove or at least loosen the material using a steel shim. The following procedure is suggested by Majer Precision Engineering (www.majerprecision.com).

Clogged pins may be cleaned using a combination of both sonication in warm water as described in the main protocol and cleaning with a 0.025-mm stainless steel shim stock. The shim stock can be purchased from MSC Industrial Supply Co. (Part No. 02467751; www.mscdirect.com or [800] 645-7270).

Because the shim material is thin, it can be cut easily with scissors into a pie shape. Carefully slide the shim material into the top of the tip's slot. Slowly and gently work it toward the end of the pin. If the shim gets wedged or stuck in the slot, do not force it out to the end. The build-up of residue could widen the slot as it exits the tip. In the case of heavy build-up, use the shim material to carefully loosen the material from the side of the slot until the shim can move all the way through. A sonication bath should then be used to remove any loose residue.

ARRAYERS AND PINS USED FOR CONTACT PRINTING OF MICROARRAYS

Currently, contact printing devices are by far the most commonly used systems for fabrication of microarrays. An ordered arrangement of pins, housed in the print head, collects small amounts of probes from a source plate and then transfers nanoliter quantities of fluid to discrete areas on a microscope slide. Please see Table 2-1 for comparative information of some of the arrayers available commercially, and Figure 2-7 for a comparison of the use of various arraying instruments in custom microarray facilities.

Features of the Arrayer

The components of a pin-based printing robot are described below. An illustration of the printer and its various features is given in Figure 2-8.

- *A stable and rigid printing platform* that provides very sturdy support and efficient vibration-damping properties and a surface that is flat to 100 μm or better.

- *A three-axis mechanical robotic arm* that provides very precise positioning with a repeatability error of less than 10 μm anywhere on the surface. Strategies for positioning involve either navigating the print head in turn to a series of slides resting on a fixed platen or moving a traveling platen of slides underneath a print head. Although both methods are effective, the latter has advantages in terms of simplicity and cost. For example, a robot fitted with an overhead gantry capable of visiting 300 slides is more expensive, slower, and more complex than a robot fitted with simple linear servo arm.

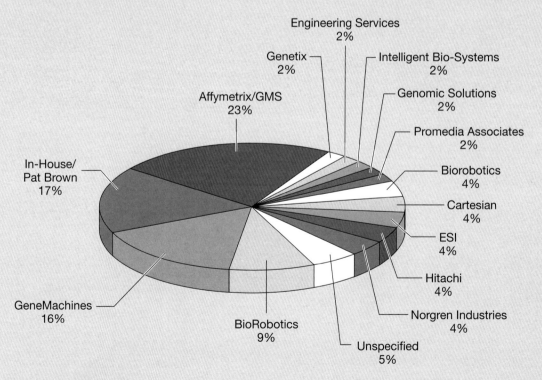

FIGURE 2-7. Comparison of use of arrayers. The chart shows the relative use of various brands of slide arraying instruments used by ~50 custom microarray facilities. (Redrawn from 2000/2001 ABRF Microarray Research Group Study [http://abrf.org/ABRF/Research].)

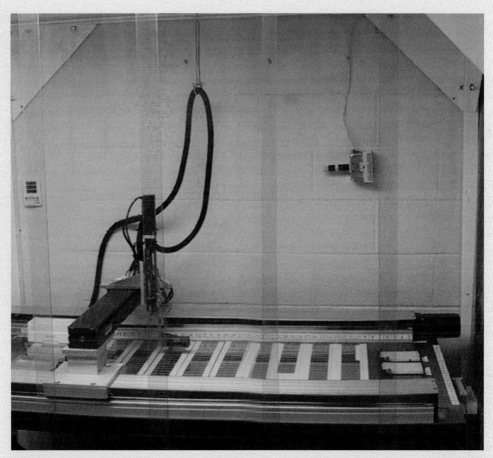

FIGURE 2-8. Arrayer. Illustrated here are the various components of a typical pin-based slide arraying instrument.

- *A servo controller,* whose dedicated electronics should accurately control the amplifiers and motors that drive the mechanism. The servo controller consists of a high-speed digital circuit board that can reside either within a computer or in the amplifier assembly. Various sensors may interface with the controller to monitor mechanical operation and personnel safety interlocks.

- *Computer control.* The system is usually controlled by a personal computer running a custom application program. The software allows the operator to configure the print run by specifying the locations of components, defining the operating parameters, and scheduling the order of events. The computer transmits high-level instructions to the servo controller and performs a supervisory role by monitoring status and performance.

- *Plate mounting.* A means of precisely mounting one or more standard 96- or 384-well plates on the platen to an accuracy of ~100 μm is required. A flexible structure that permits lateral translation to correct misalignment is highly desirable. Optional robotic arms that feed the plates from a hotel structure to the printer may be used to process large numbers of plates in a totally automatic mode.

- *Slide mounting.* The microscope slides must be immobilized on the table surface to permit accurate printing of thousands of spots during a period that may extend over several days. Various methods can be used, including attachment with common labo-

FIGURE 2-9. Slides. Layout and mounting of slides on the table surface.

ratory tape, mechanical slots with spring-loaded restraints, plates with vacuum manifolds, and magnets (please see Figure 2-9).

- *Wash and dry stations (Figure 2-10).* Cleaning the pins at the end of each cycle allows the same set of pins to be used to array many different clones without significant cross-contamination. At a minimum, cleaning involves washing with water followed by vacuum drying. Some arrayers are equipped with sonicating baths to provide more stringent cleaning. For further details on the cleaning of quill pins, please see Protocol 4. The results of a contamination test are shown in Figure 2-11.

FIGURE 2-10. Wash and dry station.

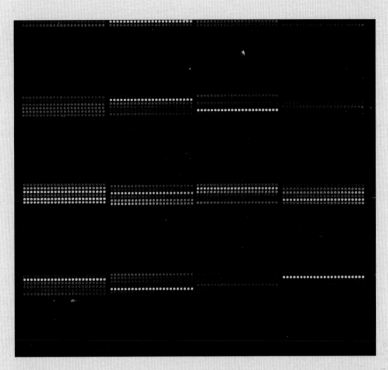

FIGURE 2-11. Contamination test. A series of genes were selected to reflect the range of hybridizations across the surface of a larger array (both in color and intensity). These clones were then re-arrayed, with each pin printing 24 spots before being washed. The next clone that each pin printed was chosen to be either of a different color or intensity. This process was repeated five times for 16 pins. Finally, the pins printed a row of 24 spots of printing buffer. Evaluation of the results showed that there was no carryover from the previous cDNA clone printed. Furthermore, the row of buffer printed was not significantly different from the local background. The slide was evaluated by competitive hybridization with Cy3-labeled Jurkat RNA vs. Cy5-labeled MCF-7 RNA. Results from experiments such as these suggest that the pin-cleaning routine commonly used (and described in Protocol 4) is effective at removing unprinted cDNA solution from the pins.

- **Environmental control.** Particulates in ambient air can easily contaminate the spotted slides, and, if they land in the printed area, they can cause problems during hybridization and scanning. Printing should therefore be carried out in a room or enclosure that provides laminar-flow HEPA-filtered air. The humidity of the air should be continuously monitored and controlled. If the humidity is too low, the solution may dry in the pin tip before the end of the print cycle. Low humidity also increases the rate of evaporation of the solutions in the source plates, interfering with DNA pickup, and increasing DNA concentrations. This problem can be partially offset by drying down the DNA solutions remaining in the printing plate at the end of each run (so that the amount of drying is not cumulative) and reconstituting the sample at the next printing.

  Excessive humidity (>65%) can cause spots to spread to an undesirably large size and to assume irregular shapes (Hegde et al. 2000). During the printing of high-density arrays, adjacent dots can become cross-contaminated as a result of variability in spot size caused by high humidity. The ideal humidity for printing varies according to the composition of the arraying solution (please see the information panel on **SUBSTRATES FOR PRINTING**). However, a temperature of ~20ºC and a relative humidity of 50–60% provide good conditions for printing with most of the commonly used arraying solutions. A moderate rate of evaporation from the spot slide allows time for the

FIGURE 2-12. Print head (please see text for details).

DNA to diffuse uniformly across the spot, minimizing the formation of "doughnut" shaped spots and improving homogeneity of spot morphology. Some printers may generate substantial heat through movement of the robot arm in the enclosed printing space. It is therefore important to monitor temperature *during* a print run, not just at the outset.

- *Printing head.* The end effector of the microarray robot is the printing head, an example of which is shown in Figure 2-12. This assembly can hold a variable number of pen tips in a precise arrangement that matches the wells from which the material to be printed is drawn. Shown are 48 pen tips spaced 4.5 mm apart (used with 384-well titer plates) in a 4 × 12 pattern that fits within the area of one microscope slide. The pin can be gravity or spring loaded to allow vertical motion while maintaining accurate lateral positioning. It is useful to limit the ability of the pins to rotate in the head. If the pins become bent, their rotation will result in improper spacing of spots (please see example in Section 3). The duration of a printing run is inversely proportional to the number of pins in the head. However, increasing the number of pins becomes nonproductive at a certain point since the chances of encountering a damaged or blocked pin, which compromises the quality of the entire set of arrays, also increase proportionately. In addition, the greater the number of pins, the greater the cost of disasters such as dropping the pin head or misaligning it with the source plate. It is therefore advisable to scale up pin numbers with care. The number of pins must be a whole number of wells in the source plate. For example, a 4 × 5 pin matrix cannot be used with a 384-well plate, but arrangements such as 4 × 4 or 4 × 8 can be used. Further details of pin design are given below.

Operating Parameters of the Arrayer That Affect Print Quality

Commercial arrayers are programmed with factory-set operating parameters. However, the settings in most machines can be adjusted to obtain optimal printing performance.

- The force and speed of impact on the microscope slide surface should be slow enough to minimize deformation of the pin tips but sufficient to impart downward acceleration to the liquid within the capillary. If contact speeds are too high, the pin tips and/or slide substrate can be damaged (please see Section 3). The distance that the springs are compressed when touching the slide (over-travel) should be minimized, although a certain amount of over-travel is necessary to ensure that every pin contacts every slide despite variations in the thickness of the slides and the unevenness of the platter. The amount of over-travel needed can be limited by selecting pin tips that are of uniform length.

- Spot morphology is dependent on the amount of material carried in the pins and the period of time the pin is in contact with the slide (dwell time). The longer the dwell time, the greater the amount of material deposited. When pins have difficulty picking up material from the well, select a longer dwell time in the plates in order to increase the amount of fluid drawn into the pins. Some printer robots allow the dwell time on the slide surface to be adjusted independently. This provides rough-and-ready control over the amount of material that is delivered and, hence, of the spot size.

- Environmental control (temperature and humidity) is discussed above.

Other factors that affect spot morphology, including the composition of the arrayed material and the characteristics of the slide surface are discussed in Protocol 2 and in the information panel on **SUBSTRATES FOR PRINTING**. However, as discussed below, pin design is perhaps the most critical factor affecting arraying speed, spot uniformity, element size, and spot morphology.

Pin Design

- ***Solid pins.*** The simplest type of arraying tool carries a bank of solid steel pins, which are robust, highly uniform, and relatively easy to manufacture (please see Figure 2-13). The blunt head allows printing on a variety of substrates including both glass and semiporous substrates such as nylon-coated glass slides. Solid pins are easily cleaned between printing cycles. However, a major disadvantage is that simple solid pins are capable of only one round of printing per visit to the source plate. Evaporation from the source plates can be a problem with simple pin printers because of the slowed printing cycle and because constant movement of the printing head between source plates and slides generates heat. The diameter of spots generated by solid pins is generally larger (200–300 μm) than other types of pins (100–150 μm). BioRobotics (www. Biorobotics.com) supplies solid pins for use in their printing machines and others.

- ***Quill pins.*** These pins, which fill by capillary action, were developed to allow continuous printing of slides after the pins have been fully charged at the source plate. The pins have a groove or slit 25–50 μm wide and a reservoir cut into the tip of the pin that allows nanoliter quantities of probe solution to be drawn into the pin. Capillary forces set up when the loaded pin touches the arraying surface allow deposition of spots of probe solution. The DNA solution tends to rush from the tip in the first few

FIGURE 2-13. Solid steel pins (please see text for details).

contacts made by the pins following filling, and the tips are therefore blotted on a blank slide before commencing the print run. Quill pins are capable of printing features in the 90–250-μm range, making them suitable for high-density microarrays. The number of elements that can be printed per visit to the probe solution is dependent on the size of the reservoir cut into the pin, the humidity in which the arraying takes place, and the solution in which the probes are dissolved. With the refinement of quill pin design, the number of slides that can be usefully printed is often limited more by the slide capacity of the arrayer platform than the amount of material available when the last slide is printed. Some pin designs allow printing of >200 slides per loading.

Generally, quill pins are not used to print on semiporous substrates, as the solution wicks from the reservoir when they contact filters, and the sharp pin tips damage delicate surfaces. One of the drawbacks of using quill pins is the sensitivity of the pin to damage and blockage. Retention of particulates within capillary slots can be a serious problem, leading to large and irregular spots, contamination, uneven flow of DNA, and blockage. Furthermore, because the spotting solution is retained in a recessed slot, careful cleaning between samples is essential to prevent cross-contamination or carryover between the wells of different source plates. The extent of contamination of pins is very dependent on the adequacy of the washing cycle during the print run and the composition of the arrayed material. In particular, residual proteins (enzymes) or poorly resuspended particulate DNA will rapidly clog quill pins. Cleaning is achieved using cycles of washing, vacuum drying, and, on some arrayers, sonication. Details for thoroughly cleaning quill pins are provided in Protocol 4. Pins available from BioRobotics (www.Biorobotics.com), Telechem (www.ArrayIt.com), and Majer Precision Engineering (www.majerprecision.com) are in common use on a range of contact printing robots. A comprehensive overview of some quill pin designs may be found on the Brown laboratory Web Site (http://cmgm.stanford.edu/pbrown/mguide/tips.html). The MicroSpot quill pin (split pin) from BioRobotics is shown in Figure 2-14.

- **Ring and pin.** The Affymetrix cDNA microarrayer (www.Affymetrix.com) uses a combination of a ring and a pin to array material (Figure 2-15). The ring acts as the

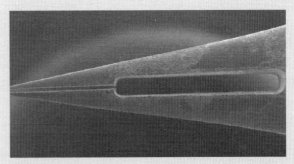

FIGURE 2-14. Quill pin. The image shows the MicroSpot split pin (from J. Pearson et al. [2001] *SPIE* 4407, 281) (please see text for details).

reservoir for 0.5–1.0 µl of probe solution collected from the source plate. The solid pin passes through the center of the meniscus of probe solution held by the ring to deliver a uniform amount to the surface of the array. Printing will be interrupted if the meniscus collapses. Although the ring and pin system consumes large amounts of probe solution, it has several advantages over quill pins. It provides the benefits of solid pins, including the ability to produce arrays on nylon membranes. Although it can theoretically print hundreds of spots from each sample collection, the slide capacity of the array may not be able to take advantage of this capability. The pin and ring combination requires no blotting and is less affected by particulate material in the print solution or by differences in the viscosity of the spotting solution. For this reason, the pin and ring printer can use material that has not been purified following PCR amplification (please see Section 4, Protocol 1). Carryover is generally less of a problem due to the relative ease of cleaning the large bore ring that holds the printing solution. The smallest pin available is 125 µm which produces a spot size of 150 µm (+/– 10), and deposits ~50 pl of material, allowing a spot density from 1000 to 2500 spots per square centimeter (or 10,000 to 25,000 spots per slide). Pins of 300 and 500 µm are available for delivering larger amounts of material; however, these are typically used for spotting protein.

FIGURE 2-15. Pin and Ring. The image shows the pin and ring system used by Affymetrix (please see text for details). (©2002, Affymetrix, Inc. All rights reserved.)

Pin Materials

Hard durable metal is required that does not oxidize easily in the high-salt environment of microarray printing. Pins are usually made of hardened stainless steel. When dipping into the titer plate wells, quill pins ideally should pick up material only within the capillary slot and not on the outside surface. Surface roughness increases the amount of DNA solution that adheres to the outside pin surface, contributing to variability in spot size and wasting material by making larger spots than is desirable. In addition, surface roughness promotes the formation of caked-on spots of DNA on the pin. The outer surface of the pin should therefore be as smooth as possible, should have neutral affinity to the DNA solution, and should not be hydrophobic or charged. If the tip of the pin is too sharp, it will initially produce very small spots due to poor capillary delivery to the slide. Sharp pin tips are also more prone to damage and are likely to damage the slide substrate. On damaged substrates, the DNA will not adhere to these puncture holes and when the slide is hybridized, the spots will appear with a characteristic "smiling face" (please see Section 3). New pins may function poorly because they are too sharp or because the two prongs are slightly uneven. It is best to carry out test printings with new pins so that their tips become slightly blunted and more uniform through wear, with consequent improvement in capillary action.

SUBSTRATES FOR PRINTING

Glass slides have been a favored solid support for immobilization of probes because of their easy availability, low intrinsic fluorescence, high transparency, good thermal properties, excellent rigidity, and straightforward chemistries for modification of the surface. Due to the nonporous nature of glass, the labeled targets have direct access to immobilized probes without limitations of internal diffusion.

Both conventional microscope slides and specifically manufactured glass slides (e.g., those available from www.arrayit.com) are used to support DNA microarrays. Several types of coatings provide surfaces to which spotted DNA can be tethered. These coatings attach firmly to the slide and bind tightly to DNA spotted onto the surface. Binding can be noncovalent (e.g., hydrophobic or electrostatic) or covalent, the latter occurring either throughout the length of the DNA molecule or by fixation of the extremities, for example, binding of 5′-aminated oligonucleotides to coatings with free aldehyde groups. Although this type of oriented attachment may provide better access for targets, the binding of oligonucleotides to glass slides that have been simply acid-washed also works well in microarray experiments (Call et al. 2001). In this case, the mechanism of binding is not known but may occur through stable hydrogen bonding or electrostatic interactions. Whatever form the bonding takes, it is obviously important that the DNA attached to the coating retain a strong ability to hybridize to targets.

At the time of writing, no consistent view exists among investigators as to the most appropriate slide surface. Poly-L-lysine is the most common material used for in-house coating of glass slides. It is not only inexpensive, but also readily accessible, by contrast to commercially produced slides, orders for which sometimes take weeks to be filled. Whatever the source of slides, it is important to check that they are of entirely regular dimension so that when laid out on a printing platter, they remain in register with the printing head. This is not always the case, even with slides produced specifically for microarray use (for an example, please see Figure 2-1 in Protocol 2).

Some batches of slides—from commercial sources as well as home-coated poly-L-lysine slides—occasionally may have high backgrounds that appear as fluorescent patches or areas of general fluorescent "haze." It is therefore advisable to scan a representative number of slides routinely before using them for printing to ensure that no areas of fluorescence interfere with array analysis.

Several slide types, including those available commercially, which are generally consistent and of high quality, are described below.

Poly-L-Lysine

Poly-L-lysine coating was used for the construction of the first DNA microarrays (Schena et al. 1996) and still enjoys wide popularity because of its ease of manufacture, accessibility, and generally good performance. The binding of DNA to poly-L-lysine is complex but essentially involves charge interactions that can be converted to covalent bonding by baking or UV-irradiation. A good poly-L-lysine-coated slide, properly blocked, will usually yield low background signals and good signal intensities. However, poly-L-lysine is not very durable, may be punctured by the printing pins, may peel away if the slide is boiled during the denaturing step of slide preparation, and is easily damaged during hybridization, especially at higher temperatures. Peeling of the coating exposes unblocked surfaces and can result in a background tint. Storing poly-L-lysine-coated slides for several weeks before using them, a process known as aging, can prevent some of these problems. The use of poly-L-lysine slides that have been stored for more than 4 months is generally not recommended. For a description of the preparation of poly-L-lysine slides, please see Protocol 1.

Commercial providers:

Menzel-Gläser: http://www.menzel.de/menzel/index/html
Sigma: http://www.sigma.com

Amino Silane (Silanated)

Amino silane is a popular coating alternative to poly-L-lysine. Various amine-modified silanes have been produced that react with the silanol glass surface. DNA is bound to the substrate through an electrostatic interaction between the amine groups of the silane, which are positively charged at neutral pH, and the negatively charged phosphodiester backbone of the DNA (please see Halliwell and Cass 2001 and references therein). UV-irradiation enhances and stabilizes the interaction by generating free-radical-mediated coupling of thymidine residues and carbon atoms on the alkyl amine. Amino-silane coating is much less sensitive to high temperature and does not appear to exhibit the same peeling problems as poly-L-lysine. Should nonuniform coating occur, or if the unused coating surface suffers from incomplete blocking, parts of the slide will fluoresce with a reddish background signal. Inexpensive amino-silane-coated slides intended for histological applications may have uneven coatings that result in high background signals and artifacts. High-quality amino-silane coatings designed for microarray use are available commercially and generally yield better results. The spot size of DNA microarrays produced with this type of coating can vary greatly among suppliers, indicating a varying degree of hydrophobicity among the several commercial formulations. Shelf life does not appear to be an issue with this coating.

Commercial providers:

Corning Microarray Technology (CMT) (http://www.corning.com): Gamma amino propyl silane (CMT-GAPS II)

Telechem/ArrayIt.com (http://www.arrayit.com):   SuperAmine

Clontech: http://www.clontech.com/Type I, Type II. Type I amino-silane slides are recommended for use with >200 bp DNA, and Type II slides are recommended for use with shorter DNA probes (>50 bp).

Eppendorf (www.brinkman.com): Creative Chip Oligo and Creative Chip PCR slides.

Aldehyde (Silylated)

DNA can be coupled to aldehyde groups on neutral hydrophobic coatings by covalent linkage to a 5′-amine linker on chemically modified DNA or to aromatic amines of G, C, and A residues within the DNA strand. The unreacted aldehyde groups in the coating are subsequently reduced to primary alcohols through reaction with sodium borohydride. DNA for printing can be prepared with a 5′-terminal amine group by use of an amine-linked PCR primer (please see Table 1-1 in Section 1) or by the use of modified phosphoamidites during synthesis of long oligonucleotides (please see Table 1-6 in Section 1). Coupling to the substrate via a 5′ amino group is more efficient than the reaction with native amine groups within DNA. This consideration may be especially important for oligonucleotides compared with the cDNA fragments, where there are more opportunities for reactions with bases located within the DNA chain. Aldehyde substrates have a high binding capacity, provide robust attachment, exhibit a low degree of background fluorescence, and were superior in at least one head-to-head comparison of several commonly used substrates (Zammatteo et al. 2000). However, prolonged storage of aldehyde-coated slides in air may result in the loss of some of the aldehyde groups due to oxidation to carboxylic acids.

Commercial providers:

Telechem/ArrayIt.com (http://www.arrayit.com):   SuperAldehyde
Genpak (http://www.genpakdna.com/slid2.shtml):   Silylated
Quantifoil (http://www.quantifoil.com):   QMT aldehyde

Activated Polymer Coating

This coating is formed by long-chain hydrophilic polymers, containing amine-reactive groups, that form interchain cross-links and links to the glass slide surface. The polymeric coating binds covalently to amine-terminated PCR products and oligonucleotides, holding the DNA away from the slide surface, thereby making it more available for hybridization while obviating the need for poly(dT) or PEG spacers on oligonucleotides. The hydrophilic nature of the polymer reduces nonspecific binding to the slide surface, giving lower background. Amine-terminated DNA samples are suspended in 150 mM sodium phosphate for printing, and printed slides are reacted overnight in a humidified chamber and then washed and blocked as described in Protocol 2. The activated slides have a shelf life of greater than 1 year.

Commercial provider:

Motorola Life Sciences (http://www.motorola.com/lifesciences)

Other Approaches

Binding of 5′-disulfide-modified oligonucleotides to mercaptosilane-coated surfaces (Rogers et al. 1999) represents an approach that is conceptually similar to the use of amine-modified DNA and aldehyde surfaces.

REFERENCES

Call D.R., Chandler D.P., and Brockman F. 2001. Fabrication of DNA microarrays using unmodified oligonucleotide probes. *BioTechniques* **30:** 368–376.

Diehl F., Grahlmann S., Beier M., and Hoheisel J.D. 2001. Manufacturing DNA microarrays of high spot homogeneity and reduced background signal. *Nucleic Acids Res.* **29:** E38.

Halliwell C.M. and Cass A.E. 2001. A factorial analysis of silanization conditions for the immobilization of oligonucleotides on glass surfaces. *Anal. Chem.* **73:** 2476–2483.

Hegde P., Qi R., Abernathy K., Gay C., Dharap S., Gaspard R., Hughes J.E., Snesrud E., Lee N., and Quackenbush J. 2000. A concise guide to cDNA microarray analysis. *BioTechniques* **29:** 548–556.

Rogers Y.H., Jiang-Baucom P., Huang Z.J., Bogdanov V., Anderson S., and Boyce-Jacino M.T. 1999. Immobilization of oligonucleotides onto a glass support via disulfide bonds: A method for preparation of DNA microarrays. *Anal. Biochem.* **266:** 23–30.

Schena M., Shalon D., Davis R.W., and Brown P.O. 1995. Quantitative monitoring of gene expression patterns with a complementary DNA microarray. *Science* **270:** 467–470.

Schena M., Shalon D., Heller R., Chai A., Brown P.O., and Davis R.W. 1996. Parallel human genome analysis: Microarray-based expression monitoring of 1000 genes. *Proc. Natl. Acad. Sci.* **93:** 10614–10619.

Yue H., Eastman P.S., Wang B.B., Minor J., Doctolero M.H., Nuttall R.L., Stack R., Becker J.W., Montgomery J.R., Vainer M., and Johnston R. 2001. An evaluation of the performance of cDNA microarrays for detecting changes in global mRNA expression. *Nucleic Acids Res.* **29:** E41.

Zammatteo N., Jeanmart L., Hamels S., Courtois S., Louette P., Hevesi L., and Remacle J. 2000. Comparison between different strategies of covalent attachment of DNA to glass surfaces to build DNA microarrays. *Anal. Biochem.* **280:** 143–150.

WWW RESOURCES

http://abrf.org/ABRF/Research Grills G. et al. 2000/2001. ABRF Microarray Research Group study: A current profile of microarray laboratories.
http://affymetrix.com Affymetrix homepage.
http://arrayit.com TeleChem International, Inc. homepage.
http://cmgm.stanford.edu/pbrown/mguide/index.html The Brown lab's complete guide to microarraying for the molecular biologist.
http://majerprecision.com Majer Precision Engineering, Inc. homepage.
http://www.Biorobotics.com BioRobotics Ltd. homepage.
http://www.cartesian.com Cartesian homepage.
http://www.clontech.com Clontech homepage.
http://www.corning.com/CMT Corning homepage.
http://www.genetix.com Genetix Ltd. homepage.
http://www.genpakdna.com/slid2.shtml GenPak's aldehyde coated (silyated) slides.
http://www.menzel.de/menzel/index.html Menzel-Gläser homepage.
http://www.motorola.com/lifesciences Motorola Life Sciences homepage.
http://www.mscdirect.com MSC Industrial Supply Company homepage.
http://www.packardbiochip.com Packard BioScience microarray and biochip technologies.
http://www.probes.com Molecular Probes homepage.
http://www.quantifoil.com Quantifoil zur deutschen homepage.
http://www.sigma.com Sigma-Aldrich homepage.
http://www.virtekbiotech.com Virtek Biotechnology homepage.

3 Expression Analysis of RNA

INTRODUCTION

The objective of many microarray projects is to identify genes expressed at different abundances in complex samples of RNA extracted from different types of cells or from the same cells growing under different conditions.

Over the years, a number of procedures have been developed to measure the abundance of a target messenger RNA (mRNA) in a preparation of total or poly(A)$^+$ RNA. The most popular of these procedures—northern blots and ribonuclease protection—remain in common use today. Both methods suffer from the same limitations: They utilize labeled, specific nucleic acid probes to detect one (or at best a few) specific mRNA in the preparation; quantification of mRNA is achieved indirectly by comparing the signal obtained from the target mRNA with that of a standard housekeeping gene, or of a known concentration of an artificial target RNA (for further discussion, please see Chapter 7, Introduction to Northern Hybridization; Sambrook and Russell 2001). Similar deficiencies apply to other techniques, such as quantitative reverse transcriptase–polymerase chain reaction (RT-PCR). Despite their limitations, methods to analyze the abundance of one or a few species of mRNAs have provided keen insight into the biology and pathology of a variety of "single-gene" diseases. However, understanding, classifying, and treating more complex diseases, such as cancer, require global analysis of the gene expression.

Many of the principles of modern microarrays were established in the late 1980s and early 1990s, when cloned cDNAs, arrayed on membrane filters, were hybridized to complex targets and used to quantify differences in expression of mRNAs over a wide dynamic range (Freimert et al. 1989; Lennon and Lehrach 1991; Gress et al. 1992; Takahashi and Ko 1994; Maier et al. 1994; please also see Section 4). A major breakthrough came in the mid 1990s, when Pat Brown, Ron Davis, and their colleagues published papers describing the use of a two-color, internally comparative hybridization technique to probe cDNAs arrayed robotically at high density on solid substrates (Schena et al. 1995, 1996; DeRisi et al. 1996). These studies led to the development of DNA microarrays to screen the relative abundance of thousands of mRNAs simultaneously. The various detection schemes and applications of cDNA microarrays are depicted in Figure 3-1.

This section describes how DNA microarrays are used to draw global profiles of the mRNAs expressed in cells and tissues. Part 1 (Protocols 1–12) describes ways to prepare RNA from a variety of sources in a state suitable for expression analysis. Protocol 11 outlines how small amounts of RNA can be amplified in vitro to provide a sufficient template for labeling, either directly or indirectly (Protocols 13 and 14). Part 2 (Protocols 13–20) continues with a description of techniques used to hybridize labeled RNAs to DNA microarrays (Protocol 20) with an extensive troubleshooting guide.

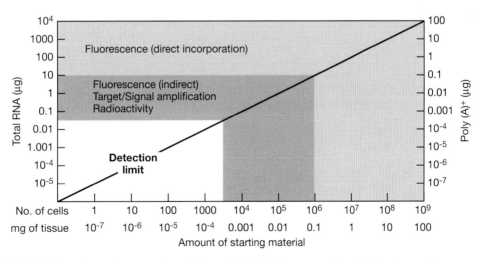

FIGURE 3-1. Detection schemes and application of cDNA microarrays. Quantitative changes in gene expression can be detected using several schemes for which the limits of detection vary. Direct incorporation of fluorescent nucleotides into the cDNA target can be used to examine expression profiles from 10 μg or more of total RNA. Indirect fluorescence, as well as target and signal amplification and radioactivity, on the other hand, can be used to detect expression profiles from as little as 50 ng of total RNA. This detection limit allows for the investigation of expression profiles from numerous biological sources including cell culture, clinical biopsies (including autopsy material), and histological samples. (Redrawn, with permission, from Duggan et al. 1999.)

Part 1: Isolating RNA

INTRODUCTION

Success in expression analysis hinges on the quality of the RNA (Schena and Davis 2000). RNA contaminated with salts, polysaccharides, DNA, protein, or lipid will label inefficiently and may generate high backgrounds during hybridization. If the RNA is partially degraded, labeling may be biased either toward sequences that lie at the 3′ termini or toward sequences that are relatively resistant to attack by RNases. This may distort the relative proportions of various RNA species detected by hybridization to DNA microarrays. Accurate and sensitive estimation of the relative and absolute amounts of mRNA therefore depends on the ability of the investigator to generate RNA preparations that are pure and undamaged.

Once a tissue has been removed from an animal, the overall rate of mRNA synthesis decreases, whereas the speed of degradation increases. The keys to successful isolation of RNA for expression analysis are care in the preparation and harvesting of cells and tissues and speed in lysing them. By preparing and lysing tissues and cells in a manner that inhibits RNases, even the inept can succeed. Table 3-1 outlines methods that are commonly used to harvest and lyse tissue and cells in preparation for extraction and purification of total RNA. These methods are detailed in Protocols 1–10, which describe the isolation of RNA from animal tissues and cells, plants, and yeast. Further information is available in the information panel on GUANIDINIUM-BASED EXTRACTION OF RNA and in Table 3-2. The isolation of RNA from small amounts of material or single cells is described in Protocol 11; other methods for the recovery of RNA from small numbers of cells in complex tissues using laser dissection techniques may be found in Section 5 of this manual. Finally, in designing studies that involve many different RNA preparations, the use of a common reference set provides a distinct advantage in reducing the complexity (and enormity) of the task. The production and use of RNA common reference sets are described in Protocol 12.

PREVENTING DEGRADATION BY RNASES FROM ANIMAL CELLS

The reactive hydroxyl groups on the 2′ and 3′ positions of ribose residues opens RNA to easy attack by RNases. Ubiquitous and stable, these enzymes are released from cells upon lysis and are present on the skin. Although many an experiment has been ruined by contamination with RNase, problems can be entirely avoided by vigilance and common sense. Sensible precautions are listed in two information panels on SPECIAL CONSIDERATIONS FOR WORKING WITH RNA and INHIBITING RNASES.

CHECKING THE INTEGRITY OF PREPARATIONS OF RNA FROM ANIMAL CELLS

After electrophoresis of RNA in the presence of ethidium bromide, the 28S and 18S species of ribosomal RNA (rRNA) should be clearly visible under UV illumination, as should a more diffuse, fast-migrating band composed of transfer RNA (tRNA) and 5S ribosomal RNA. If the

RNA preparation is undegraded, the 28S rRNA band should be stained at approximately twice the intensity of the 18S band, and no smearing of either band should be visible. mRNA is invisible unless the gel is overloaded (please see Figure 3-27). Below are three other methods that can be used to check the integrity of RNA.

- *Analysis of the size of cDNA synthesized using oligo(dT) as a primer.* Radioactive complementary DNA (cDNA) is synthesized in a pilot first-strand cDNA reaction. cDNA synthesized from mammalian mRNA should run as a continuous smear from ~600 bases to >5 kb. The bulk of the radioactivity should lie between 1.5 kb and 2 kb, and no bands of cDNA should be visible unless the mRNA was prepared from highly differentiated cells (e.g., reticulocytes and B lymphocytes) that express large quantities of a particular set of proteins.

- *Using radiolabeled poly(dT) as a probe in a pilot northern hybridization* (Fornace and Mitchell 1986; Hollander and Fornace 1990). Poly(A)$^+$ RNA will generate an autoradiogram with a continuous smear from 600 bases to >5 kb. The bulk of the radioactivity should lie between 1.5 kb and 2 kb, and, once again, no specific bands of cDNA should be visible unless the mRNA was prepared from cells that express large quantities of specific mRNAs.

- *Using northern hybridization to detect a target mRNA of known size.* For example, an mRNA that is expressed from a housekeeping gene such as glucose-6P dehydrogenase (GAPDH) mRNA, whose size in most types of mammalian cells is ~1.3 kb. Significant smearing of the band into lower-molecular-weight regions generally indicates that significant degradation of the mRNA populations has occurred. Fuzziness, on the other hand, is a sign of problems with the agarose gel system (e.g., the presence of ions in the glyoxal). For further details, please see Chapter 7 of *Molecular Cloning: A Laboratory Manual* (Sambrook and Russell 2001).

CONTAMINATION WITH DNA

After gel electrophoresis of a preparation of total RNA, the presence of material stained with ethidium bromide close to the loading well is a sure sign that genomic DNA is still present. A more stringent test is to use aliquots of the RNA preparation as templates in PCRs primed by oligonucleotides corresponding to sequences a known distance apart within a single intron. If the reactions generate a product of the predicted size, the preparation is contaminated with DNA. In this case, the preparation of total RNA should be treated with an RNase-free preparation of DNase (e.g., QIAGEN RNase-free DNase used in conjunction with RNeasy/QIAamp columns); alternatively, poly(A)$^+$ RNA can be isolated from the preparation of total RNA. DNA contamination arises when the aqueous phase becomes contaminated with material from the interface between the organic and aqueous phases, during extraction of cell lysates with chloroform.

TABLE 3-1. Preparing Biological Samples for Isolation of RNA

Preparation	Storage conditions[a]	Method of lysis
Human and Animal Tissue Samples (Protocols 1, 2, 5)		
Chill human biopsy and surgical specimens quickly on ice; deliver them to the pathologist as quickly as possible. With the patient's consent, the pathologist will provide tissue not needed for diagnosis. Most pathologists prefer to dissect fresh untreated tissue. Some, however, allow the tissue to be stored in RNA*later*[b] (Ambion 7020) before dissection and fixation for histological examination. RNA*later* preserves the integrity of the RNA for microarray analysis without compromising the histological and immunohistochemical techniques used for pathological diagnosis (e.g., please see Florell et al. 2001). Under no circumstances should the diagnosis be compromised by sampling of the tissue; all decisions involving handling of the tissue and the amount to be given for research must lie with the pathologist.	Process samples used for isolation of RNA as soon after collection as possible. Quickly cut the tissue removed from an animal or provided by a pathologist into pieces with a maximum thickness of 0.5 cm in any one dimension; place the pieces of tissue in 5 volumes of RNA*later*. Store the samples for 5 minutes at room temperature before transferring them to 4°C for storage of up 1 month or to –20°C for longer-term storage. For long-term storage, treat the samples with RNA*later*, as described above, and then transfer them to cryovials. Immediately snap-freeze the tissue in liquid nitrogen. Transfer the vials to –80°C for long-term storage.	Before addition of the lysis agent, pulverize tough (skin, bone) or fibrous (muscle) tissue into a powder, using a mortar and pestle chilled in liquid nitrogen. Transfer the powder to a polypropylene tube containing a monophasic lysis agent[c] (see Protocol 1). In general, lyse soft tissues such as spleen and liver in monophasic lysis reagent in a rotor-stator homogenizer (e.g., Polytron) (see Protocol 1). For more details, please see the information panel on HOMOGENIZATION OF ANIMAL CELLS AND TISSUES.
Cultured Cell Samples (Protocols 1, 2, 5)		
Standardize the growth of cells as much as possible. To facilitate comparison of results from different experiments, try to replicate growth conditions as exactly as possible. Use cultures of the same density, growing in identical flasks, in the same batch of medium, under identical conditions of temperature/humidity. Minimize the time between incubation and freezing/lysing the cells. Make sure that the cultures are free of mycoplasma.	Recover cells grown in monolayers by scraping and collect them by centrifugation or lyse them in situ. Collect cells grown in suspension by centrifugation. If the cells are to be stored before RNA is extracted, resuspend the pellets in a small (~200 µl) amount of PBS and freeze them at the bottom of the tube to facilitate rapid exposure to lysis buffer on thawing. (Resuspend the cells in PBS as a slurry; tilt the tube on its side and immerse it in liquid nitrogen as it is rotated.) Alternatively, store the cells for up to 1 month at 4°C or at –20°C indefinitely, after adding 5–10 volumes of RNA*later*.	Resuspend washed pellets of cells grown in suspension in monophasic lysis solution. Chill cells grown in monolayers and then lyse them directly on the plates. Tranfer cell lysates to a polypropylene tube and vortex vigorously or pipette up and down to ensure that the cells are completely disrupted (see Protocol 1).
Plant Samples (Protocols 3, 4, 7)		
Care with growth chamber conditions, day length, temperature, and CO_2 tension are obvious potential sources of variation between samples. Generally overlooked aspects of plant growth and handling (fertilization conditions, plant age, growth media, buffers, hormones,	Wash fresh tissues from plants in RNA*later* (*optional*) and immediately lyse in TRIzol. Alternatively, freeze washed tissue indefinitely at –80°C. Pulverize the frozen tissue in a mortar and pestle under liquid nitrogen and store as a powder.	Disrupt soft fresh tissues from plants such as *Arabidopsis* and *Nicotiana* by homogenization in lysis buffer with a rotor-stator homogenizer, a mixer mill (e.g., Model MM300, QIAGEN), or a Polytron. Other tissues from hardy, woody plants may require freezing

and grinding in liquid nitrogen. Reduce the viscosity of plant lysates in monophasic lysis agents by passage through a shredder spin column (e.g., QIAshredder, QIAGEN).

and other additives) may also be a source of variation. To avoid problems, the light intensity and spectrum, time of day of tissue treatment, and harvest should be identical for all samples. If possible, use growth conditions that minimize the accumulation of plant polysaccharides and complex organic compounds. These substances, which are common and persistent contaminants of preparations of plant nucleic acids, are inhibitors of many enzymatic reactions, including thermostable polymerases and reverse transcriptases.

Yeast Samples (Protocol 9)

Expression analysis of autonomous organisms such as yeast is generally aimed at cataloging the changes in abundance of gene transcripts in response to a specific stimulus or genetic alteration (e.g., please see Schena et al 1995; DeRisi et al. 1997; Gasch et al. 2000). The conditions used to grow yeast cultures for analysis by DNA microarrays are therefore dictated chiefly by the nature of the environmental stimulus or the genetic constitution of the yeast strain. However, most experiments involve growth of control cultures under standard conditions such as YPD medium (Sherman 1991) supplemented with 0–25% w/v glucose. Cultures are usually grown at 30°C and shaken at 250–300 rpm in volumes that do not exceed 25% of the flask capacity.

The use of RNA*later* is generally unnecessary. Cells grown to early to mid log phase (OD$_{600}$ 0.2–0.6) can be simply collected by centrifugation and resuspended in 50 ml of an appropriate lysis buffer, snap-frozen in liquid nitrogen, and stored at –80°C until RNA is extracted.

Lyse yeast cells by the addition of acid phenol (please see Protocol 9). However, enzymatic digestion is often used to dissolve cell wall structures that may not be efficiently broken by freezing or other mechanical forces. RNA can then be extracted with H$_2$O-saturated phenol at 65°C and then precipitated with isopropanol or ethanol. Alternatively, use a kit such as QIAGEN RNeasy (please see Protocol 1).

For many investigators, an economical alternative is to buy monophasic lysis solutions and resins in non-kit form from the appropriate manufacturers: TRIzol reagent (Invitrogen/GIBCO); TRI Reagent (Molecular Research Center); RNA STAT60 (Tel-Test, Friendswood, Texas); TOTALLY RNA (Ambion). Although all of these are undoubtedly fine products, TRIzol is currently the most widely used to purify RNA for expression analysis on DNA microarrays. TRIzol is a monophasic solution of phenol, guanidine, ammonium thiocyanates, sodium acetate, phenol red, and glycerol (for recipe, please see http://afgc.stanford.edu/afgc_html/AFGCProtocols-fev2001.pdf). The chaotropic action of the thiocyanate salts dissolves cellular components and denatures proteins, while leaving nucleic acids intact. Addition of chloroform to the lysate causes the solution to separate into two phases. The lower red organic phase contains phenol and chloroform. RNA is recovered from the aqueous phase by precipitation with isopropanol in the presence of high concentrations of salt. A subsequent chromatography step further purifies the RNA from DNA and salts carried over from the phase separation. For further details, please see the information panel on GUANIDINIUM-BASED EXTRACTION OF RNA.

[a]Maintain a database containing all of the relevant information on the samples, including the length of time between initial acquisition and storage and the length of time that the tissue spends at each temperature before being transferred to RNA*later* or –80°C. Label the storage tubes with ethanol-resistant markers or Tough Tags or Tough Spots (Diversified Biotech, Boston Massachusetts).

[b]RNA*later* is an aqueous, nontoxic reagent for tissue and cell storage. According to the literature supplied by the manufacturer (Ambion), the reagent in RNA*later* permeates the tissue within minutes (<0.5 cm in any one dimension) and inactivates RNases. Tissue samples can be stored at 4°C in 5 volumes of RNA*later* for up to 1 month, or indefinitely at –20°C. When isolating RNA, recover the cells/tissues from the RNA*later* solution by centrifugation and lyse them in a monophasic lysis agent (please see Protocol 1).

[c]At last count, there were 55 commercial kits on the market to isolate total RNA from cells (http://www.biocompare.com). Most of them contain combinations of various lysis agents—not necessarily monophasic—together with resins and solutions that are used for postlysis purification of the RNA (for review of the components of lysis agents, please see Defrancesco 1998). Although these kits are expensive, there a strong reasons to use them to prepare RNA for microarray experiments. The kits are generally simple to use, efficient, and, above all, reproducible. When comparing the expression patterns of a series of samples, a major aim should be to minimize variation in handling and processing of tissues and reagents.

TABLE 3-2. Troubleshooting Guide for Guanidinium-based Extration of RNA

Problem	Possible causes	Suggested solutions
Degraded RNA	Delay between harvesting cells or tissues and lysis.	Minimize the length of time between harvesting and lysis. Chill the cells and tissues immediately after harvesting. Wash/store cells and tissues in RNA*later*. If the cells are growing in monolayers, add monophasic lysing reagent (e.g., TRIzol) directly to the plate.
	Overloading the capacity of the reagents used to inactivate/purify the RNA (common problem).	Use the recommended ratios of reagents to tissues/cells. Do not skimp! In general, use 1 ml of TRIzol for every 0.05 g of tissue or every 100-mm culture dish (please see Table 3-3).
	Contamination of the aqueous phase with material from the interface.	Take care when pipetting. Resist the temptation to capture the last drop of aqueous phase.
	Viscosity, caused by high concentrations of high-molecular-weight DNA, disrupts the interface during pipetting.	Use appropriate volumes of TRIzol. Shear the DNA by homogenization or passage through a fine needle.
	RNA kept unfrozen and unprotected in aqueous solution.	Minimize time at temperatures >0°C. Store the RNA in ethanol (please see the information panel on STORAGE AND RECOVERY OF RNA).
	Buffers or equipment contaminated with RNase.	Follow advice given in the information panel on SPECIAL CONSIDERATIONS FOR WORKING WITH RNA.
	Starting tissue rich in nucleases (spleen, pancreas, thymus).	Minimize the length of time between harvesting and processing. Freeze the tissue in liquid nitrogen and then grind it into a powder while keeping the tissue frozen. Add TRIzol immediately after pulverization is complete.
Low yield of RNA	Tissues and cells not completely homogenized in TRIzol reagent.	Efficient homogenization is always important, and becomes critical when dealing with fibrous tissue such as heart and skeletal muscle. Prepare the tissue for homogenization by freezing it in liquid nitrogen and then grind it into a powder while keeping the tissue frozen. Make sure that no particulate matter is visible at the end of the pulverization process. After addition of TRIzol, incubate the preparation for 5 minutes at room temperature after homogenization. If fibrous matter is still visible, homogenize the lysate in a Polytron homogenizer for 30 seconds. If necessary, remove any remaining insoluble material by centrifugation before proceeding.
	Cells not completely removed from the flask/dish during incubation with TRIzol.	Add TRIzol to the flask/dish, tilting the solution back and forth. Let the flask/dish stand for 3–5 minutes. Use a rubber policeman to scrape the cells to one side of the flask/dish. Let the flask/dish stand for a further 3–5 minutes, and then use a pipette to vigorously wash the surface of the flask/dish with the lysate. Transfer the lysate to a tube and incubate for 5 minutes at room temperature.
	RNA not solubilized completely.	Do not allow the pellet of RNA to dry after precipitation with ethanol or isopropanol. Do not dry the pellet under vacuum. Completely dehydrated RNA is very difficult to dissolve. Try solubilizing the RNA in RNase-free H$_2$O at 55°C.
	Cells/tissue less transcriptionally active than expected.	Primary cultures of cells, confluent monolayers of nondividing cells, and tissues with a high content of fat all yield low quantities of RNA.

Problem	Possible cause	Solution
Low $A_{260/280}$ ratio (<1.70)	Residual organic solvents (phenol, chloroform) in the preparation.	Make sure that phase separation is complete. If in doubt, recentrifuge. Take great care not to carry any of the organic phase into the RNA sample.
		Reprecipitate the RNA with 2.5 volumes of ethanol.
	An insufficient amount of TRIzol was added to the sample.	In general, use 1 ml of TRIzol for every 0.05 g of tissue or every 100-mm culture dish (see Table 3-3).
	pH of the solution is acidic.	Dissolve the RNA in TE instead of H_2O.
	Residual guanidine isothiocyanate in the preparation.	Add 0.1 volume of a 2 M solution of sodium acetate (pH 4). Add 1 volume of isopropanol. Store the solution for 30 minutes at −20°C. Recover the RNA by centrifugation. Wash the pellet carefully in 70% ethanol and allow it to dry in the air. Dissolve the pellet while it is still slightly damp in DEPC-treated H_2O and reprecipitate the RNA with ethanol (3 volumes of ethanol for every volume of RNA solution). Recover the RNA by centrifugation.
	A_{260} or A_{280} outside linear range of the spectrophotometer.	Read the OD of a diluted sample of the RNA preparation.
RNA preparation contains some DNA	Part of the interface was transferred with the aqueous layer.	Be sure to stay well away from the interface when recovering the aqueous phase.
	An insufficient amount of TRIzol was added to the sample.	In general, use 1 ml of TRIzol for every 0.05 g of tissue or every 100-mm culture dish (see Table 3-3).
	The tissue was not completely solubilized.	Make sure that no particulate matter is visible at the end of homogenization. Incubate the preparation for 5 minutes at room temperature after homogenization. If necessary, remove the insoluble material by centrifugation before proceeding.
	Ratio of lysis reagent:tissue is too low. For tissues such as spleen and thymus, which contain large amounts of DNA, it may be necessary to increase the amount of TRIzol reagent to reduce the viscosity of the lysate to manageable levels. If the problem persists, shear the DNA by homogenization or passage through a needle.	Increase the ratio of TRIzol:tissue; centrifuge at a higher speed and for a longer time to separate the organic and aqueous phases; carry out multiple extractions to ensure partitioning of the DNA into the acid phenol phase; avoid the interface when recovering the aqueous phase. If a white precipitate forms after addition of isopropanol to the acid phenol phase, DNA contamination is still present. In this case, recover the precipitate, resuspend it in RNase-free H_2O, and re-extract several times with chloroform.
Aqueous phase containing the RNA has color (yellowish-brown or pink)	Fat globules have not floated to the top of the aqueous phase during centrifugation. Phenol red in the reagent becomes packaged in the fat micelles.	Centrifuge the preparation before addition of chloroform, and use a Pasteur pipette attached to a vacuum line to discard the surface layer of yellowish fat.
	If the samples were rich in blood, the RNA preparation may contain residual hemoglobin.	Increase the ratio of lysis reagent to sample during lysis.
	Aqueous phase turns yellow after addition of isopropanol.	Use a fresh bottle of isopropanol.
RNA is intact but is an inefficient template for reverse transcriptase	RNA preparation is contaminated with polysaccharides and/or polyphenols. This problem arises frequently in preparations of plant RNA.	Treat the plant tissue lysate with polyvinylpyrrolidone before isolating the RNA (please see Pine Tree Method of Isolation of RNA in Protocol 4).

Some of the material in this table is reproduced from the Invitrogen, Promega, and Ambion Web Sites.

Purification of Total RNA from Mammalian Cells and Tissues

Jun S. Wei and Javed Khan

Advanced Technology Center, Pediatric Oncology Branch, National Cancer Institute, NIH, Gaithersburg, Maryland 20877

Chaotropic lysis in the presence of organic solvents is the method of choice for extraction of RNA from most types of mammalian tissues and cultured cells (please see the information panel on GUANIDINIUM-BASED EXTRACTION OF RNA). In this protocol, lysis in TRIzol is followed by phase separation, which removes DNA and protein. RNA is then purified and recovered from the chaotropic solution by binding to, washing on, and release from a chromatographic matrix, in this case, RNeasy columns (please see Figure 3-2). This approach has several advantages. By eliminating the concentration and precipitation steps in the early steps, formation of complexes between RNA and polysaccharides and proteoglycans is avoided. These complexes prevent solubilization of RNA after precipitation and inhibit reverse transcription reactions. The use of both phase separation and chromatography, each of which fractionate molecules on a different physical basis, provides significantly better purification than either alone. Direct comparison of signal strength indicates that the cDNA prepared from total RNA yields a signal that is approximately three times stronger than the signal from poly(A)$^+$ RNA (Wildsmith et al. 2001). This is thought to be due to the potential loss of mRNA during poly(A)$^+$ RNA isolation and therefore confers no advantage over using total RNA.

Although the technique described here has been successfully applied to a wide variety of cells and tissues, it is not recommended when extracting RNA from adipose tissues that are rich in triglycerides. RNA is best prepared from these fatty sources by a modification of the methods of Chirgwin et al. (1979), described by Tavangar et al. (1990). See also Protocol 8 in this section.

Recommendations for the successful extraction of RNA from small amounts of tissue is described in the panel at the end of this protocol. Also at the end of this protocol is an alternative protocol: RNA EXTRACTION FROM OCT-EMBEDDED PATHOLOGY SAMPLES.

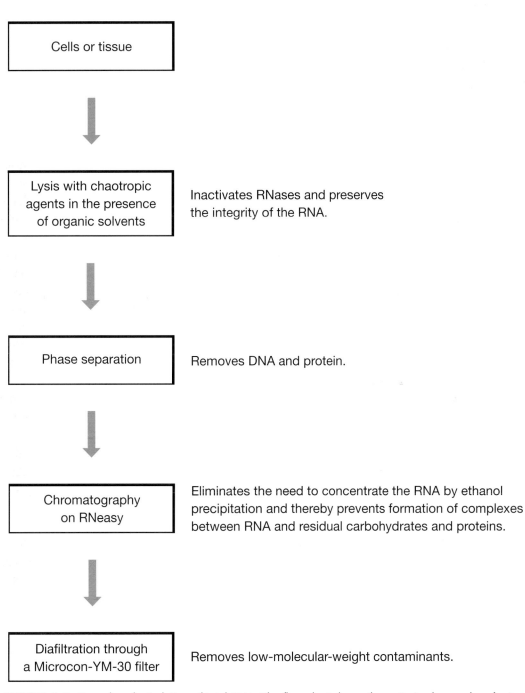

FIGURE 3-2. Procedure for isolation of total RNA. The flow chart shows the optimized procedure for isolation of total RNA from cells and tissues, in preparation for fluorescent labeling (for experimental details, please see below).

MATERIALS

CAUTION: Please see Appendix 3 for appropriate handling of materials marked with <!>.

IMPORTANT: Prepare all reagents used in this protocol with DEPC-treated H_2O (please see the information panel on SPECIAL CONSIDERATIONS FOR WORKING WITH RNA).

Buffers and Solutions

Please see Appendix 2 for components of stock solutions, buffers, and reagents.
Dilute stock solutions to the appropriate concentrations.

Chloroform <!>

DEPC-treated H_2O <!> (please see the information panel on INHIBITING RNASES)

Ethanol (absolute)
> Some batches of absolute ethanol (100% or 200 proof) have been reported to contain fluorescent contaminants that generate high backgrounds in microarray experiments; 95% ethanol does not have this problem. To avoid difficulties, either use 95% ethanol or identify a brand of absolute ethanol that performs reliably. Absolute ethanol (USP-grade ethyl alcohol 64-17-5) purchased from Warner-Graham Co. (Cockeysville, Maryland) performs consistently well.

Monophasic lysis solution (15596, TRIzol, GIBCO) (please see Tables 3-3 and 3-4)

Phosphate-buffered saline (PBS), lacking Ca^{2+} and Mg^{2+} (14190-136, GIBCO)

RNA*later* stabilization reagent (221462, QIAGEN)

RNase*Zap* (9780, Ambion)

Sodium acetate (3 M, pH 5.2)

TABLE 3-3. Amount of Monophasic Lysis Reagent Required for Isolation of RNA from Monolayers of Cells

Culture dish	Surface area (cm²)	Minimum volume of standard monophasic lysis reagent (e.g., TRI Reagent) (in ml)	Minimum volume of concentrated monophasic lysis reagent (e.g., TRI Reagent LS) (in ml)
One well of 6-well dish	10.0	0.8	0.6
10-cm dish	78.5	7.8	2.75
T75 flask	75.0	5.25	2.65
T150 flask	150.0	10.5	5.30

The amount of monophasic lysis reagent is determined by the area of the dish and not the density of the cells. The volumes of reagent shown in the table are sufficient both to cover the surface of the plate or flask completely and to overcome the buffering effects of residual medium or phosphate-buffered saline.

Some manufacturers sell monophasic lysis reagents at different concentrations, e.g., the standard TRIzol and the more concentrated TRIzol LS. The figures in the table for TRI Reagent are taken from the Web Site, Molecular Research Center Inc, whose versions of monophasic lysis reagent are TRI Reagent (equivalent to TRIzol) and TRI Reagent LS (equivalent to TRIzol LS) (http://www.mrcgene.com/tbl-rna.htm).

TABLE 3-4. Monophasic Lysis Reagents

Reagent	Commerical supplier
TRIzol	Invitrogen (Carlsbad, California)
TRI Reagent	Molecular Research Center (Cincinnati, Ohio)
Trisolv	Biotecx Laboratories (Houston, Texas)
RNA STAT60	Tel-Test (Friendswood, Texas)
Isogen	Nippon Gene (Toyama, Japan)

Always check the manufacturer's instructions when using commercial reagents.

Cells and Tissues

Monolayers or suspension cultures of mammalian cells or fresh tissues

Special Equipment

Barrier micropipette tips of various sizes

Centrifuge tubes (15-ml screw cap; 60-540, Sarstedt, Newton, North Carolina)

Clinical tabletop centrifuge

Homogenizer

The Polytron PT1200 homogenizer (Kinematica AG, Switzerland) or equivalent equipped with Probe 9100071 (Brinkmann 27 13 700-8) is used to disrupt cells and tissues. Before use, clean the Polytron so that it is free of RNase. Take apart the probe and wash the pieces first in H_2O, then in absolute ethanol, and finally in RNaseZap, which degrades RNA. Reassemble the probe and run the homogenizer in H_2O. For a discussion of various instruments used for homogenization of tissues, please see the information panel on HOMOGENIZATION OF ANIMAL CELLS AND TISSUES.

Microcon YM-30 (42410, Millipore)

Mortar and pestle

These are required for disruption of large amounts (>500 mg) of soft tissue or any amount of hard, fibrous tissue (see Step 1) (12-061-5B, Fisher Scientific, Pittsburgh Pennsylvania).

Refrigerated centrifuge (Sorvall RT 6000/H1000 rotor or equivalent)

RNeasy RNA isolation kit (75144 for Midi kit; 75162 for Maxi kit, QIAGEN)

SpeedVac

METHOD

1. Prepare cells or tissue samples for isolation of RNA:

   For Tissues: Wherever possible, keep the tissues either frozen at –80ºC or in liquid nitrogen or in RNA*later* until they are homogenized.

   a. Weigh the tissue.

   b. Place ~100 mg of frozen tissue in a 50-ml polypropylene screw-top centrifuge tube containing 4 ml of TRIzol.

   c. Homogenize the tissues with a Polytron homogenizer or in batches of 100 mg in a FastPrep instrument (please see Protocol 2).

      Most tissues can be processed using either of these methods. For information about these instruments, and on the methods commonly used to disrupt tissues, please see the information panel on HOMOGENIZATION OF ANIMALS CELLS AND TISSUES.

   d. For hard tissues or tissues larger than 500 mg, use a prechilled (with liquid nitrogen) mortar and pestle to grind up tissues before homogenization in TRIzol solution.

   e. Transfer TRIzol into a 15-ml screw-top polypropylene centrifuge tube.

   For Cells Grown in Suspension:

   a. Harvest cells by centrifugation in a precooled centrifuge at 400g for 10 minutes at 4ºC.

   b. Remove the medium by aspiration and gently resuspend the cell pellets in a volume of ice-cold PBS equivalent to 0.5 times the volume of the original culture.

   c. Repellet the cells by centrifugation, remove the PBS, and add 1 ml of TRIzol solution per 5×10^6 cells.

   d. Without delay, transfer the cell suspension to a 15-ml screw-top polypropylene centrifuge tube, and vortex vigorously for 1 minute at room temperature.

   For Cells Grown in Monolayers:

   a. Remove the medium and rinse the cell monolayers twice with ice-cold PBS.

b. Without delay, remove the PBS and add 1 ml of TRIzol solution for each 10 cm^2 of monolayer culture.

c. Use a plastic policeman to scrape the cells into the TRIzol solution.

d. Without delay, transfer the cell lysate to a 15-ml screw-top polypropylene centrifuge tube and vortex vigorously for 1 minute at room temperature.

> Do not skimp on the TRIzol solution. The amounts recommended are required to overcome the buffering effects of residual PBS and medium.

> Some types of mammalian cells contain particularly tough structures (e.g., melanosomes) that are not disrupted during lysis nor removed by chromatography. These complexes can be removed by incubating the lysate for 5 minutes at 65°C before proceeding to Step 2.

2. Stand the tube for 2–3 minutes at room temperature, and then add 0.2 volume of chloroform. Do not use 200-µl tips; instead, use 1-ml filtered pipette tips to prevent the chloroform from "creeping" into the filters. Invert the closed tube and shake it vigorously for 15–20 seconds.

3. Stand the tube for 5 minutes at room temperature, and then centrifuge the tube at 12,000g for 15 minutes at 4°C.

4. Use a Pasteur pipette to transfer the supernatant to a fresh polypropylene tube. Record the volume of the supernatant.

> To reduce the possibility of contamination with DNA, take care to avoid the white interface between the organic (lower) and the upper (aqueous phase). If this step proves to be difficult, consider using Phase Lock Gel to segregate the organic and aqueous phases (please see the alternative protocol in Protocol 9 or www.brinkman.com).

5. While vortexing, slowly add 1 volume of 70% ethanol to the supernatant.

> Add the ethanol drop by drop and make sure that the ethanol and the supernatant are mixed completely before the next drop is added. If the mixing is inadequate, the RNA will precipitate in locally high concentrations of ethanol. When addition is complete, the final proportion of ethanol in the mixture should be 35%.

6. Apply the sample to an RNeasy spin column. The expected total RNA (follow manufactures recommendations as per protocol) determines choice of spin column. The RNeasy Midi column has a maximum binding capacity of 1 mg (equivalent to 5 x 10^6 to 1 x 10^8 cells or 20–250 mg of tissue), whereas that of the RNeasy Maxi spin column is 6 mg (equivalent to 5 x 10^7 to 5 x 10^8 cells or 0.15–1 g of tissue).

7. Centrifuge the RNeasy column at 3000g in a clinical centrifuge equipped with a swing-out rotor for 5 minutes at room temperature.

8. Transfer the flow-through to the top of the same column and centrifuge again at 3000g for 5 minutes.

> A significant fraction of the RNA is not captured by the column matrix during the first centrifugation step.

> After centrifugation, check that no buffer is visible in the bottom tip of the spin column. If buffer is present, repeat the centrifugation step after removing the flow-through from the collection tube by pipetting.

9. Discard the flow-through from the column and add 4 ml of RW1 buffer for Midi (15 ml for Maxi) to the top of the column. Centrifuge the column at 3000g for 5 minutes at room temperature.

10. Discard the flow-through and add 2.5 ml of RPE buffer for Midi (10 ml for Maxi) to the top of the column. Centrifuge the column at 3000*g* for 5 minutes at room temperature.

11. Repeat Step 10 once. Centrifuge the column at 3000*g* for another 5 minutes to dry.

12. Discard the flow-through and transfer the column to a fresh 15-ml centrifuge tube for Midi columns (50-ml tube for Maxi columns).

13. To elute RNA, add 150–200 µl of H_2O to the top of the Midi column (0.8–1.2 ml of H_2O to the top of the Maxi column). Let the column stand for 1 minute at room temperature before centrifuging at 3000*g* for 5 minutes at room temperature.

14. Repeat the elution in Step 13, and combine the eluates.

15. Quantify the RNA by absorption spectrophotometry at 260 and 280 nm or by fluorescence after staining with RiboGreen (please see the information panel on QUANTIFICA-TION OF RNA).

16. Prepare aliquots of the desired quantity of RNA plus an additional 10% (for estimated losses in Steps 15–20) for individual labeling reactions into 1.5-ml microfuge tubes.

17. Precipitate RNA by adding 1/10 volume of 3 M sodium acetate (pH. 5.2) to each aliquot. Mix the solutions by vortexing briefly and then add 2.5 volumes of absolute ethanol to each tube. Again mix by vortexing.

18. Freeze the RNA preparations on dry ice until solid.

19. Thaw and recover the RNA by centrifugation at 12,000*g* for 15 minutes at 4ºC.

20. Wash the RNA pellet in 75% ethanol, recovering the RNA by centrifugation at 12,000*g* for 5 minutes at 4ºC.

    The RNA pellet can be stored safely in 75% ethanol at –80ºC.

21. On the day before labeling, repellet the RNA by centrifugation at 12,000*g* for 15 minutes at 4ºC. Remove all the ethanol carefully, and dry the pellet of RNA in a rotary evaporator with medium heat (42ºC) for a maximum of 2 minutes. Resuspend the RNA in 450 µl of DEPC-treated H_2O.

    Overdrying may result in difficulties in redissolving the RNA, and ethanol carry over will interfere with the labeling reaction.

22. Concentrate the RNA to the desired volume (17 µl, depending on the labeling protocol used) using the Microcon YM-30 filter unit, according to the manufacturer's instructions. Check the filter as necessary to determine the rate of concentration.

    This step removes many residual salts and small to medium-sized molecules that may inhibit the reverse transcription reaction.

    For labeling, total RNA is required at a concentration of 7 mg/ml.

23. Before using the RNA in microarray experiments, check its integrity by electrophoresis through a formaldehyde–1% agarose gel (please see the information panel on MAM-MALIAN, PLANT, AND BACTERIAL RNAs).

    Probes prepared from total RNA purified from animal cells and tissues by a single extraction with TRIzol sometimes generate high background when hybridized to oligonucleotide arrays. This problem can often be solved by extracting the RNA a second time with TRIzol as follows: Dissolve the RNA in 50–100 µl of H_2O. Add 1 ml of TRIzol, and then follow the manufacturer's recommendation for extracting RNA. Redissolve the RNA as described in Step 21.

EXTRACTION OF RNA FROM LIMITING AMOUNTS OF TISSUE (<50 MG)

Some cDNA microarray experiments, for example, those that involve indirect labeling using amino-allyl dyes (Protocol 14), require that significant amounts of RNA be isolated from limiting amounts of tissue without amplification.

The successful extraction of RNA from small amounts of tissue depends on adequate homogenization of the tissue in an appropriate buffer. For tissues that are particularly fibrous and otherwise difficult to homogenize, the use of TRIzol followed by purification through RNeasy columns, described in this protocol, is appropriate. To avoid potential loss of tissue that may result from processing in TRIzol, the use of RLT buffer for homogenization is recommended (please refer to the alternative protocol on the following page, beginning with Step 4). Note that adequate amounts of RLT buffer should be used; for example, up to 50 mg of tissue may be suspended in 600 μl of RLT buffer.

The yield of RNA varies according to the quantity of starting material as well as the tissue type and the transcriptional activity of the tissue. In general, ~1 μg of RNA per 1 mg of tissue can be achieved. An example of approximate amounts of tissue that may be obtained from various forms of biopsies is listed below: Figure 3-3 illustrates examples of an endoscopic biopsy and trucut biopsy, respectively.

Type of biopsy	Tissue weight
Endoscopic biopsies (standard spiked forceps)	~10 mg/biopsy
Trucut biopsies (core biopsies with bioptigun [14-gauge])	~100 mg/cm length
Fine-needle aspirate (FNA)	<5 mg/biopsy

This panel was contributed by Alex Boussioutas (Peter MacCallum Cancer Research Institute, Melbourne, Australia).

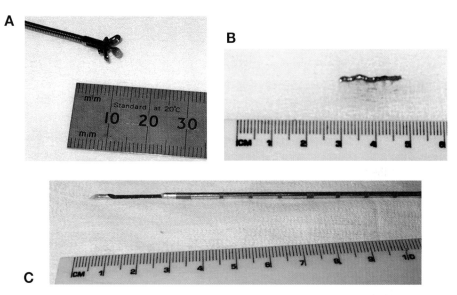

FIGURE 3-3. Biopsy samples. (*A*) Endoscopic biopsy; (*B*) trucut liver biopsy; (*C*) trucut needle.

ALTERNATIVE PROTOCOL: RNA EXTRACTION FROM OCT-EMBEDDED PATHOLOGY SAMPLES

Sophie Katsabanis
Peter MacCallum Cancer Research Institute, Melbourne, Australia

Optimal Cutting Temperature (OCT) compound, commonly used for embedding tissues, is primarily composed of carbohydrate and polyvinyl alcohol. There are a number of approaches to obtaining good quality RNA from OCT-embedded tissues; the appropriate choice is dictated by the nature of the downstream applications.

For RT-PCR analysis, for example, sufficient RNA can be obtained from a number of pooled sections. Irving et al. (1996) describe a method in which five 20-μm cryostat sections are stored frozen at –20°C in a GITC (guanidine isothiocyanate) solution. After thawing, the samples are homogenized and RNA is isolated by CsCl ultracentrifugation. In a modified approach undertaken by Nichols et al. (1997), five frozen tissue sections (10-μm thick) were cut from the OCT block at –20°C and attached to glass slides. After air-drying for 5 minutes at room temperature, the OCT was manually scraped away with a sterile razor blade, and the tissue was transferred to an extraction tube. Total RNA was isolated from the pooled sections using the QIAGEN RNeasy kit.

Downstream applications that utilize larger amounts of RNA (e.g., northerns and microarrays) require a different approach. There are a number of options, depending on the availability of the required equipment. The main objective with any method is to remove as much of the OCT compound as possible prior to RNA isolation. After this, any aqueous-based commercial kit (QIAGEN RNeasy, Ambion RNAqueous) can be used to isolate the RNA. GITC disruption and CsCl ultracentrifugation can also used with equal success, although throughput will be compromised due to the smaller capacity of the centrifuge rotor and extended centrifugation times.

To obtain larger amounts of tissue embedded in OCT, a freezing microtome (–80°C or lower) is used to cut 100-μm sections through the whole-tissue block until only the OCT remains, which is discarded. The tissue sections are placed in GITC, and RNA is isolated by CsCl ultracentrifugation as described in Protocol 8. Alternatively, the sections may be placed directly into RLT buffer (from the QIAGEN RNeasy kit). The remaining OCT will dissolve into the buffer, as RLT is an aqueous solution. After brief centrifugation to pellet the tissue pieces, the RLT is removed and replaced with fresh RLT buffer. This is an important step, as large amounts of carbohydrate released from the OCT will clog the RNeasy column, leading to reduced RNA yields. Following this, the RNeasy protocol is followed as per manufacturer's instructions.

Additional Materials

Freezing microtome (–80°C or lower)
RLT lysis buffer including β-mercaptoethanol <!> (provided in the RNeasy kit)

Method

1. Use a razor blade to remove the bulk of the OCT from the tissue.

   It is advisable to maintain the block at –80°C while cutting to minimize thawing of the tissue and therefore RNA degradation from RNase activity. If this is not possible, remove the OCT block from the liquid nitrogen storage and allow it to thaw only very slightly for easy cutting.

2. Place the tissue in RNA*later* (tissue stabilization buffer) in a 50-ml falcon tube.

   For a 10 x 10-mm OCT block, use ~5 ml of RNA*later*.

   It is important that the embedded tissue be no more than 5-mm thick, as the RNA*later* solution cannot penetrate fast enough to protect the whole sample. Diffusion is also hampered by the tissue being frozen. For best results, especially if the size of the embedded tissue piece is unknown, or is known to be larger than 5 mm, the block should be cut in half longitudinally. This exposes a second tissue face, allowing for quicker diffusion of RNA*later* into the tissue.

3. Vortex the tissue block vigorously in RNA*later* solution until the OCT begins to dissolve.

   The OCT will not dissolve completely, instead, a sort of shell or skin will remain around the tissue. All that is required is for the OCT to be soft enough to allow physical separation of the tissue from the OCT, using a pair of tweezers/forceps.

4. Remove the tissue and place it into a fresh tube and weigh the sample.

5. Add an appropriate amount of RLT lysis buffer including β-mercaptoethanol (refer to RNeasy protocol) and homogenize the tissue with an Ultraturax or similar rotor-stator homogenizer.

6. Transfer the homogenate to a 15-ml screw-cap centrifuge tube.

7. Continue to purify RNA using the RNeasy column, beginning with Step 2 of the main protocol.

Isolation of Total RNA from Tissues Using the FastPrep Instrument

The FastPrep FP 120 instrument (Q-Biogene 6000-120) is used to homogenize tissues that weigh less than 100 mg. Tissue samples are disrupted in impact-resistant 2-ml BioPulverizer tubes containing a lysing matrix to mechanically disrupt and homogenize tissues in 1 ml of TRIzol. The instrument agitates up to 12 tubes with a twisting and throwing motion at extremely high speed. Homogenization is usually complete within a few seconds. However, tough tissues such as mouse tails or bone may require longer periods of homogenization. Because each sample is contained in its individual tube, cross-contamination between samples is eliminated.

MATERIALS

Buffers and Solutions

Please see Appendix 2 for components of stock solutions, buffers, and reagents.
Dilute stock solutions to the appropriate concentrations.

Monophasic lysis solution (TRIzol 15596, GIBCO)
Please see Tables 3-3 and 3-4 in Protocol 1.

Special Equipment

BioPulverizer tubes (2 ml) containing lysing matrix D (6513-001, Q-Biogene Inc., Carlsbad California)
FastPrep FP 120 instrument (6000-120, Q-Biogene Inc., Carlsbad California)

Additional Reagents

This protocol may require reagents listed in Protocol 1.

METHOD

1. Preset the FastPrep instrument at 6 m/s for 25 seconds.

2. Measure the mass of tissue. Do not use more than 100 mg of tissue in a 2-ml BioPulverizer tube.

3. Add 0.5 ml of TRIzol to each BioPulverizer tube. Store the tube on ice for 5 minutes.

4. Quickly transfer the freshly excised tissue into the BioPulverizer tube containing TRIzol. Make sure the cap is tightly closed.

    An air space of ~0.5 ml is required. Less air space will cause the sample to leak because of tube failure or deformation around the cap.

5. Place the tubes into the FastPrep instrument, making sure that the cap lock prongs are directly over the sample tubes. Screw down the prongs tightly.

6. Close the lid and start the run.

7. After the run, immediately remove the tubes and place them on ice for 2 minutes.

8. If the tissue is not completely homogenized, repeat the homogenization step two or three more times. Be sure to place the tubes on ice for 2 minutes between each shake, otherwise they may explode because of heat expansion of the TRIzol solution.

9. When homogenization is complete, transfer the tubes from the FastPrep instrument to an ice bucket. Immediately add 0.5 ml of TRIzol to the homogenates. Mix the solutions thoroughly.

10. Follow Steps 2–18 of Protocol 1.

Isolation of Total RNA from Plant Tissue Using TRIzol*

Damares Monte*† and Shauna Somerville*

*Carnegie Institution of Washington, Stanford, California 94305; †E.M.B.R.A.P.A.
(Brazilian Agricultural Research Corporation) Genetic Resources and Biotechnology,
Brasilia, Brazil

> You work that you may keep pace with the earth and the soul of the earth. For to be idle is to become a stranger unto the seasons, and to step out of life's procession, that marches in majesty and proud submission towards the infinite.
>
> Kahlil Gibran

High-throughput DNA microarray technology (Schena et al. 1995) has already generated extensive catalogs of the patterns of gene expression in plants of several species grown under different conditions (for review, please see Kehoe et al. 1999; Richmond and Somerville 2000). The earliest arrays typically contained only a few hundred genes (Ruan et al. 1998; Aharoni et al. 2000; McGonigle et al. 2000; Reymond et al. 2000). However, as genomic sequencing of plant genomes has progressed, the number of genes on spotted arrays has expanded to several thousand (Arabidopsis Functional Genomics Consortium, http://afgc.stanford.edu) (Harmer et al. 2000; Maleck et al. 2000; Wang et al. 2000; Zhu and Wang 2000).

RNA of the quality required for microarray analysis is more difficult to prepare from plant tissues than from animal tissues. Unless great care is taken during the extraction and purification process, plant RNA may be contaminated with polyphenols, polysaccharides, proteins, or DNA, all of which will inhibit in vitro cDNA synthesis and labeling. The presence of these contaminants and/or of small nucleic acid fragments (<200 bases) may cause background hybridization to increase markedly. In addition, secondary structure elements intrinsic to many plant RNA transcripts may impede access of reverse transcriptase or may cause premature termination of cDNA synthesis (Zhu and Wang 2000). These problems, singly or in combination, may constrict the already limited dynamic range of microarray experiments (Bertucci et al. 1999; Lipshultz et al. 1999) to the point where low-abundance transcripts become undetectable.

Because polyphenols and proteoglycans bind to RNA and compromise the overall performance of microarray analysis, choosing the best method(s) for RNA isolation and purification from a particular plant species or tissue is an essential step for success. This protocol and Protocol 4 describe two methods for the purification of total RNA that yield plant RNA of high quality. Protocol 3 describes how the TRIzol method can be used to purify RNA from a variety of soft plant tissues. Protocol 4 describes the pine tree method, introduced by Chang et al. (1993), which is recommended for extraction of RNA from recalcitrant plant species

*The authors thank Sue Thayer, Bi-Huei Hou, and Lorne Rose for their kind revision of the manuscript.

and woody tissues that are rich in polyphenols and proteoglycans. Although derived originally for the isolation of RNA from pine cones, this method has been used successfully to isolate RNA of high purity from a number of plant species such as *Arabidopsis thaliana*. The yield of RNA from the two protocols varies widely according to the source and type of the plant tissue. This protocol typically yields 1.7 mg of total RNA from 1 g of *Arabidopsis* leaf tissue, whereas Protocol 4 yields ~240 μg of total RNA from pine seedlings and cones. For a smaller-scale preparation, the use of commercial kits provides an alternative method (e.g., the RNeasy Plant Kit from QIAGEN).

MATERIALS

CAUTION: Please see Appendix 3 for appropriate handling of materials marked with <!>.

IMPORTANT: Prepare all reagents used in this protocol with DEPC-treated H$_2$O (please see the information panel on SPECIAL CONSIDERATIONS FOR WORKING WITH RNA).

Buffers and Solutions

Please see Appendix 2 for components of stock solutions, buffers, and reagents.
Dilute stock solutions to the appropriate concentrations.

Chloroform <!>
Diethylpyrocarbonate (DEPC) <!>
Ethanol (95% and 75%)
> Some batches of absolute ethanol (100% or 200 proof) have been reported to contain fluorescent contaminants that generate high backgrounds in microarray experiments; 95% ethanol does not have this problem. To avoid difficulties, either use 95% ethanol or identify a brand of absolute ethanol that does not generate high levels of background fluorescence. Absolute ethanol (USP-grade ethyl alcohol 64-17-5) purchased from Warner-Graham Co. (Cockeysville, Maryland) performs consistently well.

Isopropanol (2-propanol)
Liquid nitrogen <!>
Monophasic lysis solution (e.g., TRIzol; please see Tables 3-3 and 3-4 in Protocol 1)
RNase inhibitor of choice (please see the information panel on INHIBITING RNASES)
RNA precipitation solution
> 0.8 M sodium citrate
> 1.2 M NaCl
> No adjustment of pH is required.

Centrifuges and Rotors

Clinical centrifuge (Eppendorf 5810R or equivalent)
Eppendorf rotor (F-34-6-38 or equivalent)

Special Equipment

Mortar and pestle (prechilled in liquid nitrogen) (Fisher Scientific)
Polytron homogenizer
> The Polytron is used to disrupt cells and many types of tissue (Kinematica Model 1 PT3100, equipped with Probe 9100071; Brinkmann). Before use, clean the Polytron so that it is free of RNase. Take apart the probe and wash the pieces first in H$_2$O, then in absolute ethanol, and finally in RNase*Zap*, which degrades RNA. Reassemble probe and run the homogenizer in H$_2$O.

Water bath preset to 60°C

METHOD

IMPORTANT: Place the centrifuge tubes in liquid nitrogen before beginning the protocol. In addition, when processing multiple samples simultaneously, keep the centrifuge tubes containing powdered tissue in liquid nitrogen while processing other samples.

1. Harvest and store plant tissue as described in Table 3-1. Use a prechilled mortar and pestle to grind 1 g of tissue, under liquid nitrogen, to a fine powder.

2. Transfer the powdered tissue to a 50-ml sterile plastic screw-cap centrifuge tube prechilled in liquid nitrogen. Store the tube in liquid nitrogen while processing other samples.

3. Remove the tube containing the powdered plant tissue from liquid nitrogen and immediately add 15 ml of TRIzol reagent.

4. Mix the powdered plant tissue into the TRIzol lysis solution by vigorously inverting the tube, making sure that the powdered tissue is exposed to the reagent as soon as it thaws.

   RNases trapped in the membrane fractions can be very active if not immediately neutralized by the RNase inhibitor present in the TRIzol solution.

   WARNING: Handle the polypropylene tube containing the buffer and the powdered tissue very carefully. Release of the dissolved nitrogen can blow the lid off. Wear safety glasses at all stages involving the handling of the homogenization buffer.

5. Incubate the lysate for 5 minutes at room temperature or if the tissue is hard and stringy.

6. Homogenize the tissue in a Polytron homogenizer for two bursts of 15 seconds. Vent the tube once between shaking and vortexing.

7. Centrifuge the samples at 10,000g (9000 rpm) for 10 minutes at 4°C.

8. Transfer the supernatant into a fresh sterile 50-ml sterile plastic screw-cap centrifuge tube. Discard the pellet.

9. Add 3 ml of chloroform to the tube.

10. Mix the phases by shaking the tubes vigorously and vortexing for 15 seconds. Vent the tube once between shaking and vortexing.

11. Store the tubes for 2–3 minutes at room temperature.

12. Separate the phases by centrifugation at 10,000g (9000 rpm) for 15 minutes at 4°C.

13. Carefully transfer the aqueous phase into a fresh screw-cap centrifuge tube. Take great care not to transfer any material from the interface or the lower phase. Discard the interphase and lower organic phase.

    If this step proves to be difficult, consider using Phase Lock Gel to segregate the organic and aqueous phases (please see the panel on ALTERNATIVE PROTOCOL: PURIFICATION OF RNA USING PHASE LOCK GELS in Protocol 9).

14. Measure the volume of aqueous phase and then precipitate the RNA by adding 0.5 volume of isopropanol and 0.5 volume of RNA precipitation solution. Seal the tube and mix the contents by gentle inversion.

15. Store the tube for 10 minutes at room temperature.

16. Recover the RNA by centrifugation at 10,000*g* (9000 rpm) for 10 minutes at 4ºC.

17. Carefully pour off the supernatant and wash the RNA pellet with 20 ml of 75% ethanol. Vortex briefly to wash the sides of the tube.

18. Recover the RNA by centrifugation at 10,000*g* (9000 rpm) for 10 minutes at 4ºC. Discard the supernatant and stand the open tube in a chemical fume hood for 5–10 minutes (no longer!) until no visible traces of the supernatant remain.

19. Resuspend the RNA in 250 μl of DEPC-treated H_2O by pipetting the solution up and down a few times.

20. Transfer the sample to a microfuge tube at room temperature. Remove any material that does not redissolve by centrifugation at maximum speed in a bench top microfuge for 5 minutes at room temperature.

21. Transfer the RNA solution (supernatant) to a fresh tube. Quantify the RNA by absorption spectrophotometry at 260 and 280 nm or by fluorescence after staining with RiboGreen (please see the information protocol on QUANTIFICATION OF RNA).

22. Store the RNA by one of the methods outlined in the information panel on STORAGE AND RECOVERY OF RNA. (Optional) Add an RNase inhibitor (e.g., RNasin), according to manufacturer's directions (see Sambrook and Russell 2001, page 7.83).

    Before using the RNA in microarray experiments, check its integrity by electrophoresis through a formaldehyde–1% agarose gel (please see the information panel on MAMMALIAN, PLANT, AND BACTERIAL RNAs).

Pine Tree Method for Isolation of Plant RNA*

Damares Monte*† and Shauna Somerville*

*Carnegie Institution of Washington, Stanford, California 94305; †E.M.B.R.A.P.A.
(Brazilian Agricultural Research Corporation) Genetic Resources and Biotechnology,
Brasilia, Brazil

Plant tissues from a variety of species contain large amounts of polyphenolic compounds, lipopolysaccharides, and proteins that may contaminate the RNA preparation. This causes difficulties in solubilizing the RNA after precipitation with alcohols, reduces the efficiency of cDNA synthesis and labeling, and generates background hybridization.

The pine tree method was developed by Chang et al. (1993) based on the techniques originally described by Schneiderbauer et al. (1991) and Katterman and Shattuck (1983) for the isolation of total RNA from pine tree seedlings, which are rich in ribonucleases, polysaccharides, and polyphenols. In general, extraction of RNA from these types of plant tissues by traditional phenol methods results in low yield and a brownish precipitate containing oxidized phenolic compounds that are bound tenaciously to the RNA. This problem can be overcome by including polyvinylpyrrolidone (PVP) in the lysis buffer, which binds contaminants, β-mercaptoethanol (a reducing agent), and hexadecyltrimethylammonium bromide (CTAB), a cationic detergent. Proteins are removed by chloroform instead of phenol.

This method avoids the use of phenol, guanidinium hydrochloride, or guanidinium isothiocyanate and does not require ultracentrifugation. The recovered RNA is usually intact and colorless, and the yield ranges from 100 to 240 μg/g tissue with an A_{260}/A_{280} ratio usually above 1.7. Because the method requires a lengthy precipitation of RNA with lithium chloride (LiCl), the time required to complete the protocol varies from 4 hours to overnight, depending on the amount of RNA in the preparation. The longer the exposure to LiCl, the higher the recovery of total RNA. The RNA can be used directly for DNA microarray hybridization, after testing that it is DNA-free, and as a source of purified poly(A)$^+$ RNA to prepare labeled targets.

*The authors thank Sue Thayer, Bi-Huei Hou, and Lorne Rose for their kind revision of the manuscript and Jeff Landgrof for recommending this protocol.

MATERIALS

CAUTION: Please see Appendix 3 for appropriate handling of materials marked with <!>.

IMPORTANT: Prepare all reagents used in this protocol with DEPC-treated H_2O (please see the information panel on SPECIAL CONSIDERATIONS FOR WORKING WITH RNA).

Buffers and Solutions

Please see Appendix 2 for components of stock solutions, buffers, and reagents.
Dilute stock solutions to the appropriate concentrations.

Chloroform:isoamyl alcohol (24:1) <!>
Extraction buffer
    2% (w/v) CTAB
    2% (w/v) PVP K 30
    100 mM Tris-HCl (pH 8.0)
    25 mM EDTA
    2.0 M NaCl
    0.5 g/liter spermidine
    2% β-mercaptoethanol <!>
        Mix all ingredients, except β-mercaptoethanol. Divide the solution into small aliquots and sterilize by autoclaving on liquid cycle for 15 minutes. Add β-mercaptoethanol to the extraction buffer just before use.
LiCl (8 M, F.W. = 42.39)
        Add 33.9 g of LiCl to 50 ml of H_2O. Adjust the volume of the solution to 100 ml. After all of the LiCl has dissolved, sterilize the solution by autoclaving for 15 minutes on liquid cycle.
RNase inhibitor of choice (please see Sambrook and Russell 2001)
SSTE
    1.0 M NaCl
    0.5% (w/v) SDS <!>
    10 mM Tris-HCl (pH 8.0)
    1 mM EDTA (pH 8.0)

Centrifuges and Rotors

Clinical centrifuge (Eppendorf 5810R or equivalent)
Eppendorf rotor (F-34-6-38 or equivalent)

Special Equipment

Mortar and pestle (prechilled in liquid nitrogen) (12-061-5B, Fisher Scientific)
Water bath, preset to 65ºC

METHOD

1. Transfer 15 ml of extraction buffer (containing β-mercaptoethanol) to a 50-ml polypropylene tube. Close the tube and heat the buffer to 65ºC in a water bath.

2. Use a mortar and pestle to grind 2–3 g of plant material in the presence of liquid nitrogen to a fine powder.

3. Immediately transfer the powdered tissue to the prewarmed 15 ml of extraction buffer. Mix the powder and the buffer thoroughly by inverting the tube several times.

   WARNING: Handle the polypropylene tube containing the buffer and the powdered tissue very carefully. Release of the dissolved nitrogen can blow the lid off. Wear safety glasses at all stages involving the handling of the homogenization buffer.

4. Extract the tissue solution twice with an equal volume of chloroform:isoamyl alcohol (24:1), separating the phases by centrifugation at 10,000*g* (9000 rpm) for 5 minutes at room temperature. When recovering the upper (aqueous) layer, it is important to avoid the interface. After the second extraction, transfer the aqueous phase to a fresh 50-ml centrifuge tube.

   If it proves difficult to recover the aqueous phase free of material from the interface, consider using the Phase Lock Gel to segregate the organic and aqueous phases (please see the panel on ALTERNATIVE PROTOCOL: PURIFICATION OF RNA USING PHASE LOCK GELS *in Protocol 9).*

5. Add 0.3 volume of 8 M LiCl to the aqueous phase. Mix the solution by inverting the tube several times. Store the tube for 12–16 hours at 4ºC. Harvest the RNA by centrifugation at 10,000*g* (9000 rpm) for 20 minutes at 4ºC.

   LiCl is a strong dehydrating agent that lowers the solubility of RNA (Hearst and Vinograd 1961a,b) and strips proteins from chromatin (Kondo et al. 1979). High-molecular-weight RNA can be precipitated by high concentrations (≥0.8 M) of LiCl and recovered by low-speed centrifugation (Barlow et al. 1963). After 1, 2, and 6 hours of precipitation, the yield of RNA is 30%, 65%, and 90%, respectively, of that obtained after overnight precipitation.

6. Solubilize the pellet of RNA in 500 µl of SSTE.

   When poly(A)⁺ RNA is to be extracted, dissolve total RNA in 0.5% SDS instead of SSTE and proceed to Protocol 7. Otherwise, proceed to Step 7 of this protocol.

7. Extract the RNA solution once with an equal volume of chloroform:isoamyl alcohol (24:1). Separate the phases by centrifugation at 10,000*g* (9000 rpm) for 10 minutes at 4ºC. Transfer the upper (aqueous) phase to a fresh centrifuge tube.

8. Add 2 volumes of ethanol and precipitate the RNA for at least 30 minutes at –80ºC, or 2 hours at –20ºC.

9. Collect the RNA by centrifugation at maximum speed in a microfuge for 20 minutes. Remove the supernatant by aspiration and store the open tube in a chemical fume hood for a few minutes until the last visible traces of supernatant have evaporated. Resuspend the RNA pellet in DEPC-treated H_2O. The expected yield of total RNA varies between 100 and 240 µg/g of original material. Aim to dissolve the RNA at a concentration of ~7 mg/ml.

10. Transfer the RNA solution to a fresh tube. Quantify the RNA by absorption spectrophotometry at 260 and 280 nm or by fluorescence after staining with RiboGreen (please see the information panel on QUANTIFICATION OF RNA).

11. Store the RNA by one of the methods outlined in the information panel on STORAGE AND RECOVERY OF RNA. (Optional) Add an RNase inhibitor (e.g., RNasin) according to the manufacturer's directions (please see Sambrook and Russell 2001, page 7.83).

    Before using the RNA in microarray experiments, check its integrity by electrophoresis through a formaldehyde–1% agarose gel (please see the information panel on MAMMALIAN, PLANT, AND BACTERIAL RNAs).

Isolation of Poly(A)$^+$ RNA Using FastTrack

Jun S. Wei and Javed Khan

Advanced Technology Center, Pediatric Oncology Branch, National Cancer Institute, National Institutes of Health, Gaithersburg, Maryland 20877

Stronger signals and lower backgrounds in experiments to analyze patterns of gene expression are usually obtained when total RNA rather than poly(A)$^+$ RNA is used as a template to generate probes (Wildsmith et al. 2001). The inferior signal-to-noise ratio is often a result of inherent losses encountered when purifying mRNA by binding to oligo(dT)-cellulose. This is a particularly important problem when the amounts of cells and tissue are limiting. However, there are two potential advantages for using poly(A)$^+$ RNA. First, when total RNA is used as the template, the specificity of the labeling reaction depends entirely on the ability of the oligo(dT) to select mRNA molecules as templates. Because the synthesis of fluorescently labeled cDNA rarely extends the entire length of the mRNA, priming with oligo(dT) is appropriate when the hybridization targets on the microarray correspond to the 3′ region of transcripts. When purified poly(A)$^+$ RNA is available, other options for labeling become possible. For example, synthesis of first-strand cDNAs can be primed by oligonucleotide primers of random sequence, which initiate synthesis along the length of the mRNAs and generate cDNAs that are small but represent a high proportion of the mRNA sequences. Second, the procedure used to isolate poly(A)$^+$ RNA—affinity chromatography on oligo(dT) columns of beads—provides another dimension of purification, which can be used to eliminate contaminants such as polysaccharides and polyphenols that may partition with RNA during extraction of tissues with monophasic lysis agents.

This protocol and Protocol 6 are included in this manual for investigators who wish to use poly(A)$^+$ RNA as a template for synthesis of fluorescently labeled targets. This protocol uses a commercial kit (FastTrack 2.0, a kit sold by Invitrogen), whereas Protocol 6 describes a variant of conventional oligo(dT) chromatography.

FastTrack 2.0 can be used to isolate poly(A)$^+$ RNA directly from cells and tissues, or from total RNA prepared as described in Protocol 1. The protocol is designed to purify mRNA from 1×10^7 to 5×10^8 cultured mammalian cells, 400 mg to 1 g of tissue, or 0.2 to 1.0 mg of total RNA.

MATERIALS

Buffers and Solutions

Please see Appendix 2 for components of stock solutions, buffers, and reagents.
Dilute stock solutions to the appropriate concentrations.

Ethanol (absolute)

Some batches of absolute ethanol (100% or 200 proof) have been reported to contain fluorescent contaminants that generate high backgrounds in microarray experiments; 95% ethanol does not have this problem. To avoid difficulties, either use 95% ethanol or identify a brand of absolute ethanol that performs reliably. Absolute ethanol (USP-grade ethyl alcohol, 64-17-5) purchased from Warner-Graham Co. (Cockeysville, Maryland) performs consistently well.

NaCl (5 M)

Phosphate-buffered saline (PBS), lacking Ca^{2+} and Mg^{2+} (14190-136, GIBCO)

RNA*later* stabilization reagent (221462, QIAGEN)

RNase*Zap* (9780, Ambion)

Sodium acetate (3 M, pH 5.2)

Nucleic Acids and Oligonucleotides

Total RNA, prepared as described in Protocol 1 (please see Step 3)

Cells and Tissues

Monolayers or suspension cultures of mammalian cells or fresh/frozen tissues (please see Step 1)

Special Equipment

FastTrack 2.0 kit (K1593-02, K1593-03, Invitrogen)

Homogenizer

The Polytron PT1200 homogenizer (Kinematica AG, Switzerland) or equivalent equipped with Probe 9100071 (Brinkmann 27 13 700-8) is used to disrupt cells and tissues. Before use, clean the Polytron so that it is free of RNase. Take apart the probe and wash the pieces first in H_2O, then in absolute ethanol, and finally in RNase*Zap*, which degrades RNA. Reassemble the probe and run the homogenizer in H_2O. Other equivalent instruments can be used (FastPrep instrument). For a discussion of various instruments, please see the information panel on **HOMOGENIZATION OF ANIMAL CELLS AND TISSUES**.

Mortar and pestle

These are required for disruption of large amounts (>500 mg) of soft tissue or any amount of hard, fibrous tissue (please see Step 1) (12-061-5B, Fisher Scientific)

METHOD

1. Prepare cells or tissue samples for isolation of RNA:

For Tissues: Wherever possible, keep the tissues either frozen at –80ºC or in liquid nitrogen or in RNA*later* until they are homogenized.

   a. Weigh the tissue.

b. Add 100-mg chunks directly to a 50-ml conical polypropylene tube containing FastTrack 2.0 lysis buffer. Each milliliter of lysis buffer can accommodate ~60 mg of tissue.

c. Without delay, homogenize the tissue for 30 seconds with a rotating blade tissue homogenizer (Polytron).

> Less than 500 mg of soft tissue can be homogenized easily. Larger amounts of tissue can be processed in batches of 500 mg. Hard tissues should be ground to a powder using a mortar and pestle prechilled with liquid nitrogen. The powder can then be homogenized in a Polytron homogenizer for 30 seconds in an appropriate volume of FastTrack 2.0 lysis buffer.

d. After homogenization, run the Polytron probe in a 15-ml conical tube containing 2 ml of lysis buffer and then add the solution to the tissue lysate. If particulate matter is still visible, centrifuge the samples at 12,000g (Sorvall or equivalent) for 30 minutes at 4ºC.

For Cells Grown in Suspension:

a. Harvest the cells by centrifugation at 400g in a precooled centrifuge for 10 minutes at 4ºC.

b. Remove the medium by aspiration and gently resuspend the cell pellets in ice-cold PBS equivalent to 0.5 times the volume of the original culture.

c. Harvest the cells by centrifugation as in Step a, remove the PBS by centrifugation, and add 1 ml of FastTrack 2.0 lysis buffer per 10^6 cells.

d. Without delay, transfer the cell suspension to a polypropylene tube and pass the cell lysate through a 21-gauge needle several times to break open the cells and shear genomic DNA.

> This step involves drawing the lysate into a syringe through the needle and expelling from the syringe, again through the needle. Repeat this process five times. Alternatively, homogenize the cells in a Polytron homogenizer for 15–30 seconds at room temperature. After homogenization, run the Polytron probe in a 15-ml conical tube containing 2 ml of lysis solution and then add the solution to the tissue lysate.

For Cells Grown in Monolayers:

a. Rinse the cells twice with ice-cold PBS and add 1 ml of FastTrack 2.0 lysis buffer per 10^6 cells.

b. Without delay, scrape the cells into the buffer and transfer the cell suspension to a polypropylene tube. Pass the cell lysate through a 21-gauge needle several times to break open the cells and shear genomic DNA.

> This step involves drawing the lysate into a syringe through the needle and expelling from the syringe, again through the needle. Repeat this process five times. Alternatively, homogenize the cells in a Polytron homogenizer for 15–30 seconds at room temperature. After homogenization, run the Polytron probe in a 15-ml conical tube containing 2 ml of lysis solution and then add the solution to the tissue lysate.

2. Incubate the cell lysates for 30–60 minutes at 45ºC.

3. Add 950 µl of 5 M NaCl for each 15 ml of FastTrack 2.0 lysis buffer (final concentration of NaCl = 0.5 M). If the lysate is noticeably viscous, shear the DNA by passage through a 21-gauge needle, as described in Step 1 of this protocol. Proceed to Step 4.

   Make sure that no particulate matter remains at the end of this step. The next part of the protocol requires the addition of oligo(dT) resin and recovery of bound RNA by centrifugation. Particulate material will be recovered in the pellet and may compromise the remainder of the protocol.

For Isolating mRNA from Total RNA: It is best to process total RNA in batches of 1 mg. The expected yield of poly(A)$^+$ RNA is 10–50 µg per batch, depending on the source of the tissue or cells.

   a. Precipitate the total RNA with ethanol as in Steps 17–20 in Protocol 1.

   b. Resuspend the pellet in 100 µl of elution buffer (included in the FastTrack 2.0 kit).

   c. Add the RNA solution to 10 ml of FastTrack lysis buffer in a 50-ml centrifuge tube.

   d. Incubate the solution for 5 minutes at 65ºC, and then immediately place the tube on ice for exactly 1 minute.

   e. Place the tube at room temperature and add 650 µl of 5 M NaCl. Mix the solution by gentle inversion.

   f. Proceed to Step 4.

4. Add oligo(dT)-cellulose (included in the FastTrack 2.0 kit). Estimate the amounts of resin required by assuming that 10^6 cultured mammalian cells or 20 mg of tissue contain 0.75 µg of mRNA; 1 mg of resin is required for each microgram of mRNA.

5. Store the tube for 1–2 minutes at room temperature to allow the resin to rehydrate. Vortex the sample to resuspend the resin completely. Attach the tube to a rocking device and rock the tube gently in a horizontal position for 60–90 minutes at room temperature.

6. Centrifuge the slurry at 3000*g* for 5 minutes at room temperature. Make sure that the brake is turned off or set at "Low" for this step and all subsequent centrifugation steps. Remove the supernatant by gentle aspiration, trying not to disturb the pellet.

7. Gently resuspend the oligo(dT) resin in 20 ml of binding buffer (included in the FastTrack 2.0 kit). Repeat Step 6.

8. Gently resuspend the oligo(dT) resin in 10 ml of binding buffer. Repeat Step 6.

9. Gently resuspend the oligo(dT) resin in 10 ml of low-salt wash buffer (included in the FastTrack 2.0 kit). Repeat Step 6.

10. Repeat Step 9 until there are no bubbles in the buffer after centrifugation. As many as five repetitions of Step 9 may be required.

11. Use a serological pipette to resuspend the resin in the smallest possible amount of low-salt wash buffer. Transfer the resin to a spin column seated in a microfuge tube (included in the kit). Centrifuge the spin column in the microfuge tube at 5000*g* for 10 seconds. Discard the fluid in the microfuge tube.

12. Repeat Step 11 until all of the resin has been transferred to the spin column.

13. Wash the spin column with ~500 µl of low-salt wash buffer by mixing the resin with a pipette tip. *Be careful not to damage the membrane!* Centrifuge the column at 5000*g* for 10 seconds. Read the OD_{260} of the fluid in the microfuge tube.

14. Repeat Step 13 until the OD_{260} of the flow-through is <0.05. Then transfer the column to a fresh microfuge tube.

15. Add 200 µl of elution buffer (included in the FastTrack 2.0 kit) to the column. Mix the buffer into the resin with a pipette tip. Centrifuge at 5000*g* for 10 seconds.

16. Repeat Step 15 once. The volume of the eluate in the microfuge tube should now be ~400 µl.

17. Recover the eluate from the microfuge tube and add 0.15 volume (~60 µl) of 2 M sodium acetate (included in the kit) and 2.5 volumes of absolute ethanol.

18. Freeze the tube on dry ice or at –80°C until the eluate is frozen hard.

19. Thaw the eluate at room temperature and then centrifuge it in a microfuge at maximum speed (16,000*g*) for 15 minutes at 4°C.

20. Carefully aspirate all of the ethanol, taking care not to disturb the mRNA pellet. Stand the open tube in a chemical fume hood until the last visible traces of ethanol have disappeared.

21. Dissolve the mRNA pellet in 20–50 µl of 10 mM Tris-Cl (pH 7.8), 0.1 mM EDTA.

22. Quantify the mRNA by absorption spectrophotometry at 260 and 280 nm or by fluorescence after staining with RiboGreen (please see the information panel on QUANTIFICATION OF RNA).

23. Store the mRNA by one of the methods outlined in the information panel on STORAGE AND RECOVERY OF RNA.

    Before using the RNA in microarray experiments, check its integrity by electrophoresis through a formaldehyde–1% agarose gel (please see the information panel on MAMMALIAN, PLANT, AND BACTERIALS RNAs).

Isolation of Membrane-bound Polysomal RNA

Maximilian Diehn

Department of Biochemistry, Stanford University School of Medicine, Stanford, California 94305

DNA microarrays are most often used to compare and catalog the transcripts in RNA extracted from matched sets of mammalian cells or tissues. An assumption inherent in this experimental design is that the abundance of the mRNAs in preparations of total RNA is an accurate measure of gene expression. However, because different mRNAs are translated at different efficiencies, the abundance of transcripts in total RNA may not reflect the pattern of protein synthesis in the cells. In principle, a more accurate picture of gene expression may be obtained by using DNA microarrays to analyze mRNAs isolated from polysomes, i.e., mRNAs caught in the act of translation. Another interesting characteristic of mRNAs is their subcellular localization. This property, in combination with expression levels and translation rates, can yield important insights into the biological properties of the encoded gene products.

There are numerous documented examples in eukaryotes ranging from yeast to humans, where the localization of mRNA within a cell has an important biological role in the functioning of that cell or organism. A complete understanding of gene expression will require integration of knowledge of the expression levels of mRNAs, their rates of translation, and their subcellular localization.

Perhaps the most fundamental example of differential subcellular localization of mRNAs is the spatial segregation of transcripts that encode cytosolic or nuclear proteins from those that encode membrane-associated or secreted proteins. The proteins in the latter group are cotranslationally inserted into the rough endoplasmic reticulum (ER) by ribosomes attached to the cytoplasmic surface of the rough ER, whereas the first group is translated by ribosomes that are free in the cytosol of the cell. Spatial segregation of protein synthesis creates distinct pools of mRNAs that can be separated on the basis of the presence or absence of an association with cellular membranes. Once separated, the two fractions can be hybridized to DNA microarrays and subsequent analyses can yield two important types of information:

- The subcellular localization of proteins encoded by the mRNAs can be inferred from the subcellular localization of their transcripts.

- Unexpected associations of mRNAs with cellular membranes can be identified and marked for further study.

A number of potential approaches exist for separating membrane-associated and free mRNAs. One approach takes advantage of the relatively low density of cellular lipid structures to separate membranes from denser components by sedimentation equilibrium (Mechler 1987). A second set of methods uses differential extractions with detergent coupled with sedimentation velocity centrifugation (Stoltenburg et al. 1995) to separate the two pop-

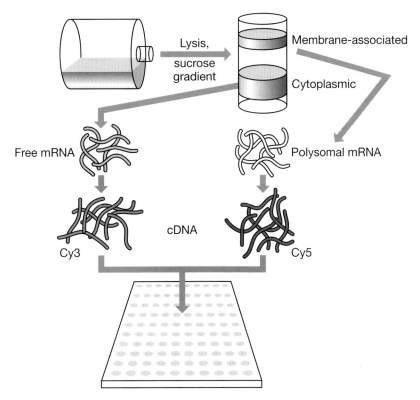

FIGURE 3-4. Procedure for isolating membrane-bound polysomes from cell lines. Cells are hypotonically lysed, and membrane-bound RNA is separated from free RNA by equilibrium density centrifugation in a sucrose gradient. Total RNA is isolated separately from the fractions containing membrane-bound or free ribosomes. cDNA is synthesized from mRNA isolated from membrane-bound and free ribosomes and labeled with the fluorescent dyes Cy5 and Cy3, respectively, for hybridization to a DNA microarray. (Modified, with permission, from Diehn et al. 2000.)

ulations of mRNAs. It is also possible to isolate rough-ER-associated mRNAs by antibody-based purification protocols that are directed against components of the signal-peptide recognition machinery. The following protocol employs sedimentation equilibrium centrifugation in a sucrose gradient. Although the experimental details are specific to this approach, the method of analysis that is described can be applied in principle to any experimental approaches that subfractionate RNAs. The overall scheme of the protocol is shown in Figure 3-4.

An important consideration in designing experiments studying the subcellular compartmentalization of RNA is the inclusion of control probes in the DNA microarrays. Probes corresponding to transcripts of known subcellular localization serve as controls for two important reasons. First, the success of the fractionation procedure can be assessed by examining the distribution of fluorescence ratios for mRNAs whose subcellular locations are known. Second, the observed fluorescence ratios for known mRNAs can be used to identify additional transcripts with similar properties. In the case of experiments with membrane-associated polysomes, DNA microarrays should contain as many probes encoding proteins of known subcellular localization as possible. Minimally, several hundred of the array elements should be of this type.

MATERIALS

CAUTION: Please see Appendix 3 for appropriate handling of materials marked with <!>.

IMPORTANT: Prepare all reagents used in this protocol with DEPC-treated H_2O (please see the information panel on SPECIAL CONSIDERATIONS FOR WORKING WITH RNA).

Buffers and Solutions

Please see Appendix 2 for components of stock solutions, buffers, and reagents.
Dilute stock solutions to the appropriate concentrations.

Chloroform (without any additives, such as isoamyl alcohol) <!>

Cycloheximide (10 mg/ml in H_2O) (Sigma) <!>

> Cycloheximide is unstable in alkaline solutions. Cycloheximide inhibits protein synthesis in eukaryotes, but not prokaryotes, by interacting directly with the translocase enzyme and blocking translocation of peptidyl tRNA from the A site to the P site within the ribosome. The drug is a competitive inhibitor of FKBP and related enzymes and is an inducer of apoptosis.

Ethanol (75% and 95%)

> Some batches of absolute ethanol (100% or 200 proof) have been reported to contain fluorescent contaminants that generate high backgrounds in microarray experiments; 95% ethanol does not have this problem. To avoid difficulties, either use 95% ethanol or identify a brand of absolute ethanol that performs reliably. Absolute ethanol (USP-grade ethyl alcohol, 64-17-5) purchased from Warner-Graham Co. (Cockeysville, Maryland) performs consistently well.

Gradient buffer

> 150 mM KCl
>
> 5 mM $MgCl_2$
>
> 50 mM Tris-Cl (pH 7.4)
>
> > Autoclave the solution before use.

Hypotonic-lysis buffer

> 10 mM KCl
>
> 1.5 mM $MgCl_2$
>
> 10 mM Tris-Cl (pH 7.4)
>
> > Sterilize the solution by autoclaving. Add cycloheximide to a final concentration of 10 µg/ml just before use.

Isopropanol

Phosphate-buffered saline (PBS)

> Add cycloheximide to a final concentration of 10 µg/ml just before use.

RNA precipitation solution

> 0.8 M sodium citrate
>
> 1.2 M NaCl

Sodium acetate (2 M)

Sucrose buffer (1.95 M) and Sucrose gradient buffer (1.3 M)

> Prepare these solutions by appropriate dilution of the 2.5 M sucrose stock with gradient buffer. Each gradient requires 13 ml of 1.95 M sucrose buffer and 6 ml of 1.3 M sucrose buffer. Just before use in a gradient, add cycloheximide to a final concentration of 10 µg/ml.
>
> It is a good idea to test these solutions by constructing a mock gradient and checking for proper layering before constructing any gradients containing actual lysate.

Sucrose gradient buffer (2.5 M)

> This solution is extremely viscous and must be made carefully.
>
> 1. Add 855.75 g of sucrose in ~150-g increments to 250 ml of gradient buffer heated to 65ºC in a 2-liter beaker.
> 2. Stir the buffer on a hot plate using an appropriately sized stirring bar and maintain the temperature of the solution near 65ºC. If the solution becomes too viscous, add a small amount of gradient buffer (65ºC).

    3. Once all of the sucrose has been added, adjust the final volume to 1 liter with gradient buffer (65°C). It is possible, although not usually necessary, to measure the concentration of sucrose in the solution using a refractometer and to adjust the strength of the solution accordingly.

    4. Just before use in a gradient, add cycloheximide to a final concentration of 10 µg/ml. Each gradient requires 15 ml of the 2.5 M sucrose buffer.

Tris-Cl (10 mM, pH 7.4)

TRIzol LS (GIBCO)

    TRIzol LS is a concentrated version of TRIzol and contains phenol and guanidine thiocyanate in a monophasic solution. TRIzol LS is the reagent of choice for isolation of RNA from liquid samples.

Centrifuges and Rotors

    Sorvall centrifuge or equivalent
    SS-34 centrifuge rotor
    SW28 ultracentrifuge rotor
    Ultracentrifuge (Beckman or Sorvall)

Special Equipment

    Ball bearing homogenizer or 5–10-ml glass Dounce homogenizer
    Barrier tips for micropipettes
    Electronic pipette pump
    Hemocytometer
    Microfuge tubes (2 ml)
    Oak Ridge polypropylene centrifuge tubes (50 ml) (Nalge Nunc International)
    Plastic pipettes (2 ml, 10 ml, and 25 ml)
    Needles (1 inch, 18-gauge)
    Roller bottles or spinner flasks for tissue culture
    Spectrophotometer
    Ultra-Clear 25 x 89-mm centrifuge tubes (344058, Beckman or equivalent)

METHOD

Preparation of Tissue Culture Cells

1. Grow the tissue culture cells under the appropriate conditions.

    Because a large number (5×10^8) of cells are required for each sucrose gradient, it is advisable to grow cells in roller bottles or as suspension cultures in spinner flasks; however, cells can also be grown in monolayers using Petri dishes. Suspension cultures should not be grown to a concentration of greater than 5×10^5 cells per milliliter as overcrowding may lead to down-regulation of protein synthesis and therefore lower yields of polysomal mRNA.

2. Add cycloheximide to the cell cultures to a final concentration of 10 µg/ml, and return them to the incubator or warm room. Incubate the cycloheximide-treated cells for 5–10 minutes at 37°C before proceeding.

    IMPORTANT: From this point on, perform all steps at 4°C or on ice.

3. Collect the cells:

For Roller or Suspension Cultures:

   a. Transfer the cell suspension to 250-ml centrifuge bottles.

   b. Rinse the empty bottles briefly with several hundred milliliters of ice-cold PBS containing 10 μg/ml cycloheximide and harvest any residual cells adherent to the flask walls with a scraper.

   c. Harvest the cells by centrifugation at 1000g for 10 minutes at 4°C.

   d. Discard the supernatant and wash the cells twice with 125 ml (per 250-ml centrifuge bottle) of ice-cold PBS supplemented with 10 μg/ml cycloheximide.

For Monolayer Cultures Growing on Petri Dishes:

   a. Remove the medium by aspiration.

   b. Add a small volume of ice-cold PBS (containing 10 μg/ml cycloheximide), and scrape the cells from the dish using a rubber policeman.

   c. Combine cells in 250-ml centrifuge bottles, and harvest them by centrifugation at 1000g for 10 minutes at 4°C.

   d. Discard the supernatant and wash the cells twice with 125 ml (per 250-ml centrifuge bottle) of ice-cold PBS supplemented with 10 μg/ml cycloheximide.

4. Recover the cells by centrifugation, and resuspend the cell pellets in 10 ml of ice-cold PBS containing 10 μg/ml cycloheximide.

5. Transfer all of the cells into a single centrifuge tube and count them using a hemocytometer. Transfer aliquots containing 5×10^8 cells to a series of 15- or 50-ml conical centrifuge tubes. Recover the cells by centrifugation at 1000g for 10 minutes at 4°C.

   It is possible to stop at this stage and freeze the cell pellets in liquid nitrogen. Store the pellets at –80°C. Cell pellets can be used for at least 6 months after freezing.

Hypotonic Lysis and Gradient Construction

6. Resuspend the cell pellet at a concentration of 2.5×10^8 cells/ml in ice-cold hypotonic-lysis buffer. Allow the cells to swell on ice for 5–10 minutes.

   It may be necessary or desirable to include RNase inhibitors in the lysis buffer and subsequent gradient fractions. Because cell lines and tissues vary in the amount of RNase activity, this decision must be made on a case-by-case basis.

7. Homogenize the cells with 10 strokes in a tight-fitting Dounce homogenizer or with 10 passes through a ball-bearing homogenizer. If desired, freeze a small aliquot of the lysate at –80°C as a source of total cellular RNA.

8. Centrifuge the homogenate at 2000g for 2 minutes at 4°C to remove nuclei and unbroken cells. The pellet will be very soft and of varying size depending on the cell type. Remove the supernatant and adjust its volume to 2 ml using ice-cold hypotonic-lysis buffer.

9. Add 2 ml of the volume-adjusted supernatant (Step 8) to 11 ml of 2.5 M sucrose gradient buffer in a 50-ml conical tube and mix the solutions well by vortexing.

10. Construct a sucrose step gradient in Ultra-Clear 25 x 89-mm centrifuge tubes.

    a. Place 4 ml of the 2.5 M sucrose gradient buffer in the bottom of the Ultra-Clear tube.

    b. Carefully layer the lysate (13 ml) from Step 9 onto the 2.5 M sucrose cushion.

    c. Layer 13 ml of 1.95 M sucrose gradient buffer and 6 ml of 1.3 M sucrose gradient buffer onto the gradient.

       The layers are most easily constructed using an electronic pipette pump and a 10-ml plastic pipette. Set the pump to its lowest speed and slowly allow the sucrose solution to flow out of the pipette. Keep the tip of the pipette above, but very close to the top of the meniscus of the gradient. While layering, try not to disturb the section on the top. The resulting gradient should have visible planes between the layers resulting from diffraction differences of the various sucrose solutions.

11. Centrifuge the gradient in an SW28 ultracentrifuge rotor at 90,000g for 5–6 hours.

    It is critical to balance the tubes accurately. If an even number of gradients are used, balance them with 1.3 M sucrose gradient buffer. If an odd number of gradients are used, additionally prepare a mock gradient using 2 ml of H_2O instead of homogenate in Step 8 and balance all of the gradients with 1.3 M sucrose gradient buffer.

    After centrifugation, a layer containing membrane material should be visible at the interface of the 1.95 M sucrose and 1.3 M sucrose solutions.

12. Harvest the gradients by puncturing the bottoms of the centrifuge tubes with an 18-gauge needle and collecting 1.5-ml fractions in 2-ml microfuge tubes. Alternatively, to minimize the risk of contamination with free RNA, isolate the membrane fraction by first removing 10 ml from the top of the tube using a P1000 Pipetman. The remainder of the gradient (containing the cytosolic fraction) is then harvested by the puncture method.

    To hold the ultracentrifuge tubes during harvesting of the gradients, carefully cut a polypropylene 50-ml conical tube in half using a sharp knife or razor blade and discard the top half of the tube. Next, cut off the very tip of the conical section remaining on the bottom of the tube. This device can be suspended over the bench using a standard clamp and ring stand and has the correct diameter to snugly fit an ultracentrifuge tube. To collect the fractions, manually slide a microfuge tube rack containing open 2-ml microfuge tubes under the punctured gradient tube.

13. Use a spectrophotometer to measure the absorbance of each fraction at 260 nm to determine the presence of nucleic acid.

    Free ribosomes and mRNA will be present in the loading region of the gradient, whereas membrane-associated ribosomes and mRNA will be located at the interface between the 1.95 M and 1.3 M sucrose solutions.

RNA Isolation

14. Using the OD_{260} measurements as a guide, make separate pools of fractions corresponding to the load zone (Free RNA) and to the interface between the 1.95 M and 1.3 M

sucrose buffers (membrane-associated RNA). Isolate total RNA from each pool with TRIzol LS reagent:

a. Transfer the pooled fractions to 50-ml Oak Ridge polypropylene tubes. Add 3 volumes of TRIzol LS for each volume of the pooled fractions.

b. Mix the samples by pipetting and vigorous vortexing.

c. Stand the tubes for 5 minutes at room temperature and then add 0.2 volume of chloroform per 0.75 ml of TRIzol LS. Use glass pipettes with an electronic pipette pump or 1-ml filtered micropipette tips to prevent the chloroform from "creeping" into the filters of smaller tips. Invert the closed tubes and shake them vigorously for 15–20 seconds.

d. Stand the tubes for 5 minutes at room temperature and then centrifuge them at 12,000g for 15 minutes at 4°C.

e. Use a 10-ml pipette to transfer the aqueous phase to a fresh polypropylene tube. The volume of the aqueous phase should be ~70% of the volume of TRIzol LS used in Step a. Add 0.25 ml of isopropanol per milliliter of TRIzol LS added in Step a. Then add 0.25 ml of RNA precipitation solution per milliliter of TRIzol LS added in Step a. Mix the solution.

f. Store the samples for 10 minutes at room temperature and then recover the RNA by centrifugation at 12,000g for 10 minutes at 4°C.

g. Remove the supernatant by aspiration and then wash the RNA pellet with 75% ethanol by gentle inversion and centrifugation at 12,000g for 5 minutes at 4°C.

h. Remove the supernatant and allow the RNA pellet to dry in the air for 10–20 minutes. Resuspend the RNA pellet in 400 µl of 10 mM Tris-HCl (pH 7.4) and transfer it to a 1.5-ml microfuge tube.

i. Perform an additional ethanol precipitation by adding 60 µl of 2 M sodium acetate and 1 ml of 95% ethanol to the RNA in a microfuge tube. Freeze on dry ice or in a –80°C freezer until solid. Thaw and centrifuge at maximum speed for 30 minutes at 4°C.

j. Remove the supernatant by aspiration and then wash the RNA pellet with 500 µl of 75% ethanol. Centrifuge at maximum speed for 15 minutes at 4°C.

k. Remove the supernatant and allow the RNA pellet to dry in the air for 10–20 minutes. Resuspend the RNA pellet in 40–200 µl of DEPC-treated H$_2$O. Store the RNA by one of the methods outlined in the information panel on **STORAGE AND RECOVERY OF RNA**.

> Yields of RNA in the two fractions can vary significantly depending on the source. The yield of membrane-associated polysomal RNA can range from 10 µg to several hundred micrograms, whereas the amount of "free" RNA yield is generally 10–150 times greater.
>
> In general, a hybridization using 30–50 µg of total RNA as input will work well on a DNA microarray. If less then this amount is recovered from the gradient in the membrane fraction, it is desirable to amplify the two fractions using an in vitro transcription-based amplification strategy (Van Gelder et al. 1990; Eberwine et al. 1992; Phillips and Eberwine 1996; Wang et al. 2000) (please see Protocols 15 and 16).

Isolation of Poly(A)$^+$ RNA by Batch Chromatography*

Damares Monte*† and Shauna Somerville*

*Carnegie Institution of Washington, Stanford, California 94305; †E.M.B.R.A.P.A.
(Brazilian Agricultural Research Corporation) Genetic Resources and Biotechnology,
Brasilia, Brazil

Virtually all eukaryotic mRNAs carry a homopolymeric tract of adenine residues at their 3′ termini and can therefore be purified from the bulk of cellular RNA by affinity chromatography on oligo(dT)-cellulose. This method, first described by Edmonds et al. (1971) and Aviv and Leder (1972), exploits the ability of the poly(A) tails to form stable RNA-DNA hybrids with short chains of oligo(dT) (usually 18–30 nucleotides in length) covalently linked to a supporting matrix of cellulose. Because only a few dT-A base pairs are formed, binding of mRNA to the oligo(dT) occurs only in buffers of high ionic strength. After nonpolyadenylated RNA molecules have been washed from the matrix, a buffer of low ionic strength is used to destabilize the double-stranded structures and to release mRNAs from the from the resin.

This protocol describes a variant of oligo(dT)-cellulose chromatography (Celano et al. 1993) that is recommended for three situations: when the preparation of total RNA may contain contaminants (such as proteins and polysaccharides) that can clog columns, or when working with small amounts of total RNA (<50 μg), or when handling many samples concurrently. Alternatively, poly(A)$^+$ RNA may be isolated by batch chromatography using commercially available kits, for example, the Oligotex mRNA kit from QIAGEN. For a list of commercial references of products for working with RNA, please see Table 3-5.

MATERIALS

CAUTION: Please see Appendix 3 for appropriate handling of materials marked with <!>.

IMPORTANT: Prepare all reagents used in this protocol with DEPC-treated H$_2$O (please see the information panel on SPECIAL CONSIDERATIONS FOR WORKING WITH RNA).

Buffers and Solutions

Please see Appendix 2 for components of stock solutions, buffers, and reagents.
Dilute stock solutions to the appropriate concentrations.

Ammonium acetate (10 M) <!>
DEPC-treated H$_2$O, ice-cold
Ethanol (95% and 75%)

> Some batches of absolute ethanol (100% or 200 proof) have been reported to contain fluorescent contaminants that generate high backgrounds in microarray experiments; 95% ethanol does not have this problem. To avoid difficulties, either use 95% ethanol or identify a brand of absolute ethanol that does not generate high levels of background fluorescence. Absolute ethanol (USP-grade ethyl alcohol, 64-17-5) purchased from Warner-Graham Co. (Cockeysville, Maryland) performs consistently well.

*The authors thank Sue Thayer, Bi-Huei Hou, and Lorne Rose for their kind revision of the manuscript.

TABLE 3-5. Web Resources for Commercial Products

Source	Web Site address	Kits/Products[a]
QIAGEN	www.qiagen.com	kits for RNA purification and cleanup
Millipore	www.millipore.com	cleanup
Ambion	www.ambion.com	kits for RNA preparation
GIBCO	www.lifetech.com	enzymes, reagents
Amersham Biosciences	www.apbiotech.com	enzymes, reagents, fluorescent dyes

[a]Always follow manufacturer's instructions when using commercial products.

NaCl (5 M)
Na-TES
   This is TES containing 0.5 M NaCl.
Oligo(dT)$_{18-30}$-cellulose (GIBCO or equivalent)
   Type III cellulose (binding capacity 58–100 OD$_{260}$ units/g) is hydrated by washing three times in Na-TES buffer at room temperature and resuspended in Na-TES at a final concentration of 100 mg/ml.
TES
   10 mM Tris-HCl (pH 7.5)
   1 mM EDTA (pH 8.0)
   SDS (0.1% w/v) <!>

Nucleic Acids and Oligonucleotides

Eukaryotic RNA, total
   Prepare as described in Protocol 2, 3, or 4 of this chapter.

Special Equipment

Microfuge with speed control
Water baths preset to 37ºC, 55ºC, and 65ºC

METHOD

1. Transfer ~1 mg of total RNA dissolved in DEPC-treated H$_2$O to a sterile microfuge tube. Adjust the volume to 600 µl with TES buffer.

2. Heat the RNA for 5 minutes in a 65ºC water bath to eliminate secondary structures. Remove the microfuge tube from the water bath and immediately plunge it into an ice-water bath.

3. Add 60 µl of 5.0 M NaCl. Mix the contents of the tube by vortexing.

4. Add 600 µl (~60 mg) of hydrated oligo(dT)-cellulose. Use a disposable pipette tip to mix the resin with the RNA solution.

5. Incubate the slurry for 10 minutes at 37ºC with occasional gentle mixing by inversion.

6. Pellet the oligo(dT)-cellulose by centrifuging the microfuge tube at maximum speed for 5 minutes at room temperature. Discard the supernatant.

7. Resuspend the pellet in 1.0 ml of Na-TES and centrifuge as described in Step 6. Discard the supernatant.

8. Resuspend the pellet in 1.0 ml of ice-cold, DEPC-treated H_2O and centrifuge once again. Discard the supernatant.

9. Elute the polyadenylated RNA by resuspending the pellet of oligo(dT)-cellulose in 400 µl of DEPC-treated H_2O and heating for 5 minutes to 55ºC. Centrifuge as before, this time retaining the supernatant.

10. Repeat Step 9 twice more, keeping each supernatant separate.

11. Quantify the mRNA in each supernatant by absorption spectrophotometry at 260 and 280 nm or by fluorescence after staining with RiboGreen (please see the information panel on **QUANTIFICATION OF RNA**). Pool the fractions with the highest yields and precipitate the poly(A)⁺ RNA with 0.2 volume of 10 M ammonium acetate and 2 volumes of absolute ethanol. Recover the RNA by centrifugation and dissolve the RNA pellet in DEPC-treated H_2O containing an RNase inhibitor such as RNasin (optional). (For choices of RNase inhibitors, please see Sambrook and Russell 2001.)

    The amount of mRNA varies from cell type to cell type. As a rule of thumb, between 1% and 4% of the total RNA is recovered from the oligo(dT)-cellulose matrices as poly(A)⁺ RNA.

Isolation of RNA by Ultracentrifugation through CsCl Solution

In this method (Chirgwin et al. 1979), cultured cells or tissues are homogenized in 4 M guanidinium isothiocyanate, and the lysate is layered onto a dense cushion of cesium chloride. Because the buoyant density of RNA in CsCl (1.8 g/ml) is much greater than that of other cellular components, rRNA and mRNA migrate to the bottom of the tube during ultracentrifugation (Glisin et al. 1974; Ullrich et al. 1977). As long as the step gradients are not overloaded, proteins remain in the guanidinium lysate while the DNA floats in the CsCl cushion. Because the Chirgwin method yields RNA of very high quality and purity and is not labor-intensive, it became the standard technique during the early 1980s for isolation of nondegraded high-molecular-weight RNA. Although the method has since been displaced by the single-step procedure of Chomczynski and Sacchi (1987) (please see Protocol 1), there are circumstances in which the Chirgwin technique is preferred. For example:

- When extracting RNA from adipose tissues that are rich in triglycerides (Tavangar et al. 1990).

- When extracting RNA from cells or tissues containing large amounts of polysaccharides and/or proteoglycans. These contaminants are reported to prevent solubilization of RNA after precipitation with alcohols and to inhibit reverse transcriptase reactions (Groppe and Morse 1993; Schick and Eras 1995).

The method described below is based on a protocol provided by Nadia Traficante (Peter MacCallum Cancer Institute, Melbourne, Australia).

MATERIALS

CAUTION: Please see Appendix 3 for appropriate handling of materials marked with <!>.

Buffers and Solutions

Please see Appendix 2 for components of stock solutions, buffers, and reagents.
Dilute stock solutions to the appropriate concentrations.

CsCl (5.7 M)/0.01 M EDTA (pH 7.5)
> The CsCl/EDTA solution is made in 100-ml batches by dissolving 96.0 g of CsCl in 90 ml of 0.01 M EDTA (pH 7.5) and adding DEPC to a final concentration of 0.1%. Allow the solution to stand for 30 minutes and then autoclave for 20 minutes at 15 psi (1.05 kg/cm^2). When the solution has cooled, adjust the volume to 100 ml with DEPC-treated H$_2$O.

EDTA (10 mM, pH 8.0)
Ethanol (75%)
Guanidinium thiocyanate homogenization buffer
> 4 M guanidinium thiocyanate (M_r = 118.1)
> 0.1 M Tris-Cl (pH 7.5)
> 1% β-mercaptoethanol <!>

Dissolve 50 g of guanidinium thiocyanate in 10 ml of 1 M Tris-Cl (pH 7.5) and add H_2O to 100 ml. Filter the solution through a Whatman No. 1 filter or equivalent. The solution is stable and can be stored indefinitely at room temperature. Just before use, add β-mercaptoethanol to a final concentration of 1% (0.14 M).

NaOH (0.1 N) <!>

Sodium lauryl sarcosinate (20% w/v)

Cells and Tissues

Cells in monolayer culture

Cells grown in monolayers should be washed once with PBS, drained well, and either used immediately or snap-frozen in liquid nitrogen and stored at –80ºC. This can be achieved as follows:

- Make a shallow tray from aluminum foil and arrange the tissue culture plates (with their covers on) in this tray. Do not stack the plates on top of one another.
- Slowly pour liquid nitrogen into the tray so that it runs underneath the bottom of the plates. After the residual liquid in the plates has frozen, quickly wrap the plates in the aluminum foil and store them at –80ºC.

Frozen monolayers of cells stored at –80ºC should be thawed directly in guanidinium thiocyanate homogenization buffer at room temperature. Frozen tissues and pellets of cells should be powdered under liquid nitrogen using a mortar and pestle prechilled in liquid nitrogen. Use a large pestle to prevent "blasting" the powder out when liquid nitrogen is added to the mortar.

Cells in suspension culture

Cells grown in suspension should be recovered by centrifugation, washed once with PBS, recentrifuged, drained well, and either used immediately or snap-frozen in liquid nitrogen and stored at –80ºC.

Tissues

Tissues should be freshly harvested, cut into small (100 mg) pieces, and placed directly into guanidinium thiocyanate homogenization buffer or, if not to be processed immediately, snap-frozen in liquid nitrogen and stored at –80ºC.

Special Equipment

Beckman SW41 rotor (or equivalent) and polyallomer ultracentrifuge tubes

Polytron homogenizer

The Polytron PT1200 homogenizer (Kinematica AG, Switzerland) or equivalent equipped with Probe 9100071 (Brinkmann 27 13 700-8) is used to disrupt cells and tissues. Before use, clean the Polytron so that it is free of RNase. Take apart the probe and wash the pieces first in H_2O, then in absolute ethanol, and finally in RNase*Zap*, which degrades RNA. Reassemble probe and run the homogenizer in H_2O. Other equivalent instruments can be used (FastPrep instrument). For a discussion of the various instruments, please see the information panel on HOMOGENIZATION OF ANIMALS CELLS AND TISSUES.

Scalpel blades and hemostat

Sorvall centrifuge and SS-34 rotor (or equivalent)

METHOD

1. *For Powdered Tissues:* Add the powder to guanidinium thiocyanate homogenization buffer in a polypropylene tube at room temperature; 1 g of powdered tissue requires 10–20 ml of homogenization buffer.

   It is better to add too much liquid than too little, but first consider the capacity of the rotor and the number of samples. An SW41 rotor can accommodate six tubes with a total volume of ~42 ml of homogenate.

WARNING: Handle the polypropylene tube containing the buffer and the powdered tissue very carefully. Release of the dissolved nitrogen can blow the lid off. Wear safety glasses at all stages involving the handling of the homogenization buffer.

For Lysates of Cultured Cells: Transfer the lysates to polypropylene tubes.

2. Homogenize the lysates in a Polytron homogenizer at high speed for 1–2 minutes. Add sodium lauryl sarcosinate to a final concentration of 0.5% and mix the suspension well.

   Homogenization in a Polytron shears the nuclear DNA and prevents formation of an impenetrable mat on top of the cushion of CsCl, which might block sedimentation of the RNA to the bottom of the centrifuge tube. Homogenization increases the yield of RNA by a factor of ~2.

3. Centrifuge the suspension at 5000*g* for 10 minutes at room temperature. Repeat the centrifugation step until all floating debris has been removed from the suspension.

4. Wash the polyallomer ultracentrifuge tubes in 0.1 M NaOH and rinse them thoroughly with H_2O. Shake the tubes dry. To each tube, add 5.0 ml of 5.7 M CsCl, 10 mM EDTA and then carefully layer the supernatant from Step 3 onto the CsCl cushion. Use a waterproof marker to mark the position of the top of the cushion on the outside of the tubes. If necessary, use guanidinium thiocyanate homogenization buffer to equalize the weights of the tubes. Centrifuge the step gradients at 150,000*g* for 18 hours at 20°C.

5. Take care not to disturb the gradients when removing the tubes from the centrifuge. Draw a line on each tube ~0.5 cm from the bottom. Use a vacuum aspirator to remove the supernatant down to the level of the CsCl cushion (upper line on the outside of the tube). Use a fresh pipette to remove the fluid above the lower mark on the tube.

6. Use a red-hot scalpel blade held in a hemostat to cut off the bottom of the tube. *Do not drop it!* Invert the bottom of the tube over a pad of Kimwipes. The pellet of RNA on the bottom of the tube should be clear and gelatinous.

7. Fill the bottom of the tube with 70% ethanol at room temperature. Invert the tube remnant and drain off the ethanol, making sure that the pellet is not dislodged. Allow the pellet of RNA to dry at room temperature and then redissolve it in ~200 μl of 1 mM EDTA (pH 8.0) by pipetting up and down with a P200 pipettor.

8. Transfer 10 μl of the RNA to a fresh microfuge tube and add 400 μl of 1 mM EDTA (pH 8.0). Measure the absorbance of the RNA solution at 260 nm and 280 nm, using 1 mM EDTA (pH 8.0) as a reference. Calculate the yield of RNA.

9. Store the RNA by one of the methods outlined in the information panel on STORAGE AND RECOVERY OF RNA.

Purification of Total RNA from Yeast

Charles B. Epstein* and Ron Butow[†]

*Aventis Pharmaceuticals, Cambridge, Massachusetts; [†]University of Texas Southwestern
Medical Center, Dallas, Texas

Isolation of RNA is achieved by treatment of yeast with hot acid phenol. This extraction procedure yields high-molecular-weight RNA with very little contaminating DNA. The protocol is based on the method of Köhrer and Domdey (1991) who used extraction with acid phenol followed by chloroform to exclude DNA and other cellular components from the aqueous phase. However, separation and recovery of the aqueous phase and removal of residual contaminants can also be facilitated by the use of Phase Lock Gels, as described in the panel ALTERNATIVE PROTOCOL: PURIFICATION OF RNA USING PHASE LOCK GELS.

MATERIALS

CAUTION: Please see Appendix 3 for appropriate handling of materials marked with <!>.

IMPORTANT: Prepare all reagents used in this protocol with DEPC-treated H_2O (please see the information panel on SPECIAL CONSIDERATIONS FOR WORKING WITH RNA).

Buffers and Solutions

Please see Appendix 2 for components of stock solutions, buffers, and reagents.
Dilute stock solutions to the appropriate concentrations.

Acid phenol (pH 5.0–5.1) <!>
   To make acid phenol, heat a fresh bottle (100 g) of crystalline phenol to 65°C. The liquefied phenol should be clear and free of color. Discard batches of phenol that are yellow or pink. Add 20 ml of a solution of 10 mM sodium acetate (pH 5.1), 50 mM NaCl, and 1.0 mM EDTA (pH 8.0). Mix the contents of the bottle by stirring. Let the liquefied phenol cool to room temperature and then add another 10 ml of the buffer. Wrap the bottle in aluminum foil and store it at 4°C. To test the pH of the phenol, refer to the instructions in the information panel on EXTRACTION OF PROTEINS AND DNA WITH PHENOL.

AE buffer
   50 mM sodium acetate (pH 6.0)
   10 mM EDTA

Ammonium acetate (7.5 M)

Chloroform:isoamyl alcohol (24:1) <!>

DEPC-treated H_2O

Ethanol (absolute)
   Some batches of absolute ethanol (100% or 200 proof) have been reported to contain fluorescent contaminants that generate high backgrounds in microarray experiments; 95% ethanol does not have this problem. To avoid difficulties, either use 95% ethanol or identify a brand of absolute ethanol that performs reliably. Absolute ethanol (USP-grade ethyl alcohol, 64-17-5) purchased from Warner-Graham Co. (Cockeysville, Maryland) performs consistently well.

Isopropanol
Phenol:chloroform <!>
    50% liquefied phenol
    50% chloroform, equilibrated in AE buffer and stored at 4°C in light-proof bottles
    SDS (10% w/v)
Sodium acetate (3 M, pH 5.2)

Media

YPD or other appropriate yeast growth medium

Cells and Tissues

Yeast cells, freshly grown as overnight culture

Centrifuges and Rotors

Centrifuge with capacity to accept 250-ml bottles
Oak Ridge tubes (phenol-resistant)
Sorvall centrifuge, SS-34 and GSA rotors (or equivalent) at room temperature

Special Equipment

Water bath set at 65°C

METHOD

Harvesting of Yeast and Extraction of RNA

1. Inoculate and grow yeast cultures (250 ml) under appropriate conditions to an A_{600} of 0.8.

   Standard conditions for growth of yeast cultures are 30°C in a shaking incubator in YPD medium. An inoculum of ~25 μl of an overnight culture of a wild-type yeast strain into 250 ml of YPD medium generates a culture with an A_{600} of ~0.72 after 16 hours incubation. For isolation of RNA from exponentially growing cells, the A_{600} of the culture should be between 0.5 and 1.0.

2. Harvest the cells by centrifugation at 2500g for 5 minutes at room temperature. Discard the supernatant.

   At this stage, the cells may be stored as a frozen pellet in liquid nitrogen or used immediately for extraction and purification of RNA.

   Centrifugation is carried out at room temperature to avoid cold-shock, which will alter the transcriptional pattern of the cells.

3. Resuspend the cells in 10 ml of AE buffer. Transfer the cell suspension to a 50-ml polypropylene centrifuge tube.

4. Add 1 ml of 10% SDS and 11 ml of acid phenol, equilibrated to 65°C. Mix the contents of the tube by vortexing for 15–20 seconds. Transfer the tube to a water bath for 1 hour at 65°C, vortexing at maximum speed for 15 seconds at 10-minute intervals.

5. After the final vortexing, cool the tube to room temperature by agitation in a bath containing ice water.

   Do not allow the emulsion to cool to <15°C, otherwise the SDS may precipitate.

6. Separate the phases by centrifugation at 2500g for 5 minutes at room temperature.

7. Use a pipette to remove and discard 10 ml of the lower (organic) phase, leaving the interface and cell debris in the tube.

8. Add 10 ml of hot acid phenol to the tube and transfer it to the 65°C water bath for 15 minutes, vortexing at maximum speed for 15 seconds at 5-minute intervals.

9. Cool the emulsion to room temperature and separate the phases by centrifugation at 2500g for 5 minutes at room temperature.

10. Transfer the upper aqueous phase (~11 ml) to a fresh polypropylene tube containing 11 ml of chloroform:isoamyl alcohol (24:1). Mix the contents by vortexing the closed tube vigorously for 30 seconds and separate the phase by centrifugation at 2500g for 5 minutes.

Purification of RNA

11. Transfer the upper aqueous phase (~11 ml) to a fresh polypropylene tube. Add 2.6 volumes of absolute ethanol containing 0.3 M ammonium acetate. Mix the solution well and store it for at least 6 hours at –20°C.

12. Recover the RNA by centrifugation at 3500g for at least 20 minutes. Without delay, carefully decant the ethanolic supernatant into a fresh tube and store the tube at –20°C until the protocol is completed and the yield of RNA is shown to be satisfactory.

13. Add 15 ml of ice-cold 75% ethanol, mix the contents by vortexing the tube briefly and then recentrifuge. Carefully decant the ethanolic supernatant into a fresh tube and store it at –20°C until the protocol is completed and the yield of RNA is shown to be satisfactory.

14. Carefully aspirate the last drops of ethanol from the sides of the tube and allow the pellet of RNA to dry in the air.

15. Dissolve the barely damp pellet in 0.5–1.0 ml of 10 mM Tris (pH 8.0). Transfer the solution to a microfuge tube and heat it for 5 minutes to 65°C to assist the RNA to dissolve.

16. Centrifuge the tube in a microfuge at 12,000g for 2 minutes at room temperature. Transfer 250-µl aliquots of the supernatant to fresh microfuge tubes. Discard the microfuge tube containing the pellet, which consists mostly of carbohydrate and cell wall components.

17. Add 2.5 volumes of ice-cold ethanol containing 0.3 M ammonium acetate. Store the tubes for 1 hour at –20°C and then recover the RNA by centrifugation in a microfuge at 12,000g for 15 minutes.

18. Remove the supernatants by aspiration and allow the pellets of RNA to dry in the air. Dissolve each of the pellets in ~200 µl of 10 mM Tris (pH 8.0). If the pellets do not dissolve immediately, warm the solutions to 45°C for 10 minutes and then store them overnight at 4°C.

19. Remove any particulate matter by centrifugation in a microfuge at 12,000g. Combine the supernatants and quantify the RNA by absorption spectrophotometry at 260 nm and 280 nm or by fluorescence after staining with RiboGreen (please see the information panel on QUANTIFICATION OF RNA).

20. Store the RNA by one of the methods outlined in the information panel on STORAGE AND RECOVERY OF RNA.

> Before using the RNA in microarray experiments, check its integrity by electrophoresis through a formaldehyde–1% agarose gel (please see the information panel on MAMMALIAN, PLANT, AND BACTERIALS RNAs). The gels should show prominent bands of rRNA and low-molecular-weight RNAs overlaid by a very light smear of mRNA.

> A 250-ml culture of a healthy, wild-type strain of yeast grown to an OD_{600} of 0.5–1.0 should yield 5–10 mg of total RNA.

ALTERNATIVE PROTOCOL: PURIFICATION OF RNA USING PHASE LOCK GELS

The Phase Lock Gel, contained in the tubes supplied by the manufacturer, migrates under centrifugal force to form a barrier between the organic and aqueous phases. The interface, together with the underlying organic material, is effectively separated from the upper aqueous layer. The gel is sufficiently leakproof to allow the supernatant aqueous phase to be poured into a fresh tube without significant contamination from the material trapped at the interface. The Phase Lock Gel is available in a variety of formulations and in tubes of several sizes. For details, please consult the manufacturer's literature or www.brinkman.com.

Additional Materials

Phase Lock Gel tubes (50 ml) (955 15 409-6, Brinkmann Eppendorf)
Tabletop centrifuge

Method

1. Carry out Steps 1–6 of the main protocol.

2. Pellet the Phase Lock Gel in a 50-ml tube by centrifugation at 1500g for 1 minute. Add the supernatant from Step 6 to the tube containing the Phase Lock Gel. Add 15 ml of chloroform and then mix the phases thoroughly by shaking the tube. *Do not vortex the tube!*

3. Separate the phases by centrifugation in a tabletop centrifuge at 1500g for 5 minutes at room temperature.

4. Carefully decant the upper aqueous phase into a fresh Oak Ridge tube.

5. Measure the volume of the solution. Add 0.1 volume of 3 M sodium acetate (pH 5.2) and 1.1 volumes of isopropanol. Store the tube for 10 minutes at room temperature.

6. Recover the precipitate of RNA by centrifugation in a Sorvall SS-34 rotor at 16,000g for 45 minutes at 15°C.

7. Remove the supernatant by gentle aspiration and then wash the pellet and the sides of the tube with 70% ethanol. Recentrifuge in a Sorvall SS-34 rotor at 16,000g for 20 minutes at 15°C.

8. Carry out Steps 15–20 of the main protocol.

Purification of RNA from *E. coli*

Virgil Rhodius

University of California, San Francisco, California 94143

Isolation of RNA is achieved by treatment of the bacterial lysate with hot acid phenol. Extraction with acid phenol followed by chloroform is used to exclude DNA and other cellular components from the aqueous phase. Subsequent treatment with DNase I is required before reverse transcription of the RNA. This extraction procedure yields high-molecular-weight RNA with very little contaminating DNA. The expected yield from a 10-ml culture is in the range of 70–300 µg, depending on the conditions of growth and harvesting. This protocol is adapted from www.microarrays.org/protocols.html and the techniques used at the Cold Spring Harbor Laboratory Microarray Courses.

MATERIALS

CAUTION: Please see Appendix 3 for appropriate handling of materials marked with <!>.

IMPORTANT: Prepare all reagents used in this protocol with DEPC-treated H_2O (please see the information panel on **SPECIAL CONSIDERATIONS FOR WORKING WITH RNA**).

Buffers and Solutions

Please see Appendix 2 for components of stock solutions, buffers, and reagents.
Dilute stock solutions to the appropriate concentrations.

Chloroform <!>
Ethanol (absolute and 80%)
> Some batches of absolute ethanol (100% or 200 proof) have been reported to contain fluorescent contaminants that generate high backgrounds in microarray experiments; 95% ethanol does not have this problem. To avoid difficulties, either use 95% ethanol or identify a brand of absolute ethanol that performs reliably. Absolute ethanol (USP-grade ethyl alcohol, 64-17-5) purchased from Warner-Graham Co. (Cockeysville, Maryland) performs consistently well.

Ethanol/phenol stop solution <!>
> H_2O-saturated phenol (pH <7.0) in ethanol (5% v/v).
> The recipe for this solution was provided by Jon Berstein (University of California, San Francisco).

Phenol, H_2O-saturated (pH <7.0)
> Prepare the phenol solution from Ultra-Pure phenol (redistilled, crystalline; 15509, Invitrogen/GIBCO). Note that H_2O-saturated acid phenol should be used for RNA extractions.

Phenol:chloroform (1:1 v/v) <!>
SDS (10% and 5% w/v) <!>
Sodium acetate (1 M and 3 M, pH 5.2)
Tris (10 mM, pH 8.0)

Enzymes and Buffers

Lysozyme solution
   500 µg/ml in 10 mM Tris (pH 8.0)
   1 mM EDTA (pH 8.0)
      Prepare the lysozyme solution fresh just before use.
5x DNase I buffer
   50 mM $MgCl_2$
   50 mM Tris-Cl (pH 7.5)
   5 mM EDTA (pH 8.0)
   5 mM dithiothreitol (DTT)
RNase-free DNase (10 units/µl) (776785, Boehringer Mannheim)
RNase inhibitor (799017, Boehringer Mannheim)

Media

Bacterial medium, appropriate for growth of *E. coli* strain

Bacterial Strains

E. coli strain of choice for preparation of RNA

Special Equipment

Sorvall RC5C, SS-34 rotor (or equivalent)
Water bath set at 64°C

METHOD

Harvesting of Total RNA

1. Inoculate a culture of the appropriate strain of *E. coli* and grow it overnight at 37°C to saturation.

2. Dilute 1 ml of the overnight culture in 100 ml of an appropriate medium. Grow the culture to mid-log phase.

3. Transfer 10 ml of the culture to a 15-ml conical tube containing 1.25 ml of ice-cold ethanol/phenol stop solution.

   This step stops the degradation of mRNA.

4. Recover the cells by centrifugation at 6000*g* for 2 minutes at 4°C. Remove the medium by aspiration.

   At this stage, the cells can be frozen in liquid nitrogen and stored at –80°C as required or used immediately for extraction of RNA.

5. Resuspend the cell pellet in 500 µl of lysozyme solution. Adjust the volume of the cell suspension to 800 µl by adding more lysozyme solution. Transfer the lysate into a 2-ml microfuge tube containing 80 µl of 10% SDS. Mix the contents of the tube with a pipette tip. Incubate the cell lysate for 2 minutes at 64°C.

   During incubation, the lysate should clear.

6. Add 88 µl of 1 M sodium acetate solution (pH 5.2) to the cleared lysate and mix by inverting the tube.

Extraction of RNA with Hot Phenol

7. To the lysate add an equal volume (~1 ml) of H_2O-saturated phenol. Close the top of the tube and mix the contents by inverting the tube 10–12 times. Incubate the tube in a water bath for 6 minutes at 64°C. Mix the contents of the tube every 40–60 seconds during the incubation.

8. Transfer the tube to an ice-bath for 2 minutes. Centrifuge the emulsion at maximum speed (16,000g) in a microfuge for 10 minutes at 4°C.

9. Transfer the upper (aqueous) layer to a fresh 2-ml microfuge tube, and then add an equal volume of chloroform. Close the top of the tube and mix the contents by inverting the tube 8–10 times.

10. Separate the phases by centrifugation at maximum speed (16,000g) in a microfuge for 5 minutes at 4°C.

11. Recover the upper (aqueous) phase. Divide the solution equally between two 1.5-ml microfuge tubes. Add 0.1 volume of 3 M sodium acetate (pH 5.2), and 2.5 volumes of cold ethanol (absolute). Store the solution for at least 1 hour at –20°C.

12. Recover the RNA by centrifugation at 12,000g in a microfuge for 30 minutes at 4°C.

13. Wash the pellet of RNA in 80% ice-cold ethanol. Centrifuge at maximum speed (16,000g) in a microfuge for 5 minutes at 4°C. Carefully remove the ethanol solution by aspiration and stand the open tube in a chemical fume hood until the last traces of ethanol have evaporated.

14. Dissolve each pellet of RNA in ~100 µl of H_2O. Pool the solution from the pair of tubes.

DNase Treatment

15. To each RNA preparation (200 µl) add:

RNase inhibitor (20 units)	0.5 µl
DNase I buffer	50 µl
RNase-free DNase (10 units/µl)	1.0 µl

    Incubate the reaction for 30 minutes at 37°C.

16. Extract the solution with an equal volume of H_2O-saturated phenol (pH <7.0). Centrifuge the emulsion at maximum speed (16,000g) in a microfuge for 2 minutes. Transfer the upper (aqueous) phase to a fresh microfuge tube.

17. Extract the solution with an equal volume of phenol:chloroform. Invert the tube several times to mix, and centrifuge the emulsion at maximum speed (16,000g) in a microfuge for 2 minutes. Transfer the upper (aqueous) phase to a fresh microfuge tube.

    Some strains of *E. coli* may require additional extractions with phenol and/or chloroform to remove contaminating RNases. It may be advisable to include two additional extractions with chloroform (by repeating Steps 9 and 10) before proceeding. After the extraction(s), transfer the aqueous phase to a fresh microfuge tube and proceed to Step 18.

18. Add 0.1 volume of 3 M sodium acetate (pH 5.2) and 2.5 volumes of ethanol. Store the solution for at least 1 hour or overnight at –20°C.

19. Recover the RNA by centrifugation at maximum speed (16,000*g*) in a microfuge for 30 minutes at 4°C.

20. Wash the pellet of RNA in 1 ml of 80% ice-cold ethanol. Centrifuge at maximum speed (16,000*g*) in a microfuge for 5 minutes at 4°C. Carefully remove the ethanol solution by aspiration and stand the open tube in a chemical fume hood until the last traces of ethanol have evaporated (~15 minutes).

Assessing the Yield and Quality of the RNA

21. Dissolve each pellet of RNA in ~50 μl of 10 mM Tris (pH 8.0).

22. Quantify the RNA by absorption spectrophotometry at 260 nm and 280 nm or by fluorescence after staining with RiboGreen (please see the information panel on QUANTIFICATION OF RNA).

    The yield of RNA should be 70–300 μg, depending on the strain of *E. coli*, the growth conditions, and the density of culture at the time of harvest.

23. Store the RNA by one of the methods outlined in the information panel on STORAGE AND RECOVERY OF RNA.

    E. coli RNA may be stored for several months at –20°C. For longer-term storage, precipitate the solution in ethanol and store at –80°C.

    Before using the RNA preparation in microarray experiments, check its integrity by electrophoresis through a formaldehyde–1% agarose gel (please see the information panel on MAMMALIAN, PLANT, AND BACTERIAL RNAs). The gels should show prominent bands of 23S and 16S rRNA and low-molecular-weight RNAs. The 23S band should stain about two times more intensely than the 16S band. A heavy smear or intensely staining bands of low-molecular-weight RNA are indicators of RNA degradation or DNA contamination.

Isolation and Amplification of RNA from Single Cells and Small Amounts of Tissues

James Eberwine,*† Paolo Marciano,‡ Tracy McIntosh,‡
and Janet Estee Kacharmina*†
*Departments of *Pharmacology, †Psychiatry, and ‡Neurosurgery, University of Pennsylvania*
Medical Center, Philadelphia, Pennsylvania 19104

Standard protocols for analyzing gene expression by DNA microarrays were developed and optimized for use with large amounts of RNA isolated from millions of freshly harvested cells or milligrams of freshly dissected tissue. Because tissues rarely consist of only one cell type, the large-scale preparations of mRNA required for expression profiling have been isolated in most cases from complex and heterogeneous mixtures of cell types. The resulting estimates of where and when a particular gene is expressed are therefore imprecise at best.

Neurological tissues provide a graphic illustration of the problem. In the central nervous system, the hippocampal region of the brain is involved in learning and memory. The hippocampus is composed of many types of cells including various categories of neurons and glia. If one wanted to profile changes in gene expression associated with a learning challenge, it would almost certainly be fruitless to analyze mRNA harvested from the whole hippocampus. Both the three-dimensional complexity and cellular specificity of response would then be lost. Ideally, it would be advantageous to analyze the mRNA in only selected cells of interest, or even a single cell (Figure 3-5). As described in the following protocols, RNA amplification provides a means to achieve these goals and to generate labeled targets from single cells, in this case, fixed neurons.

mRNA isolated from fixed tissue samples has been very difficult to analyze because fixatives such as glutaraldehyde, formalin, and paraformaldehyde form cross-links between primary amines. In tissues fixed with these agents, nucleic acids and proteins become covalently attached to one another. Consequently, RNA isolated from fixed tissue is usually fragmented because the polyribonucleotide chains cannot break free from their shackles unless they are cleaved. Fortunately, however, RNA does not need to be extracted from a fixed tissue to generate labeled targets for microarray analysis. Instead, the mRNA present in the tissue section can be copied in situ into cDNA directly on the tissue section. Figure 3-6 shows the steps involved in the reverse transcription and amplification of RNA derived from a tissue section (please see the panel ALTERNATIVE PROTOCOL: IN SITU TRANSCRIPTION OF RNA IN TISSUE SECTIONS at the end of this protocol).

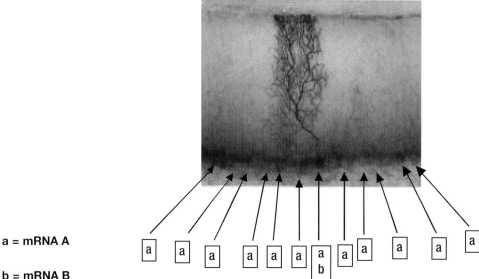

a = mRNA A

b = mRNA B

FIGURE 3-5. Cell dilution effect. The CA1 region of a rat hippocampus is shown in this figure. A single pyramidal cell is labeled with biocytin to show the various aspects of the cell. The line of cell bodies present in the CA1 region is highlighted by the arrows. If the whole CA1 area is harvested, then the mRNA from the biocytin-labeled cell will be diluted by the RNA from the other cells. If a particular mRNA A is present in all cells, then it will be relatively easy to detect using microarray analysis; if, however, mRNA B is present only in the biocytin-labeled cell, then its concentration will be diluted at least tenfold, making it more difficult to quantify the mRNA complement from this individual cell.

- Isolation of a single cell by microdissection, followed by first-strand synthesis, primed by the oligo(dT)$_{24}$–T7 primer to produce cDNA.

  or

- In situ hybridization of an mRNA-specific primer to the tissue section, usually the oligo(dT)$_{24}$–T7 primer used in the conventional antisense RNA (aRNA) technique (main protocol). The oligo(dT) section of the primer anneals to the poly(A) tail of the mRNA in the tissue section and provides a 3′-hydroxyl terminus that is extended in situ in a conventional reverse transcriptase reaction. Reverse transcriptase copies the mRNA template, jumping over the cross-linked nucleotides, generating relatively long cDNA copies of the fixed mRNA. Single cells are recovered from the tissue section by micromanipulation and single-stranded cDNA is extracted.

- Second-strand cDNA is synthesized from the first-strand product recovered either from a single cell or from a tissue section in a self-priming reaction that leaves a single-stranded hairpin loop at one end of the molecule.

- After cleavage of the hairpin loop with a single-strand-specific nuclease, the double-stranded DNA is used as the template for transcription of aRNA.

- The aRNA is again converted into double-stranded DNA which, after polishing of frayed ends, is used as the template for a further round of in vitro transcription into aRNA. By this stage, the RNA is amplified to the point where it can be used efficiently as a template to generate fluorescently labeled targets for DNA microarrays.

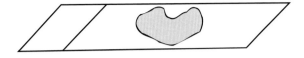

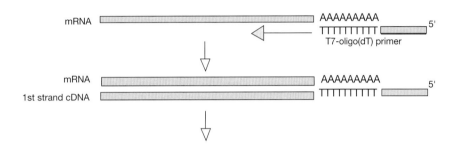

Harvest cDNA from desired region of section with a microelectrode

or

Extract DNA from entire section with 0.2 N NaOH/1%SDS

Perform aRNA amplification

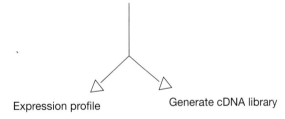

Expression profile   Generate cDNA library

FIGURE 3-6. cDNA synthesis in fixed tissue sections. In situ reverse transcription is performed on fixed tissue sections of cell cultures. Synthesis of first-strand cDNA is primed by an oligo(dT) primer equipped with a bacteriophage T7 promoter. The cDNA may be harvested from individual cells with a microelectrode or extracted from the entire section by alkali/SDS.

The main protocol describes the isolation of a single cell with subsequent amplification of RNA, whereas the alternative protocol provides a method for the copying of RNA into cDNA in situ. An additional protocol (ADDITIONAL PROTOCOL: ACRIDINE ORANGE STAINING OF SECTIONS) describes the immunostaining of cells using acridine orange to detect the presence of RNA, and thereby to determine the feasibility of proceeding with single-cell isolation or in situ transcription.

MATERIALS

CAUTION: Please see Appendix 3 for appropriate handling of materials marked with <!>.

IMPORTANT: Prepare all reagents used in this protocol with DEPC-treated H_2O (please see the information panel on SPECIAL CONSIDERATIONS FOR WORKING WITH RNA).

Buffers and Solutions

Please see Appendix 2 for components of stock solutions, buffers, and reagents.
Dilute stock solutions to the appropriate concentrations and sterilize by filtration.

Dithiothreitol (DTT) (100 mM) <!>

Ethanol (absolute or 95%)
> Some batches of absolute ethanol (100% or 200 proof) have been reported to contain fluorescent contaminants that generate high backgrounds in microarray experiments; 95% ethanol does not have this problem. To avoid difficulties, either use 95% ethanol or identify a brand of absolute ethanol that does not generate high levels of background fluorescence. Absolute ethanol (USP-grade ethyl alcohol, 64-17-5) purchased from Warner-Graham Co. (Cockeysville, Maryland) performs consistently well.

Formaldehyde (37%) <!>

Formamide (deionized) <!>

10x MOPS

Phenol:chloroform (1:1 v/v) <!>

10x RNA amplification buffer
  400 mM Tris-base (pH 7.5)
  70 mM $MgCl_2$
  100 mM NaCl
  20 mM spermidine
> Filter prior to the addition of spermidine.

10x Second-strand buffer
  1 M Tris-base (pH 7.4)
  200 mM KCl
  100 mM $MgCl_2$
  400 mM $(NH_4)_2SO_4$
> Store in small aliquots at –20°C.

Sodium acetate (3 M) or NaCl (5 M)

Trichloroacetic acid (TCA) (10% w/v) <!>

Enzymes and Buffers

AMV-RT (25,000 units/ml, 2000 units) (avian myeloblastosis virus reverse transcriptase) (800-237-4512, Cape Cod Inc., formerly Seikagaku America)
> AMV is the preferred reverse transcriptase to use in this protocol, as the enzyme contains traces of RNase H that helps with priming of the second strand. In the authors' experience, AMV has been observed to provide longer cDNA products and higher yields than does SUPERSCRIPT II.

10x AMV-RT buffer
  500 mM Tris-base (pH 8.3)
  1.2 M KCl
  100 mM $MgCl_2$

Klenow fragment of *E. coli* DNA polymerase I (2 units/μl; labeling grade) (Roche, 800-262-1640)

10x KFI (Klenow filling-in) buffer

200 mM Tris-base (pH 7.5)

100 mM $MgCl_2$

50 mM NaCl

50 mM DTT

DTT may be omitted from the buffer and added directly to the reaction (as it tends to precipitate out of the buffers over time).

Nuclease S1 (100 units/µl)

Dilute nuclease S1 in 1x nuclease S1 buffer to 1 unit/µl just before use.

10x Nuclease S1 buffer

2 M NaCl

500 mM sodium acetate (pH 4.5)

10 mM $ZnSO_4$

RNasin (40 units/µl)

T4 DNA polymerase (1 unit/µl) (Roche, 800-262-1640)

T7 RNA polymerase (1000 units/µl) (Epicentre Technologies, 800-284-8474)

Nucleic Acids and Oligonucleotides

Carrier RNA (*E. coli* tRNA)

CTP (1.0 mM)

[α-^{32}P]CTP (300 Ci/mmole; 1 mCi/100 µl) <!>

dNTP solution containing all four dNTPs, each at a concentration of 2.5 mM

NTP solution containing all four NTPs, each at a concentration of 2.5 mM

3 NTP solution containing ATP, GTP, and UTP, each at a concentration of 2.5 mM

Random Hexamers (Roche, 800-262-1640)

1 A_{260} unit = 40 µg

50 A_{260} = 50 x 40 µg = 2 mg

T7–Oligo(dT)$_{24}$ oligonucleotide (100 ng/µl)

AAA CGA CGG CCA GTG AAT TGT AAT ACG ACT CAC TAT AGG CGC (T)$_{24}$

For a description of this primer, please see the protocol introduction.

Gels

Agarose gel (1%), containing 2.2 M formaldehyde <!>

For details, please see Sambrook and Russell (2001).

10x Gel-loading dye

Cells and Tissues

Tissue section, fixed to slide

Special Equipment

Electrode holder (3 port; Warner Instruments, Connecticut)

Microelectrode for dissection

The microelectrode is autoclaved and pulled on a Sutter P-97 Puller (Sutter Instruments Co, California) to have an opening of ~3 µm.

Millipore filters (pore size 0.025 µm)

Narishige manipulator, coarse (Narishige Internations, New York)

Narishige microminipulator, fine (Narishige Internations, New York)

PE tubing (2-mm diameter; Tygon)

METHOD

Harvesting of a Single Cell

1. Deliver ~200 μl of DEPC-treated ddH$_2$O onto the tissue section to hydrate it.

2. Back-fill the microelectrode to be used for the dissection with 20 μl of DEPC-treated ddH$_2$O and mount it on a 3-port electrode holder.

3. Create a suction device by attaching one end of the PE tubing to the third port on the Warner electrode holder and secure the holder to the microscope. Attach the other end of the tubing to the housing of a 1-ml syringe.

4. Use a coarse Narishige manipulator to lower the electrode into the DEPC-treated ddH$_2$O, and a fine Narishige microminipulator to lower the electrode into the field of view.

5. With both electrode and tissue in the field of view, move the electrode from side to side, and then lower it until it begins to touch the cell of interest. Once the electrode is in position, slowly microdissect the cell by separating the cell membrane from the surrounding tissue.

    This procedure must be done slowly and carefully to avoid disrupting the nearby tissue or contaminating the electrode with other cellular mRNAs.

6. Once the cell is free from the extracellular matrix, apply suction to the 1-ml syringe and aspirate the cell into the electrode. Use the course manipulator to lift the electrode containing the cell off the tissue (for an illustration of the tissue before, during, and after selection of the single cell, please see Figure 3-7).

7. Expel the contents of the electrode into a microfuge tube.

cDNA Synthesis

8. Prepare a reaction mixture consisting of the following reagents:

DEPC-treated ddH$_2$O	4.5 μl
dNTP solution (2.5 mM each)	4.0 μl
10x RT buffer	4.0 μl
T7–oligo(dT)$_{24}$ (100 ng/μl)	2.5 μl
DTT (100 mM)	1.0 μl
RNasin (40 units/μl)	1.0 μl
AMV-RT	3.0 μl

    Transfer the contents of the tube from Step 7 into the mixture and incubate the reaction for 60 minutes at 37°C.

9. Extract the mixture with an equal volume of phenol:chloroform and then add 1/10 volume salt (3 M NaOAc or 5 M NaCl) to the aqueous phase.

10. To the aqueous phase, add 2.5 volumes of 95% ethanol and 0.5 μg of *E. coli* tRNA. Precipitate the sample by storing it for 30 minutes at 4°C; recover the nucleic acids by centrifugation in a microfuge at maximum speed (16,000g) for 20 minutes at 4°C.

11. Remove the ethanol; immediately invert the tubes and dry the pellet in the air for 10 minutes. Resuspend the pellet in 20 μl of DEPC-treated ddH$_2$O.

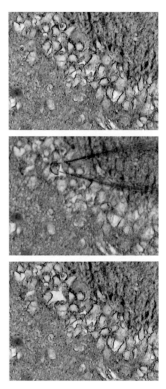

FIGURE 3-7. Mechanical harvesting of single cells. (*Top*) Section of mouse brain in which various cells can be seen after in situ transcription, but before harvesting. (*Middle*) Apposition of the patch pipette onto a cell that will be harvested. (*Bottom*) Section post-cell harvesting. The hole where the cell was removed is easily visible.

Second-strand cDNA Synthesis

12. To denature the RNA-DNA hybrid, heat the sample for 5 minutes at 85°C, and then place it immediately on ice.

13. To the denatured sample, add the following reagents:

DEPC-treated ddH$_2$O	10 µl
10x second-strand buffer	4 µl
dNTP solution (2.5 mM each)	4 µl
T4 DNA polymerase (1 unit/µl)	1 µl
Klenow fragment (2 units/µl)	1 µl

    Incubate the reaction for 4 hours to overnight at 14°C.

    This is a self-priming reaction in which the 3′ end of first-strand cDNA is used to prime second-strand synthesis.

14. To facilitate loop excision, add the following reagents:

DEPC-treated H$_2$O	319 µl
10x nuclease S1 buffer	40 µl
nuclease S1 (diluted in S1 buffer to 1 unit/µl)	1 µl

    Incubate the reaction for 5 minutes at 37°C.

15. Extract the reaction with an equal volume (400 µl) of phenol:chloroform.

16. Precipitate the sample by adding 1 ml of ice-cold ethanol and incubating the solution for 30 minutes at –80°C. Recover the nucleic acids by centrifugation in a microfuge at maximum speed (16,000*g*) for 20 minutes at 4°C. Resuspend the pellet in 18.5 µl of DEPC-treated ddH$_2$O.

    To prevent a large pellet, do not add additional salt.

17. To polish the ends of the double-stranded DNA product, add the following reagents:

10x KFI buffer	2.5 µl
(optional) DTT (100 mM)	1.0 µl
dNTP solution (2.5 mM each)	2.0 µl
T4 DNA polymerase	1.0 µl

    Incubate the reaction for 15 minutes at 37°C, and then add 25 µl of DEPC-treated ddH$_2$O for a total volume of 50 µl.

18. Extract the reaction with an equal volume (50 µl) of phenol:chloroform, and then add 5 µl of 3 M sodium acetate or 5 M NaCl to the aqueous phase.

19. Precipitate the sample by adding 125 µl of ice-cold 95% ethanol and incubating the solution for 30 minutes at –80°C. Recover the nucleic acids by centrifugation in a microfuge at maximum speed (16,000*g*) for 20 minutes at 4°C.

aRNA Amplification (Round One), Approximate Yield of 2000x

IMPORTANT: Use only DEPC-treated and autoclaved ddIH$_2$O. Use only autoclaved and freshly opened microfuge tubes, pipette tips, or filter tips.

20. To remove unincorporated dNTPs that will inhibit T7 RNA polymerase, purify the sample by drop dialysis:

    a. Resuspend the DNA pellet in 20 µl of DEPC-treated H$_2$O.

    b. Dialyze 10 µl of the sample for 4 hours against 50 ml of DEPC-treated H$_2$O using Millipore filters (pore size 0.025 µm).

       This is best accomplished by gently floating the filter in a sterile 50-ml conical tube containing H$_2$O. The filter is placed there with "baked" RNase-free forceps. It is advisable to dialyze only half of the sample at a time to prevent loss of material (e.g., if the filter were to sink). The size of the sample may change upon dialysis.

    c. When the dialysis is finished, transfer the sample to a fresh, sterile microfuge tube.

21. Deliver one fifth of the amount of sample recovered from dialysis (~2 µl) into a fresh microfuge tube and add the following reagents:

DEPC-treated ddIH$_2$O	11.5 µl
10x RNA amplification buffer	2.0 µl
DTT (100 mM)	1.0 µl
NTP solution (2.5 mM each)	2.0 µl
RNasin (20 units)	0.5 µl
T7 RNA polymerase (1000 units/µl)	1.0 µl

    Incubate the reaction for 4 hours at 37°C, and then add 30 µl of DEPC-treated H$_2$O to a total volume of 50 µl.

       For analysis of the size distribution of the reaction products, set up a "hot" reaction as described in the panel below.

22. Extract the reaction with an equal volume (50 µl) of phenol:chloroform and then add 5 µl of 3 M sodium acetate.

23. Precipitate the sample by adding 125 µl of cold ethanol and 0.5 µg of tRNA and incubating the solution for 30 minutes at –80°C. Recover the nucleic acids by centrifugation in a microfuge at maximum speed (16,000g) for 20 minutes at 4°C.

Reamplification: First-strand cDNA Synthesis

24. Resuspend the pellet of amplified RNA from Step 23 in 17 µl of DEPC-treated ddH$_2$O.

25. Denature 8–17 µl of the aRNA sample by heating it for 5–7 minutes at 85°C, and then cool the sample immediately on ice.

ASSESSING THE SIZE DISTRIBUTION OF AN RNA POPULATION

1. Prepare a reaction mixture containing a radiolabeled dNTP that can be used to analyze the size distribution of amplified RNA. Deliver ~2 µl of the sample recovered from dialysis in Step 20 into a microfuge tube and add the following reagents:

DEPC-treated ddlH$_2$O	7.5 µl
10x RNA amplification buffer	2.0 µl
DTT (100 mM)	1.0 µl
3 NTPs (ATP, GTP, UTP, 2.5 mM each)	2.0 µl
CTP (100 µM; 5 µM final conc.)	1.0 µl
RNasin (20 units)	0.5 µl
[α-^{32}P]CTP (3000 Ci/mmole; 1 mCi/100 µl)	3.0 µl
T7 RNA polymerase (1000 units/µl)	1.0 µl

   Incubate the reaction for 3.5 to 4 hours at 37°C.

2. To 2–4 µl of the hot aRNA product, add the following reagents:

DEPC-treated H$_2$O	to 20 µl
37% formaldehyde	3.5 µl
10x MOPS	2.0 µl
deionized formamide	10 µl

3. Heat denature the sample for 5–7 minutes at 85°C, and then add 2 µl of 10x gel-loading dye.

4. Analyze the samples by electrophoresis through a 1% denaturing gel until the leading dye front is almost at the bottom of the gel.

   Do not run dye front from the gel or the gel box will become contaminated with radioactivity.

5. To remove the unincorporated label, gently shake the gel in 10% TCA for 1–2 hours, changing the 10% TCA solution at 15–20-minute intervals.

6. Blot the gel dry overnight by capillary action as follows:

   a. Place the gel on parafilm or Saran Wrap.

   b. Cover the gel with two pieces of 3 MM Whatman paper and paper towels.

   c. Place a weight on top of the setup.

7. The gel should be flat and dry on the following day. Wrap the gel in Saran Wrap and appose directly to a phosphor imaging screen or onto film for 6–12 hours at –80°C. For an example of the expected aRNA size distribution data, see Figure 3-8.

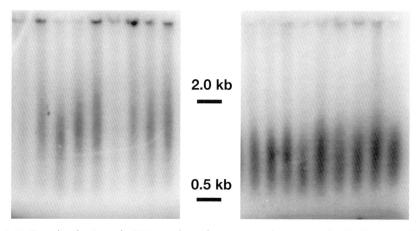

FIGURE 3-8. Size distribution of aRNA products from one and two rounds of aRNA amplification. After aRNA amplification, the length of the aRNA products can be visualized on a denaturing agarose gel. (*Left*) Products of the first amplification; (*right*) products of the second amplification. The length distribution of the aRNA is an indication of how well the cDNA synthesis and aRNA amplification have worked. Normally, the average size of an mRNA population is 1–2 kb. As can be seen from these figures, the aRNA population is similar in size to the parental RNA, suggesting that the aRNA is of high quality.

26. To the denatured sample, add the following reagents:

10x RT buffer	3 µl
DTT (100 mM)	3 µl
dNTP solution (2.50 mM)	3 µl
random hexamers (100 ng/µl)	1 µl
RNasin (40 units)	1 µl
AMV-RT (50 units)	2 µl
DEPC-treated H_2O	to 30 µl

Incubate the reaction for 1 hour at 37ºC, and then add 20 µl of DEPC-treated H_2O to a total volume of 50 µl.

27. Extract the reaction with an equal volume (50 µl) of phenol:chloroform, and then add 5 µl of 3 M sodium acetate to the aqueous phase.

28. Precipitate the sample by adding 125 µl of ice-cold 95% ethanol and incubating the solution for 30 minutes at –80ºC. Recover the nucleic acids by centrifugation in a microfuge at maximum speed (16,000*g*) for 20 minutes at 4ºC. Resuspend the pellet in 12 µl of DEPC-treated ddH_2O.

Reamplification: Second-strand cDNA Synthesis

29. Denature the sample by heating it for 5 minutes at 85ºC, and then place it on ice.

30. Prepare a second-strand reaction by adding the following reagents to the denatured sample:

10x second-strand buffer	2.0 µl
oligo(dT)–T7 amplification primer (100 ng/µl)	1.0 µl
dNTP solution (2.5 mM each)	2.0 µl
DTT (100 mM)	1.0 µl
T4 DNA polymerase (1 unit/µl)	1.0 µl
Klenow fragment (2 units/µl)	1.0 µl

Incubate the reaction for 4–16 hours at 14°C, and then add 30 μl of DEPC-treated ddH$_2$O to a total volume of 50 μl.

31. Extract the sample with an equal volume (50 μl) of phenol:chloroform, and then add 5 μl of 3 M sodium acetate.

32. Precipitate the sample by adding 125 μl of ice-cold 95% ethanol and incubating the solution for 30 minutes at –80°C. Recover the nucleic acids by centrifugation in a microfuge at maximum speed (16,000g) for 20 minutes at 4°C. Resuspend the pellet in 18 μl of DEPC-treated ddH$_2$O.

33. To fill in the ends of the double-stranded DNA product, add the following reagents:

10x KFI buffer	2.5 μl
dNTP solution (2.5 mM each)	2.5 μl
T4 DNA polymerase (1 unit/μl)	1.0 μl
Klenow fragment (2 units/μl)	1.0 μl

    Incubate the reaction for 30 minutes at 37°C, and then add 25 μl of DEPC-treated ddH$_2$O to a total volume of 50 μl.

34. Extract the sample with an equal volume (50 μl) of phenol:chloroform, and then add 5 μl of 3 M sodium acetate.

35. Precipitate the sample by adding 125 μl of ice-cold 95% ethanol and incubating the solution for 30 minutes at –80°C. Recover the nucleic acids by centrifugation in a microfuge at maximum speed (16,000g) for 20 minutes at 4°C. Resuspend the pellet in 18 μl of DEPC-treated ddH$_2$O.

aRNA Amplification (Second Round)

36. Follow the procedures for aRNA amplification (first round, Step 20).

    The aRNA probe generated using these procedures may be labeled and used in screening microarrays. A representative result that may be obtained using an aRNA probe generated from a single cell is shown in Figure 3-9. In these studies, the aRNA obtained from two rounds of amplification was converted into fluorescently labeled cDNA and used to screen an Incyte GEM microarray. The scattergram for these data (Figure 3-10) shows that the abundance of most of the cellular mRNAs are within 1 standard deviation of the line identity where an mRNA would be equally abundant in both cell types. Such data are reproducibly generated when there is enough probe to hybridize well to the microarray (a fluorescent signal >400 units).

TROUBLESHOOTING/RECOMMENDATIONS

- The amplification step must be kept strictly RNase-free.

- The glycerol in the enzyme stocks will inhibit T7 RNA polymerase if the total volume of the enzyme (RNasin and T7) is greater than one-tenth of the total volume of the reaction mixture. T7 is also inhibited by excessive tRNA, as well as competively inhibited by dNTPs (rationale for dialyzing template).

- The average length of the aRNA population is decreased if the concentration of [^{32}P]CTP in the reaction mixture is increased. This problem is caused primarily by post-synthetic radiolysis.

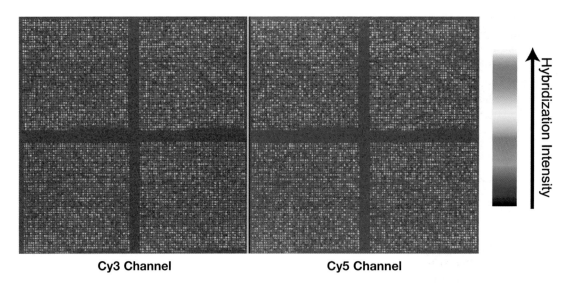

Cy3 Channel   **Cy5 Channel**

FIGURE 3-9. Microarray result from screening of the aRNA made from a single cell. These results show a typical microarray (Incyte microarray) after hybridization with fluorescently tagged cDNA made from the aRNA generated from a single cell.

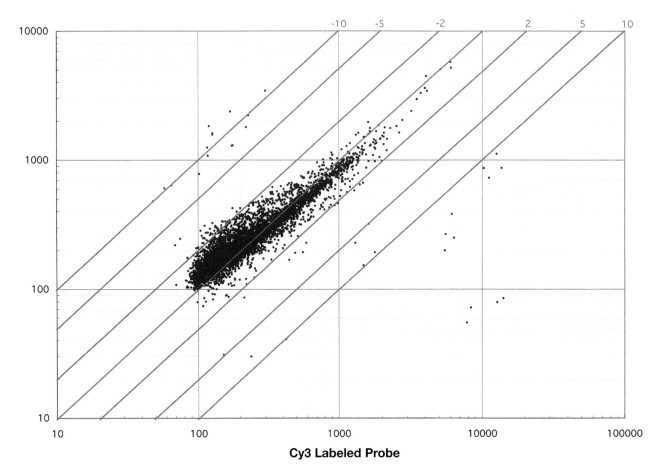

FIGURE 3-10. Scattergram of single-cell microarray results: Expression of Cy5-labeled probe vs. Cy3-labeled probe. This scattergram shows the relative abundances of various mRNAs from two different types of cells. Any spot that falls on the 45° diagonal represents those mRNAs whose abundances are the same between the cells. The correlation coefficient of these data is 0.91.

ALTERNATIVE PROTOCOL: IN SITU TRANSCRIPTION OF RNA IN TISSUE SECTIONS

mRNA may be copied directly into cDNA in situ by incubating the selected tissue section in a reaction mixture including an oligo(dT)$_{24}$–T7 primer (used in the main protocol), dNTPs, and reverse transcriptase. The first-strand cDNA product is recovered from the section and used for production of double-stranded cDNA and subsequent RNA amplification. Figure 3-6 illustrates the overall process.

Additional Materials

CAUTION: Please see Appendix 3 for appropriate handling of materials marked with <!>.

Carrier DNA (*E. coli* DNA; 10 mg/ml)
DTT (100 mM) <!>
Formamide, deionized <!>
IST buffer
    50 mM Tris (pH 8.3)
    120 mM KCl
    6 mM MgCl$_2$
KCl (1.2 M)
MgCl$_2$ (1 M)
NaOH (0.2 N)/0.1% SDS <!>
    Optional, please see Step 10.
20x SSC
Tris (0.2 M, pH 7 and 1 M, pH 8.3)
Water bath, preset to 95°C

Method

Hybridization with the Amplification Primer

1. If the tissue sections are frozen, thaw the slides to room temperature and allow them to dry.

2. Prepare an excess of the following hybridization solution. For 1 ml:

formamide	0.5 ml (50% formamide)
20x SSC	0.25 ml (5x SSC)
oligo(dT)–T7 primer (100 ng/µl)	10 µl (final conc. 1 ng/µl)
DEPC-treated ddH$_2$O	0.24 ml

3. Pipette the hybridization solution onto the tissue sections (the exact volume is not critical), and allow the primer to hybridize to the sections in a humidified chamber overnight (8–12 hours) at room temperature.

In Situ Transcription (IST)

4. Pipette the hybridization solution from the slides and wash off the excess primer by rinsing the sections in an excess of 2x SSC for 2 hours at room temperature.

5. Remove the sections from the wash and pipette 1x IST buffer (RNase-free) onto the sections.

6. Incubate the sections for 30 minutes at room temperature to change the buffer conditions on sections.

   This step is very important for an efficient IST procedure.

7. Pipette the IST buffer from the slides and replace it with the IST reaction mix:

For 1 ml		Composition of IST Reaction Mix
1 M MgCl$_2$	6 µl	6 mM MgCl$_2$
1 M Tris (pH 8.3)	50 µl	50 mM Tris (pH 8.3)
1.2 M KCl	100 µl	120 mM KCl
100 mM DTT	71 µl	7 mM DTT
DEPC-treated H$_2$O	660 µl	
dNTP solution (2.5 mM)	100 µl	250 µM four dNTPs
RNasin (40 units/µl)	3 µl	0.12 unit/µl RNasin
AMV-RT (20 units/µl)	10 µl	1 µl RT/100 µl mix

IMPORTANT: Add the AMV-RT to each tube individually.

Adding DTT to the reaction mix before adding RNasin creates the appropriate reducing environment; add reverse transcriptase at the very end. Incubate the IST reaction for 90 minutes at 37°C.

8. Wash the sections in an excess of 0.5x SSC (need not be RNase-free) for 2 hours at room temperature or overnight at 4°C, and then allow the sections to dry in the air.

These slides are now ready to be further processed, or they can be stored at room temperature for several weeks or at 4°C indefinitely. Store the slides in a slide tray.

Recovery of cDNA from the Tissue Sections

9. Remove the fixed cell containing the in-situ-transcribed cDNA by using a micropipette to scrape and aspirate the cell into a microfuge tube containing 10 µl of DEPC-treated H$_2$O.

Alternatively, remove the surrounding tissue area, leaving the cell on the slide. Then transfer the cell into the microfuge tube using the microelectrode.

10. Separate the cDNA from the cell debris by heating for 5 minutes at 95°C, followed by quick cooling.

Alternatively, chemically denature the cDNA by adding 10 µl of 0.1 N NaOH/0.1% SDS.

11. Add 10 µl of 0.2 M Tris (pH 7) and 1 µl of 10 mg/ml *E. coli* DNA (carrier) to the cDNA, and recover the cDNA by ethanol precipitation.

Do not extract with phenol:chloroform, because residual protein will act as a carrier to help in the precipitation.

12. Remove the ethanol, immediately invert the tubes, and dry the pellet in the air for 10 minutes. Resuspend the pellet in 20 µl of DEPC-treated ddH$_2$O.

13. Dissolve the cDNA pellet in 20 µl of DEPC-treated H$_2$O and proceed to Step 12 of the main protocol to continue with second-strand synthesis of cDNA.

ADDITIONAL PROTOCOL: ACRIDINE ORANGE STAINING OF SECTIONS

Before spending the time and money required for analysis of RNA extracted from single cells recovered from sections of fixed tissue, it is sensible to sacrifice one section to find out whether the RNA has survived the tissue-harvesting and fixation processes. This is easily done by dipping a slide containing an appropriate section into an acridine orange solution (Figure 3-11). At the proper pH, acridine orange will stain single-stranded nucleic acid (such as RNA) orange, whereas double-stranded DNA will appear green. If an orange color is present when the stained tissue section is examined under fluorescent illumination, then RNA is present. Most of the stain is contributed by ribosomal and other abundant RNAs. However, if these RNA species have survived, there is good chance that the sections treated with citric acid–sodium phosphate buffer are appropriate for in situ transcription single-cell aRNA protocols.

Additional Materials

Acridine orange
   Prepare a solution of acridine orange (0.6 µg/ml) in citric acid–sodium phosphate buffer.
Citric acid–sodium phosphate buffer
   60 mM citric acid
   80 mM Na_2HPO_4 (pH 4.1)

Method

1. Rinse the tissue sections with DEPC-treated ddH_2O for 5 minutes.

2. Incubate the sections for 5 minutes in citric acid–sodium phosphate buffer.

3. Incubate the sections for 15 minutes in acridine orange.

4. Rinse the sections three times for 5 minutes each time in citric acid–sodium phosphate buffer.

5. Visualize the single-stranded RNA (orange) and double-stranded DNA (green) with a fluorescent microscope at a wavelength of 488 nm.

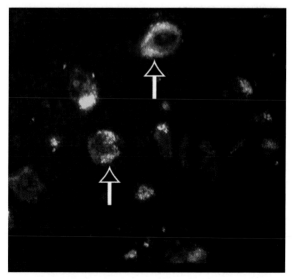

FIGURE 3-11. Acridine orange staining of a section for mRNA. The orange-stained mRNA is visible in this section. This procedure can be used on archival tissue specimens.

RNA Common Reference Sets

Jonathan R. Pollack

Department of Pathology, Stanford University School of Medicine, Stanford, California 94305

To measure gene expression using microarrays, two different mRNA preparations are labeled, using different fluors, and cohybridized to a cDNA microarray. For each gene-specific element in the array, the ratio of intensity of the two fluors reflects the relative abundance of that particular mRNA in the two preparations.

The use of two-color labeling has the important property of robustly eliminating effects due to variation in the amount of DNA spotted on the arrays, variation in the stringency of the hybridization (salt concentration, temperature, and duration of hybridization), and variation in the local concentration of labeled sample during hybridization. Any changes in these parameters should affect the numerator and denominator of fluorescence ratios equally and thus would not influence measured fluorescence ratios.

In studies that include many different RNA preparations, it becomes impractical to hybridize all pair-wise combinations of samples. The solution is to hybridize each of the experimental samples against the same common reference RNA preparation, and to calculate the level of each mRNA relative to the reference. The relative abundances of mRNAs among the different experimental samples are then calculated indirectly, from the ratio of ratios.

For many experiments, a "natural" RNA reference sample is available, for example, when quantifying changes in mRNA abundance over time (reference = time zero sample) or after treatment with a drug (reference = control unexposed to drug). However, in certain instances, such as in the measurement of mRNA abundances in different tumor samples, no natural reference exists. In such cases, an mRNA "common reference set" can be used (Eisen and Brown 1999). If each test (i.e., tumor) sample is compared to the same common reference set, then the relative intensity of gene expression among the samples can be calculated. In this type of experiment, the common reference set becomes the denominator for all measured fluorescence ratios.

An ideal common reference set should hybridize with sufficient signal intensity to all or nearly all of the DNA elements in the array, should be easy and cost-effective to prepare, and should be easily reproduced to allow comparison of samples over time and between locations. Note that the common reference set need not have any particular biological purpose or property and need not include RNA from every cell type under investigation. However, a good reference set should generate a readable signal from most elements on the array. In addition, for the reference set to be useful to a broad group of researchers, it should be constructed from validated sources that are readily available. In practical terms, a common reference comprising pooled RNA from stable lines of cultured cells meets many of these criteria.

This protocol outlines the preparation of an RNA common reference set used extensively by the cDNA microarray community at Stanford University (Perou et al. 1999, 2000; Ross et al. 2000). This reference set is produced from 11 different established cell lines (see Table 3-6), many of which are available from the American Type Culture Collection. These cell lines are easy to grow and, in combination, hybridize to a large majority of arrayed cDNA elements. Although the optimal number of cell lines used in a reference set has not been established experimentally, it is perhaps important not to use too many different cell types. The pooled RNA may dilute to the point of invisibility low-abundance transcripts that are expressed in only one or a few of the cell lines in the set.

Most laboratories with the infrastructure required for DNA microarrays should be able to reproduce the Stanford common reference set. In general, the work load involved in producing a batch of the common reference set typically could require a period of 2–3 months of full-time work to grow up the 11 cell lines and purify sufficient RNA for several thousand array hybridizations. However, for some investigators, a commercial reference set may be the best option. Stratagene Inc. sells a common reference set of RNA extracted from ten human cell lines (Novoradovskaya et al. 2000). However, unlike the Stanford set, few details are available about the cell lines and their provenance.

Both the Stanford and the Stratagene common reference sets allow rational comparison of microarray results within and between laboratories. Other possible reference sets, less commonly used, that may be able to fulfill the same purpose include labeled genomic DNA or RNA generated by transcription of a pool of cDNAs in vitro.

WHY USE A COMMON REFERENCE SET?

Consider an experiment whose goal is to identify genes that are expressed at different levels in tumors and normal cells. Two experimental designs are possible:

- Tumor versus tumor versus normal
  Samples: T1, T2, N1, N2

  Options for comparison:
  T1 vs. N1, T2 vs. N2, T1 vs. N2, T2 vs. N1, T1 vs. T2, N1 vs. N2
  This matrix provides a comparison of all possible combinations and has the advantage that questions are addressed by direct comparison: How does one tumor compare with another? How does tumorous tissue compare with normal? How does normal compare with normal? However, this approach is only practical when the number of samples is very small, as the number of combinations increases exponentially with the number of samples.

- Tumor versus reference, normal versus reference
  Samples: T1, T2, N1, N2, R

  Options for comparison:
  T1 vs. R, T2 vs. R, N1 vs. R, N2 vs. R
  Here, all samples are tested against a common reference RNA and comparison is made indirectly with respect to the reference. The number of combinations is manageable as they increase linearly with the number of samples. In addition, comparisons can be made between experiments and investigators who use a common reference. A potential disadvantage is that inferences are made indirectly between samples, via the reference, potentially reducing the resolving power of the experiment. The ideal common reference therefore should be widely accessible, available in unlimited amounts, and should provide a signal over a wide range of genes. These issues are considered in more detail in Section 7.

Figure 3-12 illustrates the differences in these two experimental designs.

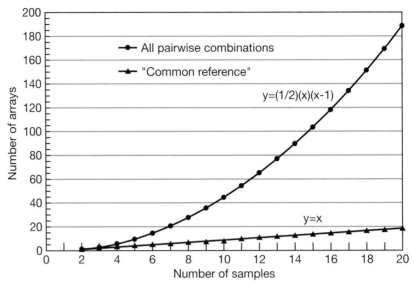

FIGURE 3-12. Differences in performing all pairwise combinations vs. using a common reference.

MATERIALS

CAUTION: Please see Appendix 3 for appropriate handling of materials marked with <!>.

Buffers and Solutions

Please see Appendix 2 for components of stock solutions, buffers, and reagents.
Dilute stock solutions to the appropriate concentrations.

ATRA (all-*trans* retinoic acid; R 2625, Sigma)
   Prepare a 10 mM stock in DMSO.
Cell culture media
   RPMI 1640 (GIBCO or equivalent)
   10% fetal bovine serum (Hyclone or equivalent)
   penicillin and streptomycin (1x concentration, GIBCO)
Phosphate-buffered saline (PBS), lacking Ca^{2+} and Mg^{2+}
1x Trypsin-EDTA

Gels

Agarose gel (1%) containing 2.2 M formaldehyde <!>
   For details, please see Sambrook and Russell (2001).

Special Equipment

FastTrack 2.0 mRNA isolation kit (Invitrogen)
Humidified incubator with an atmosphere of 5% CO_2
Laminar flow hood for passaging and harvesting of cells
Roller bottles and appropriate incubator (alternative to tissue culture dishes)
Tissue culture dishes (15 cm)
UV spectrophotometer

TABLE 3-6. Cell Lines Used in Stanford "Common RNA Reference"

Name	Description	Growth properties	ATCC catalog No. or Reference
MCF7	breast adenocarcinoma-derived cell line	adherent	ATCC HTB-22
Hs578T	breast adenocarcinoma-derived cell line (stromal-like)	adherent	ATCC HTB-126
NTERA2	teratoma-derived cell line	adherent	ATCC CRL-1973
Colo205	colon tumor-derived cell line	mixed	ATCC CCL-222
OVCAR-3	ovarian tumor-derived cell line	adherent	ATCC HTB-161
UACC-62	melanoma-derived cell line	adherent	Stinson et al. (1992)
MOLT-4	T cell leukemia-derived cell line	suspension	ATCC CRL-1582
RPMI 8226	multiple myeloma-derived cell line	suspension	ATCC CCL-155
NB4+ATRA	acute promyelocytic leukemia-derived cell line	suspension	Lanotte et al. (1991)
SW872	liposarcoma-derived cell line	adherent	ATCC HTB-92
HepG2	liver tumor-derived cell line	adherent	ATCC HB-8065

Cells and Tissues

Cell lines

Please see Table 3-6 for a listing and description of cell lines used in the Stanford common reference set of RNAs. Of the 11 cell lines, 9 are currently available from the American Type Culture Collection (www.atcc.org). However, because NB4 and UACC-62 are not at present distributed by the ATCC, it is impossible to replicate the Stanford Common Reference Set from publicly available sources. We therefore recommend that HL-60 cells (ATCC CCL-240) be substituted for NB4 cells and that the SK-MEL-2 melanoma cell line (ATCC HTB-68) be substituted for UACC-62 cells. Because the aim should be to preserve the "commonality" of the reference set as far as possible, other substitutions by individual laboratories are discouraged.

METHOD

Growing Cell Lines

The 11 cell lines listed in Table 3-6 are easy to maintain and grow in either monolayer or suspension culture. This protocol is designed for cells growing in culture dishes. If suspension cultures are grown in flasks or roller bottles, adjust the protocol accordingly.

1. Maintain the 11 cell lines in RPMI 1640 supplemented with 10% fetal calf serum in 15-cm tissue culture dishes at 37°C in an atmosphere of 5% CO_2 in air.

   Cells should be passaged when approaching confluence at ~1:5 dilution using standard trypsinization procedures for adherent lines.

   Record passage numbers of cell lines in a log book or database. Store master cultures of early passages in liquid nitrogen in small aliquots in medium containing 10% DMSO.

   Discard cell lines after ten passages in cell culture and replace them from frozen master cultures.

   Wherever possible, use the same batch of fetal calf serum to grow the 11 cell lines. Serum is probably a significant source of batch-to-batch variation in reference RNAs. Record the batch numbers of serum and medium used for each passage of each cell line.

2. Expand the cell numbers so that 10–20 15-cm tissue culture dishes of each cell line can be grown.

3. Change the media 48 hours before harvesting the cells for isolation of mRNA.

   Media changes produce alterations in the pattern and intensity of gene expression. To minimize variation between preparations of common reference RNAs, establish standardized protocols for growing and refeeding cells and follow them faithfully.

4. Add all-*trans* retinoic acid (ATRA) to a final concentration of 10 μM to the culture medium of NB4 cells (or substituted HL-60 cells) ~48 hours before harvesting the cells.

> NB4 and HL-60 cells are derived from cases of human promyelocytic leukemia. Addition of ATRA induces, over the course of 48 hours, the expression of genes specific to granulocytic differentiation with concomitant maturation of the cells.

5. Harvest the cells for mRNA isolation at ~80% confluence.

> Patterns of gene expression change as cell cultures approach confluence. To minimize variation among preparations of common reference RNAs, standardize protocols for growing and harvesting cells and follow them faithfully.

Preparation of mRNA

6. Prepare mRNA from the cell lines using, for example, the FastTrack 2.0 (Invitrogen) mRNA isolation kit.

   a. Remove the media from the culture by aspiration.

   b. Lyse the cells on the surface of the dishes using the lysis buffer supplied by the manufacturer.

   c. Isolate the mRNA by batch chromatography on oligo(dT)-cellulose.

   > A number of methods can be used to prepare either total RNA or mRNA from cell lines. The Stanford group routinely uses the FastTrack 2.0 (Invitrogen) mRNA isolation kit. The FastTrack kit yields mRNA of high quality for labeling and hybridization to DNA microarrays, although less expensive alternatives are likely to be equally effective.

   > An outline of the procedure is given here; for details please see Protocol 6.

7. Determine the yield and purity of mRNA by UV spectrophotometry or staining with RiboGreen (please see the information panel on QUANTIFICATION OF RNA).

8. Assess the quality and integrity of the mRNA by denaturing gel electrophoresis through formaldehyde-agarose gels (please see information panel on MAMMALIAN, PLANT, AND BACTERIAL RNAs).

9. If the quantity and quality of the isolated mRNA are satisfactory, combine equal amounts (weight) of mRNA from each cell line and mix well. Distribute the pooled RNA mixture into small aliquots (10–20 μg), and store them at –80°C or as described in the information panel on STORAGE AND RECOVERY OF RNA.

CALIBRATING DIFFERENT BATCHES OF COMMON REFERENCE RNA

Although every effort is taken to grow the cell lines and isolate the mRNA in a uniform and standardized manner, even slight differences in the treatment of cells, or in the quantification of mRNA, may change the abundances of mRNA species in the reference set. To correlate results obtained from experiments using different batches of the reference sets, it may be necessary to quantify and correct for batch-to-batch variation. This correction may be achieved by labeling different batches of reference sets with Cy3 and Cy5 and hybridizing them in pair-wise crosses to DNA microarrays. After this experiment has been repeated several times, accurate batch-specific "calibration" coefficients can be calculated for each gene on the array. These coefficients may be used to correct for systematic differences caused by batch-to-batch variation in the common reference sets.

Part 2: Labeling and Hybridization

INTRODUCTION

The first global surveys of gene expression were undertaken in the mid 1970s. Polysomal RNA isolated from lines of cultured mammalian cells was transcribed in vitro into radiolabeled single-stranded cDNA, which was then hybridized with an excess of its unlabeled mRNA template. Hybridization kinetics indicated that the mRNA comprised three kinetic classes, differing in their abundance in the mRNA population (Bishop et al. 1974; Getz et al. 1975, 1977). The most abundant transcripts contributed 30–90% of the mass of mRNA, but only 0.1% of its sequence complexity. Moderately abundant mRNA accounted for ~50–60% of the mass of the mRNA and 2–5% of it sequence complexity. Rare mRNAs made a negligible contribution by mass but provided >85% of the sequence complexity of the polysomal RNA (please see Table 3-7).

Work carried out during the next 25 years amply confirmed these general conclusions. Over the course of a quarter century, a number of mRNAs belonging to each abundance class were cataloged, mapped, and quantified by a combination of northern blotting, RNase protection, and more recently, real-time PCR. It was always clear, however, that integrated comprehensive maps of cellular transcription could not be built, bottom up, from studies of individual mRNAs and that new techniques would be needed to monitor the expression of many genes simultaneously. For a while in the early 1990s, differential display seemed to be a potential, if partial, solution to the problem. But, by the middle of the decade, at about the same time that the first papers on DNA microarrays were published, differential display had begun to founder because of a lack of power and the failure to develop robust automated methods.

TABLE 3-7. Abundance Classes of mRNA in Mammalian and Plant Cells

Total number of mRNA species	$1.0–3.4 \times 10^4$
Sequence complexity	$1–3 \times 10^7$ nucleotides
Total number of mRNA molecules per cell	
High-abundance mRNA species	
Number of species	7–10
Sequence complexity	$\sim 1–3 \times 10^4$ nucleotides
Number of molecules/cell	4,500–10,000 molecules/cell
Medium-abundance mRNA species	
Number of species	500–800
Sequence complexity	2×10^5 to 1.5×10^6 nucleotides
Number of molecules/cell	300–1000 molecules/cell
Low-abundance mRNA species	
Number of species	10,000–34,000
Sequence complexity	$1–3 \times 10^7$ nucleotides
Number of molecules/cell	3–100 molecules/cell

Data from Bishop et al. (1974); Getz et al. (1975); Goldberg et al. (1978).

It is estimated that ~85% of expressed genes are present at ≤5 copies per cell (<1:100,000); ~97% of the mass of mRNA in a cell contains only ~20% of the transcribed genes.

DNA microarrays, now the dominant technique in RNA profiling, have satisfied all reasonable tests of robustness and power and, with smaller organisms, at least, have fulfilled the promise of quantifying the transcription products of a cell and of describing clusters of genes that respond in similar ways to specific external stimuli.

But these are still the early days of a young technology, and it will take several more years of work before comprehensive and reliable databases of gene expression in higher eukaryotes are available. At present, our picture of global gene expression in the complex tissues and cells of mammals and plants is both incomplete and of low resolution: the former because only a subset of the cellular transcription units are represented in currently used DNA microarrays; the latter because transcripts belonging to the lowest abundance class lie at, or just beyond, the limit of sensitivity of standard microarray technology. Head-to-head comparisons suggest that, at present, the sensitivity of DNA microarrays is approximately equal to that of oligonucleotide chips, northern blotting, and other methods of RNA analysis (e.g., please see Chen et al. 1998; Bertucci et al. 1999; Wang et al. 1999; Yang et al. 1999; Taniguchi et al. 2001).

A useful measure of the sensitivity of a microarray experiment is the smallest fraction of mRNA that can be reliably detected by hybridization to its cognate arrayed DNA element(s) (Bertucci et al. 1999). In an ideal experiment, this fraction would be 1–2 parts per million, enough to detect an RNA present at a few molecules per cell. The intensity of the signal emitted by mRNA hybridized to a display element in a typical DNA microarray is affected by several variables, including those described below.

Quality of the Preparations of RNA

At all stages of purification, it is essential to take precautions to avoid contamination with RNases. mRNAs that have been partially degraded by RNase may generate truncated cDNAs that are smaller than their cognate display elements, with consequent reduction in signal intensity. Differences in spectral signals emerging from array elements hybridized with pairs of Cy3- and Cy5-labeled targets may therefore reflect differences in the quality of the two RNA preparations, rather than transcriptional regulation. This problem can be minimized by using oligo(dT) as the primer for synthesis of fluorescently labeled cDNA from preparations of total RNA or purified poly(A)$^+$ mRNA. Unless the RNA preparation is severely degraded, targets ~300–500 bases in length, derived from the 3′ termini of transcripts, are unlikely to be truncated. Targets shorter than 300 bp have been reported to produce unreliable data in microarray experiments (Yang et al. 1999). The quality of RNA preparations can be assessed as described in the information panel on **MAMMALIAN, PLANT, AND BACTERIAL RNAs**.

Nature of the Primer

Some, perhaps a majority, of investigators prefer to use total RNA as the starting material for direct fluorescent labeling. In this case, the use of oligo(dT) as a primer for first-strand synthesis is obligatory and the fluorescent cDNA product is biased toward sequences in the 3′ region of the mRNA. Alternatively, purified poly(A)$^+$ or polysomal mRNA can be used as templates for direct labeling, in reactions primed either by oligo(dT) alone or by a combination of oligo(dT) and random primers. Random priming increases both the yield and sequence complexity of the fluorescently labeled cDNA, and the selection for reverse transcription of mRNA sequences is eliminated, along with the bias toward sequences in the 3′

region of mRNA. However, other types of RNAs (ribosomal and low-molecular-weight RNAs) that frequently contaminate mRNA preparations will also be copied into labeled cDNA, which may raise the increase of background hybridization. Random priming is advantageous when the array elements are composed of entire cDNA sequences or amplified segments of genomic DNA containing predicted open reading frames. Priming with oligo(dT) or anchored primers is obligatory when the array elements consist of sequences derived from the 3′ regions of mRNAs.

Type, Density, and Number of Fluorescent Groups Carried on the Targets

As outlined in Table 3-7, there are many ways in which fluorochromes can be incorporated into or attached to target sequences. A popular method is direct labeling in which nucleotides conjugated to the carbocyanine dyes Cy3 and Cy5 (Yu et al. 1994; Zhu et al. 1994; Zhu and Waggoner 1997) are incorporated directly into first-strand cDNA in a reaction catalyzed by reverse transcriptase or into second-strand cDNA in a reaction catalyzed by the Klenow fragment of *E. coli* DNA polymerase. In both cases, the goal is to achieve a density of labeling in which an average of 1 base in 8 carries a fluorescent label. Labeling at a higher density is counterproductive because quenching between adjacent fluorescent nucleotides reduces the fluorescent yield and the intensity of the signal (Randolph and Waggoner 1997).

The popularity of Cy3- and Cy5-labeled dNTPs as reagents for direct labeling of cDNAs may not last much longer. A range of alternative dyes (Alexa fluor) have recently become commercially available (Molecular Probes, Inc) that exhibit enhanced fluorescence, improved photostability, and greater resistance to changes in pH (Panchuk-Voloshina et al. 1999). In a head-to-head comparison, cDNAs labeled with Alexa 456 generate signals that are between ~2.5 and 3 times higher than signals from cDNAs labeled with Cy3 (Wildsmith et al. 2001). For further information, please see the information panel on **ALEXA DYES**.

Enzyme Used for Reverse Transcription of the RNA Template

Thermostable DNA-dependent DNA polymerases vary over a two- to threefold range in their ability to incorporate cyanine-conjugated dUTP (Panchuk-Voloshina et al. 1999). Similar claims are made by manufacturers of reverse transcriptases. The most popular enzyme for synthesis of fluorescently labeled cDNA targets is currently SUPERSCRIPT II RT (GIBCO), an engineered version of Moloney murine leukemia virus (Mo-MLV) reverse transcriptase that lacks RNase H activity and is not significantly inhibited by rRNA or tRNA. However, because the enzyme is sterically inhibited by bulky cyanine adducts, labeling reactions should be incubated for the full 2 hours recommended by the manufacturer.

Although SUPERSCRIPT II RT has become the standard enzyme for direct labeling of cDNA, many other versions of reverse transcriptase are commercially available that, judging from the literature supplied by the manufacturers, may be equivalent to or better than SUPERSCRIPT II RT (e.g., CyScribe from Amersham Pharmacia Biotech and Omniscript from QIAGEN).

Density and Amount of DNA in the Array Element

During hybridization, each immobilized probe DNA must be in tenfold or more molar excess over its complementary labeled target sequences. This arrangement ensures that hybridization will follow pseudo-first-order kinetics over a wide range of target concentrations. The strength of the signal emitted by any one element is determined by the initial concentration of the cognate target in the hybridization mixture. Thus, a twofold increase in target concentration will produce a twofold increase in signal, and abundant RNAs will generate stronger signals than RNAs of lower abundance. When the amount of immobilized probe DNA is limiting, the dynamic range of the system is constricted and estimates of differential expression are compressed (Heller et al. 1997; Yue et al. 2001). Probes (cDNAs or PCR products) in expression analysis are generally printed onto microarrays at a concentration of 100–500 ng/µl (Schena et al. 1996; Welford et al. 1998; for review, please see Deyholos and Galbraith 2001). Operationally, the dynamic range of the microarray system is probably defined more by the scanners than by the concentration of target RNA. Scanners are typically 16-bit machines, i.e., 2^{16}, a dynamic range of $\simeq 65,000$.

Concentration of the Target

If the concentration of the target in the hybridization mixture is too low, annealing will be slow and the attenuated signal may not be detected by the fluorescence scanner. The minimum quantity of target required for hybridization should contain just enough molecules of the lowest-abundance RNA in the sample to generate a readable signal after hybridization. This quantity can be estimated by multiplying the fractional detection limit (see above) by the total number of target molecules in the hybridization mixture. Because both the ratio of signal to background and the dynamic range improve as the quantity of RNA increases, hybridization mixtures usually contain three or four times the calculated minimum quantity of target. However, if the concentration of the target is too high, say >10 times the calculated minimal amount, the dynamic range of the signal may be reduced and the signal to background ratio may either deteriorate or show no further improvement (Yue et al. 2001). As a rule of thumb, an amount of labeled target equivalent to at least 1 µg of poly(A)$^+$ RNA (~100 µg of total RNA) should be used in a standard microarray hybridization mixture (please see Protocol 20). If these amounts are not available, the RNA preparation should be amplified before labeling (e.g., please see Guatelli et al. 1990; Van Gelder et al. 1990; Eberwine et al. 1992; Luo et al. 1999). For details of the linear amplification of RNA populations, please see Protocols 15 and 16.

Signal-to-Noise Ratio

The characteristic dot patterns of microarrays become detectable when the ratio of signal to background is >1.5–2.0. Many factors affect the signal-to-noise ratio, including:

- ***Quality of the mRNA preparation.*** The quality of the RNA varies according to the tissue of origin and the method of preparation. Labeled targets synthesized from degraded RNA may hybridize ineffectively to their cognate microarray elements and may bind nonspecifically to noncognate elements. Furthermore, nonspecific noise may be introduced into the assay by molecules that can bind to the substrate or DNA immobilized on the array, and simultaneously bind fluorochromes.

- ***Characteristics of the reverse transcriptase used in direct labeling.*** Some types of reverse transcriptases do not cope well with templates rich in guanine and cytosine, whereas others inefficiently catalyze the incorporation of nucleotides carrying cyanine dye adducts.

- *Number and density of the fluorescent adducts carried on the targets.*

- *Proportion and quantity of misprimed products generated in the labeling reaction.* Small fragments of RNA and DNA in the RNA sample may act as ectopic primers and generate a population of labeled fragments with the potential to hybridize to many array elements.

- *Surface characteristics of the glass slide containing the array elements and the composition of the spotting solution.* Slides coated with polylysine bind DNA noncovalently. The DNA may therefore leach from the slide when incubated at high temperature in solutions of high salt. The spotting solution can markedly effect the efficiency with which DNA binds to the surface of the slides. Inhomogeneities in the surface of the slide may lead to unequal distribution of DNA in different regions of the slide.

- *Stringency of the hybridization conditions and effectiveness of the blocking agents included in the hybridization reaction.* Detergents and blocking agents suppress nonspecific hybridization, but they may also increase the rate of leaching of DNA from the slide surface.

- *The efficiency of the wash procedure.* Failure to remove hybridization solutions—particularly those containing SDS—can result in elevated temperatures.

These problems and others that can cause deterioration in the ratio of signal to noise are discussed in many areas throughout the text of this manual. The point to be made here is that microarray experiments are a continuum, welded from many components. Mistakes or bad judgment at almost any stage may later come to haunt the investigator.

Fluorescent Labeling of First-strand cDNA Using Reverse Transcriptase

Michael Bittner

National Human Genome Research Institute, National Institutes of Health, Bethesda, Maryland 20892

The direct synthesis of fluorochrome-labeled first-strand cDNA is carried out in a reaction catalyzed by reverse transcriptase that contains mRNA as a template, dye-conjugated deoxynucleotide triphosphates as substrates, and either oligo(dT)$_{12-18}$ or anchored oligo(dT)$_{12-18}$ as a primer. The investigator will need to choose among the various brands of reverse transcriptases offered commercially and among the nucleotides conjugated to carbocyanine or Alexa dyes (please see the information panel on **ALEXA DYES**). The standard combination used in this protocol (SUPERSCRIPT II and Cy3/Cy5-labeled dUTP) is highly reliable and satisfies the needs for high levels of incorporation of fluorescently tagged nucleotide, good spectral separation of the emitted light, and fit of the absorption peak with available laser illumination sources.

In general, dye-conjugated nucleotides are incorporated less efficiently than unmodified dNTPs into cDNA in reactions catalyzed by reverse transcriptase. Because incorporation of a cyanine-labeled nucleotide often leads to chain termination at a nearby nucleotide (Zhu and Waggoner 1997), the median length of the fluorescent cDNAs synthesized is inversely proportional to the concentration of dye-conjugated nucleotide in the reaction mixture. Under the conditions of labeling described in this protocol, the fluorescent cDNAs are comparatively short (400–1000 nucleotides).

Cy5-substituted nucleotides are incorporated less efficiently than Cy3-substituted nucleotides. For this reason, testing of the chain lengths of the Cy5-labeled cDNAs by electrophoresis through a 2% agarose gel is recommended as a quality control step. After electrophoresis, the gel is scanned with a fluorescence scanner. Figure 3-13 shows an electropherogram of two failed labelings and one successful labeling.

The efficiency of the labeling reaction and the quality of the labeled products may be directly tested by hybridizing the fluorescently labeled cDNAs to DNA microarrays. Two types of tests are commonly used:

- *Self-tests.* In this test, the same RNA preparation is labeled in two separate reactions with Cy3- and Cy5-labeled dUTP. A mixture of the labeled samples is then hybridized to the DNA probes immobilized on a microarray(s). Because the experiment is, in essence, a comparison of the sample to itself, the ratio of the two fluorescent signals emitted by all of elements on the array should be constant. The scatter plot depicted

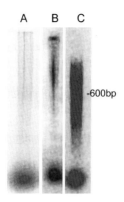

A B C

-600bp

FIGURE 3-13. An electropherogram of Cy5-labeled cDNA. Labeled cDNAs resulting from three different labelings are shown. A 10% sample from each labeling was run on a 2% agarose gel (Tris-acetate, EDTA buffer), and the gel was imaged on a fluorescent scanner equipped for 630 nm excitation and 650 nm emission. Lanes *A* and *B* show the results of two labelings. Lane *A* is typical of results obtained when fragmented RNA is used as a template. Lane *B* shows aggregation of labeled cDNA that typically occurs when the template RNA is purified only by phase separation. Lane *C* shows the result of a successful experiment: The fluorescently labeled cDNA population exhibits a reasonable range of chain lengths with no evidence of aggregation.

in Figure 3-14 is an example of plots of the mean intensities of the two fluorescent signals obtained from a self-test. The ratio of the two fluorescent signals emitted from the great majority of elements is close to 1.

- *Disparate sample pairs.* In testing for the reproducibility of labeling, pairs of samples with different patterns of gene expression are analyzed by hybridization to DNA microarrays. Many of the array elements should display wide differences in the intensity of the two fluorescent signals. When the experiment is repeated several times, the variance in the observed ratios of the two fluorescent signals can be calculated. Figure 3-15 shows scatter plots of the three experiments comparing the ratios of the fluorescent signals emitted when Cy3- and Cy5-labeled cDNAs, prepared from two different samples of RNA, were mixed and hybridized to the same DNA microarrays.

The following protocol is designed for labeling of total RNA, prepared as described in Protocol 1, with Cy3- or Cy5-labeled dUTP. However, it can easily be adapted to label puri-

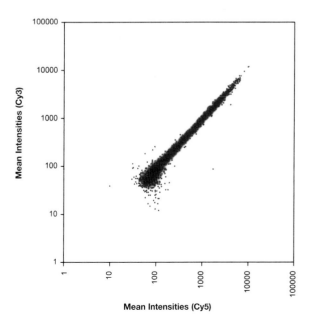

FIGURE 3-14. Autocorrelation plot. The mean intensities from a hybridization of a single RNA species labeled with two separate dyes and hybridized to 6336 arrayed cDNAs are plotted on log scales.

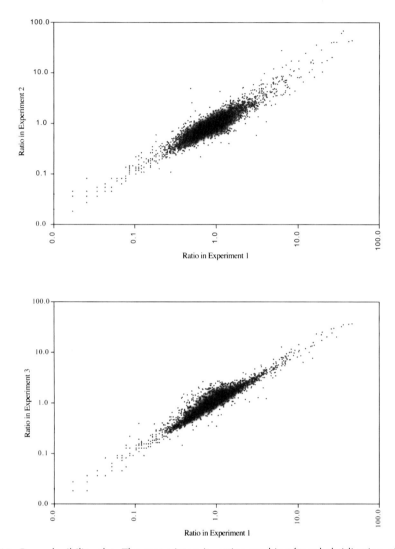

FIGURE 3-15. Reproducibility plot. The mean intensity ratios resulting from hybridization of two different species of independently labeled RNA to 6336 arrayed cDNAs were determined in three separate experiments. Pairwise comparisons of the ratios from measurements passing a minimal quality detection threshold (3683 genes) are plotted on log scales.

fied mRNA, by using as starting material 1–3 μg of poly(A)$^+$ or polysomal RNA (Protocol 5 or 6). Whether total RNA or mRNA is used, the starting material should also include appropriate control RNAs (please see the information panel on CONTROLS USED IN SPOTTED MICROARRAYS in Section 1). This protocol consists of four major processes:

- Annealing of primers to the RNA.
- Synthesis of first-strand cDNA catalyzed by reverse transcriptase.
- Alkaline hydrolysis of the template RNA, followed by concentration of the labeled cDNA and removal of low-molecular-weight contaminants.
- Checking the quality of the labeled cDNA.

MATERIALS

CAUTION: Please see Appendix 3 for appropriate handling of materials marked with <!>.

IMPORTANT: Prepare all buffers and solutions in DEPC-treated H_2O and store frozen in small aliquots.

Buffers and Solutions

Please see Appendix 2 for components of stock solutions, buffers, and reagents.
Dilute stock solutions to the appropriate concentrations.

Dithiothreitol (DTT) (0.1 M) <!>

EDTA (0.5 M, pH 8.0)

NaOH (1 N) <!>
   Prepare fresh each month and store in well-filled plastic containers.

50x TAE (Tris-acetate eletrophoresis) buffer

TE (pH 7.4 and 7.5)

Tris-HCl (1 M, pH 7.5)

Enzymes and Buffers

First-strand cDNA buffer (as supplied by the manufacturer of the enzyme)
   If buffer supplied by the manufacturer is not available, use the following 5x first-strand buffer:
      250 mM Tris-Cl (pH 8.3)
      375 mM KCl
      15 mM $MgCl_2$

RNasin RNase inhibitor (30 units/µl), stored –20ºC

SUPERSCRIPT II RNase H⁻ reverse transcriptase kit (GIBCO), or equivalent

Nucleic Acids and Oligonucleotides

Cy3-labeled dUTP (1 mM) and Cy5-labeled dUTP (1 mM) (Amersham Biosciences)
   dNTPs conjugated to carbocyanine dyes are light-sensitive and should be stored at –20ºC in light-proof containers.

   If desired, Cy3- and Cy5-labeled dCTP can be used in place of fluorochrome-coupled dUTP. In this case, the low dTTP mix described below should be replaced by a low dCTP mix.

10x dNTP/low-dTTP solution
   Prepare a solution containing dATP, dCTP, dGTP, each at a concentration of 5 mM, and dTTP at 2 mM. Store the solution in small aliquots at –20ºC. For instructions on preparing and storing dNTPs, please see Appendix 2.

Human C_0t-1 DNA (available from a variety of commercial suppliers)

Oligo(dT)$_{12-18}$
   Resuspend the oligonucleotide at a concentration of 1 mg/ml in H_2O. Store the solution in small aliquots at –20ºC.

OR

Anchored primer (5′-TTT TTT TTT TTT TTT TTT TTT TTV-3′)
   Resuspend the oligonucleotide at a concentration of 2 mg/ml in H_2O. Store the solution in small aliquots at –20ºC.

   Anchored primers are a mixture of four synthetic oligonucleotides, consisting of an oligo(dT) backbone and an A, G, or C residue in the 3′-terminal position. Priming with an anchored primer ensures that cDNA synthesis is initiated at the 5′ end of the poly(A) tract of the mRNA. This method of priming is recommended if the hybridization probes on the microarrays correspond to the 3′ ends of the transcripts. Anchored primers can be ordered from Sigma and other commercial suppliers.

Total RNA (>7 mg/ml)

> Prepare as described in Protocol 1. The efficiency of labeling depends on the quality of the RNA. The higher the purity and the greater the integrity of the RNA, the more efficient the labeling. Standard labeling reactions contain 40–60 µg of total RNA. However, when all of the steps from the harvesting of cells to purification of RNA are working well, as little as 25 µg of total RNA can be used as the template for labeling. When the supply of RNA is not limiting, up to 200 µg of total RNA can be used in each reaction. Alternatively, mRNA, isolated as described in Protocol 5, or polysomal RNA, isolated as described in Protocol 6, may be used as starting material.

Gels

6x Anemic gel-loading buffer containing 0.08% (w/v) bromophenol blue <!>, 0.08% (w/v) xylene cyanol FF <!>, and 40% sucrose in H_2O

Conventional 2% agarose gel (6.0 cm wide x 8.5 cm long, with 2-mm wide slots), cast in 1x TAE buffer

> Do not add ethidium bromide to the gel or running buffer.

Centrifuges and Rotors

Desktop centrifuge (high-speed 14,000*g* for 1.5-ml microfuge tubes)

Special Equipment

Fluorescence scanner (e.g., Molecular Dynamics Typhoon or equivalent)

Microcon YM-100 (42412 Millipore) or Microcon YM-30 (42411 Millipore)

> Please see Steps 8–10 of this protocol. YM-100 centrifugal devices retain >90% of single-stranded cDNAs whose sizes exceed 300 nucleotides. For YM-30 devices, the nominal cutoff for single-stranded cDNAs is ~50 nucleotides (see table below).

Property	Microcon YM-100	Microcon YM-30
Color of device	blue	clear
Filtration area (cm²)	0.32	0.32
Nominal cut off (in daltons)	100,000	30,000
Maximum allowable *g*-force	500*g* in a fixed-angle rotor	14,000*g* in a microfuge
Time of centrifugation	5–15 minutes at 25ºC	5–8 minutes at 25ºC
Capacity of device (ml)	0.5	0.5
Retention volume (µl)	10	10

PCR tubes (0.2-ml thin-walled)

Spectrophotometer

Thermal cycler

> The cycler should accommodate 0.2-ml thin-walled PCR tubes. Set the thermal cycler to 65ºC.

Water baths set at 42ºC and 65ºC

METHOD

Annealing the Primer to the mRNA

1. Prepare an annealing reaction.

If using an anchored oligo(dT) primer: Mix in an 0.2-ml thin-walled PCR tube:

	Addition for Cy5 labeling	Addition for Cy3 labeling
Total RNA (>7 mg/ml)	40–60 µg	40–60 µg
Anchored primer (2 µg/µl)	1 µl	1 µl
H$_2$O	to 17 µl	to 17 µl

If using an oligo(dT)$_{12-18}$ primer: Mix in an 0.2-ml thin-walled PCR tube:

	Addition for Cy5 labeling	Addition for Cy3 labeling
Total RNA (>7 mg/ml)	40–60 µg	40–60 µg
oligo(dT)$_{12-18}$ primer (1 µg/µl)	1 µl	1 µl
H$_2$O	to 17 µl	to 17 µl

2. Heat the reaction mixture(s) in a thermal cycler for 10 minutes at 65ºC. Cool the mixture(s) for 2 minutes on ice.

Synthesis of First-strand cDNA

3. Add to each of the annealing mixtures:

5x first-strand buffer (SUPERSCRIPT reverse transcriptase kit)	8 µl
10x dNTP/low dTTP solution	4 µl
Cy5- or Cy3-labeled dUTP (1 mM)	4 µl
0.1 M DTT	4 µl
RNasin (30 units/µl)	1 µl
SUPERSCRIPT II (200 units/µl)	2 µl

Reverse transcriptases are very sensitive to denaturation at air/liquid interfaces, so be very careful to avoid foaming when mixing the components of the reaction. This is sometimes difficult because many preparations of reverse transcriptases are supplied in buffers containing nonionic detergents such as Nonidet P-40 or Triton X-100.

Mo-MLV (SUPERSCRIPT II) is temperature-sensitive and should be stored at –20ºC until the last possible moment and be returned to the freezer at the first possible opportunity.

4. Incubate the reactions for 30 minutes at 42ºC, and then add an additional 2 µl of SUPERSCRIPT II. Make sure that the enzyme is well mixed into the reaction volume and continue incubation for an additional 30–60 minutes at 42ºC.

Although labeling reactions can be incubated for up to 4 hours without problems, the production of labeled cDNA usually ceases after 60–90 minutes. If the yield of labeled cDNA is unsatisfactory, the time course of incorporation of Cy3- and Cy5-labeled dUTP should be checked as described in the information panel on **MEASURING THE EFFICIENCY OF DYE-LABELING OF DNA.**

Hydrolysis of RNA

5. To each reaction, add 5 µl of 0.5 M EDTA.

   Make sure to mix the reaction mixture well after the addition of EDTA before proceeding with addition of NaOH (Step 6). Nucleic acids precipitate in alkaline magnesium solutions.

6. Add 10 µl of 1 N NaOH to each reaction and incubate the solutions for 30 minutes at 65°C to hydrolyze RNA. Allow the reaction to cool to room temperature.

   Because Cy5 is alkali-labile, carry out hydrolysis of RNA for the minimum time possible. Two factors affect the success of the reaction:

   - ***The purity of the sodium hydroxide solution.*** Contamination with metals or prolonged storage of the hydroxide in a glass vessel exposed to light can produce a solution that will degrade Cy5, turning the solution yellow.
   - ***The purity of the RNA.*** Contaminated preparations of RNA sometimes contain substances that promote degradation of the fluor.

   If degradation of fluorophores appears to be a problem, replace the NaOH solution, repurify the RNA, and try reducing the time of hydrolysis to 20 minutes.

7. Neutralize each of the reactions by adding 25 µl of 1 M Tris-Cl (pH 7.5).

Purification and Fluorescently Labeled cDNA

Centrifugal ultrafiltration through a Microcon YM-100 cartridge is used to purify and concentrate fluorescently labeled cDNAs whose size is greater than ~250–300 nucleotides. Cy3- and Cy5-labeled targets can be processed independently or, if the labeled cDNAs are to be hybridized to the same microarrays, the Cy3- and Cy5-labeling reactions (Step 7) can be mixed together and copurified. Of course, the reactions should not be mixed if unincorporated cyanine nucleotides are to be recovered from the reaction mixture (please see Protocol 19).

A cartridge of smaller pore size (e.g., Microcon YM-30) may be used to harvest all labeled products >50–100 bp in size. Please see the panel on **ALTERNATIVE PROTOCOL: PURIFICATION AND CONCENTRATION OF FLUORESCENTLY LABELED cDNA (MICROCON YM-30)**.

8. Transfer to a Microcon YM-100 cartridge:

   neutralized solution(s) (Step 7)
   350 µl of TE (pH 7.5)
   20 µg of human C_0t-1 DNA

   Mix the components by gentle pipetting and then centrifuge the cartridge at 500g for 10 minutes. Discard the flow-through.

   The goals of this step are to desalt the DNA and to remove the products of alkaline degradation (Step 6).

   When handling precious samples, it is worthwhile to test the cartridges for leaks by loading 200 µl of H_2O and centrifuging at 500g for a few seconds. If the filter is not properly sealed to the cartridge or has other defects, the H_2O will pass through. If most of the H_2O is retained, it can be removed and replaced by the sample.

   The inclusion of a ubiquitous blocker such as human C_0t-1 DNA is mandatory in hybridization mixtures. However, different investigators add the blocker at different stages: Some investigators add blocker when assembling the hybridization mixture, whereas others, as described in this protocol, prefer to add the blocker at a convenient stage during purification of the fluorescently labeled target. The bulk DNA then serves as a carrier to minimize loss of the labeled DNA through binding to surfaces. Adding the blocker before centrifugation assists in the removal of salts and other impurities that may contaminate the C_0t-1 DNA.

9. Wash the fluorescent first-strand cDNA by adding 200 μl of TE (pH 7.5) and concentrate the solution to a volume of ~20–30 μl, usually achieved by centrifugation at 500g for 8–10 minutes. Discard the flow-through.

   When concentrating solutions by centrifugal filtration, the centrifugation times required to achieve the desired final volume are variable. Exceedingly long spins can remove nearly all the solvent from the solution. When fluorochrome-labeled nucleic acids are concentrated onto the filter in this fashion, they become very difficult to recover. To minimize problems, approach the desired volume incrementally by conservative estimations of centrifugation times. If necessary, the final concentration step can be achieved by evaporating liquid in a SpeedVac. Vacuum evaporation, if not carried to dryness, does not affect the performance of the labeled cDNA.

   After the second centrifugation step, the labeled cDNA retained by the filter is usually significantly darker in color than the flow-through, as it has a higher concentration of light-absorbing fluors.

10. Recover the concentrate by inverting the Microcon cartridge over a clean collection tube and centrifuging at 500g for 3 minutes.

    In some cases, the Cy5-labeled cDNA will become trapped in a gelatinous blue precipitate, which is recovered in the concentrated solution. The greater the quantity of precipitate, the lower the amount of cDNA that can be recovered. The blue gel may be solubilized by heating, but this is little consolation since the fluorescent cDNA then binds in a uniform, nonspecific fashion to the immobilized DNA probes. The nature of the precipitate is unknown, but it is likely to contain a high proportion of carbohydrate. Cy5 has a strong affinity for binding to concentrated carbohydrates such as glycogen. Possible sources of carbohydrate could be the preparation of template RNA or the C_0t-1 DNA used as blocker.

Checking the Quality of the Labeled cDNA

11. Remove a 2–3-μl sample of the Cy5-labeled cDNA for analysis, leaving 18–28 μl for hybridization. Store the labeled cDNA in a foil-wrapped tube at 4°C.

12. Analyze the sample by electrophoresis through a 2% agarose gel, cast and run in 1× TAE buffer.

    For maximal sensitivity, use anemic gel-loading buffer (see Materials list) which contains a minimal amount (30% of the usual concentration) of bromophenol blue and xylene cyanol. Do not add ethidium bromide to the gel or running buffer.

13. Scan the gel on a fluorescence scanner (e.g., Molecular Dynamics Typhoon).

    Successful labeling produces a dense smear of labeled cDNA from 400 to >1000 nucleotides in length, with a minimum of low-molecular-weight transcripts (as in Figure 3-13, lane C). Weak labeling and/or significant levels of low-molecular-weight material are indicators of inefficient labeling (as in Figure 3-13, lane A).

    If desired, the efficiency of labeling may be measured by spectrometry. For details, please see the information panel on **MEASURING THE EFFICIENCY OF DYE LABELING OF DNA**.

ALTERNATIVE PROTOCOL: PURIFICATION AND CONCENTRATION OF FLUORESCENTLY LABELED cDNA (MICROCON YM-30)

For purifying and concentrating fluorescently labeled cDNA products in the size range of >50–100 bp, some investigators prefer to use a cartridge of smaller pore size (e.g., Microcon YM-30).

Additional Materials

Cy3- and Cy5-labeling reactions (Step 8 of the main protocol)
C_0t-1 human DNA (20 mg/ml) (GIBCO)
Microcon YM-30 ultracentrifugal filtration device (Millipore)
Poly(A)$^+$ RNA (10 mg/ml) (P 9403, Sigma).
TE (pH 8.0)
Yeast tRNA (10 mg/ml) (15401-011, GIBCO)

Method

1. Add 380 µl of TE (pH 8.0) to the reservoir of a Microcon YM-30 ultrafiltration device.

2. Add ~60 µl of the Cy5-labeling reaction (Step 8) and 60 µl of the Cy3-labeling reaction to the same filtration device.

3. Insert the loaded device into one of the vials provided by the manufacturer.

4. Centrifuge the device in a microfuge at 14,000g for 7–8 minutes at room temperature.

5. Remove the flow-through from the vials and add 450 µl to the reservoir of the device.

6. Centrifuge the device again in a microfuge at 14,000g for 7–8 minutes at room temperature.

7. Remove the flow-through and add to the reservoir:

TE (pH 8.0)	450 µl
C_0t-1 human DNA	20 µg
poly(A)$^+$ RNA	20 µg
yeast tRNA	20 µg

8. Discard the original collection vial and replace it with a fresh vial. Insert the ultrafiltration device into the fresh vial. Centrifuge the device in a microfuge at 14,000g for 7–8 minutes at room temperature.

   If necessary, continue the centrifugation until the volume of the retentate is reduced to 5–10 µl. These low volumes are attained after the center of the membrane is dry and the target forms a ring of liquid at the rim of the membrane. Make sure not to dry the membrane completely.

9. Invert the device into a clean tube and centrifuge at 500g for 2 minutes to recover the fluorescently labeled cDNA.

   The target usually has a purple color at this stage.

Indirect Fluorescent Labeling of DNA with Amino-Allyl Dyes

Joseph DeRisi

Department Biochemistry and Biophysics, University of California, San Francisco, California 94143

Typically, fluorescently labeled cDNA is generated by incorporation of dye-conjugated nucleotides during reverse transcription of RNA templates. However, the large bulk of the fluorescent dyes presents such serious steric problems for RNA-dependent DNA polymerases that the fluorescent dNTPs are incorporated into cDNA with much lower efficiency than unsubstituted dNTPs. This generates unevenly labeled cDNA of low fluorescent intensity, reduces the sensitivity with which low-abundance mRNAs can be detected, and increases the variability between replicate experiments. Further truncation in sensitivity results from the difference in efficiency with which Cy3-dUTP and Cy5-dUTP are incorporated into labeled DNA. The financial penalty for the inefficient and variable incorporation of cyanine-dye-coupled nucleotides is high, as fluorescent nucleotide analogs such as Cy3- and Cy5-labeled dNTPs are expensive. Clearly, a cheaper, more efficient labeling method would be of great advantage.

One attractive possibility is to incorporate into cDNA, either by chemical synthesis or by enzymic catalysis, a more accommodating nucleotide analog carrying a chemically reactive amine group to which a fluorescent dye may later be conjugated. This idea was reduced to practice by Randolph and Waggoner (1997), who incorporated amino-allyl dUTP (please see Figure 3-16) into DNA and conjugated the resulting primary amine groups to a succinimidyl ester of Cy3 (please see Figure 3-17). The Randolph paper provides a clear and concise description of the effects of amino-allyl substitution and Cy3 conjugation on the melting temperature, extinction coefficient of the DNA, and the quantum yield of the dye as a function of fluor density and length of the arm linking the dye to the nucleotide. Maximum signal was obtained when the density of labeling was ~1 fluorophore per 6 nucleotides—a higher ratio than can be achieved by direct labeling with dye-conjugated nucleotides. Labeling

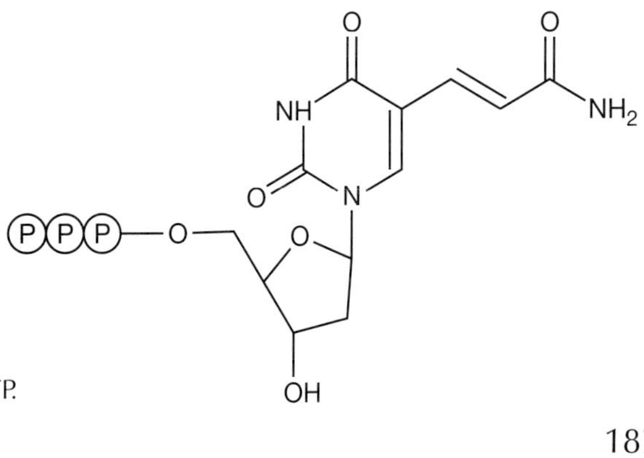

FIGURE 3-16. Amino-allyl substitution of dUTP.

187

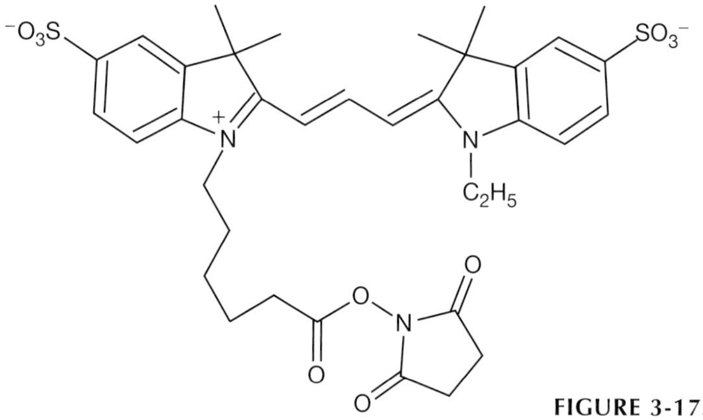

FIGURE 3-17. Structure of Cy3.

with amino-allyl dyes at still higher dye:nucleotide ratios is possible, but at a price: The intensity of the fluorescent signal is decreased, as is the quantum yield. These effects are most likely due to nonproductive fluor:fluor and fluor:nucleotide interactions that result in the quenching of the fluorescent signal. Although chemical coupling of dyes to nucleic acids has been used for many years in immunochemistry, DNA sequencing, and in situ hybridization (Brumbaugh et al. 1988), the technique is now reemerging as a popular and viable approach in microarray analysis (Hughes et al. 2001).

Compared to direct, enzyme-catalyzed labeling, coupling of reactive dyes to amine-substituted nucleotides takes longer and requires more steps. However, the added advantages of brightness, lack of enzymatic bias, and lower cost make the extra effort worthwhile. In addition, a range of fluorescent dyes are now available as *N*-hydroxysuccinimidyl esters (including Cy3 and Cy5, Alexa dyes, fluorescein, bodipy, Texas red, FITC, and rhodamine). These esterified dyes (available from Molecular Probes and other suppliers) can be conjugated to any nucleic molecule carrying a reactive amine group (Panchuk-Voloshina et al. 1999).

The incorporation of 5-(3-amino-allyl)-2′-deoxyuridine 5′-triphosphate (aa-dUTP) into DNA can be catalyzed by a variety of RNA-dependent and DNA-dependent DNA polymerases. The efficiency of incorporation is approximately the same as that of unmodified dUTP. The density of labeling is determined by the ratio of aa-dUTP:dTTP in the reaction mixture. After synthesis of cDNA, the RNA is hydrolyzed with alkali and then neutralized with free acid or with a buffer, such as HEPES which does not contain primary amines. The following protocol is derived mainly from Randolph and Waggoner (1997) and Hughes et al. (2001), with modifications and comments from the DeRisi and Bowtell laboratories.

MATERIALS

CAUTION: Please see Appendix 3 for appropriate handling of materials marked with <!>.
IMPORTANT: Prepare all buffers and solutions in DEPC-treated H_2O and store frozen in small aliquots.

Buffers and Solutions

Please see Appendix 2 for components of stock solutions, buffers, and reagents.
Dilute stock solutions to the appropriate concentrations.

Anhydrous dimethylformamide (DMF) <!> or dimethylsulfoxide (DMSO) <!>
EDTA (1.0 M, pH 8)
HEPES (1 M, pH 7.4)
NaOH (1.0 M) <!>
Sodium acetate (3 M, pH 5.2)
Sodium bicarbonate buffer (1 M, pH 9.0)

Enzymes and Buffers

First-strand cDNA buffer (as supplied by the manufacturer of the enzyme)
> If the buffer supplied by the manufacturer is not available, prepare the following 5x first-strand buffer:
>> 250 mM Tris-Cl (pH 8.3)
>> 375 mM KCl
>> 15 mM $MgCl_2$

RNasin RNase inhibitor (30 units/μl)
> Store at –20ºC.

SUPERSCRIPT II RNase H^- reverse transcriptase kit (GIBCO), or equivalent (e.g., StrataScript reverse transcriptase from Stratagene, Inc. or PowerScript reverse transcriptase from CLONTECH)

Nucleic Acids

For instructions on making and storing solutions of dNTPs, please see **Appendix 2**.

dATP, dCTP, dGTP, dTTP (each at a concentration of 100 mM)

dNTP/Low-dTTP solution
> Prepare a solution containing dATP, dCTP, dGTP, each at a concentration of 5 mM, and dTTP at 2 mM. Store the solution in small aliquots at –20ºC. For instructions on preparing and storing dNTPs, please see Appendix 2.

Human C_0t-1 DNA (available from a variety of commercial suppliers)

Oligo(dT)$_{12-18}$
> Resuspend the oligonucleotide at a concentration of 1 mg/ml in H_2O. Store the solution in small aliquots at –20ºC.

OR

Anchored primer (5'-TTT TTT TTT TTT TTT TTT TTT TTV-3')
> Resuspend the oligonucleotide at a concentration of 2 mg/ml in H_2O. Store the solution in small aliquots at –20ºC.

> Anchored primers are a mixture of four synthetic oligonucleotides, consisting of an oligo(dT) backbone and an A, T, G, or C residue in the 3'-terminal position. Priming with an anchored primer ensures that cDNA synthesis is initiated at the 5' end of the poly(A) tract of the mRNA. This method of priming is recommended if the hybridization probes on the microarrays correspond to the 3' ends of transcripts. Anchored primers can be ordered from Sigma and other commercial suppliers.

Poly(A)$^+$ or polysomal RNA or amplified cRNA (~200 µg/ml)
> Prepare as described in Protocols 5 and 7.

Random primers (4 µg/µl in TE at pH 7.6)
> Because of their uniform length and lack of sequence bias, synthetic oligonucleotides of random sequence are the primers of choice. Oligonucleotides of optimal length (hexamers and heptamers; Suganuma and Gupta 1995) can be purchased from commercial sources (e.g., Pharmacia or Boehringer Mannheim) or synthesized locally on an automated synthesizer. Store the solution of primers at –70ºC in small aliquots.

> The factors influencing the choice between random priming and 3´-biased priming are discussed in the Introduction to this section.

Special Reagents

aa-dUTP (5-[3-amino-allyl])-2´-deoxyuridine 5´-triphosphate sodium salt) (Sigma)
> Dissolve the aa-dUTP in H$_2$O to make a 100-mM solution.

Fluorolink Cy3 and Cy5 Monoreactive Dye-5 Packs (Amersham Biosciences)
> For instructions on making and storing solutions of Cy dye esters, please see Steps 13–15 of this protocol.

> Amersham ships succinimidyl esters of the cyanine dyes as dried pellets sealed in a foil bag with a small amount of desiccant. If the desiccant has turned from dark blue to a light pink, moisture may have contaminated the sample. Contaminated dye packs should be returned to Amersham for a refund. When esters of carbocyanine dyes are exposed to water, the reactive part of the dye is rapidly hydrolyzed. It is essential to store the lyophilized dyes in a desiccator in the dark.

Special Equipment

Desktop centrifuge (high-speed 16,000g) for 1.5-ml microfuge tubes

Microcon YM-30 (Millipore)

QIAquick PCR purification kit (50) (28104, QIAGEN)

SpeedVac rotary evaporator

Water baths (constant temperature), heating blocks, or thermal cyclers set to 70ºC, 65ºC, and 42ºC

METHOD

Incorporation of aa-dUTP into First-strand cDNA by Reverse Transcription

1. Prepare the 50X dNTP + aa-dUTP mixture by combining the following dNTPs:

100 mM dATP	10 µl
100 mM dCTP	10 µl
100 mM dGTP	10 µl
100 mM dTTP	6 µl
100 mM aa-dUTP	4 µl

   Prepare aliquots of the 50X mixture into convenient amounts and store frozen at –20ºC or –80ºC.

   The intensity of labeling depends on the molar ratio of dTTP:aa-dUTP in the reaction mixture. Ratios between 1:1 (Hughes et al. 2001) and 3:2 (used here) are generally suitable for labeling first-strand cDNA from yeast or mammalian cells. However, if the intensity of labeling is inadequate, determine the optimal ratio of dTTP:aa-dUTP in preliminary experiments using a range of ratios. The density of labeling can be determined as described in the information panel on **MEASURING THE EFFICIENCY OF DYE LABELING OF DNA.**

2. To anneal the primer to the mRNA, mix the following:

poly(A)$^+$ RNA or polysomal RNA (~200 µg/ml)	2 µg
primer (1–2 µg/ml)	1 µl
H$_2$O	to 15.5 µl

    When using purified mRNA as a template, synthesis of first-strand cDNA is usually primed by oligo(dT)$_{12\text{-}18}$ or a set of anchored primers. However, random primers can also be used, in combination with either oligo(dT)$_{12\text{-}18}$ or a set of anchored primers.

3. Incubate the reaction mixture for 8 minutes at 70ºC, and then transfer the reaction mixture to an ice bath.

4. Assemble the master mix for cDNA synthesis:

5x first-strand cDNA buffer	6 µl
50x aa-dNTP	0.6 µl
DTT (0.1 M)	3 µl
SUPERSCRIPT II RT (500 units/µl)	2 µl
RNasin (30 units/ml) (optional)	2 µl
H$_2$O	to 14.5 µl

    The volumes shown are those required for each labeling reaction.

    Reverse transcriptases are very sensitive to denaturation at air/liquid interfaces, so be very careful to avoid foaming when mixing the components of the reaction. This is sometimes difficult because many preparations of reverse transcriptases are supplied in buffers containing nonionic detergents such as Nonidet P-40 or Triton X-100.

    Mo-MLV (SUPERSCRIPT II) is temperature-sensitive and should be stored at –20ºC until the last possible moment and be returned to the freezer at the first possible opportunity.

5. Add 14.5 µl of the master mix to each priming reaction (Step 2)

6. Incubate the complete reaction mixtures for 2 hours at 42ºC.

Hydrolysis and Cleanup of the First-strand Product

7. To each reaction mixture, add 3 µl of 0.1 M EDTA.

    Make sure to mix the reaction mixture well after the addition of EDTA before proceeding with the addition of NaOH (Step 8). Nucleic acids precipitate in alkaline magnesium solutions.

8. To the reaction mixture, add 3.5 µl of 0.1 M NaOH. Incubate the reactions for 10 minutes at 65ºC.

9. Neutralize the hydrolysis reaction by the addition of HEPES (pH 7.0) to a final concentration of 500 mM.

    Tris carries a free amine group and should not be used for neutralization because it will interfere with the subsequent coupling reaction.

    In place of the purification outlined in Steps 10–12, the first-strand reaction product may be purified by chromatography using the QIAquick purification column (please see the panel on **PURIFICATION OF AMINO-ALLYL-LABELED CDNA** below Step 12). However, the standard elution buffer supplied by QIAGEN contains Tris-base, which carries an amino group that will interfere with subsequent coupling of the aa-cDNA to esterified dyes. Therefore, rather than QIAGEN's EB buffer, use H$_2$O to elute the aa-cDNA from the QIAquick column (see panel below Step 12).

10. Adjust the volume of the reaction to 500 μl with H_2O. Concentrate the cDNA product by centrifugation through a Microcon YM-30 concentrator.

> Try to reduce the volume of the sample to <10 μl. This can usually be accomplished by centrifuging the reaction at maximum speed (16,000g) for 6–10 minutes in a typical microfuge. Do not spin to dryness as this can make the cDNA difficult to recover.

11. Adjust the volume of the concentrated solution to 500 μl with H_2O and repeat Step 10 at least twice more.

> The goal of this step is to remove the hydrolyzed RNA, NaOH, and buffer components.

12. The amino-allyl-substituted cDNA (<10 μl) may now be stored indefinitely at –20ºC.

PURIFICATION OF AMINO-ALLYL-LABELED FIRST-STRAND CDNA

Some investigators prefer to prepare the first-strand cDNA for labeling by absorption to a column, followed by precipitation with ethanol. QIAquick columns, which are sold as part of the QIAquick PCR purification kit (QIAGEN), are fitted with silica-gel membranes that bind DNA in a pH- and salt-dependent manner. Purify each dye-labeled sample separately by following the manufacturer's directions, as modified below. The following sequence replaces Steps 10 to 12. In brief, after Step 9 (above):

a. Add 500 μl (5 volumes) of PB buffer (QIAGEN) to the neutralized solution of cDNA. Mix the solution by gentle vortexing.

b. Place a QIAquick column in a 2-ml collection tube. Apply the cDNA solution to the center of the QIAquick column, and centrifuge at 10,000g (13,000 rpm) for 1 minute. Discard the flow-through.

c. Add the appropriate amount of ethanol to PE buffer (QIAGEN) (see instructions on bottle). Add 750 μl of PE buffer containing ethanol to the QIAquick column.

d. Centrifuge at 10,000g for 1 minute. Discard the flow-through. Repeat the wash with another 750 μl of PE buffer containing ethanol. Then centrifuge again at 10,000g for 1 minute. Discard the eluate.

e. Place the QIAquick column in a 1.5-ml microfuge tube. Add 30 μl of H_2O to the center of the column, wait 2 minutes, and then centrifuge at 10,000g for 1 minute. Collect the eluate.

> **IMPORTANT:** Do not use QIAGEN EB buffer for elution (see note to Step 9, above).

f. Repeat Step e, collecting the eluate in the same tube.

g. Add 0.1 volume of 3 M sodium acetate (pH 5.2) (~10 μl), and then add 2.5 volumes of ethanol (~275 μl).

> Some investigators add an inert carrier (e.g., 20 μg of glycogen) to improve the efficiency of precipitation.

h. Store the solution for 30 minutes at –20°C and then recover the cDNA by centrifugation at 13,000g for 10 minutes at 4°C.

i. Wash the pellet with 500 ml of cold 75% ethanol. Recover the cDNA by centrifugation at 13,000g for 10 minutes at 4°C.

j. Remove the ethanol by careful aspiration, taking care not to disturb the pellet of cDNA. Allow the cDNA to dry in the air until the last visible traces of ethanol have evaporated.

k. Dissolve the cDNA in 10 μl of H_2O and proceed directly to Step 13 or store the DNA at –20°C until needed.

> Some investigators prefer to dry the samples under vacuum after Step f, rather than precipitating them with ethanol (Steps g–j).

Aliquoting Cy-Dye Esters

13. Resuspend the solid pellet of the Cy dye ester in 12 μl of anhydrous DMF or DMSO.

14. Because a single tube of esterified dye usually provides sufficient material to label at least 12 samples, transfer 1-μl aliquots of the resuspended dye into separate screw-cap tubes. Dry down the aliquots using a SpeedVac rotary evaporator, without heat.

15. Store the dried dye aliquots at 4°C, in a light-proof box, preferably under vacuum and in the presence of a large amount of desiccant.

    Storing the dyes in this manner will prevent them from becoming contaminated with moisture.

Coupling the Amino-Allyl-substituted cDNA to *N*-hydroxysuccinimidyl-esterified Dyes

16. To the labeled cDNA (10 μl from Step 12), add 1.5 μl of freshly made 1 M sodium bicarbonate buffer (pH 9.0).

17. Remove an aliquot of the succinimidyl dye from storage (Step 15), and use the bicarbonate-buffered cDNA solution to resuspend the pellet by vigorously pipetting up and down.

18. Incubate the coupling reaction in the dark for at least 60 minutes at room temperature.

19. (*Optional*) Some investigators quench the coupling reaction by adding hydroxylamine to a final concentration of 1.5 M before proceeding to the QIAquick clean up (Step 21). However, others (including the DeRisi laboratory) think that hydroxylamine quenching is unnecessary and possibly deleterious.

Removal of Free Esterified Dye

20. Purify each dye-labeled sample separately by chromatography through QIAquick columns as described in Steps a–g of the panel below Step 12.

21. Concentrate the final eluate obtained in Step g (see panel) to the desired volume in a Microcon YM-30 concentrator or a vacuum evaporator.

22. Store the labeled cDNA in a foil-wrapped tube at 4°C. Analyze a sample of the fluorescently labeled DNA by gel electrophoresis and calculate the efficiency of labeling as described in Steps 12 and 13 of Protocol 13.

    A good probe should contain >1 dye residue per 75 nucleotides.

Amplification of mRNA Preparations to Generate Targets for Screening DNA Microarrays

James Eberwine,*† Paolo Marciano,‡ Tracy McIntosh,‡ and Janet Estee Kacharmina*†

*Departments of *Pharmacology, †Psychiatry, and ‡Neurosurgery, University of Pennsylvania Medical Center; Philadelphia, Pennsylvania 19104*

When DNA microarrays are used to detect and measure changes in the patterns of gene expression, the labeled targets should faithfully reflect the abundance of mRNAs in the original tissues or cells. The opportunity for serious bias is minimal when fluorescently labeled targets are copied directly from mRNA templates, for example, in a single enzymatic reaction in which RNA-dependent DNA polymerase transcribes mRNA into fluorescently labeled first-strand cDNA. However, the direct conversion of mRNA into labeled cDNA requires substantial quantities of template that are not available, for example, from microdissected tissues or from small populations of rare cells isolated by fluorescence-activated cell sorting. In such cases, the preparation of mRNA must be amplified to an amount sufficient for synthesis of an adequate quantity of target. In this protocol, we discuss the commonly used antisense RNA (aRNA) amplification method to generate a template for target synthesis. We then describe how small amounts of RNA (~1 ng of total RNA) can be copied into cDNA and amplified by in vitro transcription using bacteriophage T7 DNA-dependent RNA polymerase. Methods to isolate and amplify RNA from microdissected fixed paraffin-embedded tissue are discussed further in Protocol 11 and in Section 5.

AMPLIFIED cDNA GENERATED BY RT-PCR

In this method (Figure 3-18), the mRNA is copied into first-strand cDNA, using as primers oligo(dT) molecules carrying a unique arbitrary sequence at their 5′ ends. After completion of first-strand synthesis, terminal deoxynucleotidyl transferase is used to catalyze the addition of dG residues to the 3′ end of the first-strand cDNAs. The homopolymeric dG 3′ tail and the unique sequence at the 5′ end of the synthetic oligo(dT) primer are then used as annealing sites for primers in a standard PCR catalyzed by *Taq* DNA polymerase. Although such PCRs are relatively efficient, they have the capacity to alter the relative abundances of the original mRNAs. During PCR, some of the cDNAs will be more efficiently amplified than others because of differences in lengths and secondary structures. For example, in an experiment to measure the relative abundance of two cDNAs, if cDNA 1 is amplified at 90% the efficiency of cDNA 2, then the molar ratio of cDNA 1 to cDNA 2 after one round of PCR is

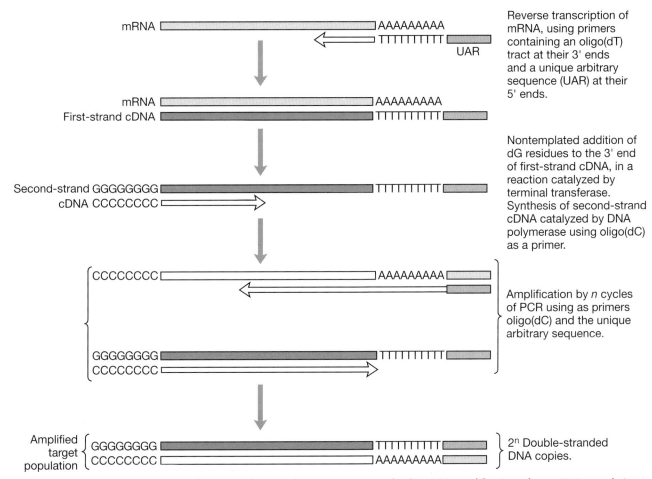

FIGURE 3-18. Schematic diagram of RT-PCR, showing the major steps involved in PCR amplification of an mRNA population. Any bias for or against a particular species of mRNA is exponentially amplified in this procedure, resulting in a target population that does not accurately reflect the abundance of an mRNA species in the initial population.

skewed by a factor of 9/10. If the PCR is repeated 35 times with the difference in efficiency of amplification remaining constant, then the fractional percentage of cDNA 1 relative to cDNA 2 after 35 rounds of PCR is $(9/10)^{35}$ or 0.028% of the original abundance. The population of cDNAs produced by multiple rounds of amplification may therefore bear little resemblance to the population of mRNAs that engendered it. Because of the potential for strong skewing, it is inappropriate to screen microarrays with targets generated during many cycles of PCR.

ARNA AMPLIFIED BY T7 RNA POLYMERASE

The aRNA procedure, first developed in 1990 by Van Gelder et al., has been used for a variety of purposes including generation of targets for microarray analysis. The aRNA procedure uses bacteriophage-encoded RNA polymerases to transcribe a DNA template into RNA (Figure 3-19), which is accomplished through synthesis of single-stranded cDNA copies of the mRNA population using either oligo(dT) or random hexamer primers whose 5′ ends encode syn-

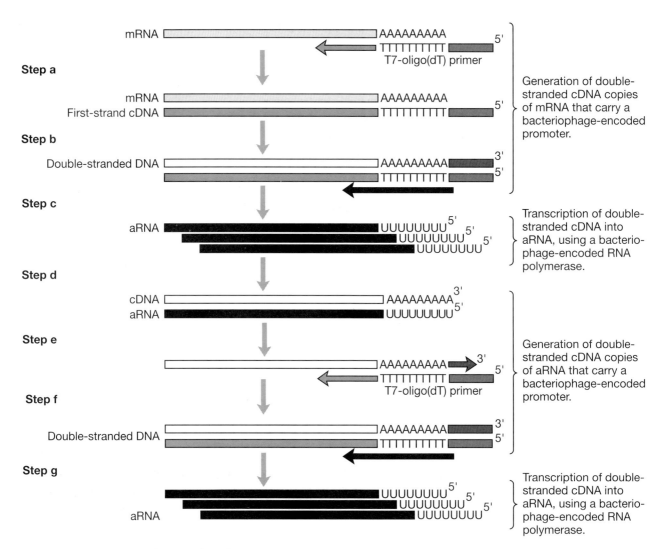

FIGURE 3-19. Synthesis of aRNA. This schematic diagram shows the steps involved in the synthesis of antisense RNA copies of mRNA. Two rounds of aRNA synthesis are shown (Steps a–c and Steps d–g). The aRNA produced in the first round is used as the template for the second round of synthesis. The steps in the protocol are summarized in the following table. For further details, please see protocol.

Step	Template	Primer	Enzyme	Product
a	mRNA	T7–oligo(dT)	reverse transcriptase	mRNA-cDNA hybrid
b	cDNA	random hexamers	E. coli DNA polymerase I	double-stranded cDNA
c	double-stranded cDNA	none	T7 RNA polymerase	aRNA
d	aRNA	random hexamers	reverse transcriptase	aRNA-cDNA hybrid
e/f	cDNA	T7–oligo(dT)	E. coli DNA polymerase I	double-stranded cDNA
g	double-stranded cDNA	none	T7 RNA polymerase	aRNA

thetic promoters for T3, SP6, or T7 DNA-dependent RNA polymerases. Conversion of the single-stranded DNA to double-stranded cDNA generates templates that may be transcribed into aRNA by the appropriate DNA-dependent RNA polymerase. The key features of the procedure are (1) that aRNA accumulates at a linear rate (as opposed to an exponential rate in PCR) and (2) that the aRNA is not used as a template for reiterative rounds of amplification. Because skewing of the abundance of mRNAs is minimized during the linear amplification process, the final aRNA target accurately represents the size, complexity, and abundance of mRNAs in the original mRNA population (please see Van Gelder et al. 1990; Eberwine et al. 1992). Either total RNA or mRNA may be used as the starting templates.

When the procedure is optimized, the amount of aRNA synthesized in vitro can be 1000–2000-fold greater than the initial quantity of mRNA. Amplification at such high efficiency allows expression analysis to be carried out on DNA microarrays with a few nanograms of starting RNA. If even less mRNA is available, a second round of aRNA amplification will be required. Two rounds of amplification carried out sequentially should, in theory, result in a million-fold amplification of the starting mRNA. In practice, two rounds of amplification result in an approximate 10^5-fold increase in the amount of aRNA, with very little concomitant increase in random or systematic bias (Wang et al. 2000). Sufficient high-fidelity aRNA is obtained in two rounds of amplification to allow analysis of the minute quantity of mRNA extracted from a single cell (0.1–1.0 pg) (Kacharmina et al. 1996; Crino and Eberwine 1997) (please see Protocol 11)

Fluorescently tagged ribonucleotides are incorporated inefficiently in aRNA molecules synthesized in vitro. Three approaches have been described to overcome this problem and to generate targets from aRNA:

- ***Incorporation of biotinylated nucleotides into the aRNA chain.*** After hybridization of the biotinylated aRNA target to DNA microarrays, the biotin is detected by using fluorescently tagged avidin or antibiotin antibodies. For experimental details of target preparation, please see Protocol 18.

- ***Conversion of the aRNA product into cDNA using reverse transcriptase*** and random primers labeled at their 5′ end with a fluorescent tag. The 5′-labeled cDNA is used as a target to hybridize to the array.

- ***Incorporation of fluorescently tagged deoxynucleotides into randomly primed cDNA*** synthesized from aRNA templates by reverse transcriptase. The internally labeled cDNA is then used as a target. This is essentially the standard method of target synthesis (Protocol 13), except that aRNA is used as template instead of mRNA or total RNA. Experimental details of target preparation are described in this protocol.

SYNTHESIS OF ARNA AND DOUBLE-STRANDED DNA FROM SMALL AMOUNTS OF TOTAL OR POLY(A)$^+$ RNA

This protocol generates enough aRNA template to allow fluorescently labeled targets to be produced from very small amounts (~1 ng) of either total or poly(A)$^+$ RNA. When larger amounts of RNA are available (>50 μg of total RNA or >2 μg of poly(A)$^+$ RNA), amplification of the template is unnecessary, and labeled targets can be synthesized by conventional methods as described in Protocols 13 and 14. The method consists of three sets of enzymatic reactions:

- Conversion of RNA to double-stranded cDNA (Steps 1–4).
- Transcription of double-stranded cDNA into aRNA (Steps 5–7).
- Conversion of aRNA to double-stranded cDNA (Steps 7–14).

The double-stranded cDNA can be used as a template for a second round of synthesis of aRNA, or it can be labeled by random primed incorporation of fluorescent nucleotides as described in the panel on **ADDITIONAL PROTOCOL: LABELING aRNA.**

MATERIALS

CAUTION: Please see Appendix 3 for appropriate handling of materials marked with <!>.
IMPORTANT: Prepare all buffers in DEPC-treated H_2O and store frozen in small aliquots.

Buffers and Solutions

Please see Appendix 2 for components of stock solutions, buffers, and reagents.
Dilute stock solutions to the appropriate concentrations and sterilize by filtration.

Dithiothreitol (DTT) (0.1 M) <!>
Ethanol (absolute)

> Some batches of absolute ethanol (100% or 200 proof) have been reported to contain fluorescent contaminants that generate high backgrounds in microarray experiments; 95% ethanol does not have this problem. To avoid difficulties, either use 95% ethanol or identify a brand of absolute ethanol that performs reliably. Absolute ethanol (USP-grade ethyl alcohol, 64-17-5) purchased from Warner-Graham Co. (Cockeysville, Maryland) performs consistently well.

Linear polyacrylamide
Phenol:chloroform (75:25) <!>
Sodium acetate (3 M, pH 7.0)

Enzymes and Buffers

Bacteriophage T4 DNA ligase
Bacteriophage T4 DNA polymerase (2500 units/ml)
Bacteriophage T7 DNA-dependent RNA polymerase (1000 units/μl)
E. coli DNA ligase (1000–4000 units/ml)
E. coli DNA polymerase I (10,000 units/ml)
E. coli RNase H (1000 units/ml)
10x First-strand buffer

> 500 mM Tris-Cl (pH 8.3)
> 1.2 M KCl
> 100 mM $MgCl_2$

Reverse transcriptase

> Recombinant murine reverse transcriptase (RT) is available from several manufacturers. We strongly recommend the use of a mutated form of the enzyme that lacks RNase H activity. The enzyme used in this protocol is SUPERSCRIPT II reverse transcriptase (Invitrogen/GIBCO). However, the protocol can easily be adapted for use with other commercial preparations of RNase H⁻ forms of Mo-MLV RT. The specific activity of preparations of reverse transcriptase depends on the particular cDNA clone used to express the enzyme in *E. coli* and varies among manufacturers. Follow the individual manufacturer's directions (i.e., units/μg input RNA and incubation temperature) for the enzyme at hand. Mo-MLV RT is temperature-sensitive and should be stored at –20°C until needed.

10x RNA amplification buffer

> 400 mM Tris-Cl (pH 7.5)
> 70 mM $MgCl_2$
> 100 mM NaCl
> 20 mM spermidine
> Filter prior to the addition of spermidine.

RNase inhibitor

> Protein inhibitors of RNase bind to and inhibit the activity of most RNases but do not affect the RNase activity of wild-type Mo-MLV RT. These inhibitors are sold by several manufacturers under different trade names (e.g., RNasin from Promega and Prime Inhibitor from 5-Prime→3-Prime).

10x Second-strand buffer
1 M Tris-Cl (pH 7.4)
200 mM KCl
100 mM $MgCl_2$
400 mM $(NH_4)_2SO_4$

Nucleic Acids and Oligonucleotides

dNTP solution containing all four dNTPs, each at a concentration of 10 mM
Store the solution in small aliquots at –20ºC. For instructions on preparing and storing dNTPs, please see Appendix 2.

NTP solution containing all four ribonucleotide triphosphates, each at a concentration of 2.5 mM
Store the solution in small aliquots at –20ºC. For instructions on preparing and storing NTPs, please see Appendix 2.

Oligo$(dT)_{24}$–T7 promoter
5′AAA CGA CGG CCA GTG AAT TGT AAT ACG ACT CAC TAT AGG CGC $(T)_{24}$

This promoter sequence is much longer than the consensus sequence for the T7 promoter defined by Dunn and Studier (1983), and sold by New England Biolabs and Stratagene (TAAT-ACGACTCACTATAGGGAGA). In the oligonucleotide defined here, the T7 promoter is embedded in a sequence that provides a 5′-flanking region, which provides space for T7 RNA polymerase to bind and a 3′-flanking trinucleotide that stimulates T7 enzymatic activity. Dissolve the synthetic oligonucleotide in H_2O at a concentration of 100 pmoles/µl (~2 µg/µl).

The synthetic oligonucleotide should be purified by polyacrylamide gel electrophoresis (Sambrook and Russell 2001) and dissolved in H_2O at a concentration of ~25 pmoles/µl (~0.5 µg/µl).

Random primers
Because of their uniform length and lack of sequence bias, synthetic oligonucleotides of random sequence are the primers of choice for efficient copying of aRNA into cDNA (Steps 8–10 of this protocol). Oligonucleotides of optimal length (hexamers, heptamers, or octamers; Suganuma and Gupta 1995) can be purchased from a commercial source (e.g., Pharmacia or Boehringer Mannheim) or synthesized locally on an automated DNA synthesizer. Resuspend the random primers at 1.0 µg/ml in TE (pH 7.6). Store the solution of primers at –20ºC in small aliquots.

Total RNA (1 µg/ml) or poly(A)$^+$ RNA (1–10 ng) purified from the appropriate source(s) by one of the methods described in Protocols 1–10.

Special Equipment

Microcon YM-50 column or equivalent
Water baths set at 73ºC, 70ºC, 42ºC, and 16ºC

METHOD

Synthesis of First-strand and Second-strand cDNA

1. To synthesize first-strand cDNA, mix the following in a microfuge tube:

1 ng/µl total RNA	1 µl
100 pmoles/µl oligo$(dT)_{24}$–T7 promoter	1 µl
H_2O	to 13 µl

Seal the tube and incubate the mixture for 10 minutes at 70ºC. Remove the tube from the 70ºC bath, allow it to stand for 5 minutes at room temperature, and then add:

10x first-strand buffer	2 μl
0.1 M DTT	1 μl
2.5 mM dNTP solution	2 μl
RNase inhibitor	1 μl
SUPERSCRIPT II (200 units)	1 μl

Mix the reagents by gentle vortexing and centrifuge the reaction mixture briefly to eliminate any bubbles. Incubate the sealed microfuge tube for 1 hour at 42ºC.

2. To synthesize the second strand, add the following directly to the first-strand reaction:

10x second-strand buffer	10 μl
2.5 mM dNTP solution	10 μl
E. coli DNA polymerase I (40 units)	4 μl
E. coli RNase H (1 unit)	1 μl
H₂O	to 80 μl

Mix the reagents by gentle vortexing and centrifuge the reaction mixture briefly to eliminate any bubbles. Incubate the closed microfuge tube for 2 hours at 16ºC.

E. coli DNA ligase is used during second-strand synthesis to seal adjacent 5′- and 3′-hydroxyl ends of DNA. The bacterial enzyme is preferred to bacteriophage T4 DNA ligase for this purpose because it is unable to join adjacent DNA and RNA segments that arise during synthesis of the second strand of cDNA (Oakayama and Berg 1982).

3. Add 2 μl (5 units) of bacteriophage T4 DNA polymerase and incubate the reaction mixture for 10 minutes at 16ºC.

T4 DNA polymerase is used to polish the termini of the completed double-stranded DNAs.

4. Extract the reaction mixture with 150 μl of phenol:chloroform (75:25). Centrifuge the tube briefly to separate the phases and then transfer 130 μl of the aqueous (upper) phase to a fresh microfuge tube. Store the tube on the bench. To further purify the double-stranded cDNA product:

a. Add 100 μl of H₂O to the tube containing the phenol:chloroform.

b. Mix the phases by vortexing and centrifuge the tube briefly to separate the phases.

c. Transfer 120 μl of the aqueous phase to the microfuge tube that contains 130 μl of the aqueous phase from the first extraction.

d. Add 250 μl of H₂O to the pooled aqueous phases.

e. Transfer the pooled aqueous phases to a spin column such as a Microcon YM-50 column.

f. Centrifuge the column at 13,000g for 5 minutes at room temperature.

g. Wash the column with 500 μl of H₂O and centrifuge as in Step f.

h. Invert the column into a fresh microfuge tube. Centrifuge the tube at 1000g for 3 minutes to collect the sample (~15 μl).

Transcription of Double-stranded cDNA into aRNA

5. Transfer 14 µl of the cDNA preparation (Step 4) to a fresh microfuge tube and add:

10x RNA amplification buffer	2.0 µl
0.1 M DTT	1.0 µl
2.5 mM NTP solution	2.0 µl
RNasin (20 units)	0.5 µl
T7 RNA polymerase (1000 units/µl)	1.0 µl

   Mix the reagents by gentle vortexing and then incubate the reaction for 4 hours at 37°C.

6. Add 20 µl of H_2O to the reaction, followed by 40 µl of phenol:chloroform (75:25). Centrifuge the tube briefly to separate the phases and then transfer 30 µl of the aqueous (upper) phase to a fresh microfuge tube. Store the tube on the bench. To further purify the aRNA product:

   a. Add 20 µl of H_2O to the tube containing the phenol:chloroform.

   b. Mix the phases by vortexing, and centrifuge the tube briefly to separate the phases.

   c. Transfer 20 µl of the aqueous phase to the microfuge tube that contains 30 µl of the aqueous phase from the first extraction.

   d. Add 5 µl of 3 M sodium acetate (pH 7.0) to the pooled aqueous phases, followed by 8 µl of 0.25% linear acrylamide and 130 µl of ethanol.

   e. Store the solution for 4–8 hours at –20°C.

   f. Recover the aRNA by centrifugation at 15,000g for 10 minutes at 4°C

   g. Remove the ethanol by gentle aspiration and allow the pellet to dry for 15–20 minutes at room temperature.

7. Dissolve the pellet of RNA in 12.5 µl of H_2O.

Conversion of aRNA to Double-stranded cDNA for Reamplification

8. To the purified RNA, add 1 µl of 1 µg/µl random primers and incubate the solution for 10 minutes at 70°C. Chill the solution rapidly on ice and then store it for 10 minutes at room temperature.

9. For first-strand synthesis, add the following components:

10x first-strand buffer	2 µl
0.1 M DTT	2 µl
10 mM dNTP solution	0.5 µl
RNase inhibitor	1 µl
SUPERSCRIPT II (200 units/µl)	1 µl

   Mix the components and incubate the solution (final volume ~20 µl) for 1 hour at 37°C.

10. Heat the reaction mixture for 2 minutes at 94°C and then chill it rapidly on ice.

11. Add 1 µl of 1 µl oligo(dT)$_{24}$–T7 promoter (100 pmoles/µl) and incubate the reaction mixture for 5 minutes at 70°C, followed by 3 minutes at 42°C.

12. For second-strand synthesis, add the following components:

10x second-strand buffer	15 µl
10 mM dNTPs	7.5 µl
E. coli DNA polymerase I (40 units)	4 µl
E. coli RNase H (1 unit)	1 µl
H$_2$O	to 100 µl

    Mix the solution and incubate it for 2 hours at 16ºC.

13. Add 2 µl of T4 DNA polymerase and incubate the solution for 10 minutes at 16ºC.

    T4 DNA polymerase is used to polish the termini of the completed double-stranded DNAs.

14. Purify the resulting double-stranded cDNA as described in Step 4.

15. To generate the second round of aRNA, amplify this double stranded cDNA by repeating Steps 5 through 7.

    It is assumed that mRNA represents ~1% of the total DNA population; therefore, a 10^3-fold overall amplification of 1 ng of total RNA should yield ~10 ng of double-stranded RNA.

    The quality and size distribution of the second round aRNA product can be monitored by electrophoresis through agarose-formaldehyde gels (Sambrook and Russell 2001).

    The cDNA is ready for labeling using one of the methods described below in the additional protocol.

ADDITIONAL PROTOCOL: LABELING aRNA

Depending on how the aRNA target will be used, the second-round aRNA T7 in vitro transcription product can be labeled using a variety of procedures. For microarrays using ^{33}P-labeled targets, the procedure in Section 4, Protocol 2 may be followed for incorporating ^{33}P-labeled ribonucleotides into the aRNA as it is synthesized. One fluorescent detection method that has been used to screen microarrays successfully is based on the use of the RNA labeling kit from Enzo Diagnostics, Inc. Fluorescent NTPs typically are incorporated poorly by RNA polymerases into the RNA product; however, the Enzo kit overcomes this problem by promoting the synthesis of RNA utilizing biotinylated ribonucleotides. After hybridization to an array, biotin-labeled RNAs are detected using fluorescently tagged antibodies or avidin that bind to biotin with high affinity. The synthesis of biotinylated aRNA utilizing the Enzo labeling kit is described in this protocol. Alternatively, the aRNA can be reverse-transcribed into cDNA using random primers incorporating Cy3- and Cy5-labeled nucleotides into the cDNA product.

Additional Materials

RNA labeling kit (Enzo Diagnostics, Inc.; www.EnzoBio.com)
   The kit components include biotin-labeled ribonucleotides and HY reaction buffer.
RNeasy column (QIAGEN)
   Optional, please see Step 2.

Method

1. Add the following reagents to a tube containing products from either the first or second round of aRNA amplification (Step 15 of the main protocol).

10x HY reaction buffer	4 μl
biotin-labeled ribonucleotides	4 μl
0.1 M dithiothreitol	4 μl
RNase inhibitor	4 μl
T7 RNA polymerase (1000 units/μl)	2 μl
H_2O	to 40 μl

    Mix the reagents and incubate the reaction mixture for 4 hours at 37°C.

2. Purify the labeled cRNA product using either phenol:chloroform extraction and ethanol precipitation described in Step 6 of the main protocol or the RNeasy column methodology from QIAGEN (see manufacturers instructions or Protocol 1 for details).

Amplification of Small Quantities of mRNA for Expression Analysis

Ena Wang and Francesco M. Marincola

HLA and Immunogenetics Laboratory, National Cancer Institute, National Institutes of Health, Bethesda, Maryland 20892

Many biological processes occur in cellular compartments that are too small in size to yield enough RNA for expression analysis using DNA microarrays. Attempts to extend the sensitivity of cDNA microarrays by intensifying the fluorescent signals (Chen et al. 1998; Zejie et al. 1998; Rajeevan et al. 1999) have resulted in only modest improvements. Consequently, microarray technology has until recently been limited to systems from which RNA can be extracted in large amounts (~50–200 μg of total RNA or 2–5 μg of poly(A)$^+$ RNA). However, in the last few years, in vitro methods to amplify mRNA or cDNA populations have been developed (Lockhart et al. 1996; Phillips and Eberwine 1996; Trenkle et al. 1998) that have the potential to reduce by orders of magnitude the amounts of total RNA or poly(A)$^+$ RNA required for microarray analysis. Although these amplification procedures are gaining wide acceptance (Van Gelder et al. 1990; Eberwine et al. 1992; Lockhart et al. 1996; Kacharmina et al. 1999; Luo et al. 1999), very little systematic work has so far been done to assess their limits or to compare the efficiency of the available experimental schemes. We recently described a modified procedure (Wang and Marincola 2000), based on Eberwine's pioneering work, to optimize the amplification of complex populations of mRNA by combining aRNA amplification (Phillips and Eberwine 1996) with template switching (Matz et al. 1999). We validated the method by showing that the fidelity of aRNA amplified from very small quantities of mRNA (1/10,000 to 1/100,000 of normal input) yielded expression profiles comparable to those obtained from conventional arrays using poly(A)$^+$ RNA or total RNA (Wang et al. 2000). In this protocol, we briefly review the RNA amplification methods and describe in detail our amplification procedure.

Amplifying populations of mRNAs without skewing the relative abundances remain a hot field of research. Linear amplification methods have been developed that in theory should maintain the proportionality of each RNA species present in the original sample. In vitro transcription of double-stranded cDNAs equipped with a bacteriophage T7 promoter (Van Gelder et al. 1990) provides an efficient way to amplify mRNA sequences (aRNA) and thereby generate templates for synthesis of fluorescently labeled single-stranded DNAs (Van Gelder et al. 1990; Eberwine et al. 1992; Lockhart et al. 1996; Phillips and Eberwine 1996; Kacharmina et al. 1999; Luo et al. 1999). However, validation of these methods has relied on northern analysis or in situ hybridization with a limited number of genes to demonstrate linearity and reproducibility of mRNA amplification (Van Gelder et al. 1990; Eberwine et al.

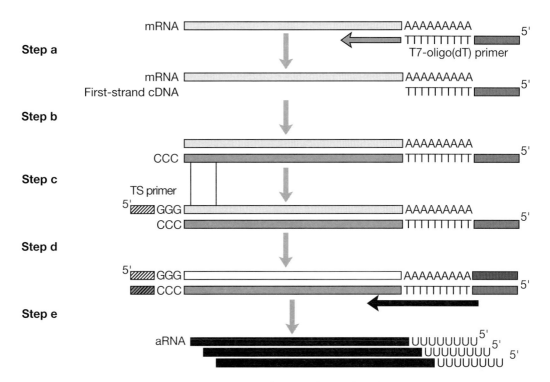

FIGURE 3-20. Amplification of mRNA using template switching. The schematic diagram shows the conversion of mRNA to double-stranded cDNA that can be either transcribed into aRNA by a bacteriophage-encoded RNA polymerase or amplifed by PCR. The steps in the protocol are summarized in the following table. For further details, please see the protocol. (Modified, with permission, from Figure 1 of CLONTECH Atlas Smart™ Probe Amplification Kit User Manual ©2000.)

Step	Template	Primer	Enzyme	Product
a	mRNA	T7–oligo(dT)	reverse transcriptase	mRNA-cDNA hybrid
b	mRNA-cDNA hybrid	none	reverse transcriptase	C-tailed mRNA-cDNA hybrid
c/d	C-tailed mRNA-cDNA hybrid	TS primer	reverse transcriptase, RNase H DNA polymerase	double-stranded cDNA
e	double-stranded cDNA	none	T7 RNA polymerase	aRNA

1992; Lockhart et al. 1996; Phillips and Eberwine 1996; Kacharmina et al. 1999; Luo et al. 1999). Nevertheless, conventional aRNA amplification remains vulnerable to bias because of possible underrepresentation of 5′ sequences of mRNAs and because of the low temperature at which the double-stranded cDNA is synthesized (Phillips and Eberwine 1996), which provides opportunities for false priming during second-strand synthesis. Although underrepresentation of 5′ sequences could in theory be overcome by using hairpin loop priming of second-strand cDNA synthesis, rather than the more efficient Gubler-Hoffman (1983) method (Kacharmina et al. 1999), lack of bias still cannot be guaranteed because of the possibility of nonspecific priming at low temperature. Thus, at the moment, it is still unclear whether conventional aRNA amplification results in significant skewing of mRNA abundances (Bertucci et al. 1999).

In this protocol, outlined in Figure 3-20, we describe a modified procedure to generate large quantities of full-length aRNA for use in high-throughput cDNA microarray analysis. On the basis of conventional aRNA amplification (Eberwine et al. 1992; Phillips and Eberwine 1996; Kacharmina et al. 1999), the modified procedure uses template switching by reverse transcriptase at the 5′ end of the mRNA template to generate full-length double-stranded cDNA (Chenchik et al. 1998; Matz et al. 1999) that can be transcribed in vitro of the T7 RNA polymerase.

First-strand cDNA synthesis is initiated by an oligo(dT)–T7 primer whose 5′ sequence contains a T7 promoter recognized by the bacteriophage-encoded RNA polymerase. Second-strand cDNA synthesis utilizes the intrinsic terminal transferase activity and template switching ability of Mo-MLV reverse transcriptase (Chenchik et al. 1998; Matz et al. 1999; SMART PCR cDNA Synthesis Kit User Manual). This enzyme adds few nontemplated nucleotides (mostly C residues) to the 3′ end of the first-strand cDNA upon reaching the 5′ end of the RNA template. When an oligonucleotide (TS primer) carrying a short stretch of dG residues at its 3′ end is then added to the reaction mixture, it hybridizes to the protruding dC residues attached to the 5′ end of the newly synthesized cDNA. Reverse transcriptase is then able to extend the cDNA beyond the dC tract, using the TS primer as the template, to create a short segment of double-stranded DNA. After treatment with RNase H to remove the original mRNA and addition of a thermostable DNA polymerase, the TS primer initiates double-stranded cDNA synthesis, using the first-strand cDNA as a template. The resulting full-length double-stranded DNA is then purified and used as the template for in vitro transcription catalyzed by bacteriophage T7-encoded RNA polymerase. The resulting aRNA can be used as a template either for labeling of cDNA by random priming or for further rounds of amplification by PCR.

This method overcomes the bias generated by amplification methods that use terminal transferase to catalyze addition of nucleotides to the 3′ terminus of first-strand cDNAs, irrespective of their length. The linear amplification efficiency is greater than 2000-fold in the first-round amplification, 800,000-fold in the second-round amplification, and reliably reflects the relative levels of gene expression observed in the starting total RNA. The fidelity of this method was recently assessed by gene profiling analysis (Wang et al. 2000) and more recently by comparing estimates of gene expression in amplified and nonamplified RNAs using quantitative real-time PCR (Ohnmacht et al. 2001). These experiments confirm that proportionality of gene expression in different RNA populations is maintained through multiple rounds of amplification.

MATERIALS

CAUTION: Please see Appendix 3 for appropriate handling of materials marked with <!>.

IMPORTANT: Prepare all reagents used in this protocol with DEPC-treated H_2O (please see the information panel on **SPECIAL CONSIDERATIONS FOR WORKING WITH RNA**).

Buffers and Solutions

Please see Appendix 2 for components of stock solutions, buffers, and reagents.
Dilute stock solutions to the appropriate concentrations.

Ammonium acetate (7.5 M)
Dithiothreitol (DTT) (0.1 M) <!>

Dissolve 0.31 g of DTT in 20 ml of 0.01 M of sodium acetate (pH 5.2). Sterilize the solution by filtration and store it in small aliquots at –20ºC. Under these conditions, DTT is stable to oxidation by air.

Ethanol (absolute)

> Some batches of absolute ethanol (100% or 200 proof) have been reported to contain fluorescent contaminants that generate high backgrounds in microarray experiments; 95% ethanol does not have this problem. To avoid difficulties, either use 95% ethanol or identify a brand of absolute ethanol that performs reliably. Absolute ethanol (USP-grade ethyl alcohol, 64-17-5) purchased from Warner-Graham Co. (Cockeysville, Maryland) performs consistently well.

Linear polyacrylamide

> Linear polyacrylamide is an efficient neutral carrier for precipitating picogram amounts of nucleic acids with ethanol (Gaillard and Strauss 1990). To make linear polyacrylamide, prepare a 5% solution of acrylamide (without bis-acrylamide) in 40 mM Tris-Cl, 20 mM sodium acetate, 1 mM EDTA (pH 8.0). Add 1/100 volumes of fresh 10% ammonium persulfate and 1/1000 volumes of TEMED. When the solution becomes viscous, precipitate the polymer with 2.5 volumes of ethanol. Dissolve the pellet in 20 volumes of H_2O by shaking overnight. The 0.25% solution of linear polyacrylamide is stable for several years at 4°C.

Monophasic lysis solution (TRIzol 15596, GIBCO)

NaOH (1 M) containing 2 mM EDTA

Phenol:chloroform:isoamyl alcohol (25:24:1) <!>

Enzymes and Buffers

Advantage DNA polymerase (CLONTECH) and Advantage PCR buffer

> This product contains a mixture of an amino-terminal deletion mutant of *Taq* DNA polymerase and a second thermostable DNA polymerase that provides 3′→5′ proofreading activity. The combination of these two enzymes allows efficient amplification of full-length cDNAs with an error rate lower than that of conventional PCR (Barnes 1994).

First-strand cDNA buffer (as supplied by the manufacturer of the enzyme)

> If buffer supplied by the manufacturer is not available, use the following 5x first-strand buffer:
>> 250 mM Tris-Cl (pH 8.3)
>>
>> 375 mM KCl
>>
>> 15 mM $MgCl_2$

In vitro transcription kit (Ambion T7 MEGAscript kit)

Reverse transcriptase

> Recombinant murine reverse transcriptase (RT) is available from several manufacturers. We strongly recommend the use of a form of the enzyme carrying a point mutation that inactivates its RNase H activity. The enzyme used in this protocol is SUPERSCRIPT II reverse transcriptase (Invitrogen/GIBCO). However, the protocol can easily be adapted for use with other commercial preparations of RNase H⁻ point mutants of Mo-MLV RT. The specific activity of preparations of reverse transcriptase depends on the particular cDNA clone used to express the enzyme in *E. coli* and varies between manufacturers. Follow the individual manufacturer's directions (i.e., units/µg input RNA and incubation temperature) for the enzyme at hand. Mo-MLV RT is temperature-sensitive and should be stored at –20°C until needed.

RNase H (2 units/µl)

RNase inhibitor

> Store the inhibitor at –20°C. Protein inhibitors of RNase bind to and inhibit the activity of most RNases but do not affect the RNase activity of wild-type Mo-MLV RT. These inhibitors are sold by several manufacturers under different trade names (e.g., RNasin from Promega and Prime Inhibitor from 5-Prime→3-Prime).

Nucleic Acids and Oligonucleotides

ATP, GTP, CTP, UTP (*each* at a concentration of 75 mM; part of Ambion MEGAscript T7 kit)

dNTP/Low-dTTP solution

> Prepare a solution containing dATP, dCTP, dGTP, each at a concentration of 5 mM, and dTTP at 2 mM. Store the solution in small aliquots at –20°C. For instructions on preparing and storing dNTPs, please see Appendix 2.

dNTP solution containing all four dNTPs, each at a concentration of 10 mM
>Store the solution in small aliquots at –20ºC. For instructions on preparing and storing dNTPs, please see Appendix 2.

Oligo(dT)$_{15}$–T7 promoter
>5′ AAA CGA CGG CCA GTG AAT TGT AAT ACG ACT CAC TAT AGG CGC (T)$_{15}$

>This promoter sequence is much longer than the consensus sequence defined by Dunn and Studier (1983) and sold by New England Biolabs and Stratagene. In the extended sequence shown here, the consensus sequence is embedded between a 5′-flanking region that provides space for the T7 RNA polymerase to bind and a 3′-flanking trinucleotide that stimulates transcription catalyzed by the enzyme.

>The synthetic oligonucleotide should be purified by polyacrylamide gel electrophoresis (Sambrook and Russell 2001) and dissolved in H$_2$O at a concentration of ~25 pmoles/μl (~0.5 μg/μl).

Random primers
>Because of their uniform length and lack of sequence bias, synthetic oligonucleotides of random sequence are the primers of choice for efficient copying of aRNA into cDNA (this protocol). Oligonucleotides of optimal length (hexamers, heptamers, or octamers; Suganuma and Gupta 1995) can be purchased from a commercial source (e.g., Pharmacia or Boehringer Mannheim) or synthesized locally on an automated DNA synthesizer. Resuspend the random primers at 1.0 μg/ml in TE (pH 7.6). Store the solution of primers at –20ºC in small aliquots.

Total RNA
>Between 0.01 μg and 5 μg of total RNA is required for this protocol, prepared as described in Protocol 1. The total RNA content of mammalian cells is in the range of 20–40 pg (Roozemond 1976; Uemura 1980) and only 0.5–1.0 pg of this is mRNA. The protocol is optimized for use with RNA extracted from 500 to 2.5 x 10^5 cells purified from the appropriate source by one of the methods described earlier in this section (please see the protocols in Part 1 of Section 3)

TS primer 5′ AAG CAG TGG TAA CAA CGC AGA GTA CGC GGG 3′
>According to the data of Chenchik et al. (1998), the best results are obtained when the 3′GGG sequence is built from ribonucleotides rather than from deoxyribonucleotides. However, the authors have used TS primers with ...dGdGdG3′ many times without any problem.

>The synthetic primer should be purified by gel electrophoresis (Sambrook and Russell 2001) and dissolved in H$_2$O at a concentration of ~30 pmoles/μl (~0.5 μg/μl) and dissolved in H$_2$O at a concentration of ~25 pmoles/μl (~0.5 μg/μl).

Centrifuges and Rotors

Desktop centrifuge (high-speed 16,000g) for 1.5-ml microfuge tubes

Special Equipment

Micro Bio-Spin column (Bio-Gel P6, Bio-Rad)
PCR tubes (0.2-ml thin-walled)
Phase Lock Gel (heavy) (0.5-ml tube; Brinkmann Eppendorf)
Thermal cycler
Water baths at 42ºC and 65ºC.

METHOD

Synthesis of First-strand and Second-strand cDNA

1. To synthesize first-strand cDNA, mix the following in a 0.2-ml thin-walled PCR tube:

total RNA	(0.01–0 5 µg)
oligo(dT)$_{15}$–T7 promoter (100 pmoles/ml)	1 µl
H$_2$O	to 8 µl

   Seal the tube and incubate it for 5 minutes at 70°C. Remove the tube from the water bath or thermal cycler and allow it to stand for 5 minutes at room temperature.

   > The amount of oligo(dT)–T7 primer used in this reaction varies according to the amount of total RNA used in the reaction. Although the primer should always be in molar excess, too much primer can lead to nonspecific amplification at later stages of the protocol (Baugh et al. 2001). Before committing valuable samples to the protocol, carry out a series of test reactions and amplifications containing different amounts of template RNA and different molar ratios of primer. The aim should be to find the ratios of primer:template that generate the maximum yields of aRNA.

2. To the contents of the RNA/oligo(dT) mix, add:

5x first-strand buffer	4 µl
TS (template switch) primer (30 pmoles/µl)	1 µl
0.1 M DTT	2 µl
RNase inhibitor	1 µl
10 mM dNTP solution	2 µl
SUPERSCRIPT II RT (200 units/µl)	2 µl

   Mix the reagents by gentle vortexing and centrifuge the reaction mixture briefly to eliminate any bubbles. Incubate the sealed microfuge tube for 90 minutes at 42°C in a thermal cycler.

3. To synthesize second-strand cDNA, add the following reagents directly to the first-strand reaction mixture:

H$_2$O	106 µl
Advantage PCR buffer	15 µl
10 mM dNTP solution	3 µl
RNase H (2 units/µl)	1 µl
Advantage cDNA polymerase mix (CLONTECH)	3 µl

   Mix the reagents by gentle vortexing and transfer the tube to a thermal cycler, programmed as follows:

   > 37°C for 5 min (to digest the mRNA component of the first-strand:cDNA hybrid)
   > 94°C for 2 min (to denature the DNA-DNA hybrid at the 3′ end of the first-strand cDNA)
   > 65°C for 1 min (to allow the primers to bind)
   > 75°C for 30 min (to allow for extension of the primers into full-length cDNA strands)

   > Since the TS primer that initiates the second-strand cDNA synthesis is already present in the first-strand cDNA synthesis reaction mixture and has been used as a primer to generate the extension to the 3′ end of the first-strand cDNA, no further addition of primer is required at this step.

4. Stop the reaction by adding 7.5 μl of 1 M NaOH solution containing 2 mM EDTA and incubate the reactions for 10 minutes at 65°C.

   > The NaOH increases the pH of the reaction mixture, which enhances the efficiency of extraction with phenol:chloroform:isoamyl alcohol (Step 5) and inactivated enzymes. The reaction can be stored at –20°C at this stage.

Purification of Double-stranded cDNA

This step is designed to prevent carryover of unincorporated dNTP, primers, and inactivated enzymes into the subsequent in vitro transcription reaction.

5. Transfer the reaction mixture to a 1.5-ml microfuge tube containing:

linear acrylamide (0.1 μg/μl)	1 μl
phenol:chloroform:isoamyl alcohol	150 μl

   Close the tube and mix the reagents by gentle vortexing.

6. Transfer the emulsion to a Phase Lock Gel tube and centrifuge the tube at 10,000g for 5 minutes at room temperature.

7. Transfer the aqueous phase to a fresh 1.7-ml microfuge tube and add 70 μl of 7.5 M ammonium acetate followed by 1 ml of absolute ethanol. Close the tube and mix the reagents by gentle vortexing. Proceed without delay to the next step.

8. Centrifuge the ethanolic solution at 10,000g for 20 minutes at room temperature (to prevent coprecipitation of oligonucleotide primers).

9. Discard the supernatant and wash the pellet with 800 μl of 75% ethanol. Centrifuge again at 10,000g for 10 minutes. Repeat the washing step one more time.

10. Discard the final supernatant and allow the pellet to dry in the air. Dissolve the double-stranded cDNA in 70 μl of H_2O.

11. Prepare a Micro Bio-Spin chromatography column (Bio-Gel P6 column in Tris) as follows:

    a. Invert the column several times to resuspend the settled gel and remove any bubbles.

    b. Snap off the tip and place the column in a collection tube.

    c. Remove the cap and allow the buffer to drain out.

    d. Discard the drained buffer and apply 700 μl of H_2O to the column.

    e. Discard the flow-through and repeat the washing step three times.

    f. Centrifuge the column at 700g for 2 minutes at room temperature.

       > When opening the column, sometimes a gel will be attached to the underside of the cap. Try to recover as much of the gel as possible and replace it in the column, and then aspirate any remaining gel from the lid.
       >
       > Because the collection tubes provided by the manufacturer are not RNase-free, collect the eluate from the column using RNase-free tubes prepared locally.

12. Insert the column into a fresh RNase-free collection tube. Load the DNA preparation (70 μl, Step 9) into the center of the column and centrifuge the column at 700g for 4 minutes.

13. Evaporate the sample to damp-dryness in a rotary evaporator (e.g., SpeedVac) and dissolve it in 8 μl of H_2O.

In Vitro Transcription of Double-stranded cDNA

All reagents and master mixes (except for the T7 RNA polymerase!) should be thawed completely, mixed well, and centrifuged briefly before use. Store the polymerase in the freezer until all other reagents of the master mix have been added. Check the 10x reaction buffer supplied with the MEGAscript kit for precipitation. If a precipitate is visible, warm the buffer to 37°C until the precipitate is no longer visible (5–10 minutes). Vortex the buffer gently and centrifuge it briefly to deposit the fluid in the bottom of the tube.

The reagents used in this part of the protocol are supplied as part of the Ambion T7 MEGAscript kit.

14. To the sample of double-stranded cDNA (Step 13), add:

ATP (75 mM)	2.0 μl
GTP (75 mM)	2.0 μl
ATP (75 mM)	2.0 μl
GTP (75 mM)	2.0 μl
10x reaction buffer	2 μl
enzyme mixture (RNase inhibitor and T7 RNA polymerase)	2 μl

Incubate the reaction mixture for 6 hours at 37°C.

According to Ambion, the incubation can be interrupted by storing the reaction tube at –20°C and resuming the incubation later without losing efficiency.

Purification of aRNA

15. Purify the RNA synthesized in Step 14 by standard extraction with phenol:chloroform (as decribed in Step 6 of Protocol 15). Alternatively, use a monophasic reagent such as TRIzol, as summarized below.

   a. Add 1 ml of TRIzol solution to the transcription reaction. Mix the reagents well by pipetting or gentle vortexing.

   b. Add 200 μl of chloroform per 1 ml of TRIzol solution. Mix the reagents by inverting the tube for 15 seconds. Allow the tube to stand for 2–3 minutes at room temperature.

   c. Centrifuge the tube at 10,000*g* for 15 minutes at 4°C.

   d. Transfer the aqueous phase to a fresh tube and add 500 μl of isopropanol per 1 ml of TRIzol reagent.

   e. Store the sample for 10 minutes at room temperature and then centrifuge at 10,000*g* for 15 minutes.

   f. Wash the pellet twice with 1 ml of 70% ethanol.

   g. Allow the pellet to dry in the air for 15–20 minutes and then dissolve it in 20 μl of H_2O.

   h. Measure the quantity of RNA concentration spectrophotometrically.

Second Round of Amplification

16. Mix in a 0.2-ml thin-walled PCR tube:

aRNA (Step 15)	0.5–1 μg
random primers (1 μg/μl)	2 μl
H₂O	to 10 μl

    Heat the mixture to 70ºC for 5 minutes and then allow the tube to cool on the bench for 5–10 minutes.

17. Add the following reagents to the mixture prepared in Step 14:

5x first-strand buffer	4 μl
oligo(dT)$_{15}$–T7 promoter (100 pmoles/ml)	1 μl
0.1 M DTT	2 μl
RNase inhibitor	1 μl
10 mM dNTP solution	2 μl
SUPERSCRIPT II RT (200 units/μl)	2 μl

    Mix the reagents by gentle vortexing and centrifuge the reaction mixture briefly to eliminate any bubbles. Incubate the sealed microfuge tube in a thermal cycler for 90 minutes at 42ºC.

18. From this point on, follow the previously described procedures for synthesis of second-strand cDNA (Steps 3–4), purification of double-stranded cDNA (Steps 5–13), in vitro transcription (Step 14) with 40 μl of reaction mixture instead of 20 μl, and isolation of aRNA (Step 15).

    The quality of the second-round aRNA can be monitored by electrophoresis through denaturing gels (Sambrook and Russell 2001). The size of the RNA obtained from the first-round amplification ranges from 500 to 6000 nucleotides and from 500 to 4000 nucleotides obtained from the second-round amplification (please see Table 3-8 and Figure 3-21).

    The aRNA can now be used as a template for synthesis of fluorescently labeled cDNA, catalyzed by reverse transcriptase as described in Protocol 13.

TABLE 3-8. Concentration and Ratios of RNA

Sample Mel 888	Total RNA
Fragment name	
1	18S
2	28S
Corrected RNA area	2,386.00
RNA concentration (ng/μl)	1,477.54
rRNA ratio (28S/18S)	**1.58**

	1st IVT
Corrected RNA area	529.66
RNA concentration (ng/μl)	327.99
rRNA ratio (#2/#1)	**0**

	2nd IVT
Corrected RNA area	1,057.73
RNA concentration (ng/μl)	655
rRNA ratio (#2/#1)	**0**

Data derived from Figure 3-21, panel B.

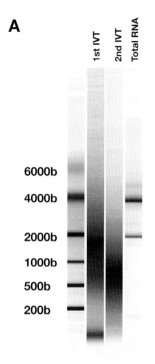

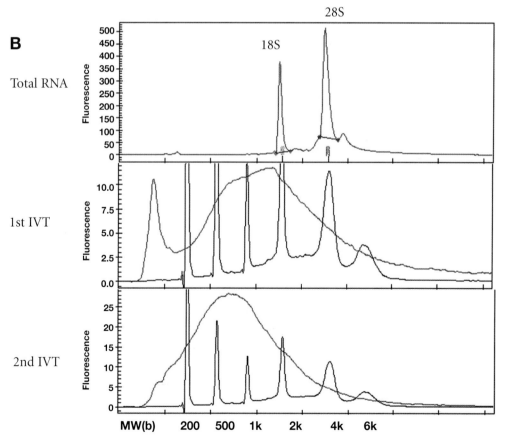

FIGURE 3-21. Analysis of products of in vitro transcription (IVT). (*A*) RNA products of in vitro transcription separated by electrophoresis on an RNA 6000 chip using an Agilent Bio-Analyzer 2100. (*B*) Quality analysis electropherograms of amplified RNA obtained using an Agilent Bio-Analyzer. (*Blue*) Molecular ladder; (*red*) sample.

Labeling Second-strand DNA Using the Klenow Fragment of *E. coli* DNA Polymerase

In the following protocol, the preparation of single-stranded cDNA is labeled with fluorescent nucleotides in a reaction primed by random hexamers and catalyzed by the Klenow fragment of *E. coli* DNA polymerase. Because of their uniform length and lack of sequence bias, synthetic oligonucleotides of random sequence are the primers of choice for labeling cDNAs, for example, cDNAs generated by amplification of RNA (Protocols 15 and 16). An alternative protocol at the end of this protocol describes labeling of double-stranded genomic DNA using the Klenow fragment.

MATERIALS

CAUTION: Please see Appendix 3 for appropriate handling of materials marked with <!>.
IMPORTANT: Prepare all buffers and solutions in DEPC-treated H_2O and store frozen in small aliquots.

Buffers and Solutions

EDTA (0.5 M, pH 8.0)

Enzymes and Buffers

Klenow fragment of *E. coli* DNA polymerase I (e.g., high-concentration, exonuclease-free Klenow 50 units/µl from New England Biolabs)
5x Random priming buffer
  250 mM Tris (pH 8.0)
  100 mM NaCl
  25 mM $MgCl_2$
  10 mM dithiothreitol (DTT) <!>
  1 M HEPES (adjusted to pH 6.6 with 4 M NaOH <!>)
    Sterilize the buffer by filtration and store it in small aliquots at –20ºC.
RNase H (1–5 units/µl)

Nucleic Acids

Cy3-labeled dUTP (1 mM) and Cy5-labeled dUTP (1 mM) (Amersham Biosciences)
  dNTPs conjugated to carbocyanine dyes are light-sensitive and should be stored at –20ºC in light-proof containers.
10x dNTP/Low-dTTP solution
  Prepare a solution containing dATP, dCTP, dGTP, each at a concentration of 5 mM, and dTTP at 2 mM. Store the solution in small aliquots at –20°C. For instructions on preparing and storing dNTPs, please see Appendix 2.
Oligo(dT)$_{12-18}$ or anchored primers (2 µg/µl)

Random primers (4 µg/µl in TE at pH 7.6)
> Oligonucleotides of optimal length (hexamers and heptamers; Suganuma and Gupta 1995) can be purchased from commercial sources (e.g., Amersham Biosciences or Boehringer Mannheim) or synthesized locally on an automated synthesizer. Store the solution of primers at –70°C in small aliquots.

Total RNA or poly(A)⁺ RNA
> Prepare as described in Protocol 1, 5, or 6.

Centrifuges and Rotors

Desktop centrifuge (high-speed 16,000g) for 1.5-ml microfuge tubes

Special Equipment

Microcon YM-100 (42412, Amicon)
Molecular Dynamics Storm fluorescence scanner (or equivalent)
PCR tubes (0.2-ml thin-walled)
QIAquick PCR purification kit (50) (28104, QIAGEN)
Thermal cycler
> The cycler should be able to accommodate 0.2-ml thin-walled PCR tubes.

METHOD

Annealing the Primer to the mRNA

1. In a thin-walled 0.2-ml PCR tube, mix:

total RNA	50 µg
or	
poly(A)⁺ RNA	1 µg
oligo(dT)$_{12-18}$ or anchored primers (2 µg/µl)	0.5 µl
H$_2$O	to 22.5 µl

2. Heat the reaction mixture in a thermal cycler for 10 minutes to 65°C. Cool the mixture on ice for 2 minutes.

Synthesis of Unlabeled First-strand cDNA

3. Add to the mixture from Step 2:

5x first-strand cDNA buffer	8.0 µl
0.1 M DTT	4.0 µl
5 mM dNTPs	4.0 µl
SUPERSCRIPT II RT (200 units/µl)	1.5 µl

   Reverse transcriptases are very sensitive to denaturation at air/liquid interfaces, so be very careful to avoid foaming when mixing the components of the reaction. This is sometimes difficult because many preparations of reverse transcriptase are supplied in buffers containing nonionic detergents such as Nonidet P-40 or Triton X-100.

   Mo-MLV (SUPERSCRIPT II) is temperature-sensitive and should be stored at –20°C until the last possible moment and be returned to the freezer at the first possible opportunity.

4. Incubate the reaction mixture for 1 hour at 42ºC.

5. Add 0.25 µl of RNase H (1–5 units/µl).

6. Incubate the reaction mixture for 30 minutes at 37ºC.

Cleanup of First-strand cDNA

7. Add 160 µl of TE (pH 7.4) and mix the reaction mixture thoroughly by gentle vortexing.

8. Transfer the reaction mixture to a Microcon YM-30 cartridge. Centrifuge the cartridge at 16,000*g* for 5 minutes. Discard the flow-through.

9. Add 200 µl of TE (pH 7.4) to the cartridge. Again centrifuge the cartridge at 16,000*g* for 5 minutes. Discard the flow-through.

10. Recover the concentrate by inverting the cartridge in a fresh collection tube. Centrifuge the inverted cartridge at ~1000*g* for 1 minute. The volume of the concentrate should be ~2 µl.

    When concentrating solutions by centrifugal filtration, the centrifugation times required to achieve the desired final volume are variable. Overly long spins can remove nearly all of the solvent from the solution. When fluorochrome-labeled nucleic acids are concentrated onto the filter in this fashion, they become very difficult to recover. To minimize problems, approach the desired volume incrementally by conservative estimations of the required spin times.

11. Add 40 µl of H_2O to the cartridge. Insert the inverted column in the same collection tube (Step 10). Centrifuge the inverted cartridge in a microfuge at ~1000*g* for 1 minute.

12. Adjust the volume of the flow-through to 58 µl with H_2O.

13. Transfer 29 µl of the flow-through to a fresh 0.2-ml thin-walled PCR tube. The remaining 29 µl can be stored at –20ºC or used for labeling.

Synthesis of Fluorescent Second-strand cDNA

14. Mix the following components:

first-strand cDNA (Step 13)	29 µl
10x Klenow buffer	4 µl
random primer (4 µg/µl)	1 µl

15. Incubate the tube for 2–3 minutes at 100ºC in a thermal cycler. Allow the tube to cool to room temperature on the bench.

16. Add the following components to the tube:

10x low-dNTP solution	4 µl
Cy3-labeled or Cy5-labeled dUTP (1 mM)	1 µl
Klenow fragment (50 units/µl)	1 µl

    Incubate the reaction for 3 hours at 37ºC.

Cleanup of Fluorescent Second-strand cDNA

17. Remove the contaminants from the fluorescently labeled DNA using QIAquick PCR purification columns (QIAGEN). Follow the instructions in the panel below Step 12 in Protocol 14.

ALTERNATIVE PROTOCOL: LABELING GENOMIC DNA USING THE KLENOW FRAGMENT OF *E. COLI* DNA POLYMERASE

In this protocol, fragmented genomic DNA is labeled with fluorescent nucleotides in a reaction catalyzed by the Klenow fragment of *E. coli* DNA polymerase and primed by random hexamers. The labeled DNA can be used as a target in comparative genomic hybridization experiments (please see Section 5).

Additional Materials

Genomic DNA, fragmented by sonication to an average length of 500 bp to 1 kb
  Prepare the sonicated DNA according to the method described on pages 12.15–12.16 of Sambrook and
  Russell (2001).
Microcon YM-30 (Millipore)
5x Three dNTP solution, containing dATP, dCTP, dGTP, each at a concentration of 5 mM
Water baths set at 95°C and 37°C

Method

1. In a 1.5-ml microfuge tube, mix the fragmented genomic DNA and random primers:

fragmented genomic DNA	1 μg
random primers (4 mg/ml)	2 μl
H$_2$O	to 20 μl

2. Heat the mixture for 2 minutes to 95°C in a thermal cycler. Cool the mixture for 2 minutes on ice.

3. Prepare the labeling mix:

5x random priming buffer	10 μl
5x three dNTP solution	5 μl
H$_2$O	12 μl

4. Transfer the labeling mix to the tube containing the genomic DNA and add:

Cy3- or Cy5-labeled dUTP (1 mM)	2 μl
Klenow fragment (50 units/μl)	1 μl

   Incubate the reaction for 3 hours at 37°C in the dark.

5. Add 2.5 μl of EDTA (0.5 M, pH 8.0) to stop the reaction.

6. Remove unincorporated dNTPs as follows:
   a. Add 470 μl of H$_2$O to the reaction.
   b. Transfer the diluted reaction mixture to a Microcon YM-30 filtration unit in a collection tube.
   c. Reduce the volume to 20–30 μl by centrifugation at 13,000g for 8–10 minutes.
   d. Add 450 μl of H$_2$O to the 20–30 μl of fluid in the upper portion on the Microcon YM-30.
   e. Repeat the centrifugation step.
   f. Add 450 μl of H$_2$O to the 20–30 μl of fluid in the upper portion on the Microcon YM-30.
   g. Repeat the centrifugation step until the volume is reduced to ~10 μl.
   h. Place the filtration unit into a fresh microfuge tube and centrifuge at 3000g for 3 minutes.

   Store the labeled genomic DNA at 4°C in the dark until ready to proceed with hybridization.

Labeling of Amplified RNA with Biotinylated Nucleotides for Hybridization to Oligonucleotide Arrays

Ed Tom, Jerry Lee, Dorian Willhite, Suzanne Ybarra, and Richard Glynne

Eos Biotechnology, South San Francisco, California 94080

In general, preparations of mRNA are not hybridized directly to oligonucleotide arrays. Instead, a derivative of the mRNA is synthesized that contains labeled nucleotides. In this protocol, the mRNA is converted into unlabeled double-stranded cDNA carrying the bacteriophage T7 promoter. The cDNA is then used as a template for an in vitro transcription reaction catalyzed by T7 DNA-dependent RNA polymerase in the presence of biotinylated nucleotides. Biotinylated bases are used for labeling because fluorescent nucleotides are poor substrates for bacteriophage-encoded RNA polymerases. Since each cDNA template is transcribed many times, the mRNA sequences (or more precisely, complementary copies of them) become amplified several thousandfold in a linear fashion, and, simultaneously, are labeled with biotinylated bases that can be used to detect hybrids on oligonucleotide arrays. The biotinylated cRNA is then chemically fragmented, mixed with control cRNA fragments, and hybridized to the oligonucleotide array. The biotinylated cRNA is detected by binding of streptavidin-phycoerythrin and scanning with a confocal laser scanner.

This labeling protocol has been tested on spotted oligonucleotide arrays, but not, as yet, with cDNA arrays. The results show that oligonucleotide-biotinylated RNA hybrids can be detected with approximately the same sensitivity as hybrids labeled by Cy3 or Cy5.

The transcription of double-stranded cDNA tagged with the T7 promoter was originally developed to amplify small quantities of mRNA without significantly affecting mRNA copy levels (Van Gelder et al. 1990; Eberwine et al. 1992; Phillips and Eberwine 1996; Luo et al. 1999; Wang et al. 2000). The first stage of this method—the conversion of mRNA to T7-tagged double-stranded cDNA—is detailed in Steps 1–4 of Protocol 15, which should be completed before beginning the labeling protocol described here.

MATERIALS

CAUTION: Please see Appendix 3 for appropriate handling of materials marked with <!>.

IMPORTANT: Prepare all reagents used in this protocol with DEPC-treated H_2O (please see the information panel on **SPECIAL CONSIDERATIONS FOR WORKING WITH RNA**).

Buffers and Solutions

Please see Appendix 2 for components of stock solutions, buffers, and reagents.
Dilute stock solutions to the appropriate concentrations.

Ammonium acetate (5 M)

Ethanol (absolute) at room temperature and 80% chilled to –20°C

Ethanol (absolute)

> Some batches of absolute ethanol (100% or 200 proof) have been reported to contain fluorescent contaminants that generate high backgrounds in microarray experiments; 95% ethanol does not have this problem. To avoid difficulties, either use 95% ethanol or identify a brand of absolute ethanol that performs reliably. Absolute ethanol (USP-grade ethyl alcohol) purchased from Rossville (Gold Shield) performs consistently well.

Phenol:chloroform:isoamyl alcohol (25:24:1) <!>

Enzymes and Buffers

T7 RNA polymerase (part of Ambion MEGAscript T7 kit)

10x T7 transcription buffer (part of Ambion MEGAscript T7 kit)

Nucleic Acids and Oligonucleotides

ATP, GTP, CTP, UTP (each at a concentration of 75 mM; part of Ambion MEGAscript T7 kit)

Bio-11-CTP (10 mM) (Enzo)

Bio-16-UTP (10 mM) (Roche)

Double-stranded cDNA, tagged with a bacteriophage T7 promoter sequence

> The cDNA is prepared from 10 µg of total RNA or 1 µg of poly(A)$^+$ RNA as described in Protocol 15, Steps 1–4; the volume after cDNA synthesis should be ~155 µl.

Marker/ladder of DNA or RNA (MBI Fermentas)

Special Reagents and Kits

Linear polyacrylamide (0.25%) (please see Protocol 16)

RNeasy kit (QIAGEN)

T7 MEGAscript kit (Ambion)

Special Equipment

PCR tubes (0.2-ml thin-walled)

> For larger numbers of samples, strip tubes and caps can be used.

Phase Lock Gel Light tubes (Brinkmann Eppendorf or 5 Prime→3 Prime)

Picofuge (Stratagene) or equivalent centrifuge

Thermal cycler fitted with a heated lid (MJ Research) or equivalent

METHOD

Concentrating the cDNA

After converting total RNA or poly(A)$^+$ RNA into double-stranded cDNA tagged with the bacteriophage T7 promoter (Steps 1–4, Protocol 15), the cDNA is purified in Phase Lock Gel Light tubes, as described below.

1. Centrifuge one Phase Lock Gel Light tube for each reaction at 13,000g or greater for 1 minute at room temperature.

2. Add cDNA sample (~155 μl) to Phase Lock Gel Light tube.

3. Add equal volume (~155 μl) of phenol:chloroform:isoamyl alcohol (25:24:1).

4. Invert the tube and shake vigorously or vortex for 1–2 seconds.

5. Centrifuge Phase Lock Gel Light tubes at 13,000g or greater in a microfuge for 2 minutes at room temperature.

6. Transfer the upper aqueous layer (~150 μl) into a fresh microfuge tube.

7. Precipitate the cDNA by adding:

linear acrylamide (0.25%)	0.5 μl
aqueous phase	150 μl
5 M ammonium acetate (equal volume to aqueous phase)	150 μl

   Mix the reagents by gentle vortexing.

8. Add ethanol equivalent to 2.5x volume of aqueous phase phus 5 M ammonium acetate, which is usually 750 μl. Mix the reagents by gentle vortexing and then store the solution for at least 20 minutes at –20°C.

9. Recover the cDNA by centrifugation at 12,000g or greater for 30 minutes at 16°C.

10. Carefully remove the ethanol from the faint, whitish pellet.

11. Wash the pellet twice with 500 μl of 80% ethanol prechilled to –20°C, each time recovering the DNA by centrifugation at 13,000g or greater for 5 minutes at 16°C.

12. After the final centrifugation, carefully remove the ethanol and store the open tube on the bench or chemical fume hood until the pellet is damp-dry.

13. Dissolve the pellet in 3 μl of H_2O.

Transcribing the cDNA In Vitro, Using the Ambion T7 MEGAscript Kit

14. Prepare the Transcription Master Mix. Multiply the volumes for each reaction by (x +1/2), where x is the total number of reactions.

ATP (75 mM)	2.0 μl
GTP (75 mM)	2.0 μl
CTP (75 mM)	1.5 μl
UTP (75 mM)	1.5 μl
Bio-11-CTP (10 mM)	3.75 μl
Bio-16-UTP (10 mM)	3.75 μl
10x T7 transcription buffer	2.0 μl
T7 RNA polymerase (100 units/μl)	2.0 μl

15. Add 18.5 µl of the Transcription Master Mix to a 0.2-ml thin-walled PCR tube.

16. Add 1.5 µl of the T7-promoter-tagged, double-stranded cDNA(s) (Step 13). Mix the reagents by gentle pipetting. Store the unused portion of the cDNA at –20ºC.

17. Centrifuge the tube(s) briefly in a picofuge to deposit the fluid in the bottom of tube.

18. Transfer the tubes to a thermal cycler and incubate the tube(s) for 6 hours at 37ºC, with postincubation hold temperature automatically set at 4ºC. Use the heated lid of the thermal cycler to prevent condensation.

    The biotinylated RNA can be stored for up to 1 week at –20ºC or for longer periods at –80ºC. The expected yield is 50–100 µg of cRNA from ~0.5 µg of double-stranded cDNA.

Purifying the Biotinylated RNA with the QIAGEN RNeasy Kit

19. Add 80 µl of H_2O to each sample of biotinylated RNA (Step 18). Mix the solution by pipetting and then transfer the mixture to a fresh 1.5-ml microfuge tube.

20. Add 350 µl of RLT buffer (QIAGEN) and mix thoroughly by gentle vortexing.

21. Add 250 µl of absolute ethanol. Mix by gentle vortexing.

22. Apply the sample (700 µl) to an RNeasy spin column.

23. Centrifuge the column at 10,000*g* in a microfuge for 15–20 seconds at room temperature.

24. Transfer the flow-through from the collection tube to a fresh microfuge tube. Store the flow-through at room temperature until the recovery of RNA is confirmed.

25. Discard the collection tube.
    IMPORTANT: Replace it with a fresh collection tube.

26. Add 500 µl of RPE buffer (QIAGEN) to the spin column.

    The fresh bottle of RPE buffer should be mixed with 95–100% ethanol before use, as prescribed by the QIAGEN manual.

27. Centrifuge the column at 10,000*g* for 15–20 seconds at room temperature.

28. Discard the flow-through, and then repeat Steps 26 and 27.

29. Discard the flow-through and centrifuge the column at 16,000*g* or greater for 2 minutes at room temperature.

    After centrifugation, check that no buffer is visible in the bottom tip of the spin column. If buffer is present, repeat the centrifugation step after removing the flow-through from the collection tube by pipetting.

30. Transfer the spin column to a fresh microfuge tube. Add 50 µl of H_2O directly to the center of the RNeasy membrane and store the column for 5 minutes at room temperature.

31. Centrifuge the column at 16,000*g* or greater for 2 minutes at room temperature.

32. Add another 50 µl of H_2O directly to the center of the RNeasy membrane and store the column for 5 minutes at room temperature.

33. Centrifuge the column at 16,000*g* or greater for 2 minutes at room temperature.

34. Discard the spin column and measure the amount of RNA in the flow-through spectrophotometrically at 260 nm and 280 nm.

35. Analyze 200–300 ng of the RNA by electrophoresis through a 1% agarose gel. As markers, use either an RNA ladder (low range) or a DNA ladder (100-bp spacing).

> A native agarose gel may work as well as a fully denaturing gel in verifying RNA integrity. The cRNA should appear as a smear with a median size of 600–1000 bases relative to a 100-bp DNA ladder.
>
> The cRNA need not be heated before loading onto the native agarose gel.
>
> Before hybridization to oligonucleotide microarrays, the cRNA is fragmented as described below in the additional protocol.

ADDITIONAL PROTOCOL: FRAGMENTATION OF BIOTINYLATED cRNA

To increase hybridization kinetics and reduce secondary structure, the biotinylated cRNA, prepared in the main protocol, is fragmented into products of 50–100 bases by heating in the presence of magnesium ions.

Additional Materials

Biotinylated cRNA
Filter (0.2 μm)
Magnesium acetate
Potassium acetate
Tris-acetate (1 M, pH 8.1)
  Trizma base. Adjust pH with acetic acid.

Method

1. Transfer 15 μg of biotinylated cRNA in a volume equal to or less than 16 μl into PCR tubes (concentrate by ethanol precipitation if necessary).

2. Adjust the cRNA volume to 16 μl with RNase-free H_2O.

3. Prepare the 5x fragmentation buffer:

Reagent	Amount	Final Concentration
1 M Tris-acetate (pH 8.1)	4.0 ml	200 mM
MgOAc	0.64 g	150 mM
KOAc	0.98 g	500 mM

Adjust the final volume to 20 ml with RNase-free H_2O, and filter through a 0.2-μm filter.

4. Add 4 μl of 5x fragmentation buffer to the cRNA and incubate the mixture for 35 minutes at 95°C in thermal cycler with heated lid.

   IMPORTANT: The use of microcentrifuge tubes in a heat block is not recommended as evaporation of buffer occurs during the incubation.

5. Centrifuge the tube(s) in a picofuge to collect any condensation and place the tubes on ice.

   The fragmented cRNA is ready to be used for hybridization.

Recovery of Unincorporated Cy Dyes: Repurification by HPLC*

Chih Long Liu

Biological and Biomedical Sciences, Division of Biomedical Sciences, Harvard Medical School, Boston, Massachusetts 02115

One of the barriers to microarray analysis is the high cost of fluorescent nucleotides used in labeling the cDNA for cDNA microarray hybridization and analysis. A typical labeling reaction, in which reverse transcriptase copies mRNA into Cy3- or Cy5-labeled cDNA, consumes ~3 nmoles of the dye. At current market prices ($295/25 nmoles, October 2001), costs can become quickly prohibitive if a large number of samples are analyzed (a typical tumor profiling assay may involve hundreds of samples, resulting in costs of tens of thousands of dollars for the dye alone).

Reverse transcriptases do not efficiently incorporate the dye-conjugated nucleotides into cDNA. Incorporation rates as high as 5% have been reported, but the typical incorporation rate is more on the order of 2–4% (Yu et al. 1994; unpubl.). Among the factors contributing to this low efficiency are (1) the lability of the dye (especially Cy5 dUTP) and (2) steric inhibition by the bulky fluorescent chromophore. Dye nucleotides are used in reactions at concentrations, generally close to K_m, that generate a satisfactory yield of product, labeled to an appropriate specific activity, that hybridizes efficiently. Decreasing the concentration of Cy3- and Cy5-labeled nucleotides in the labeling reaction will not reduce costs since the rates of incorporation into cDNA, already low, will be decreased still further.

The expense, however, can be lowered by recovering unincorporated dyes from the reaction mixture. In the method described here, based on a protocol for separation of dNTPs by high-performance liquid chromatography (HPLC), the dyes are recovered from a spent reaction mixture containing unincorporated unlabeled nucleotides, reverse transcriptase, buffer components, degraded RNA, DNA primers, and aborted cDNA transcripts. The HPLC column contains an anion-exchange, reversed-phase C-18 resin. The anionic and neutral components of the reaction mixture are washed from the resin by anionic exchange. Unincorporated unlabeled nucleotides, which lack the hydrocarbon chain present in the cyanine nucleotides, have low retention times because of the reversed-phase qualities of the column. The combination of anion-exchange and reversed phase has the advantage of enabling the separation of the desired triphosphate form of the dye-nucleotide from the mono- and diphosphorylated forms. Aborted cDNA transcripts most likely account for labeled components with retention times longer than those of the cyanine-linked nucleotides. Please note that this protocol cannot be used to recover amino-allyl dyes.

*Kathleen Hayashibara (Perkins-Elmer Biosystems) and Linda McAllister (Celera Diagnostics) former members of the Pat Brown laboratory assisted with this protocol. The method for purification of Cy dyes by HPLC is based on a protocol by Suzanne Admiraal, a former member of the Herschlag Lab.

In general, the activity of purified, recycled Cy3 and Cy5 dyes is comparable to the activity of the stock dyes and that any variation in activity present is within the variation of array-to-array/day-to-day hybridization. Because there is no chemical reason why the stock and repurified dyes should behave differently from one another, any observed artifacts are most likely due to problems with the purification process itself or to nonconventional components that for some reason were added to the original labeling reaction. The protocol involves:

- An initial desalting step that permits a large initial load on the column.

- A lyophilization step to reduce the volume of the sample.

- Filtration through a Microcon or Centricon filter to remove unincorporated material or high-molecular-weight components of the original labeling reaction.

- Purification by HPLC.

- Several cycles of lyophilization-resuspension to evaporate the TEAA buffer used in HPLC purification.

MATERIALS

CAUTION: Please see Appendix 3 for appropriate handling of materials marked with <!>.

Buffers and Solutions

Please see Appendix 2 for components of stock solutions, buffers, and reagents.
Dilute stock solutions to the appropriate concentrations.

Acetonitrile <!>

Cyanine-dye nucleotides (Cy-labeled dNTPs), recovered from labeling reactions

For handling cyanine dyes: Cy-labeled dNTPs are usually collected from the labeling reaction at the stage when the labeled DNA is concentrated through Microcon filters. In the Brown laboratory, the flow-through from the filters is collected into separate tubes until the final wash is completed. This allows the probe to be rescued from the collected flow-through in the event of a Microcon filter failure. The tubes containing the flow-through are then combined after the final wash. Adding phosphate buffer (pH 7) at this stage to a concentration of 10 mM minimizes degradation of the triphosphate nucleotides into mono- and diphosphate forms. Unpurified dyes can then be stored for up to 1 year at –20ºC. Avoid storing the dyes in the freezer (the doors are frequently opened) since exposure accelerates degradation of the dyes (please see the panel on FINAL CONSIDERATIONS at the end of this protocol).

High-salt buffer (HSB)

1 M triethylammonium acetate (pH 8.0)

10% acetonitrile

Pass the buffer through a nylon 0.22-μm filter. Sparge the buffer in helium immediately before use in HPLC.

Low-salt buffer (LSB)

25 mM triethylammonium acetate (pH 8.0)

10% acetonitrile

Prepare a 40-fold dilution of HSB, and add acetonitrile to 10%. Pass the buffer through a nylon 0.22-μm filter. Sparge the buffer in helium immediately before use in HPLC.

Phosphate buffer (0.5 M and 10 mM, pH 7.0)

Triethylammonium acetate (TEAA) (1 M, pH 8.0)

Triethylammonium acetate (15 mM, pH 8.0)

Prepare by mixing 0.750 ml HSB with 49.25 ml of H_2O and passing the solution through a 0.22-μm filter.

Special Equipment

HPLC column (Dionex NucleoPac 9 × 250 PA-100; P/N 43011 [anion exchange])
HPLC equipment (Perkin Elmer Series 200 LC Pump, Perkin Elmer UV/Vis Detector LC 295)
Sep-Pak cartridges, C18; 1 column per Cy dye, per three sequential runs (20515, Waters Corp.)
Syringes (12 ml, 1 per dye)

METHOD

Sep-Pak Purification

1. Prepare the following materials in 50 ml tubes:

   acetonitrile (a set of three runs consumes ~40 ml)
   ddH$_2$O, filtered through an 0.22-μm Millipore filter
   15 mM TEAA

2. To preload, wash the Sep-Pak column with 10 ml of acetonitrile, followed by 5 ml of H$_2$O and 10 ml of 15 mM TEAA.

3. Add 1 M TEAA to the sample, to a final concentration of 15 mM TEAA (50 μl for a 3.25-ml volume). This addition usually boosts the yield by 1–2%.

   The column may be loaded with up to 150 OD$_{260}$ units of sample, lyophilized to a volume of 3–5 ml. Loading larger volumes of 6.5–7.5 ml can provide reasonable yields. Volumes of up to 10 ml have been used, but with a reduction in yield.

4. Load the sample onto the column. The dye will be visible near the top of the column. Wash the column with 5 ml of 15 mM TEAA.

5. Elute the Cy-labeled dNTPs from the column with 3 ml of acetonitrile, at a rate of ~1–2 drops per second. Discard the initial colorless drops, collect the colored drops into a 2-ml centrifuge tube, and discard the remaining drops.

   The expected collected volume will be ~1.0–2.0 ml. Some color may remain in the column after the elution.

6. Immediately wash the column, using the preload protocol (described in Step 2). Process up to two additional samples sequentially, rewashing the column between samples, and keeping the dyes separate.

   If the column is allowed to sit for more than 5 minutes, there may be a few drops of color during the washing of the column with H$_2$O in the preload protocol, and yields may decrease by 5–10% (or more). Avoid reusing the column more than twice (a total of three uses), as yields may begin to diminish.

7. Pool the colored samples and measure the UV absorbance (at the absorbance maximum for each dye). Use the extinction coefficient of the dye to calculate the yield (please see the information panel on MEASURING THE EFFICIENCY OF DYE LABELING OF DNA). Expected yields at this stage are 70–80% for each Cy-labeled dNTP.

   One wash–load–wash–elute cycle usually takes 15 minutes to complete and requires the use of a ring stand. It is possible, however, to increase throughput by scaling up the column size and using a vacuum rack apparatus to process several columns in parallel. Such columns and apparatuses are available in the Waters catalog (please see the panel on FINAL CONSIDERATIONS at this end of this protocol).

HPLC Purification

8. In a lyophilizer, reduce the volume of the pooled material from the Sep-Pak purification series (from Step 7) to ~0.5–1.0 ml, keeping the dyes separate.

    This will usually take 12–18 hours. The material may or may not dry completely during lyophilization; this is normal. If necessary, dissolve the dried pellet or adjust the volume of the liquid with 0.2 M TEAA so that the approximate concentration of the Cy-labeled dNTP is 200 nmoles (dye) per milliliter. The concentration of TEAA in the final solution is not critical: Anywhere within the range of 0.01–0.1 M TEAA is acceptable.

9. Centrifuge the sample through a Microcon 0.40-µm filter at 14,000*g* until the liquid level reaches the filter membrane. This usually takes ~10–20 minutes, depending on the concentration of the sample.

    This step removes any high-molecular-weight material that may have formed by aggregation during storage of the samples.

10. Measure the absorbance of the filtrate, and if necessary, dilute the sample to a concentration that will not exceed the capacity of the HPLC column (10 µmoles for the column specified below).

11. Equilibrate the HPLC column in the following buffer system, at a flow rate of 3 ml/minute (for the general purge method).

    5 minutes LSB
    2 minutes gradient to 100% HSB
    5 minutes HSB
    2 minutes gradient to 60% LSB
    5 minutes 60% LSB

12. Load the sample into the injection loop.

    For sample size and other issues, please see the panel on FINAL CONSIDERATIONS.

13. Run the gradient according to the following program (3 ml/minute flow, chart recorder 0.5 cm/minute).

    5 minutes 60% LSB, 40% HSB
    10 minutes gradient to 80% HSB
    1 minute gradient to 100% HSB
    10 minutes 100% HSB
    1 minute gradient to 60% LSB
    5 minutes 60% LSB

    The peak corresponding to the Cy-labeled dNTP should be separated from any other species present by at least 1–2 fractions of 1.8 ml.

    Retention times should be ~11–12 minutes for Cy3-labeled dUTP and 12.5–13 minutes for Cy5-labeled dUTP. Shorter retention times indicate that the effective separation capacity of the column is low and that the column is nearing the end of its useful life. The retention time of the column used for producing this protocol shortened by more than 20% over a period of 3 years, with a commensurate reduction in separation capacity.

Final Preparative Procedures: Lyophilization and Redilution

A preparative run of ~150 nmoles of Cy-labeled dNTP (please see the panel on FINAL CONSIDERATIONS) should yield ~5 ml of buffer containing the Cy-labeled nucleotide. In the final steps of the protocol, lyophilization is used to remove the buffer salts from the Cy-labeled dNTP.

14. Transfer the samples from the collection tubes to 50-ml plastic conical tubes, fitted with caps that have holes (an 18-gauge needle can be used to punch holes in the caps).

    Avoid filling more than half the volume of the tube, as the samples have a tendency to splatter and travel up the tube during lyophilization.

15. Freeze the samples on dry ice and transfer them to a lyophilization chamber. Wrap the chamber with foil to protect the samples from light.

16. Lyophilize the samples for 6–15 hours.

    Lyophilization carried out after Sep-Pak purification may be complete after 6–10 hours, because of the presence of volatile acetonitrile. Lyophilization is complete when the sample resembles a film and/or specks of solid residue.

17. Resuspend the samples in 8–10 ml with H_2O and lyophilize them to dryness; this is a lengthy process that may require up to 24 hours.

18. Repeat Step 17 and then resuspend the sample in 10 mM phosphate buffer (pH 7.0).

    Aim to dissolve the Cy-labeled dNTP at a concentration of 1 nmole/µl (based on the estimate of amount of material applied to the HPLC column). The Brown laboratory usually processes batches of ~50–200 nmoles of Cy-labeled dNTPs and, at this stage, uses 50 µl of buffer to redissolve the recovered material. If the liquid is too viscous, add additional buffer in 500-µl increments. After quantifying the recovered Cy-labeled dNTP (Step 19), adjust the concentration to 1 nmole/µl.

    Bear in mind that some of the Cy-labeled dNTP will coat the upper regions of the tube walls and may not be visible to the naked eye. To recover this residue, pipette the liquid onto the upper regions of the tube walls and roll the tube, ensuring that the drop travels across the entire surface area of the tube. The drop will often acquire the color of the dye even before visible specks of residue have been resuspended.

19. Measure the absorbance of the sample. $A_{560/660}/A_{260}$ ratios should be ~17 for Cy3-labeled dNTP and 25 for Cy5-labeled dNTP. Lower ratios indicate that TEAA buffer is still present.

    Expected overall yield for Cy3-labeled dNTP is 50–70% and for Cy5-labeled dNTP, 45–65%.

FINAL CONSIDERATIONS

An optimal lot for injection into an HPLC column contains ~150 nmoles of Cy-labeled dNTP, depending on the contents and concentration of the Microcon filtrate. HPLC purification can be used without Sep-Pak purification, but the effective capacity of the column is then reduced from 150 nmoles to <50 nmoles and the overall yields tend to be lower. The post Sep-Pak lyophilization step is still necessary and may take longer to complete because of the high concentration of buffer salts in the samples.

The rate-limiting step for the entire protocol will most likely be the Sep-Pak purification step, especially if large amounts of Cy-labeled dNTP filtrate have accumulated. Larger C18 columns and filtration apparatuses for purification of several columns in parallel are available from Waters Corp. However, optimization would be necessary for significant scaling-up of the wash, load, and elution volumes.

The most likely causes for low yields of dye are excessive exposure to light, excessive freeze-thaw cycles, and storage for more than 1 year. The protocol can be performed under ambient laboratory lighting conditions, although steps should be taken to minimize direct exposure to light. Tubes or containers should be wrapped in foil or otherwise kept dark (e.g., in a closed ice bucket) during lengthy procedures (e.g., lyophilization) or inbetween steps of the protocol.

It may be possible to separate mixtures of Cy3- and Cy5-labeled dNTP from each other, although this protocol has not been optimized for that purpose. Collecting smaller fractions, modifying the initial LSB-HSB mix, and decreasing the slope of the gradient would be possibilities to consider when optimizing separation of the two dye nucleotides.

Hybridization and Posthybridization Washing

Trey Ideker,* Suzanne Ybarra,† and Sean Grimmond‡

*Whitehead Institute for Biomedical Research, Cambridge, Massachusetts 02142;
†Eos Biotechnology, South San Francisco, California 94080; ‡ARC-SRC for Functional
and Applied Genomics, Gene Expression Profiling Facility, Institute of Molecular Bioscience,
University of Queensland St Lucia, QLD, 4072 Australia

As in any hybridization, the following are the goals when annealing labeled targets to spotted DNA microarrays:

- To achieve the highest possible ratio of signal-to-background noise.

- To minimize cross-hybridization between labeled targets and arrayed elements that share small regions of homology.

- To ensure that the strength of the signal is proportional to the concentration of labeled target.

These goals are achieved by optimizing a number of experimental parameters, including the conditions and time of prehybridization and hybridization, the volume of the hybridization mixture, the ionic and buffering conditions, and the amount of labeled target in the hybridization mixture. For specific considerations of experimental design, please refer to Section 7.

In general, labeled targets are hybridized to DNA microarrays under conditions similar to those used for conventional Southern or northern hybridizations. Buffers of high ionic strength are used to reduce electrostatic repulsion and to promote association of complementary strands; blocking agents and detergents are used to minimize background noise; and hybridization and washing are carried out under conditions of moderate to high stringency to suppress cross-hybridization.

During hybridization, each immobilized target DNA must be in tenfold or more molar excess over its complementary, labeled target sequences. This arrangement ensures that hybridization will follow pseudo-first-order kinetics over a wide range of target concentrations. The strength of the signal emitted by any one element is determined by the initial concentration of the cognate target in the hybridization mixture. Thus, a twofold increase in target concentration will produce a twofold increase in signal, and abundant RNAs will generate stronger signals than RNAs of lower abundance. When the amount of immobilized target DNA is limiting, the dynamic range of the system is constricted and estimates of differential expression are compressed (Heller at al 1997; Yue et al. 2001). Targets (cDNAs or PCR products) in expression analysis are generally printed onto microarrays at a concentration of 100–500 ng/µl (Schena et al. 1996; Welford et al. 1998; for review, please see Deyholos and Galbraith 2001).

The characteristic dot patterns of microarrays become detectable when the signal-to-background ratio is greater than 1.5–2.0. A useful measure of the sensitivity of a microarray experiment is the smallest fraction of mRNA that can be reliably detected by hybridization to its cognate arrayed DNA element(s) (Bertucci et al. 1999). In an ideal experiment, this fractional detection limit would be 1–2 parts per million—enough to detect an RNA present in a few molecules per cell.

If the concentration of target in the hybridization mixture is too low, annealing will be slow and the attenuated signal may not be detected by the fluorescence scanner. The minimum quantity of target required for hybridization should contain just enough molecules of the lowest-abundance RNA in the sample to generate a readable signal after hybridization. Because both the ratio of signal to background and the dynamic range improve as the quantity of RNA increases, hybridization mixtures usually contain three or four times the calculated minimum quantity of target. However, if the concentration of the target is too high— for example, >10 times the calculated minimal amount—the dynamic range of the signal may be reduced, and the signal-to-background ratio may either deteriorate or may show no further improvement (Yue et al. 2001). As a rule of thumb, an amount of labeled target equivalent to at least 1 µg of poly(A)$^+$ RNA (~100 µg of total RNA) should be used in standard (15–35 µl) microarray hybridization mixtures. If these amounts are not available, the RNA preparation should be amplified before labeling (e.g., please see Guatelli et al. 1990; Van Gelder et al. 1990; Eberwine et al. 1992; Luo et al. 1999). Poly(A)$^+$ RNA (1 µg) typically corresponds to 10–40 pmoles of incorporated fluorescent dye.

This protocol describes the steps for prehybridization, hybridization, and washing of microarrays. An additional protocol on hybridization using microarray slide stacking may be found at the end of the main protocol.

BEFORE BEGINNING: MAKE A CLEAN WORK SURFACE

Dust is one of the most common contaminants in microarray experiments. Before setting up hybridization reactions, clean and cover all laboratory benches with a dust-free sheet placed over the work area. Two common dust-free sheetings include aluminium foil or absorbent bench coating, with the plastic side up. Conventional use of bench coating (absorbent side up) provides a source of contaminating fibers and dust particles that are attracted to clean dry slides by electrostatic forces. Wear powder-free nitrile gloves. Avoid exposing the labeled targets to strong light.

MATERIALS

CAUTION: Please see Appendix 3 for appropriate handling of materials marked with <!>.

Buffers and Solutions

Please see Appendix 2 for components of stock solutions, buffers, and reagents.
Dilute stock solutions to the appropriate concentrations.

Bovine serum albumin (BSA) (10% w/v, Worthington)
50x Denhardt's solution
Formamide, molecular-biology grade (100%) (BP227-100, Fisher Scientific) <!>
    Please see the information panel on FORMAMIDE.
Isopropanol (HPLC grade)
SDS (20%) (US75932, USB) <!>
20x SSC (pH 7.0) (US19629, USB) *or* 20x SSPE

Nucleic Acids and Oligonucleotides

C_0t-1 DNA (20 mg/ml, human or mouse as appropriate) (GIBCO)
Poly(A) (10 mg/ml) (P 9403, Sigma)
Target DNA, labeled as described in Protocol 13 <!>
tRNA (10 mg/ml) (15401-011, GIBCO)

Special Equipment

Coverslips (e.g., HS40, HybriSlips, Grace BioLabs; *or* Corning Cover Glass, 2935-246, Fisher Scientific, 12-548-5P)

IMPORTANT: TO CLEAN COVERSLIPS:

- Briefly submerge coverslips in dH_2O, then dip them several times into a second container with dH_2O, and then dip them several times into a container containing 100% isopropanol.

- Wipe away isopropanol with a Kimwipe.

- Blow away dust with compressed air. Check that the coverslip is relatively clean and free of dust.

Coplin jars (S 5516, Sigma) or Microscope slide staining trays (VWR 25461-003)
Light-proof washing containers
    Washing containers may be Coplin jars (see above), large Petri dishes that have been covered in foil tape, or containers or staining dishes (VWR 13197-274) with matching slide racks (VWR 13197-272).
Microarray scanner (please see Table 3-9)
Microconcentrator (e.g., Microcon YM-100)
Microduster III (8 oz. refill; VWR 21899-092)
Slide racks (900234, Wheaton)

METHOD

Prehybridization

Prehybridization is used to:

- Wash unbound DNA from the slide prior to addition of the target.

- Block reactive groups on the surface of the slide (e.g., free amine groups) that can bind labeled target DNA nonspecifically.

    Prehybridization reduces nonspecific background but increases the risk of damaging or contaminating the slides during handling. Although opinion is mixed on its value for poly-L-lysine slides, prehybridization is recommended for gamma-amino propyl silane (GAPS) slides (Corning Microarray Technology), but is not absolutely required with Telechem SuperAmine slides; however, some investigators find that prehybridization of these slides is beneficial.

---

1. Transfer the slides to a Coplin jar filled with a solution of 0.1-1.0% (w/v) BSA, 5x SSC, 0.1% SDS at ambient temperature. Place the Coplin jar in a water bath for 30–45 minutes at 42ºC.

    All prehybridization and hybridization washes are carried out either in Coplin jars (as described here) or in microscope slide staining trays.

    An alternative method for preparing the slides is given in the panel below Step 4.

2. Wash the slides with several changes of H_2O at ambient temperature.

3. Rinse the slides in 100% isopropanol (HPLC grade).

    Some investigators report that the use of isopropanol adversely affects hybridization. If this is a problem, please use the alternative protocol immediately below.

4. Dry the slides in the air or by centrifugation (at 2000*g* for 5 minutes at room temperature, with array side facing out), prior to addition of the hybridization solution.

    Use the slides immediately for hybridization. The efficiency of hybridization is likely to decrease rapidly if the slides are allowed to dry for more than 1 hour.

The following alternative sequence of steps may be used instead of Steps 1–4 for cleaning slides.

- Submerge the slides in 5x SSC/0.2% SDS (pH 7.0) for ~40 minutes at 55°C. This incubation time is highly variable and depends on the batch of slides used. Use a Coplin staining jar placed inside a water bath, with no agitation.

- Immediately dip the slides five times in dH$_2$O at room temperature.

- Dry the slides by blowing with nitrogen or by centrifugation.

Hybridization of Labeled Targets

Hybridization solutions generally contain:

- 2.5–5x SSC or SSPE. SSPE has better buffering capacity, but SSC is more commonly used. SSPE should always be used in hybridization solutions that contain formamide, which is sometimes acidic.

- 0.1–0.25% SDS

In addition, hybridization solutions commonly contain combinations of the following constituents. Filter all components through a 0.22-μm filter before the hybridization solution is assembled.

- 50% formamide. Addition of formamide lowers the melting temperature of hybrids and allows hybridization to be performed at lower temperatures, reducing the tendency for evaporation. Hybridizations performed with formamide-containing solutions are incubated at 42°C, compared with 65°C for aqueous solutions.

- tRNA (0.75 mg/ml)*

- C_0t-1 DNA (1.0 mg/ml)*

- poly(A) (1 mg/ml)*

- BSA (0.2 mg/ml) or 5x Denhardt's solution

- salmon sperm DNA (100 μg/ml)

*These blocking agents are often used in combination. Some investigators choose to add these to the labeled target DNAs just before final clean up (Protocol 13, Step 8) to reduce losses by absorption to ultrafiltration membranes. A typical hybridization mixture might contain 50% formamide, 5x SSC, 0.1% SDS, 5x Denhardt's solution.

---

5. Mix together appropriate amounts of the Cy3- and Cy5-labeled target DNAs and concentrate the mixture to a final volume of ~6 μl in a Microcon YM-100 device as described in Steps 8 and 9 of Protocol 13.

6. Prepare the hybridization solution containing target DNAs and components listed below in the following volumes (~16 μl for a 24 x 24-mm coverslip, ~24 μl for a 24 x 40-mm coverslip, 32 μl for a 24 x 60-mm coverslip):

20x SSPE	10 μl
formamide	20 μl
C_0t-1 DNA	2.0 μl
poly(A)	2.0 μl
SDS (10%)	0.5 μl
labeled target	~6.0 μl

The above are components of a typical hybridization solution; however, the components may be varied as described in the panel preceding Step 5.

7. (*Optional*) Centrifuge the final mixture in a microfuge at 10,000*g* for 5 minutes, and then transfer the supernatant to a fresh tube.

Some investigators include a centrifugation step to remove small amounts of glass fiber and other high-molecular-weight particles that may have been introduced during clean-up of the target.

8. Heat the supernatant for 2 minutes at 100ºC. Cool the solution for 30 seconds in a 30ºC water bath.

Heating the hybridization mixture reduces the background. Do not place the solution on ice as SDS will precipitate.

9. Transfer the appropriate amount of hybridization solution to the DNA microarray. Carefully place a coverslip on the slide.

One of the more technically challenging steps in the microarray process involves setting up the hybridization reaction. This is a tricky process and should be practiced with dummy slides. The hybridization solution must be applied evenly to the surface of the microarray, and once deposited, it must be protected against evaporation, usually by placing a coverslip over the solution and incubating the microarray inside a humid chamber. Because these steps occur toward the end of the microarray protocol, subsequent to microarray fabrication and cDNA labeling, any associated problems may forfeit hours of prior laboratory work and, at the very least, will have a large impact on the quality of the resulting microarray image. In part due to these challenges, a number of automated processing "stations" have recently appeared on the market that attempt to automate the hybridization and washing steps. These machines are, however, still evolving: In our hands, the highest-quality microarray images obtained to date have been produced by careful, manual placement of the hybridization solution and coverslip. Two procedures are described in Figures 3-22 and 3-23. Both achieve the same end, in that once mastered, they yield fairly reproducible results. The choice between them is a matter of personal preference.

Do not add large amounts of target to the center of the microarray, as this is likely to cause air bubbles to form beneath the coverslip.

If the volume of the hybridization solution is too large, then the coverslip will float around the slide surface. With subsequent handling of the slide (e.g., placing it in the hybridization chamber or walking to the water bath), the coverslip may no longer rest over the printed array surface. It is tricky to lay the coverslip down with the hybridization solution in the center of the spotted area. Instead, the hybridization solution should be placed near the left inner edge of the spotted area allowing the air to be displaced by the hybridization solution as the coverslip is slowly lowered.

Standard histological coverslips may not be clean enough for microarray experiments and should therefore be cleaned as described in the panel in the Materials list. Dirty coverslips trap bubbles during set up, resulting in high background and/or black holes (please see the Troubleshooting Guide at the end of this protocol). Fine bubbles are not usually a problem, as they disappear as the solution warms up. Moving the coverslip in an attempt to remove or reposition small bubbles will cause harm.

10. Because hybridization is performed in a small volume, it is important to prevent dehydration by incubating the slide in a sealed humid environment. Satisfactory results can be obtained from any of the following arrangements:

    - A 25-place plastic slide storage box (light-proof), containing a piece of wet 3M Whatman paper (1 ml of 3x SSC for a 25-place slide box).

    - An empty pipette tip box, in which the lower part has been filled with 5 ml of 3x SSC and the slide placed flat over the perforated surface.

    - Commercial hybridization cassettes from Telechem or Corning, which provide a complete seal around the slide and can therefore be immersed in a water bath.

        Details for constructing hybridization of single-slide hybridization chambers are publicly available at: http://cmgm.stanford.edu/pbrown/mguide/index.html.

11. Incubate the slide for 14–16 hours at 42°C (if using a hybridization solution containing formamide) or 65°C (is using an aqueous hybridization solution).

    It is important to get the level of humidity just right: too dry, and the coverslip will adhere to the microarray, and high background will be seen; too humid, and condensation floods the area around the coverslip, reducing the strength of the signal.

Washing the Hybridized Arrays

IMPORTANT: Do not let slides dry out *at any stage* during the washing procedure. Do not use excessive amounts of SDS, which must be completely removed before scanning to avoid high background. Washes are generally performed at room temperature, although some investigators perform Washes 1 and 2 at temperatures of up to 55°C. The optimal wash temperature for a particular set of targets should be determined empirically.

Turn the scanner on to warm up while the slides are being washed.

12. Prepare the following wash solutions and pass them through 0.22-μm disposable filters:
    Wash 1: 0.5x SSC, 0.01% SDS
    Wash 2: 0.5x SSC
    Wash 3: 0.1x SSC
    Wash 4: 0.01x SSC

13. Disassemble the hybridization chamber. If the chamber has been submerged in a water bath, carefully remove all traces of water, especially between the two halves, before unscrewing.

14. Fill a Coplin jar with Wash 1. Remove the slide from the hybridization chamber, and immediately immerse it in Wash 1 until the coverslip detaches.

    Gentle agitation may be necessary to remove the coverslip. Do not attempt to remove the coverslip manually. If there is some resistance and the coverslip does not appear to be moving, place the slide back in the slide box and pour some of Wash 1 on top of the slide. Let it sit for ~1 minute, and then try again. Use a fresh batch of Wash 1 for each slide.

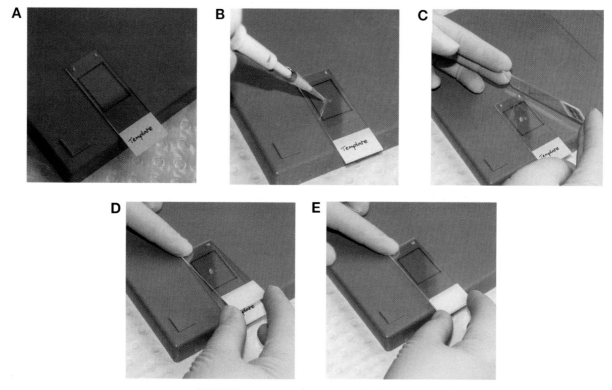

FIGURE 3-22. (*See facing page for legend.*)

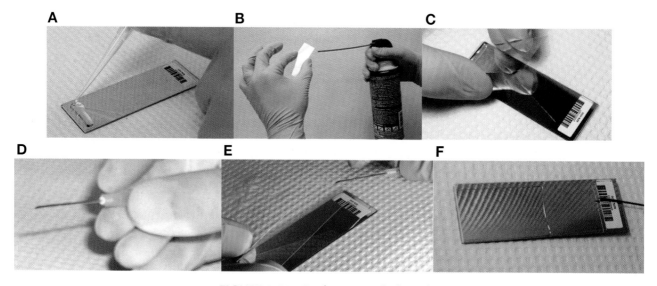

FIGURE 3-23. (*See facing page for legend.*)

FIGURE 3-22. Setting up the hybridization reaction: Manual transfer of the hybridization solution from the coverslip onto the inverted microarray. Place appropriate coverslip onto a template slide (*A*) and apply the hybridization solution to the middle of the coverslip (*B*), taking care to avoid introducing air bubbles. Invert the slide with the printed and processed array over the coverslip (*C*), slowly lowering the slide until it makes contact with the hybridization mixture (*D*) and the coverslip is transferred to the array slide (*E*). Invert the microarray slide so that the coverslip is on the top surface. *Take care not to allow the array slide to come into full contact with the template slide, otherwise the target will sandwich the two slides together, and they will not be able to be separated.*

FIGURE 3-23. Setting up the hybridization reaction: Manual placement of the solution and coverslip prior to hybridization. The photographs shown in panels *A–F* illustrate the setup of a hybridization reaction using a microarray printed on a standard 25 x 70-mm (1 x 3-inch) microscope slide coated with a reflective material (APBiotech Type 7 RPK0328). To begin, remove any dust from the surface of the microarray slide with several blasts of compressed nitrogen, and then lay the slide flat on a clean bench top. Use a micropipette fitted with a standard P200 tip to draw up ~40–50 μl of hybridization solution (labeled cDNA samples reconstituted in hybridization buffer) and deposit it in a uniform bead near one of the long ends of the microarray slide (see panel *A*). The exact volume necessary will depend on the particular surface chemistry of the slide and on the hybridization buffer used—the goal being to eventually spread the solution over the entire surface of the microarray without wasting solution over the edges. Occasionally during this process, one or more air bubbles may be expelled from the pipette tip and onto the surface of the hybridization solution. Because these bubbles may later lodge beneath the surface of the coverslip and interfere with hybridization, it is good practice to remove them before continuing the procedure. Bubbles are burst easily using the tip of a medium- to small-gauge needle (see panel *D*). It is also possible to draw the bubbles directly back into the pipette tip, but this method will inevitably also draw up (and waste) some of the hybridization solution itself. With practice, it is possible to pipette the solution in such a way as to avoid depositing air bubbles altogether. Immediately after depositing the bead of hybridization solution, pick up a clean coverslip and clear it of dust using brief blasts of compressed nitrogen (panel *B*). The coverslip should be large enough to completely cover the area of the slide containing the microarray: Hold the coverslip by its edges and toward its center so as to minimize chances of breaking it with the force of the nitrogen blasts. Align it in the same orientation as the microarray slide, but angled up and away from the bead of hybridization solution (panel *C*). Starting with the lower edge of the coverslip *behind the slide*, slowly drag the coverslip forward so the edge meets the bead. Once contact has been made, let the lower edge of the coverslip rest against the slide surface. Now, slowly transfer support of the elevated end of the coverslip to the tip of a small- to medium-gauge needle (a Becton-Dickinson 20G11/2 needle is shown in panel *D*). If the needle has a beveled tip, the longer side of the tip should be oriented downward. To ensure that the transfer goes smoothly, secure the base of the needle (yellow plastic in the photograph) firmly against the bench top. Hinging the needle at this point, bring the tip upward to support the raised edge of the coverslip (panel *E*). Release the coverslip from the fingers and thumb, so that it rests hands-free, supported at one end by the microarray slide and at the opposite end by the needle tip. Stabilizing the base of the needle on the bench top, gradually lower the needle tip and thus the elevated edge of the coverslip. As the inside surface of the coverslip approaches the surface of the microarray slide, the hybridization solution will begin to wick horizontally between the two. Be careful not to drop the coverslip. Rather, continue to lower the coverslip until it is almost entirely parallel to and resting on the slide surface. At this point, the hybridization solution will have traveled one half to two thirds of the way down the slide (panel *F*). When it becomes difficult to lower the needle any further, slip the needle out from beneath the surface of the coverslip. Do not worry about scratching the slide surface with the needle tip; it causes minimal damage to the microarray. The hybridization solution will quickly advance to fill the remaining space between coverslip and slide. If the solution does not wick far enough, or spills out from the edges of the coverslip, try increasing or decreasing the amount of hybridization solution deposited on the slide at the beginning of this procedure. *Note:* Depositing the solution at one end of the slide and wicking it down the slide's long dimension (vs. depositing the solution along the long dimension and wicking it across) allows for slower and more precise lowering of the coverslip and will minimize the chance of bubble formation during the wicking process.

15. Once the coverslip has been removed, place the slide in a slide holder, and immerse it in a light-proof container filled with ~250 ml of Wash 1. Place the container on an orbital shaker and agitate the slide for 2 minutes.

16. Transfer the slide and holder to a container filled with ~250 ml of Wash 2, and again agitate the slide on a shaker for 3 minutes.

17. Transfer the slide and holder to a container filled with ~250 ml of Wash 3, and again agitate the slide on a shaker for 3 minutes.

18. Repeat Step 17 twice more, washing for 1 minute each time.

19. Quickly (<10 seconds) transfer the slide and its holder to a container filled with ~250 ml of Wash 4. *Immediately* place the slide on two layers of 3M Whatman paper in a centrifuge microtiter plate holder. *Immediately* dry the slide by centrifuging at low speed for ~5 minutes.

20. Place the slide in a light-proof box until ready for scanning. Scan the microarray on the same day, as the signal will decrease over time.

> For further details on scanning/imaging hybridized microarrays, please see Table 3-9 and the panel on **MICROARRAY READERS** below.

MICROARRAY READERS

Two types of instruments are used for collecting data from targets hybridized to microarrays. Confocal microscopes, also known as laser scanners, rely upon the use of one or more lasers as excitation sources to scan the microarray in a point-by-point manner. In this system, photomultiplier tubes serve as detectors. The laser(s) may scan the array samples in sequence or simultaneously. By contrast, imaging systems for reading arrays make use of a charge-coupled device (CCD) camera. CCD-based imagers typically use a beam of white light as the excitation source, directed through a filter block or wheel, to collect a series of images from the array, section by section. The suppliers and features of various microarray readers are described in Table 3-9. For the most current information for these systems, please consult the suppliers' Web Sites.

ADDITIONAL PROTOCOL: MICROARRAY SLIDE STACKING

Sean Grimmond

ARC-SRC for Functional and Applied Genomics, Gene Expression Profiling Facility, Institute of Molecular Bioscience, University of Queensland St Lucia, QLD, 4072, Australia

Slide stacking is used to hybridize two microarray slides fitted with spacers to a single aliquot of target. The two slides are laid face to face, with the top slide offset ~2 mm to create a lip onto which hybridization solution can be pipetted. This alignment creates a void into which hybridization solution can be injected. Many commercial microarray substrates come prelabeled with an adhesive bar code at one end. These make ideal spacers for array stacking.

Originally, stacking was performed with CMT GAPS slides that came with a bar code sticker on one end. These bar codes formed a spacer between the slides. Since then, CMT GAPS slides have changed their bar code so that it is embedded in the glass. These slides may still be used for slide stacking. Note that microarray stacks do not fit many commercial hybridization chambers.

Method

1. Orient the two slides with bar codes (or other spacers) so that they are aligned head to tail, with the printed surface facing upward. Flip one slide over the other so that the printed surfaces face one another. Slide the top slide a further ~1–2 mm to facilitate injection of the hybridization solution.

2. Prepare the labeled target and hybridization solution as described in Step 6 of the main protocol. A larger amount (usually ~80–100 μl) of hybridization solution is required for stacked hybridizations.

   If a slide with an adhesive bar code sticker is used, then the hybridization volume required is 80–100 μl. If the slide has no bar code (or has an embedded bar code), then 40–50 μl of hybridization volume is required.

3. Introduce the hybridization solution in one single pipetting motion into the gap between the two slides at a point approximately one-third from the end of the slides. A single application of hybridization solution prevents injection of bubbles. Once all the solution has been transferred, use forceps to push the two slides flush with each other for hybridization. Avoid contact with the edge of the slide sandwich as capillary action can draw hybridization solution from the stack.

TABLE 3-9. Features of Array Scanners

Company	Basic design	Resolution (in μm)	Speed to scan 10K slide	Sensitivity	Lasers and excitation range	Associated software	Other features
Affymetrix (www.affymetrix.com)							
418 Array Scanner	rotational laser scanning microscope	10	<2 min to scan a slide with 10,000 spots	<1 fluor/μm² (signal to noise >3.5)	red diode, excites at 635 nm, emission filter at 665 nm; green doubled YAG excites at 532 nm, emission filter at 570 nm; 3rd emission filter allows detection of up to 10 dyes	instrument control and analysis integrated with Jaguar 2.0 software; MicroDB 2.0 and DMT 2.0 allow data mining	linear dynamic range over three to five orders of magnitude; integration of 2 additional lasers and 3 additional filters
Agilent (www.chem.agilent.com)							
	scanning laser	5	<8 min per slide	<1 chromophore/μm²	SHG-YAG laser, 532 HeNe laser, 633	PC data system; data extraction and data analysis software	scanner focus is continually adjusted
Amersham (Molecular Dynamics) (www.apbiotech.com)							
Typhoon 9400	scanning and/or imaging for detection of storage phosphor, fluorescence, chemiluminescence	10			red excited fluorescence at 633 nm; green excited fluorescence at 532 nm; blue excited fluorescence at 457 and 488 nm	ImageQuant image analysis software	linear dynamic range over five orders of magnitude
Alpha Innotech (www.alphainnotech.com)							
AlphaArray Reader	CCD-based imager	whole array	<1.5 sec	0.06 fluor/μm²	8 excitation wavelengths to detect numerous fluorophores	imaging and data analysis software	high-throughput imager optical management system (NovaRay light management) reduces acquisition time

	Type	Resolution (µm)	Scan time	Sensitivity	Lasers/excitation	Software	Features
Axon Instruments (www.axon.com)							
GenePix 4000B	scanning laser	5–100	12 min at 5 µm	0.1 fluor/µm² for Cy3, Cy5	409, 473, 532, 594, 635, 670, 690	GenePix Pro 3.0 array analysis software	small footprint available (13.5 × 8.75 × 17.5 inches); adjustable focus
GeneFocus (www.genefocus.com)							
DNAscope IV, V	scanning confocal laser	5, 10, or 20	6 min at 10 µm	<1 fluor/µm²	532, 635, 488	MACROview	up to 3 lasers, 4 filter sets
DNAscope LM	scanning confocal laser	5, 10, 20	6 min at 10 µm	<1 fluor/µm²	532, 635	MACROview	up to 3 lasers, 4 filter sets
Packard BioScience (www.packardbiochip.com)							
ScanArray Lite / ScanArray 4000 / ScanArray 5000	laser confocal optics	5, 10, 20, 30, and 50	≤5 min for full scan field	<0.1 molecule fluor/µm²	Laser choices: 488, 514, 543, 594, 612, and 633 nm	QuantArray microarray analysis software	up to 11 emission filters available; bar code and 20-cassette autoloader options
Cyclone Gene Array System	storage Phosphor imager with helical scanning design	42	3–10 min	<2 dpm/mm²/hr five orders of magnitude dynamic range		OptiQuant and QuantArray microarray analysis software	imaging area: 240–537.5 cm² radioisotope labeling
Perkin Elmer (www.perkinelmer.com)							
GenTac LSIV	nonconfocal scanning laser	2–30 (user defined)	1 sec to 10 min (preset or automatic)	0.1 fluor/µm²	4 excitation lasers and 2 additional photomultipliers	Microsoft SQL server 7.0-db engine	high-throughput can image up to 24 microarrays at a time; dark-field illumination, fluorescence filters allow high-quality image, low background
Virtek Vision Corp (www.virtekbiotech.com)							
Chipreader	scanning laser confocal; 2 PMT detectors; lasers and PMTs individually controlled	10–80 (Chip-reader) 5–40 (high res.) 3–24 (extreme)	25 scan lines/sec; full scan = 6 min at 10 µm	16-bit dynamic range	532 and 635 nm	CR 2.0	small footprint available (11 × 9 × 12 inches)

Troubleshooting Guide*

PART 1: TROUBLESHOOTING SPOTTED ARRAYS

PART 2: TROUBLESHOOTING AFFYMETRIX ARRAYS

*Contributed by Carolyn Best, Trey Ideker, Javed Khan, Damares Monte, Ed Tom.

IMAGE 1: Ideal Image

The image has a dynamic range in excess of two orders of magnitude (spot intensities ranging from 200 to 50,000 counts); minimal background fluorescence (<200 intensity counts in both Cy3 and Cy5 channels); strong spatial uniformity in both dynamic range and background intensity (i.e., from one side of the image to the other); round, evenly spaced spots; and virtually no dust, scratches, speckles, or other artifacts.

IMAGE 2: Bubbles

Problem: A large bubble under the coverslip during hybridization has excluded the target resulting in poor signal in this region. Bubbles partially or completely impede hybridization to the spots in their vicinity. Bubbles can also cause a large amount of fluorescence to accumulate at their perimeters. *Note:* Small bubbles at setup usually disappear as slide warms during hybridization.

Causes:

- Poor setup technique.
- Particulate material in hybridization solution.
- Dirty coverslip.

Possible Solutions:

- Practice setup technique (see Figures 3-22 and 3-23).
- Clean the coverslip with water and ethanol prior to use.
- Use oil-free compressed N_2 to clean the slide and coverslip prior to use.
- Use coverslips designed for microarrays, such as Hybrislips.
- Centrifuge the hybridization solution prior to application to microarray.

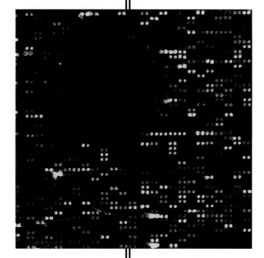

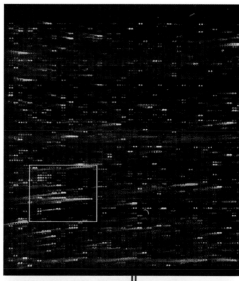

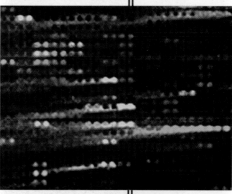

IMAGE 3: Comets

Problem: Comet tails: Smearing of DNA from point of spotting. (*Top*) DNA trails out in a smear from right to left across the entire slide. Comets are traveling in same direction, with the DNA probably released during the blocking or postprinting wash. The problem with this slide was traced to defective UV cross-linking. (*Middle*) Detail of boxed area from indicated region. In some places, the spots are silhouetted as black holes because binding of the released DNA to these regions is blocked by DNA previously deposited. (*Bottom*) Generally good spot morphology, but with severe comet with one sample, due to excessive DNA concentration. Note that there is some slight smearing of some of the other spots, and suboptimal fixation may have exacerbated the problem.

Causes:

- Overloading the binding capacity of the slide due to high concentration of DNA in arraying material.
- Inadequate fixation of DNA to slide due to poor UV cross-linking or inadequate baking.
- Poor postprinting wash technique.
- Defective batch of slides.
- Comets are more apparent with the brightest spots. This problem is not necessarily due to excess DNA. Rather, it may be a general problem of all spots on the slide, manifested most readily with genes that are highly expressed and generate strong signals that reveal displaced DNA.

Possible Solutions:

- Resuspend the PCR products for arraying at 150–250 µg/ml.
- A general problem (*top* and *middle* figures) is more likely due to inadequate fixation. Check temperature of baking oven. Replace and calibrate UV bulbs in cross-linking device.
- If just a few spots (*bottom*) on the slide are affected, then the problem is more likely due to excess DNA in those samples. Check levels of DNA (see Section 1, Protocol 4).
- Rapidly submerge the slides and agitate them during postprinting wash.
- Check the batch of slides. Use alternative slide substrates.

IMAGE 4: Damaged Substrate

Problem: Damage to substrate. (*Top*) Scratches in slide substrate caused by repositioning the coverslip. (*Bottom*) Chipping of poly-L-lysine substrate by pins causing red background hybridization (*arrow*).

Causes:

- Scratches due to moving coverslip once applied, or forced removal during washing.
- Chipping of substrate due to pin tip design or to excessively rapid contact of the pin with the slide.

Possible Solutions:

Scratches

- Do not reposition coverslip, but if this is necessary, slide the coverslip by applying gentle pressure from the edge rather than the top.
- Avoid excessive slide drying, which makes coverslip removal during washing difficult.

Chipping

- If chipping occurs predominantly with one pin, check the pin tip for damage.
- In general, reduce contact speed and/or overstrike distance.
- Consider the use of a more durable slide substrate. Poly-L-lysine is fairly delicate.

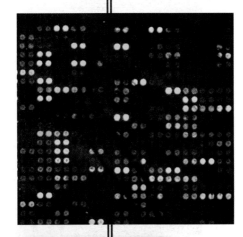

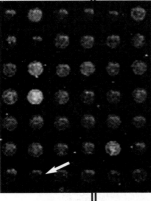

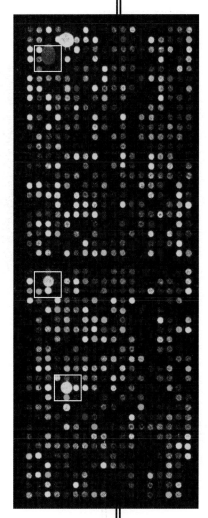

IMAGE 5: Dilated Spots

Problem: Excessive delivery of DNA during printing, causing large irregular spots. May be worse in the slide at the beginning of a print run. The figure shows a generally good microarray but with occasional probes with large irregular spot morphology (*boxed areas*), which obscure adjacent spots.

Causes:

Occasional spot
- Too large a volume in wells of source plate.
- Pin slightly dirty or damaged.

Problem with individual macrogrid
- Exterior of pin dirty or damaged and collecting too much sample.

General problem
- Source plate overfull in many or all wells.
- Inadequate blotting at start of print run (quill pins).
- Excessive dwell time during pickup in source plate or during slide contact.
- Excessive vertical acceleration during printing.
- Incompatible pin/surface chemistry, e.g., disparity in hydrophobicity index.
- Excessive humidity.

Possible Solutions:
- Check volume of DNA in source plate. Depth should not exceed 1 mm or ~8 µl in 384-well plate.
- Examine and clean pins.
- Check and modify the performance settings of the arrayer with respect to the blotting, dwell, and acceleration times.
- Use recommended pin/substrate combination. Check slide batch.
- Relative humidity should be 50–60%.

IMAGE 6: Doughnuts

Problem: Irregular distribution of DNA within the spot. Deposition of DNA involves an interplay between the geometry of the pin head, hydrophobicity of substrate, wetting characteristics of arraying solution, humidity during printing, downward force during contact, and upward acceleration as pin head moves away. (*Top*) Irregular deposition of DNA within spot, with annular or "doughnut" pattern. (*Bottom*) Detail of boxed area in above figure.

Causes:

- Inappropriate combination of pin, slide, and/or array buffer composition.
- Inappropriate settings for arrayer.
- Rapid drying of slides.

Possible Solutions:

- Try different slide substrates, with attention to substrates of differing hydrophobicities.
- Compare different pins.
- Include DMSO or betaine in the array solution.
- Print at 50–60% humidity.
- Experiment with contact speed and upward acceleration of print head.
- Rehydrate slides after printing (please see Section 2).

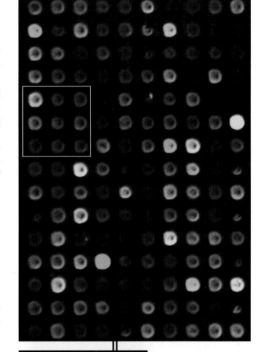

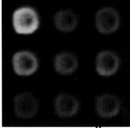

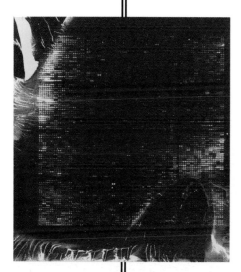

IMAGE 7: Edge Drying

Problem: Severe background hybridization predominantly located at periphery of slide due to drying during hybridization. Difficulty in removing coverslip is also an indication of excessive drying.

Causes:

- Failure to provide adequate humidity during hybridization.
- The problem tends to be more severe with hybridization performed at 65°C.
- Overly long hybridization time.

Possible Solutions:

- Include wetted Whatman paper in hybridization chamber.
- Consider using different hybridization chamber setup.
- Consider use of hybridization solution containing formamide and incubate at 42°C.
- Experiment with dummy slides to ensure that correct balance of humidity is met and drying/condensation is avoided.
- Perform hybridizations for ~16 hours.

IMAGE 8: Edge Fading

Problem: Image progressively fades near the edge of the microarray.

Causes:

- Uneven target distribution during setup.
- Diffusion-limited access of probes to target.
- Condensation around the edge of the coverslip dilutes target.

Possible Solutions:

- Follow correct setup procedure.
- Consider altering hybridization volume.
- Consider using a hybridization station that allows mixing of target during hybridization.
- Ensure proper humidity; do not allow condensation to build up on slide surface.

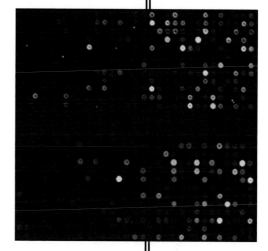

IMAGE 9: High Background: Fluorescence

Problem: (*Top*) High irregular background. (*Bottom*) Severe background, with pattern indicating it has washed over the slide, during the final centrifugation.

Causes:

- High inherent background fluorescence of slide substrate.
- Failure to adequately remove unincorporated nucleotides from target.
- Failure to heat target prior to hybridization.
- Hybridization solution is intensely fluorescent: Inadequate washing.
- Failure of coverslip to fall away from slide in first washes.
- Failure to remove residual solutions (particularly SDS) at end of wash steps.
- Drying during wash steps.
- Oils from skin or latex in gloves.
- Ethanol used in preparation of targets generates fluorescence.

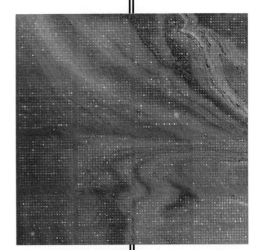

Possible Solutions:

- Check new batches of slides by scanning prior to printing.
- Perform adequate target cleanup.
- Heat target to 100°C for 2 minutes immediately before hybridization.
- Use large wash volumes and clean containers; avoid washing multiple slides without buffer change.
- Wash for recommended times, with agitation.
- Ensure coverslip release.
- Avoid excessive use of SDS in wash buffers and ensure that all SDS is removed during wash.
- Do not allow the slide to dry out during washes. Work quickly; set up containers in advance of moving slides.
- Centrifuge slides immediately at end of washing. Do not rack and batch for long periods.
- Wear powder-free nitrile gloves.
- Change brand of ethanol; use ethanol from either Gold Seal or Warner-Graham.

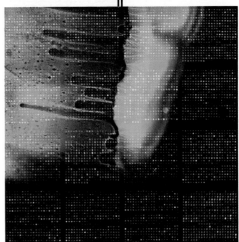

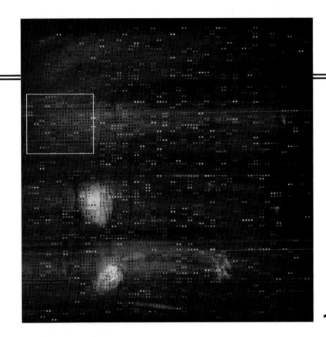
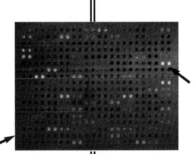

IMAGE 10: High Background: Black Holes

Problem: Signal reversal: Black holes. (*Left*) High background binding of labeled targets to substrate, in which many spots appear as "black holes," i.e., the fluorescent intensity of the spot is beneath that of the surrounding background. (*Right*) Detail of boxed area showing that the presence of DNA in spotted area acts as a blocking agent, preventing target binding (*left arrow*). Unavailability of target for hybridization results in low signal over spots, except for strongly expressed genes (*right arrow*).

Causes:

- Failure to adequately block slides after printing.
- Omission of blocking agents in hybridization solution.
- Incorrect target preparation.

Possible Solutions:

- Ensure correct blocking. Prepare blocking solution immediately prior to use.
- Check that the hybridization solution is matched to the slide substrate.
- Follow recommended procedure for target preparation, including cleanup.
- Consider using slide substrates with less-stringent blocking requirements.

IMAGE 11: Irregular Spot Morphology

Problem: Irregular spot morphology or placement due to pin defects. (*Top*) Unevenly shaped spots due to poor pin tip design or damaged pin tip. (*Bottom*) Erratic spot-to-spot spacing caused by a slight bend in one of the pins making up the print head. Substantial error in spot position occurs if bent pins are free to rotate in their housing, as shown here.

Causes:

- Poor pin design.
- Bent pins.
- Damaged pin tip.

Possible Solutions:

- New pins. Pins are too fine to attempt to remachine.
- Take extreme care in handling pins, especially when removing or replacing in print head or during sonication.

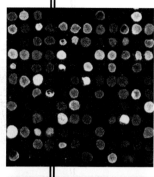
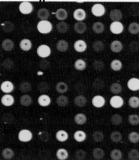

IMAGE 12: Low Signal Intensity

Problem: Low signal intensity. Although many of the spots are detected, the dynamic range is limited and most signals are only a fewfold above background. The low-level hybridization at many of the spots is suggestive of a nonspecific signal.

Causes:

- Impure or inadequate concentration of material arrayed.
- Dilute hybridization conditions.
- Inadequate RNA.
- Poor labeling.
- Scanner defect.

Possible Solutions:

Step through the process systematically. Be sure to include appropriate contols at all steps. Follow the recommended procedures for:

- PCR quantitation and cleanup.
- RNA purification and labeling.
- Check dye and enzyme batches. QC probe on gels.
- Replace hybridization reagents.
- Check scanner performance. Faulty laser may be the problem.
- Compare experiences with other users of the facility.
- Keep a QC reference set: Store a proven set of slides, RNA, and reagents for troubleshooting.

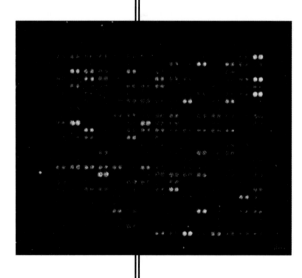

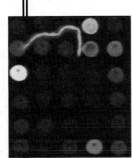

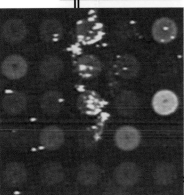

IMAGE 13: Particle Contamination

Problem: Interference with spot quantitation. (*Top*) Contamination with fiber. (*Bottom*) Powder or particulates from target.

Causes:

- Particulate material from work area (bench coat, gloves, tissues, general environment).
- Dirty slides or coverslips.
- Resin from target cleanup not removed by centrifuge.
- Particulates in wash buffers.

Possible Solutions:

- Use foil or bench coat plastic side up for setup.
- Use powder-free nitrile gloves.
- Use oil-free compressed N_2 to remove dust from the slides and coverslips prior to setup.
- Use coverslips designed for microarrays, such as those with a protective backing.
- Centrifuge target at 10,000g for 5 minutes before setting up slides. Do not disturb pellet.
- Filter hybridization solutions and wash buffers before use.

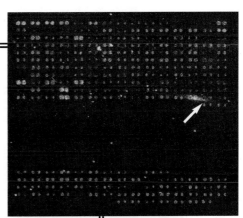

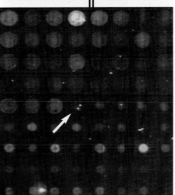

IMAGE 14: Pin Blockage

Problem: Pin blockage (quill pins). Complete (*top*) or partial (*bottom*) blockage interfering with probe deposition at the indicated positions (*arrows*).

Causes:

- Poor preparation of array material.
- Inadequate cleaning of pins during the print run.
- Poor pin design.

Possible Solutions:

- Prepare array material (see Section 1, Protocols 1, 2, and 3) with special care to remove particulate and protein material.
- Check operation of wash station. Wash stations that incorporate sonication baths are preferable.
- Clean pins as described in Section 2, Protocol 4.

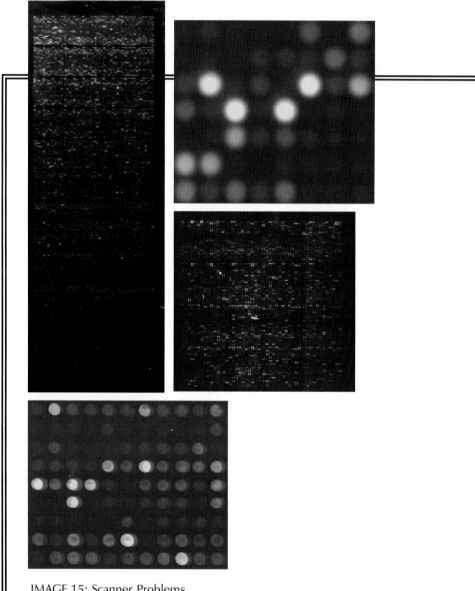

IMAGE 15: Scanner Problems

Problems: *Slide position in scanner: (Left, top)* Signal diminishes along the axis of the slide, because slide is not lying flat in the scanning tray. *(Right, top)* Good spot morphology but slides are out of focus. *Defective scanner optics: (Right, bottom)* Regular pattern of high and low intensity across the slide. *(Left, bottom)* Spots are in relatively good focus, but the red and green color channels are out of alignment.

IMAGE 16: Day-to-Day Variation in Printing

This graph measures intensities plotted by day of printing of a microarray. The microarray was generated by printing during a period of 5 days using a 16-pin print head. Each pin printed a 19 x 21 macrogrid. The slide was hybridized with the same RNA, labeled with either Cy3 or Cy5. The x axes correspond to each coordinate in the 19 x 21 grid, gradually assembled during the 5 days of printing. The y axis is the average intensity of each of 16 spots, i.e., for a given coordinate position. The panels depict (D) the intensity in the Cy3 channel (Log_2 G); (C) the intensity in the Cy5 channel (Log_2 R), the overlay (B), which is the average value of the sum of the intensities (0.5x) (Log_2 R + Log_2 G); and the relative intensity (A) of each channel (Log_2 R/G). Substantial variation in signal intensity between samples is seen, which coincides with the day of printing.

Problems:

Intensity variation in signal output as a function of printing time.

Causes:

The causes of this variation are not clear, but they may have been associated with differences in humidity, pin performance, or operator-dependent issues.

Solutions:

As the cause of the problem is unclear, the remedy is not obvious. The finding does underscore the fact that printing-dependent sources of variation between experiments should be considered.

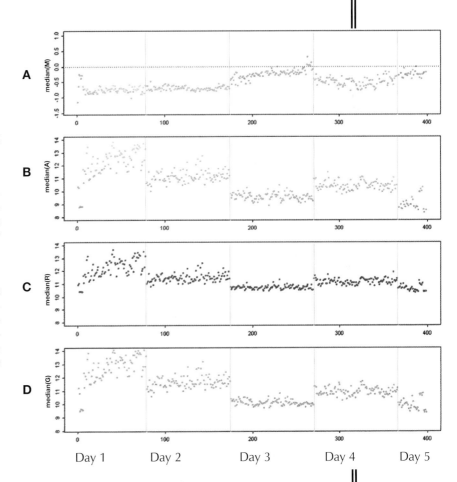

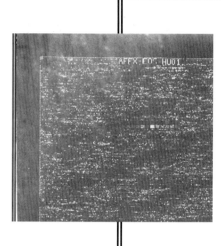

IMAGE 17: High Irregular Background

Problem: High level of irregular diffuse background.

Causes: Grease or dirt on the outer surface of chip, or glue on the inner surface.

Solution: Check to ensure that the glass surface is clean, then rescan. If problem persists, the sample must be rehybridized.

IMAGE 18: Particle Contamination

Problem: Fine particulate material. Particulate back-ground at a low, acceptable level (*left*) or severe level requiring repeat experiment (*right*).

Causes: Salt, protein, or particles in hybridization/ sample solution.

Solution: Prefilter hybridization sample solution with a 0.2-μm filter. If problem persists, a buffer formulation containing an additional blocking reagent is available from Affymetrix Technical Support.

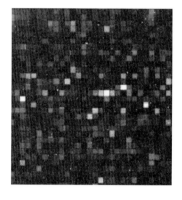
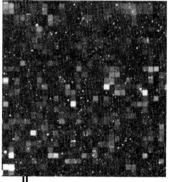

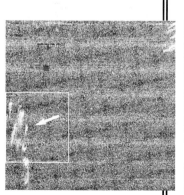
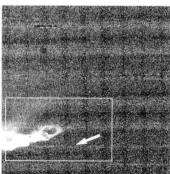

IMAGE 19: Bright Patches

Problem: Bright patches/streaks. High local background appearing in streaks (*left*) or patches (*right*) (see *arrows*).

Causes: Glue, and nonspecific binding of streptavidin-phyco-erythrin.

Solution: If flaw covers a substantial portion of chip, then sample must be rehybridized. If necessary, remove the chip.

The periodic intensity striations evident in some of these images are not actually present in the data but are image aliasing artifacts resulting from the extreme compression of the original raster image to printable pixel densities.

IMAGE 20: Nonspecific Signal

Problem: General low-level signal with little discrimination between features

Causes: Low target quality or inappropriate hybridization or wash buffer for mutations, or temperature, or aged or bleached stain preparations.

Solution: Check for this problem in other hybridizations on chips from the same lot; test other chips from this lot using previously successful hybridization samples. If chip synthesis is the problem, repeat hybridizations on chips from a different lot. Otherwise, if the target is the problem, reprocess the target from starting RNA and rehybridize. Check temperature of hybridization oven. Check scripts used for automated washing protocols. Compare results from different wash station modules.

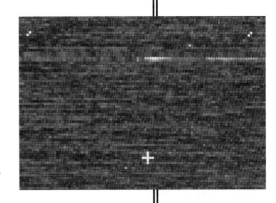

IMAGE 21: Scanner Problem: Loss of Signal

Problem: Graded loss of the signal across the chip surface.

Causes: Out-of-focus scanning, uneven washing or staining.

Solution: Rescanning the chip (in another scanner, if possible) may fix the focusing problem. Otherwise, sample must be rehybridized on another chip.

 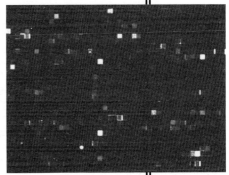

IMAGE 22: Chip Defects

Possible defects in chip manufacture. (*Left*) Pitting of features, including hole (*arrow*). Pitting can be caused by an anti-foam reagent in old versions of Affymetrix protocols. Newer formulations without this component are less susceptible to pitting. (*Right*) Bright edges on features may be possible problems with fragmentation of cDNA.

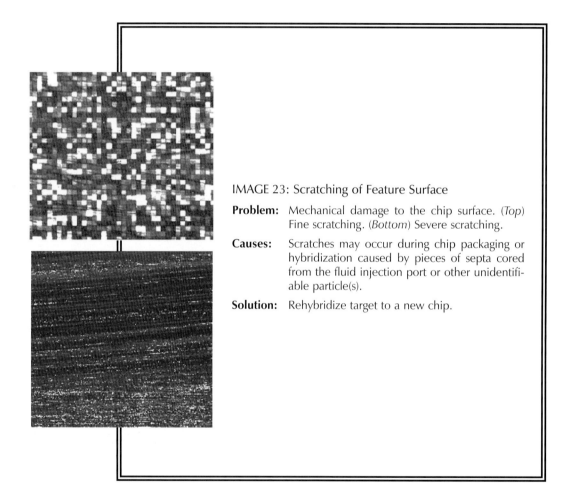

IMAGE 23: Scratching of Feature Surface

Problem: Mechanical damage to the chip surface. (*Top*) Fine scratching. (*Bottom*) Severe scratching.

Causes: Scratches may occur during chip packaging or hybridization caused by pieces of septa cored from the fluid injection port or other unidentifiable particle(s).

Solution: Rehybridize target to a new chip.

ALEXA DYES

Alexa dyes are a proprietary series of seven fluorescent compounds synthesized and sold by Molecular Probes, Inc. (www.molecularprobes.com). The names of the dyes (Alexa 350, 430, 488, 532, 546, 594, 658) indicate their approximate excitation maxima (see Figures 3-24 and 3-25). The dyes were obtained by sulfonation of the ring hydrogen atoms of coumarin or rhodamine, a process known to increase the brightness of many other fluorescent compounds in aqueous media (Wessendorf and Brelje 1992; Mujumdar et al. 1993). By contrast to the sulfonated cyanine dyes Cy3 and Cy5, Alexa dyes are insensitive to a broad range of pH values and are more resistant to photobleaching. In addition, their succinimidyl esters are soluble in aqueous solutions, allowing conjugation in the absence of organic solvents (Panchuk-Voloshina et al. 1999).

Alexa 546 is an orange dye that is available as a succinimidyl ester or conjugated to dUTP (546-14-dUTP, Molecular Probes, Inc). Like other rhodamines, it exhibits a high molar extinction coefficient (ε = 104,000; please see the information panel on MEASURING THE EFFICIENCY OF DYE LABELING OF DNA). In head-to-head comparisons, first-strand cDNAs labeled with Alexa 546-14-dUTP emitted an approximately threefold stronger signal from DNA microarrays than cDNAs labeled with Cy3-dUTP (Wildsmith et al. 2001). Although both dyes gave comparable results in hybridization experiments using labeled second-strand cDNAs (please see Figure 3-25), labeling with Alexa 546 was slightly more efficient (L. Rose, unpubl.). Unincorporated Alexa 546, like Cy3, can be recovered from spent labeling reactions as described in Protocol 19.

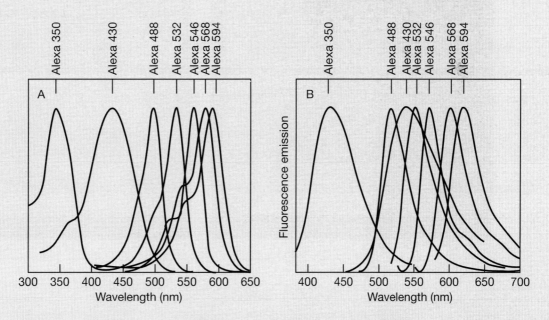

FIGURE 3-24. Normalized absorption (*A*) and emission (*B*) spectra of the Alexa dyes conjugated to goat anti-mouse antibody. With the exception of few nanometers shift of the excitation/emission maxima toward the red region of the spectrum, the profile of the conjugates' spectra closely resembles that of the free Alexa dyes. (Redrawn, with permission, from Panchuk-Voloshina et al. 1999.)

At the time of this writing, only one nucleotide conjugate of an Alexa dye (546-14-dUTP) is commercially available. As more conjugates reach the market, the Alexa dyes will provide a real challenge to the dominance of the sulfoindocyanine dyes as labels for targets in DNA microarray experiments, especially if they retain their current price advantage.

FIGURE 3-25. Comparison between the Alexa-Fluor 546-14-dUTP and Cy-dUTP dyes. RNA from the wild-type *Arabidopsis thaliana*, labeled either with Alexa-Fluor 546-14-dUTP (Molecular Probes) (*left*) or Cy3-dUTP (Amersham) (*right*), was competitively hybridized with the Cy5-labeled (Amersham) *cim-7* mutant of *A. thaliana*. Incorporation was tested using the same RNA on a set of three arrays for each dye. Standard second-strand cDNA-labeling reactions (Protocol 13 and http://afgc.stanford.edu/afgc_html/AFGCProtocols-fev2001.pdf) and hybridization methods (please see Protocol 20) were used for both slides. Scans were taken using a Packard Bioscience Scanarray 4000 (Perkin Elmer). Cy3-dUTP and Alexa-Flour 546-14-dUTP channel images were scanned at a laser power of 77 and PMT of 77, and the Cy5 channel was taken at laser power of 70 and PMT of 70. The dyes gave comparable results. (Images provided by Lorne Rose, Carnegie Institution of Washington.)

BACTERIAL MICROARRAYS

During the course some 50 years, bacterial geneticists have mapped, sequenced, mutated, and transposed virtually all genes and operons in *E. coli* to which a phenotype can be attached. They have cataloged the gene clusters involved in particular metabolic functions, and they have identified the sensors of physiological change and have explored in detail the responsive regulatory circuits used to switch banks of relevant genes on and off. If all this has been achieved by elegant genetics and biochemistry, is there a need for DNA microarrays to study gene expression in prokaryotes?

Genetics is at its most powerful when the investigator can apply selective pressure for and against the gene functions of interest. Genes that have no known function and are not associated with a phenotype are generally ignored by geneticists or are invisible to them. This became all too apparent in 1997, when the complete 4.6-Mbp sequence of the *E. coli* genome was published (Blattner et al. 1997): No less than 30% of the open reading frames in the *E. coli* chromosome turned out to have no known function. The ability of DNA microarrays to quantify changes in RNA levels for every gene when *E. coli* is grown under a variety of physiological circumstances and genetic states offers a possibility of analyzing the global response of the genome to specific physiological responses and of assigning functions to these new-found genes.

The first attempt at global analysis of gene expression in *E. coli*, published in 1993, used an ordered, overlapping set of bacteriophage λ genomic recombinants arrayed in 21 x 21 matrices on nylon membranes (Chuang et al. 1993). Because the inserts in the recombinant clones were so large (9–21 kb) that they encompassed several genes, the resolution of the system analysis was low by today's standards. Nevertheless, it was possible to identify regions containing genes whose expression levels were affected by a variety of environmental changes including heat and osmotic shock, starvation for various nutrients, low oxygen tension, and chemical inducers. Although more detailed expression profiling became possible after the full genomic sequence was available, global analysis of gene expression in prokaryotes lagged behind similar studies in eukaryotes—perhaps because the brief half-life of bacterial mRNA and the lack of a poly(A) tail thwarted isolation or selective labeling of RNA in the overwhelming presence of the rRNA and tRNA. These problems have largely been overcome, and, in the last few years, the flow of papers on expression analysis in prokaryotes has increased steadily.

Most of the experiments used for expression profiling of prokaryotes are similar in both design and execution to those developed in the Brown Lab for yeast. The arrays are composed of a comprehensive set of genomic elements, and the experimental design typically involves comparing the abundance of target sequences in a control RNA with a series of experimental RNAs isolated from cultures exposed to drugs, inducers, or various forms of metabolic and environmental stresses. Data are collected and analyzed in the same manner as data collected from yeast profiling experiments.

In principle, DNA microarrays can be used to analyze global gene expression in any prokaryote whose genome has been completely sequenced. However, the interpretation of microarray data is both simplified and enriched when a wealth of genetic knowledge about the organism is available and the phenotypes of mutants are well-characterized. At the time of this writing, the complete genomic sequences of >20 prokaryotes are known. However, most of the work on expression profiling has concentrated on *E. coli*, as summarized below.

- **Construction of arrays.** The most popular type of array consists of PCR products corresponding to every open reading frame, spotted onto glass slides. In the case of *E. coli*, 4290 open reading frames are amplified from a genomic DNA template (30 ng) using specific primer pairs (Richmond et al. 1999). Primers are generally designed to start at the putative initiating ATG and to end at the stop codon. If desired, the primers can be designed with a 5′ sequence containing a restriction site that facilitates cloning. Amplification is usually performed in two steps to reduce the amount of template DNA that would otherwise be spotted onto the array. The products of the first amplification reactions are diluted ~500-fold and used as templates for reamplification. The size and yield of the products of the second round of PCR are confirmed by gel electrophoresis before purification with 96-well PCR purification kits (QIAGEN) and arraying. With some experimentation (Richmond et al. 1999), 99.5% of the *E. coli* open reading frames can be successfully amplified and used in microarrays experiments (Wei et al. 2001). The genes on the arrays can be categorized into the functional groups defined by Riley and Labedan (1996; please see Smulski et al. 2001; Wei et al. 2001).

  Selinger et al. (2000) have described a different approach in which both coding and noncoding regions of the *E. coli* genome are displayed on 544 x 544 grids of 25-mer oligonucleotides of defined sequence. The total array consists of 295,936 oligonucleotides synthesized in situ on a derivatized glass surface (Pease et al. 1994; Lockhart et al. 1996). The large number of oligonucleotide allows transcripts to be probed at high resolution (intergenic regions every 6 bases, open reading frames every 60 bases on average). Although the sensitivity of the system is approximately the same as conventional spotted arrays (~0.2 copies of RNA per cell), its high resolution and its ability to monitor changes in transcripts of noncoding regions may be of value to some investigators.

- **Labeling RNAs.** RNA for expression analysis is generally prepared from *E. coli* using QIAGEN RNeasy columns (e.g., please see Richmond et al. 1999; Khodursky et al. 2000), although more elaborate methods are preferred by some groups of workers (Wei et al. 2001). Total RNA (6–50 µg) may be labeled in random priming reactions using commercially available random hexamers, reverse transcriptase, and Cy3- or Cy5-labeled deoxynucleotides. Alternatively, 3′ termini of bacterial mRNAs can be selectively polyadenylated in the presence of total cellular RNA in an in vitro reaction catalyzed by poly(A) polymerase. The polyadenylated molecules may then be purified by oligo(dT) chromatography (Wendish et al. 2001). After labeling and hybridization, comparable signal intensities are obtained with ~1% as much oligo(dT)-purified mRNA as total RNA. However, the signal ratios obtained from the two types of targets are approximately equal, indicating that enrichment of mRNA may not be of significant advantage.

  Alternative methods of labeling include terminal transferase-catalyzed biotinylation of first-strand cDNA (used in hybridization to Affymetrix-type arrays; Selinger et al. 2000) and genome-directed primers for selective labeling of transcripts (Talaat et al. 2000). This method uses a computer algorithm to define the minimum number of oligonucleotides of defined length that are capable of priming synthesis from genomic copies of all known genes.

- ***Normalization of data.*** Hybridization signals obtained with fluorescently labeled cDNA may be normalized by dividing the signal generated from fluorescently labeled sheared genomic DNA (Richmond et al. 1999; Wei et al. 2001). In addition, most researchers include in their microarrays a set of DNAs that serve as internal controls. For example, Wei et al. (2001) spotted onto each slide 76 specific *E. coli* PCR products, 8 amplified genes of *Klebsiella pneumoniae*, and 12 plant cDNA clones. The internal controls are used to derive equivalent readings among the slides that comprise the entire genomic array.

Although expression profiling has been by far the most common application of DNA microarrays in studies of prokaryotes, array technology has also been used in comparative studies to detect and rapidly map gene-specific differences between closely related prokaryotic genomes and to develop phylogenetic trees showing their evolutionary relationships (Murray et al. 2001).

EXTRACTION OF PROTEINS AND DNA WITH PHENOL

Until the mid 1950s, the standard method of purifying DNA involved stripping protein from the nucleic acid with detergent and strong salt solutions (e.g., perchlorate). Final deproteinization was achieved by several extractions with chloroform laced with isoamyl alcohol (Sevag et al. 1938). The first reported use of phenol to purify nucleic acids was published by Kirby (1956), who was aware of the power of phenol to extract proteins from aqueous solution (Grassmann and Defner 1953). In his initial paper, Kirby showed that extraction of homogenates of mammalian tissue with a two-phase phenol-water mixture led to partitioning of RNA into the aqueous layer at room temperature. DNA remained associated with protein at the interface. Kirby quickly realized that replacement of water by solutions of anionic salts released both DNA and RNA into the aqueous phase (Kirby 1957; for review, please see Kirby 1964). Although the use of anionic salts to release proteins from DNA was quickly abandoned in favor of strong anionic detergents such as SDS, Kirby's original description of phenol extraction forms the basis of many purification methods in common use today. The function of the phenol is probably that of a protein solvent, in that it extracts protein that has been separated from nucleic acids by anionic salts or detergents. So efficient is this process that pure preparations of nucleic acids are obtained after just two or three extractions with phenol.

The pH of the phenol determines partitioning of DNA and RNA between the organic phase and the aqueous phase (Perry and Kelley 1972; Brawerman et al. 1972). At slightly alkaline pH, DNA and RNA are both almost quantitatively partitioned into the aqueous phase. However, at acid pH (e.g., pH 5.2), DNA denatures and precipitates into the organic phase and the interface. RNA, on the other hand, is retained in the aqueous phase. Isolation of RNA free of significant contamination by DNA therefore requires an acidic solution of phenol or phenol:chloroform. The pH of phenol supplied by manufacturers should be checked before use and adjusted to the appropriate pH by equilibration with 0.01 M Tris (pH <7.00) or, in the case of acid phenol, by equilibration in 10 mM sodium acetete (pH 5.1), 50 mM NaCl, and 1 mM EDTA (pH 8.9). The bottle of equilibrated phenol should be wrapped in aluminum foil and stored at 4°C.

Purified phenol has a specific gravity of 1.07 and therefore forms the lower phase when mixed with water. However, the organic and aqueous phases may be difficult to separate or may invert when phenol is used to extract protein from aqueous solutions containing high concentrations of solutes. This problem is largely alleviated when a 50:50 mixture of phenol:chloroform is used because the higher density of chloroform (1.47) ensures separation of the two phases. Denatured proteins collect at the interface between the two phases, whereas lipids partition efficiently into the organic layer. Isoamyl alcohol is often added to the phenol:chloroform mixture to reduce foaming. The combination of organic solvents is believed to reduce the partitioning of RNA into the organic phase and the formation of insoluble RNA-protein complexes at the interface.

Pure phenol is supplied as a white crystalline mass (melting point 43°C). However, on exposure to air and light, phenol is prone to redden, a process that is accelerated by alkalinity. Pigmented batches of crystalline phenol must be redistilled at 182°C to remove oxidation products such as quinones that cause the breakdown of phosphodiester bonds or promote cross-linking of nucleic acids.

The liquefied form of phenol provided by many manufacturers contains ~8% water and can be stored frozen at –20°C. Liquefied phenol, if colorless, can be used in molecular cloning without redistillation. These days, only occasional batches of liquefied phenol are pink or yellow. These should be rejected and returned to the manufacturer. (Saturated phenols are available from several manufacturers, including Ambion.)

CHECKING THE PH OF EQUILIBRATED PHENOL

- *Acid phenol:* Mix 2 ml of the organic phase with 8 ml of methanol and 10 ml of H_2O. Measure the pH of the final solution with a standard reference electrode.

- *Neutral phenol:* Mix 2 ml of the organic phase with 5 ml of methanol and 13 ml of H_2O. Measure the pH of the final solution with a standard reference electrode.

FORMAMIDE

Formamide is used as an ionizing solvent in aqueous buffers. Many batches of high-grade formamide are sufficiently pure to be used without further treatment. However, as a rule of thumb, if any yellow color is present or if there is even the hint of a smell of ammonia, the formamide should be purified. A more rigorous test of purity is to measure conductivity, which rises as the formamide breaks down to ammonium formate. The conductivity of pure formamide is 1.7 (Casey and Davidson 1977) and the conductivity of a 10^{-3} M solution of ammonium formate is ~650 μmho. The conductivity of formamide used in reannealing experiments should be <2.0 μmho.

Formamide can be deionized by stirring for 1 hour on a magnetic stirrer with a mixed bed ion-exchange resin (e.g., Dowex AG8, Bio-Rad AG 501-X8, 20-50 mesh or X8[D]). The solution is then filtered through Whatman #1 paper and stored in small aliquots at –20ºC, preferably under nitrogen. Each resin can be reused several times. X8(D) contains an indicator that changes color when the resin is exhausted.

Formamide is used in hybridization reactions, to resolve complex compressions in sequencing gels and to denature RNA before electrophoresis as described below.

Denaturing RNA before Electrophoresis

Formamide (50%) is used to assist in denaturation of RNA before electrophoresis through denaturing formaldehyde-agarose gels (Lehrach et al. 1977).

Hybridization Reactions

Bonner et al. (1967) were the first to use formamide as a solvent in hybridization reactions. At the end of their brief paper, they wrote:

> That formamide should take the place of elevated temperature in the hybridization process is to be expected. Aqueous solutions of formamide denature DNA as has been shown by Helmkamp and Ts'o (1961) and Marmur and Ts'o (1961). The concentrations of formamide required for DNA-RNA hybridization, 30–40 vol%, are well below the 60 vol% found by Marmur and Ts'o to be required for denaturation of native DNA (in 0.02 M NaCl–0.002 M sodium citrate).
>
> What has now been found by serendipity is that hybridization as conducted in aqueous formamide possesses distinct advantages over hybridization conducted at elevated temperatures. These advantages include increased retention of immobilized DNA by the nitrocellulose filters and decreased nonspecific background absorption. These two factors combine to result in an increased reproducibility of replicates with the hybridization procedure. Hybridization in formamide solution at low temperature is helpful also in minimizing scission of nucleic acid molecules during prolonged periods of incubation.
>
> In addition to these advantages, increased flexibility is introduced into the design of reaction conditions for a given experiment. It is more convenient to control this stringency of hybridization with formamide rather than through adjustment of the incubation temperature.

HYBRIDIZATION IN BUFFERS CONTAINING FORMAMIDE

Depression of the melting temperature (T_m) of duplex DNA is a linear function of the formamide concentration (McConaughy et al. 1969; Casey and Davidson 1977). For DNAs whose G+C content is in the range of 30–75%, the T_m is depressed by 0.63°C for each percentage of formamide in the hybridization mixture. Thus, the T_m of the hybrid formed between a probe and its target may be estimated from the following equation, which is modified from Bolton and McCarthy (1962):

$$T_m = 81.5°C + 16.6 \ (\log_{10}[Na^+]) + 41 \ (\text{mole fraction } [G+C]) - 0.63 \ (\%\text{formamide}) - 500/n$$

where n is the length of the DNA in nucleotides. This equation applies to the reversible T_m defined by optical measurement of hyperchromicity at OD_{260}. The "irreversible" T_m (Hamaguchi and Geiduschek 1962), which is more important for autoradiographic detection of DNA hybrids, is usually 7–10°C higher than that predicted by the equation. Similar equations have been derived for RNA probes hybridizing to immobilized RNA (Bodkin and Knudson 1985):

$$T_m = 79.8°C + 18.5 \ (\log_{10} [Na^+]) + 58.4 \ (\text{mole fraction } [G+C]) + 11.8 \ (\text{mole fraction } [G+C])^2$$
$$- 0.35 \ (\%\text{formamide}) - 820/n$$

and for DNA-RNA hybrids (Casey and Davidson 1977):

$$T_m = 79.8°C + 18.5 \ (\log_{10} [Na^+]) + 58.4 \ (\text{mole fraction } [G+C]) + 11.8 \ (\text{mole fraction } [G+C])^2$$
$$- 0.50 \ (\%\text{formamide}) - 820/n$$

Comparison of these equations shows that the relative stability of nucleic acid hybrids in high concentrations of formamide decreases in the following order: RNA-RNA (most stable), RNA-DNA (less stable), and DNA-DNA (least stable). In 80% formamide, the T_m of an RNA-DNA hybrid is ~10°C higher than a DNA-DNA hybrid of equivalent base composition. It is therefore possible to find hybridization conditions that allow the formation of RNA-DNA hybrids and discourage the formation of DNA-DNA hybrids (Casey and Davidson 1977). This ability to suppress reannealing of DNA was extremely useful when S1 mapping of RNA was carried out with double-stranded DNA probes (Berk and Sharp 1977). However, the development of efficient methods to prepare single-stranded probes now allows annealing of RNA to DNA to be carried out under standard hybridization conditions without fear of competition from the complementary strand of DNA. As a consequence, the annealing conditions established by Casey and Davidson (1977) are today used only very rarely.

• The rate of DNA-DNA hybridization in 80% formamide is slower than in aqueous solution (Casey and Davidson 1977). Increasing the concentration of formamide decreases the rate of DNA:DNA renaturation by 1.1% for every 1% increase in the concentration of formamide (Hutton 1977). Therefore, the optimal rate in 50% formamide is 0.45 times the optimal rate in aqueous solution (Hutton 1977). In 80% formamide, the rate of DNA-DNA hybridization is three- to fourfold slower than in aqueous solution (Casey and Davidson 1977). This effect is a consequence of increased viscosity of the hybridization solution at the temperatures used for renaturation.

• The breakdown of formamide that occurs during prolonged incubation at temperatures in excess of 37°C can cause the pH of the hybridization buffer to drift upward (Casey and Davidson 1977). When formamide is included in the hybridization buffer, 6x SSPE is preferred to 6x SSC because of its greater buffering power.

(Reprinted from Sambrook and Russell 2001.)

GUANIDINIUM-BASED EXTRACTION OF RNA

Most modern methods for the purification of RNA from animal and plant cells are based on the use of guanidinium salts, which are among the most effective protein denaturants and inactivators of ribonucleases. The first guanidinium salt to be used as a deproteinization agent during isolation of RNA was the chloride (Cox 1968). A succession of papers appeared in the 1970s describing the use of the more powerful isothiocyanate salt to isolate total cellular RNA from cultured cells and fresh tissues (Glisin et al. 1974; Ullrich et al. 1977; Chirgwin et al. 1979). By the early 1980s, these methods had replaced older techniques based on extraction with organic solvents for purification of RNA from "difficult" sources, such as ribonuclease-rich pancreatic tissue. However, the early guanidinium-based methods were capable of processing only a few samples simultaneously since they used ultracentrifugation of cell and tissue lysates through a CsCl cushion to separate the RNA from the remainder of the cellular components. It was not until 1987, when Chomczynski and Sacchi eliminated the requirement for ultracentrifugation that guanidinium-based methods could be used to process more samples simultaneously than an ultracentrifuge rotor can hold.

Further modifications included recovery of RNA from the cell lysate by 0.5 volume of isopropanol and 0.5 volume of high-salt solution, an improvement that eliminates contaminating polysaccharides from the final RNA preparation (Chomczynski and Mackey 1995). The initial commercial reagents that were developed based on this method, RNAzol and RNAzol B (Cinna Scientific, Cincinnati, Ohio), provided a fast, inexpensive, and simple procedure to obtain high-quality undegraded RNA from a variety of biological specimens. In a series of papers published in the 1990s, Chomczynski (1993, 1994, 1999) introduced a variation that allows the simultaneous recovery of RNA, DNA, and protein. In this method, cells and tissues are lysed with a monophasic solution of guanidinium isothiocyanate, ammonium thiocyanate, and phenol, and the TRI or TRIzol reagent, which is currently available under different trade names from various companies (please see footnote c to Table 3-1 in Part 1 of this section). The addition of chloroform to the cell lysate generates a second (organic) phase into which DNA and proteins are extracted, leaving RNA in the aqueous supernatant. If care is taken to avoid the interface, the RNA recovered from the aqueous phase by precipitation with isopropanol can be used without further purification for hybridization to DNA microarrays or as a source of intact poly(A)$^+$ RNA. However, some investigators prefer to isolate poly(A)$^+$ RNA, using, for example, the FastTrack 2.0 kit (Invitrogen) (please see Protocol 2).

Monophasic lysis agents containing guanidinium isothiocyanate disrupt cells and denature proteins very efficiently, and they are the buffers of choice for isolation of RNA from all animal tissues and most plant tissues. However, for disruption of certain plant tissues, lysis agents containing guanidinium chloride are preferred. For example, endosperm of corn forms a heavy precipitate in the presence of guanidinium isothiocyanate but is soluble in lysis solutions containing the chloride salt. The RNeasy Plant Mini Kit sold by QIAGEN contains both types of lysis solutions and offers advice about which to use when extracting RNA from different plant tissues.

Monophasic lysis reagents are available in a large variety of kits from commercial manufacturers (please see footnote c to Table 3-1 in Part 1 of this section). Details of the composition of some monophasic lysis agents are available in published patents (see Chomczinski 1989, 1994).

HOMOGENIZATION OF ANIMAL CELLS AND TISSUES

The following are two types of power-driven homogenizers in common use.

- ***The Kinematica Polytron*** PT3100 instrument equipped with probe 9100071 (Brinkmann) is used to disrupt cells and tissues weighing >100 mg. Although the Polytron can deal with only one sample at a time, its powerful and speed adjustable motor allows several grams of tissue to be homogenized in the same run. Samples need not be thawed before homogenization. A disadvantage of the Polytron is the possibility of cross-contamination between samples. Because the levels of gene expression differ by several orders of magnitude, even slight contamination of a homogenate with a lysate from a previous sample can affect the profile of gene expression on DNA microarrays. To clean the Polytron between samples:

  1. Take apart the probe and clean off any bits of tissue that may have been caught inside the rotor and blade assembly. Boil the rotor and blade for a few minutes in a large volume of H_2O. Be aware that the H_2O tends to boil up inside the probe. It is therefore essential to submerge the full probe in large volumes of H_2O that are changed once or twice.

  2. Run the reassembled Polytron in 50 ml of fresh H_2O.

  3. Wipe the Polytron probe dry with clean Kimwipes.

- ***The FastPrep instrument*** (Q-Biogene, 6000-120) is used to disrupt tissues that weigh <100 mg and can process up to 12 samples simultaneously. Because each sample is contained in its individual tube, the opportunities for cross-contamination of samples are minimized. Depending on the types of tissues, multiple runs may be needed to achieve complete homogenization. When the fat content of the sample is high, larger amounts of the sample may be needed to obtain sufficient amounts of RNA. For more details, please see Protocol 2.

Although power-driven homogenizers have largely replaced manual methods of tissue disruption, the older techniques outlined below are still used to prepare RNA from bone or gristly tissues, from plant material, or from tissues rich in degradative enzymes.

Speed is the key to success when dealing with tissues such as pancreas or gut that are rich in ribonucleases. It is best to cut the freshly dissected tissue into small pieces (~100 mg) and to drop them immediately into liquid nitrogen. The snap-frozen tissue can be stored for several months at –80ºC without affecting the yield or integrity of the RNA. For extraction of RNA:

1. Transfer ~100 mg of the frozen tissue to a mortar prechilled in liquid nitrogen and pulverize the tissue using a prechilled pestle. The tissue can be kept frozen during pulverization by the addition of liquid nitrogen. Use a large mortar, constantly topped up with liquid nitrogen, to prevent "blasting" the powder out when the nitrogen is added.

2. Transfer the powdered tissues to TRIzol solution (1 ml/100 mg of powder) for processing in a Polytron homogenizer (Protocol 1) or in batches of 100 mg in a FastPrep instrument (see Protocol 2).

Snap freezing and pulverization are not always necessary. Tissues that are less rich in ribonucleases may be minced into small pieces and either lysed immediately in TRIzol or transferred to RNA*later* (Ambion) for short-term storage (please see Table 3-1).

Very hard tissues such as bone and cartilage should be ground to a powder using a mortar and pestle prechilled with liquid nitrogen. The powder can then be homogenized in a Polytron homogenizer for 30 seconds in an appropriate volume of TRIzol solution. During this process, the tissue becomes fully solubilized in TRIzol and the DNA is sheared. After homogenization, run the Polytron probe in a 15-ml conical tube containing 3 ml of TRIzol solution and then add the TRIzol to the tissue lysate. If particulate matter is still visible, centrifuge the samples at 12,000*g* in a Sorvall (or equivalent) for 30 minutes at 4°C.

Instead of grinding in a mortar, frozen tissue may placed inside a homemade bag of plastic film and pulverized with a blunt instrument, for example, a hammer (Gramza et al. 1995). Only certain types of plastic film are tough enough to withstand hammering at low temperature, for example, Write-On Transparency Film AF 4300 from 3M. A further adaptation is to use a steel piston and pestle (please see Figure 3-26) prechilled on dry ice. Having a number of these inexpensive devices available speeds the processing of multiple samples.

The methods discussed here have been developed for use with animal cells and tissues. Different techniques are required to homogenize plant tissues (please see Protocols 2 and 3).

FIGURE 3-26. Steel piston homogenizer.

INHIBITING RNASES

RNases are robust and powerful enzymes that seriously threaten the integrity of RNA at all stages of its isolation and characterization. Described below are three types of inhibitors that are commonly used to keep the activity of RNases in check.

Diethylpyrocarbonate

DEPC is a highly reactive alkylating agent, and it is used to inactivate RNases in buffers and glassware (Penman et al. 1970; Williamson et al. 1971). Because DEPC modifies proteins and RNA indiscriminately, it cannot be used during isolation and purification of RNA and is incompatible with some buffers. DEPC is a highly reactive alkylating agent that destroys the enzymatic activity of RNase chiefly by ethoxyformylation of histidyl groups.

In aqueous solution, DEPC hydrolyzes rapidly to CO_2 and ethanol, with a half-life in phosphate buffer of ~20 minutes at pH 6.0 and 10 minutes at pH 7.0. This hydrolysis is greatly accelerated by Tris and other amines, which themselves become consumed in the process. DEPC therefore cannot be used to treat solutions that contain these buffers. Samples of DEPC that are free of nucleophiles (e.g., H_2O and ethanol) are perfectly stable, but even small amounts of these solvents may cause complete conversion to diethyl carbonate. For this reason, DEPC should be protected against moisture. Store DEPC in small aliquots under dry conditions and never open a bottle at a lower temperature than that of the environment.

To decontaminate glassware, fill the items with a solution of 0.1% DEPC in H_2O and allow them to stand for 2 hours at 37°C. Rinse the items several times with RNase-free H_2O and then autoclave them for 15 minutes at 15 psi (1.05 kg/cm^2) on liquid cycle.

H_2O purified through well-maintained, modern reverse-osmosis systems is free of RNase (Huang et al. 1995). However, poorly maintained purification systems may become contaminated by microbial growth. This is commonly the case in large centralized systems with many meters of piping and storage vats in which H_2O can stagnate. In such cases, it may be necessary to generate RNase-free H_2O by DEPC treatment, as described above.

DEPC can carboxymethylate unpaired adenine residues in RNA. mRNAs that have been exposed to DEPC are translated with reduced efficiency in in vitro protein-synthesizing systems (Ehrenberg et al. 1976). However, the ability of DEPC-treated RNA to form DNA-RNA or RNA-RNA hybrids is less seriously affected unless a large fraction of the purine residues have been modified.

Removal of DEPC by thermal degradation generates small amounts of ethanol and CO_2, which can increase the ionic strength and lower the pH of unbuffered solutions. Do not use DEPC I solutions containing free amine groups (e.g., Tris buffers).

> **CAUTION:** DEPC is toxic and is suspected to be a carcinogen. Wear gloves and safety glasses to prevent DEPC from contacting the skin and eyes. Handle the chemical in a properly vented chemical fume hood.

This information panel is modified from Sambrook and Russell (2001).

Vanadyl Ribonucleoside Complexes

These complexes are transition state analogs that bind to the active sites of many RNases and inhibit their catalytic activity almost completely (Berger and Birkenmeier 1979). Because vanadyl ribonucleases do not covalently modify RNases, they must be used at all stages of RNA extraction and purification. However, because these complexes inhibit RNA polymerases and in vitro translation, they must be removed from the final preparation of RNA by multiple extraction with phenol containing 0.1% hydroxyquinoline. Vanadyl ribonucleoside complexes are available from several commercial suppliers.

Protein Inhibitors of RNases

Many RNases bind very tightly, albeit noncovalently, to ~50-kD proteins that are found in the cytoplasm of virtually all mammalian tissues and can be isolated in abundance from placenta (Blackburn et al. 1977). In vivo, these protein inhibitors belong to the pancreatic RNase superfamily, notably angiogenin, a blood vessel-inducing and eosinophyll-derived neurotoxin. The 1:1 complexes between these protein inhibitors and their targets are among the tightest on record (1–70 fM; Lee et al. 1989; for reviews, please see Lee and Vallee 1993).

Protein inhibitors of RNase derived from several sources are sold by several manufacturers under various trade names (e.g., RNasin from Promega Corp. and Prime Inhibitor from 5 Prime→3 Prime). Although these vary in their requirement for sulfhydryl reagents, all of them display a broad spectrum of inhibitory activities against RNases, but do not inhibit other nucleases, polymerases, or in vitro translation systems (e.g., please see Murphy et al. 1995).

Because the inhibitors do not form covalent complexes with RNase, they cannot be used in the presence of denaturants such as SDS and guanidine that are commonly used to lyse mammalian cells in the initial stages of extraction of RNA. However, the inhibitors can be included at all stages during subsequent purification of RNA. Inhibitors must be replenished several times during the purification procedure, since they are removed by extraction with phenol.

MAMMALIAN, PLANT, AND BACTERIAL RNAs

Mammalian RNAs

A typical mammalian cell contains ~0.5×10^{-5} to 1.0×10^{-5} μg of RNA, the bulk of which is in the cytoplasm. The four species of rRNA (5S, 5.8S, 18S, and 28S) constitute 80–85% of cytoplasmic RNA, whereas the population of tRNAs accounts for another 15% or so. The abundant RNAs are of defined size and sequence and can be isolated in virtually pure form by gel electrophoresis, HPLC, anion-exchange chromatography, or density gradient centrifugation. By contrast, mRNAs, which make up between 1% and 5% of the total cellular RNA, are heterogeneous in size (from a few hundred bases to many kilobases in length), in abundance (from 1–2 molecules per cell up to several thousand), and in sequence. Most mammalian mRNAs carry at their 3′ termini a tract of polyadenylate residues that is generally long enough to allow mRNAs to be purified by affinity chromatography on oligo(dT)-cellulose (please see the information panel on OLIGO(dT)-CELLULOSE). The resulting heterogeneous collection of molecules collectively encodes virtually all of the polypeptides of the cell.

Plant RNAs

Plant RNAs consist of a heterogeneous population of molecules that can be separated into three classes by zone sedimentation: 23–25S, 16S–17S, and 4S. The first two classes consist of rRNAs, whereas the 4S class includes tRNAs and other small RNA molecules, such as small nuclear RNAs (Brown and Shaw 1998; Sugiura and Takeda 2000). The RNAs in the three classes are abundant and stable and can be easily visualized as intensely fluorescent bands in agarose gels stained with ethidium bromide. The rRNAs are components of three types of ribosomes (i.e., cytoplasmic, plastid, and mitochondrial) that are found in all photosynthetic eukaryotes, including plants and algae.

TABLE 3-10. Components of Mammalian Cytoplasmic RNA

Type of RNA	Size (in nucleotides)	Approximate molecular mass (in daltons)[a]	Number of species per cell	Percentage by weight of cytoplasmic RNA
18S ribosomal	1868[b]	0.58×10^6	1	~20
28S ribosomal	5025[b]	1.56×10^6	1	~57
5.8S ribosomal	158	4.9×10^4	1	~1.5
5.0S ribosomal	120	3.70×10^4	1	~1.5
tRNAs	73–91	heterogeneous	~100	15–17
mRNA	several hundred to several thousand	heterogeneous	>10^4	1–5
Small RNAs	100–330	heterogeneous	~60	<2

[a]Calculated using a molecular mass of 310 daltons per nucleotide.
[b]The sizes given are those of human 18S and 28S ribosomal RNAs.

mRNAs are far less abundant in plant cells than in animal cells, usually representing only 1–2% of the total cellular RNA. Like mRNAs from animals, plant mRNAs are heterogeneous in sequence, stability, and size, ranging from a few hundred bases in length to many kilobases (Spremuli 2000). A typical plant cell contains slightly less than 1 pg of mRNA, depending on the cell type, developmental stage, and growth conditions (Okamura and Goldberg 1989). If one assumes an average length of 2 kb and 0.6 pg of mRNA, a plant cell may have ~5×10^5 mRNA molecules. In addition, the level of expression of mRNAs varies from highly abundant, as usually is the case of photosynthetic genes in certain plant tissues, to moderate and rare. For example, the transcript for the small subunit of the ribulose-1,5-biphosphate carboxylase/oxygenase (Rubisco) enzyme was ~3% of total transcript population in tomato (Pichersky et al. 1986); for cyclophilin, ~0.3%; and for actin, ~0.04% in tomato leaves (Karrer et al. 1995). mRNAs are produced in the nucleus and some undergo posttranscriptional processing before entering the cytoplasm. Because plant cells have hard cell walls, most procedures for RNA isolation require grinding of the entire cell, and thus the RNA pool obtained may contain heterogeneous nuclear transcripts (i.e., unprocessed and semi-processed transcripts). To obtain only cytoplasmic RNA, consider extracting RNA from gently lysed plant protoplasts, a method that allows intact nuclei to be separated and discarded.

A poly(A)$^+$ tail at the 3´ ends of plant mRNAs makes them distinct from the remaining RNA population, and this unique characteristic allows their purification and separation from the other RNA species, as is the case of other eukaryotes.

Bacterial RNAs

Approximately 4% of the total RNA in an *E. coli* cell is mRNA, whereas ~80% is rRNA (16S and 23S) and 15% is tRNA. The sequence of the *E. coli* genome predicts 4290 open reading frames, ~70% of which have been assigned functions (Blattner et al. 1997). Unlike eukaryotic mRNAs, prokaryotic mRNAs are not uniformly polyadenylated and hence cannot be purified by chromatography on oligo(dT)-cellulose. The short half-life of bacterial mRNAs and the inability to selectively label them in the presence of the more abundant tRNA and rRNA species have undoubtedly contributed to the comparatively slow penetration of microarrays as a method to censor global gene expression in prokaryotes. However, these problems are not insurmountable, and the pace of expression profiling of bacteria is rapidly increasing (for further details, please see the information panel on **BACTERIAL MICROARRAYS**).

Quality Control

Whatever their source, the quality of preparations of RNA used for expression profiling should be checked by gel electrophoresis (please see Figures 3-27 and 3-28). Other methods of checking the integrity of mammalian and plant RNAs include the following:

- *Analysis of the size of cDNA synthesized using oligo(dT) as a primer.* Radioactive cDNA is synthesized in a pilot first-strand cDNA reaction. cDNA synthesized from mammalian mRNA should run as a continuous smear from ~600 bases to >5 kb. The bulk of the radioactivity should lie between 1.5 kb and 2 kb, and no bands of cDNA should be visible unless the mRNA was prepared from highly differentiated cells (e.g., reticulocytes and B lymphocytes) that express large quantities of a particular set of proteins.

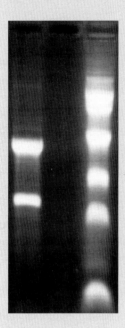

FIGURE 3-27. After electrophoresis of mammalian RNA in the presence of ethidium bromide, the 28S and 18S species of rRNA should be clearly visible under UV illumination, as should a more diffuse, fast-migrating band composed of tRNA and 5S rRNA. If the RNA preparation is not degraded, the 28S rRNA band should be stained at approximately twice the intensity of the 18S band and no smearing of either band should be visible. Staining close to the loading well is a sign that DNA is still present in the preparation. mRNA is invisible unless the gel is overloaded (it is a smear).

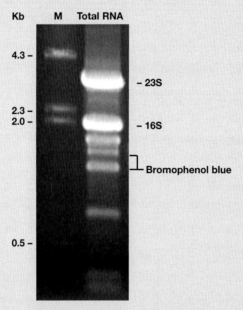

FIGURE 3-28. Total RNA from leaf tissue, where chloroplast RNA is abundant, is separated by electrophoresis through 1.2% agarose. Higher-plant chloroplasts contain 70S ribosomes, consisting of a large and a small subunit, 50S and 30S, respectively. The large subunit contains the 23S rRNA with a molecular weight of 1.1×10^6 and the small subunit contains a 16S rRNA with a molecular weight of 0.56×10^6 (Kissil and Buetow 1982; Leaver 1982). On the basis of their stoichiometry within the ribosome, it would be expected that the 23S RNA would outweigh the 16S species by almost twofold. However, most RNA preparations contain less 23S rRNA than predicted, most probably because of degradation. Thus, rRNAs isolated from plants always contain degradation products, as shown in the figure. Note also that plant ribosomes contain a short 5S rRNA molecule which is absent from animal mitochondria (Spremuli 2000). (Image provided by Bi-Huei Hou, Carnegie Institute of Washington, Stanford University.)

- *Using radiolabeled poly(dT) as a probe in a pilot northern hybridization* (Fornace and Mitchell 1986; Hollander and Fornace 1990). Poly(A)$^+$ RNA will generate an autoradiogram with a continuous smear from 600 bases to >5 kb. The bulk of the radioactivity should lie between 1.5 kb and 2 kb, and, once again, no specific bands of cDNA should be visible unless the mRNA was prepared from cells that express large quantities of specific mRNAs.

- *Using northern hybridization to detect mRNA of known size* expressed from a house-keeping gene, for example, glucose-6P dehydrogenase (GAPDH) mRNA, whose size in most mammalian cells is ~1.3 kb. Significant smearing of the band into lower-molec-ular-weight regions generally indicates that significant degradation of the mRNA pop-ulations has occurred. Fuzziness, on the other hand, is a sign of problems with the agarose gel system (e.g., the presence of ions in the glyoxal).

MEASURING THE EFFICIENCY OF DYE LABELING OF DNA

The best way to evaluate the quality of labeled targets is by agarose gel electrophoresis, which provides information on the length of the targets and their intensity of labeling (please see Protocol 13). However, the efficiency of labeling can be also be measured by standard spec-troscopy, as described here. This technique is useful when estimating the amounts of Cy3- and Cy5-labeled nucleotides that should be used in hybridization reactions.

The efficiency of dye labeling, expressed as the ratio of bases to dye molecules, can be esti-mated by (1) measuring the absorbance of the nucleic acid at 260 nm and the absorbance of the dye at its absorbance maximum (λ) and (2) applying the Beer-Lambert law:

Absorbance = extinction coefficient × path length × concentration

The extinction coefficients (ε) and absorption maxima (λ_{max}) of fluorescent dyes com-monly used to label nucleic acids are shown in Table 3-11.

1. Measure the absorbance (A) of the labeled DNA sample at 260 nm and at the λ_{max} of the dye. To perform these measurements, the solution should contain >5 µg/ml of the DNA-dye conjugate.

2. Correct for the contribution of the dye to the A_{260} reading, using the correction factors $A_{base} = A_{260} - (A_{dye} \times CF_{260})$.

TABLE 3-11. Absorption Properties of Fluorescent Dyes

Dye	λ_{max} (nm)	ε (cm^{-1}M^{-1})	Correction factor (CF$_{260}$)
Alexa Fluor 488	492 (green)	62,000	0.30
Alexa Fluor 532	525 (yellow)	82,300	0.24
Alexa Fluor 546	555 (orange)	104,000	0.21
Alexa Fluor 568	576 (red)	93,000	0.45
Alexa Fluor 594	588 (red)	80,400	0.45
Cy3	550 (orange)	150,000	0.08
Cy5	649 (far red)	250,000	0.05

TABLE 3-12. Extinction Coefficients for Nucleic Acids

Nucleic acid	ε (cm^{-1}M^{-1})	MW$_{base}$
Double-stranded DNA	6,600	330
Single-stranded DNA	8,920	330
Oligonucleotide	10,000	330

The information in this table was assembled from literature provided by Amersham Biosciences, Molecular Probes, Inc., and the Ed Tom Lab.

3. Calculate the ratio of bases to dye molecules, using the following equation: base:dye = $(A_{base} \times \varepsilon_{dye})/(A_{dye} \times \varepsilon_{base})$, where ε_{dye} is the extinction coefficient of the fluorescent dye and ε_{base} is the extinction coefficient for a base in double-stranded DNA, single-stranded DNA, or oligonucleotides (please see Table 3-12).

When labeling with Cy3 or Cy5, the base:dye ratio varies between 8 and 65 depending on the properties of the template RNA (e.g., G+C) content and the characteristics of the reverse transcriptase. Because SUPERSCRIPT II catalyzes the incorporation of Cy3 more efficiently than Cy5, the density of Cy3 labeling is usually greater than that of Cy5 labeling by a factor of 4/3.

The concentration (C) of nucleic acid in the sample can be calculated from the following equation: C (in mg/ml) = $(A_{base} \times 330)/(\varepsilon_{base} \times$ path length). Because the amount of nucleic acid is generally small, spectroscopic measurements are usually taken using small cuvettes (100–200-μl capacity). The path length of these cuvettes is sometime shorter than the conventional 1 cm. UV translucent microtiter plates can also be used if an absorbance plate reader is available. The path length of these readers varies according to the model and manufacturer. The instruction manual should contain the necessary data.

MOLONEY LEUKEMIA VIRUS REVERSE TRANSCRIPTASE

Mo-MLV reverse transcriptase contains two independently functional, nonoverlapping domains (Tanese et al. 1985; Tanese and Goff 1988; for review, please see Prasad 1993). The large amino-terminal domain (~450 residues) contains the DNA polymerase activity, whereas the carboxy-terminal domain (~220 residues) encompasses the RNase H activity. The DNA polymerase is rather sluggish and prone to pausing at regions of the RNA template rich in secondary structure (Matson et al. 1980; Gerard et al. 1989). In addition, RNase H activity has the capacity to hydrolyze the RNA template near the point of chain growth, which can result in dissociation of the DNA-RNA hybrid and termination of the first-strand cDNA. Up to 50% of the first-strand cDNA molecules initiated by Mo-MLV reverse transcriptase may be prematurely terminated by one or another of these mechanisms (Berger et al. 1983).

Solving the three-dimensional structure of Mo-MLV reverse transcriptase in the early

1990s (Arnold et al. 1992; Kohlstaedt et al. 1992; Georgiadis et al. 1995) was an important step forward because it opened the way to rational genetic engineering of the enzyme. However, by then, one of the chief problems had already been solved by the creation of a mutant of Mo-MLV that retained DNA polymerase activity but lacked RNase H activity (Kotewicz et al. 1988). Surprisingly, inactivation of the RNase H domain by deletion or point mutation led to a dramatic increase in the ability of the enzyme to catalyze the synthesis of cDNA at elevated temperature (Gerard et al. 1989, 1992). Until this serendipitous discovery, Mo-MLV had been used at temperatures no greater than 42°C. However, certain mutants of Mo-MLV deficient in RNase H can efficiently catalyze the synthesis of cDNA at temperatures as high as 50°C (Gerard et al. 1989, 1992), whereas RNase H$^-$ forms of the avian enzyme can be safely used at 60°C (for review, please see Gerard 998).

The elimination of the RNase H activity from reverse transcriptase increases the ability of the enzyme to generate full-length cDNA molecules at standard temperatures. Various commercially marketed forms of these variants include a mutant of Mo-MLV reverse transcriptase that lacks RNase H activity and contains five additional residues at the carboxyl terminus. Other commercial mutant forms of Mo-MLV reverse transcriptase that lack RNase H include StrataScript from Stratagene, SUPERSCRIPT and SUPERSCRIPT II from Invitrogen/GIBCO. SUPERSCRIPT carries a deletion that eliminates RNase H activity, whereas StrataScript and SUPERSCRIPT II carry point mutations.

OLIGO(dT)-CELLULOSE

Oligo(dT) continues to be heavily exploited as an affinity ligand to isolate and purify poly(A)$^+$ mRNA, essentially as described by Aviv and Leder (1972) and Nakazato and Edmonds (1972). For this purpose, thymidylate oligomers 12–18 residues in length are covalently attached to a solid matrix (usually cellulose). The standard method of synthesis of the oligomers, which was pioneered by Gilham (1964, 1971), involves polymerization of thymidine monophosphate in the presence of a carbodiimide. Cellulose is then added, to which the oligothymidylate molecules become attached by reaction between their 5′-phosphoryl groups and the hydroxyl groups of cellulose. Gilham (1964) used oligo(dT)-cellulose columns chiefly to explore affinity chromatography of polynucleotides, showing that various oligomers of adenylic acid could be eluted from an oligo(dT)-cellulose column in a temperature-dependent fashion. For isolation of mRNA, however, it is more convenient to exploit the salt dependence of the hybridization reaction, as described in Protocol 7. For further information, please see Sambrook and Russell (2001).

QUANTIFICATION OF RNA

Because it is rapid, simple, and nondestructive, absorption spectroscopy has long been the method of choice to measure the amount of DNA and RNA in concentrated pure solutions. Table 3-13 shows the relationship between the absorbance at 260 nm and the concentration of nucleic acid in a solution.

It is not good practice to estimate the concentration of solutions of nucleic acids and oligonucleotides by measuring their absorption at a single wavelength (260 nm). The absorbance of the sample should be measured at several wavelengths since the ratio of absorbance at 260 nm to the absorbance at other wavelengths is a good indicator of the purity of the preparation. Significant absorption at 230 nm indicates contamination by phenolate ion, thiocyanates, and other organic compounds (Stulnig and Amberger 1994), whereas absorption at higher wavelengths (330 nm and higher) is usually caused by light scattering and indicates the presence of particulate matter. Absorption at 280 nm indicates the presence of protein, because aromatic acids absorb strongly at 280 nm.

For many years, the ratio of the absorbance at 260 nm and 280 nm (OD_{260}:OD_{280}) has been used as a measure of purity of isolated nucleic acids. This method dates back to 1942, when Warburg and Christian showed that the ratio is a good indicator of contamination of protein preparations by nucleic acids. The reverse is not true! Because the extinction coefficients of nucleic acids at 260 nm and 280 nm are so much greater than that of proteins, significant contamination with protein will not greatly change the OD_{260}:OD_{280} ratio of a nucleic acid solution (Warburg and Christian 1942; Glasel 1995; Manchester 1995, 1996; Wilfinger et al. 1997). In theory, the $A_{260:280}$ ratio of RNA should be 1.9 to 2.0. However, the $A_{260:280}$ ratio of nucleic acids is significantly affected by the pH and ionic strength of the solution (Beavan et al. 1955; Wilfinger et al. 1997). In water, the $A_{260:280}$ ratio increases from 1.55 to 1.97 as the pH rises from 5.2 to 6.1. In 100 mM NaCl, the ratio is 1.5, and in 1 M NaCl, it is 2.1. Preparation of nucleic acids contaminated with significant amounts of phenol absorbs strongly at 230 nm.

Despite its simplicity, absorption spectroscopy is comparatively insensitive. With most laboratory spectrophotometers, nucleic acid concentrations of at least 1 μg/ml are required to obtain reliable estimates of A_{260}. In addition, absorption spectroscopy cannot readily distinguish between DNA and RNA, and it cannot be used with crude preparations of nucleic acids. Because of these limitations, a number of alternative methods have been devised to measure the concentration of RNA.

TABLE 3-13. Absorbance of Nucleic Acids at 260 nm

Absorbance at 260 nm	Extinction coefficient	Weight of nucleic acid in one OD_{260} unit
RNA and single-stranded DNA	7.4	40 μg/ml
Double-stranded DNA	6.6	50 μg/ml
Oligonucleotides	8.6	33 μg/ml

The values shown in the table are (1) valid for 1-cm path-length cuvettes and (2) should be regarded as approximate since they are affected by the base composition and the degree of secondary structure in single-stranded nucleic acids.

RiboGreen

RiboGreen is an unsymmetrical cyanine dye sold by Molecular Probes, Inc. The free dye is essentially nonfluorescent, but it exhibits a 1000-fold enhancement of fluorescence at 520 nm when bound to RNA. As little as 10 ng/ml RNA can be detected in a spectrophotometer, a fluorescence plate reader, or a filter-based fluorometer equipped with standard fluorescein filters (e.g., Turner Designs TD-700). The sensitivity of RiboGreen is 200-fold higher for RNA than for ethidium bromide and 100-fold higher than absorbance at 260 nm. The assay requires two concentration of dye to cover its full dynamic range (1 mg/ml to 1 mg/ml RNA). The major disadvantages are (1) cost and (2) the inability of the dye to distinguish between RNA and DNA, a problem solved by treating the samples with DNase before assay. The concentration of RNA in the test samples is determined by interpolation into a standard curve, constructed using samples containing known amounts of RNA. Details of the assay are available on the Molecular Probes Web Site (www.molecularprobes.com) and in the literature provided as part of the RiboGreen kits.

SPECIAL CONSIDERATIONS FOR WORKING WITH RNA

It is easy but unnecessary to become paranoid about RNase. Problems with endogenous RNases can usually be eliminated by careful handling of tissues. Ideally, tissues are fresh frozen in liquid nitrogen, stored in RNA*later,* or immediately homogenized in TRIzol. For further details, please see Table 3-1.

The greatest risk to RNA lies between the time that a tissue is isolated and the time it is either frozen or lysed in a denaturing solution. Minimizing this time and avoiding damage to tissue are essential if endogenous RNases are not to destroy the RNA. If RNA cannot be extracted immediately, store the tissue in RNA*later* (Ambion) (please see Table 3-1).

Particular care is also required toward the end of the purification process, when the RNA is transferred into aqueous solvents and loses the protection afforded by reagents such as phenol or guanidinium ions. If RNases have not been removed or inactivated by this stage or if they are introduced, even in minute amounts, they will inexorably degrade the RNA. Always work quickly with RNA and minimize the time spent at >0°C (please see the information panel on STORAGE AND RECOVERY OF RNA).

In our experience, contamination with exogenous RNase frequently arises from a breakdown in aseptic technique, in that solutions become contaminated with bacteria or other microorganisms, or by transfer from automatic pipetting devices that have previously been used to dispense solutions of RNase, for example, during processing of plasmid preparations. Effective methods to avoid contamination with RNases include the following:

- Keep a special set of automatic pipettors for use when handling RNA.

- Set aside items of glassware, batches of plasticware, and buffers that are to be used only for experiments with RNA. Alternatively, use disposable plasticware, which generally does not require cleaning before use. Disposable pipette tips and microfuges are available that are certified by the manufacturer(s) to be free of RNase. To reduce the chances for contamination, it is best to use sterile forceps when transferring these small items from their original packages to laboratory racks.

- Store solution/buffers in small aliquots and discard each aliquot after use. Avoid materials or stock solutions that have been used for any other purposes in the laboratory.

- Never assume that anything in the laboratory is free of RNase unless steps have personally been taken to remove or inactivate the enzyme, as described below.

- Set aside special tanks used for gel electrophoresis of RNA. Clean these tanks with detergent solution, rinse them in H_2O, dry them with ethanol, and then fill them with a 3% solution of H_2O_2. After 10 minutes at room temperature, rinse the electrophoresis tank thoroughly with H_2O treated with diethylpyrocarbonate (DEPC). Solutions containing primary amines (e.g., Tris) cannot be treated with DEPC (please see the information panel on INHIBITING RNASES).

- Prepare all solutions and buffers with RNase-free glassware, H_2O, and chemicals reserved for work with RNA that are handled with baked spatulas (for 4 hours at 300°C). Where feasible, treat the solutions with 0.1% DEPC for at least 12 hours at 37°C and then heat for 15 minutes to 100°C or autoclave for 15 minutes at 15 psi (1.05 kg/cm^2) on liquid cycle (for further information, please see the information panel on INHIBITING RNASES). Filter the solutions that are heat-labile through 0.2-μm filters and store in RNase-free glassware or plasticware.

- Wear gloves when handling weighing boats or working with RNA. Change gloves frequently.

- Autoclaved glassware may not be sufficient to inactivate RNase. Bake all glassware for 4 hours at 300°C or fill with 0.5 N NaOH for 30 minutes, followed by rinsing several times with sterile, RNase-free H_2O.

- Microfuge tubes may be rendered free of RNase by soaking overnight in 0.1% DEPC, followed by rinsing with sterile, RNase-free H_2O and autoclaving.

- Decontaminate shared equipment, such as rotary evaporators, by wiping them before use with RNase-Off (CPG Inc.) or other RNase decontaminating agent.

STORAGE AND RECOVERY OF RNA

Storage of RNA

After precipitation with ethanol, store the RNA as follows:

- Dissolve the precipitate in deionized formamide and store at –20ºC (Chomczynski 1992). This provides a chemically stable environment that also protects the RNA against degradation by RNases. Purified, salt-free RNA dissolves quickly in formamide up to a concentration of 4 mg/ml. At such concentrations, samples of the RNA can be analyzed directly by gel electrophoresis and RT-PCR or used as a template for cDNA synthesis catalyzed by reverse transcriptase, thereby saving time and avoiding potential degradation. If necessary, recover the RNA from formamide by precipitation with 4 volumes of ethanol as described by Chomczynski (1992) or by diluting the formamide fourfold with 0.2 M NaCl and then adding the conventional 2 volumes of ethanol (Nadin-Davis and Mezl 1982).

- Dissolve the precipitate in an aqueous buffer and store at –80ºC. Buffers commonly used for this purpose include TE (pH 7.4) or RNase-free H_2O containing 0.1 mM EDTA (pH 7.5) containing SDS (0.1–0.5%). A disadvantage of this method is that the SDS must be removed by chloroform extraction and ethanol precipitation before the RNA can be used as a template for reverse transcriptase. Furthermore, accessing aliquots of the sample requires that it be warmed, which leaves the RNA prey to lingering RNases.

- Store the precipitate of RNA as a suspension at –20ºC in ethanol. Samples of the RNA can be removed, as needed, with an automatic pipetting device. Advantages of storing RNA in ethanol are (1) that the low freezing point allows recovery of an aliquot with warming the sample to temperatures >0ºC and (2) that RNases are inactive in ethanol. However, because precipitates of RNA are lumpy, vortex the suspension immediately before sampling.

Recovery of RNA from Storage

RNA is usually stored in formamide, ethanol, or a solution of Tris/EDTA containing SDS.

- Precipitate the RNA stored in formamide with 4 volumes of ethanol, as described by Chomczynski (1992). Then proceed to Step 1.

- Precipitrate the RNA stored in TE/SDS by addition of 0.1 volume of 3 M sodium acetate (pH 5.2) and 3 volumes of absolute ethanol. Proceed to Step 1.

- Recover the precipitates of RNA stored in ethanol by centrifugation as described in Step 1.

1. Recover the RNA by centrifugation at 12,000g for 10 minutes at 4ºC.

   If large amounts of RNA (>150 µg) are centrifuged in a microfuge tube for long periods of time, a compact, hard pellet is formed that does not dissolve easily. When processing large quantities of RNA, centrifuge the sample for 30 seconds to recover most of the RNA, transfer most of the supernatant to a new tube, and recover the remaining RNA by centrifuging at 12,000g for a further 10 minutes. Process the two batches of RNA separately for the next three steps, recombining them at Step 5.

2. Remove the supernatant by gentle aspiration and then add 1 ml of 75% ethanol. Invert the closed tube several times and then recentrifuge at 12,000*g* for 5 minutes at 4ºC.

3. Carefully pour off the supernatant. Recentrifuge the tube briefly and then use a automatic pipette to remove the residual ethanol from the pellet.

4. Stand the open tube in a ventilated hood until the pellet of RNA is just dry, but no longer.

5. Resuspend the RNA in 50 μl of 10 mM Tris-Cl (pH 7.5), 0.1 mM EDTA.

   For microarray experiments, the RNA must be concentrated at >7 mg/ml.

6. Incubate the closed tube for 5–10 minutes at 65ºC. Vortex the tube briefly to deposit the fluid in the bottom of the tube.

   The pellet of RNA will rapidly become translucent in aqueous buffer; it is thus necessary to hold the sample to the light while swirling the solution to check that the RNA is redissolved.

7. Quantify the RNA by absorption spectrophotometry at 260 and 280 nm, or by fluorescence after staining with RiboGreen (please see the information panel on QUANTIFICATION OF RNAS).

   Before using the RNA in microarray experiments, check its integrity by electrophoresis through a formaldehyde–1% agarose gel (please see the information panel on MAMMALIAN, PLANT, AND BACTERIAL RNAS).

REFERENCES

Aharoni A., Keizer L.C.P., Bouwmeester H.J., Sun Z., Alvarez-Huerta M., Verhoeven H.A., Blaas J., van Houwelingen A.M.M.L., De Vos R.C.H., van der Voet H., Jansen R.C., Guis M., Mol J., Davis R.W., Schena M., van Tunen A.J., and O'Connell A.P. 2000. Identification of the SAAT gene involved in strawberry flavor biogenesis by use of DNA microarrays. *Plant Cell* **12:** 647–661.

Arnold E., Jacobo-Molina A., Nanni R.G., Williams R.L., Lu X., Ding J., Clark Jr., A.D., Zhang A., Ferris A.L., Clark P., et al. 1992. Structure of HIV-1 reverse transcriptase/DNA complex at 7 Å resolution showing active site locations. *Nature* **357:** 85–89.

Aviv H. and Leder H. 1972. Purification of biologically active globin messenger RNA by chromatography on oligothymidylic acid cellulose. *Proc. Natl. Acad. Sci.* **69:** 1408–1412.

Barlow J.J., Mathias A.P., and Williamson R. 1963. A simple method for the quantitative isolation of undegraded high molecular weight ribonucleic acid. *Biochem. Biophys. Res. Commun.* **13:** 61–66.

Barnes W.M. 1994. PCR amplification of up to 35-kb DNA with high fidelity and high yield from lambda bacteriophage templates. *Proc. Natl. Acad. Sci.* **91:** 2216–2220.

Baugh L.R., Hill A.A., Brown E.L., and Hunter C.P. 2001. Quantitative analysis of mRNA amplification by in vitro transcription. *Nucleic Acids Res.* **29:** E29.

Beavan G.H., Holiday E.R., and Johnson E.A. 1955. Optical properties of nucleic acids and their components. In *The nucleic acids: Chemistry and biology* (ed. E. Chargaff and J.N. Davidson), vol. 1, pp. 493–553. Academic Press, New York.

Berger S.L. and Birkenmeier C.S. 1979. Inhibition of intractable nucleases with ribonucleotide-vanadyl complexes: Isolation of messenger ribonucleic acid from resting lymphocytes. *Biochemistry* **18:** 5143–5149.

Berger S.L., Wallace D.M., Puskas R.S., and Eschenfeldt W.H. 1983. Reverse transcriptase and its associated ribonuclease H: Interplay of two enzyme activities controls the yield of single-stranded complementary deoxyribonucleic acid. *Biochemistry* **22:** 2365–2372.

Berk A.J. and Sharp P.A. 1977. Sizing and mapping of early adenovirus mRNAs by gel electrophoresis of S1 endonuclease-digested hybrids. *Cell* **12:** 721–732.

Bertucci F., Bernard K., Loriod B., Chang Y.C., Granjeaud S., Birnbaum D., Nguyen C., Peck K., and Jordan B.R. 1999. Sensitivity issues in DNA array-based expression measurements and performance of nylon microarrays for small samples. *Hum. Mol. Genet.* **8:** 1715–1722.

Bishop J.O., Morton J.G., Rosbash M., and Richardson M. 1974. Three abundance classes in HeLa cell messenger RNA. *Nature* **250:** 199–204.

Blackburn P., Wilson G., and Moore S. 1977. Ribonuclease inhibitor from human placenta. Purification and properties. *J. Biol.Chem.* **252:** 5904–5910.

Blattner F.R., Plunkett III G., Bloch C.A., Perna N.T., Burland V., Riley M., Collado-Vides J., Glasner J.D., Rode C.K., Mayhew G.F., Gregor J., Davis N.W., Kirkpatrick H.A., Goeden M.A., Rose D.J., Mau B., and Shao Y. 1997. The complete genome sequence of *Escherichia coli* K-12. *Science* **277:** 1453–1474.

Bodkin D.K. and Knudson D.L. 1985. Assessment of sequence relatedness of double-stranded RNA genes by RNA-RNA blot hybridization. *J. Virol. Methods* **10:** 45–52.

Bolton E.T. and McCarthy B.J. 1962. A general method for isolation of RNA complementary to DNA. *Proc. Natl. Acad. Sci.* **48:** 1390–1396.

Bonner J., Kung G., and Bekhor I. 1967. A method for the hybridization of nucleic acid molecules at low temperature. *Biochemistry* **6:** 3650–3653.

Brawerman G., Mendecki J., and Lee S.Y. 1972. A procedure for the isolation of mammalian messenger ribonucleic acid. *Biochemistry* **11:** 637–641.

Brown J.W.S. and Shaw P.J. 1998. Small nucleolar RNAs and pre-rRNA processing in plants. *Plant Cell* **10:** 649–657.

Brown N.L. 1984. DNA sequencing. *Methods Microbiol.* **17:** 259–313.

Brumbaugh J.A., Middendorf L.R., Grone D.L., and Ruth J.L. 1988. Continuous, on-line DNA sequencing using oligodeoxynucleotide primers with multiple fluorophores. *Proc. Natl. Acad. Sci.* **85:** 5610–5614.

Casey J. and Davidson N. 1977. Rates of formation and thermal stabilities of RNA:DNA and DNA:DNA duplexes at high concentrations of formamide. *Nucleic Acids Res.* **4:** 1539–1552.

Celano P., Vertino P.M., and Casero Jr. R.A. 1993. Isolation of polyadenylated RNA from cultured cells and intact tissues. *BioTechniques* **15:** 26–28.

Chang S., Puryear Y., and Cairney J. 1993. A simple and efficient method for isolating RNA from pine trees. *Plant Mol. Biol. Rep.* **11:** 113–116.

Chen J.J., Wu R., Yang P.C., Huang J.Y., Sher Y.P., Han M.H., Kao W.C., Lee P.J., Chiu T.F., Chang F., Chu Y.W., Wu C.W., and Peck K. 1998. Profiling expression patterns and isolating differentially expressed genes by cDNA microarray system with colorimetry detection. *Genomics* **51:** 313–324.

Chenchik A., Zhu Y.Y., Diatchenko L., Li R., Hill J., and Siebert P.D. 1998. Generation and use of high-quality cDNA from small amounts of total RNA by SMART™ PCR. In *Gene cloning and analysis by RT-PCR* (ed. P.D. Siebert and J.W. Larrick), pp. 305–319. Eaton Publishing/BioTechniques Book Division, Natick, Massachusetts.

Chirgwin J.M., Przybyla A.E., MacDonald R.J., and Rutter W.J. 1979. Isolation of biologically active ribonucleic acid from sources enriched in ribonuclease. *Biochemistry* **18:** 5294–5299.

Chomczynski P. 1989. Product and process for isolating RNA. U.S. Patent 4,843,155.

———. 1992. One-hour downward alkaline capillary transfer for blotting of DNA and RNA. *Anal. Biochem.* **201:** 134–139.

———. 1993. A reagent for the single-step simultaneous isolation of RNA, DNA and proteins from cell and tissue samples. *BioTechniques* **15:** 532–534.

———. 1994. Shelf-stable product and process for isolating RNA, DNA and proteins. U.S. Patent 5,346,994.

———. 1999. Product and process for isolating DNA, RNA and proteins. U.S. Patent 5,945,515.

Chomczynski P. and Mackey K. 1995. Modification of the TRI Reagent™ procedure for isolation of RNA from polysaccharide- and proteoglycan-rich sources. *BioTechniques* **19:** 942–945.

Chomczynski P. and Sacchi N. 1987. Single-step method of RNA isolation by acid guanidinium thiocyanate-phenol-chloroform extraction. *Anal. Biochem.* **221:** 303–305.

Chuang S.E., Daniels D.L., and Blattner F.R. 1993. Global regulation of gene expression in *Escherichia coli.* *J. Bacteriol.* **175:** 2026–2036.

Cox R.A. 1968. The use of guanidinium chloride in the isolation of nucleic acids. *Methods Enzymol.* **12B:** 120–129.

Crino P.B. and Eberwine J. 1997. Cellular and molecular basis of cerebral dysgenesis. *J. Neurosci. Res.* **50:** 907–916.

Defrancesco L. 1998. Need for speed II. *The Scientist* **12:** 20–26.

Deyholos M.K. and Galbraith D.W. 2001. High-density microarrays for gene expression analysis. *Cytometry* **43:** 229–238.

DeRisi J.L., Iyer V.R., and Brown P.O. 1997. Exploring the metabolic and genetic control of gene expression on a genomic scale. *Science* **278:** 680–686.

DeRisi J., Penland L., Brown P.O., Bittner M.L., Meltzer P.S., Ray M., Chen Y., Su Y.A., and Trent J.M. 1996. Use of a cDNA microarray to analyze gene expression patterns in human cancer. *Nat. Genet.* **14:** 457–460.

Diehn M., Eisen M.B., Botstein D., and Brown P.O. 2000. Large-scale identification of secreted and membrane-associated gene products using DNA microarrays. *Nat. Genet.* **25:** 58–62.

Duggan D.J., Bittner M., Chen Y., Meltzer P. and Trent P.M. 1999. Expression profiling using cDNA microarrays. *Nat. Genet.* (suppl.) **21:** 10–14.

Dunn J.J. and Studier F.W. 1983. Complete nucleotide sequence of bacteriophage T7 DNA and the locations of T7 genetic elements. *J. Mol. Biol.* **166:** 477–535.

Eberwine J., Yeh H., Miyashiro K., Cao Y., Nair S., Finnell R., Zettel M., and Coleman P. 1992. Analysis of gene expression in single live neurons. *Proc. Natl. Acad. Sci.* **89:** 3010–3014.

Edmonds M., Vaughn Jr. M.H. and Nakazato H. 1971. Polyadenylic acid sequences in the heterogeneous nuclear RNA and rapidly-labeled polyribosomal RNA of HeLa cells: Possible evidence for a precursor relationship. *Proc. Natl. Acad. Sci.* **68:**1336–1340.

Ehrenberg L., Fedorcsak I., and Solymosy F. 1976. Diethyl pyrocarbonate in nucleic acid research. *Prog. Nucleic Acid Res. Mol. Biol.* **16:** 189–192.

Eisen M.B. and Brown P.O. 1999. DNA arrays for analysis of gene expression. *Methods Enzymol.* **303:** 179–205.

Florell S.R., Coffin C.M., Holden J.A., Zimmermann J.W., Gerwels J.W., Summers B.K., Jones D.A., and Leachman S.A. 2001. Preservation of RNA for functional genomic studies: A multidisciplinary tumor bank protocol. *Mod. Pathol.* **14:** 116–128.

Fornace Jr. A.J. and Mitchell J.B. 1986. Induction of B2 RNA polymerase III transcription by heat shock enrichment for heat shock induced sequences in rodent cells by hybridization subtraction. *Nucleic Acids Res.* **14:** 5793–5811.

Freimert C., Erfle V., and Strauss G. 1989. Preparation of radiolabeled cDNA probes with high specific activity for rapid screening of gene expression. *Methods Mol. Cell. Biol.* **1:** 143–153.

Gaillard C. and Strauss F. 1990. Ethanol precipitation of DNA with linear polyacrylamide as carrier. *Nucleic Acids Res.* **18:** 378.

Gasch A.P., Spellman P.T., Kao C.M., Carmel-Harel O., Eisen M.B., Storz G., Botstein D., and Brown P.O. 2000. Genomic expression programs in the response of yeast cells to environmental changes. *Mol. Biol. Cell* **11:** 4241–4257.

Georgiadis M.M., Jessen S.M., Ogata C.M., Telesnitsky A., Goff S.P., and Hendrickson W.A. 1995. Mechanistic implications from the structure of a catalytic fragment of Moloney murine leukemia virus reverse transcriptase. *Structure* **3:** 879–892.

Gerard G.F. 1998. Reverse transcriptase: A historical perspective. *Focus* (Life Technologies) **20:** 65–67.

Gerard G.F., D'Alessio J.M., and Kotewicz M.L. 1989. cDNA synthesis by cloned Moloney murine leukemia virus reverse transcriptase lacking RNase H activity. *Focus* (Life Technologies) **11:** 66–69.

Gerard G.F., Schmidt B.J., Kotewicz M.L., and Campbell J.H. 1992. cDNA synthesis by Moloney murine leukemia virus RNase H-minus reverse transcriptase possessing full DNA polymerase activity. *Focus* (Life Technologies) **14:** 91–93.

Getz M.J., Birnie G.D., Getz M.J., Birnie G.D., Young B.D., MacPhail E., and Paul J. 1975. A kinetic estimation of base sequence complexity of nuclear poly(A)-containing RNA in mouse Friend cells. *Cell* **4:** 121–129.

Getz M.J., Reiman Jr. H.M., Siegal G.P., Quinlan T.J., Proper J., Elder P.K., and Moses H.L. 1977. Gene expression in chemically transformed mouse embryo cells: Selective enhancement of the expression of C type RNA tumor virus genes. *Cell* **11:** 909–921.

Gilham P.T. 1964. Synthesis of polynucleotide celluloses and their use in fractionation of oligonucleotides. *J. Am. Chem. Soc.* **86:** 4982–4989.

———. 1971. The covalent binding of nucleotides, polynucleotides and nucleic acids to cellulose. *Methods Enzymol.* **21:** 191–197.

Glasel J.A. 1995. Validity of nucleic acid purities monitored by 260nm/280nm absorbance ratios (comments). *BioTechniques* **18:** 62–63.

Glisin V., Crkvenjakov R., and Byus C. 1974. Ribonucleic acid isolated by cesium chloride centrifugation. *Biochemistry* **13:** 2633–2637.

Goldberg R.B., Hoschek G., Kamalay J.C., and Timberlake W.E. 1978. Sequence complexity of nuclear and polysomal RNA in leaves of the tobacco plant. *Cell* **14:** 123–131.

Gramza A.W., Lucas J.M., Mountain R.E., Schuller D.E., and Lang J.C. 1995. Efficient method for preparing normal and tumor tissue for RNA extraction. *BioTechniques* **18:** 228–231.

Grassman W. and Deffner G. 1953. Verteilungschromatographisches verhalten von proteinen un peptiden in phenolhaltigen lösungsmitteln. *Hoppe-Seyler's Z. Physiol. Chem.* **293:** 89–98.

Gress T.M., Hoheisel J.D., Lennon G.G., Zehetner G., and Lehrach H. 1992. Hybridization fingerprinting of high-density cDNA-library arrays with cDNA pools derived from whole tissues. *Mamm. Genome* **3:** 609–619.

Groppe J.C. and Morse D.E. 1993. Isolation of full-length RNA templates for reverse transcription from tissues rich in RNase and proteoglycans. *Anal. Biochem.* **210:** 337–343.

Guatelli J.C., Whitfield K.M., Kwoh D.Y., Barringer K.J., Richman D.D., and Gingeras T.R. 1990. Isothermal, in vitro amplification of nucleic acids by a multienzyme reaction modeled after retroviral replication. *Proc. Natl. Acad. Sci.* **87:** 7797.

Gubler U. and Hoffman B.J. 1983. A simple and very efficient method for generating cDNA libraries. *Gene* **25:** 263–269.

Hamaguchi K. and Geiduschek P. 1962. The effect of electrolytes on the stability of the deoxynucleate helix. *J. Am. Chem. Soc.* **84:** 1329–1338.

Harmer S.L., Hogenesch J.B., Straume M., Chang H.S., Han B., Zhu T., Wang X., Kreps J.A., and Kay S.A. 2000. Orchestrated transcription of key pathways in *Arabidopsis* by the circadian clock. *Science* **290:** 2110–2113.

Hearst J.E. and Vinograd J. 1961a. The net hydration of deoxyribonucleic acid. *Proc. Natl. Acad. Sci.* **47:** 825–830.

———. 1961b. The net hydration of T4 bacteriophage deoxyribonucleic acid and the effect of hydration on buoyant behavior in a density gradient at equilibrium in the ultracentrifuge. *Proc. Natl. Acad. Sci.* **47:** 1005–1014.

Heller R.A., Schena M., Chai A., Shalon D., Bedilion T., Gilmore J., Woolley D.E., and Davis R.W. 1997. Discovery and analysis of inflammatory disease-related genes using cDNA microarrays. *Proc. Natl. Acad. Sci.* **94:** 2150–2155.

Helmkamp G. and Ts'o P.O.P. 1961. The secondary structures of nucleic acids in organic solvents. *J. Am. Chem. Soc.* **83:** 138–142.

Hollander M.C. and Fornace Jr. A.J. 1990. Estimation of relative mRNA content by filter hybridization to a polythymidylate probe. *BioTechniques* **9:** 174–179.

Huang Y.H., Leblanc P., Apostolou V., Stewart B., and Moreland R.B. 1995. Comparison of Milli-Q® PF Plus water to DEPC-treated water in the preparation and analysis of RNA. *BioTechniques* **19:** 656–661.

Hughes T.R., Mao M., Jones A.R., Burchard J., Marton M.J., Shannon K.W., Lefkowitz S.M., Ziman M., Schelter J.M., Meyer M.R., Kobayashi S., Davis C., Dai H., He Y.D., Stephaniants S.B., Cavet G., Walker W.L., West A., Coffey E., Shoemaker D.D., Stoughton R., Blanchard A.P., Friend S.H., and Linsley P.S. 2001. Expression profiling using microarrays fabricated by an ink-jet oligonucleotide synthesizer. *Nat. Biotechnol.* **19:** 342–347.

Hutton J.R. 1977. Renaturation kinetics and thermal stability of DNA in aqueous solutions of formamide and urea. *Nucleic Acids Res.* **4:** 3537–3555.

Irving J.A., Cain G., Parr A., Howard M., Angus B., and Cattan A.R. 1996. OCT embedded sections of pathological specimens as a source of high quality RNA for reverse transcriptase/polymerase chain reaction. *J. Clin. Pathol.* **49:** 258–259.

Kacharmina J.E., Crino P.B., and Eberwine J. 1999. Preparation of cDNA from single cells and subcellular regions. *Methods Enzymol.* **303:** 3–18.

Karrer E.E., Lincoln J.W., Hogenhout S., Bennett A.B., Bostock R.M., Martineau B., Lucas W.J., Gilchrist D.G., and Alexander D. 1995. *In situ* isolation of mRNA from individual plant cells: Creation of cell-specific cDNA libraries. *Proc. Natl. Acad. Sci.* **92:** 3814–3818.

Katterman F.R.H. and Shattuck V.I. 1983. An effective method of DNA isolation from the mature leaves of *Gossipium* species that contain large amounts of phenolic terpenoids and tannins. *Prep. Biochem.* **13:** 347–359.

Kehoe D.M., Villand P., and Somerville S. 1999. DNA microarrays for studies of higher plants and other photosynthetic organisms. *Trends Plant Sci.* **4:** 38–41.

Khodursky A.B., Peter B.J., Cozzarelli N.R., Botstein D., Brown P.O., and Yanofsky C. 2000. DNA microarray analysis of gene expression in response to physiological and genetic changes that affect tryptophan metabolism in *Escherichia coli. Proc. Natl. Acad. Sci.* **97:** 12170–12175.

Kirby K.S. 1956. A new method for the isolation of ribonucleic acid from mammalian tissues. *Biochem. J.* **64:** 405–408.

———. 1957. A new method for the isolation of deoxyribonucleic acids; evidence on the nature of bonds between deoxyribonucleic acid and protein. *Biochem. J.* **66:** 495–504.

———. 1964. Isolation and fractionation of nucleic acids. *Prog. Nucleic Acid Res. Mol. Biol.* **3:** 1–31.

Kissil M.S. and Buetow D.E. 1982. Preparation of in vivo labelled, high specific activity [^{32}P]chloroplast rRNA from *Euglena gracilis.* In *Methods in chloroplast molecular biology* (ed. M. Edellman et al.), pp. 377–403. Elsevier Biomedical Press, New York.

Kohlstaedt L.A., Wang J., Friedman J.M., Rice P.A., and Steitz T.A. 1992. Crystal structure at 3.5 Å resolution of HIV-1 reverse transcriptase complexed with an inhibitor. *Science* **256:** 1783–1790.

Köhrer K. and Domdey H. 1991. Preparation of high molecular weight RNA. *Methods Enzymol.* **194:** 398–405.

Kondo T., Nakajima Y., and Kawakami M. 1979. Effect of salts and chromatin concentrations on the buoyant density of chromatin in metrizamide gradient. *Biochim Biophys Acta* **561:** 526–534.

Kotewicz M.L., Sampson C.M., D'Alessio J.M., and Gerard G.F. 1988. Isolation of cloned Moloney murine leukemia virus reverse transcriptase lacking ribonuclease H activity. *Nucleic Acids Res.* **16:** 265–277.

Lanotte M., Martin-Thouvenin V., Najman S., Balerini P., Valensi F., and Berger R. 1991. NB4, a maturation inducible cell line with t(15;17) marker isolated from a human acute promyelocytic leukemia (M3). *Blood* **77:** 1080–1086.

Leaver C.J. 1982. Isolation of intact 16S and 23S ribosomal RNAs from higher plants. In *Methods in chloroplast molecular biology* (ed. M. Edellman et al.), pp. 369–375. Elsevier Biomedical Press, New York.

Lee F.S. and Vallee B.L. 1993. Structure and action of mammalian ribonuclease (angiogenin) inhibitor. *Prog. Nucleic Acid Res. Mol. Biol.* **44:** 1–30.

Lee F.S., Shapiro R., and Vallee B.L. 1989. Tight binding inhibition of angiogenin and ribonuclease A by placental ribonuclease inhibitor. *Biochemistry* **28:** 225–230.

Lehrach H., Diamond D., Wozney J.M., and Boedtker H. 1977. RNA molecular weight determinations by gel electrophoresis under denaturing conditions: A critical reexamination. *Biochemistry* **16:** 4743–4751.

Lennon G.G. and Lehrach H. 1991. Hybridization analyses of arrayed cDNA libraries. *Trends Genet.* **7:** 314–317.

Lipshultz R.J., Fodor S.P.A., Gingeras T.R., and Lockhart D.J. 1999. High density synthetic oligonucleotides arrays. *Nat. Genet.* **21:** 20–24.

Litt M., Hauge X., and Sharma V. 1993. Shadow bands seen when typing polymorphic dinucleotide repeats: Some causes and cures. *BioTechniques* **15:** 280–284.

Lockhart D.J., Dong H., Byrne M.C., Follettie M.T., Gallo M.V., Chee M.S., Mittmann M., Wang C., Kobayashi M., Horton H., and Brown E.L. 1996. Expression monitoring by hybridization to high-density oligonucleotide arrays. *Nat. Biotechnol.* **14:** 1675–1680.

Luo L., Salunga R.C., Guo H., Bittner A., Joy K.C., Galindo J.E., Xiao H., Rogers K.E., Wan J.S., Jackson M.R., and Erlander M.G. 1999. Gene expression profiles of laser-captured adjacent neuronal subtypes. *Nat. Med.* **5:** 117–122.

Maier E., Meier-Ewart S., Ahmadi A.R., Curtis J., and Lehrach H. 1994. Application of robotic technology to automated sequence fingerprint analysis by oligonucleotide hybridisation. *J. Biotechnol.* **35:** 191–203.

Maleck K., Levine A., Eulgen T., Morgan A., Schmid J., Lawton K.A., Dangl J.L., and Dietrich R.A. 2000. The transcriptome of *Arabidopsis* during systemic acquired resistance. *Nat. Genet.* **26:** 403–410.

Manchester K.L. 1995. Value of A_{260}/A_{280} ratios for measurement of purity of nucleic acids. *BioTechniques* **19:** 208–210.

———. 1996. Use of UV methods for measurement of protein and nucleic acid concentrations. *BioTechniques* **20:** 968–970.

Marmur J. and T'so P.O.P. 1961. Denaturation of deoxyribonucleic acid by formamide. *Biochim. Biophys. Acta* **51:** 32–36.

Martin R. 1987. Overcoming DNA sequencing artifacts: Stops and compressions. *Focus* (Life Technologies) **9:** 8–10.

Matson S.W., Fay P.J., and Bambara R.A. 1980. Mechanism of inhibition of the avian myeloblastosis virus deoxyribonucleic acid polymerase by adriamycin. *Biochemistry* **19:** 2089–2096.

Matz M., Shagin D., Bogdanova E., Britanova O., Lukyanov S., Diatchenko L., and Chenchik A. 1999. Amplification of cDNA ends based on template-switching effect and step-out PCR. *Nucleic Acids Res.* **27:** 1558–1560.

McConaughy B.L., Laird C.D., and McCarthy B.J. 1969. Nucleic acid reassociation in formamide. *Biochemistry* **8:** 3289–3295.

McGonigle B., Keeler S.J., Lau S.MC., Koeppe M.K., and O'Keefe D.P. 2000. A genomics approach to the comprehensive analysis of the glutathione *S*-transferase gene family in soybean and maize. *Plant Physiol.* **124:** 1105–1120.

Mechler B.M. 1987. Isolation of messenger RNA from membrane-bound polysomes. *Methods Enzymol.* **152:** 241–248.

Mujumdar R.B., Ernst L.A., Mujumdar S.R., Lewis C.J., and Waggoner A.S. 1993. Cyanine dye labeling reagents: Sulfoindocyanine succinimidyl esters. *Bioconjug. Chem.* **4:** 105–111.

Murphy N.R., Leinbach S.S., and Hellwig R.J. 1995. A potent, cost-effective RNAse inhibitor. *BioTechniques* **18:** 1068–1073.

Murray A.E., Lies D., Li G., Nealson K., Zhou J., and Tiedje J.M. 2001. DNA/DNA hybridization to microarrays reveals gene-specific differences between closely related microbial genomes. *Proc. Natl. Acad. Sci.* **98:** 9853–9858.

Nadin-Davis S. and Mezl V.A. 1982. Optimization of the ethanol precipitation of RNA from formamide containing solutions. *Prep. Biochem.* **12:** 49–56.

Nakazato H. and Edmonds M. 1972. The isolation and purification of rapidly labeled polysome-bound ribonucleic acid on polythymidylate cellulose. *J. Biol. Chem.* **247:** 3365–3367.

Nichols B.L., Dudley M.A., Nichols V.N., Putman M., Avery S.E., Fraley J.K., Quaroni A., Shiner M., and Carrazza F.R. 1997. Effects of malnutrition on expression and activity of lactase in children. *Gastroenterology* **112:** 742–751.

Novoradovskaya N., Payette T., Novoradovsky A., Braman J., Chin N., Pergamenschikov A., Fero M., and Botstein D. 2000. Pooled, high quality reference RNA for human microarrays. *Strategies Newsletter* **13:** 121–122. Stratagene, Inc., LaJolla, California.

Okamuro J.K. and Goldberg R.B. 1989. Regulation of plant gene expression: General principles. In *The biochemistry of plants: A comprehensive treatise* (ed. A. Marcus et al.), vol. 15, pp.1–82, Academic Press, New York.

Ohnmacht G.A., Wang E., Mocellin S., Abati A., Fetsch P.A., Rosenberg S.A., and Marincola F.M. 2001. Short-term kinetics of tumor antigen expression *in vivo. J. Immunol.* **167:** 1809–1820.

Panchuk-Voloshina N., Haugland R.P., Bishop-Stewart J., Bhalgat M.K., Millard P.J., Mao F., and Leung W.Y. 1999. Alexa dyes, a series of new fluorescent dyes that yield exceptionally bright, photostable conjugates. *J. Histochem. Cytochem.* **47:** 1179–1188.

Pease A.C., Solas D., Sullivan E.J., Cronin M.T., Holmes C.P., and Fodor S.P. 1994. Light-generated oligonucleotide arrays for rapid DNA sequence analysis. *Proc. Natl. Acad. Sci.* **91:** 5022–5026.

Penman S., Fan H., Perlman S., Rosbach M., Weinberg R., and Zylber E. 1970. Distinct RNA synthesis systems of the HeLa cells. *Cold Spring Harbor Symp. Quant. Biol.* **35:** 561–575.

Perou C.M., Jeffrey S.S., van de Rijn M., Rees C.A., Eisen M.B., Ross D.T., Pergamenschikov A., Williams C.F., Zhu S.X., Lee J.C., Lashkari D., Shalon D., Brown P.O., and Botstein D. 1999. Distinctive gene expression patterns in human mammary epithelial cells and breast cancers. *Proc. Natl. Acad. Sci.* **96:** 9212–9217.

Perou C.M., Sorlie T., Eisen M.B., van de Rijn M., Jeffrey S.S., Rees C.A., Pollack J.R., Ross D.T., Johnsen H., Akslen L.A., Fluge O., Pergamenschikov A., Williams C., Zhu S.X., Lonning P.E., Borresen-Dale A.L., Brown P.O., and Botstein D. 2000. Molecular portraits of human breast tumours. *Nature* **406:** 747–752.

Perry R.P. and Kelley D.E. 1972. The production of ribosomal RNA from high molecular weight precursors. 3. Hydrolysis of pre-ribosomal and ribosomal RNA by a 3′-OH specific exoribonuclease. *J. Mol. Biol.* **70:** 265–279.

Phillips J. and Eberwine J.H. 1996. Antisense RNA amplification: A linear amplification method for analyzing the mRNA population from single living cells. *Methods* **10:** 283–288.

Pichersky E., Bernatzky R., Tanksley S.D., and Cashmore A.R. 1986. Evidence for selection as a mechanism in the concerted evolution of *Lycopersicon esculentum* (tomato) genes encoding the small subunit of ribulose-1,5-bisphosphate carboxylase/oxygenase. *Proc. Natl. Acad. Sci.* **83:** 3880–3884.

Prasad V.R. 1993. Genetic analysis of retroviral reverse transcriptase structure and function. In *Reverse transcriptase* (ed. A.M. Skalka and S.P. Goff), pp. 135–162. Cold Spring Harbor Laboratory Press, Cold Spring Harbor, New York.

Rajeevan M.S., Dimulescu I.M., Unger E.R., and Vernon S.D. 1999. Chemiluminescent analysis of gene expression on high-density filter arrays. *J. Histochem. Cytochem.* **47:** 337–342.

Randolph J.B. and Waggoner A.S. 1997. Stability, specificity and fluorescence brightness of multiply-labeled fluorescent DNA probes. *Nucleic Acids Res.* **25:** 2923–2929.

Reymond P., Weber H., Damond M., and Farmer E.E. 2000. Differential gene expression in response to mechanical wounding and insect feeding in *Arabidopsis. Plant Cell* **12:** 707–719.

Richmond T. and Somerville S. 2000. Chasing the dream: Plant EST microarrays. *Curr. Opin. Plant Biol.* **3:** 108–116.

Richmond C.S., Glasner J.D., Mau R., Jin H., and Blattner F.R. 1999. Genome-wide expression profiling in *Escherichia coli* K-12. *Nucleic Acids Res.* **27:** 3821–3835.

Riley M. and Labedan B. 1996. *Escherichia coli* gene products: Physiological functions and common ancestries. In Escherichia coli *and* Salmonella: *Cellular and molecular biology*, 2nd edition (ed. F.C. Neidhardt et al.), pp. 2118–2202. American Society for Microbiology, Washington, D.C.

Roozemond R.C. 1976. Ultramicrochemical determination of nucleic acids in individual cells using the Zeiss UMSP-I microspectrophotometer. Application to isolated rat hepatocytes of different ploidy classes. *Histochem. J.* **8:** 625–638.

Ross D.T., Scherf U., Eisen M.B., Perou C.M., Rees C., Spellman P., Iyer V., Jeffrey S.S., Van de Rijn M., Waltham M., Pergamenschikov A., Lee J.C., Lashkari D., Shalon D., Myers T.G., Weinstein J.N., Botstein D., and Brown P.O. 2000. Systematic variation in gene expression patterns in human cancer cell lines. *Nat. Genet.* **24:** 227–235.

Ruan Y., Gilmore J., and Conner T. 1998. Towards *Arabidopsis* genome analysis: Monitoring expression profiles of 1400 genes using cDNA microarrays. *Plant J.* **15:** 821–833.

Sambrook J. and Russell D.W. 2001. *Molecular cloning: A laboratory manual*, 3rd edition. Cold Spring Harbor Laboratory Press, Cold Spring Harbor, New York.

Schena M. and Davis R.W. 2000. Technology standards for microarray research. In *Microarray biochip technology* (ed. M. Schena), pp. 1–18. Eaton Publishing/ BioTechniques Book Division, Natick, Massachusetts.

Schena M., Shalon D., Davis R.W., and Brown P.O. 1995. Quantitative monitoring of gene expression patterns with a complementary DNA microarray. *Science* **270:** 467–470.

Schena M., Shalon D., Heller R., Chai A., Brown P.O., and Davis R.W. 1996. Parallel human genome analysis: Microarray-based expression monitoring of 1000 genes. *Proc. Natl. Acad. Sci.* **93:** 10614–10619.

Schick B.P. and Eras J. 1995. Proteoglycans partially co-purify with RNA in TRI reagent and can be transferred to filters by northern blotting. *BioTechniques* **18:** 574–578.

Schneiderbauer A., Sandermann Jr. H., and Ernst D. 1991. Isolation of functional RNA from plant tissues rich in phenolic compounds. *Anal. Biochem.* **197:** 91–95.

Selinger D.W., Cheung K.J., Mei R., Johansson E.M., Richmond C.S., Blattner F.R., Lockhart D.J., and Church G.M. 2000. RNA expression analysis using a 30 base pair resolution *Escherichia coli* genome array. *Nat. Biotechnol.* **18:** 1262–1268.

Sevag M.G., Lackman D.B., and Smolens J. 1938. The isolation of the components of streptococcal nucleoproteins in serologically active form. *J. Biol. Chem.* **1254:** 425–436.

Sherman F. 1991. Getting started with yeast. *Methods Enzymol.* **194:** 3–21.

Smulski D.R., Huang L.L., McCluskey M.P., Reeve M.J., Vollmer A.C., Van Dyk T.K., and LaRossa R.A. 2001. Combined, functional genomic-biochemical approach to intermediary metabolism: Interaction of acivicin, a glutamine amidotransferase inhibitor, with *Escherichia coli* K-12. *J. Bacteriol.* **183:** 3353–3364.

Spremuli L. 2000. Protein synthesis, assembly and degradation. In *Biochemistry and molecular biology of plants* (ed. B.B. Buchanan et al.), pp. 412–454, American Society of Plant Physiologists, Rockville, Maryland.

Stinson S.F., Alley M.C., Kopp W.C., Fiebig H.H., Mullendore L.A., Pittman A.F., Kenney S., Keller J., and Boyd M.R. 1992. Morphological and immunocytochemical characteristics of human tumor cell lines for use in a disease-oriented anticancer drug screen. *Anticancer Res.* **12:** 1035–1053.

Stoltenburg R., Wartmann T., Kunze I., and Kunze G. 1995. Reliable method to prepare RNA from free and membrane-bound polysomes from different yeast species. *BioTechniques* **18:** 564–568.

Stulnig T.M. and Amberger A. 1994. Exposing contaminating phenol in nucleic acid preparations. *BioTechniques* **16:** 402–404.

Suganuma A. and Gupta K.C. 1995. An evaluation of primer length on random-primed DNA synthesis for nucleic acid hybridization: Longer is not better. *Anal. Biochem.* **224:** 605–608.

Sugiura M. and Takeda Y. 2000. Nucleic acids. In *Biochemistry and molecular biology of plants* (ed. B.B. Buchanan et al.), pp. 260–310. American Society of Plant Physiologists, Rockville, Maryland.

Takahashi N. and Ko M.S. 1994. Toward a whole cDNA catalog: Construction of an equalized cDNA library from mouse embryos. *Genomics* **23:** 202–210.

Talaat A.M., Hunter P., and Johnston S.A. 2000. Genome-directed primers for selective labeling of bacterial transcripts for DNA microarray analysis. *Nat. Biotechnol.* **18:** 679–682.

Tanese N. and Goff S.P. 1988. Domain structure of the Moloney murine leukemia virus reverse transcriptase: Mutational analysis and separate expression of the DNA polymerase and RNase H activities. *Proc. Natl. Acad. Sci.* **85:** 1777–1781.

Tanese N., Roth M., and Goff S.P. 1985. Expression of enzymatically active reverse transcriptase in *Escherichia coli. Proc. Natl. Acad. Sci.* **82:** 4944–4948.

Taniguchi M., Miura K., Iwao H., and Yamanaka S. 2001. Quantitative assessment of DNA microarrays— Comparison with northern blot analyses. *Genomics* **71:** 34–39.

Tavangar K., Hoffman A.R., and Kraemer F.B. 1990. A micromethod for the isolation of total RNA from adipose tissue. *Anal. Biochem.* **186:** 60–63.

Trenkle T., Welsh J., Jung B., Mathieu-Daude F., and McClelland M. 1998. Non-stoichiometric reduced complexity probes for cDNA arrays. *Nucleic Acids Res.* **26:** 3883–3891.

Uemura E. 1980. Age-related changes in neuronal RNA content in rhesus monkeys (*Macaca mulatta*). *Brain Res. Bull.* **5:** 117–119.

Ullrich A., Shine J., Chirgwin J., Pictet R., Tischer E., Rutter W., and Goodman H. 1977. Rat insulin genes: Construction of plasmids containing the coding sequences. *Science* **196:** 1313–1319.

van Gelder R.N., von Zastrow M.E., Yool A., Dement W.C., Barchas J.D., and Eberwine J.H. 1990. Amplified RNA synthesized from limited quantities of heterogeneous cDNA. *Proc. Natl. Acad. Sci.* **87:** 1663–1667.

Wang Y., Rea T., Bian J., Gray S., and Sun Y. 1999. Identification of the genes responsive to etoposide-induced apoptosis: Application of DNA chip technology. *FEBS Lett.* **445:** 269–273.

Wang E., Miller L.D., Ohnmacht G.A., Liu E.T., and Marincola F.M. 2000. High-fidelity mRNA amplification for gene profiling. *Nat. Biotechnol.* **18:** 457–459.

Warburg O. and Christian W. 1942. Isolierung und kristallisation des gärungsferments enolase. *Biochem. Z.* **310:** 384-421.

Wei Y., Lee J.M., Richmond C., Blattner F.R., Rafalski J.A., and LaRossa R.A. 2001. High-density microarray-mediated gene expression profiling of *Escherichia coli. J. Bacteriol.* **183:** 545–556.

Welford S.M., Gregg J., Chen E., Garrison D., Sorensen P.H., Denny C.T., and Nelson S.F. 1998. Detection of differentially expressed genes in primary tumor tissues using representational differences analysis coupled to microarray hybridization. *Nucleic Acids Res.* **26:** 3059–3065.

Wendisch V.F., Zimmer D.P., Khodursky A., Peter B., Cozzarelli N., and Kustu S. 2001. Isolation of *Escherichia coli* mRNA and comparison of expression using mRNA and total RNA on DNA microarrays. *Anal. Biochem.* **290:** 205–213.

Wessendorf M.W. and Brelje T.C. 1992. Which fluorophore is brightest? A comparison of the staining obtained using fluorescein, tetramethylrhodamine, lissamine rhodamine, Texas red, and cyanine 3.18. *Histochemistry* **98:** 81–85.

Wildsmith S.E., Archer G.E., Winkley A.J., Lane P.W., and Bugelski P.J. 2001. Maximization of signal derived from cDNA microarrays. *BioTechniques* **30:** 202–208.

Wilfinger W.W., Mackey K., and Chomczynski P. 1997. Effect of pH and ionic strength on the spectrophotometric assessment of nucleic acid purity. *BioTechniques* **22:** 474–476, 478–481.

Williamson R., Morrison M., Lanyon G., Eason R., and Paul J. 1971. Properties of mouse globin messenger ribonucleic acid and its preparation in milligram quantities. *Biochemistry* **10:** 3014–3021.

Yang G.P., Ross D.T., Kuang W.W., Brown P.O., and Weigel R.J. 1999. Combining SSH and cDNA microarrays for rapid identification of differentially expressed genes. *Nucleic Acids Res.* **27:** 1517–1523.

Yu H., Chao J., Patek D., Mujumdar R., Mujumdar S., and Waggoner A.S. 1994. Cyanine dye dUTP analogs for enzymatic labeling of DNA probes. *Nucleic Acids Res.* **22:** 3226–3232.

Yue H., Eastman P.S., Wang B.B., Minor J., Doctolero M.H., Nuttall R.L., Stack R., Becker J.W., Montgomery J.R., Vainer M., and Johnston R. 2001. An evaluation of the performance of cDNA microarrays for detecting changes in global mRNA expression. *Nucleic Acids Res.* **29:** E41.

Zejie Y., Ziaoyi W., Yu T., and Huan H. 1998. The method of microdisplacement measurement to improve the space resolution of array detector. *Med. Eng. Phys.* **20:** 149–151.

Zhu T. and Wang X. 2000. Large-scale profiling of the *Arabidopsis* transcriptome. *Plant Physiol.* **124:** 1472–1476.

Zhu Z. and Waggoner A.S. 1997. Molecular mechanism controlling the incorporation of fluorescent nucleotides into DNA by PCR. *Cytometry* **28:** 206–211.

Zhu Z., Chao J., Yu H., and Waggoner A.S. 1994. Directly labeled DNA probes using fluorescent nucleotides with different length linkers. *Nucleic Acids Res.* **22:** 3418–3422.

WWW RESOURCES

http://afgc.stanford.edu Arabidopsis Functional Genomics Consortium (AFGC)

http://cmgm.stanford.edu/pbrown/mguide/index.html The MGuide Version 2.0. The Brown Lab's complete guide to microarraying for the molecular biologist.

http://www.ambion.com Ambion, Inc. homepage

http://www.apbiotech.com Amersham Biosciences homepage

http://www.atcc.org American Type Culture Collection homepage

http://www.clontech.com BD Biosciences Clontech homepage

http://www.lifetech.com Invitrogen homepage

http://www.microarrays.org/protocols.html Microarray protocols maintained at the University of California, San Francisco, Department of Biochemistry and Biophysics.

http://www.millipore.com Millipore Corporation homepage

http://www.molecularprobes.com Molecular Probes, Inc. homepage

http://www.mrcgene.com Molecular Research Center homepage

http://www.qiagen.com QIAGEN homepage

Membrane-based Spotted cDNA Arrays

Kevin G. Becker, William H. Wood III, and Chris Cheadle

*DNA Array Unit, National Institute on Aging, National Institutes of Health,
Baltimore, Maryland 21224*

INTRODUCTION

Many of the concepts and strategies of modern microarrays were developed in the 1980s when membrane filters were used for differential screening of complementary DNA (cDNA) libraries with complex targets (Sargent and Dawid 1983; Friemert et al. 1989; Gress et al. 1992). After sequenced cDNA libraries became available, filter-based methods were used to analyze the expression patterns of tissues derived from human fetal brain, *Drosophila*, and mouse embryos, among others (Lennon and Lehrach 1991; Gress et al. 1992; Maier et al. 1994; Takahashi and Ko 1994). Soon afterward, robotic spotting of membrane arrays (Maier et al. 1994), glass cDNA microarrays (Schena et al. 1995), and the development of oligonu-cleotide "chips" (Lockhart et al. 1996) allowed more powerful systematic comparisons of gene expression.

Membrane-based arrays have been commercialized successfully, chiefly because of the ease of integration of membrane technologies into existing laboratory protocols (e.g., please see www.resgen.com; www.clontech.com). For the average molecular biology laboratory, the use of commercially produced membrane arrays provides a straightforward entry into genomic-scale gene expression studies without the need to purchase large numbers of cDNA clones or specialized arraying and scanning equipment. In addition, custom-made membrane arrays providing flexible content can be generated locally and used to complement commercial products at low cost.

Glass- and membrane-based microarrays, both of which can be manufactured in academic laboratories, are sometimes regarded as alternative technologies. In reality, each format has strengths and weaknesses, and the two technologies should probably be seen as complementary, rather than competing options. Arrays of genes can be spotted at a higher density on glass supports (microarrays) than on membranes (macroarrays). More importantly, glass microarrays can be used with an internal reference probe in a simultaneous two-color hybridization as a control for slide-to-slide variation in manufacture. The ability to include controls of this type is a key difference between the two systems. Operationally, the relative sensitivity of glass and membrane arrays is likely to be dependent on the quality of the arrays and on the ability of the investigator to produce a labeled target that hybridizes with low background. Strengths of membrane/radioactive array systems include:

- *Labeling of cDNA to higher specific activity with radioactive precursors rather than fluorescent compounds.* The higher efficiency of incorporation of radiolabeled, rather than Cy5- or Cy3-labeled, dNTPs allows labeling to be carried out with much less RNA. Instead of the 50–200 µg of total RNA typically used for labeling with fluorescent dNTPs, only 1–10 µg is required when labeling with [^{33}P]dNTPs. In this sense, radioactive targets hybridized to membrane-based arrays provide 100-fold greater sensitivity than fluorescent targets hybridized to glass microarrays (Bertucci et al. 1999). Although it is important not to confuse the amount of RNA required for an experiment with the ability to detect differences in gene expression, membrane arrays nevertheless offer a greater opportunity to replicate the experiment without resorting to amplification of targets. Increasing the number of replicate hybridizations can improve the statistical significance of an experiment (Andrews et al. 2000; Barrett et al. 2001) (for a further discussion, please see Section 7, Part 1).

- *Using a single labeling system (^{33}P) can be an advantage over dual fluorescent labeling.* Cy3- and Cy5-labeled dUTPs are incorporated into DNA at different rates, with Cy5-labeled dUTP incorporation being less efficient. Variation in incorporation rates can lead to biases that require correction by normalization algorithms, a process that can introduce errors. Furthermore, the detection of differential expression of some genes appears to be sensitive to the dye combinations used (Taniguchi et al. 2001).

- *Preparation and processing of nylon arrays can be performed relatively quickly and easily.* By contrast, the production of glass arrays, including coating and aging of slides, printing, denaturation, and chemical processing, is a lengthy procedure. Some of the array devices used for producing membrane arrays can make use of unpurified polymerase chain reaction (PCR) products, substantially shortening the workup of probe sets. Arraying a set of ~1000 concentrated PCR products onto nylon membranes typically takes ~1 day for membrane preparation, arraying, and UV cross-linking.

- *The costs associated with membrane-based arrays are fairly low for a variety of reasons,* including the ability to use unpurified PCR products for spotting, the use of commonly available labeling and hybridization protocols, the relatively low cost of radioactivity compared with fluorescent nucleotides, the ability to rehybridize the arrays three to five times, and the use of standard radioactivity detection methods (film or phosphoimager screens). Collectively, these factors may result in lower setup and operational costs and a shorter time from setup to generation of data.

In summary, membrane-based cDNA array gene expression studies have proven to be highly sensitive, reproducible, inexpensive, and flexible. They generally require less specialized and less expensive equipment and reagents than do other array formats. In the authors' experience in running a cDNA array core facility, nylon membranes require less training of students and postdoctoral fellows and are easily moved from a specialty array facility to a standard molecular laboratory or to collaborating laboratories. These advantages allow rapid training of personnel and less time to generate high-quality microarray data.

Part 1: Preparation and Hybridization of Membrane Arrays

Part 1 of this section describes the progression of steps for setting up microarray experiments using membrane-based arrays. First, amplified cDNA clones, isolated as described in Section 1, are printed onto nylon membranes using standard robotic arrayers and are subsequently fixed to the membrane by UV-irradiation. Typically, the printing process is more straightforward than that for printing onto solid-support surfaces (described in Section 2). Alternatively, mammalian and yeast clone sets or open reading frames (ORFs), arrayed onto reusable nylon membranes, are commercially available from ResGen (www.resgen.com) or from CLONTECH (www.clontech.com). Next, target RNA, prepared as described in Section 3, Part 1, is radiolabeled by direct incorporation of $[\alpha\text{-}^{33}P]dCTP$ using reverse transcriptase. After template RNA has been hydrolyzed in base, the labeled target cDNA is purified by spin-column chromatography. The labeled target DNA is then hybridized to membrane microarrays under conditions similar to those used for conventional Southern hybridizations, typically at high stringency. The hybridization results are imaged using standard radioisotope detection (phosphorimaging) techniques and analyzed as described in Part 2.

The following sequence of protocols describes:

- Printing cDNA arrays onto nylon membranes and subsequent processing (Protocol 1).
- Preparation and radiolabeling of RNA to prepare the target (Protocol 2).
- Hybridization of the labeled target to membrane arrays (Protocol 3).

Printing Membrane Arrays

Printing cDNA arrays on nylon membranes with robotic arrayers is somewhat more forgiving than printing onto glass surfaces. Less time is required to optimize printing because the binding of nucleic acids to nylon is efficient and based on protocols that have been developed over many years of use. Printing arrays on membranes is best done with a blunt pin as opposed to a split or quill-pen-type printing pin, which may damage the filter. In addition, the wicking effect of quill pins on membrane surfaces produces spots of variable sizes, whereas a blunt pin produces spots of uniform diameter and DNA quantity. A further advantage of solid pins is that impure PCR products, which would normally clog quill pins, can be used for arraying. In the authors' laboratory, an Affymetrix 417 arrayer with a pin-and-ring printing system is used. This system allows a single pickup of PCR product to produce identical spots over 42 arrays. For further details on printing systems, in particular of the pin and ring setup, please see the information panel on **ARRAYERS AND PINS USED FOR CONTACT PRINTING OF MICROARRAYS** in Section 2.

Membranes must be held in a stable position for printing. In the authors' laboratory, stainless steel forms are manufactured that are the same size as standard microscope slides (75 x 175 x 1.5 mm), and the membrane is temporarily bound to these forms for printing. The adaptation of the Affymetrix 417 arrayer and the use of stainless steel forms in place of microscope slides to immobilize the membranes during printing are shown in Figure 4-1.

PREPARATION OF PROBES FOR MEMBRANE ARRAYS: PCR AMPLIFICATION OF cDNA CLONES

Material for spotting on membrane filters can be prepared as described in Section 1 (Probes for Spotted Arrays). The amplification of cDNA clones is performed as described in Section 1, Protocol 2, except that purification of the PCR-amplified material is not required. Following standard PCR amplification, the 100-μl reactions are concentrated to ~24 μl by evaporation, by returning the reactions to a 96-well PCR machine, and heating them with the lids open for ~1–2 hours at 70°C.

Evaporation, unlike ethanol precipitation or column purification of PCR products, requires no additional transfer or handling of amplicons. Unlike glass substrates, nylon membranes can accommodate minor contaminants in the spotting mixture, such as free nucleotides, enzymes, and residual PCR primers. However, unpurified PCR-amplified material can be used only with array systems that can accommodate impure material without clogging the pins, such as the pin-and-ring-based machine described above. PCR products should be checked for yield and for the amplification of single bands as described in Section 1, Protocol 4.

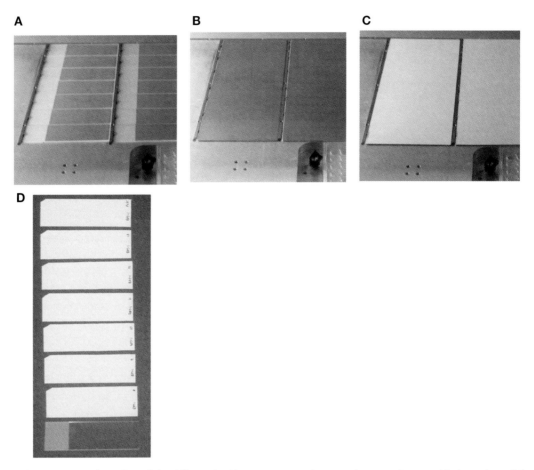

FIGURE 4-1. Adaptation of the Affymetrix 417 arrayer to print on nylon membranes. (*A*) A section of the array platen loaded with seven standard microscope slides; (*B*) replacement of the same seven-slide area with stainless steel forms; (*C*) forms with nylon membranes glued onto forms; (*D*) seven postprinting cut and labeled 75 x 25-mm nylon arrays.

MATERIALS

CAUTION: Please see Appendix 3 for appropriate handling of materials marked with <!>.

Buffers and Solutions

Please see Appendix 2 for components of stock solutions, buffers, and reagents.
Dilute stock solutions to the appropriate concentrations.

NaOH (1 N) <!>

Nucleic Acids and Oligonucleotides

cDNA probes
Prepare the probes as described in Section 1, Protocol 2. For further details on preparation and concentration of probes for printing on membrane arrays, please see the panel on the previous page.

Special Equipment

Arrayer (e.g., Affymetrix 417)
Koh-I-Noor rapidograph pen (with Rapid-draw 3084-F ink)
Krylon repositional adhesive (7020, Krylon, Inc.)
Nitrile gloves, powder-free
Nytran$^+$ Supercharge nylon membrane (10416296, Schleicher & Schuel)
Plastic plate sealer
Stainless steel forms for holding membranes for printing (75 × 175 × 1.5 mm)
> These forms may be made to specifications in a machine shop.

Stratalinker 2400 (Stratagene)

METHOD

Membrane Preparation

1. Wearing powder-free nitrile gloves, cut the Nytran$^+$ Supercharge nylon membrane to fit each of six 75 × 175 × 1.5-mm stainless steel forms.

   > The membrane is best cut with a straight edge and razor through the membrane support paper.

2. Spray Krylon repositional adhesive lightly onto each steel form. This adhesive remains tacky and does not dry. Position a membrane on each form and press through the membrane support paper to secure the membrane to the form.

3. Place the form/membrane in the arrayer into the appropriate platen position, covering the entire printable area. Make sure that each form/membrane unit is flat against the platen area and that there are no high spots over the entire platen.

Printing Arrays on Nylon Membranes

4. *Just before the first printing* of each set of three 96-well microtiter plates, add 1 N NaOH (~5 µl) to each cDNA sample (usually ~20 µl) to give a final concentration of 0.2 N NaOH. Mix the samples by gently vortexing the plate for a few seconds. Centrifuge briefly to collect the samples.

   > Plates that have been printed once will not need additional NaOH, but they may need to have 5–10 µl of H$_2$O added to correct for evaporation. A minimum of 10 µl of material is required in the wells to ensure that the ring is filled during sample pickup.

5. Load the first three plates into the arrayer.

6. Spot the probes, using a 300-µm pin, with center-to-center spot spacing of 665 µm.

   > This procedure allows 2304 individual spots to be printed onto an area the size of a 25 × 75-mm microscope slide and produces 16 identical 12 × 12 grids or subarrays from 24 96-well plates. In many cases, the authors print 12 plates in duplicate on this same area, which allows 1152 spots to be arrayed in duplicate. Approximately 8 hours of continuous printing is required to produce 42 identical arrays. For additional details on printing arrays, please see Section 2, Protocol 2.

7. After printing each set of three plates, remove the 96-well plates from the arrayer, seal them with plastic plate sealers, and store them at –20°C.

    A standard PCR can be printed 5–10 times for a total of ~200–400 individual arrays. Ideally, the material should be printed in a concerted fashion to minimize artifacts associated with long-term storage. Long-term storage of PCR plates for many months at –20°C seems to result in a weaker signal. It is unclear why this occurs; however, it does *not* seem to be due to storage of the DNA in NaOH.

Postprinting Processing of Membranes

Postprinting processing takes ~1 hour and produces arrays ready for immediate hybridization.

8. At the end of the print run, fix the spotted DNA to the membranes by placing the stainless steel forms, with printed membranes still attached, into a Stratalinker 2400 UV cross-linker, and UV cross-link for ~1 minute at 120 mJ/second.

9. Use a razor blade to divide the column of membrane-attached forms.

10. Label the membranes with a Koh-I-Noor rapidiograph using Rapid-draw 3084-F ink, which binds radiolabeled target, thereby allowing identification of the filter directly from the scanned image.

    If the printed membranes are not used right away, store them between sheets of standard photocopy paper at room temperature.

RNA Preparation and Labeling

For methods of isolating total RNA for labeling, please see Section 3, Part 1. cDNA targets are prepared by the direct incorporation of $[\alpha\text{-}^{33}P]dCTP$ using reverse transcriptase (RT) (Whitney et al. 1999). The following protocol appears to be insensitive to minor contaminants that inhibit fluorescent labeling, perhaps because of the more efficient incorporation of both radiolabeled nucleotides. A typical reaction uses 5 μg of total RNA per sample; however, useful signals can be obtained with as little as 1 μg of total RNA if longer exposure times are used. Using more than 10 μg of RNA is unlikely to yield more information.

If filters larger than those described here are used, it may be necessary to increase the amount of RNA in proportion to the increased volume of the hybridization solution.

MATERIALS

CAUTION: Please see Appendix 3 for appropriate handling of materials marked with <!>.

Buffers and Solutions

Please see Appendix 2 for components of stock solutions, buffers, and reagents.
Dilute stock solutions to the appropriate concentrations.

Dithiothreitol (DTT) (0.1 M)
EDTA (0.5 M, pH 8.0)
NaOH (0.1 M) <!>
Tris (1 M, pH 8.0)

Enzymes and Buffers

5x First-strand buffer (18084-014, GIBCO)
RNaseOUT (10777-019, GIBCO)
SUPERSCRIPT II RT (18084-014, GIBCO)

Nucleic Acids and Oligonucleotides

$[\alpha\text{-}^{33}P]dCTP$ (3000 Ci/mmole) (58430, ICN) <!>
dNTP solution, lacking dCTP, each at a concentration of 8 mM (27-20X0-0, Pharmacia)
Oligo(dT)$_{10\text{-}20}$ primer (1 μg/μl) (Poly TGF, Research Genetics)
Total RNA preparation
    Prepare RNA preparation as described in one of the protocols of Section 3, Part 1.

Special Equipment

Bio-Spin P-30 spin column (Bio-Rad)

METHOD

First-strand Synthesis of cDNA

1. Set up an annealing reaction by mixing 1–10 μg of total RNA with 1 μl of oligo(dT)$_{10\text{-}20}$ primer (1 μg/μl), and adding H_2O to 15 μl. Heat the mixture for 5 minutes at 65ºC, and then incubate it for 2 minutes on ice.

2. Prepare a reverse transcription reaction mixture by adding the following components to 15 μl of the annealing reaction:

5x first-strand buffer	8 μl
20 mM dNTP solution (without dCTP)	4 μl
0.1 M DTT	4 μl
RNaseOUT (40 units)	1 μl
[α-^{33}P]dCTP (3000 Ci/mmole)	5 μl
H_2O	to a final volume of 38 μl

3. Add 2 μl of SUPERSCRIPT II RT (200 units/μl) to the reaction and incubate the mixture for 35 minutes at 42ºC.

   Reverse transcriptases are very sensitive to denaturation at air/liquid interfaces, so be very careful to avoid foaming when mixing the components of the reaction. This is sometimes difficult because many preparations of reverse transcriptases are supplied in buffers containing nonionic detergents such as Nonidet P-40 or Triton X-100.

4. Add an additional 2 μl of SUPERSCRIPT II RT (200 units/μl) and incubate the reaction further for 35 minutes at 42ºC.

Hydrolysis of RNA

5. Add 5 μl of 0.5 M EDTA to halt the reaction.

   Make sure to mix the reaction mixture well after addition of EDTA before proceeding with the addition of NaOH (Step 6). Nucleic acids precipitate in alkaline magnesium solutions.

6. Add 10 μl of 0.1 M NaOH, mix well and centrifuge briefly, and then incubate the samples for 30 minutes at 65ºC to hydrolyze the template RNA.

7. Add 25 μl of 1 M Tris (pH 8.0) to the neutralize samples.

Cleanup of Labeled Target with a Bio-Rad Bio-Spin P-30 Spin Column

8. Place the column in a microfuge tube and centrifuge it briefly to settle the resin.

9. Remove the cap from the column and break off the bottom of the column.

10. Place the column into a 2-ml reservoir tube.

11. Centrifuge the column at low speed (1000 rpm) in a microfuge for 2 minutes at room temperature.

12. Discard the effluent and repeat the centrifugation (Step 11) until all liquid is removed from the column.

13. Place the column into a fresh microfuge tube.

14. Apply the labeled sample (up to 82 µl) to the column.

15. Centrifuge the column at low speed (1000 rpm) in a microfuge for 4 minutes, and recover the flow-through (~82 µl).

    The column can be stored at –20°C.

16. Count a 1-µl aliquot of the sample in a scintillation counter.

    A typical labeling reaction (75 µl) generally yields 3×10^7 to 5×10^7 total cpm.

Hybridization of Target to Membrane Arrays

In general, membrane microarrays are hybridized under conditions similar to those used for conventional Southern hybridizations. Buffers of high ionic strength are used to promote association of complementary strands, and various blocking agents are used to minimize background interference. The hybridization and washing steps are typically carried out under conditions of high stringency to suppress cross-hybridization. For further details and special considerations of the hybridization reaction, please refer to the introduction to Section 3, Protocol 20. In this protocol, target cDNA radiolabeled with $[\alpha\text{-}^{33}\text{P}]\text{dCTP}$ (Protocol 2) is hybridized to spotted membrane arrays. After hybridization (and subsequent analysis), the target may be stripped from the membrane, allowing the membrane to be reused for subsequent hybridizations as described in the additional protocol at the end of this protocol.

Various problems together with possible solutions are presented in the troubleshooting guide in Figure 4-3.

MATERIALS

CAUTION: Please see Appendix 3 for appropriate handling of materials marked with <!>.

Buffers and Solutions

Please see Appendix 2 for components of stock solutions, buffers, and reagents.
Dilute stock solutions to the appropriate concentrations.

Dextran sulfate (50%)
2x SSC
1x SSC/0.1% SDS <!>
2x SSC/0.1% SDS
Microhyb (Hyb250.GF, Research Genetics)

Nucleic Acids and Oligonucleotides

DNA arrays, printed onto nylon membranes as described in Protocol 1
Human C_0t-1 DNA (1 mg/ml) (15279-001, LTI, Inc.)
Poly(dA) (8 mg/ml) (P 9403, Sigma)
Target cDNA (~75 µl, 3×10^7 to 5×10^7 cpm), labeled as described in Protocol 2

Special Equipment

Falcon tubes (35-2098, Falcon)
Glass or metal plates
   Please see Step 8.
Hybridization oven with rotary movement (e.g., HS 9360, HybAid, Inc.)
PhosphorImager (e.g., Molecular Dynamics STORM)
Phosphorimaging screens (e.g., Molecular Dynamics)

METHOD

Prewashing the Filters

1. Load the cDNA arrays, printed onto 25 x 75-mm nylon membranes, into empty 50-ml disposable Falcon tubes with the spotted face of the membrane facing inward.

    Up to three membranes may fit around the wall of the tube without overlap for hybridization with the target.

2. To prewash the filters, fill the tube with 50 ml of 2x SSC. Decant the fluid and drain the last drops by inverting the tube on a paper towel.

    This process attaches the membrane to the side wall of the tube.

3. Align the arrays edge to edge and remove any bubbles under the membrane by rolling a 5-ml plastic pipette against the membrane.

Hybridizing the Arrays

4. Prepare the hybridization buffer by combining:

Microhyb with 10% dextran sulfate (final concentration)	4 ml
1 mg/ml human C_0t-1 DNA, denatured for 5 minutes at 95ºC prior to use	10 µl
8 mg/ml poly(dA), denatured for 5 minutes at 95ºC prior to use	10 µl

5. Transfer the hybridization solution into the Falcon tube containing the arrays, and prehybridize the membranes in a standard hybridization oven with rotary movement for 2 hours at 42ºC.

6. After prehybridization, denature the entire volume of labeled probe (~75 µl, 3×10^7 to 5×10^7 cpm) for 5 minutes at 95ºC, and add it to the Falcon tube (Step 5) containing the arrays and the hybridization buffer (~4 ml).

7. Carry out hybridization by incubating the tube with rotory movement for 12–18 hours at 42ºC.

8. After hybridization, decant the hybridization solution from the filters into a tube suitable for storage at –20ºC.

    Although it appears that targets may be effectively reused, at the time of this writing, the efficiency of reused hybridization solution has not been extensively characterized. Investigators should themselves therefore establish the validity of reuse. Prehybridize the filters as described above. Denature stored hybridization solution for 5 minutes at 100ºC, cool to 42ºC for 5 minutes, and then add the solution to the filters that have been drained of hybridization buffer.

Washing the Filters

IMPORTANT: Do not allow the filters to dry out *at any stage* during the washing procedure. It is recommended that the washes be performed at temperatures up to 50ºC, although the optimal wash temperature for a particular set of targets should be determined experimentally.

9. Wash the hybridized arrays quickly in the original tube with 50 ml of 2x SSC/0.1% SDS (preheated to 50°C), followed by two washes in 2x SSC/0.1% SDS with rotary movement for 15 minutes each time at 50°C.

> Monitor the arrays with a survey meter at each wash step. The need for further washing should be determined empirically. If more stringent washing is needed, wash the filters in 1x SSC/0.1% SDS for 5–15 minutes at 65°C.

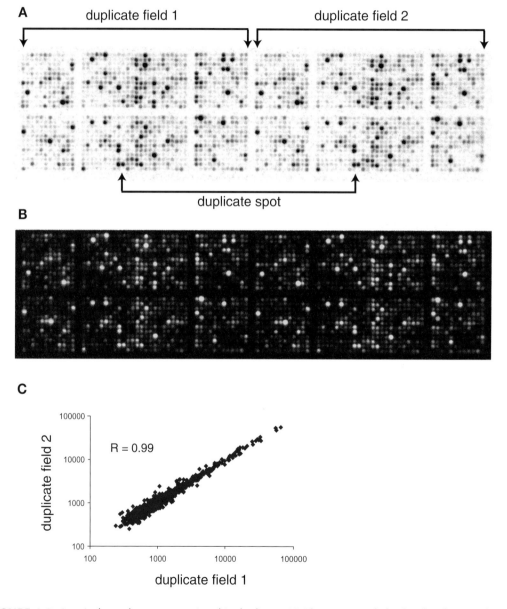

FIGURE 4-2. A typical membrane array printed in duplicate. (*A*) The array was hybridized with 5 μg of total RNA from a PC12 cell line. This array contains 1152 unique cDNAs spotted in widely spaced duplicate fields. (*B*) Pseudocolor overlay of two radioactive images; (*C*) comparison of total non-normalized intensities with the correlation between the duplicate fields.

10. Align the wet membrane arrays on a glass or metal plate. Remove all excess fluid and micro-bubbles by rolling with a pipette. Cover the filters *very tightly* with plastic wrap, which is taped securely to the back of the plate.

    If filters are to be reused (see panel below), *do not* let them dry out. To keep the filters moist, place a small piece of moistened blotting paper at the bottom of the plate.

11. Expose the microarrays to phosphorimager screens for 1–3 days, and then scan the screens in a phosphorimager (e.g., Molecular Dynamics STORM PhosphorImager) at 50-μm resolution.

    The hybridization results may be analyzed as described in Part 2. Figure 4-2 shows the results obtained with a typical membrane array experiment. Possible problems and their solutions are described in Figure 4-3.

    Note that the filters may be stripped of labeled target for reuse as described in the panel below.

ADDITIONAL PROTOCOL: TARGET STRIPPING AND REUSE OF MEMBRANES

The following sequence of steps describes a method for stripping the arrays of hybridized target so that the membranes may be used again.

Additional Materials

CAUTION: Please see Appendix 3 for appropriate handling of materials marked with <!>.

Stripping solution
  0.4 N NaOH <!>
  0.1% SDS <!>
Washing solution
  0.2 M Tris-HCl (pH 8.0)
  1x SSC
  0.1% SDS

Method

1. To remove the labeled target, wash the hybridized membranes twice in ~200–300 ml of stripping solution for 30 minutes at 65°C with vigorous shaking.

2. Wash the membranes twice in washing solution for 10 minutes at room temperature each time.

3. Allow the membranes to dry in the air, and then expose them to a phosphorimager screen overnight to determine the efficiency of stripping.

    Filters can be reused approximately three times before there is a substantial loss in signal.

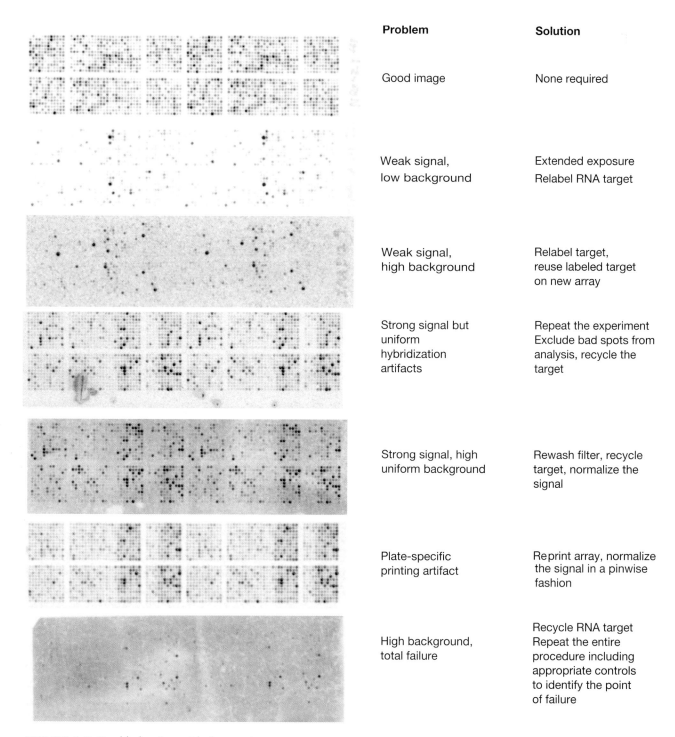

Problem	Solution
Good image	None required
Weak signal, low background	Extended exposure Relabel RNA target
Weak signal, high background	Relabel target, reuse labeled target on new array
Strong signal but uniform hybridization artifacts	Repeat the experiment Exclude bad spots from analysis, recycle the target
Strong signal, high uniform background	Rewash filter, recycle target, normalize the signal
Plate-specific printing artifact	Reprint array, normalize the signal in a pinwise fashion
High background, total failure	Recycle RNA target Repeat the entire procedure including appropriate controls to identify the point of failure

FIGURE 4-3. Troubleshooting guide for membrane arrays.

Part 2: Data Analysis and Interpretation

Quantitative data can be acquired from raw phosphoimages with a number of software programs, including ImageQuant from Molecular Dynamics (http://www.mdyn.com/products/ImageQuant), ArrayVision from Imaging Research (http://www.imagingresearch.com), Array-Pro Analyzer from Media Cybernetics (http://www.mediacy.com/), AIDA Array from Raytest (http://www.raytest.de/bio-imag/bio_imag.html), and P-Scan from the Center for Information Technology, National Institutes of Health (http://cit.nih.gov). AtlasImage is designed for analysis of CLONTECH membranes (http://www.clontech.com).

Programs for the acquisition of primary data generally have similar functions and perform similar tasks. Primary images are usually composites of many smaller membrane arrays. These primary images are first segmented into images of individual arrays. Subarray spot patterns are identified through predetermined grid patterns or by automatic spot-calling algorithms. Intensities are quantified either with no background correction or with background automatically corrected by an algorithm. Once raw values of intensities are acquired, the data are analyzed using approaches similar to those used for glass-based arrays, the chief difference being that the basic unit of measure is generally a single value of raw intensity as opposed to a ratio of test:control, as is the case with two-color array formats.

As with other array formats, normalization is critical to correct for variance due to labeling or hybridization differences between samples in a series. No single method of normalization corrects for all variations or errors, and different approaches are appropriate for different experimental conditions. It is important to understand the reasons for normalization and the appropriate choices.

Non-uniform local hybridization anomalies on membranes come in many forms and generally do not recur with experimental repetition. Consequently, the most effective way to deal with local anomalies may be to repeat the experiment. Minor local anomalies can then be noted and omitted from the analysis.

Baseline differences in background may be reproduced in duplicate experiments. The contribution of uniform background may be simply subtracted or removed by more sophisticated normalization techniques (e.g., please see Schuchhardt et al. 2000; Tanaka et al. 2000), which can be used for global normalization, pinwise background correction, or similar regional background corrections.

An alternative approach to normalization is through Z-transformation of intensity values (Vawter et al. 2001). Raw values of intensity are transformed to log values, thereby reducing the effects of outliers and allowing intensities to be presented as units of standard deviation (s.d.). (For example, Z values of 1,2,3... represents 1,2,3... standard deviations from the mean of that array.) Because the normalization function is to each individual array and not to another sample, Z values become comparable across samples and across experiments.

Once raw intensities have been normalized or transformed, most approaches to further analysis of membrane-derived data are similar to those used to analyze data from other array formats (for a detailed discussion of data analysis, please see Section 7, Parts 2 and 3). Variance and correlation measurements between duplicate spots and repeat labeling of the same RNA (technical repeats) as well as repeat experiments (biological repeats) are used to monitor array quality and experimental reproducibility. Statistical assessment, pattern recognition strategies, and visual display of membrane-based array data are similar if not identical to other array formats (Eisen et al. 1998; Toronen et al. 1999; Tusher et al. 2001).

REFERENCES

Andrews J., Bouffard G.G., Cheadle C., Lu J., Becker K.G., and Oliver B. 2000. Gene discovery using computational and microarray analysis of transcription in the *Drosophila melanogaster* testis. *Genome Res.* **10:** 2030–2043.

Barrett T., Cheadle C., Wood W.H., Teichberg D., Donovan D.M., Freed W.J., Becker K.G., and Vawter M.P. 2001. Assembly and use of a broadly applicable neural cDNA microarray. *Restor. Neurol. Neurosci.* **18:** 127–135.

Bertucci F., Bernard K., Loriod B., Chang Y.C., Granjeaud S., Birnbaum D., Nguyen C., Peck K., and Jordan B.R. 1999. Sensitivity issues in DNA array-based expression measurements and performance of nylon microarrays for small samples (erratum *Hum. Mol. Genet.* [1999] **8:** 2129). *Hum. Mol. Genet.* **8:** 1715–1722.

Eisen M.B., Spellman P.T., Brown P.O., and Botstein D. 1998. Cluster analysis and display of genome-wide expression patterns. *Proc. Natl. Acad. Sci.* **95:** 14863–14868.

Friemert C., Erfle V., and Strauss G. 1989. Preparation of radiolabeled cDNA probes with high specific activity for rapid screening of gene expression. *Methods Mol. Cell. Biol.* **1:** 143–153.

Gress T.M., Hoheisel J.D., Lennon G.G., Zehetner G., and Lehrach H. 1992. Hybridization fingerprinting of high-density cDNA-library arrays with cDNA pools derived from whole tissues. *Mamm. Genome* **3:** 609–619.

Lennon G.G. and Lehrach H. 1991. Hybridization analyses of arrayed cDNA libraries. *Trends Genet.* **7:** 314–317.

Lockhart D.J., Dong H., Byrne M.C., Follettie M.T., Gallo M.V., Chee M.S., Mittmann M., Wang C., Kobayashi M., Horton H., and Brown E.L. 1996. Expression monitoring by hybridization to high-density oligonucleotide arrays. *Nat. Biotechnol.* **14:** 1675–1680.

Maier E., Meier-Ewert S., Ahmadi A.R., Curtis J., and Lehrach H. 1994. Application of robotic technology to automated sequence fingerprint analysis by oligonucleotide hybridization. *J. Biotechnol.* **35:** 191–203.

Sargent T.D. and Dawid I.B. 1983. Differential gene expression in the gastrula of *Xenopus laevis. Science* **222:** 135–139.

Schena M., Shalon D., Davis R.W., and Brown P.O. 1995. Quantitative monitoring of gene expression patterns with a complementary DNA microarray. *Science* **270:** 467–470.

Schuchhardt J., Beule D., Malik A., Wolski E., Eickhoff H., Lehrach H., and Herzel H. 2000. Normalization strategies for cDNA microarrays. *Nucleic Acids Res.* **28:** E47.

Takahashi N. and Ko M.S. 1994. Toward a whole cDNA catalog: Construction of an equalized cDNA library from mouse embryos. *Genomics* **23:** 202–210.

Tanaka T.S., Jaradat S.A., Lim M.K., Kargul G.J., Wang X., Grahovac M.J., Pantano S., Sano Y., Piao Y., Nagaraja R., Doi H., Wood III W.H., Becker K.G., and Ko M.S. 2000. Genome-wide expression profiling of mid-gestation placenta and embryo using a 15,000 mouse developmental cDNA microarray. *Proc. Natl. Acad. Sci.* **97:** 9127–9132.

Taniguchi M., Miura K., Iwao H., and Yamanaka S. 2001. Quantitative assessment of DNA microarrays—Comparison with Northern blot analyses. *Genomics* **71:** 34–39.

Toronen P., Kolehmainen M., Wong G., and Castren E. 1999. Analysis of gene expression data using self-organizing maps. *FEBS Lett.* **451:** 142–146.

Tusher V.G., Tibshirani R., and Chu G. 2001. Significance analysis of microarrays applied to the ionizing radiation response. *Proc. Natl. Acad. Sci.* **98:** 5116–5121.

Vawter M.P., Barrett T., Cheadle C., Sokolov B.P., Wood III W.H., Donovan D.M., Webster M., Freed W.J., and Becker K.G. 2001. Application of cDNA microarrays to examine gene expression differences in schizophrenia. *Brain Res. Bull.* **55:** 641–650.

Whitney L.W., Becker K.G., Tresser N.J., Caballero-Ramos C.I., Munson P.J., Prabhu V.V., Trent J.M., McFarland H.F., and Biddison W.E. 1999. Analysis of gene expression in mutiple sclerosis lesions using cDNA microarrays. *Ann. Neurol.* **46:** 425–428.

WWW RESOURCES

http://cit.nih.gov Center for Information Technology homepage, National Institutes of Health
http://www.clontech.com BD Biosciences Clontech homepage
http://www.resgen.com ResGen, trademark of Intvitrogen Corporation
http://www.imagingresearch.com Imaging Research Inc. homepage
http://www.mdyn.com/products/ImageQuant Molecular Dynamics image analysis software
http://www.mediacy.com MediaCybernetics homepage
http://www.raytest.de/bio-imag/bio_imag.html Raytest's bioimaging products and applications

5 | Tissue Microdissection

Carolyn J.M. Best, Isabel M. Leiva, John W. Gillespie,
Rodrigo F. Chuaqui, and Michael R. Emmert-Buck
Pathogenetics Unit, Laboratory of Pathology and Urologic Oncology Branch,
National Cancer Institute, Bethesda, Maryland 20892

Renate Burgemeister and Karin Schütze
P.A.L.M. Microlaser Technologies AG, Bernried, Germany

INTRODUCTION

Tissues are composed of multiple interacting cell populations in a complex three-dimensional arrangement, with each cellular phenotype reflecting a different pattern of expression of messenger RNA (mRNA) and protein. An important goal of many biological studies is to study the molecular expression profile of specific cell types within the specimen (Figure 5-1). However, the cells of interest might constitute only a small proportion of the cells within a specimen and may be separated from one another by other components of the tissue. Retrieval of such topologically inaccessible cells involves the use of microdissection techniques that allow target cells to be separated from their neighbors. Before these techniques were developed, immunohistochemistry and in situ hybridization were the primary tools for measuring protein and mRNA levels in specific cell types in tissues. Although still useful, these tools are generally limited to analysis of single genes or gene products and are unsuitable for global studies of genomic rearrangements or mRNA expression.

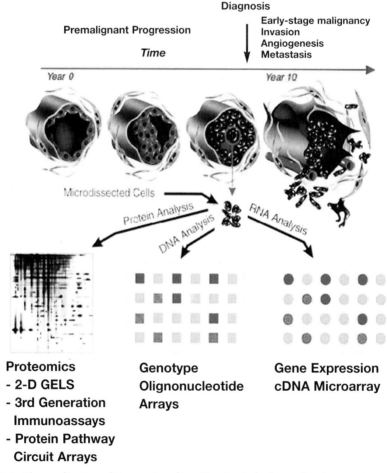

FIGURE 5-1. The application of tissue microdissection to study the molecular events associated with cancer progression. The molecular profile of proteins (two-dimensional gel analysis or immunoassays), the DNA genotype (e.g., mutation analysis and loss of heterozygosity), or the molecular profile of RNA (e.g., cDNA libraries and microarrays) can be compared within the tissue of a single patient. Normal epithelium, stroma, precancerous lesions, invasive cancer cells, and inflammatory cells can each be sampled and compared.

METHODS OF MICRODISSECTION

Isolating a specific population of cells from a heterogeneous tissue sample under direct microscopic visualization is simple in concept. In practice, however, the approach is technically challenging and has evolved through several developmental stages (please see Table 5-1):

- ***Manual microdissection.*** Early efforts entailed gross removal of tissue from a frozen histological slide using a scalpel blade to scrape sections and procure cells of interest. Subsequently, manual or micromanipulator-guided needles with adhesive tips were used to improve the accuracy and reliability of microdissection (Going and Lamb 1996).

- ***Microdissection of membrane-mounted native tissue (MOMeNT).*** MOMeNT, a refinement of manual microdissection, involves placing a tissue section onto a 6-μm-thick polyethylene membrane attached to a glass slide. The membrane serves as a backbone that keeps the entire tissue together. Thus, large tissue areas can be manually circumscribed with a scalpel and captured with forceps (Böhm and Wieland 1997). Later versions of this method used thinner foils that allowed laser dissection to be used to outline groups of target cells, which were then retrieved manually with needles or forceps (Böhm et al. 1997; Gjerdrum et al. 2001; Ling et al. 2001; Specht et al. 2001; Walch et al. 2001; Fink et al. 2002).

- ***Ablation of cells with UV irradiation.*** A technical advance known as selective ultraviolet radiation fractionation (SURF) allows cold ablation of unwanted cells by UV-irradiation. In this approach, a UV transilluminator (wavelength of 302 nm within the UV-C range) illuminates the entire slide, causing single-strand nicks and destroying cell viability. The cells of interest are protected from damage with ink and are subsequently recovered using a micromanipulator (Shibata et al. 1992).

- ***Laser capture microdissection (LCM).*** LCM is a laser-based method of microdissection that uses an infrared laser integrated into the illumination path of a standard inverted microscope. Pulses of light from an infrared laser are directed through a transparent rigid plastic cap, the surface of which is lined with a thermoplastic ethylene vinyl acetate film. This specially designed molded cap has stand-off rails at its perimeter so that when the cap is lowered onto the surface of a routinely prepared tissue section, a 12-μm gap is created between the thermoplastic membrane and the tissue. The tissue section is examined microscopically, and a laser diode is activated in areas where target cells underlie the transfer film. The heating effect of the laser pulse (980 nm) causes localized melting of an area of film equivalent to the focal spot size of the laser (60, 30, 15, or 7.5 μm). The melted film flows onto the tissue section, where it rapidly cools, forming a strong bond with the target cells. When the film is removed, the areas of tissue selected by the investigator are harvested from the section. Spatially complex arrangements of target cells are captured by repeating the process at different locations until a number of cells sufficient for analysis have been bonded to the film.

- ***Laser pressure catapulting (LPC).*** "Noncontact" LPC utilizes a focused UV-A laser to transport a single cell or group of cells directly—without mechanical contact—to an appropriate collection surface (e.g., the buffer-filled cap of a standard microfuge tube) (Fink et al. 1998; Schütze and Lahr 1998; Lahr 2000; Lehman et al. 2000; Glöckner et al. 2001; Imamichi et al. 2001; Scheidl et al. 2002; Westphal et al. 2002). The captured samples are easily transferred into the tube by a simple centrifugation step. A pulsed low-energy 337-nm nitrogen laser is integrated via the epifluorescence path of a standard microscope and focused through the objective. The physical force for catapulting is believed to be the pressurized gas that develops under the target area as a consequence of ablation induced by the massive photon flux within the focal plane of the laser. Depending on the nature of the specimen, microdissection can be performed before catapulting. This process is known as laser microdissection and pressure catapulting (LMPC). This fully automated approach facilitates the fast preparation of pure and homogeneous samples. The laser beam is maneuvered to cut around the periphery of a desired region of cells, thereby separating them from the neighboring components of the tissue. It also may be directed to specific regions of tissue to eliminate unwanted material within a precisely selected area. The focused laser beam causes localized photodecomposition and ablates the unwanted tissue in its limited focal spot.

The principles and characteristics of the major methods of microdissection in current use are summarized in Table 5-1. For further details concerning laser capture microdissection (LCM) and LMPC, please see the introductions to Protocols 2 and 10, respectively, as well as the introductions to Parts 1 and 2 of this section.

THE IMPORTANCE OF TISSUE PROCESSING

Materials used for microdissection are of various biological origins; they are often biopsy specimens that have been surgically removed from patients and sent to a histopathology laboratory (Figure 5-2). At first glance, how these samples are acquired and processed may seem to be of little concern to the molecular biologist or the bioinformatician who is analyzing molecular profiling data sets. However, changes in the molecular profiles of cells may occur as a sample is being removed from the patient, in the period before processing, and/or during processing itself. The factors that affect the recovery and analysis of the RNA are the time between surgical removal of samples and processing in the pathology laboratory, the type of fixative and the embedding medium, the length of fixation time, and the processing temperature. All of these variables significantly affect the yield and quality of macromolecules extracted from samples recovered from tissues by LCM and LMPC (e.g., please see Goldsworthy et al. 1999; Fend et al. 1999a,b; Kleeberger et al. 2000; Lahr 2000; Lahr et al. 2000; Lehmann et al. 2000; Gillespie et al. 2001; Hoffmann et al. 2001; Scheidl et al. 2002). When planning microarray experiments, it is critical to establish a system to optimize the acquisition and processing of tissue as it moves from the surgeon to the pathologist and finally to the laboratory. Points to consider are:

- The types and numbers of tissue samples that are potentially available.
- How to obtain informed consent from the patient.
- How and when to acquire samples.
- How samples are to be processed by the pathology laboratory.
- How to track, log, and if necessary, de-identify the samples as they move through the process.
- How to store and process the samples after they arrive in the custody of the microarray laboratory.

TABLE 5-1. Summary of Methods Used for Microdissection of Tissue Sections

	Manual tissue microdissection[a]	MOMeNT[a]	LCM[a]	LPC[a]	LMPC[a]
Principle	Manual dissection by procurement of large areas of sectioned tissues using a sterile needle or scalpel with or without an inverted microscope.	Manual dissection of tissue using polyethylene foil as supporting membrane to cut out groups of cells from tissue sections.	Selected individual or groups of cells are transferred from a tissue section to a thermoplastic film by heat generated by an infrared laser.	Noncontact catapulting procedure: gas pressure created by UV-A laser lifts single cells or groups of cells from the object slide; desired cells recovered by "noncontact" laser catapulting; no heat formation.	Noncontact microdissection procedure; UV-A laser-based circumscription separates selected specimen from surrounding area; selective elimination of unwanted cells within tissue area.
Method used to recover sample	Manual capture (sterile needle or scalpel) or micromanipulator; transfer into PCR tubes	Manual capture (sterile needles, scalpels, tweezers, or micromanipulator) facilitated by use of membrane.	Thermoplastic transfer membrane procures attached cells directly on LCM cap.	Laser catapulting directly onto collection surface (buffer-filled caps, strips, or microtiter plates).	Laser catapulting directly onto collection surface (buffer-filled caps, strips, or microtiter plates).
Minimum size of recovered sample	$\geq$50–100 μm	50–100 μm	>7.5 μm	<1 μm	<1 μm
Preferred use	Recovery of large, homogeneous areas of cells.	Recovery of large, homogeneous areas of cells.	Individual and small groups of cells (5–50).	Single cells or small groups of cells (50–100).	Chromosomes, nuclei, single cells, groups of cells (1–10,000), living cells.
Specimen preparation	FFPE, FF	FFPE, FF	FFPE, FF, cell smears; cytospins.	FFPE, FF, cell smears, cytospins.	FFPE, FF, cell smears, cytospins, cell cultures.
Preparation time	5–10 min for >10^4 cells.	5–10 min for 1–10 cells.	<10 sec for up to 30 cells.	<1 sec for 1–30 cells; <10 min for up to 10,000 cells.	<1 sec for 1–30 cells; <5 min for up to 10,000 cells.
Cost of equipment	low	low	high	high (automated)	high (automated)
Advantages	Simple and rapid.	Rapid method to isolate defined groups of cells with minimal contamination.	Very rapid method for retention of RNA integrity; direct visual confirmation of captured cells.	Very rapid and easy to handle method for retention of DNA, RNA, and protein integrity.	Very rapid and easy to handle; high precision for recovery of cells groups; allows recovery of live cells from cultures; direct visual conformation.
Disadvantages	High risk of contamination; unsuitable for small lesions or for tissues consisting of several types of intermixed cells.	Sophisticated preparations of tissue sections, exclusively unsuitable for use with membrane-mounted tissue sections; excludes the use of routinely processed glass slides.	Transfer film required; unsuitable for live-cell capture.	Disintegration of morphology during catapulting.	Membrane-mounted specimen required to preserve morphology.

This table is adapted from Walch et al. (2001).

[a] Abbreviations: (FFPE) Formalin-fixed, paraffin-embedded tissue; (FF) fresh-frozen tissue; (MOMeNT) microdissection of membrane-mounted native tissue; (LCM) laser-capture microdissection; (LPC) laser pressure catapulting; (LMPC) laser microdissection and pressure catapulting.

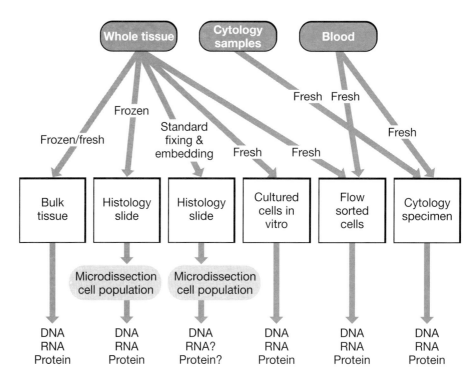

FIGURE 5-2. Effects of sample processing on the results of molecular analysis. For each type of human sample, decisions about processing must be made with consideration for the chosen downstream analysis. Each processing method has particular strengths and weaknesses in terms of subsequent molecular analyses, and investigators must select an appropriate approach consonant with the specific goals of their study. For recommendations regarding the use of each processing method, please refer to http://cgap-mf.nih.gov/BtoB/BtoBMolAnal.html.

A crucial issue is the method used by the pathology laboratory to process the tissue. In routine practice, the pathologist has three immediate options: to freeze a biopsy sample, to keep it fresh, or to fix and embed it. Most surgical and biopsy specimens are fixed in 10% neutral buffered formalin, followed by embedding in paraffin. The embedding process begins with a series of dehydration steps using increasing concentrations of alcohol, followed by a "clearing" step in xylene that allows the paraffin to penetrate throughout the tissue. The paraffin block is then sectioned onto glass slides for staining, microscopic visualization, and finally, preparation of microdissected cell populations.

Pathology samples are routinely fixed in formalin because the architecture of the specimen is better preserved than by freezing, After diagnosis is complete, most pathology laboratories will retain some of the blocks of embedded material for archival storage from where it can be retrieved should the need arise, for example, to confirm or extend a diagnosis. However, with the patient's informed consent and with the approval of the Institutional Human Research Ethics Committee, a portion of the biopsy material not required for diagnosis or storage may be made available for research projects. Typically, 5-μm sections of formalin-fixed tissues cut from paraffin blocks on a microtome are mounted on standard glass slides and analyzed microscopically after staining with hematoxylin and eosin, Methyl Green, or Fast Red (e.g., please see Burton et al. 1998). Tissue sections are sometimes stained immunohistologically before microdissection to identify particular types of target cells (Fend et al. 1999a,b; Noack et al. 1999; Buerger et al. 2000a,b; Kaserer et al. 2000; Persson et al. 2000; Gjerdrum et al. 2001; Ling et al. 2001). Although tissues fixed in formalin retain their morphology better than frozen material, the use of formalin-fixed, paraffin-embedded tissue specimens for high-throughput expression array samples has been problematic, chiefly because cross-linking of proteins and RNA occurs during fixation.

Frozen sections are currently regarded as the best material available for microdissection because they yield DNA, RNA, and protein of high quality (Goldsworthy et al. 1999). Sections are prepared by freezing freshly resected tissue in an embedding compound such as OCT and then cutting sections on a cryostat (Hiller et al. 1996; Ponten et al. 1997; Kaserer et al. 2000; Persson et al. 2000; Stoehr et al. 2000; Ling et al. 2001). Unfortunately, the cellular histology of the tissues is sometimes disrupted during this process, making it difficult to identify the target cell populations. Clearly, to satisfy the needs of both pathologists and molecular biologists, improved strategies for fixation and embedding of samples must be developed. The goals should be to provide a level of histologic detail that is acceptable to the pathologist, allow efficient microdissection of selected cells, and maintain the integrity of transcripts within the tissue. Investigators should be prepared to invest some time in establishing a system that

- allows recovery of RNA of sufficient quality for analysis by real-time PCR, for amplification in vitro, for generation of fluorescent or radioactive targets for expression profiling (Luo et al. 1999; Glöckner et al. 2000; Lehmann et al. 2000; Nagasawa et al. 2000; Ohyama et al. 2000; Bertheau et al. 2001; Hoffmann et al. 2001; Specht et al. 2001; Scheidl et al. 2002), and for construction of cDNA libraries (Peterson et al. 1998) and

- yields images of specimens that allow unambiguous identification of cell types. The better the images, the more secure the link between the cellular pathology of the samples and downstream molecular analysis (Emmert-Buck et al. 1996, 2000; Bonner et al. 1997, Simone et al. 1998; Banks et al. 1999; Dietmaier et al. 2000; Vona et al. 2000; Gjerdrum et al. 2001; Westphal et al. 2002). Digital images of the tissue section before and after microdissection provide an indispensable record of the experiment.

A good place to start is to read the paper by Goldsworthy et al. (1999). These authors compared the effects of various fixation methods on cellular morphology and the amplification of RNA from samples captured by LCM from sections of mouse livers. As expected, the quality of RNA obtained from paraffin-embedded material was poor. Ethanol (70%) was the fixative of choice for optimal morphology and microdissection. Extraction is best achieved from fresh-frozen tissue. Similar results have been obtained with human prostate samples (Gillespie et al. 2002). However, the experimenter should be prepared to try a variety of fixation procedures since it seems unlikely that a single process will be ideal for all types of tissues and conditions.

ACKNOWLEDGMENTS

We gratefully acknowledge the scientists at Arcturus, Inc. and P.A.L.M. Microlaser Technologies for their assistance in the preparation and review of this chapter: James Stanchfield, Steve Kunitake, Anna Mennis, and Rachel Goodrich.

Part 1: Manual Dissection and Laser Capture Microdissection

Carolyn J.M. Best, Isabel M. Leiva, John W. Gillespie, Rodrigo F. Chuaqui, and Michael R. Emmert-Buck

Pathogenetics Unit, Laboratory of Pathology and Urologic Oncology Branch, National Cancer Institute, Bethesda, Maryland 20892

INTRODUCTION

During the past decade, molecular profiling has emerged as a dynamic new discipline, capable of generating a global view of mRNA, protein patterns, and DNA alterations in various cell types and disease processes. Molecular profiling integrates information from the expanding genetic databases of the Human Genome Project with newly developed technologies for expression analysis. This approach holds great promise for facilitating an understanding of the still largely unknown relationship between genotype and phenotype in humans and for developing new diagnostic and therapeutic targets for clinical intervention.

Recent advances in sequencing and amplification methods have facilitated the analysis of DNA and RNA from small, discrete biological samples (e.g., cytological smears and tissue biopsies). The success and precision of these methods depend, however, on the integrity and purity of the cell populations under study. Manual or mechanical approaches to separate discrete populations of the cells of interest, although effective for projects of limited scope, can become quite time-consuming and labor-intensive for broad-range projects.

A new microdissection technology, which relies upon the use of a low-energy infrared laser integrated into a standard microscope, allows the recovery of specific cell populations from standard histological tissue sections. LCM was first developed at the National Institute of Child Health and Human Development (NICHD) and the National Cancer Institute (NCI) of the National Institutes of Health (NIH) (Emmert-Buck et al. 1996, 1997; Bonner et al. 1997). Working with the NIH as part of a Cooperative Research and Development Agreement, Arcturus, Inc., a company devoted to the design and expansion of molecular diagnostic technologies, has developed LCM into a commercially available system. For further details on LCM technology, applications, and protocols, please see the Arcturus Web Site at www.arctur.com.

In the Pathogenetics Unit of the NCI, we have concentrated on a tissue microdissection-based approach to molecular profiling (e.g., please see Figure 5-3). LCM is being used in the Cancer Genome Anatomy Program (CGAP) to catalog the development of cells from normal to diseased state. The technology can be applied to any disease process which is accessible through tissue sampling, such as premalignant cancer lesions, multiple sclerosis, arteriosclerosis, and Alzheimer's disease. For additional information, please see the Molecular Profiling Initiative Web Site at http://cgap-mf.nih.gov/index.html.

The series of protocols in Part 1 provide details for various approaches to and applications of tissue microdissection in current use.

- Protocol 1 describes manual microdissection for dissecting stained tissue samples with a 30-gauge needle and an inverted microscope.

- Protocol 2 presents the dissection of tissue samples by LCM.

- Protocol 3 describes immunostaining of specific, selected cell populations in preparation for LCM.
- Protocol 4 presents various approaches for recovering RNA from microdissected samples.

For additional protocols, information, and references on LCM and laser-dissecting microscopes, please see the Arcturus Web Site at www.arctur.com. A series of protocols found in Section 3 (Protocols 13 to 18) describe further downstream processing of microdissected samples in preparation for microarray experiments. Protocol 20 in Section 3 describes the setup and process of the hybridization to microarrays.

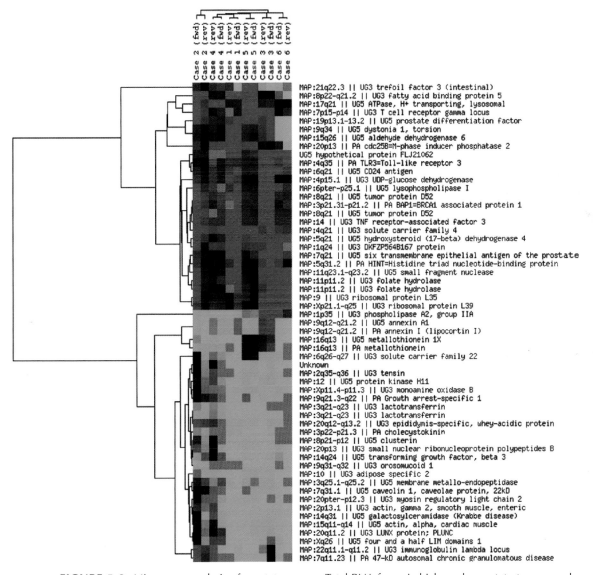

FIGURE 5-3. Microarray analysis of prostate cancer. Total RNA from six high-grade prostate tumors and a reference sample pooled from normal prostate tissue were used to generate fluorescent first-strand cDNA targets. The probes were hybridized in duplicate (with forward and reverse fluorescent reactions) to 6.4K human cDNA microarrays (NCI Array Facility, Gaithersburg, Maryland). Hierarchical cluster analysis was performed for all genes up-regulated or down-regulated at least twofold on at least half of the arrays. The tumors clustered tightly together, and 52 genes were identified as demonstrating consistent changes in a majority of the tumors.

Manual Microdissection

Manual microdissection and subsequent molecular analysis can be carried out on slides containing standard formaldehyde-fixed 5-μm tissue sections stained with hematoxylin and eosin or more rarely by Methyl Green or Fast Red. Tissue sections are dissected with a 30-gauge needle using an inverted microscope. Although many investigators choose to use microscopes fitted with long-distance working optics (10x and 50x dry lens objectives), we have not found it necessary to use microscopes fitted with special optics. With normal optics, the highest-power objective that can be used for practical purposes is 10x, which allows for relatively precise manual microdissections. Using the minimal amount of staining required to visualize the tissue for microdissection significantly improves recovery of macromolecules. Because the tissue sections are microdissected from slides without coverslips, the refractive indices of the sample and the air differ significantly. This causes distortions of images in the optical axis and substantial light scattering, which typically generates "dark" images. Decreasing stain concentrations to ~10% of their standard concentrations improves both image quality and molecular recovery.

MATERIALS

CAUTION: Please see Appendix 3 for appropriate handling of materials marked with <!>.

Buffers and Solutions

Please see Appendix 2 for components of stock solutions, buffers, and reagents.
Dilute stock solutions to the appropriate concentrations.

Complete miniprotease inhibitor cocktail tablets (1 836 153, Roche)
> For all protein analyses, dissolve one protease inhibitor cocktail tablet per 10 ml of each reagent except xylene.

Deionized H_2O

Eosin Y solution (Sigma)

Ethanol (70%, 95%, 100%)
> Some batches of absolute ethanol (100% or 200 proof) have been reported to contain fluorescent contaminants that generate high backgrounds in microarray experiments; 95% ethanol does not have this problem. To avoid difficulties, either use 95% ethanol or identify a brand of absolute ethanol that performs reliably. Absolute ethanol (USP-grade ethyl alcohol, 64-17-5) purchased from Warner-Graham Co. (Cockeysville, Maryland) performs consistently well.

Extraction buffer for microdissected sample (choose a buffer appropriate for the microdissected sample, i.e., DNA, RNA, or protein analysis: please see Step 15)
> DNA extraction buffer
> 50 mM Tris-Cl (pH 7.6)
> 1 mM EDTA (pH 8.0)
> 1% Tween-20
> 2 mg/ml proteinase K

RNA extraction buffer

> RNA can be recovered from microdissected cells using any of a number of commercially available kits. Typically, the cells are homogenized in a standard guanidinium-thiocyanate-based buffer containing β-mercaptoethanol and the RNA is then purified using, for example, the RNeasy kit from QIAGEN. In most cases, digestion with DNase I is used to remove residual genomic DNA before the washing steps while the RNA is still bound to the silica gel membrane. For further details, please see Section 3, Protocol 1 or Protocol 4 in this section.

Protein extraction buffer

> If proteins are to be analyzed by electrophoresis, lyse the cells in a buffer containing:
>
> > 8 M urea
> > 2 M thiourea
> > 2% (w/v) CHAPS
> > 1% (w/v) dithiothreitol (DTT) <!>
> > 0.8% Pharmalyte (pH 3–10)
>
> For more information, please see Banks et al. (1999), Emmert-Buck et al. (2000), and Ornstein et al. (2000).
>
> If native proteins are to be recoverd and analyzed from frozen sections, please see the introduction to **ALTERNATIVE PROTOCOL: MICRODISSECTION OF FROZEN TISSUE SAMPLES** at the end of this protocol.

Glycerol (ultrapure, GIBCO)

Hematoxylin solution (Mayer's, Sigma)

Xylene (mixed) (ACS reagent, Sigma) <!>

Cells and Tissue Samples

Tissue sections

> Sections cut from formalin-fixed, paraffin-embedded sections are mounted on slides and stored at or below room temperature. Do not deparaffinize the sections until immediately prior to microdissection. Sections embedded in low-melt polyester are stored at 4°C. Frozen sections are stored at –80°C or below.

Special Equipment

Inverted microscope (standard)

Microdissecting tool (30-gauge needle on a syringe)

METHOD

Slide Processing

For paraffin-embedded sections, begin at Step 1; for frozen-embedded sections, begin at Step 4. For polyester-embedded sections, immerse the slides twice in absolute ethanol for 5 minutes each time (to dewax the sections), and then begin at Step 3.

1. To deparaffinize tissue sections, immerse the slide(s) in fresh xylene for 5 minutes.

2. Transfer the slides into fresh xylene, and immerse them for 5 minutes.

3. Transfer the slides into absolute ethanol, and immerse them for 30 seconds.

4. Transfer the slides into 95% ethanol, and immerse them for 30 seconds.

5. Transfer the slides into 70% ethanol, and immerse them for 30 seconds.

6. Transfer the slides into deionized H_2O, and immerse them for 30 seconds.

7. Transfer the slides into Mayer's hematoxylin solution, and immerse them for 30 seconds.

8. Transfer the slides into deionized H_2O for 15 seconds; repeat once.

9. Transfer the slides into 70% ethanol, and immerse them for 30 seconds.

10. Transfer the slides into eosin Y, and immerse them for 15 seconds.

11. Transfer the slides into deionized H_2O, and immerse them for 30 seconds; repeat once.

12. Transfer the slides into 3% glycerol in deionized H_2O, and immerse them for 30 seconds.

    Soaking in 3% glycerol is particularly helpful in preparing the tissue for microdissection because it renders the tissue less brittle. Dissected tissue fragments are easier to procure.

13. Remove the slides from the 3% glycerol solution and gently shake them to remove the layer of glycerol/H_2O.

    It is important to ensure that the thin coat of fluid covering the slide after removal from the glycerol/H_2O is removed. Dissection with this fluid layer present results in diffusion of tissue fragments, with potential for "contamination" of samples. Additionally, dissection of the tissue under fluid produces large strips of tissue that are not easily homogenized in extraction buffers.

Dissection

Perform the microdissection within the next 5–10 minutes, if possible. During this time, the tissue is dry but retains a soft consistency. If the dissection takes more than a few minutes, the tissue will become increasingly brittle and the dissected fragments may be repelled as the needle is brought in proximity to the tissue. If the tissue becomes overly dry, resoak it in the 3% glycerol/H_2O solution for 1–2 minutes.

14. While viewing the tissue through a microscope, gently scrape the cell population of interest with a 30-gauge needle inserted into a syringe. The dissected cells will become detached from the slide and form small dark clumps of tissue that can be collected on the needle by electrostatic attraction. Several small tissue fragments can be procured simultaneously. Collect the first fragment of tissue on the tip of the needle to assist in procuring subsequent tissue.

    To ensure a stable dissecting hand, prop an elbow on a solid surface adjacent to and at the same height as the stage of the microscope. It is helpful to rest the ulnar aspect of the dissecting hand on the stage of the microscope and move the needle into the microscopic field, a few millimeters above the tissue. In this way, both the dissecting arm and hand can rest on solid support surfaces.

15. Carefully place the tip of the needle with the procured tissue fragments into a 1.5-ml microfuge tube containing 100 μl of the appropriate extraction buffer for the tissue under study. Gently shake the tube to ensure that the tissue detaches from the tip of the needle.

    Pressing down on the shaft of the syringe to inject an air bubble into the extraction solution helps to detach the tissue from the needle and prevents any fragments from remaining lodged in the barrel of the needle.

16. Continue to procure cell or tissue samples by repeating Steps 14 and 15.

    The number of cells or tissue samples to be collected depends on the type of tissue as well as the goals of the experiment. In the case of prostate tissue, we recommend collecting 5000 cells for RNA amplification (e.g., prior to microarray analysis) and 100,000 cells for two-dimensional protein gels.

ALTERNATIVE PROTOCOL: MICRODISSECTION OF FROZEN TISSUE SAMPLES

The placement of frozen tissue sections directly on agarose-coated slides can be helpful in maintaining stability if proteins are to be recovered in native form from a frozen section. The agarose gels can be prepared or soaked in appropriate buffers that will bathe the frozen section prior to and during the microdissection. The pH, salt concentration, proteinase inhibitors, etc., of the buffer should be tailored to the properties of the desired target proteins. Agarose-coated slides may also be used in microdissection for the recovery of mRNA.

Additional Materials

Agarose solution (2%) in appropriate buffer, warmed to 45°C
Cryostat
Microscope slides (standard uncoated glass)

Method

1. To prepare slides for microdissection, place 200 µl of warm 2% agarose solution on standard uncoated glass slides, cover them with a glass coverslip, and allow the gel to set.

2. Remove the glass coverslip from the slide and immediately transfer the freshly cut tissue section from the cryostat onto the agarose-coated slide.

3. Use a 30-gauge needle to "tease" the tissue apart.
   The tissue will remain bathed in the fluid from the gel and can be gently pulled apart, separating along tissue planes (e.g., stroma and epithelium will easily separate from each other).

4. Gently pick up the dissected tissue from the slide, or, alternatively, use the needle to physically cut the agarose and procure both the agarose and the tissue fragment together.

Laser Capture Microdissection

In laser capture microdissection (LCM), specific cell populations are recovered from standard histological sections through the use of a low-energy infrared laser integrated into a standard microscope equipped with a continuous imaging system. The method was originally developed by the laser technology group working at the National Institutes of Health (Emmert-Buck et al. 1996, 1997; Bonner et al. 1997) and commercialized through a Collaborative Research and Development Agreement with Arcturus, Inc. (Mountain View, California). For information about laser dissection microscopes and their use, please see the company's Web Site, and for additional protocols and information on LCM and laser-dissecting microscopes, please visit the Arcturus Web Site at www.arctur.com.

Once the tissue has been properly processed, sectioned, stained, and dehydrated, it is ready for microdissection (please see Figure 5-4). A CapSure device (small cap) coated with a thermoplastic film is placed directly on the surface of a prepared tissue section. A low-power near-infrared laser beam activates the membrane to contact selected cells and lifts them from the surrounding tissue. The tissue is visualized under the microscope and an initial road map image and predissection, postdissection, and cap images are taken to document the histology, the steps of microdissection, and the microdissected cells (please see Figure 5-5).

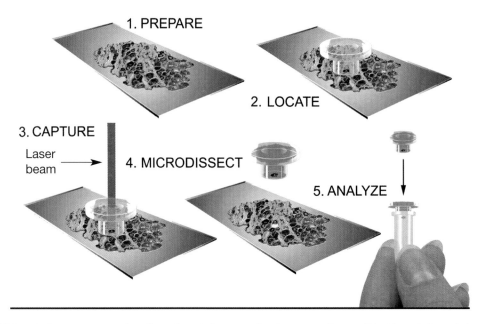

FIGURE 5-4. Laser capture microdissection. A tissue section is prepared on a slide (*1*) and viewed through a standard inverted light microscope. The slide is positioned so that the desired cells will be directly underneath the target (*2*). A microfuge cap, coated on the bottom with the transfer membrane, is placed on top of the cells, and a brief pulse from a low-power infrared laser is shot through the cap and membrane (*3*). The membrane melts and intercalates with the microtopology of the cells it directly contacts. The cap is lifted off the tissue (*4*) and the desired cells are isolated for subsequent molecular analysis (*5*).

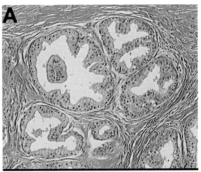

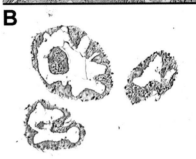

FIGURE 5-5. Laser capture microdissection of normal prostate epithelium. Immediately prior to microdissection, the section was stained with hematoxylin and eosin and dehydrated with xylene. (*A*) Normal prostate epithelium is part of a complex milieu of several cell types. A laser was used to attach only the epithelial cells to a transparent thermoplastic film. (*B*) The film was lifted off of the tissue section, removing all microdissected cells, and viewed, showing effective capture of the desired tissue uncontaminated by other cell types.

The focal spot size of the infrared laser can at present be adjusted to diameters of 7.5–30 μm; therefore, capture of single cells with the standard LCM system is limited to target cells that are large or are well-isolated (Luo et al. 1999). However, a modified LCM microscope has been described recently, in which a cylindrical, 40-μm-wide membrane surface is positioned onto the sample with minimal contact force and is rotated as single cells are rapidly captured and concentrated (Suarez-Quian et al. 1999). In addition, Arcturus has developed high-sensitivity low-volume caps for capture of LCM samples, where the cap sits above the tissue section without contacting it and the laser melts the film sufficiently to allow it to reach the surface of the section and bond to the desired cells.

MATERIALS

CAUTION: Please see Appendix 3 for appropriate handling of materials marked with <!>.

Buffers and Solutions

Please see Appendix 2 for components of stock solutions, buffers, and reagents.
Dilute stock solutions to the appropriate concentrations.

Complete miniprotease inhibitor cocktail tablets (Roche)
> For all protein analysis, dissolve one protease inhibitor cocktail tablet per 10 ml of each reagent except xylene.

Deionized H_2O

Eosin Y solution (Sigma)

Ethanol (70%, 95%, absolute)
> Some batches of absolute ethanol (100% or 200 proof) have been reported to contain fluorescent contaminants that generate high backgrounds in microarray experiments; 95% ethanol does not have this problem. To avoid difficulties, either use 95% ethanol or identify a brand of absolute ethanol that performs reliably. Absolute ethanol (USP-grade ethyl alcohol, 64-17-5) purchased from Warner-Graham Co. (Cockeysville, Maryland) performs consistently well.

Extraction buffer for microdissected sample (choose a buffer appropriate for the particular study (i.e., DNA, RNA, or protein analysis; please see Step 20)

DNA extraction buffer

50 mM Tris-Cl (pH 7.6)

1 mM EDTA (pH 8.0)

1% Tween-20

2 mg/ml proteinase K

RNA extraction buffer
> RNA can be recovered from microdissected cells using any of a number of commercially available kits. An RNA isolation kit designed specifically for LCM samples is available from Arcturus (www.arctur.com). Typically, the cells are homogenized in a standard guanidinium-thiocyanate-based buffer containing β-mercaptoethanol, and the RNA is then purified using, for example, the RNeasy kit from QIAGEN. In most cases, digestion with DNase I is used to remove residual genomic DNA before the washing steps while the RNA is still bound to the silica gel membrane. For further details, please see Section 3, Protocol 1 or Protocol 4 in this section.

Protein extraction buffer
> If proteins are to be analyzed by electrophoresis, lyse the cells in a buffer containing:
>> 8 M urea
>> 2 M thiourea
>> 2% (w/v) CHAPS
>> 1% (w/v) dithiothreitol (DTT) <!>
>> 0.8% Pharmalyte (pH 3–10)
>
> For more information, please see Banks et al. (1999), Emmert-Buck et al. (2000), and Ornstein et al. (2000).
>
> If native proteins are to be recovered and analyzed from frozen sections, please see the introduction to **ALTERNATIVE PROTOCOL: MICRODISSECTION OF FROZEN TISSUE SAMPLES** in Protocol 1.

Glycerol (ultrapure, GIBCO)

Hematoxylin solution (Mayer's, Sigma)

Xylene (mixed) (ACS reagent, Sigma) <!>

Cells and Tissue Samples

Tissue sections
> Sections cut from formalin-fixed, paraffin-embedded sections are mounted on slides and stored at or below room temperature. Do not deparaffinize the sections until immediately prior to microdissection. Sections embedded in low-melt polyester are stored at 4°C. Frozen sections are stored at –80°C or below.

Special Equipment

Adhesive pad (e.g., CapSure Cleanup Pad, Arcturus, Inc.)
GeneAmp PCR tubes (0.5-ml thin-walled, RNase-free) (Applied Biosystems)
> These tubes are recommended because they do not leak when the LCM cap is in place and the tube is inverted.

Laser capture microdissection system (PixCell II LCM Instrument, Arcturus, Inc.) <!>
LCM caps with transfer membranes (Arcturus, Inc.)

METHOD

Slide Processing

If a paraffin-embedded section is to be stained, begin the protocol at Step 1. If the section was frozen-embedded, melt it gently (e.g., on the back of the hand) for ~30 seconds after removal from the freezer, and then begin the protocol at Step 4. This process will create greater tissue adhesion to the slide and a "rougher" tissue surface and allow for better adhesion to the LCM cap. For polyester-embedded sections, immerse the slides twice in absolute ethanol for 5 minutes each time (to dewax the sections), and then begin at Step 3.

1. To deparaffinize tissue sections, immerse the slide(s) in fresh xylene for 5 minutes.

2. Transfer the slides into fresh xylene, and immerse them for 5 minutes.

3. Transfer the slides into absolute ethanol, and immerse them for 30 seconds.

4. Transfer the slides into 95% ethanol, and immerse them for 30 seconds.

5. Transfer the slides into 70% ethanol, and immerse them for 30 seconds.

6. Transfer the slides into deionized H_2O, and immerse them for 30 seconds.

7. Transfer the slides into Mayer's hematoxylin solution, and immerse them for 30 seconds.

8. Transfer the slides into deionized H_2O for 15 seconds; repeat once.

9. Transfer the slides into 70% ethanol, and immerse them for 30 seconds.

10. Transfer the slides into eosin Y, and immerse them for 15 seconds.

11. Transfer the slides into 95% ethanol, and immerse them for 15 seconds.

12. Transfer the slides into 95% ethanol, and immerse them for 15 seconds.

13. Transfer the slides into absolute ethanol, and immerse them for 15 seconds.

14. Transfer the slides into absolute ethanol, and immerse them for 15 seconds.

15. Transfer the slides into xylene to ensure dehydration of the sections. Immerse the slides for 60 seconds.

16. Dry the slides in the air for ~2 minutes or gently use an air gun to completely remove xylene.

> The tissue section should be completely dry before LCM. Use an Accuduster or similar device to facilitate drying for efficient microdissection.

Dissection

To preserve RNA integrity, it is essential that microdissection proceed immediately after slide preparation as significant RNA degradation may occur in fully dehydrated tissue sections after just 1 hour at room temperature. Stained slides may be kept for short periods in xylene until drying just before microdissection. Following capture, cells should be extracted with denaturing buffer as soon as possible.

17. Place the instrument cap directly over the surface of the tissue.

    It is essential that there are no irregularities in the tissue surface in or near the area to be microdissected. Wrinkles will elevate the LCM cap away from the tissue surface and decrease the membrane contact during laser activation. In addition, subtle irregularities sometimes occur on the tissue surface (under the LCM cap) that cannot be detected visually. However, these can be noted by a decrease in the laser activation spot size. This problem can be partially or completely alleviated by adding an extra weight to the cap support arm or temporarily increasing the laser power.

18. Focus the laser beam according to the PixCell instructions. Deliver a pulse using the low-power infrared laser.

    The appropriate duration of the pulse and the mAmp of laser power delivered should be quickly determined empirically prior to microdissection of different tissue types. Briefly, the longer the pulse and the higher the power, the larger the area of captured cells. Power and duration settings for the desired spot size can be optimized by test firing in an area devoid of tissue.

    The laser activates the membrane to make contact with the tissue, and the desired cells adhere to the membrane of the LCM cap. The size of the laser beam may be adjusted from 7.5 μm to 30 μm to allow microdissection of either groups of cells or single cells, depending on the intent of the study.

19. After the microdissection is complete, lift the cap with microdissected cells from the slide and use an adhesive pad to remove cells that may have attached nonspecifically to the LCM cap. Place the cap on the adhesive pad three separate times, and then view it microscopically to ensure that all nonspecific material has been removed.

    Arcturus Engineering has developed a new type of cap (HS LCM caps) that eliminates collateral pickup of unwanted cells. With these caps, the film is held 12-μm from the tissue and only the cells that are targeted come into contact with the film. This approach eliminates the need to remove material that adheres nonspecifically during LCM. For details, please see www.arctur.com/technology/lcm_steps.htm.

20. Place the cap onto a 0.5-ml GeneAmp tube containing 100 μl of the appropriate extraction buffer for molecular analysis (e.g., denaturing buffer for RNA extraction). Invert the tube to allow lysis of the cells.

    When ExtracSure devices are used in combination with CapSure HS, the samples can be extracted with 10 μl of buffer.

    Details of the method used to isolate RNA from microdissected tissue are given in Protocol 4 of this section. Arcturus has developed an RNA isolation kit called the PicoPure RNA Isolation Kit (www.arctur.com) that is designed specifically for LCM samples.

Protocol 3

Immuno-LCM

Microdissection of routinely stained or unstained frozen sections of tissues has been used successfully to obtain purified cell populations for the analysis of gene expression. However, the precision and usefulness of microdissection are frequently limited by difficulty in identifying cell types and structures by morphology alone. Consequently, procedures for rapid immunostaining have been developed that can be used in tandem with LCM and extraction of RNA from frozen sections (Fend et al. 1999a). Immunostaining allows analysis of mRNA extracted from specific cell populations that have been identified by their immunophenotype or expression of function-related antigens. Excellent immunostaining of sections fixed in acetone, methanol, or ethanol/acetone can be obtained after 12–25 minutes total processing time. Frozen tissue sections may be immunostained under RNase-free conditions using a rapid three-step streptavidin-biotin technique followed by dehydration. The immunostained sections are ready for dissection using LCM (Protocol 2). The specificity, precision, and speed of microdissection are markedly increased due to the improved identification of desired (or undesired) cell types. The mRNA recovered from immunostained tissue is of high quality: Single-step polymerase chain reaction (PCR) can be used to amplify fragments of more than 600 bp from both housekeeping genes (e.g., β-actin) and cell-specific messages (e.g., CD4 or CD19) using cDNA corresponding to <500 immunostained, microdissected cells.

MATERIALS

CAUTION: Please see Appendix 3 for appropriate handling of materials marked with <!>.

Buffers and Solutions

Please see Appendix 2 for components of stock solutions, buffers, and reagents.
Dilute stock solutions to the appropriate concentrations.

Acetone
DEPC-treated H_2O (Research Genetics)
Diaminobenzidine (DAB) <!>
Ethanol (70%, 95%, absolute)
Hematoxylin solution (Mayer's, Sigma)
Phosphate-buffered saline (PBS) (pH 7.4)
Phosphate-buffered saline, with Ca^{2+} and Mg^{2+}
Placental RNase inhibitor (Perkin Elmer, Branchburg)
Xylene (mixed) (ACS grade, Sigma) <!>

Cells and Tissue Samples

Tissue block, snap frozen

325

Special Equipment

Cryostat

DAKO Quick Staining kit (DAKO Corp.)

> The kit provides materials for a three-step streptavidin-biotin-staining procedure with predilut-
> ed mono- or polyclonal (rabbit) primary antibodies optimized for very brief staining times. The
> dilutions for primary antibodies, which are supplied by the investigator, should be determined
> individually. Secondary antibodies are supplied in prediluted form in the DAKO Quick Staining
> kit. Add placental RNase inhibitor to the primary antibody and the DAB solution at a concen-
> tration of 200–400 units/ml. Prepare all solutions with DEPC-treated H_2O.

Glass slides (Superfrost Plus, Fisher Scientific)

METHOD

1. Use a new disposable cryostat blade to cut 8-µm serial sections of snap-frozen tissue blocks on a standard cryostat.

2. Mount the tissue sections on Superfrost Plus glass slides and immediately transfer the slides to a –80ºC freezer.

3. Thaw the frozen sections for 30–60 seconds at room temperature.

4. Fix the samples by immersing them immediately in cold acetone for 5 minutes.

5. Rinse the slides briefly in PBS.

6. Using the DAKO Quick Staining kit, immunostain the tissue sections by incubating the slides at room temperature with the primary and secondary antibodies and the tertiary reagent for 90–120 seconds each, rinsing briefly with PBS between each step.

7. Develop the color with DAB for 3–5 minutes and counterstain with hematoxylin for 15–30 seconds.

8. Dehydrate the sections by sequential immersion in a series of 70%, 95%, absolute ethanol for 15 seconds each.

9. Immerse the sections in xylene for 2 minutes, repeat once.

10. Allow the samples to dry in the air.

    > The immunostained sections are now ready for LCM as described in Protocol 2.

Processing of Microdissected Tissue for Expression Analysis

The following protocol describes the recovery of total RNA from microdissected samples using the Micro RNA isolation kit from Stratagene, Inc. (Ohyama et al. 2000). Other methods proven to be successful for RNA isolation from LCM- or LPC-derived samples are described, for example, in Luo et al. (1999) and Bernsen et al. (1998), respectively. Please also see the panel on **COMMERCIAL KITS FOR ISOLATION OF RNA FROM SMALL NUMBERS OF MICRODISSECTED CELLS** at the end of this protocol. RNA recovered from microdissected samples may be labeled and hybridized to microarrays as described in the protocols in Section 3, Part 2 of this manual.

MATERIALS

CAUTION: Please see Appendix 3 for appropriate handling of materials marked with <!>.

Buffers and Solutions

Please see Appendix 2 for components of stock solutions, buffers, and reagents.
Dilute stock solutions to the appropriate concentrations.

β-mercaptoethanol (14.2 M) <!>
Chloroform:isoamyl alcohol (24:1) <!>
Glycogen (10 mg/ml) in H_2O
Isopropanol (ice-cold) <!>
Phenol (water-saturated, pH 5.2) <!>
RiboGreen RNA quantitation agent (Molecular Probes, Inc)
RNA denaturing buffer (GITC)
    4 M guanidine isothiocyanate (GITC)
    0.02 M sodium citrate
    0.5% Sarcosyl
Sodium acetate (2 M) adjusted to pH 4.0 with acetic acid <!>

Enzymes and Buffers

DNase I (10 units/µl) (GenHunter)
10x DNase buffer
Protein inhibitor of RNase (e.g., RNasin from Promega Inc. or Prime Inhibitor from 5 Prime→3 Prime)

Cells and Tissue Samples

Microdissected tissue on LCM cap (from Protocol 2)

Special Equipment

Bioanalyzer (Agilent Technologies)
    Optional, please see Step 27.

GeneAmp PCR tubes (0.5-ml thin-walled, RNase-free) (Applied Biosystems)

> These tubes are recommended because they do not leak when the LCM cap is in place and the tube is inverted.

Spectrofluorometer (reduced volume, e.g., TD-60 from Turner Designs)

METHOD

IMPORTANT: Before beginning the protocol, clean all pipettors with a product that will inactivate RNases (e.g., RNase*Zap* Wipes, Ambion Inc.).

Extraction of RNA

1. For each cap of tissue to be processed, prepare a GeneAmp microfuge (0.5-ml) thin-walled PCR tube containing 200 µl of RNA denaturing buffer and 1.6 µl of β-mercaptoethanol.

   > For an alternative protocol for extracting RNA from microdissected material, please see Protocol 8.

2. Place the LCM cap carrying microdissected tissue onto the GeneAmp tube prepared in Step 1. Invert the capped tube several times over the course of 2 minutes to recover the tissue from the cap.

   > For specimens that have been paraffin-embedded, it is helpful to include an incubation step (with the tube inverted) of 20 minutes at 60°C to further liberate the RNA from the tissue.

3. Remove the solution from the PCR tube and place it into a sturdy RNase-free 1.5-ml microfuge tube.

4. Add 20 µl (one-tenth volume) of 2 M sodium acetate (pH 4.0) to the sample.

5. Add 220 µl (equal volume) of H_2O-saturated phenol.

6. Add 60 µl (one-third volume of phenol) of chloroform:isoamyl alcohol.

7. Shake the tube vigorously for 15 seconds.

8. Place the tube on wet ice for 15 minutes.

9. Centrifuge the tube in a microfuge for 30 minutes at 4°C to separate the aqueous and organic phases.

   > Phase separation can also be performed with precentrifuged Phase Lock Gel tubes (5 Prime→3 Prime).

Recovery of RNA

10. Transfer the upper aqueous layer to a fresh tube.

    > Any of the lower organic phase accidentally transferred with the aqueous phase may interfere with the subsequent isopropanol precipitation. To remove any residual organics from the aqueous layer, add 1 volume of 100% chloroform, mix well, and centrifuge for 10 minutes at 4°C to separate the aqueous and organic phases. Transfer the upper layer to a fresh tube.

11. To the aqueous layer, add 1–2 µl of glycogen (10 mg/ml) and 200–300 µl (equal volume) of cold isopropanol.

Glycogen facilitates visualization of the pellet, which can be problematic when using small amounts of RNA.

12. Place the samples for at least 30 minutes (or overnight) at –80ºC.

    Before centrifuging, the tubes may need to be thawed slightly if they have solidified during the isopropanol precipitation.

13. Recover the RNA by centrifugation at maximum speed in a microfuge for 30 minutes at 4ºC, with the cap hinges pointing outward so that the location of the pellet can be better predicted.

14. Discard the supernatants, wash the pellets with 300 µl of cold 70% ethanol, and then centrifuge for 5 minutes at 4ºC.

15. Discard the supernatants.

16. Allow the pellets to dry on ice to remove any residual ethanol.

    Overdrying will prevent the pellets from resuspending easily.

17. Store the pellets at –80ºC until use or treat them with DNase I as described in the steps below.

    DNase treatment of RNA recovered from microdissected cells is highly recommended. Contamination of RNA preparations with genomic DNA can be a problem, possibly due to small DNA fragments created during tissue processing.

DNase Treatment of RNA

18. To each RNA pellet, add 15 µl of DEPC-treated H_2O and 1 µl (20 units) of RNasin or other protein inhibitor of RNase. Mix the components by gently flicking the side of each tube until the pellets are dissolved.

19. Centrifuge the samples briefly in a microfuge.

20. To each sample, add 2 µl of 10x DNase buffer and 20 units (2 µl) of DNase I. Incubate the tubes for 2 hours at 37ºC.

    Some investigators omit DNase I treatment since it may demand another round of RNA purification with the attendant loss of valuable material. These investigators argue that a low level of contamination with genomic DNA is unlikely to affect the transcription pattern since (i) reverse transcription from genomic DNA will be a rare event and (ii) DNA-derived signals emanating from spots on the DNA microarrays are easily identified since they will be neutral with respect to cell type.

    If treatment with DNase as described in this protocol leads to significant losses of RNA, it may be better to purify RNA by a spin-matrix method. This allows digestion with DNase to be performed while the RNA is still bound to the matrix (please see the panel on **COMMERCIAL KITS FOR ISOLATION OF RNA FROM SMALL NUMBERS OF MICRODISSECTED CELLS** at end of this protocol)

21. Extract the RNA by adding to each sample:

2 M sodium acetate (pH 4.0)	2 µl
phenol (H_2O-saturated)	22 µl
chloroform:isoamyl alcohol	6 µl

22. Shake the tubes vigorously for 15 seconds and place them on wet ice for 5 minutes.

23. Centrifuge the tubes at maximum speed in a microfuge for 10 minutes at 4ºC.

24. Transfer the upper layer to a fresh tube.

    > Any of the lower organic phase accidentally transferred may contaminate the aqueous phase and may interfere with the subsequent isopropanol precipitation. To remove any residual organics from the aqueous layer, add 1 volume of 100% chloroform, mix well, and centrifuge for 10 minutes at 4°C to separate the aqueous and organic phases. Transfer the upper layer to a fresh tube.

25. Continue with the RNA extraction by repeating Steps 11–15 above, adjusting the volume of isopropanol accordingly.

26. Dry the pellet, but take care not to overdry it. Resuspend the pellet in 19 μl of DEPC-treated H$_2$O and 1 μl of RNase inhibitor and store at –80°C.

27. If possible, check the quality of RNA.

    > Until recently, it has been very difficult to assess the quality of these samples because the amount of RNA recovered from LCM was so small and the loss involved in checking quality by standard means was not sufficiently advantageous. However, with the recent availability of the BioAnalyzer (from Agilent Technologies), which can assess the quality of amounts of RNA as low as 5 ng or so, it has become increasing feasible to check RNA quality prior to any subsequent analyses.

28. Quantify the RNA.

    > The amounts of RNA recovered from microdissected samples are generally too small to be measured by conventional spectrophotometry. Instead, RNA is quantified using, for example, RiboGreen RNA quantitation agent (Molecular Probes, Inc) and a reduced volume spectrofluorimeter (e.g., TD-60 from Turner Designs). Please note that reagents such as RiboGreen bind to both DNA and RNA. Quantification of RNA should therefore be performed on samples that have been treated with DNase I.

    > The samples are now ready for subsequent processing, and may be labeled for microarray analysis according one of the protocols in Section 3, Part 2.

COMMERCIAL KITS FOR ISOLATION OF RNA FROM SMALL NUMBERS OF MICRODISSECTED CELLS

Several kits are commercially available that greatly simplify the task of isolating total RNA from small numbers of cells recovered from tissue sections by LCM. The best results are obtained with kits that use spin-matrix columns, for example, as described below.

- **Absolute RNA Kit** (Stratagene) (http://www.stratagene.com/cellbio/purification/absolutely_rna_micro.htm). Cells recovered by LCM are lysed, mixed with ethanol, and applied to silica-based fiber resin. Digestion to remove residual genomic DNA is performed with DNase I before the washing step while the RNA is still bound to the silica-gel resin. The column is then washed and the RNA is eluted in a small volume.

- **PicoPure Kit** (Arcturus, Inc.) (http://www.arctur.com/products/picopure_rna_isolation.htm). This kit is very similar to the Absolute RNA kit from Stratagene, except that digestion with DNase I is performed after the RNA is eluted from the column. The kit is optimized for recovery of RNA from 10 to 1000 or more cells isolated by LCM.

- **Micro RNA Isolation Kit** (Stratagene). Total RNA is purified by lysing cells in a guanidine/β-mercaptoethanol-based buffer, followed by extraction with phenol:chloroform and precipitation with ethanol in the presence of glycogen. After the RNA is redissolved, it is treated with DNase I to remove contaminating genomic DNA. The method is very similar to that described above in Protocol 4.

- **RNeasy Minikit** (QIAGEN) http://www.qiagen.com/literature/brochures/pcr/pdf/pcrcha28.pdf. This minikit is used essentially as described in Section 3, Protocol 1. For details, please see Ohyama et al. (2000).

Part 2: Laser Pressure Catapulting

Karin Schütze,[a] Bernd Becker,[b] Monique Bernsen,[c] Tone Björnsen,[d] Dieter Brocksch,[e] Christer Bush,[d] Annette Clement-Sengewald,[f] Marcory C.R.F. van Dijk,[c] Gabriele Friedemann,[a] Wolfgang Heckl,[i] Georgia Lahr,[j] Per Lindahl,[k] Annette Mayer,[l] Sven Nilsson[k], Stefan J. Scheidl,[k] Monika Stich,[j] Wilhelm Stolz,[b] Minoru Takemoto,[k] Stefan Thalhammer,[i] Thomas Vogt,[b] and Renate Burgemeister[a]

[a]*P.A.L.M. Microlaser Technologies AG, Bernried, Germany;* [b]*Universität Regensburg, Regensburg, Germany;* [c]*Academisch Ziekenhuis Nijmegen, Nijmegen, The Netherlands;* [d]*University Hospital, Department of Pathology, Regionsykehuset Tromso-RiTo, Tromsoe, Norway;* [e]*Carl Zeiss, Business Group Microscopy, Göttingen, Germany;* [f]*Frauenklinik der Ludwig Maximilians Universität, Munich, Germany;* [i]*Institute of Cristallography, Ludwig Maximilians Universität, Munich, Germany;* [j]*Academic-Hospital München-Harlaching, Munich, Germany;* [k]*Göteborg University, Department of Medical Biochemistry, Göteborg, Sweden;* [l]*Institute of Anthropology and Human Genetics, Goethe University, Frankfurt/Main, Germany*

INTRODUCTION

Laser pressure catapulting (LPC) was developed by the founding investigators at P.A.L.M. GmbH (www.PALM-Microlaser.com) as a method to isolate cell populations or even single cells of interest. LPC allows gas pressure created by laser-induced photodecomposition to lift single cells or parts of tissue out of the plane and catapult them—up to several centimeters—into a buffer-filled collecting vessel, usually the cap of a regular microfuge tube or a microtiter plate, mounted in the path of the laser beam (please see Figure 5-6) (Schütze and Lahr 1998; Lahr et al. 2000; Bertheau et al. 2001; Westphal et al. 2002). The captured specimens are centrifuged into the tip of the microfuge tube. Depending on the nature of the tissue and the applied preparation method, the laser may be used first to circumscribe a single cell or a selected area on a tissue section, creating a gap between the target cells and their unwanted neighbors. Unwanted material within a desired area can be selectively eliminated, thereby providing capture of a pure sample in a process known as laser microdissection and pressure catapulting (LMPC) (please see Figure 5-7) (Buerger et al. 2000a; Lahr et al. 2000; Stoehr et al. 2000; Vona et al. 2000; Hoffmann et al. 2001; Specht et al. 2001; Fink et al. 2002; Scheidl et al. 2002; Westphal et al. 2002).

The cutting size of the laser is dependent on the wavelength and quality of the laser beam, the magnification and numerical aperture of the objective, and the absorption behavior of the selected specimen. For accurate focusing, a laser of high beam quality and an objective with a numerical aperture (n.a.) >1 is required. The use of a 100x oil immersion objective (n.a. 1,3) will allow precise isolation of single nuclei, filaments, chromosomes, or even chromosomal parts. Within the narrow focus of the laser beam, a density of power >1 MW/cm^2 is generated, enough to destroy the chemical bonds of biological matter. During laser cutting, material is photofragmented into atoms and small molecules, which are blown away at supersonic velocities. Because the process is photochemical and rapid (sub-microsecond), collater-

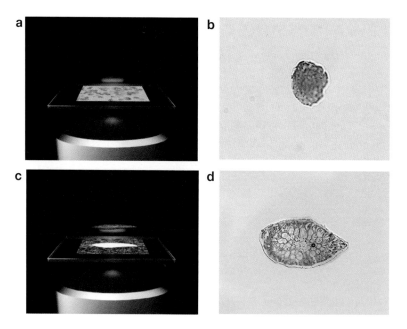

FIGURE 5-6. Scheme of laser pressure catapulting (LPC). (a) A single cell is catapulted from a cyto-centrifuged specimen, and (b) visualized within the capture cap. (c) A selected area is microdissected and catapulted from a membrane-mount tissue section, and (d) visualized within the capture cap.

al damage to the adjacent material is negligible (Srinivasan 1986). Furthermore, as the cell(s) of interest can be catapulted from the section without mechanical contact, there is no possibility of contamination with nonselected tissue. This allows the recovery in the same collection device of multiple elements from geographically different areas or from multiple slides (e.g., serial sections). LPC or LMPC is fully automated and can be applied with any cell or tissue preparation technique and staining method in conjunction with simultaneous fluorescence illumination. Using computer graphic tools or working with image analysis, the investigator selects, outlines, and color-codes the cells or areas of interest (Figure 5-8). The outlined samples are assembled within a list of elements and subsequently processed automatically (please see Table 5-2).

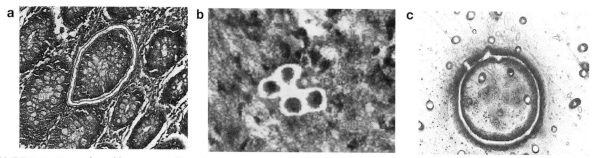

FIGURE 5-7. Examples of laser microdissection and microsurgery. (a) Circumscription of a large gland from a membrane-mount tissue section (viewed with 20x objective); (b) microdissection of single tumor cells; (c) microdissection around circulating tumor cells retained on a routine blood filter (Teflon; 20 μm-thick) for subsequent genetic evaluation (viewed with a 40x objective).

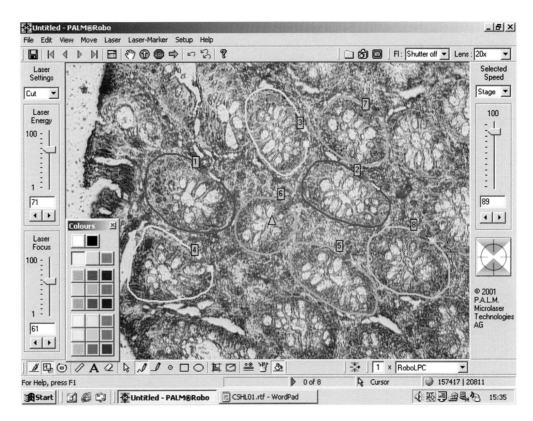

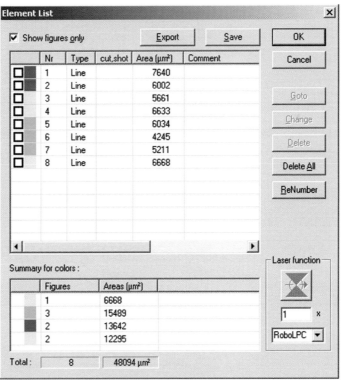

FIGURE 5-8. Preselection with color-coding and automated microdissection. (*Top*) Color-coded outlining of selected samples and display of the RoboLPC line with the catapulting sites shown as magenta-colored dots. The Microbeam automatically circumscribes the outlined samples and immediately catapults them into the capture vial. (*Bottom*) The list of elements allows specimen grouping with respect to color-coded preselection; only the outlined areas are captured by laser treatment.

TABLE 5-2. Laser Actions and Automated Microdissection and Catapulting Procedures

Cut		The laser cuts along the predefined line.
CloseCut		An open figure is closed and subsequently cut.
LPC	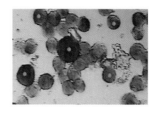	Only dot-marked specimens are catapulted.
AutoLPC (for glass-mounted specimens only)		The outlined area is catapulted with multiple shots (the LPC pattern is preselected within the laser "Setup menu" and is displayed at the screen). Please see Figure 5-9.
CloseCut&AutoLPC	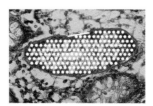	An open figure is closed and the outlined area is cut prior to AutoLPC to avoid contamination with neighboring tissue.
RoboLPC		The outlined specimen is cut up to a small jointing segment, from where the entire area is catapulted with one single shot (the size of the joint is pre-selected within the laser "Setup menu" and displayed together with the LPC-dot).

INSTRUMENTATION

Details of the PALM Microbeam, the motorized microscope stage, and the software for automated microdissection and catapulting (including current sets of instructions for using the PALM system for a growing number of applications) are described in the literature supplied by PALM and on the company's Web Site at www.PALM-Microlaser.com. The software (RoboSoftware) controls the motor-driven laser energy and focus settings, as well as the motion of the motorized stage. Instrument settings differ between applications and with the particular optical system of the LMPC microscope.

Catapulted specimens are collected within the cap of a routine microfuge tube or any other appropriate vial (i.e., microtiter plates) positioned above the objective and within the line of laser beam. For optimal visualization, caps with a flat nonfrosted clear surface are recommended. The use of a flat cap with a tiny rim (<1 mm) improves the efficiency of laser capture and enables the cap surface to be focused with a 5x, 10x, and a long-distance 40x objective. To achieve tight attachment of the catapulted sample within the collecting cap, the cap should be filled with a small amount of buffer (e.g., RNA lysis buffer), which allows easy transfer of the catapulted specimen into the tube by a quick centrifugation step. Alternatively, the samples may be catapulted into flat 8-cap strips filled with a semi-adherent silicone.

PREPARATION OF SPECIMENS

Specimens for LPC can be prepared by any of the techniques commonly used in molecular pathology. They can be frozen in liquid nitrogen and stored at −80°C; they can be fixed in formalin, embedded in paraffin, and stained with any standard fluorescent, immunohistological, or chromogenic-histological stain; or they can be embedded and stored in OCT (optimal cutting temperature embedding compound or Tissue-Tek).

- Among fixatives, precipitating agents such as methanol, ethanol, and acetone perform well with respect to RNA integrity and recovery, but they are incompatible with cryosectioning.

- Tissues fixed with cross-linking agents such as paraformaldehyde and formalin yield less RNA than snap-frozen or ethanol-fixed tissues.

- Morphology is superior in paraffin-embedded sections, but RNA recovery is significantly reduced compared with frozen samples embedded in OCT.

- Sections cut from OCT-embedded material often display microscopic rifts, but the relative positions of cells are well preserved. OCT, like most embedding compounds (including paraffin), interferes with laser cutting and must be removed from sections before LPC or LMPC (please see Protocol 7).

Glass-mount Specimens

Sections of tissue can be mounted on regular glass slides or onto charged (+) slides, which are plasma-treated to improve adhesion of tissue or cells (please see Protocol 5). Specimens (e.g., individual cells from cytocentrifuged samples; please see Figure 5-9a–c) on routine glass slides are easily catapulted with single laser shots focused slightly below the desired cells.

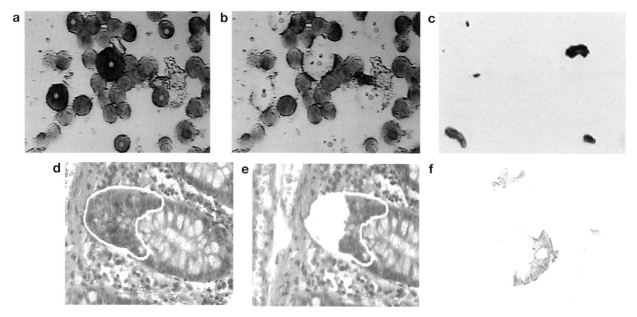

FIGURE 5-9. Direct catapulting of single cells and tissue areas from cytocentrifuged specimen. (a) Cells are marked with computer graphics tools; (b) each marked cell is automatically relocated and separately ejected with a single laser shot, leaving a corresponding gap on the slide; (c) the catapulted cells sometimes arrive broken within a routine microfuge cap. This does not interfere with recovery of DNA, RNA, or protein. (d) Microdissection and catapulting of a glass-mount tissue section: Microdissection prior to catapulting yields a clear-cut gap between the selected and the nonselected material to provide a pure sample preparation. (e) With multiple laser shots, the selected sample is ejected piece by piece leaving corresponding empty spots on the slide. (f) Catapulting with multiple shots usually results in tissue flakes within the collection cap; however, the samples are derived from a morphologically defined origin, and the recovery of DNA, RNA, or proteins is not affected.

For catapulting larger specimens or entire tissue areas, multiple laser shots are required, since the laser can only grab a small portion with each shot. Catapulting from glass usually results in cell fragments or tissue flakes within the sampling cap. Fragmentation of the specimen tissue, however, does not impair subsequent molecular analysis (please see Figure 5-9d–f) (Lahr 2000; Lahr et al. 2000; Bertheau et al. 2001; Scheidl et al. 2002; Westphal et al. 2002).

Membrane-mount Specimens

For certain applications, the specimen may be mounted onto a special membrane, which acts as a backbone, supporting the desired sample during catapulting and preserving its morphology (please see Figure 5-10). During laser microdissection, both the selected region of

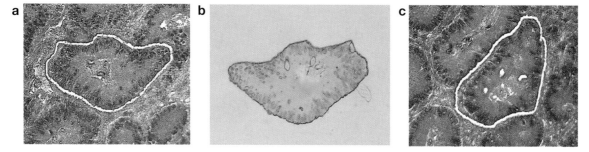

FIGURE 5-10. Microdissection and catapulting of membrane-mount specimen. (a) The laser circumscribes the selected area of a histological tissue section simultaneously cutting the underlying membrane (viewed with a 40x objective); (b) the catapulted sample arrives in the capture cap with its morphology preserved intact (visualized with a 40x long-distance objective); (c) microdissection and selective destruction of unwanted material prior to catapulting (viewed with a 40x objective).

tissue and the underlying membrane are simultaneously circumscribed by the laser beam and catapulted with one single laser shot. Membrane-mounting is recommended for the following.

- Fragile specimens and for material that sticks tightly to the substratum (e.g., extended single cells, blood smears, or cytological smears) (Burgemeister et al. 1999), chromosomes, or filaments.

- Large cell areas from histological sections. This way, areas up to 1 mm in diameter corresponding to thousands of cells are captured within a few seconds.

- Types of cells that can be cultured on membranes. These cells may be fixed prior to microdissection and catapulting or may be catapulted and collected in a viable state. Cells survive microdissection and catapulting quite well and are amenable to subsequent cultivation and cloning (Mayer et al. 2002).

The protocols in this part of Section 5 describe the types of slides used in tissue sectioning (Protocol 5), the preparation of tissues for sectioning (Protocols 6 through 8), and the protection of tissue sections using a "liquid coverslip" (Protocol 9). A final protocol for capture of live cells is given in Protocol 10. For details of the instrumentation and procedures for catapulting, please see the PALM Web Site at www.PALM-Microlaser.com. Also found here is an updated list of publications using the PALM MicroBeam for various applications.

Preparation of Slides for Tissue Sectioning for LMPC

Laser microdissection and pressure catapulting can be performed with routinely fixed and paraffin-embedded tissue (Protocol 6) or with fresh or frozen specimens (Protocol 7). Depending on the nature of the tissue, precoating of glass slides or PALM MembraneSlides (described in the protocols below) may be necessary to increase tissue adhesion.

Two types of membrane slides are available that differ in the chemical compounds and in the laser-cutting behavior of the supporting membrane. The use of a particular type of slide depends on the application—either may be used.

- *PEN Membrane.* The PEN (polyethylene naphthalate) membrane (available through PALM) is 1.35 μm thick and is highly absorptive in the UV-A range, which facilitates laser cutting. The PEN membrane is mostly used for routine tissue preparations, for example, to microdissect single cells or large cell areas. However, it may also be used to recover cells from cell smears or from cells cultured on membranes.

- *POL Membrane.* The POL (polyester) membrane is 0.9–1.0 μm thick and is less sensitive to UV light than the PEN membrane. The POL membrane is used primarily for preparations where critical neighboring material or part of the specimen itself must be removed prior to catapulting to avoid contamination with unwanted material. After unwanted regions of tissue have been discarded, the selected specimen is circumscribed using a somewhat higher laser energy to yield a small "membrane-specimen island" that is subsequently catapulted into the collection cap.

Special "double-membrane" slides have been developed by PALM that consist of a thicker Teflon membrane—resembling the glass slide—and a tightly attached membrane (either POL or PEN). These PALM DuplexSlides are resistant to chemical treatment and enable LMPC even with objectives of high numerical aperture but short working distance. In some special cases, a "membrane-tissue-membrane" sandwich is of help to prevent an unattached or vital specimen from floating. A special MembraneFrame is used in this case to top the membrane slide. During microdissection, the PALM laser is powerful enough to cut simultaneously through both membranes together with the sandwiched specimen.

To cultivate and subsequently catapult living cells (please see Protocol 10), special PALM ChamberSlides (slides with attached flasket) as well as PALM DuplexDishes have been developed.

MATERIALS

Buffers and Solutions

Please see Appendix 2 for components of stock solutions, buffers, and reagents. Dilute stock solutions to the appropriate concentrations.

Poly-L-lysine solution (0.1% w/v) (P 8920, Sigma)

Special Equipment

Superfrost Plus glass microscope slides (61661155, Fisher Scientific) or PALM MembraneSlides

METHOD

1. To coat the glass slide, distribute a drop of poly-L-lysine solution over the slide.

2. Use a second slide or a pipette tip to distribute the solution over the surface of the slide.

3. Allow the slide to dry for 30 minutes at room temperature.

4. Prepare the tissue samples for sectioning onto the glass or membrane-coated slides (please see Protocol 6, 7, or 8).

Protocol 6

Preparation of Paraffin-embedded Tissue Sections for LMPC

In general, if RNA is to be extracted from the captured material, the sections should be cut and processed under conditions that minimize the possibility of exposure to RNases. All instruments and staining chambers should be treated with RNase-decontaminating agents such as RNaseZap, and all solutions should be freshly prepared with ingredients that are RNase-free. For further details, please see the information panel on **SPECIAL CONSIDERATIONS FOR WORKING WITH RNA** in Section 3.

MATERIALS

CAUTION: Please see Appendix 3 for appropriate handling of materials marked with <!>.

IMPORTANT: Prepare all reagents used in this protocol with DEPC-treated H$_2$O (please see the information panel on **SPECIAL CONSIDERATIONS FOR WORKING WITH RNA** in Section 3).

Buffers and Solutions

Please see Appendix 2 for components of stock solutions, buffers, and reagents.
Dilute stock solutions to the appropriate concentrations.

Ethanol (absolute, 96%, 70%)
> Some batches of absolute ethanol (100% or 200 proof) have been reported to contain fluorescent contaminants that generate high backgrounds in microarray experiments. To avoid difficulties, identify a brand of absolute ethanol that performs reliably. Absolute ethanol (USP-grade ethyl alcohol, 64-17-5) purchased from Warner-Graham Co. (Cockeysville, Maryland) performs consistently well.

RNaseZap (9780, Ambion)

Staining solution: Mayer's hematoxylin, Methyl Green, *or* Toluidine Blue Xylenes <!>
> It is advisable to test the influence of special staining solutions prior to the array experiments; very preliminary results show that hematoxylin-eosin staining as well as "nuclear Fast Red" staining seem to give best results.

Cells and Tissues

Tissue specimens (paraffin-embedded)

Special Equipment

Glass or membrane-coated slides (please see Protocol 5)
Microtome

METHOD

1. Select routine paraffin-embedded specimens and cut sections of 3–15 μm with a standard microtome.

2. Transfer the sections directly onto glass slides or membrane slides.

3. Dry the slides overnight at 37–56°C

4. To remove paraffin from the tissue sections, immerse the slides sequentially in the following series of solvents for the frequencies and times listed.

Solvent	Frequency and Time
xylene	2× 2 minutes
absolute ethanol	1 minute
96% ethanol	1 minute
70% ethanol	1 minute

   Rinse with H_2O.

5. To stain the deparaffinized tissue sections, immerse the slides sequentially in the following series of solutions for the times listed.

Solution	Time
Mayer's hematoxylin	45 seconds to 10 minutes
or	
Methyl Green	10 seconds
or	
Toluidine Blue	10 seconds

   Rinse with H_2O for 10 minutes.

absolute ethanol	1 minute
96% ethanol	1 minute
70% ethanol	1 minute

   Rinse with H_2O.

6. To fix the stained tissue sections, immerse the slides sequentially in the following solvents for frequencies and times listed.

Solvent	Frequency and Time
96% ethanol	2× 1 minute
absolute ethanol	2× 1 minute

   Dry the slides for 30 minutes to overnight at 37–56°C.

   For best results, microdissection should follow immediately. If necessary, the slides can be stored for several weeks. Typically, the specimen is applied to the glass slide or to the membrane and used immediately for LPC or LMPC; however, a "liquid cover" can be applied that improves visualization and prevents the specimen from contamination, but still allows LMPC and unrestricted molecular analysis (please see Protocol 9).

Preparation of Sections of Fresh-Frozen Tissue for LMPC

The specimens to be used for LPC or LMPC should be either snap-frozen in liquid nitrogen and stored at –80°C or embedded and stored in OCT (optimal cutting temperature compound) at –80°C. In the latter case, the OCT must be removed from the sections prior to LPC.

If RNA is to be extracted, the sections should be cut and processed under conditions that minimize the possibility of exposure to RNases. All instruments and staining chambers should be treated with RNase-decontaminating agents such as RNase*Zap*, and all solutions should be freshly prepared with ingredients that are RNase-free. For further details, please see the information panel on **SPECIAL CONSIDERATIONS FOR WORKING WITH RNA** in Section 3.

MATERIALS

CAUTION: Please see Appendix 3 for appropriate handling of materials marked with <!>.

IMPORTANT: Prepare all reagents used in this protocol with DEPC-treated H_2O (please see the information panel on **SPECIAL CONSIDERATIONS FOR WORKING WITH RNA** in Section 3).

Buffers and Solutions

Please see Appendix 2 for components of stock solutions, buffers, and reagents.
Dilute stock solutions to the appropriate concentrations.

Acetone (ice-cold)

Eosin Y solution alcoholic (HT110-1-16, Sigma Diagnostics, Deisenhofen, Germany)

Ethanol (absolute, 96%, 70%)
> Some batches of absolute ethanol (100% or 200 proof) have been reported to contain fluorescent contaminants that generate high backgrounds in microarray experiments. To avoid difficulties, identify a brand of absolute ethanol that performs reliably. Absolute ethanol (USP-grade ethyl alcohol, 64-17-5) purchased from Warner-Graham Co. (Cockeysville, Maryland) performs consistently well.

Mayer's hematoxylin staining solution

Methanol (70%) <!>

Poly-L-lysine (P 1274, Sigma)

RNA*later* stabilization reagent (221462, QIAGEN)
> Optional, please see Step 3.

RNase*Zap* (9780, Ambion)

Cells and Tissues

Tissue specimen

Special Equipment

Cryostat
Glass or membrane-coated slides (please see Protocol 5)

Additional Reagents

Step 1 may require reagents and materials listed in Protocol 5.

METHOD

1. Section the tissue specimen at 10-μm thickness in a cryostat at –20°C.

2. Transfer the sections directly onto the appropriate membrane slides.

3. Allow the sections to attach to the membrane-coated slide.

   Optional: Cover the section with 100 μl of RNA*later*.

4. To prepare the section for extraction of RNA, immerse the slide for 5 seconds in 70% ethanol, 70% methanol, or ice-cold acetone.

   If necessary, slides can be stored at this stage at –80°C.

5. To stain the sections, immerse the slides sequentially in the following series of solutions for the times listed.

Solution	Time
Mayer's hematoxylin	45 seconds
Rinse with H_2O.	
Rinse with H_2O (*optional:* add 1 drop of ammonia solution).	
alcoholic eosin Y	20 seconds
70% ethanol	10 seconds
70% ethanol	10 seconds
96% ethanol	20 seconds
96% ethanol	20 seconds

   Dry the slides in the air for 30 seconds and the store them (e.g., in a sterile 50-ml Falcon tube).

   For best results, microdissection should follow immediately. If necessary, the slides can be stored overnight at –80°C or on dry ice. Typically, the specimen is applied to the glass slide or membrane and used immediately for LPC or LMPC; however, a "liquid cover" can be applied that improves visualization and prevents the specimen from contamination, but still allows LMPC and unrestricted molecular analysis (please see Protocol 9).

Protocol 8

LPC of Tissues Fixed in Zincfix for mRNA Profiling

A range of histological methods have been tested for their ability to conserve RNA and for their compatibility with laser microdissection (Scheidl et al. 2002). The zinc-based fixative used in this protocol conserves RNA without compromising morphology. The RNA prepared in this protocol can be transcribed by RNA-dependent DNA polymerases into cDNA of high quality and amplified as described in Section 3, Protocols 15 and 16. The RNA must be amplified (perhaps 10^6-fold) using primers equipped with bacteriophage T7 promoters (for details, please see Section 3, Protocols 15 and 16). To avoid problems, precautions must be taken to avoid contaminating the RNA with DNA, in particular with plasmids that contain T7 promoters. Frequent cleaning of laboratory equipment and the use of barrier tips for automatic pipettors are recommended.

To obtain the amounts of RNA required for hybridization to cDNA microarrays, it is essential to avoid losses of RNA in the early stages of the protocol. The overall recovery from tissue to isolated total RNA with this protocol is estimated to be ~50%, with losses occurring mainly in the tissue fixation and RNA isolation steps. Neither the LPC procedure itself nor the handling of dry sections at room temperature will lead to significant losses of RNA (Scheidl et al. 2002).

This protocol, like many others in this manual, requires working conditions that are free from RNases. Wear gloves when appropriate and work on decontaminated surfaces, i.e., surfaces treated with an agent such as RNaseZap (Ambion). Use RNase-free enzymes and reagents.

MATERIALS

CAUTION: Please see Appendix 3 for appropriate handling of materials marked with <!>.

IMPORTANT: Prepare all reagents used in this protocol with DEPC-treated H_2O (please see the information panel on SPECIAL CONSIDERATIONS FOR WORKING WITH RNA in Section 3).

Buffers and Solutions

Please see Appendix 2 for components of stock solutions, buffers, and reagents.
Dilute stock solutions to the appropriate concentrations.

Ethanol (99.9%, 90%, 70%)

Steps 11–14 require 40 ml of each of these solutions of ethanol.

Some batches of absolute ethanol (100% or 200 proof) have been reported to contain fluorescent contaminants that generate high backgrounds in microarray experiments. To avoid difficulties, identify a brand of absolute ethanol that performs reliably. Absolute ethanol (USP-grade ethyl alcohol, 64-17-5) purchased from Warner-Graham Co. (Cockeysville, Maryland) performs consistently well.

OCT (optimal cutting temperature compound)

Phosphate-buffered saline (PBS) lacking Ca^{2+} and Mg^{2+}

RNase*Zap* (9780, Ambion)
Sucrose in Zincfix (30% w/v)
Xylene <!>
    Steps 11–14 require 40 ml of xylene.
Zincfix
    5 g of $ZnCl_2$
    6 g of zinc acetate·$2H_2O$
    0.1 g of calcium acetate
    in 1 liter of 0.1 M Tris-Cl (pH 7.4)

IMPORTANT: Zincfix is unstable and must be freshly prepared.

Cells and Tissues

Tissue specimen

Special Equipment

Cryostat
Plastic tissue molds for OCT mounting
Rocking platform at 4°C
Silica gel for dry storage
Superfrost Plus glass slides (61661155, Fisher Scientific or Menzel Gläser)

METHOD

Dissection, Fixation, and Mounting

1. Chill PBS and Zincfix solutions on ice.

2. As soon as possible after surgery, or after dissection of an animal, transfer the specimen into ice-cold PBS.

3. Transfer the specimen to ice-cold Zincfix.
    The ratio of fixative:specimen volume should be >10.

4. Incubate the specimen in Zincfix overnight at 4°C with gentle rocking.

5. Transfer the specimen to a solution of 30% (w/v) sucrose in Zincfix. Incubate the specimen at 4°C until the specimen sinks to the bottom of the container.

6. Pour OCT into a tissue mold and place the specimen into the mold in the desired position and orientation.

7. Place the mold on dry ice until the OCT freezes.
    Store the mounted specimens at –80°C until sectioning.

Sectioning

8. Section the specimen at 10-μm thickness in a cryostat at –20°C.

9. Transfer the sections to Superfrost Plus glass slides.

10. Allow the sections to dry for 30 minutes at room temperature. Store sections at –80ºC in boxes containing silica gel.

    The following alternative procedure can be used for optimal morphology:

    i.   Chill the Superfrost glass slides to –20ºC, by leaving them in the cryostat for a few minutes.

    ii. Pick up each section on a cold Superfrost glass slide and fasten it by heating with a finger from the other side of the glass.

    iii. Leave the sections to freeze-dry in the cryostat for 30 minutes.

Preparation of Slides

11. Prepare 40 ml of Zincfix, 40 ml of 70% ethanol, 40 ml of 90% ethanol, 40 ml of 99.5% ethanol, and 40 ml of xylene in 50-ml tubes, and place the tubes on ice.

12. Remove the frozen slide from the –80ºC freezer (from Step 10).

13. Wash the slide for 5 minutes in ice-cold Zincfix. Use a pair of tweezers to rock the slide gently during the last 2 minutes of this wash.

14. Immerse the slide for the times shown in the following series of dehydrating agents:

Solvent	Time
70% ethanol	30 seconds
95% ethanol	30 seconds
99.5% ethanol	30 seconds
xylene	1 minute

15. Allow the slide to dry under a ventilating hood at room temperature.

    For best results, microdissection should follow immediately. If necessary, the slides can be stored for 18–20 hours (Scheidl et al. 2002). Typically, the specimen is applied to the glass slide or membrane and used immediately for LPC or LMPC; however, a "liquid cover" can be applied that improves visualization and prevents the specimen from becoming contaminated, but still allows LMPC and unrestricted molecular analysis (please see Protocol 9).

Protocol 9

Protection of Tissue Samples with a Liquid Coverslip

For microscropic analysis, histological sections are generally embedded in "mounting" medium and covered with a coverslip. However, the presence of the mounting medium and the coverslip impairs the recovery of samples using laser pressure catapulting. Unfortunately, dispensing with the medium and the coverslip interferes with the refraction of light and reduces the quality of the image required for precise identification of target cells. This problem can sometimes be alleviated by conventional histological or fluorescent staining of sections. When these tactics are inappropriate, target cells must be identified by virtue of their morphological characteristics. In these situations, a mounting medium that improves diffraction is recommended. For short-term improvement of visualization, either 70% ethanol or a solution of 1% glycerol in PBS may be dropped onto the section on the slide. The specimen is then allowed to dry prior to laser dissection.

An improved "liquid cover" reagent for tissue sections has been evaluated by PALM that polymerizes on the section, shows a refractive index similar to that of the tissue, and has no impact on subsequent molecular analysis. This "liquid coverslip" simultaneously serves to protect the sample to minimize contamination. The following protocol, provided by Tone Björnsen and Christer Bush (University Hospital, Department of Pathology, Tromsoe, Norway), is based on a nonhazardous solution and is easily sprayed onto the slide.

The "PALM Liquid Coverslip" still allows LMPC and unrestricted molecular analysis.

MATERIALS

IMPORTANT: Prepare all reagents used in this protocol with DEPC-treated H_2O (please see the information panel on **SPECIAL CONSIDERATIONS FOR WORKING WITH RNA** in Section 3).

Buffers and Solution

Please see Appendix 2 for components of stock solutions, buffers, and reagents.
Dilute stock solutions to the appropriate concentrations.

Isopropanol
Liquid coverslip solution (PLCS, PALM)
   Turpentine oil may be used to clean or remove unwanted residual PLCS.

Cells and Tissues

Tissue sections mounted on slides, as described in Protocol 6, 7, or 8

Special Equipment

Spray-pump bottle

METHOD

IMPORTANT: Perform all steps in a chemical fume hood to minimize contamination.

1. Dilute the liquid coverslip solution (PLCS) 1:5 or 1:10 in isopropanol.

2. Use a spray-pump bottle to deliver a thin stream of the diluted solution onto the membrane-mounted sections.

3. Lay out the slides in the chemical fume hood and allow the isopropanol to evaporate from the sections.

4. Proceed with microdissection and laser pressure catapulting.

   The sections can be stored at room temperature until further processing.

Isolation of Viable Cells after Laser Microdissection and Catapulting

Laser microbeam microdissection (LMM) and laser pressure catapulting (LPC) are methods designed to retrieve cells from fixed or frozen tissues (Meier-Ruge et al. 1976; Schindler et al. 1985; Kubo et al. 1995; Emmert-Buck et al. 1996; Bonner et al. 1997; Schütze and Lahr 1998; Schütze et al. 1998; Lahr 2000). Until recently, laser-based capture of living cells typically resulted in their destruction (Schindler et al. 1985); however, a modification of the LMPC laser technique and a newly developed cell culture protocol allow microdissection and "ejection" of viable single cells or cell clusters (Mayer et al. 2002). The protocol is used with cell cultures from which selected cells are microdissected, ejected, and recovered for further propagation. The viability of the captured and catapulted cells is not affected by the procedure.

To perform LMPC of living cells, the cells are cultivated in an assembled "round open closed" (ROC) chamber or in PALM DuplixDishes. Single cells or clusters of cells are circumscribed using a 20x objective lens. Undesired cells can be eliminated from the circumscribed area by a direct laser shot. LPC is performed with a single laser shot positioned at the border of the circumscribed film-cell stack. Even large cell-film stacks (e.g., 385 x 248 μm) can be catapulted (Figure 5-11). Microdissection of single living cells is achieved within seconds, and catapulting of cell clusters requires less than 2 minutes. The isolated and catapulted cells are suspended in an appropriate volume of supplemented and conditioned medium. If less than ten cells are isolated, it is best to bring them into close contact within a so-called "hanging droplet." The cells—still in a spherical shape—aggregate at the bottom of the droplet and start to form cell-cell contacts (Figure 5-12C).

The following day, the aggregated cells are plated in a droplet of supplemented medium on the bottom of a standard culture dish. Due to the spherical shape of the droplet, the aggregated cells are forced to move to the tension-free center of the droplet, and during 1 day in culture, the cells reassume their typical morphology (Figure 5-11C). Depending on the density of the plated cells and their physiological state before microdissection, proliferation

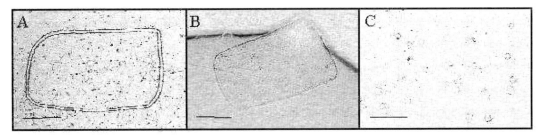

FIGURE 5-11. Microscopic illustration using LMPC to capture EJ28 cells. The images show the cells after microdissection (A), catapulted membrane with the cells (B), and cells after 1 day in culture (C). Bar, 100 μm. Objective lenses, 20x.

349

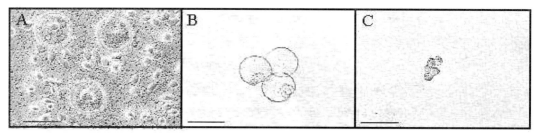

FIGURE 5-12. Images of pooled single EJ28 cells. (A) The cells after laser cutting; (B) three catapulted membrane areas with cells; (C) aggregated cells within the "hanging droplet." Bars: (A,B) 100 μm; (C) 50 μm. Objective lenses: (A,B) 20x; (C) 40x.

begins after 3 days (30 cells) up to 3 weeks (10 cells). The ability to destroy unwanted cells by precise laser shots and to recover living cells by LMPC allows homogeneous cell populations to be established from heterogeneous cell cultures (i.e., after transfection experiments). In principle, this protocol could be further adapted for the isolation of viable cells from tissues obtained from biopsies.

MATERIALS

CAUTION: Please see Appendix 3 for appropriate handling of materials marked with <!>.

Buffers and Solutions

Please see Appendix 2 for components of stock solutions, buffers, and reagents.
Dilute stock solutions to the appropriate concentrations.

Ethanol (absolute)
Hanks balanced salt solution (HBSS) (H 6136, Sigma-Aldrich)
Trypsin-EDTA solution (Sigma-Aldrich)

Cell Culture Media

Appropriate cell culture medium including 1x antibiotic-antimycotic solution (Sigma-Aldrich)
Conditioned medium for the desired cell line (Patterson and Chun 1977; Garcia-Moreno et al. 2002)
Supplemented medium (4 parts medium, 1 part conditioned medium)

Special Equipment

Culture dishes (plates and lids) for cell culture
Gassed CO_2 incubator for cell culture (Kendro Laboratory Products)
Inverted microscope (Axiovert 135, Zeiss)
Laser microscope, Robot-MicroBeam (PALM Microlaser Technologies AG, Bernried, Germany)
Microfuge tubes (PALM Microlaser Technologies)
Polyethylene-naphthalene membrane (PALM Microlaser Technologies)
ROC (round open closed) Chamber (PeCon and LaCon, Erbach-Bach, Germany) or PALM DuplixDishes (PALM Microlaser Technologies)
UV light, specifically for use within the safety hood (Kendro Laboratory Products) <!>

METHOD

IMPORTANT: To reduce the chance of contamination, wear gloves when handling cell cultures. Do not keep the cell cultures outside the incubator longer than necessary.

1. Assemble the ROC chamber as described by the manufacturer, but in addition, insert a polyethylene-naphthalene membrane.

2. Apply a droplet of absolute ethanol onto the glass bottom of the chamber to facilitate membrane mounting.

3. Cover the glass bottom of the ROC chamber with the membrane.

4. Expose the opened chamber with the membrane to UV light for 20 minutes to change the nature of the membrane from hydrophobic to hydrophilic.

5. Complete the assembly of the ROC chamber, and autoclave it for 20 minutes at 121°C (liquid cycle).

Cell Culture

6. Seed the cultured cells at the desired density to ideally produce a semiconfluent monolayer in an appropriate culture medium onto the membrane-covered base of the ROC chamber. Culture the cells for 1–2 days at 37°C in a gassed incubator. The cells are now ready for microdissection.

Lasxer Microdissection and Catapulting

7. Remove the medium completely from the ROC chamber before laser microdissection.

8. Microdissect the desired cell sample on the membrane as described in the informational material supplied by PALM.

    The parameters for laser cutting depend on the particular laser-microscope system and must be optimized.

9. Carefully pipette 10 μl of HBSS on top of the selected cells to facilitate LPC. Be careful not to wash away the microdissected specimen.

10. Pipette 5 μl of HBSS into the center of the cap of a microfuge tube and place the cap directly above the selected cells in the ROC chamber without using the manipulator.

    Alternatively, use a PALM Petriperm Holder in combination with the CapMover to capture cells.

11. Catapult the cell membrane stack with one single laser shot that is positioned at the border of the circumscribed film-cell stack.

    The energy settings should be sufficiently high to catapult the microdissected cells with the membrane into a cap. Even large cell-film stacks (e.g., 385 x 248 μm) can be catapulted.

12. After LPC, remove the ROC chamber from the microscope stage and inspect the catapulted cells in the cap.

    If several experiments are to be performed, allow the cells in the ROC chamber to recover from drying by adding medium back to the cells, and then repeat the microdissection as described beginning in Step 7. After several microdissection events, the fluid/medium enters the microspace between the membrane and the glass bottom of the ROC chamber, which makes further microdissection and catapulting more and more difficult and finally impossible.

Recovery of Catapulted Cells

13. Cover the catapulted cells in the cap with 25 μl of HBSS.

14. Seal the cells in the cap by inverting the tube onto the cap. Store the cells up to 30 minutes at room temperature to allow them to detach from the membrane.

15. Recover the cells by centrifuging the tube in a microfuge at 8000*g* for 1 minute at room temperature and discard the supernatant.

16. Resuspend the cells in 20 μl of trypsin-EDTA solution and incubate them for 10 minutes at room temperature.

17. Centrifuge the cells in a microfuge at 8000*g* for 1 minute at room temperature.

18. After centrifugation, resuspend the trypsinized cells in 15 μl (<10 cells) or 20 μl of supplemented medium (4 parts medium, 1 part conditioned medium).

    If there are less than 10 catapulted cells in the tube, proceed to Step 19; if there are 10 or more cells in the suspension, proceed to Step 23.

Cultivation of Cells

19. If less than 10 cells were recovered in the suspension, form a "hanging droplet" by transfering the 15-μl drops containing the cells to the inside of an inverted lid of a culture dish.

20. Turn the lid over and place it on the bottom culture dish. This results in "hanging droplets" in which single cells come in close contact and start aggregation.

21. Incubate the cells within the "hanging droplet" in a gassed incubator overnight at 37ºC.

22. After incubation, invert the lid again and add 5 μl of supplemented medium to the droplet (total: 20 μl).

23. Use a sterile micropipette to transfer the 2-μl droplets containing the cell suspension to the bottom of a culture dish, either alone or with sufficient space between other droplets. To avoid the possibility of cross-contamination of cells from individual droplets, outline each group of cells with silicone glue or use cloning rings.

24. Incubate the cells overnight at 37ºC.

25. After incubation, mark the droplets on the bottom of the culture dish with a permanent marker to facilitate tracing of the cells.

26. Remove the medium and fill the culture plate with 4–10 ml of fresh supplemented medium, depending on the diameter of the culture dish.

    The growing cells can be observed during the following days and weeks. Regular changes of cell culture medium are recommended.

REFERENCES

Banks R.E., Dunn M.J., Forbes M.A., Stanley A., Pappin D., Naven T., Gough M., Harnden P., and Selby P.J. 1999. The potential use of laser capture microdissection to selectively obtain distinct populations of cells for proteomic analysis—Preliminary findings. *Electrophoresis* **20:** 689–700.

Becker I., Becker K.F., Rohrl M.H., and Hofler H. 1997. Laser-assisted preparation of single cells from stained histological slides for gene analysis. *Histochem. Cell Biol.* **108:** 447–451.

Becker I., Becker K.F., Rohrl M.H., Minkus G., Schütze K., and Hofler H. 1996. Single-cell mutation analysis of tumors from stained histologic slides. *Lab. Invest.* **75:** 801–807.

Bernsen M.R., Dijkman H.B., de Vries E., Figdor C.G., Ruiter D.J., Adema G.J., and van Muijen G.N. 1998. Identification of multiple mRNA and DNA sequences from small tissue samples isolated by laser-assisted microdissection. *Lab. Invest.* **78:** 1267–1273.

Bertheau P., Plassa L.F., Lerebours F., de Roquancourt A., Turpin E., Lidereau R., de Thé H., and Janin A. 2001. Allelic loss detection in inflammatory breast cancer: Improvement with laser microdissection. *Lab Invest.* **81:** 1397–1402.

Böhm M. and Wieland I. 1997. Analysis of tumour-specific alterations in native specimens by PCR: How to procure the tumour cells. *Int. J Oncol.* **10:** 11–139.

Böhm M., Wieland I., Schütze K., and Rübben H. 1997. MicroBeam MOMeNT—Non contact laser microdissection of membrane-mounted native tissue. *Am. J. Pathol.* **151:** 63–67.

Bonner R.F., Emmert-Buck M., Cole K., Pohida T., Chuaqui R., Goldstein S., and Liotta L.A. 1997. Laser capture microdissection: Molecular analysis of tissue. *Science* **278:** 1481–1483.

Buerger H., Gebhardt F., Schmidt H., Beckmann A., Hutmacher K., Simon R., Lelle R., Boecker W., and Burkhard B. 2000a. Length and loss of heterozygosity of an intron 1 polymorphic sequence of *egfr* is related to cytogenetic alterations and epithelial growth factor receptor expression. *Cancer Res.* **60:** 854–857.

Buerger H., Simon R., Schafer K.L., Diallo R., Littmann R., Poremba C., van Diest P.J., Dockhorm-Dworniczak B., and Boecker W. 2000b. Genetic relation of lobular carcinoma in situ, ductal carcinoma in situ, and associated invasive carcinoma of the breast. *Mol. Pathol.* **53:** 118–121.

Burgemeister R., Schütze K., Minderer S., and Gloning K.-P. 1999. Single fetal cells separated by the Laser MicroBeam technique. *BIOforum Int.* **3:** 119–121.

Burton M.P., Schneider B.G., Brown R., Escamilla-Ponce N., and Gulley M.L. 1998. Comparison of histologic stains for use in PCR analysis of microdissected, paraffin-embedded tissues. *BioTechniques* **24:** 86–92.

Dietmaier W., Gänsbauer S., Beyser K., Renke B., Hartmann A., Rümmele P., Jauch K.-W., Hofstädter F., and Rüschoff J. 2000. Microsatellite instability in tumor and nonneoplastic colorectal cells from hereditary non-polyposis colorectal cancer and sporadic high microsatellite-instable tumor patients. *Pathobiology* **68:** 227–231.

Emmert-Buck M.R., Bonner R.F., Smith P.D., Chuaqui R.F., Zhuang Z., Goldstein S.R., Weiss R.A., and Liotta L.A. 1996. Laser capture microdissection. *Science* **274:** 998–1001.

Emmert-Buck M.R., Lubensky I.A., Chuaqui R.F., Debelenko L.V., Vocke C.D., Merino M.J., Duray P.H., Linehan W.M., Liotta L.A., and Zhuang Z. 1998. Applications of tissue microdissection in molecular pathology: Principles and guidelines. *Methods Mol. Med.* **14:** 269–298.

Emmert-Buck M.R., Gillespie J.W., Paweletz C.P., Ornstein D.K., Basrur V., Appella E., Wang Q.H., Huang J., Hu N., Taylor P., and Petricoin III E.F. 2000. An approach to proteomic analysis of human tumors. *Mol. Carcinog.* **27:** 158–165.

Fend F., Emmert-Buck M.R., Chuaqui R., Cole K., Lee J., Liotta L.A., and Raffeld M. 1999a. Immuno-LCM: Laser capture microdissection of immunostained frozen sections for mRNA analysis. *Am. J. Pathol.* **154:** 61–66.

Fend F., Quintanilla-Martinez L., Kumar S., Beaty M.W., Blum L., Sorbara L., Jaffe E.S., and Raffeld M. 1999b. Composite low grade B-cell lymphomas with two immunophenotypically distinct cell populations are true biclonal lymphomas. A molecular analysis using laser capture microdissection. *Am. J. Pathol.* **154:** 1857–1866.

Fink L., Seeger W., Ermert L., Hänze J., Stahl U., Grimminger F., Kummer W., and Bohle R.M. 1998. Real-time quantitative RT-PCR after laser-assisted cell picking. *Nat. Med.* **11:** 1329–1333.

Fink L., Kohlhoff S., Stein M.M., Hanze J., Weissmann N., Rose F., Akkayagil E., Manz D., Grimminger F., Seeger W., and Bohle R.M. 2002. cDNA array hybridization after laser-assisted microdissection from nonneoplastic tissue. *Am. J. Pathol.* **160:** 81–90.

Garcia-Moreno C., Mendez-Davila C., de La Piedra C., Castro-Errecaborde N.A., and Traba M.L. 2002.

Human prostatic carcinoma cells produce an increase in the synthesis of interleukin-6 by human osteoblasts. *Prostate* **50:** 241–246.

Gillespie J.W., Ahram M., Best C.J., Swalwell J.I., Krizman D.B., Petricoin E.F., Liotta L.A., and Emmert-Buck M.R. 2001. The role of tissue microdissection in cancer research. *Cancer J.* **7:** 32–39.

Gillespie J.W., Best C.J.M., Bischel V.E., Cole K.A., Greenhut S.F., Hewitt S.M., Ahram M., Gathright Y.B., Merino M.J., Strausberg R.L, Epstein J.I., Hamilton S.R., Gannot G., Baibakova G.V., Calvert V.S., Flaig M.J., Chuaqui R.F., Herring J.C., Pfeifer J., Petricoin, E.F., Linehan W.M., Duray P.H., Bova G.S., and Emmert-Buck M.R. 2002. Evaluation of non-formalin tissue fixation for molecular profiling studies. *Am. J. Pathol.* **160:** 449–457.

Gjerdrum L.M., Lielpetere I., Rasmussen L.M., Bendix K., and Hamilton-Dutoit S. 2001. Laser-assisted microdissection of membrane-mounted paraffin sections for polymerase chain reaction analysis: Identification of cell populations using immunohistochemistry and in situ hybridization. *J. Mol. Diagn.* **3:** 105–110.

Glöckner S., Lehmann U., Wilke N., Kleeberger W., Länger F., and Kreipe H. 2000. Detection of gene amplification in intraductal and infiltrating breast cancer by laser-assisted microdissection and quantitative real-time PCR. *Pathobiology* **68:** 173–179.

Glöckner S., Lehmann U., Wilke N., Kleeberger W., Länger F., and Kreipe H. 2001. Amplification of growth regulatory genes in intraductal breast cancer is associated with higher nuclear grade but not with the progression to invasiveness. *Lab Invest.* **81:** 565–571.

Going J.J. and Lamb R.F. 1996. Practical histological microdissection for PCR analysis. *J. Pathol.* **179:** 121–124.

Goldsworthy S.M., Stockton P.S., Trempus C.S., Foley J.F., and Maronpot R.R. 1999. Effects of fixation on RNA extraction and amplification from laser capture microdissected tissue. *Mol. Carcinog.* **25:** 86–91.

Heel K. and Dawkins H. 2001. Laser microdissection and optical tweezers in research. *Today's Life Sci.* March/April: 42–48.

Hiller T., Snell L., and Watson P.H. 1996. Microdissection RT-PCR analysis of gene expression in pathologically defined frozen tissue sections. *BioTechniques* **21:** 38–42.

Hoffmann M., Olson K., Cavender A., Pasqualini R., Gaikwad J., and D'Souza R.N. 2001. Gene expression in a pure population of odontoblasts isolated by laser-capture microdissection. *J. Dent. Res.* **80:** 1963–1967.

Imamichi Y., Lahr G., and Wedlich D. 2001. Laser-mediated microdissection of paraffin sections from *Xenopus* embryos allows detection of tissue-specific expressed mRNAs. *Dev. Genes Evol.* **211:** 361–366.

Kaserer K., Schmaus J., Bethge U., Migschitz B., Fasching S., Walch A., Herbst F., Teleky B., and Wrba F. 2000. Staining patterns of p53 immunohistochemistry and their biological significance in colorectal cancer. *J. Pathol.* **190:** 450–456.

Kleeberger W., Rothämel T., Glöckner S., Lehmann U., and Kreipe H. 2000. Laser-assisted microdissection and short tandem repeat PCR for the investigation of graft chimerism after solid organ transplantation. *Pathobiology* **68:** 196–201.

Kubo Y., Klimek F., Kikuchi Y., Bannasch P., and Hino O. 1995. Early detection of Knudson's two-hits in preneoplastic renal cells of the Eker rat model by the laser microdissection procedure. *Cancer Res.* **55:** 989–990.

Lahr G. 2000. RT-PCR from archival single cells is a suitable method to analyse specific gene expression. *Lab Invest.* **80:** 1477–1479.

Lahr G., Stich M., Schutze K., Blumel P., Posl H., and Nathrath W.B. 2000. Diagnosis of papillary thyroid carcinoma is facilitated by using an RT-PCR approach on laser-microdissected archival material to detect RET oncogene activation. *Pathobiology* **68:** 218–226.

Lehmann U., Glöckner S., Kleeberger W., Feist H., von Wasielewski R., and Kreipe H. 2000. Detection of gene amplification in archival breast cancer specimens by laser-assisted microdissection and quantitative real-time polymerase chain reaction. *Am. J. Pathol.* **156:** 1855–1864.

Ling G., Persson A., Berne B., Uhlén M., Lundeberg J., and Pónten F. 2001. Persistent p53 mutations in single cells from normal human skin. *Am. J. Pathol.* **159:** 1247–1253.

Luo L., Salunga R.C., Guo H., Bittner A., Joy K.C., Galindo J.E., Xiao H., Rogers K.E., Wan J.S., Jackson M.R., and Erlander M.G. 1999. Gene expression profiles of laser-captured adjacent neuronal subtypes. *Nat. Med.* **5:** 117–122.

Mayer A., Stich M., Brocksch D., Schütze K., and Lahr G. 2002. Going *in vivo* with laser-microdissection. *Methods Enzymol.* (in press).

Meier-Ruge W., Bielser W., Remy E., Hillenkamp F., Nitsche R., and Unsöld R. 1976. The laser in the Lowry technique for microdissection of freeze-dried tissue slices. *Histochem. J.* **8:** 387–401.

Nagasawa Y., Takenaka M., Matsuoka Y., Imai E., and Hori M. 2000. Quantitation of mRNA expression in glomeruli using laser-manipulated microdissection and laser pressure catapulting. *Kidney Int.* **57:** 717–723.

Noack F., Helmecke D., Rosenberg R., Thorban S., Nekarda H., Fink U., Lewald J., Schütze K., Stich M., Harbeck N., Magdolen V., Graeff H., and Schmitt M. 1999. CD87-positive tumor cells in bone marrow aspirates identified by confocal laser scan fluorescence microscopy. *Int. J. Oncol.* **15:** 617–623.

Ohyama H., Zhang X., Kohno Y., Alevizos I., Posner M., Wong D.T., and Todd R. 2000. Laser capture microdissection-generated target sample for high-density oligonucleotide array hybridization. *BioTechniques* **29:** 530–536.

Ornstein D.K., Gillespie J.W., Paweletz C.P., Duray P.H., Herring J., Vocke C.D., Topalian S.L., Bostwick D.G., Linehan W.M., Petricoin III E.F., and Emmert-Buck M.R. 2000. Proteomic analysis of laser capture microdissected human prostate cancer and in vitro prostate cell lines. *Electrophoresis* **21:** 2235–2242.

Patterson P.H. and Chun L.L. 1977. The induction of acetylcholine synthesis in primary cultures of dissociated rat sympathetic neurons. II. *Dev. Biol.* **60:** 473–481.

Persson A.E., Ling G., Williams C., Bäckvall H., Pontén J., Pontén F., and Lundeberg J. 2000. Analysis of p53 mutations in single cells obtained from histological tissue sections. *Anal. Biochem.* **287:** 25–31.

Peterson L.A., Brown M.R., Carlisle A.J., Kohn E.C., Liotta L.A., Emmert-Buck M.R., and Krizman D.B. 1998. An improved method for construction of directionally cloned cDNA libraries from microdissected cells. *Cancer Res.* **58:** 5326–5328.

Ponten F., Williams C., Ling G., Ahmadian A., Nister M., Lundeberg J., Ponten J., and Uhlen M. 1997. Genomic analysis of single cells from human basal cell cancer using laser-assisted capture microscopy. *Mutat. Res.* **382:** 45–55.

Scheidl S.J., Nilsson S., Kalèn M., Hellström M., Takemoto M., Hakansson J., and Lindahl P. 2002. mRNA expression profiling of laser microbeam microdissected cells from slender embryonic structures. *Am. J. Pathol.* **160:** 801–813.

Schindler M. 1998. Select, microdissect, and eject. *Nat. Biotechnol.* **16:** 719–720.

Schindler M., Allen M.L., Olinger M.R., and Holland J.F. 1985. Automated analysis and survival selection of anchorage-dependent cells under normal growth conditions. *Cytometry* **6:** 368–374.

Schütze K. and Lahr G. 1998. Identification of expressed genes by laser-mediated manipulation of single cells. *Nat. Biotechnol.* **16:** 737–742.

Schütze K., Pösl H., and Lahr G. 1998. Laser micromanipulation systems as universal tools in molecular biology and medicine. *Mol. Cell. Biol.* **44:** 735–746.

Shibata D., Hawes D., Li Z.H., Hernandez A.M., Spruck C.H., and Nichols P.W. 1992. Specific genetic analysis of microscopic tissue after selective ultraviolet radiation fractionation and the polymerase chain reaction. *Am. J. Pathol.* **141:** 539–543.

Simone N.L., Bonner R.F., Gillespie J.W., Emmert-Buck M.R., and Liotta L.A. 1998. Laser-capture microdissection: Opening the microscopic frontier to molecular analysis. *Trends Genet.* **14:** 272–276.

Specht K., Richter T., Müller U., Walch A., Werner M., and Höfler H. 2001. Quantitative gene expression analysis in microdissected archival formalin-fixed and paraffin-embedded tumor tissue. *Am. J. Pathol.* **158:** 419–429.

Srinivasan R. 1986. Ablation of polymers and biological tissue by ultraviolet lasers. *Science* **234:** 559–565.

Stoehr R., Hartmann A., Hindlmeyer E., Mürle K., Wieland W., and Knuechel R. 2000. Oligoclonality of early lesions of the urothelium as determined by microdissection-supported genetic analysis. *Pathobiology* **68:** 165–172.

Suarez-Quian C.A., Goldstein S.R., Pohida T., Smith P.D., Peterson J.I., Wellner E., Ghany M., and Bonner R.F. 1999. Laser capture microdissection of single cells from complex tissues. *BioTechniques* **26:** 328–335.

Vona G., Sabile A., Louha M., Sitruk V., Romana S., Schütze K., Capron F., Franco D., Pazzagli M., Vekemans M., Lacour B., Bréchot C., and Paterlini-Bréchot P. 2000. Isolation by size of epithelial tumor cells. A new method for the immunomorphological and molecular characterization of circulating tumor cells. *Am. J. Pathol.* **156:** 57–63.

Walch A., Specht K., Smida J., Aubele M., Zitzelsberger H., Höfler H., and Werner M. 2001. Tissue microdissection techniques in quantitative genome and gene expression analyses. *Histochem. Cell Biol.* **115:** 269–276.

Westphal G., Burgemeister R., Friedemann G., Wellmann A., Wernert N., Wollscheid V., Becker B., Vogt T., Knüchel R., Stolz W., and Schütze K. 2002. Non-contact laser catapulting—A basic procedure for functional genomics and proteomics. *Methods Enzymol.* (in press).

WWW RESOURCES

http://cgap-mf.nih.gov/index.html Molecular Profiling Initiative

http://www.arctur.com   Arcturus Systems for Microgenomics homepage

http://www.arctur.com/products/picopure_rna_isolation.htm Arcturus PicoPureM RNA isolation Kit

http://www.PALM-Microlaser.com P.A.L.M. Mirolaser Technologies homepage

http://www.qiagen.com/literature/brochures/pcr/pdf/pcrcha28.pdf   DiLella A.G. 2001. Department of Pharmacology, Merck Research Laboratories. Analysis of RNA from laser capture microdissected cells.

http://www.stratagene.com/cellbio/purification/absolutely_rna_micro.htm   Stratagene Absolutely RNA Microprep Kit

6 Using Microarrays for Genomic Analysis

INTRODUCTION

The vast amounts of sequence and polymorphism data now available from many organisms provide extraordinarily sensitive tools to study the structure and the function of genomes. The preceding sections of this manual have dealt with the use of microarrays to study the expression profiles of specific cell types and tissue samples. The collection of protocols in this section provide microarray-based strategies for three different types of genomic analysis: determining genomic copy number, detecting and mapping polymorphisms, and mapping DNA-protein interactions on the genome.

Part 1 of this section describes three approaches for assessing DNA copy number using microarrays. In the first two approaches, comparative genomic hybridization (CGH) is performed using the full complexity of the genomic DNA, represented either as cDNA clones (Protocol 1) or as BAC (bacterial artificial chromosome) clones (Protocols 2 and 3). In the third method, the sequence complexity of total genomic DNA is substantially reduced by the use of genomic representations, in an approach known as representational difference analysis (RDA).

Part 2 provides protocols for detecting and mapping mutations and/or genomic sequence variations. Reproducibly ordered arrays of oligonucleotide probes representing particular known sequences are well-suited for the mapping and analysis of mammalian genomes. The recent discovery and identification of large numbers of single-nucleotide polymorphisms (SNPs) in human and other genomes have provided an extensive map of physical markers that densely cover the genome. These features are the basis of various methods for detecting novel spontaneous mutations or for identifying heritable SNPs in specific genomic regions. The protocols in Part 2 describe SNP detection using either single-base extension (SBE)-Tag (Protocol 6) or generic tag arrays (Protocol 7), sequence variant detection by resequencing (Protocol 8), and the analysis of loss of heterozygosity (LOH) using SNP arrays (Protocol 9).

Finally, Part 3 describes methods for microarray hybridization that facilitate the mapping of DNA-protein interactions (Protocols 10 and 11). These approaches are based on the use of microarrays representing essentially every yeast intergenic (promoter) sequence. DNA recovered from specifically immunoprecipitated chromatin is amplified, labeled, and hybridized to the array. Although this method was developed for the yeast genome, it can be adapted for use with any genome whose sequence is completely established or for the interrogation of specific regions.

For further information on each of these methods of analysis, please see the Introductions to the various parts of the section.

Part 1: Microarray-based Detection of DNA Copy Number

INTRODUCTION

Comparative genomic hybridization (CGH) identifies and maps sites of variation in DNA copy number throughout the genome (Kallioniemi et al. 1992, 1993; du Manoir et al. 1993) in a single measurement. In CGH as originally developed, total genomic DNAs from two (or more) cell populations are labeled with different fluorescent dyes and hybridized to metaphase chromosome spreads prepared from a normal individual. The genomic DNAs can be obtained from fresh, frozen, or fixed tissue specimens. High concentrations of unlabeled repetitive DNA, typically C_0t-1 DNA, are included to block hybridization of repetitive sequences. The binding ratio of sequences from the different cell populations at the locations on the chromosomes to which they are complementary is proportional to their relative initial concentrations in the hybridization mixture. Quantitative calculation of the hybridization ratios along the genomic map provided by the chromosomes therefore supplies information on the relative copy numbers of different sequences in the genomes being hybridized. If one of the cell populations has a "normal" diploid genome, typically called the reference, then the ratio of signals emitted from different loci provides a map of variation in copy number in the "test" genome(s).

The development of CGH was motivated by the important contributions of variations in DNA copy number to problems of both reproductive and somatic health. For example, constitutional deletions and duplications at specific genomic sites are frequently involved in abnormal fetal development, leading to conditions such as Down's syndrome. In cancer, multiple alterations arise in the genomes of somatic cells as the malignancy develops. Some of these alterations involve localized loss or gain of DNA copy number and are thus potentially detectable by CGH. Because the losses reduce gene expression, they contribute to, for example, inactivation of tumor suppressor genes. Conversely, gains in copy number may increase the level of expression of genes that stimulate cellular growth. Some of the observed gains in copy number result from high-level amplification of focal regions of the genome that contain known oncogenes; others may indicate the locations of new oncogenes.

In the years since its inception, CGH has provided a wealth of information regarding regions of DNA amplification and deletion in cancer cell lines and tumor samples (for examples, please see the publications at http://www.progenetix.net/). Analyses of CGH have also directly contributed to the identification of genes with important roles in the development or progression of cancer (e.g., please see Visakorpi et al. 1995a,b; Monni et al. 1996; Hemminki et al. 1997; Collins et al. 1998). However, the mapping accuracy and the detection of small aberrations have been limited by the low cytogenetic resolution provided by the use of metaphase chromosomes as the mapping skeleton. In addition, although high-level amplifications of limited genomic regions are easily detectable, the ratios of signals emitted by two different samples do not necessarily yield a quantitative measure of the fold increase in copy number.

Microarray implementations of CGH (Solinas-Toldo et al. 1997; Pinkel et al. 1998; Pollack et al. 1999) have the potential to overcome many of the limitations of traditional cytogenetic CGH. Using arrays of mapped genomic clones permits the resolution of the measurements to be determined by the spacing of the clones on the array and their size. However, the exacting performance requirements for accurate measurement of copy number make array CGH a very demanding microarray technology. For example, one would like to be able to detect biologically relevant gains and losses of single-copy DNA in specimens that consist of more than one cell type, for example, a mixture of tumor and normal cells. This can only be achieved if CGH is sufficiently sensitive to reliably detect a ratio change of less than a factor of 2. In mammalian systems, this level of precision must be achieved for a nucleic acid preparation, the genomic DNA, which is at least ten times as complex as the corresponding mRNA pool.

Part 1 meets the challenges of detecting DNA copy number alteration. In the first two approaches, total genomic DNA is hybridized to arrays containing either:

- Polymerase chain reaction (PCR)-amplified cDNAs (Protocol 1) (Pollack et al 1999). The same cDNA microarrays can be used for expression and genomic DNA analysis, which is a significant advantage when high-quality cDNA arrays are available. Averaging fluorescence ratios from several arrayed cDNAs that are neighbors on the chromosome may permit higher-quality measurements of single-copy gain and loss.

- Genomic libraries constructed in high-capacity vectors such as P1s and BACs (Protocols 2 and 3). The use of arrays containing very large genomic inserts (Salinas-Toldo et al. 1997; Pinkel et al. 1998; Albertson et al. 2000; Bruder et al. 2001) is based on experimental observation that the intensity of the hybridization signal increases as the complexity of the DNA in the array spot is increased. Because BAC arrays provide sufficient precision to detect changes in single-copy sequences that affect only a fraction of a clone, arrays of overlapping BACs can provide resolution down to at least 50 kb (Albertson et al. 2000).

In the third method, the sequence complexity of total genomic DNA is substantially reduced by inter-*Alu* PCR (Geschwind et al. 1998) or by using restriction enzymes and PCR to generate genomic representations, an approach known as representational difference analysis (RDA) (Lucito et al. 2000) (Protocols 4 and 5). Labeled genomic representations are hybridized to arrays made from individual DNA fragments that have been cloned from similarly produced genomic representations of reduced sequence.

Table 6-1 summarizes the strength and weaknesses of the three methods currently available for array CGH. None of them currently hold a dominant position in the field and each may have advantages in particular circumstances. Their suitability for specific purposes can best be assessed by evaluation of the primary publications.

TABLE 6-1. Comparison of Different Array CGH Platforms

Platform	Array elements	Element complexity	Sample complexity	Description	Advantages/Disadvantages	References
Large insert genomic clones	BACs, PACs, P1s, cosmids	~40–150 kb	high	Arrays are constructed by spotting DNA isolated from individual clones.	Strong hybridization signal due to high complexity of spotted DNAs. Mapped BACs are progressively easier to obtain as a result of ongoing progress in analysis of the sequences of human and mouse genomes. However, preparing sufficient DNA from large-insert cloning vectors is difficult, and spotting of clones requires fragmentation of long DNA molecules.	Solinas-Toldo et al. (1997); Pinkel et al. (1998); Albertson et al. (2000)
Representations of large-insert genomic clones	Fragment pools representing genomic clones such as BACs, PACs, P1s, cosmids.	Initial sequence complexity of the clone is reduced by the methods used to create representations.	high	Ligation-mediated PCR or DOP-PCR is used to generate representations of genomic clones.	Requires only small amounts of DNA to be isolated from the clones. Ligation-mediated PCR maintains the complexity of the parental clones and hence has the ability to provide results identical to those obtained from the use of entire clones. Signal intensities decrease if the representation substantially reduces the complexity of the material in the spot.	Snijders et al. (2001; Ligation-mediated PCR); Hodgson et al. (2001; DOP-PCR)
cDNA microarrays	PCR-amplified cDNAs and ESTs	0.5–2 kb	high	Arrays are constructed by spotting PCR-amplified cDNAs.	Using commercially available libraries, well-established spotting methods allows parallel measurements of DNA copy number and gene expression. cDNA/EST libraries are not complete, and not all ESTs are accurately mapped. Averaging ratios from several array elements adjacent on the chromosome may be required to accurately identify regions of single-copy gain and loss. Sensitivity for detecting heterologous loss is less than that obtained with BAC arrays.	Pollack et al. (1999)

(Continued on following page.)

TABLE 6-1. (*Continued*)

Platform	Array elements	Element complexity	Sample complexity	Description	Advantages/Disadvantages	References
Inter-*Alu* PCR arrays	Inter-*Alu* PCR fragments	0.2–2 kb	reduced	Mapped genomic clones are amplified by inter-*Alu* PCR. Individual fragments are cloned and arrayed. Test and reference genomic DNAs can be similarly amplified, labeled, and hybridized to the array.	Preparation of DNA from genomic clones is simplified, and the DNA to be analyzed is significantly enriched. Detection of single-copy changes requires averaging over several neighboring elements of the array.	Geschwind et al. (1998)
Genomic representation arrays	Representational PCR fragments	0.2–2 kb	reduced	Genomic DNA digested with restriction enzyme(s) is ligated to primers and amplified. Individual amplified fragments are used as array elements. The complexity of the array is 2–40-fold less than that of the original genomic DNA. Labeled representations of test and reference DNAs are prepared with same restriction enzymes and hybridized to the array.	Production of the representation provides significant amplification, so that only small amounts of DNA are required for analysis. Map positions of array elements must be established. Test and reference DNAs must be from the same person unless detection of polymorphisms is desired.	Lucito et al. (1998, 2000)

Comparative Genomic Hybridization Using cDNA Microarrays

Jonathan R. Pollack

Stanford University School of Medicine, Stanford, California 94305

cDNA microarrays provide an attractive platform for array CGH analysis in part because the technology is so familiar and robust. For several years, high-density cDNA microarrays, containing tens of thousands of cDNAs, have been routinely printed and used in expression analysis (please see Section 1). These same arrays can be used for CGH, where they provide very high mapping resolution, ultimately gene by gene and exon by exon, for ratiometric measurement of variation in copy number of genomic DNA. Furthermore, the parallel analysis of mRNA expression patterns, using the same microarrays, provides ready opportunity to compare and correlate DNA copy number with variation in gene expression, both genome-wide and in targeted chromosomal regions. This can provide a basis for prioritizing candidate cancer genes for further study; for example, within amplicons, oncogenes are expected to be highly expressed when amplified.

cDNA microarrays have been used extensively to characterize mRNA levels in cancerous cells (DeRisi et al. 1996; Alizadeh et al. 2000; Perou et al. 2000). Because the sequence complexity of genomic DNA is at least an order of magnitude higher than the sequence space of the mRNA population of a mammalian cell, the use of cDNA microarrays to measure variation in the copy number of genomic DNA requires exacting protocols to achieve the necessary sensitivity and precision.

The protocol detailed here describes the preparation of genomic probes and their hybridization to cDNA microarrays for high-resolution CGH analysis (schematically depicted in Figure 6-1). These methods have demonstrated that CGH using cDNA microarrays has sufficient sensitivity to detect single-copy loss of genomic DNA sequences with high precision (coefficient of variation ~10%) (Pollack et al. 1999). For special considerations for setup of the protocol and analysis of the data, please refer to the panel on TROUBLESHOOTING at the end of the protocol.

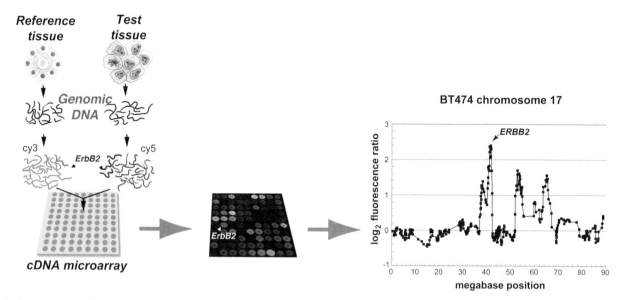

FIGURE 6-1. Schematic representation of CGH to cDNA microarrays. Test and reference genomic DNAs are labeled with two different fluors and cohybridized to a cDNA microarray. For each cDNA on the array, the ratio of intensity between the two fluors represents the relative genomic copy number for that gene. Fluorescence ratios can be plotted against chromosomal map position to obtain a high-resolution map of the variation in DNA copy number in the test sample. The results shown here describe DNA copy number variation for human breast cancer cell line BT474 across chromosome 17. (Adapted, with permission, from Pollack et al. 1999.)

MATERIALS

CAUTION: Please see Appendix 3 for appropriate handling of materials marked with <!>.

Buffers and Solutions

Please see Appendix 2 for components of stock solutions, buffers, and reagents.
Dilute stock solutions to the appropriate concentrations.

EDTA (0.5 M, pH 8.0)
2.5x Random primer mix
    125 mM Tris-Cl (pH 6.8)
    12.5 mM MgCl$_2$
    25 mM β-mercaptoethanol <!>
    750 μg/ml random octamers
        These components can be assembled separately, or the complete buffer can purchased as part of
        the BioPrime DNA Labeling System (18094-011, Invitrogen).
SDS (10%) <!>
20x SSC
TE (pH 7.4)

Enzymes and Buffers

Klenow fragment of *E. coli* DNA polymerase I (high concentration, 40–50 units/μl)
    The use of high-concentration Klenow fragment significantly enhances labeling efficiency. The
    enzyme can be purchased as part of the BioPrime DNA Labeling System (18094-011, Invitrogen),
    or separately from New England Biolabs (M0210M).

Nucleic Acids and Oligonucleotides

cDNA microarrays

cDNA microarrays, spotted on poly-L-lysine-coated glass microscope slides, can be fabricated in-house (please see Section 2, Protocol 2) or purchased commercially. Microarrays should be processed, prior to hybridization, by blocking unbound poly-L-lysine with succinic anhydride treatment (please see Section 2, Protocol 1). The use of glass surfaces coated with materials other than poly-L-lysine may result in increased background fluorescence (please see the panel on TROUBLESHOOTING at the end of this protocol).

Cy5-labeled dCTP and Cy3-labeled dCTP (1 mM stock solutions) (PA55021 and PA53021, Amersham Biosciences)

dNTP-labeling solution containing dATP, dGTP, dTTP (each at a concentration of 1.2 mM) and dCTP (at a concentration of 0.6 mM in H_2O or in TE [pH 8.0])

Use ultrapure dNTPs (e.g., 27-2035-01, Amersham Biosciences). For advice on preparing and storing stock solutions of dNTPs, please see Appendix 2.

The dNTP-labeling mix supplied with the BioPrime DNA Labeling System (Invitrogen) contains biotinylated dCTP and should not be used with this protocol.

Human C_0t-1 DNA (1 μg/μl stock solution) (15279-011, Invitrogen)

Poly(dA):Poly(dT) (P 9764, Sigma)

Prepare a 5 mg/ml stock solution in TE (pH 7.4).

Reference DNA of known concentration

Genomic DNAs prepared from normal male or normal female peripheral blood leukocytes are suitable for genomic DNA references for male and female test samples, respectively. The reference DNAs and test DNAs should be prepared by the same methods.

Test genomic DNA of known concentration

Genomic DNA prepared by any number of standard methods is of sufficient quality for array CGH analysis (please see the additional protocols). The QIAGEN Blood & Tissue Genomic DNA kit (13362) provides a convenient option. The genomic DNA should be dissolved in TE at a concentration of 200–400 μg/ml. For high-complexity DNAs (e.g., human genomic DNA), the labeling reaction works more efficiently if the size of the DNA is first reduced by digestion with a restriction enzyme such as *Dpn*II. After digestion, the DNA should be purified by phenol:chloroform extraction and precipitated with ethanol. Alternatively, the QIAquick PCR Purification kit (28106, QIAGEN) may be used.

Yeast tRNA (15401-11, Invitrogen)

Prepare a 5 mg/ml stock solution in TE (pH 7.4).

Special Equipment

Desktop centrifuge with microtiter carrying plates (e.g., Beckman Coulter Allegra 6R or equivalent)

Fluorescence scanner (two-color, e.g., Axon GenePix 3000)

Glass coverslips (22 x 60 mm) (12-544-G, Fisher Scientific)

Glass washing chambers (3) (900303, Wheaton)

Heating block, preheated to 100ºC

Hybridization chambers (510-459-9101, Monterey Industries, Richmond, California)

Metal slide racks (2) (900234, Wheaton)

Microcon YM-30 filters (42411, Millipore)

Water bath, preheated to 37ºC and to 65ºC

The 65ºC water bath must be large enough for hybridizations and washing (e.g., Hot Shaker, Bellco Glass Co.).

METHOD

Labeling of Genomic DNA Using Random Primers

1. Label two screw-top microfuge tubes, one for the test sample of genomic DNA and one for the reference sample.

2. To the appropriate tubes, add 2–4 µg of genomic DNA for the test and for the reference samples to be labeled. Adjust the volume in each tube to 21 µl with dH$_2$O.

    The use of 4 µg of genomic DNA as the starting material, when available, is desirable because it will increase the quantity of labeled product. Adding additional Klenow fragment at Step 4 or lengthening the period of incubation at Step 5 may permit adequate labeling from smaller quantities of starting DNA material.

3. To each tube, add 20 µl of 2.5x random primer mix. Place the tubes in a heating block for 5 minutes at 100°C, and then transfer them immediately onto ice.

    If necessary after cooling, centrifuge the tubes briefly to bring contents to bottom of the tubes.

4. To each reaction mixture (in ice) add:

dNTP-labeling solution	5 µl
Cy5- *or* Cy3-labeled dCTP (1 mM)	3 µl
high-concentration Klenow fragment (40 units/µl)	1 µl

    Typically, the test sample of genomic DNA is labeled with Cy5 and the reference sample of genomic DNA is labeled with Cy3. Cy-labeled dUTP may be substituted for Cy-labeled dCTP; however, the concentrations of nucleotides in the dNTP-labeling mix must then be adjusted accordingly.

5. Mix the components by gently tapping the sides of the tubes. Incubate the reaction mixtures for 2 hours at 37°C and then stop the reactions by adding 5 µl of 0.5 M EDTA (pH 8.0).

6. Purify the labeled genomic DNAs using a Microcon YM-30 filter:

    a. Combine the labeled test and reference samples and transfer them onto a single Microcon YM-30 filter. Add 450 µl of TE (pH 7.4).

    b. Centrifuge the filter unit in a microfuge at 12,000*g* for 9 minutes at room temperature. Continue centrifugation for additional intervals of 30 seconds to 1 minute until the volume of labeled DNA is 15–32 µl. Discard the flow-through.

    c. Add an additional 500 µl of TE (pH 8.0) to the filter and repeat the centrifugation until the volume of labeled DNA is again 15–32 µl. Discard the flow-through.

7. Onto the Microcon YM-30 filter, transfer:

TE (pH 7.4)	450 µl
poly(dA)-poly(dT)	20 µg
yeast tRNA	100 µg
C_0t-1 DNA (human or mouse, as appropriate)	50 µg

    As with cytogenetic CGH, it is necessary to preanneal the labeled samples of genomic DNA with a large excess of an appropriate C_0t-1 DNA. The preannealing step serves to block the annealing of labeled highly repetitive sequences to similar sequences in the cDNA microarray, such as the repetitive *Alu* elements that are present in ~5% of the 3′-untranslated regions (3′UTRs) of arrayed cDNA clones. Failure to block repetitive elements results in compression of the fluorescence ratios. We have also found empirically that it is necessary to preanneal the labeled genomic DNA samples with an excess of poly(dA)-poly(dT) to block hybridization to the 3′ tails of arrayed cDNAs (please see the panel on TROUBLESHOOTING at the end of the protocol).

8. Centrifuge the samples (~11 minutes) as described in Step 6, until the volume of labeled sample is ~15–32 μl. Reverse the filter and transfer it to a fresh microfuge tube. Recover the labeled DNA by centrifuging the tube at 12,000g for 1 minute at room temperature.

Hybridization

9. Transfer the labeled probe to a fresh screw-top microfuge tube, and adjust the volume to 32 μl with H_2O. Add 6.8 μl of 20x SSC (final concentration 3.4x SSC) and mix the reagents by gently tapping the side of the tube. Add 1.2 μl of 10% SDS (final concentration 0.3%), and again mix the reagents by gently tapping the side of the tube.

    The volume of hybridization mixture (40 μl) is sufficient for annealing to a cDNA microarray under a 22 x 60-mm glass coverslip. If coverslips of other sizes are used, adjust the volume of the hybridization mixture accordingly.

10. Place the tube into a heating block for 2 minutes at 100°C, and then incubate the tube for 25 minutes at 37°C.

    Incubation at 37°C allows poly(dA)-poly(dT) and C_0t-1 DNA to anneal to the labeled genomic DNA before the hybridization mixture is transferred to the cDNA microarray.

11. Centrifuge the sample at maximum speed in a microfuge for 5 minutes at room temperature.

    This step is optional, but it may reduce the amount of fluorescent debris on the microarray surface.

12. Place the cDNA microarray in the hybridization chamber. Transfer 40 μl of hybridization mixture to the cDNA microarray, and carefully overlay a glass coverslip (22 x 60 mm). To maintain humidity, add 20 μl of 3x SSC to the chamber reservoir. If no reservoir is available, disperse 3x SSC as ~1-μl droplets onto the surface of the coverslip.

    For setup of microarray slides, see Section 2.

13. Close the hybridization chamber, and place it into a water bath heated to 65°C. Incubate the microarray hybridization reaction for 16–20 hours at 65°C.

Washing and Scanning

14. Prepare 400 ml of each of the following series of wash solutions in separate glass washing chambers:

    2x SSC/0.3% SDS (prewarm the solution to 65°C)
    2x SSC (prewarm the solution to 65°C)
    1x SSC
    0.2x SSC

    In preparing the first wash solution, dilute the appropriate amount of 20x SSC stock solution into H_2O before adding the appropriate amount of 10% SDS stock solution or the SDS will precipitate from solution.

15. Remove the hybridization chamber(s) from the water bath and dry the exterior with absorbent paper. Remove the microarray(s) from the chamber(s) and place them immediately into a metal slide rack in the first wash solution. Wash the microarrays with gen-

tle agitation, by transferring the slide rack through the glass chambers, according to the following wash program:

	SSC	SDS	Temperature	Time
Wash 1A:	2x	0.3%	65°C	5 minutes
Wash 1B:	2x	–	65°C	brief rinse
Wash 2:	1x	–	20°C	5 minutes
Wash 3:	0.2x	–	20°C	5 minutes

During Wash 1A, take care to allow the coverslip to slide gently from the microarray, thereby minimizing the possibility of scratching the array surface. Performing the first wash at 65°C for a full 5 minutes appears to be very important for increasing the ratio of specific to non-specific hybridization signal.

During Wash 1B, rinse the microarrays briefly in 2x SSC, and then place them into a fresh slide rack in Wash 2 to prevent the carryover of SDS, which could become a source of auto-fluorescence.

16. Place the metal slide rack into a desktop centrifuge with microtiter carrier plates. Dry the microarrays by centrifuging them at 46*g* (500 rpm) for 2 minutes at room temperature.

Spin-drying the microarrays is important to reduce the fluorescence background from air-dried salt deposits.

17. Scan the cDNA microarrays using a two-color fluorescence scanner.

It is advisable to scan the hybridized microarrays within a few hours of washing, as the fluorescence signal will fade over hours to days (particularly in the Cy5 channel). Store the microarrays in a closed slide box.

DATA ANALYSIS

- *Normalization:* To compensate for differences in the initial concentration of test and reference DNAs and for differences in labeling efficiencies between the test (Cy5) and reference (Cy3) DNAs, it is necessary to normalize fluorescence ratios across all array elements. Normalization ensures that loci with no change in DNA copy number, relative to the average ratiometric value of all elements on the array, will have fluorescence ratios (test/reference) of 1.

  Ratiometric unity can be achieved by multiplying all fluorescence ratios by a factor such that the average fluorescence ratio for all well-measured genes on the array is set to 1 (this calculation is performed in log space to weight DNA amplifications and deletions equally). Note that this normalization procedure is identical to that performed routinely in most microarray analyses of mRNA levels (for further details, please see Section 7, Part 3). As with cytogenetic CGH, this method of normalization ensures that fluorescence ratios reflect gains and losses of DNA relative to the average level of gains/losses in the test sample. However, it will not be possible to distinguish between a pure tetraploid DNA sample, for example, and the diploid DNA reference.

- *Mapping fluorescence ratios onto the genome:* Individual arrayed cDNAs can be identified by gene name or, for anonymous ESTs, by UniGene clusters (Schuler 1997). Until very recently, the highest resolution mapping of cDNAs onto the human genome could be achieved using radiation hybrid map positions (Deloukas et al. 1998). With the release of the draft sequences of the human genome (Lander et al. 2001), arrayed cDNAs can now be mapped onto the human genome with a greater degree of precision in local ordering. To produce a profile of variation in DNA copy number (fluorescence ratios) across chromosomes (e.g., as seen in Figure 6-1), it is necessary to associate the cDNA accessions/gene names for arrayed elements with chromosomal nucleotide map positions. Databases such as that maintained at the University of California, Santa Cruz (http://genome.ucsc.edu/) can aid in this endeavor. Scripts to perform this task are also available as Web-based tools (e.g., CaryoScope; http://genome-www.stanford.edu/~rees; C. Rees and J. Pollack, unpubl.). For further details of imaging and data analysis, please see Pollack et al. (1999).

TROUBLESHOOTING

- ***Starting out:*** When setting up the assay for the first time, the investigator may find it useful to hybridize genomic DNAs with a known change in copy number; for example, cancer cell lines whose DNA copy number alterations have been well-characterized by cytogenetic CGH or cell lines containing varying numbers of X chromosomes (e.g., 49, XXXXX vs. 46, XX), which would model different levels of gain or loss for all arrayed cDNAs mapping to the X chromosome. A number of these genomic DNA reagents are available from the ATCC (www.atcc.org) or the NIGMS Human Genetic Mutant cell repository (locus.umdnj.edu/nigms/). As with RNA hybridizations, fluorescence ratios obtained in genomic DNA hybridizations are linearly proportional, but tend to underestimate changes in copy number (Pollack et al. 1999).

  Self-self hybridizations (e.g., 46, XX vs. self) can be performed to determine the range and standard deviation of fluorescence ratios. This information is useful for setting a threshold above or below which deviant ratios are considered indicative of real changes in DNA.

  Control spots that must always be included in the microarray include total human genomic DNA, human C_0t-1 (to assess the efficiency of blocking), yeast DNA, and 3x SSC (to assess hybridization specificity).

- ***Low signal:background ratios:*** The investigator can expect to find average signal:background ratios of 5, more than sufficient for high-precision measurements (coefficient of variation ~10%). In our hands, labeling genomic DNAs by random priming provides results superior to those obtained with labeling by nick translation. Reducing the size of the genomic DNA prior to labeling and using a high concentration of the Klenow enzyme are both important for optimal labeling and strong hybridization signal. Although the efficiency of labeling is not easily quantified, a strong labeling should result in a deep purple hybridization mixture (with significantly more color than is typically seen in an mRNA labeling reaction).

  Low signal:background ratios can result from high background, caused, for example, by the use of alternative array surfaces (this protocol is optimized for poly-L-lysine-coated slide surfaces) or inadequate processing of poly-L-lysine-coated slides (please see Chapter 2, Protocol 1). To distinguish a genomic DNA-labeling problem from a microarray slide problem, it may be useful to label and hybridize an mRNA sample, which is expected to provide high background.

- ***High signal, but compressed fluorescence ratios:*** If hybridization signals are strong, but fluorescence ratios (test:reference) significantly underestimate true ratios, then the specificity of hybridization is not optimal. Hybridization using a formamide-based hybridization solution may result in reduced specificity, compared to the use of the aqueous hybridization solution detailed in this protocol. Performing the first posthybridization wash at 65°C appears to be important for attaining a high level of hybridization specificity.

- ***High fluorescence ratios observed for a subset of cDNAs in most test (tumor) samples:*** Genomic DNA tumor samples appear to be relatively enriched for poly(dA)-poly(dT) tracts. Inclusion of poly(dA)-poly(dT) in the hybridization mixture is therefore necessary to block the annealing of these labeled sequences to the long poly(dA) tails of a subset of cDNA array elements. Inefficient blocking may cause genomic sequences that annual to these tailed cDNAs to appear to be amplified in most tumor samples.

  In the early days of cDNA microarray fabrication, cDNA clones were not necessarily colony-purified or sequence-validated. This led to the inclusion of mitochondrial DNA contaminants in a small fraction of arrayed elements. Because mitochondrial DNAs are often highly prevalent in cancer cells, fluorescence ratios for these elements will also appear elevated in the majority of tumor samples. Although this is not a significant problem with the newer arrays, it is easy to identify mitochondrial DNA contaminants by hybridization of labeled human mitochondrial DNA to the cDNA microarray.

- ***Fluorescence ratios for certain cDNAs do not reflect expected copy number variation:*** The authors have observed that a small fraction of cDNA elements present on their microarrays do not accurately measure expected variations in DNA copy number. These findings reflect, in part, cDNAs that have a high degree of sequence similarity to genes mapping on multiple chromosomes (gene families, pseudogenes) and, in part, cDNAs that have been either incorrectly identified (sequence-tracking errors) or incorrectly mapped onto the human genome. For this reason, the use of a "moving average" of fluorescence ratios (Pollack et al. 1999), averaging across arrayed elements that are neighbors on a chromosome, may produce a more accurate profile of DNA variation in copy number across chromosomes.

Preparation of BAC DNA for CGH by Ligation-mediated PCR

Antoine Snijders,*† Daniel Pinkel†,‡ and Donna Albertson*†,‡

*Comprehensive Cancer Center, †Cancer Research Institute and ‡Department of Laboratory Medicine, University of California, San Francisco, California 94143

Mapped sets of BAC (bacterial artificial chromosome) clones are becoming increasingly available (Cheung et al. 2001), greatly simplifying the identification of genomic regions containing changes in DNA copy number. The preparation of BAC DNA for spotting microarrays, however, can be a challenging task. Because BACs are single-copy vectors, the yield of DNA from bacterial cultures is low compared to yields obtained from cultures harboring high-copy-number vectors. Furthermore, achieving consistency can be difficult when spotting viscous high-molecular-weight DNA at sufficient concentration to generate signals with a high ratio of signal to noise (Snijders et al. 2001). To prepare sufficient genomic DNA for array production from inserts cloned from high-capacity vectors, various procedures for amplifying representations of the inserts have been employed, including ligation-mediated PCR (Snijders et al. 2001) and degenerate-oligomer-primed (DOP)-PCR (Hogdson et al. 2001). Ligation-mediated PCR is expected to preserve the complexity of the BAC DNA more completely and thus provide better array performance.

The method described here for generating a high-complexity representation of genomic clone DNA combines ligation-mediated PCR followed by further amplification to overcome limitations faced when using large insert clones for DNA microarray CGH (Klein et al. 1999; Snijders et al. 2001).

Figures 6-2 and 6-3 provide an overview of the steps of the protocol. BAC DNA is digested with the restriction endonuclease MseI, adaptors are annealed to the digested BAC DNA, and a first round of amplification by ligation-mediated PCR is carried out (Figure 6-2). A small amount (1 ng) of the resulting product is then used as template for a subsequent amplification. The products of the second round of amplification are purified, resuspended at a concentration of 0.8 µg/µl DNA in 20% dimethylsulfoxide (DMSO) (spotting solution), and used for spotting arrays. The overall procedure generates sufficient spotting solution to create tens of thousands of arrays from 1 ng of BAC DNA, producing essentially an unlimited supply of reagent for array production.

In replicate microarray hybridization experiments (please see Protocol 3), independently prepared representations of BACs yield highly reproducible data: The average variation of the linear ratios from two independent preparations of the same clones is 6.6%. Furthermore, the ratios measured on arrays spotted with the representations derived from a given set of BAC clones are essentially identical to those ratios obtained from arrays created by spotting unamplified BAC DNA isolated directly from the same clones (Snijders et al. 2001).

For further information about the properties of BAC vectors and purification of BAC clones, please see Chapter 4 of Sambrook and Russell (2001).

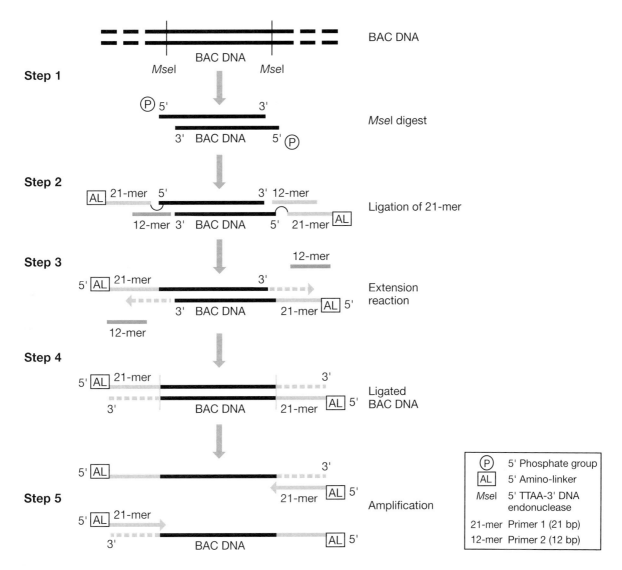

FIGURE 6-2. Schematic overview of ligation-mediated PCR. BAC DNA is digested with the restriction enzyme *Mse*I, generating a set of DNA fragments carrying protruding 5′-phosphorylated termini (Step 1). Primer 2 guides Primer 1 to the protruding sequence, allowing Primer 1 to be ligated to the fragments of BAC DNA (Step 2). Due to the lack of a phosphate group at its 5′ end, Primer 2 cannot be ligated to the 3′ termini of the DNA fragments. Heat is used to dissociate Primer 2 from the termini of the DNA fragments, and the exposed 3′ termini are then extended (*dashed line*) in a reaction catalyzed by a combination of *Taq*I and *Pwo* DNA polymerases (Steps 3 and 4). The resulting DNAs are then used as templates in an amplification reaction primed by the excess Primer 1 remaining after ligation (Step 5). A second round of amplification is carried out to generate DNA that will be made for spotting (not shown). (Adapted, with permission, from Snijders et al. 2002.)

MATERIALS

CAUTION: Please see Appendix 3 for appropriate handling of materials marked with <!>.

Buffers and Solutions

Please see Appendix 2 for components of stock solutions, buffers, and reagents.
Dilute stock solutions to the appropriate concentrations.

ATP (10 mM) (available from Invitrogen)
Store at –20ºC.

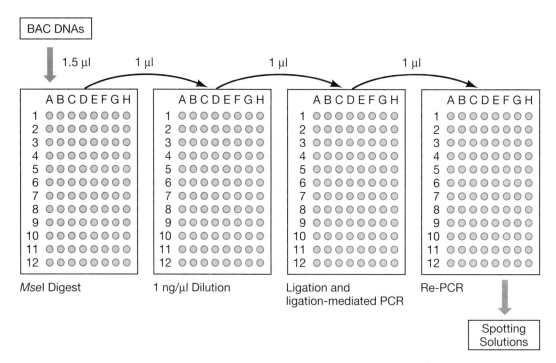

FIGURE 6-3. Schematic overview of the ligation-mediated PCR procedure for 96 BAC DNA clones. After digesting the BAC DNA, 1 μl of each digestion reaction is used to make a dilution containing 1 ng/μl DNA; 1 μl from the dilution is used for the ligation and subsequent PCR. From this PCR (50 μl), only 1 μl is used as template for a second round of PCR. The final yield of DNA is ~10–15 μg, which is precipitated and redissolved in 12 μl of 20% DMSO. This solution is then loaded into a microtiter plate for printing. Note that ~20 ng of input BAC DNA can yield ~1000 sets of printing solutions (input DNA amplification ~5 x 10^5). (Adapted, with permission, from Snijders et al. 2002.)

DMSO (20%) <!> in sterile H_2O
> Store the solution at room temperature.

dNTP solution, containing all 4 dNTPs, each at a concentration of 10 mM and of 25 mM

Ethanol (absolute, ice-cold and 70%)
> Some batches of absolute ethanol (100% or 200 proof) have been reported to contain fluorescent contaminants that generate high backgrounds in microarray experiments; 95% ethanol does not have this problem. To avoid difficulties, either use 95% ethanol or identify a brand of absolute ethanol that performs reliably. Absolute ethanol (USP-grade ethyl alcohol, 64-17-5) purchased from Warner-Graham (Cockeysville, Maryland) performs consistently well.

H_2O (sterile, e.g., autoclaved, deionized, and filtered)

$MgCl_2$ (25 mM) (Perkin Elmer)
> Store at –20ºC.

10x One-Phor-All Buffer Plus (27-0901-02, Amersham Biosciences)
> 100 mM Tris-acetate (pH 7.5)
> 100 mM magnesium acetate
> 500 mM potassium acetate
> > Store the buffer at 4ºC.
> > One-Phor-All Buffer Plus is a universal buffer, used in this protocol at 2.2x for the *Mse*I digest and at 2.5x final concentration for the ligation reaction.

Sodium acetate (3 M, pH 5.2)

TE (pH 7.4)

Enzymes and Buffers

AmpliTaq Gold DNA polymerase (5 units/µl) (Perkin Elmer)
> Store at –20°C. When in use, keep the enzyme on ice; return to –20°C as soon as possible.

DNA polymerase mix containing *Taq* and *Pwo* DNA polymerase (3.5 units/µl)
> The Expand Long Template PCR System is available from Roche.
> Store the buffer at –20°C. When in use, keep the enzyme mixture on ice; return it to –20°C as soon as possible.

*Mse*I restriction enzyme (20 units/µl) (New England Biolabs)
> Store the enzyme at –20°C.

10x PCR Buffer 1
> Store the buffer at –20°C.
> The Expand Long Template PCR System is available from Roche.

10x *Taq* Buffer II (contains no MgCl$_2$) (Perkin Elmer)
> Store the buffer at –20°C.

T4 DNA ligase (5 units/µl) (Invitrogen)
> Store the ligase at –20°C. When in use, keep the enzyme on ice; return it to –20°C as soon as possible.

Gels

Agarose gels (1%) made with Ultrapure agarose (Invitrogen), cast in 1x TBE, containing 0.5 µg/ml ethidium bromide <!>

6x Loading buffer
0.25% bromophenol blue <!>
0.25% xylene cyanol <!>
30% glycerol in H$_2$O
> Store the buffer at 4°C.

Nucleic Acids and Oligonucleotides

BAC DNA (20–500 ng), purified with minimal contamination from host DNA
> BAC DNA may be purified as described in Chapter 4 of Sambrook and Russell (2001).

Primers for ligation to BAC DNA and amplification of ligation products
Primer 1: 5′-AGT GGG ATT CCG CAT GCT AGT-3′ (50-nmolar scale containing a 5′ amino-linker)
- For the primer stock solution: Dissolve in sterile TE (pH 7.4) to 500 µM.
- For the 100 µM working solution: Dilute stock solution 1:5 in sterile H$_2$O. Store dry primer, stock solution, and working solution at –20°C.

Primer 2: 5′-TAA CTA GCA TGC-3′ (50-nmolar scale)
- For the primer stock solution: Dissolve in sterile TE (pH 7.4) to 500 µM.
- For the 100 M working solution: Dilute stock solution 1:5 in sterile H$_2$O. Store dry primer, stock solution, and working solution at –20°C.

φX174 RF DNA/*Hae*III marker (Promega)

Special Equipment

Fan (hybridization) oven (e.g., Techne Hybridiser HB-1D) capable of heating to 45°C
> The oven is used to dry down the PCR products (Step 31).

Multichannel pipettors (e.g., a Matrix Technologies 8- or 12-channel pipettor that dispenses 0.5–12.5 µl and a Matrix Technologies 8- or 12-channel pipettor that dispenses 5–250 µl)

Plate seal (96-well) (USA Scientific).

Polypropylene PCR 8-tube strips (0.2 ml) with separate 8-cap strips (USA Scientific)
> Strips and caps must be free of RNase, DNase, DNA, pyrogens, and PCR inhibitors.

Reagent reservoir with divider (25 ml) (Matrix Technologies)

Thermal cycler, capable of ramping at ~1.3°C/minute (e.g., Perkin-Elmer 9700)

UV transilluminator (e.g., Stratagene Stratalinker 2400, capable of producing 260,000 µJ UV)

METHOD

IMPORTANT: Use a multichannel pipettor when indicated in the protocol.

Digestion of BAC DNA with *Mse*I

1. Use sterile H_2O to dilute the 10x One-Phor-All Buffer Plus to a final concentration of 0.8x in a volume of 750 µl and then dispense 93 µl of the diluted buffer into each tube of an 8-tube strip.

   The restriction enzyme buffer dilution is enough for ~3 x 96 digest preparations each in a 5-µl reaction volume; the leftover dilution can be stored at 4°C after capping with an 8-cap strip.

2. Use a multichannel pipettor to dispense 2.5 µl of the 0.8x buffer solution into each tube of 12 8-tube PCR strips and seal the tubes using a 96-well plate seal to prevent evaporation and possible contamination.

   DNA/PCR contamination is possible when handling 96 different BAC DNAs at one time. Therefore, always wipe pipettors with 10 mM HCl (or other commercially available reagents). If the plate is sealed with a 96-well plate seal, centrifuge before unsealing to remove moisture around the seal, and release the seal slowly. Keep 8-tube strips, 8-cap strips, tubes, and other labware clean. Carry out amplification reactions in a confined space, either in a separate room or at a PCR workstation. Do not open tubes with PCR products in confined spaces. It is advisable to use filter pipette tips throughout the entire protocol.

3. Use a single-channel pipettor to add 1.5 µl of BAC DNA to each tube. After adding the BAC DNA to each 8-tube strip, place the strip in a different rack and seal it with a 96-well plate seal.

   BAC DNA usually ranges in concentration from 20 to 400 ng/µl. Note that 1.5 µl of BAC DNA is used for each restriction enzyme digest reaction regardless of the DNA concentration of each BAC preparation.

   During this step, only one 8-tube PCR strip is handled at a time. Keep the remaining 11 8-tube strips covered with a 96-well plate seal.

   - Roll back the plate seal of the 96-well plate (host plate), containing the digest buffer solution, until the first 8-tube strip is exposed.
   - Take out the first 8-tube strip and add BAC DNA to each tube.
   - Place this 8-tube strip in a clean 96-well plate (recipient plate) and place a 96-well plate seal on top of the plate so that it covers the whole plate (one end of the plate seal will cover the 8-tube strip, the other end of the seal will stick to the 96-well plate).
   - Return to the host plate and roll back the plate seal until the next 8-tube strip becomes exposed. Take out the strip and add BAC DNA to each tube. Partially remove the 96-well plate seal of the recipient plate while leaving the first 8-tube strip covered.
   - While holding the 96-well plate seal in one hand, place the next 8-tube strip in the recipient plate. Reseal the recipient plate and repeat this procedure until all 8-tube strips are done.

4. Use 10x One-Phor-All Buffer Plus to dilute the *Mse*I restriction enzyme to a final concentration of 2 units/µl in a volume of 120 µl. Keep the enzyme and the dilution on ice during this process. Discard any unused enzyme dilution.

5. Dispense 1 μl (2 units) of the diluted *Mse*I enzyme into each tube individually; keep the enzyme dilution on ice during this process. After adding the diluted enzyme, cover each 8-tube strip with an 8-cap strip and place the strip on ice.

   The use of a multichannel pipettor for pipetting small amounts (~1 μl) of enzyme has not been reliable. The authors have found that by pipetting the enzymes, *Mse*I, T4 DNA ligase, and the DNA polymerase resolution mixture separately using a single-channel pipettor has led to more reliable results.

6. Place the reaction in a thermal cycler for 12–16 hours (or overnight) at 37ºC.

7. Analyze 1.75-μl aliquots of the digests by conventional electrophoresis through a 1% agarose gel containing 0.5 μg/ml ethidium bromide. Include marker DNA (e.g., φX174 RF DNA/*Hae*III) to check fragment length. The digestion products should range from 100 to 1500 bp.

Ligation of Specific Primers to BAC DNA

The ligation reaction is carried out in a 10-μl reaction volume containing 5 μM Primer 1, 5 μM Primer 2, 0.5× One-Phor-All Buffer Plus, 1 mM ATP, 5 units of T4 DNA ligase, and 1 ng of digested BAC DNA.

8. Use sterile H_2O to dilute 1 μl of each digest to a final DNA concentration of 1 ng/μl.

9. Set up 12 new 8-tube strips.

   a. Individually add the calculated amount of sterile H_2O to each new tube at the locations corresponding to the locations of each digest.

   b. Use a multichannel pipettor to transfer 1 μl of each digest.

   c. Cover using a 96-well plate seal (please see Figure 6-3).

10. Set up the ligation reaction by combining the following in a 1.5-ml microfuge tube to create a primer solution (784 μl total volume):

Primer 1 (100 μM)	56 μl
Primer 2 (100 μM)	56 μl
One-Phor-All Buffer Plus	56 μl
sterile H_2O	616 μl

    Mix by pipetting and dispense 98 μl of the primer solution into each tube of an 8-tube strip.

11. Use a multichannel pipettor to withdraw 8 μl of the primer solution (Step 10) from each tube of the 8-tube strip and dispense 7 μl into the bottoms of 12 new 8-tube strips. Seal the 8-tube strips using a 96-well plate seal.

    Use a 12.5-μl multichannel pipettor to pick up 8 μl of the primer solution, dispense 7 μl, and discard the remaining 1 μl and pipette tips. The use of new pipette tips for each 8-tube strip is encouraged to ensure accuracy.

12. Add 1 μl of the 1 ng/μl BAC DNA digest prepared in Step 9 to the 7 μl of primer solution in each corresponding 8-tube strip (Figure 6-3).

    a. Carefully unseal the BAC DNA dilution plate, and then use a multichannel pipettor to withdraw 1 μl of the first 8-tube strip.

b. Unseal only the first 8-tube strip containing the primer solution, pick up the strip, add the DNA directly into the 7 µl of primer solution, and cover both 8-tube strips after adding the DNA.

13. Transfer the 12 8-tube strips into a thermal cycler. Carry out the annealing reaction for 1 minute at 65°C, and then lower the temperature to 15°C, with a ramp of ~1.3°C per minute (e.g., a ramp rate of 5% in a Perkin-Elmer 9700 thermal cycler).

14. During the annealing process, dispense 62.5 µl of 10 mM ATP solution into each tube of an 8-tube strip. Cover the 8-tube strip and place it on ice.

    The ATP solution is enough for ~5x 96 ligation reactions; the leftover ATP solution can be stored at 4°C after covering it with an 8-cap strip.

15. When the thermal cycler reaches 15°C, promptly remove the tubes from the machine and carefully open all 8-tube strips, including the 8-tube strip containing the ATP solution (Step 14). Use a multichannel pipettor set on the repeat-pipetting-mode to withdraw 12.5 µl of 10 mM ATP and dispense 1 µl on the inside wall of each of the 96 tubes containing DNA. Gently tap the rack so that the ATP slides into the DNA/primer solution. Seal the tubes with a 96-well plate seal.

    Adding the ATP in this manner reduces the probability of carryover contamination.

16. Dispense 1 µl (5 units) of T4 DNA ligase into each tube of the 96 tubes individually. Cover each 8-tube strip with an 8-cap strip after adding the enzyme and place on ice.

17. Place the reaction in a thermal cycler for 12–16 hours (or overnight) at 15°C.

Ligation Mediated PCR

18. Combine the following in a 15-ml tube for a total volume of 4480 µl:

10x PCR Buffer 1	336 µl
10 mM dNTP solution	224 µl
sterile H$_2$O	3920 µl

    Vortex briefly to mix and place the diluted dNTP solution on ice. Pour the solution into a reservoir.

    Each ligation-mediated PCR is carried out in a reaction volume of 50 µl containing 0.6x PCR Buffer 1, 0.4 mM dNTP mixture, 3.5 units of DNA polymerase mixture, and 10 µl of ligation mixture.

19. Remove the ligation reactions from the thermal cycler (Step 17), and open all the 8-tube strips carefully.

20. Use a multichannel pipettor, set on the repeat-pipetting-mode, to withdraw 205 µl of the diluted dNTP mixture, and dispense 40 µl onto the inside walls of each of the tubes in five 8-tube PCR strips. Purge the remaining 5 µl of PCR mixture back into the reservoir and discard the pipette tips.

21. Repeat this process to deliver diluted dNTP solution into the next set of five 8-tube PCR strips. Each time upon completion, purge the remaining 5 µl of diluted dNTP mixture back into the reservoir.

22. Adjust the multichannel pipettor fill volume to 85 µl leaving the dispense volume at 40 µl. Withdraw 85 µl of diluted dNTP mixture from the reservoir and dispense 40 µl onto the inside walls of the remaining two 8-tube PCR strips. Gently tap the PCR rack so that

the diluted dNTP mixture slides into the DNA/primer solution. Seal the tubes with 8-tube strips.

23. To dissociate Primer 2 from the BAC DNA, place the PCR tubes in a thermal cycler for 4 minutes at 68°C. Then remove the tubes and add 1 μl of DNA polymerase mixture (3.5 units/μl) to each tube. Open one 8-tube strip at a time, close it immediately after adding the enzyme mixture, and place on ice.

    The incubation for 4 minutes at 68°C displaces Primer 2 (12 mer; T_m = ~40°C) (please see Figure 6-2). It is critical to add the DNA polymerase mixture quickly to each 8-tube strip and to store the strip-tube on ice. Acting swiftly during this step is essential to prevent significant reannealing of Primer 2. The subsequent 3-minute incubation at 68°C will displace any reannealed Primer 2, allowing the free 3′ end of BAC DNA to be extended (please see Figure 6-2).

    The entire process of removing 12 8-tube strips from the thermal cycler, adding the enzyme mixture to each tube individually, placing the 8-tube strips on ice, and finally returning the 12 8-tube strips to the thermal cycler for amplification should take no longer than 10–15 minutes.

24. Transfer the 8-tube strips to the thermal cycler and carry out amplification using the denaturation, annealing, and polymerization times and temperatures listed below:

Cycle number	Denaturation	Annealing	Polymerization
First cycle			3 min at 68°C
Subsequent cycles (14)	40 sec at 94°C	30 sec at 57°C	1 min, 15 sec at 68°C
Subsequent cycles (34)	40 sec at 94°C	30 sec at 57°C	1 min, 45 sec at 68°C
Last cycle	40 sec at 94°C	30 sec at 57°C	5 min at 68°C

    Upon completion of the amplification, incubate the 8-tube strips at 4°C.

25. Analyze 3.5 μl of each amplification reaction by electrophoresis through a conventional 1% agarose gel containing 0.5 μg/ml ethidium bromide. Use marker DNA (e.g., φX174 RF DNA/*Hae*III Marker) to check the fragment lengths. The size of the amplification products should range from 70 to 1500 bp, with the highest concentration of product ~200–800 bp.

    If a banding pattern appears in the smear, the ligation and/or ligation-mediated PCR has not been successful and should be repeated. All of the products should have a smear ranging from 70 to 1500 bp. Any aberration from this smear, e.g., a smear ~300–600 bp or a high-molecular-weight smear, is unacceptable.

Amplification of Ligation-mediated PCR Products

The product of the ligation-mediated PCR is used as a template in a conventional amplification (Re-PCR) reaction to generate DNA for spotting microarrays. Amplification is carried out in a 100-μl reaction containing 1x *Taq* buffer II, Primer 1 (4 μM), dNTP mixture (0.2 mM), MgCl₂ (5.5 mM), 2.5 units of AmpliTaq Gold, and ligation-mediated PCR product (1 μl).

26. Prepare a PCR mixture by combining the following reagents in a 15-ml tube for a total volume of 9900 μl:

10x *Taq* Buffer II	1000 μl
Primer 1 (100 μM)	400 μl
dNTP solution (25 mM)	80 μl
MgCl₂ (25 mM)	2200 μl
AmpliTaq Gold (5 units/μl)	50 μl
sterile H₂O	6170 μl

27. Pour the PCR mixture (Step 26) into a reservoir. Use a multichannel pipettor to dispense 99 µl of the mixture into each tube of 12 8-tube strips. Seal the tubes using a 96-well plate seal.

28. Use a multichannel pipettor to add 1 µl of ligation-mediated PCR product to each corresponding 8-tube strip of PCR mixture as follows:

    a. Unseal one 8-tube strip of PCR mixture (Step 27) and one 8-tube strip containing the ligation-mediated PCR product (Step 24).

    b. Dispense 1 µl of template (ligation-mediated PCR product) into the PCR mixture, cover the 8-tube strip, and then cover the 8-tube strip containing the remaining ligation-mediated PCR.

    c. Continue to the next set of 8-tube strips, and follow Steps a and b, until all of the templates have been processed.

29. Transfer the 8-tube strips, each containing 100 µl of PCR mixture and 1 µl of ligation-mediated PCR product, to a thermal cycler and carry out amplification using the denaturation, annealing, and polymerization times and temperatures listed below:

Cycle number	Denaturation	Annealing	Polymerization
First cycle	10 minutes at 95°C		
Subsequent cycles (45)	30 seconds at 95°C	30 seconds at 50°C	2 minutes at 72°C
Last cycle			7 minutes at 72°C

Upon completion of the amplification, incubate the 8-tube strips at 4°C.

30. Analyze 4 µl of each reaction by electrophoresis through a conventional 1% agarose gel containing 0.5 µg/ml ethidium bromide. Use marker DNA (e.g., φX174 RF DNA/*Hae*III Marker) to check the fragment lengths. The size of the amplification products should range from 200 to 1500 bp.

Preparation of Spotting Solutions from Re-PCR for Array CGH

31. Reduce the volumes of the amplification products to ~50 µl by drying the samples. Uncap the 8-tube strips and place the PCR rack face-up in a fan (hybridization) oven for ~75 minutes at 45°C.

    If the heat inlet of the oven is biased toward one side of the PCR rack, rotate the rack every 15 minutes to allow even evaporation. Reducing the volumes of the Re-PCR products is necessary to accommodate the ethanol and sodium acetate to be added for DNA precipitation.

32. Recover the PCR products by precipitation with 150 µl of prechilled absolute ethanol and 5 µl of 3 M sodium acetate (deliver these solutions using a multichannel pipettor). Cover the 8-tube strips and invert the rack several times to mix.

33. Precipitate the samples in the PCR rack for 15 minutes at –20°C.

34. Recover the precipitated samples by centrifuging the rack at 1699*g* for 90 minutes at 4°C.

35. Use a multichannel pipettor to remove the supernatants carefully. Then use a multichannel pipettor to add 150 µl of 70% ethanol to each of the pellets, and cap the tubes.

36. Vortex each 8-tube strip until the pellets come loose. After vortexing all 8-tube strips, centrifuge the rack at 1699*g* for 45 minutes at 4°C.

37. Use a multichannel pipettor to remove as much 70% ethanol as possible. Dry the pellet for ~90 minutes at room temperature.

    The time required depends on the amount of ethanol remaining on the pellet. Do not dry the pellets to the point of desiccation.

38. Handling only one 8-tube strip a time, use a multichannel pipettor to add 12 µl of a 20% DMSO solution to each of the pellets and mix them by pipetting. Cap the tubes and resuspend the pellets by flicking the bottoms of the PCR tubes to loosen the pellet.

    The final DNA concentration of the spotting solution should be ~0.8–1.3 µg/µl.

39. Store the DNA solutions overnight (or longer) at 4°C. Use a multichannel pipettor to mix the solution until the pellet is completely in suspension.

    DNA solutions can be stored at 4°C. The DNA is denatured in the printing solution so that no further processing necessary.

Printing and Processing Microarrays

40. Print the DNA samples as described in Section 2, Protocol 2, and then allow them to dry in the air.

    After printing the spotting solutions on a glass surface, the spots will become nearly invisible due to the lack of salt in the spotting solutions. Breathing on the glass slide will make the arrays visible for a short period of time.

41. Place the slides with spotted arrays into a UV Stratalinker 2400, arrays facing up, and cross-link the DNA to the substrate by exposure to 260,000 µJ UV irradiation.

    The arrays should be subjected to a fixed amount of *energy* (260,000 µJ) instead of other available options the Stratalinker may have, such as *autocrosslink* or *time*. Over-cross-linking the slide may result in a decrease in fluorescent hybridization signal.

    Staining the slides with DAPI indicates that typically all of the DNA deposited by the pins remains in the spot and is retained during hybridization in 50% formamide/2x SSC.

CGH Using BAC Genomic Microarrays

Richard Segraves,* Donna Albertson,*†‡ and Daniel Pinkel*‡

*Comprehensive Cancer Center, †Cancer Research Institute and ‡Department of Laboratory
Medicine, University of California, San Francisco, California 94143-0808

Array elements consisting of genomic DNA cloned in BAC vectors yield more intense signals and better performance for detection of single-copy gains and losses than smaller clones such as cDNAs. The use of *sequence tags* in the genomic inserts cloned in high-capacity BAC and PAC (P1-derived artificial chromosome) vectors allows direct access to the genomic sequence. Labeling of genomic DNA by random priming provides sufficient amplification so that as little as 3 ng of DNA can be used for measurement of CGH on BAC arrays.

The following protocol describes the preparation and fluorescent labeling of test and reference genomic DNA samples, the conditions for their hybridization to BAC-derived microarrays, and subsequent image and data analyses. For the preparation of BAC clones for printing microarrays, please see Protocol 2.

MATERIALS

CAUTION: Please see Appendix 3 for appropriate handling of materials marked with <!>.

Buffers and Solutions

Please see Appendix 2 for components of stock solutions, buffers, and reagents.
Dilute stock solutions to the appropriate concentrations.

Blocking solution
　　　Please see Step 10.
DAPI (4′, 6-diamidino-2-phenylindole) stain mounting medium

1 μM DAPI	1 μl
*PBS, lacking Ca^{2+} and Mg^{2+}	100 μl
glycerol	900 μl

　　　*Adjust the pH of the PBS to 8.0 with 0.5 M bicarbonate buffer.
EDTA (0.5 M, pH 8.0)
Ethanol (absolute), ice-cold
　　　Some batches of absolute ethanol (100% or 200 proof) have been reported to contain fluorescent contaminants that generate high backgrounds in microarray experiments; 95% ethanol does not have this problem. To avoid difficulties, either use 95% ethanol or identify a brand of absolute ethanol that performs reliably. Absolute ethanol (USP-grade ethyl alcohol, 64-17-5) purchased from Warner-Graham (Cockeysville, Maryland) performs consistently well.
Glycerol (100%)

Hybridization mix (pH 7.0)

  1 g of dextran sulfate (sodium salt, 500,000 m.w.) (Ultrapure, Invitrogen)

  5 ml of formamide <!>

  1 ml of 20x SSC

  Distribute 1 g of powdered dextran sulfate over the entire length of a 15-ml tube. While holding the tube horizontally, squirt in 5 ml of formamide. Close the tube and shake it vigorously for 30 seconds. Add 1 ml of 20x SSC and shake the solution vigorously for 30 seconds. Store the tube overnight at room temperature to allow the dextran sulfate to dissolve. Adjust the volume of the solution to 7 ml with H_2O, and adjust the pH to 7.

10x Phosphate-buffered saline (PBS) (pH 7.4), lacking Ca^{2+} and Mg^{2+}

PN buffer

  PN buffer is prepared by mixing two components: a dibasic and a monobasic component.
  - For the dibasic component, prepare 0.1 M $Na_2HPO_4 \cdot H_2O$.
  - For the monobasic component, prepare 0.1 M $NaH_2PO_4 \cdot H_2O$.

  Adjust the pH of the dibasic component to pH 8.0 with the monobasic component. Add Nonidet P-40 (NP-40) to 0.1%.

SDS (20%) <!>

Sephadex solution

  50 g of Sephadex G-50

  500 ml of 10 mM Tris (pH 8)

  1 mM of EDTA

  0.1% SDS

Sodium acetate (3 M, pH 5.2)

Tris base (1 M, pH 7.6)

Wash buffer (pH 7), prewarmed to 45°C

  50% formamide <!>

  2x SSC

Enzymes and Buffers

Klenow fragment of *E. coli* DNA polymerase I (high concentration, 40–50 units/µl)

  The use of high-concentration Klenow significantly enhances labeling efficiency. The enzyme can be purchased as part of the BioPrime Labeling kit (GIBCO) or separately from New England Biolabs.

Gels

Agarose gels (1%), cast in 1x TBE

  Please see Step 6.

Nucleic Acids and Oligonucleotides

Cy5-labeled dCTP and Cy3-labeled dCTP (1 mM stock solutions) (PA55021 and PA53021, Amersham Biosciences)

10x dNTP labeling solution containing dATP, dGTP, dTTP (each at a concentration of 2 mM) and dCTP (at a concentration of 0.5 mM in TE [pH 7.6])

  Use ultrapure dNTPs (e.g., Pharmacia). For advice on preparing and storing stock solutions of dNTPs, please see Appendix 2.

Herring or salmon sperm DNA (10 mg/ml) (Invitrogen)

Human C_0t-1 DNA (0.7 µg/µl stock solution) (Invitrogen)

  The concentration of each new lot of C_0t-1 DNA should be 500 ng/µl or greater as measured using a fluorimeter.

Microarrays of BAC elements, prepared as described in Protocol 2

Arrays are printed on a variety of substrates including chromium-coated glass, aminosilane on glass, and Corning commercial slides (please see the information panel on SUBSTRATES FOR PRINTING in Section 2). The authors typically print arrays on chromium as this provides a good environment for CCD imaging using the home-built CCD imaging system. For commercial laser scanners, arrays are printed on glass slides and are imaged without mounting in DAPI or applying a coverslip.

2.5x Random primer solution (BioPrime Labeling Kit, 18094-011, GIBCO)

125 mM Tris-Cl (pH 6.8)

12.5 mM $MgCl_2$

25 mM β-mercaptoethanol <!>

750 μg/ml random octamers

These components can be assembled separately or the complete buffer can purchased as part of the BioPrime Labeling Kit (Invitrogen).

Reference DNA of known concentration

Test genomic DNA of known concentration

Genomic DNA prepared by any number of standard methods is of sufficient quality for array CGH analysis.

Yeast tRNA solution (50 mg) (Invitrogen)

Dissolve in sterile H_2O to 100 μg/μl.

Special Equipment

Binding clips

Clear fingernail polish

Coverslips (No. 1, Corning)

Heating block, preset to 100°C

Rocking table (e.g., VWR brand Rocker, Model 100)

Rubber cement (Ross, American Glue Corporation)

Sephadex G-50 spin column (please see Step 8) (Amersham Biosciences)

Silicone gasket (Press-to-Seal, PGC Scientific)

UV Stratalinker 2400

Water bath, preset to 45°C

METHOD

Random Primer Labeling of Genomic DNA

1. Label two screw-top microfuge tubes, one for the test sample and one for the reference sample of genomic DNA.

   Each random primer labeling reaction is carried out in a 50-μl reaction volume containing 200–300 ng of genomic DNA, 1x random primers, 40 units of Klenow fragment, Cy3- or Cy5-labeled dCTP (40 μM), and 1x dNTP mixture. The random primed DNA product typically ranges in size from 200 to 1500 bp, with the highest concentration ~400 bp. Please see Steps 2–4.

2. To the appropriate tubes, add 200–300 ng of genomic DNA for the reference and for the test samples to be labeled. Add 20 μl of 2.5x random primer solution, and bring the volume in each tube to 42 μl with H_2O.

3. Place the tubes into a heating block (or thermal cycler) and denature the DNA by incubating for 10 minutes at 99ºC, and then transfer the tubes onto ice.

   > If necessary after denaturing the DNA, centrifuge the tubes briefly to bring the contents to the bottoms of the tubes.

4. To each reaction mixture add:

dNTP labeling solution	5 µl
Cy5- *or* Cy3-labeled dCTP	2 µl
Klenow fragment (40 units/µl)	1 µl

   > Typically, the test genomic DNA sample is labeled with Cy3 and the reference genomic DNA sample is labeled with Cy5. Cy-labeled dUTP may be substituted for Cy-labeled dCTP; however, the concentrations of nucleotides in the dNTP-labeling mix should then be adjusted accordingly.

5. Mix the components by gently tapping the sides of the tubes and incubate the reactions overnight at 37ºC.

6. Analyze a small aliquot (5 µl) of each labeling reaction by electrophoresis through a 1% agarose gel.

   > The DNA fragments should appear as a smear ranging in size from ~100 to 500 bp.

7. Remove the unincorporated nucleotides by spin column chromatography, using a Sephadex G-50 column. For details, please see Protocol A8.30 in Sambrook and Russell (2001).

Hybridization to Arrays

8. To create a hybridization area on the slide, use a 200-µl pipette tip on the end of a 10-ml syringe to dispense rubber cement in a ring around the array, using a stereomicroscope to observe the area (please see Figure 6-4). Allow the rubber cement to dry in air, and then apply a second thick layer of rubber cement on top of the first layer. Allow to dry in air.

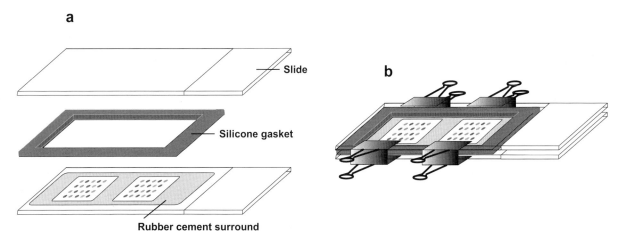

FIGURE 6-4. Overview of hybridization slide assembly. After applying the hybridization solution inside the rubber cement surround on the array, a silicone gasket is placed around the rubber cement. A clean microscope slide is placed on top of the silicone gasket and the whole slide assembly is sealed using binder clips as shown. (*a*) Expanded view, showing the array slide with rubber cement around the array at the bottom silicone gasket, and slide used as a cover at the top. (*b*) Assembled hybridization chamber with binder clips. (Adapted, with permission, from Snijders et al. 2002.)

9. Prepare the labeled probe for hybridization by mixing the following DNA samples:

human C_0t-1 DNA (~0.7 µg/µl)	100 µl
labeled test genomic DNA	50 µl
labeled reference genomic DNA	50 µl

Recover the DNA mixture by standard precipitation with ethanol. Pellet the DNA by centrifugation at 20,800g (14,000 rpm) for 30 minutes at 4°C, remove the supernatant, and allow the DNA pellet to dry in the air for 5–10 minutes.

10. Dissolve the DNA pellet in 5 µl of yeast tRNA solution and 10 µl of 20% SDS, and then add 35 µl of hybridization mix.

11. Prepare 50 µl of blocking solution for each array as follows (typically, 2–3 ml of solution is prepared and stored at room temperature):

    a. Precipitate 50 µl of salmon sperm DNA (10 mg/ml) with 2.5 volumes of ethanol and 0.1 volume of 3 M sodium acetate (pH 5.2). Mix the solution and recover the precipitate by centrifugation in a microfuge at 7750g (6400 rpm) for 1–2 minutes.

    b. Remove the supernatant and allow the pellet to dry in the air.

    c. Dissolve the DNA pellet in 5 µl of H_2O and 10 µl of 20% SDS, and then add 35 µl of hybridization mix (pH 7.0).

12. Place a silicone gasket around the array and rubber cement ring. Deliver the blocking solution (50 µl) onto the hybridization area, taking care to cover the entire area. Place a clean glass microscope slide on top of the gasket to prevent evaporation. Allow the array to block for ~30 minutes at room temperature.

    Please see Figure 6-4; note that binder clips are not required for this step.

13. Denature the DNA by incubation for 10–15 minutes at 73°C, and then continue the incubation for 1 hour at 37°C.

    The preannealing step allows the highly repetitive sequences in the DNAs to anneal so that they are no longer available to hybridize to similar sequences in the elements on the array. Failure to block repetitive elements results in severe compression of the fluorescence ratios.

14. Remove the glass cover slide from the blocked microarray. Aspirate the blocking solution with care from the array, and then quickly deliver the hybridization mixture from Step 13 onto the array inside the hybridization area.

15. Create an airtight chamber by placing a glass microscope slide on top of the gasket and clamping the slides tightly in place with binder clips (please see Figure 6-4).

16. Place the slide "chamber" on a slowly rocking table (~1 rpm) in a 37°C incubator, and incubate the microarray hybridization reaction for 34–48 hours.

17. To stop the hybridization reaction, remove the binder clips and cover slide from the array. Rinse the hybridization solution from the array slide under a stream of PN buffer.

18. Place the slide containing the hybridized array into a Coplin jar containing 50 ml of wash buffer, prewarmed to 45°C in a water bath, and incubate the microarray for 15 minutes.

19. Transfer the microarray slide into a fresh Coplin jar with 50 ml of PN buffer, and allow the jar to stand for 15 minutes at room temperature.

20. With care, use forceps to remove the rubber cement from the slide (keeping the array moist with PN buffer), and transfer the slide into fresh PN buffer for 15 minutes.

21. Remove the slide from the Coplin jar and allow the PN buffer to "roll" off the slide.

    IMPORTANT: Do not allow the slide to dry completely.

22. For imaging of the slide using a custom CCD system, stain the array with DAPI.

    a. Deliver ~200 µl of DAPI stain mounting medium onto the array.

    b. Cover the array area with a 24 x 50 No. 1 Corning coverslip, blot the excess DAPI mounting media from the edges, and seal with clear fingernail polish.

        The arrays are now ready for imaging. Images can be acquired using commercially available CCD or laser-scanning imaging systems (e.g., an Axon scanner 4000B; please also see Table 3-9 in Section 3). For further discussion of imaging, please see the panel on IMAGING AND ANALYSIS OF ARRAYS below.

        When using commercial laser scanners (please see Section 3, Table 3-9), arrays are rinsed with sterile H_2O and dried by centrifuging them in a tabletop centrifuge.

IMAGING AND ANALYSIS OF ARRAYS

Arrays printed on transparent substrates such as coated glass slides can be imaged on commercial laser scanners. They are typically imaged dry. The authors obtained somewhat better measurements using arrays printed on chromium-coated slides and imaging with a custom-built CCD system (Pinkel et al. 1998). The arrays are mounted under a coverslip in a 90% glycerol/PBS medium containing DAPI to stain the DNA in the array spots. The imaging system can obtain independent images of four fluorochromes; typically, DAPI to allow visualization of the spots, fluorescein, and Cy3 and Cy5 (or their spectral equivalents) for simultaneous comparison of up to three different genomic DNAs. Quantitative analysis of the images to obtain the ratios is performed with commercial software such as Genepix from Axon Instruments, as described in Section 7, Part 2, or with the custom program UCSF SPOT (Jain et al. 2002). UCSF SPOT uses the DAPI image to automatically find all of the spots and establish their boundaries. The boundary is thus tailored to each spot, following whatever shape irregularities may be present. The program then calculates local background for each spot, the background-corrected intensity for each fluorochrome for each pixel within the spot, various measures of fluorescence ratios, and statistical and diagnostic parameters. The authors use the ratios of the total intensities of the test and reference signals for each spot for the final data. This analysis is essentially completely automatic—operator intervention is permitted only to verify that the spot boundaries have been properly found and to make small adjustments if there are problems. Analysis of an array of ~7500 spots takes less than 1 minute on a standard lap top computer. If only test and reference images are available, as is typically the case with images obtained from laser scanners, UCSF SPOT can use either one or the sum of both in place of the DAPI image to find the spots. A second custom program takes the UCSF SPOT output, associates each spot with the clone ID and mapping information, averages replicate spots, applies quality control criteria, and outputs data ready for interpretation.

Microarray-based Representational Analysis of DNA Copy Number: Preparation of Target DNA

Robert Lucito and Michael Wigler

Cold Spring Harbor Laboratory, Cold Spring Harbor, New York 11724

Representational microarray analysis, like array-based CGH, can be used to measure differences in DNA content between two samples. This approach has its genesis in a method known as representational difference analysis used to identify the differences in sequences between two genomes (Lisitsyn and Wigler 1993; Lisitsyn et al. 1993, 1995).

Due to the complexity of the human genome, the abundance of a single-copy sequence in labeled target prepared from a total genomic DNA is very low. When hybridizing a target as complex as the human genome to a microarray for comparative measurements of DNA copy number, the ratio of signal to noise obtained from individual probes may be low unless the probe size is large, typically a BAC or YAC (yeast artificial chromosome). One way to reduce the complexity of the target is to produce a *representation* of the genome through the preferential amplification of small restriction fragments (Lucito et al. 1998). In this scheme (please see Figure 6-5), DNA is cut with a restriction enzyme and ligated to linkers that serve as primer binding sites for PCR amplification. In a standard PCR, only small fragments (typically, <1 kb) will be efficiently amplified, and thus the amplified material is a representation of the total genome rather than a faithful copy. The degree of representation depends on the restriction enzyme used (Lucito et al. 1998). For example, a low-complexity representation (~2.5% of the genome) is obtained with the enzyme *Bgl*II, which has a 6-base recognition sequence and hence produces small fragments relatively infrequently. By contrast, the enzyme *Dpn*II, which recognizes a 4-base sequence and cuts frequently, produces many small fragments and consequently a high-complexity representation (~70%). In a low-complexity representation, the proportional contribution of each labeled component is higher than in a mixture containing fragments of the entire genome. Hence, the ratio of signal to noise may be improved by using a low-complexity labeled representation set. Representation sets made from two DNA sources, such as tumor and corresponding normal tissue, can be differentially labeled with fluorescent dyes, typically Cy3 and Cy5, respectively. The labeled targets can be competitively hybridized to a microarray to detect differences in DNA copy number between the two samples (Lucito et al. 2000).

The composition of the microarray is an important consideration for representation microarray analysis. Because the representative targets are derived from random fragments of the genome, there is no selection for coding versus intergenic sequences. Hence, microarrays that contain cDNA probes are not well-suited to this approach. The authors make use of

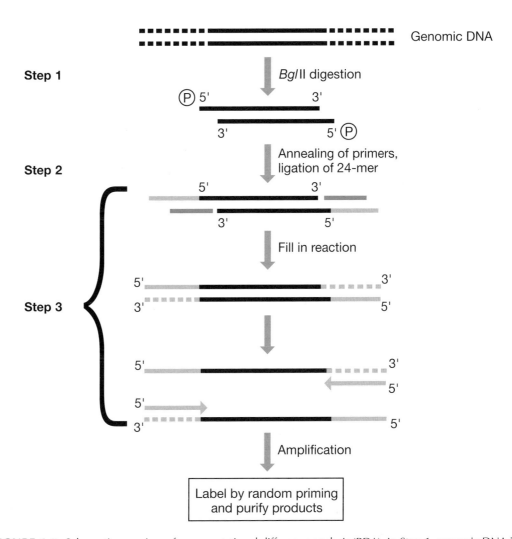

FIGURE 6-5. Schematic overview of representational difference analysis (RDA). In Step 1, genomic DNA is digested with the restriction enzyme *Bgl*II, generating a set of fragments carrying protruding 5′ termini. In Step 2, unphosphorylated oligonucleotide adaptors are ligated to the termini. The adaptors consist of a 24-mer and a partially complementary 12-mer. The 24-mer is able to ligate to the phosphorylated 5′ termini created by cleavage of genomic DNA with *Bgl*II (Step 1). Due to a lack of a phosphate group at its 5′ terminus, the 12-mer, which serves as a guide to the 24-mer, is unable to ligate to the 3′ termini of the genomic DNA fragments. During subsequent PCR (Step 3), the 12-mers are displaced, the recessed 3′ termini are filled, and the fragments of genomic DNA are amplified.

microarrays with probes from two sources for their studies: One option is to use small (<1.0 kb) genomic fragments that are randomly distributed throughout the genome or, in some cases, cloned from specific regions of interest (Lucito et al. 2000). The other class of probes, now favored by the authors, is long oligonucleotides (~70 bp). The relative merits of these probes are discussed in this protocol.

MATERIALS

CAUTION: Please see Appendix 3 for appropriate handling of materials marked with <!>.

Buffers and Solutions

Please see Appendix 2 for components of stock solutions, buffers, and reagents. Dilute stock solutions to the appropriate concentrations.

10x Amplification buffer (N808-0190, Applied Biosystems).
>Alternatively, 10x amplification buffer can be made according to the following recipe:
>>500 mM KCl
>>100 mM Tris-HCl (pH 8.3)
>>Store the buffer in small aliquots at –20°C.

Ethanol (absolute and 70%)
>Some batches of absolute ethanol (100% or 200 proof) have been reported to contain fluorescent contaminants that generate high backgrounds in microarray experiments; 95% ethanol does not have this problem. To avoid difficulties, either use 95% ethanol or identify a brand of absolute ethanol that performs reliably. Absolute ethanol (USP-grade ethyl alcohol, 64-17-5) purchased from Warner-Graham (Cockeysville, Maryland) performs consistently well.

Isopropanol <!>
MgCl$_2$ (25 mM)
Phenol:chloroform (v/v) <!>
SDS (10%) <!>
Sodium acetate (pH 5.3)
SSC
3x SSPE
>SSC and SSPE can be made in-house or purchased in an RNase-free form from companies, such as Invitrogen or Ambion.

TE (pH 8.0)

Enzymes and Enzyme Buffers

Klenow fragment of *E. coli* DNA polymerase I (5 µl) (M0210S, New England Biolabs, or 18012-021, GIBCO)
>Note that Klenow is provided with the Megaprime DNA Labeling System. This protocol will require additional enzymes (Step 11) that can be ordered from a separate supplier.

Megaprime DNA Labeling System, dCTP (RPN1607, Amersham Biosciences)
>This random-primed labeling kit is used with labeled dCTP.

Restriction endonuclease (New England Biolabs)
>Choose an endonuclease appropriate for digestion of genomic DNA (*Bgl*II is used as an example in this protocol); please see Step 1.

Taq polymerase (5 units/µl) (Perkin Elmer or Applied Biosystems)
T4 DNA ligase (4 units/µl) (New England Biolabs)

Gels

Agarose (2%) gels, homemade or precast (BioWhittaker)

Nucleic Acids and Oligonucleotides

Adaptors

The primer pairs listed below may be ordered from any reputable company synthesizing oligos. 200 nmoles of the 12 mer is a sufficient quantity for the ligation step (Step 3) unless there are plans to prepare many representation sets. 1 μmole of the 24 mer will be required as it is used as a primer in PCR amplification (Step 6) as well as for ligation (Step 3). Resuspend the primers in H_2O at a concentration of 62 pm/μl and store aliquots at –20ºC.

Three alternate adaptor pairs are shown:

RBgl24	agcactctccagcctctcaccgca
RBgl12	gatctgcggtga
NBgl24	aggcaactgtgctatccgagggaa
NBgl12	gatcttccctcg
IBgl24	tcagcatcgagactgaacgcagca
IBgl12	gatctgctgcgt

Any of these sets of adaptors may be used for ligation in the protocol. Because minor variation has been observed between different batches of primers, a single source of primers should be used for all related experiments. For construction of an oligonucleotide array, there is no need to use more than one adaptor pair. For production of fragments from representations (RDA) or representations from genomic clones such as YACs and BACs, it is advisable to alternate the use of adaptor pairs to minimize the chance of contamination or cross-hybridization.

IMPORTANT: These oligonucleotides are designed to ligate to the end of a fragment produced by a *Bgl*II restriction endonuclease digestion. The adaptor sequences can be modified as appropriate for use with any restriction endonuclease that produces a protruding 5´ end.

Carrier tRNA (5–10 μg) (Sigma)

C_0t-1 DNA

Optional, please see Step 12.

Cy3- and Cy5-labeled dCTP (Amersham Biosciences)

dNTP solution, containing all four dNTPs, each at a concentration of 10 mM (Sigma)

Genomic DNA

Genomic DNA can be isolated from sample or normal to be used as reference (obtained from CLONETECH or Sigma).

Special Equipment

Centrifugal evaporator (e.g., SpeedVac)
Heat block, set at 55ºC
Hybridization chambers (TeleChem International)
Microduster (compressed gas) (VWR)
Microcon YM-30 (Amicon)
Thermal cycler fitted with a heated lid (MJ Research or Applied Biosystems)

METHODS

Production of Amplicon Representation (please see Figure 6-6)

1. Digest genomic DNA with the desired restriction endonuclease.

   *Bgl*II is used as an example in this protocol; however, other enzymes can be used. The choice of enzyme will affect the degree of representation of the genome (Lucito et al. 1998). When digesting less than 500 ng of DNA, the reaction should be carried out in the presence of 20 ng/μl tRNA in a minimum volume of 50 μl. To minimize noise in the representation, it is important that the digestion go to completion. Allow the digestion to

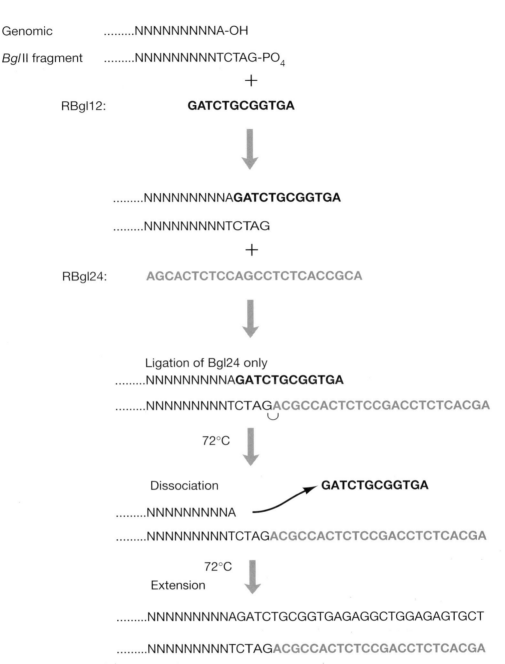

Genomic ....NNNNNNNNNA-OH

*Bgl*II fragment ........NNNNNNNNNTCTAG-PO$_4$

+

RBgl12: **GATCTGCGGTGA**

........NNNNNNNNNA**GATCTGCGGTGA**

........NNNNNNNNNTCTAG

+

RBgl24: AGCACTCTCCAGCCTCTCACCGCA

Ligation of Bgl24 only
........NNNNNNNNNA**GATCTGCGGTGA**

........NNNNNNNNNTCTAGACGCCACTCTCCGACCTCTCACGA

72°C

Dissociation **GATCTGCGGTGA**

........NNNNNNNNNA

........NNNNNNNNNTCTAGACGCCACTCTCCGACCTCTCACGA

72°C
Extension

........NNNNNNNNNAGATCTGCGGTGAGAGGCTGGAGAGTGCT

........NNNNNNNNNTCTAGACGCCACTCTCCGACCTCTCACGA

FIGURE 6-6. Use of adaptors in RDA ligation and amplification. The shorter oligonucleotide (RBgl12 in this example) is complementary to the *Bgl*II site and guides the addition of the longer oligonucleotide (RBgl24). Only RBgl24 is ligated through the PO$_4$ group on a genomic fragment.

incubate for at least 8 hours or overnight at 37°C. It is important that the normal and tumor DNAs to be compared are derived from the same individual, or polymorphisms located at the *Bgl*II sites could result in representational differences between individuals.

The quantity of genomic DNA for digestion depends on availability. Normally, if using tumor specimens, quantity can be as low or lower than 25 ng.

2. Purify the digested fragments by extraction with phenol:chloroform once. Add carrier (5–10 μg of tRNA), 2 volumes of absolute ethanol, and 1/10 volume of 3 M sodium acetate (pH 5.3). Vortex the sample and place on ice for 15 minutes.

3. Centrifuge the tubes at maximum speed (14000g) in a microfuge for 15 minutes, decant the supernatant, and wash the pellet with 70% ethanol. Decant the ethanol and dry the pellet to dampness in a SpeedVac.

    Take care to avoid loss of the pellet.

4. Resuspend the DNA in 10 µl of TE and ligate the digested DNA to adaptors. Set up the ligation reaction as follows:

purified DNA digest (Step 3)	10 µl
24-mer adaptor (62 pmoles/µl)	7.5 µl
12-mer adaptor (62 pmoles/µl)	7.5 µl
ligase buffer	3 µl

5. To facilitate annealing, cool the reaction slowly. Remove the tubes and place them on ice for several minutes. Add 2 µl of T4 DNA ligase (4 units/µl) to the reaction and incubate it overnight at 16°C.

    A convenient way to achieve slow cooling is to place the reactions in a heating block at 55°C, and then place the block in a cold room until the temperature of the block decreases to 16°C.

6. Amplify the ligation reaction using the conditions appropriate for the amount of starting material. The following sequence of steps is suitable for amplification of amounts of digested template DNA ranging from 100 ng to 1 µg (conditions for amplifying smaller amounts of DNA are given in the panel below Step c):

    a. Place 1/10 of the ligation reaction into each of two PCR tubes. To each tube add the following reagents:

H_2O (final volume 400 µl)	304.2 µl
amplification buffer	40 µl
$MgCl_2$ (25 mM)	32 µl
dNTP solution	12.8 µl
adaptor	8 µl
Taq polymerase (5 units/µl)	3 µl

    The $MgCl_2$ concentration is critical to the shape of the representation. The higher the $MgCl_2$ concentration, the larger the fragments amplified in the representation set up to a certain point. The authors have found that a magnesium concentration of 2 mM is optimal for use with Perkin Elmer *Taq* in this protocol. The shape of the representation set or size range as observed on a gel can alter with different *Taq* polymerases at the same $MgCl_2$ concentration. If using a polymerase other than Perkin Elmer *Taq*, it is best to compare results obtained with different concentrations of $MgCl_2$ with those obtained with Perkin Elmer *Taq* in a buffer containing 2 mM $MgCl_2$. A 400-µl PCR volume can be accommodated in only a few thermocyclers, including the ABI 480. The reaction can be divided between several tubes if an appropriate instrument is not available.

    b. Place the tubes in a thermocycler and incubate them for 5 minutes at 72°C to allow filling of the recessed 3′ termini.

    c. Amplify the DNA templates using the times and temperatures listed below.

Cycle number	Denaturation	Polymerization
Amplification cycles (25)	1 minute at 95°C	3 minutes at 72°C
Last cycle		10 minutes at 72°C

    The average yield from one reaction is 15–20 µg of amplified DNA.

AMPLIFICATION OF SMALL AMOUNTS OF TEMPLATE DNA

For amplification of small amounts of DNA from a small number of cells, for example, an additional step is included to help to increase the yield of the amplification product.

- **For amplification of 25–100 ng of DNA:** Follow the setup and amplification conditions described in Steps a, b, and c above, performing only 20 cycles for amplification (Step c). At this point, divide each of the reactions into two tubes, add an appropriate volume of amplification mixture (PCR reagents prepared in Step a) to bring the volume of each divided reaction to 400 μl, and perform an additional five cycles of PCR.

- **For amplification of 1000–5000 cells obtained by laser capture microdissection:** Using the *entire* ligation reaction from Step 5, follow the setup and amplification conditions described in Steps a, b, and c above, performing only 15 cycles of amplification. At this point, divide the reaction into two tubes, add an appropriate volume of amplification mixture (PCRs prepared in Step a) to bring the volume of each divided reaction to 400 μl, and perform an additional ten cycles of PCR.

---

7. Purify the PCRs by phenol:chloroform extraction. Add 1/10 volume of sodium acetate and 1 volume of isopropanol, place the reaction on ice for 15 minutes, and centrifuge at maximum speed (14,000*g*) in a microfuge for 15 minutes. Decant the supernatant, and wash the pellet with 70% ethanol. Decant the supernatant and the dry the pellet to dampness in a SpeedVac.

8. Resuspend the representation set in 1/10 its original volume of TE. Remove 1 μl and analyze the products by electrophoresis through a 2% agarose gel.

    The representation set should be predominantly in the size range of 200–1200 bp. The representation should be compared to a standard of sheared herring sperm DNA of known concentration to estimate the concentration of the representation set. When *Bgl*II representations are prepared from human DNA, there are two distinct bands present in the representation set with approximate sizes of 600 bp and 800 bp. These are the amplified products of repetitive sequences in the human genome. If the representation set is a smear or if these bands are not apparent, it is best to remake the representation set.

    One 400-μl amplification reaction yields ~15–20 μg of representation product. If less product is obtained, it is advisable to reassess the amplification conditions, the reagents, or the ligation.

Labeling and Purification

9. Label the representations by random priming using a commercial kit. A kit from Amersham Biosciences is recommended, although it is likely that random priming kits from other companies will suffice. Follow the reaction conditions described for the kit, with these modifications:

    a. Combine the following reagents in a microfuge tube:

representation set	8–12 μg
random primer (supplied with kit)	10 μl
random nonamer (supplied with kit)	5 μl

    b. Place the tube at 95°C for 3 minutes. Then centrifuge the tube briefly to mix and bring the reagents to the bottom of the tube.

c. To the tube add the following reagents:

Cy5 or Cy3 dCTP (depending on the experiment)	8–10 µl
Labeling mix (provided with random prime kit)	20 µl
Klenow fragment (provided with random prime kit)	4 µl

d. Incubate the tubes for 1 hour at 37°C.

e. Add 4 µl of Klenow fragment (from another supplier), and incubate the reaction for an additional hour at 37°C.

10. Purify the labeled representation sets using a Microcon YM-30 column.

a. Combine the two tubes, one representation set labeled with Cy5 and the other labeled with Cy3, onto the column with an additional 150 µl of TE.

b. Centrifuge the column at 12,500g in a microfuge for 10 minutes at room temperature.

11. Remove the flow-through from the column, add 400 µl of TE to the remaining material (the labeled representation set), and centrifuge the column at 12,500g in a microfuge for 10 minutes at room temperature. Remove the flow-through and repeat this step three times.

   If the target is to be hybridized to a microarray that contains genomic fragments rather than oligonucleotide probes, C_0t-1 DNA should be added to block nonspecific hybridization. If required, C_0t-1 DNA should be added before the last wash in Step 11. If added later, the final volume of the labeled sample will increase to an unacceptable level.

12. The volume of the remaining sample should be ~5–7 µl. Invert the column and place it into a fresh tube. Centrifuge the tube at 12,500g for 2 minutes at room temperature to collect the labeled sample.

13. To the collected sample, add 3× SSPE to 35 µl and add SDS to 0.2% (0.7 µl of 10% SDS).

   The labeled target is now ready for hybridization to the microarray (please see Protocol 5).

Microarray-based Representational Analysis of DNA Copy Number: Preparation of Slides and Hybridization

Robert Lucito and Michael Wigler

Cold Spring Harbor Laboratory, Cold Spring Harbor, New York 11724

Microarrays printed with oligonucleotide probes derived from low-complexity representations are hybridized to representations of genomic DNA and used to detect and identify differences (amplifications and deletions) that lead to changes in copy number. The following protocol describes hybridization of labeled, amplified representation sets to microarrays. Special considerations for setup of the protocol and analysis of data are provided in the panel on TROUBLESHOOTING at the end of the protocol.

The authors have made use of two sources of probes to construct RDA microarrays:

- ***Cloned human DNA restriction fragments of <1.0 kb.*** These fragments have been derived either from small *Bgl2*II fragments excised from specific BAC, P1, and YAC clones containing regions of human DNA of special interest, from libraries of RDA fragments, or from random cloning of *Bgl2*II fragments from human DNA (Lucito et al. 2000).

- ***Long oligonucleotides prepared to match specific sequences*** distributed across the human genome can now be generated by reference to the human DNA sequence (http://genome.ucsc.edu/). Long oligonucleotides rather than restriction fragments are preferred by the authors for several reasons. Oligonucleotides are synthesized under controlled conditions and as a result, the yields tend to be more uniform than those of PCR-amplified fragments. Thus, the variability between spots on an oligonucleotide array is often less than that on an array of PCR fragments. Additionally, it is possible to avoid various sequence-related problems, such as repetitive sequences, mononucleotide stretches, and hairpin structures that limit target access. Knowledge of the chromosomal sequence corresponding to the oligonucleotide facilitates comparison with the literature describing regions of gain or loss in various tumors. Finally, through *in silico* design, it is possible to generate several oligonucleotides that are closely adjacent in the genome, allowing the averaging of results obtained from a cluster of probes.

MATERIALS

CAUTION: Please see Appendix 3 for appropriate handling of materials marked with <!>.

Buffers and Solutions

Please see Appendix 2 for components of stock solutions, buffers, and reagents.
Dilute stock solutions to the appropriate concentrations.

Ethanol (absolute) ice-cold

Some batches of absolute ethanol (100% or 200 proof) have been reported to contain fluorescent contaminants that generate high backgrounds in microarray experiments; 95% ethanol does not have this problem. To avoid difficulties, either use 95% ethanol or identify a brand of absolute ethanol that performs reliably. Absolute ethanol (USP-grade ethyl alcohol, 64-17-5) purchased from Warner-Graham (Cockeysville, Maryland) performs consistently well.

0.2% SDS <!>
0.2% SDS/1x SSC
0.2x SSC
0.05x SSC

Nucleic Acids and Oligonucleotides

DNA microarrays, printed on slides as described in Section 2, Protocol 2

The slides used for microarrays are silanated and purchased from Corning (Corning Microarray Technology [CMT] [http://www.corning.com/CMT/]: Gamma amino propyl silane [GAPS]). Other slide surfaces may require different procedures for preprocessing. The arrays are typically printed at an oligo concentration of 35 pM.

Genomic DNA, labeled as described in Protocol 4

Special Equipment

Coverslips

Many coverslips can be used for array hybridization, but the authors recommend either lifter slips (from Erie Scientific Co.) or HybriSlips (from Grace Biolabs, HS40).

Hybridization chamber (TeleChem International)
Microduster (compressed gas) (VWR)
Slide boxes (60-6441-00, PGC Scientific or equivalent)

Additional Reagents and Equipment

Steps 1–3 require reagents and equipment listed in Section 2, Protocol 2.
Steps 5–11 require reagents and equipment listed in Section 3, Protocol 20.

METHOD

Postprint Processing of Slides

For details of postprint processing of RDA microarrays, please see Section 2, Protocol 2. Essentially the same protocol may be used here with the following modifications.

1. Rehydrate the microarrays for 2–3 minutes in a humid chamber. Remove the slides from the chamber, and fix by cross-linking in a Stratlinker, set at 60 mJ.

2. Snap-dry the slides by heating on a hot plate set at 100–140°C for ~5 seconds, and then allow them to cool in air.

3. Wash the slides in 0.2% SDS for 10–15 seconds and then transfer them into distilled H_2O for 10–15 seconds. Denature the DNA fragments by immersing the slides in boiling distilled H_2O for 3 minutes. Immerse the slides in cold ethanol for several seconds and then dry them by centrifugation.

    If arrays are composed of long oligonucleotides, denaturing in boiling H_2O is not necessary.

4. Store the slides, now ready for use, in a light-proof box, such as a plastic microscope box without a cork liner.

Hybridization

For details on hybridization, please see Section 3, Protocol 20. Essentially the same protocol may be used here with the following modifications.

5. Place the slides in the hybridization chamber, and then place a coverslip on each slide.

6. To denature the target, boil the labeled sample for 5 minutes. After boiling, do not place the sample on ice as SDS in the hybridization solution will precipitate.

    Use a lid lock (e.g., LidLock, PGC Scientific) on the microfuge tube to prevent it from opening during target denaturation. Evaporation of the sample can alter the concentration of the SSPE and the SDS and affect the hybridization conditions.

7. Centrifuge the sample briefly to collect the material condensed on the lid.

    If C_0t-1 DNA has been added to block repetitive sequences, incubate the probe for 30 minutes at 37°C before placing it onto the array. If an oligonucleotide is used, repeated sequences should have been avoided by design. Blocking is therefore unnecessary.

8. Fill the small reservoir on the two short sides of the Telechem chamber with 10–15 µl of H_2O. Add the probe to the slide by pipetting next to the coverslip and allowing capillary action to pull the fluid under the coverslip.

    To avoid formation of air bubbles when adding the target and coverslip to the microarray, and to prevent drying during the incubation of the microarray, please see Section 3, Protocol 20.

9. Place the lid onto the chamber and place the chamber into a hybridization oven. Incubate the hybridization reactions for 12–18 hours at 65°C.

Washing

10. Wash the slides with the temperature and timing described below:

0.2% SDS/1x SSC	55°C	until coverslip floats free of slide
0.2% SDS/1x SSC	55°C	1 minute
0.2x SSC	20°C	30 seconds
0.05x SSC	20°C	10 seconds

    Slides can be washed either individually or in groups by placing them in a slide holder. Coverslips are carefully removed in the first wash solution and may require a gentle shake to encourage the coverslip to detach from the slide. If the coverslip does not come off immediately, leave the slide in the first wash for a longer period. Difficulty in removing coverslips may be a consequence of drying during hybridization. This can be remedied by increasing the hybridization volume by adding a further 2–3 μl of 3x SSPE to the purified labeled sample in future experiments.

    WARNING: Do not let slides dry out at any stage during the washing procedure. Do not use excessive amounts of SDS, which must be completely removed before scanning to avoid high background.

11. Dry the slides by centrifuging them in a tabletop centrifuge at low speed.

    Slides can be placed either in a slide holder or in a 50-ml centrifuge tube with several lint-free wipes pressed into the bottom.

    Typical hybridization results are shown in Figure 6-7.

ANALYSIS

A number of software packages are available to calculate the intensity of the spots or features on the array (please see Section 7, Part 4). The authors currently use the software that is included with the Axon scanner. Once the intensities are measured, the software calculates the ratio of Cy5/Cy3. The data are saved and can be further analyzed with other software. Further analysis is performed to normalize the data so that the median ratio is 1.0 (more than half of the genome should have no change in copy number). Software packages used for analysis (e.g., Spotfire and SPlus) should have the capability of mapping copy number fluctuations to specific chromosomal sequences. Spotfire has the advantage of being user-friendly and flexible enough to change threshold criteria on the fly, and it has several clustering algorithms and various ways to examine data. One interesting function of Spotfire is that the information is linked. By selecting a spot on the graph, the user can follow the behavior of this feature in several other experiments. SPlus is more difficult to use, but it is extremely flexible, and sophisticated statistical analysis of the data can be performed. SPlus also has a scripting language that allows the design of scripts that can perform various functions including importing data, normalization of the data, and merging several experiments.

FIGURE 6-7. Gene-copy microarray analysis of primary breast cancer sample. Nuclei were prepared from a breast cancer biopsy and separated by fluorescence-activated cell sorting on the basis of DNA ploidy. For this comparison, the diploid nuclei were considered normal and the aneuploid nuclei were considered tumorous. Genomic DNA was isolated from the two types of nuclei, and representation sets were prepared, differentially labeled, hybridized to an oligonucleotide array, washed, and analyzed. The representation sets were labeled such that probes that have a gain in copy number (amplified in the tumor) appear *red* and probes with a loss of copy number appear *green*.

TROUBLESHOOTING

Representations and Labeling

- *Preparing representation sets.* It is important that representations compared on an array be prepared in the same manner. The authors have compared representations that were prepared in different tubes, on different days, and from separate digestions. Representations to be compared should be prepared with the same adaptors since large differences have sometimes been observed when representations generated with different adaptors were compared. Typically, the best results are obtained when the two samples being compared are prepared on the same day, using the same adaptors in the same PCR machine.

- *Low signal intensity on the array.* Signals of low intensity may result if the concentration of the representations was overestimated or if less than the recommended amount of representation was used. Low signal intensity may also be caused by inefficient labeling of the representation, possibly due to inefficient extension by Klenow or degraded nucleotides or primer. This problem can be solved by replacing all components of the labeling reaction.

Hybridization (please also see the Troubleshooting Guide in Section 3)

- *Extremely bright and dim regions on the scan of the array.* These features are commonly seen if the slides were not washed properly or were inadequately dried by centrifugation after washing. A possible solution is to increase the number of washes and/or to increase the centrifugation time after washing.

- *Speckles on the scan of the array.* This problem is generally caused by inefficient washing of the slides. If the problem persists, wash the slides an additional time during preparation. Speckles can also be caused by inadequate removal of SDS in the washes. Increasing the time of the final wash may alleviate this problem.

- *Bright edges on the array.* This problem can be caused if the volume of the hybridization mixture is too small, which leads to inefficient flow under the coverslip. Increase the volume of the hybridization mixture to the point where a small amount of fluid remains outside the coverslip. Too much volume will cause the coverslip to float away!

- *Dimmer regions on the side or corner of the array.* This problem is usually a result of flexing of the coverslip. The larger the array, the larger the coverslip, and the greater the flexion. As a result, the array pushes the hybridization solution away from the slide causing uneven hybridization. The solution is either to make a smaller array or to use thicker coverslips.

- *Blotches across the array.* This problem can be caused by uneven slide coating on the slide surface and may be detected at the end of printing if the slide is scanned at a very high PMT on the scanner after prehybridization.

Poor Quality of the Array

- *Spots are small on the array.* This problem arises when the slide is not properly rehydrated. Increase the time during rehydration.

- *Size of the spots varies.* This variation in size usually occurs for one of two reasons. If the fragments are precipitated after PCR amplification, and if the salt used for precipitation is not adequately removed, residual salt is left in the probe. During rehydration, the spots containing more salt will swell more than spots containing less salt. Two solutions are (1) to remove residual salt by taking more care during washing of the plates and (2) to purify the fragments by column chromatography. Members of the author's laboratory routinely use Millipore Multiscreen filter plates to purify the fragment from reagents such as primers, nucleotides, and protein and, in addition, use a programmed robotic workstation for the purification procedure. This system has proven to work extremely well—the only drawback being the loss of ~30% of the material. Variation in spot size can also be caused by failure to resuspend array material after drying. The resuspension volume is small and any pipetting error causes differing salt concentrations and the problem described above. Printing problems associated with sample preparation are usually not encountered with oligonucleotide sets.

- *Low DNA concentration of the spots.* Whether this problem is limited to specific spots or if a whole plate is affected, poor amplification or loss during subsequent purifications is an obvious possibility. This problem can usually be corrected by gel analysis immediately prior to printing.

Part 2: Mutation Detection and SNP Genotyping

INTRODUCTION

Two recent advances have fired a profound revolution in analysis and mapping of mammalian genomes: the development of large banks of informative single-nucleotide polymorphisms (SNPs) whose alleles are present in target populations at approximately equal frequencies, and the development of technologies for constructing highly ordered, site-addressable arrays comprising thousands of oligonucleotide probes. Using these arrays, construction of allelotypes from large numbers of SNPs becomes simply a matter of Cartesian geometry.

SNPs are the most common informative genetic variations between individuals of a species. The number of SNPs in public databases already exceeds 1.6 million, which corresponds to a frequency of approximately one SNP every 2000 base pairs (kb) in the human genome. In addition to their high density, SNPs offer several advantages over other types of genetic markers, for example, their evolutionary stability compared with short di- or trinucleotide repeats, and with their accessibility to scoring methods that are independent of DNA length. Instead of measuring differences in the size of particular segments of DNA (Kwok 2000; Shi 2001), discrimination of SNP alleles can be achieved by techniques such as allele-specific hybridization or allele-specific primer extension. The combination of a method for allele discrimination with a scheme for detection, such as fluorescence intensity, fluorescence polarization, microarray binding, or mass spectrometry, has resulted in several viable schemes for high-throughput genotyping. For a summary of the more commonly used methods, please see Table 6-2. These techniques can, in principle, be used to score thousands of SNPs in large numbers of genomes. Work on this scale is required for linkage studies of monogenic disorders, for association studies of particular genotypes with common diseases (multigenic disorders), and for pharmacogenomic studies.

Because of the need to score thousands of SNPs in many individuals (Chakravarti 1998; Collins et al. 1998; Wang et al. 1998), high-density microarrays are well-suited for SNP genotyping. Noncontiguous heritable polymorphisms may be analyzed in a highly parallel fashion, which allows discrimination between the various alleles that might be present at an SNP locus. In microarray-based genotyping, allele discrimination can take place directly on the array (allele-specific hybridization) or during a preliminary hybridization step (single-base extension). In both cases, since effective detection typically requires greater than fmole quantities of target DNA, sequences containing the SNPs of interest are amplified by multiplex PCR using genomic DNA as template. The arrays can be manufactured either by spotting presynthesized oligonucleotides or by photolithographically synthesizing the probes directly onto the arrays.

Microarrays can be also used to detect known or predictable variants and mutations of a particular sequence by constructing microarrays containing sets of tiled probes that span the genomic region of interest. Segments of genomic DNA from the target locus are amplified and hybridized to the array. The pattern of hybridizations reveals the particular sequence(s) present in the target sample.

TABLE 6-3. Commonly Used Methods for Genotyping

Method	Allele discrimination	Detection	Mutliplex	Reference
Restriction-fragment-length polymorphism (RFLP)	digestion	size, gel electrophoresis	no	Kiko et al. (1979)
Allele-specific amplification	extension	presence, gel electrophoresis	yes	Fortina et al. (1992)
*Taq*Man	hybridization	fluorescence, solution	no	Livak et al. (1995)
Molecular beacons	hybridization	fluorescence, solution	no	Tyagi et al. (1998)
The Invader assays	cleavage	fluorescence, solution	no	Ryan et al. (1999)
Oligonucleotide ligation assay (OLA)	ligation	fluorescence, gel electrophoresis	yes	Eggerding (1995)
Fluorescent resonance energy transfer (SBE-FRET)	extension	fluorescence, solution	no	Chen and Kwok (1999)
Fluorescent polarization (SBE-FP)	extension	fluorescence, solution	no	Chen et al. (1999)
Length-multiplex single-base extension (LM-SBE)	extension	fluorescence, gel electrophoresis	yes	Lindblad-Toh et al. (2000b)
DASH	hybridization	fluorescence, solution	no	Prince et al. (2001)
Pyrosequencing	extension	fluorescence, solution	no	Ronaghi et al. (1999)
Mass spectrometry (MALDI-TOF)	extension	size, time of flight	yes	Haff and Smirnov (1997)
SBE with flow cytometry	extension	fluorescence, flow cytometry	yes	Chen et al. (2000)
Allele-specific primer extension on microarrays	extension	fluorescence, array	yes	Pastinen et al. (2000)
Single-base extension on arrays (SBE-TAGs)	extension	fluorescence, array	yes	Hirchhorn et al. (2000)
HuSNP chip	hybridization	fluorescence, array	yes	Sapolsky et al. (1999)
Affymetrix tag arrays	extension	fluorescence, array	yes	Fan et al. (2000)

This section contains four protocols:

- *Protocol 6: SNP Genotyping Using SBE–Tag Arrays.* SNPs are amplified by PCR and annealed to a locus-specific primer. A single-base extension reaction (SBE) is then performed using fluorescently labeled dideoxynucleotide triphosphates as substrates. The amplified SNP allele specifies the incorporation of one of the labeled ddNTPs, which is detected by hybridization of a tag sequence in the extended primer to genomic probes on a spotted microarray.

- *Protocol 7: SNP Genotyping by SBE Using Affymetrix Tag Arrays.* Similar to Protocol 6, this protocol describes SNP genotyping based on the use of a generic high-density oligonucleotide Affymetrix array. The GenFlex Tag array is composed of generic 20-mer oligonucleotide tag probes that can, in principle, be used to detect any SNP when hybridized to labeled oligonucleotides.

- *Protocol 8: Sequence Variant Detection Using High-density Microarrays.* Strategies for examining, or resequencing, each base in a target region of interest can be accomplished by synthesizing arrays containing a series of tiled oligonucleotides of a defined length. Every possible oligonucleotide that is complementary to the target sequence is present on the array. Each of these probes in turn is represented by a set of at least four variants each containing a different base (A, G, C, T) at a designated interrogation position (e.g., a base near the center of the probe). The fluorescently labeled target, amplified from the genome of interest, hybridizes most strongly to the arrayed oligonucleotides that are its perfect complement. The protocol describes the application of this technology to the detection of mutations in the human *p53* gene.

- ***Protocol 9: Loss of Heterozygosity Analysis Using SNP Arrays.*** This protocol uses allele-specific hybridization to the Affymetrix GeneChip HuSNP to identify regions of DNA that have become homozygous in human cancers as a result of deletion. Germline (normal) DNA and DNA extracted from the tumor are used as templates in multiplex PCRs that are primed with 5′-tailed locus-specific oligonucleotides. Each amplified locus corresponds to an SNP displayed on the the Affymetrix GeneChip. The products of a secondary biotinylating amplification reaction are pooled, hybridized to the SNP array, and stained with streptavidin-phycoerythrin conjugates. Sites of loss of heterozygosity are detected by comparing the patterns of hybridization of the germline and tumor DNAs.

SNP Genotyping Using SBE–Tag Arrays

Kerstin Lindblad-Toh,* Yin-Mei Lim,* Joel N. Hirschhorn,*†‡
and Pamela Sklar*†§

*Whitehead Institute/MIT Center for Genome Research, Cambridge, Massachusetts;
†Harvard Medical School, Boston, Massachusetts 02115; ‡Divisions of Genetics and
Endocrinology, Children's Hospital, Boston, Massachusetts 02115; §Department of
Psychiatry, Massachusetts General Hospital, Boston, Massachusetts 02114

In microarray-based genotyping, discrimination of alleles can take place directly on the array or in a preliminary step before array hybridization. The Affymetrix HuSNP GeneChip, containing close to 1500 human SNP loci that are genotyped simultaneously, is an example of allele discrimination performed directly on the array (Sapolsky et al. 1999). The SBE-TAGS method (Single-Base Extension–Tag Arrays on Glass Slides) is an example of allele discrimination occurring prior to hybridization (please see below) (Hirschhorn et al. 2000).

Genotyping directly on a microarray can be somewhat inflexible because the number and type of alleles are determined by the composition of the microarray. However, one can use a "generic" microarray, and retain flexibility in the range of SNPs to be tested, by performing the allele discrimination prior to hybridization using bifunctional SBE-TAG primers. These primers carry (1) unique locus-specific sequences that provide allele discrimination and (2) sequences complementary to specific oligonucleotide "tags" on the microarray. Thus, a single set of tag-recognition sequences can be combined with different sets of locus-specific sequences to achieve flexibility in allele discrimination. The protocol for SBE-TAGS presented here is based on a method described by Hirschhorn et al. (2000). A similar tag strategy is used with the Affymetrix GenFlex chip (Fan et al. 2000;) (please see Protocol 7).

Tag arrays can be generated either by spotting presynthesized oligonucleotides (tag oligonucleotide), as described in this protocol, or by photolithographically synthesizing the tags directly onto the array (as for the GenFlex chip, Protocol 7). Photolithographic synthesis generates uniform spots, but the method is costly and not feasible in a standard laboratory. By contrast, spotting tag oligonucleotides onto glass slides is both inexpensive and easy, provided the tag primers are deposited uniformly and at equal concentrations. The amount of material deposited can be monitored by adding a positive control oligonucleotide to the spotting mix for each tag oligonucleotide. The positive control primer contains a unique sequence that is detected by hybridization to a complementary fluorescently labeled oligonucleotide. In this protocol, the positive control is labeled with FAM whose fluorescent output is read in a specific channel on the scanner. The positive control allows normalization of spot values to compensate for variation in spotting efficiency.

In conventional SBE (Syvanen 2001), the locus containing the SNP is amplified by PCR, using primers that flank the SNP sites. These primers are selected from DNA sequences stored in the appropriate databases. For example, the db-SNP database (www.ncbi.nlm.nih.gov/SNP/) provides information on the positions of SNPs and the sequences that flank them in the human genome. Following PCR amplification of the SNP locus, the product is purified to remove unincorporated dNTPs and unused primers. A locus-specific tag-SBE primer, which terminates one base 5′ to the SNP of interest, is then annealed to the PCR product. An SBE reaction is performed using DNA polymerase to catalyze the template-specified incorporation of fluorescently labeled ddNTP(s). As in dye-terminator sequencing, each nucleotide is labeled with a different fluorescent dye. Because dNTPs are not present in the extension reaction, only the dideoxynucleotide complementary to the SNP on the template strand will be incorporated. Typically, the products of the SBE reactions are detected using a fluorescent sequencing apparatus or plate reader.

Figure 6-8 shows a schematic diagram of the SBE-TAGS protocol. The first steps of the SBE-TAGS procedure are similar to those of a conventional SBE protocol, but differ in the way in which the labeled product is recognized. Each SBE-TAGS primer is designed with a tail that is the reverse complement of one of the tags spotted on the microarray. When SBE-TAGS products are pooled and hybridized to the microarray, SBE products from each locus will bind to a specific spot on the microarray containing the corresponding tag. The fluorescent color of each spot is then assayed and the genotype is determined (please see Figure 6-8). The PCR can be performed either in single-plex, which is simpler and less prone to error, or in a multiplex reaction, which conserves DNA template and reduces the number of PCRs. The main protocol describes a single-plex PCR SBE reaction and the alternative protocol describes a multiplex PCR approach.

Care is needed in the design of tag oligonucleotides and in the complementary sequences incorporated into the tag-SBE primer. The tag oligonucleotides must be unique with respect not only to each other, but also to the genome of the organism that is genotyped. Table 6-3 lists the 166 tags developed and tested for the protocol described below. These tags were selected from unique bacteriophage λ sequences to have a common size, GC content, and melting temperature (T_m), as well low self-similarity with no more than two consecutive identical bases (Hirschhorn et al. 2000). Tags were also selected to have low similarity to each other and to human genes by subjecting the sequences to a BLAST search against known sequences. Details of the design of the tag oligonucleotides are given in the panel on **DESIGN AND USE OF SBE-TAGS** at the end of this introduction. An alternative approach to creating tags is to consider all possible *n*-mers of a certain size, e.g., 20 mers, and then to select tags whose sequences are unique and have the lowest self-complementarity. Such a set has been used for the Affymetrix tag arrays (Protocol 7) (Fan et al. 2000).

An important feature of the SBE-TAGS method is the high degree of multiplexing that can be achieved by pooling many SNP loci into a single SBE (and/or PCR). When multiplexing, it is crucial to ensure that the loci within a pool do not share homologous segments that may cross-hybridize and cause nonspecific amplification. This problem can be avoided by arranging the primers/loci in different pools according to their degree of similarity.

A critical goal when designing tag-SBE primers is to avoid self-complementarity between tag recognition and locus-specific sequences. If a number of bases at the 3′ end of the tag-SBE primer are complementary to another region of the oligonucleotide, the primer may fold back on itself, forming a self-priming hairpin. In this situation, the next base in the primer rather than the SNP will determine the extension product, and the resulting genotype will most likely be erroneous.

In the following protocol, the tag-SBE primers are synthesized as reverse complements of the tags in Table 6-3, followed by the SBE primer sequence. Further details of tag-SBE primer design are provided in the panel at the end of this Introduction.

SUMMARY

This protocol is adapted directly from Hirschhorn et al. (2000). A summary of the main stages and their purposes is listed below:

- *Tag oligonucleotide and SBE-TAGS primer design.* A critical step that requires thought and careful planning. Please refer to the panel on DESIGN AND USE OF SBE-TAGS following Table 6-3.

- *Constructing the microarray.* Spotting tag oligonucleotides generates sufficient microarrays for several experiments. The slides can be stored for up to 3 months.

- *Genotyping.* This consists of PCR amplification followed by SBE reactions. Genotyping takes 1–2 days.

- *Hybridization.* The products of the genotyping reactions are hybridized to the microarray and scanned. Hybridization takes 1–2 days.

- *Analysis of the data.* Genotypes are determined following quality control and normalization of microarray data.

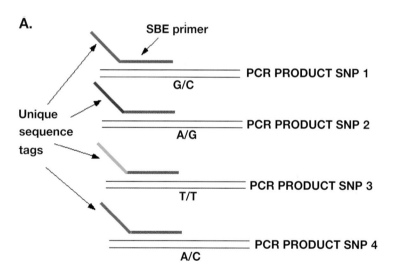

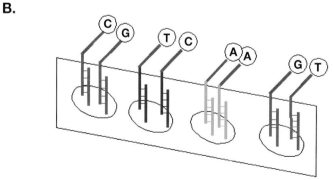

Spotted slide containing reverse complements of sequence tags for demultiplexing

FIGURE 6-8. Schematic depiction of SBE-TAGS for genotyping. (*A*) In SBE, a hybrid primer containing a generic sequence tag followed by a locus-specific sequence is hybridized to a site adjacent to the SNP and extended in the presence of fluorescent dideoxynucleotides. Each of the four extension products carries a distinct fluorescent label represented by the colored tails. (*B*) Multiple SBE reactions are performed in solution with each SBE primer marked by a different unique sequence tag. After hybridization to a generic tag array, generated by spotting the reverse complements of the sequence tags onto a glass microscope slide, the multiplex reaction is analyzed. (Reprinted, with permission, from Hirschhorn et al. 2000 [©National Academy of Sciences, U.S.A.].)

TABLE 6-3. Bacteriophage λ Tags for SBE

Tag	Tag Sequence: To be spotted on slide	Reverse Complement: To be attached to SBE primer	Tag	Tag Sequence: To be spotted on slide	Reverse Complement: To be attached to SBE primer
LT1	GCCTCCACGCACGTTGTGATATGTA	TACATATCACAACGTGCGTGGAGGC	LT84	TTATGTCAACACCGCCAGAGATAAT	ATTATCTCTGGCGGTGTTGACATAA
LT2	GCAGATCAATTAATACGATACCTGCG	CGCAGGTATCGTATTAATTGATCTGC	LT85	GTGCGTCCTGCTGATGTGCTCAGTAT	ATACTGAGCACATCAGCAGGACGCAC
LT3	GGTTCTGTTCTTCGTTGCACATGAGG	CCTCATGTCAACGAAGAACAGAACC	LT86	TTGTGCATCCATCTGATTCTCCTG	CAGGAGAATCCAGATGGATGGCACAA
LT4	TTAGTCTCCGACGGCAGGCTTCAAT	ATTGAAGCCTGCCGTCGGAGACTAA	LT87	AATGGATCGCACTCGTTATTCTCGGA	TCCGAGAATAACGAGTGGATCCATT
LT5	CTGTGACAGAGCCAACACGCAGTCT	AGACTGCGTGTTGGCTCTGTCACAG	LT88	TTAACCACCATCAGGCTCGGTGGTTCT	AGAACCACCGAGCCTGATGGTGGTTAA
LT6	CCTGGTGGTTGACTGATCACCATAA	TTATGGTGATCAGTCAACCACCAGG	LT89	AATTGCTATAAGACAGAGCATGTTGCG	CGCAACATGCTCTGTCTTATAGCAATT
LT7	GCATGTATAGAACATAAGGTGTCTC	GAGACACCTTATGTTCTATACATGC	LT90	CACTCAGGCGGCCTTGATAGTCATA	TATGACTATCAAGGCCGCCTGAGTG
LT8	GCTAGATGAAGAGAAGCGCATGGA	TCCATGCGCTTGCTCTTCATCTAGC	LT91	ACGCCTCGAGTGAAGCGGTTATTGGT	ACCAATAACCGCTTCACTCGAGGCGT
LT9	TACAACCGACAGATGTATGTAAGGC	GCCTTACATACATCGTCGGTTGTA	LT92	CAATGGCATATTGCATGGTGTGCTC	GAGCACACCATGCAATATGCCATTG
LT10	TTCAATCTGGTCTGACCTCCTTGTG	CACAAGGAGGTCAGACCAGATTGAA	LT93	GCTCTGAGCCTCAAGACGATCCTGAAT	ATTCAGGATCGTCTTGAGGCTCAGAGC
LT11	ACACGATGTGAATATATTATCGTGGC	GCCACAGATAAATATTCACATCGTGT	LT94	CATGTCGTCTGCCAGTTCTGCCTCT	AGAGGCAGAACTGGCAGACGACATG
LT12	TTGAAGTTCGCAGAATCGTATGTGT	ACACATACGATTCTGCGAACTTCAA	LT95	TACCTCTGAATCAATATCAACCTGG	CCAGGTTGATATTGATTCAGAGGTA
LT13	AACGTCGTTGAGCACATCCTGTAA	TTACAGGATGTGCTCAACGACGTT	LT96	TTCATCGTTAACCGAGTGGATGTCG	CGACATCCACTCCGGTTAACGATGAA
LT14	GGCAACTCATGCAATTATTGTGAGC	GCTCACAATAATTGCATGAGTTGCC	LT97	GGAACAGAGCGGCAATAAGTCGTCA	TGACGACTTATTGCCGCTCTGTTCC
LT15	CCAGAAGTATATTAATGAGGCAGTGCAG	CTGCACTGCTCATTAATATACTTCTGG	LT98	GGTACGCTGCGCAGGATAATGTCCGGT	ACCGGACATTATCCTGCGCAGCGTACC
LT16	AAGCAGTCTGTCAGTCAGTGCGTGAA	TTCAGCACTGACTGACAGACTGCTT	LT99	CTGTTCGACAGCTCTCACATCGATCC	GGATCGATGTGAGAGCTGTCGAACAG
LT17	AATGATGCTCTGCGTGATGTTG	CAACATCATCACGCAGAGCATCATT	LT100	ACATAATGCAGGCCTTCACGCTTCA	TGAAGCGTGAAGGCCTGCATTATGT
LT18	AATACACGAAGGAGTTAGCTGATGC	GCATCAGCTAACTCCTTCGTGTATT	LT101	TTCGCGGGTGCTTCTTCAGTACGCTA	TAGCGTACTGAAGAAGCACCCGCGAA
LT19	GCTGTTAATCATTACCGTGATAACGCC	GGCGTTATCACGGTAATGATTAACAGC	LT102	TTACTGATAAGTTCCAGATCCTCCT	AGGAGGATCTGGAACTTATCAGTAA
LT20	GCGGAACGGTCAGAGAGATTGATGT	ACATCAATCTCTCTGACGTTCCGC	LT103	TTCGCTCACTTCGAAACCTCTCGTT	AACAGAGAGGTTTCGAAGTGAGCGAA
LT21	GTTATGGTCAGTTCGAGCATAAGGC	GCCTTATGCTCGAACTGACCATAAC	LT104	GTCTTGTTCGATTAACTGCGCGAGAA	TTCTCGCGCAGTTAATCGAACAAGAC
LT22	TTACCTATGATTGATCGTGGTGATATCCG	CGGATATCACCACGATCAATCATAGGTAA	LT105	CCGTAATAGGGATGCGTAATGATGT	ACATCATTACGCATCCCTATTACGG
LT23	GCTGTGGCATTGCAGCAGATTAAGG	CCTTAATCTGCTGCAATGCCACAGC	LT106	GCCAGCGTCAGACATCATATGCAGATAC	GTATCTGCATATGATGTCTGACGCTGGC
LT24	TGACGTCATTGTAGGCGGAGAGCTA	TAGCTCTCCGCCTACAATGACGTCA	LT107	TTGAGTACGGTCATCATCTGACACT	AGTGTCAGATGATGACCGTACTCAA
LT25	TCAATAATCAAACGTAAGGCGTTCCT	AGGAACGCCTTACGTTTGATTATTGA	LT108	TGTATGCCGACTCTATATCTATACC	GGTATAGATATAGAGTCGGCATACA
LT26	TTATCGGCTACATCGGTACTGACTC	GAGTCAGTACCGATGTAGCCGATAA	LT109	CCATATCATCCAGTGGTCGTAGCAG	CTGCTACGACCACTGGATGATATGG
LT27	CCATTATCGCCTGGTTCATTCGTGA	TCACGAATGAACCAGGCGATAATGG	LT110	CAATTCGAATATTGGTTACGTCTGC	GCAGACGTAACCAATATTCGAATTG
LT28	GGCGTACCTTCGCGCGAGATATAAT	ATTATATCTCGCGCGAAGGTACGCC	LT111	ATAACTCAATGTTGGCCTGTATAGC	GCTATACAGGCCAACATTGAGTTAT
LT29	AACTGAGCGGCTAGCCACTGCTGTCC	GGACAGCAGTGGCTAGCCGCTCAGTT	LT112	ATTATCACTGTTAGTCTCCTGACGTC	GACGTCAGGAGACTAACAGTGATAAT
LT30	GTTGTGCTGAATTAAGCGAATACCG	CGGTATTCGCTTAATTCAGCACAAC	LT113	TTCGTAGGGATCAAGGCCATGAATGT	ACATTCATGGCCTTGATCCCTACGAA
LT31	TTATATCTGCACAACAGGTAAGGAC	GTCCTTACCTGTTGTGCAGATATAA	LT114	CCTCGTCTATTGTATCCATTGAGCATT	AATGCTCAATGGATACAATAGACGAGG
LT32	AAGAGCGGCGGCGCTTACTACCGATTC	GAATCGGTAGTAAGCGCCGCCGCTCTT	LT115	TTCCTTCATTGATATTTCCGAGAGCA	TGCTCTCGGAAATATCAATGAAGGAA
LT33	CGGTCACACGTTAGCAGCATGATTG	CAATCATGCTGCTAACGTGTGACCG	LT116	CAAGTACTAATAAGCCGGATAGATAGCC	GGCTATCTATCCGGCTTATTAGTACTTG
LT34	AAGAAGAGTCAATCGCAGACAACAT	ATGTTGTCTGCGATTGACTCTTCTT	LT117	TTAACACAGTGGCGAACTGTCCATGA	TCATGGACAGTTCGCCACGTGTTAA
LT35	CATATCGCGCTGTGACGATGCTAAT	ATTAGCATCGTCACAGCGCGATATG	LT118	GCTGGCAGCATTCTTGAGTCCAATA	TATTGGACTCAAGAATGCTGCCAGC
LT36	AAGGTACTGCAAGTGCTCGCAACAT	ATGTTGCGAGCGACTTGCAGTACCTT	LT119	TTATTGCTTCTCTTGACCGTAGGAC	GTCCTACGGTCAAGAGAAGCAATAA
LT37	CTGCAATTCTGCGGGTAAGCACGAACT	AGTTCGTGCTTACCCGCAGAATTGCAG	LT120	AACGGTTCGACCTTCTAATCCTATC	GATAGGATTAGAAGGTCGAACCGTT
LT38	AACCTAACATTGATTCAGGTACAGG	CCTGTACCTGAATCAATTGTTAGGTT	LT121	ACTGACCTGTGCAGCTTAATATTCT	AGAATATTAAGCTGCACAGGTCAGT
LT39	CAGTTGATCATCAGCAGGTAATCTGG	CCAGATTACCTGCTGATGATCAACTG	LT122	TTGTCAGGTTACCAACTACTAAGGT	ACCTTAGTAGTTGGTAACCTGACAA
LT40	ATATGTTATCTGCCACGCCGATTAT	ATAATCGGCGTGGCAGATAACATAT	LT123	GGATGAATGCGTTGGTGTACCTCAT	ATGAGGTACACCAACGCATTCATCC
LT41	AACTGGATACGATTGGATTCGACAA	TTGTCGAATCCAATCGTATCCAGTT	LT124	TTGCTAGGCACTGATACATAACTCT	AGAGTTATGTATCAGTGCCTAGCAA

ID	Sequence	Sequence	ID	Sequence	Sequence
LT42	CATCGTCAAGCGACGTTCTCATGTT	AACCATGAGAACGTCGTTGACGATG	LT125	AAGTATTCGTTCACTTCCGATAAGC	GCTTATCGGAAGTGAACGAATACTT
LT43	CCATTCCAGACATGCTCGTTGAAGC	GCTTCAACGAGCATGCTCTGGAATGG	LT126	CTATGTGCCGGAGCGGGACAATTACAA	TTGTAAATGTCCGCTCCGGCACATAG
LT44	GCCATCGCTGGACTATCGAAGAGTG	CACTCTTCGATAGTCCAGCGATGGC	LT127	TCGTTGCTGGAAGCCTGGAAGAAGTA	TACTTCTTCCAGGCTTCCAGCAACGA
LT45	ATCTCGTTCCGTATCGCGTCGAACT	AGTTCGACGCGATACGGAACGAGAT	LT128	GGAATATCAGAAGTGGAAACGGCACA	TGTGCCGTTCCACTTCTGTATATTCC
LT46	GAACGCAATATTCACAAGCAATGCG	CGCATTGCTTGTGAATATTGCGTTC	LT129	TTATAATCTGCTGGCCGGAACTAAT	ATTAGTTCCGGCCAGCAGATTATAA
LT47	AAGAGACCGCGACTTACCATGTATC	GATACAATGGTAAGTCGCGGTCTCTT	LT130	GGTGCACATGCGCATACAGTTGGTA	TACCAACTGTATGCGCATGTGCACC
LT48	GCAGAACTGATGAGCGATCCGAATA	TATTCGGATCGCTCATCAGTTCTGC	LT131	CTCACAGTCTGAGCGGTTCAACAGG	CCTGTTGAACGGCTCAGACTGTGAG
LT49	AACCTTCAACTACACGGCTCACCTG	CAGGTGAGCCGTGTAGTTGAAGGTT	LT132	CAGCGGTCGTGCTGTATTGTCTCAG	CTGAGACAATACAGCAGACGACGCTG
LT50	GTGTGGCGGAGACAGCGACGAAGTAT	ATACTTCGTCGCGTCTCGCCACAC	LT133	CTACCACCATGACTAACGCGCTTGC	GCAAGCGCGTTAGTCATGGTGGTAG
LT51	CCTGTATCAGGACATGGTACGGAGCTA	TAGCTCGTACCATGTCCTGATACAGG	LT134	GTCACCTGACGCACTGAATACGCTG	CAGCGTATTCAGTGGCGTCAGGTGAC
LT52	AAGGAGATTATGTACCGAGGAAGAA	TTCTTCCTCGGTACATAATCTCCTT	LT135	GTACTGGCCGCGATTGCAGATGTTA	TAACATCTGCAATGCGGGCCAGTAC
LT53	AATACCGGAACATCTCGGTAACTGC	GCAGTTACCGAGATGTTCCGGTATT	LT136	AAGATATAGCTTCAGCTGTCCGCGCTT	AAGCGCGACAGCTGAAGCTATATCTT
LT54	TTGAAGGAAGATATCTTCCTTCTCAA	CCATGCGGAGGATATCTTCCTTCTCAA	LT137	GGCGTTACAGCATGGATGTGGAGTA	TACTCCACATCCATGCTGTAACGCC
LT55	GGAATTACACCACGTGGATTGGCATC	GATGCCAATCCACGTGGTGTAATTCC	LT138	CAGTTGGCGTGGAGTGCAGGTATACAG	CTGTATACCTGCACTCCACGCCACTG
LT56	GGATATACCGCTCACCGTATTGCAG	CTGCAATACGGTGAGCGGTATATCC	LT139	GGTGGTCCGGCAGTACAATGGATTA	TAATCCATTGTACTGCCGGACCACC
LT57	TCAATGGATACACGGTTGTGAACATCCAA	TTGGATGTTCACAACCTGTATCCATGA	LT140	CACTATGAGAGCCTGCGTGGACGTT	AACGTCCACGCAGGCTCTCATAGTG
LT58	TTGCGGAGCTATTAGAGCTTATACA	TGTATAAGCTCTAATAGCTCCGCAA	LT141	GGATTAACGTGAAGTACCGTTATGA	TCATAACGGTACTTCACGTTAATCC
LT59	TTGTGGTAATAGGCCAGTCAACCAG	CTGGTTGACTGGCCTATTACCACAA	LT142	GGAAGTAAGCGTACTGTCAGCGGCA	TGCCGCTGACAGTACGCTTACTTCC
LT60	GGCCTGCTTAGGTGACGTCTCTCGT	ACGAGAGACGTCACCTAAGCAGGCC	LT143	AACCAGCACGCGTTATCTTGGTACG	CGTACCAAGATAACGCGTGCTGGTT
LT61	AACCAATCGTAGTAACCATTCAGGA	TCCTGAATGGTTACTACGATTGGTT	LT144	AACGCTCGTGTCGTCATACACTGAA	TTCAGTGTATGACGACCAGAGCGTT
LT62	AAGATGACCATCTACATTACTGAGC	GCTCAGTAATTGATGATGTCATCTT	LT145	GGAATACCAACATATCCGGTGTCACG	CGTGACACCGGATATGTTGGTATTCC
LT63	CGCAGATGAGCTTGTCCATATGACTG	CAGTCATATGGACAAAGTCATCTGCG	LT146	GATTGAAGGTCCGGTGGATGGCTTA	TAAGCCATCCACCGGACCTTCAATC
LT64	AACCTCAGCGAGCGTGGTTGATATGG	CCATATCAACCAGCTCGCTGACGTT	LT147	GAAGGGAAGGACAAACCTGAAGTCCA	TGGACTTCAGGTTGTCCTTCGCTTC
LT65	GAGCCTGGCTAACCGTGACCAGAAC	GTTCTCGTCACGGTTAGCCAGGCTC	LT148	TTCTCTCGGTGCCAGTATGGTGCTC	GAGCACCATACTGGCACCGGAGGAA
LT66	AACAATCGCCGCACAGATGGTTAACTT	AAGTTAACCATTCGTGCGGGCGATGTT	LT149	GCGCAGTTACATGAGACTCTGCCTGA	TCAGGCAGAGTCTCATGTAACTGCGC
LT67	AGAATTCTGGCGAATCCTCGACCA	TGGTCAGAGGATTCGCCCAGAATTCT	LT150	GAGCTGCTGCACCATATTCCTGAAC	GTTCAGGAATATGGTGCAGCAGCTC
LT68	AACGGTGCAATGAAGCCAGTTTAGA	TCTAACTTGGCTTCATTGCACCGTT	LT151	ATCGTGAGGATGACTGGTGGCGTAA	TTACGCCACCAGTCATCCTCACGAT
LT69	AATATGCTGCTTGAGGCTTATTCGG	CCGAATAAGCCTCAAGCAGCATATT	LT152	GCTCTGAAGGCGGGTGTATGACATGG	CCATGTCATACACCGCCTTCAGAGC
LT70	AATACTCAACTTCGGCAGAGGTAAC	GTTAACTCTGCCGGAAGTTGAGTATT	LT153	TGAATAACGTCATGTCAGAGCAGAA	TTCTGCTCTGACATGACGTTATTCA
LT71	AATCCAGATGGAGTTCTGAGGTCAT	ATGACCTCAGAACTCCATCTGGATT	LT154	AGATTGCGTCCATCCGCCAGAGTGT	ACACTCTGGCTGATGGAGCAATCT
LT72	AATCGCAATGCTTGGAACTGAGAAG	CTTCTCAGTTCCAAGCATTGCGATT	LT155	CGAGGAGGTCCGGTATGCCGGTTAAG	CTTAACCAGTGCCGTGAGTGACTCG
LT73	TCTACGAATGCGAGAGTGCGTTGCTT	AAGCAACGCACTCTCGATTCGTAGA	LT156	CAGGAGGACACTCCGTATGCCGGAAC	GTTCAGCCACGAGAGTCCTCCTG
LT74	ATCTAACACCGTGCGTGTTGACTAT	ATAGTCAACACGCACGGTGTTAGAT	LT157	AACATACTGAACTCCGTGCAGCCGT	ACGGCTGCACGGAGTTCAGTATGTT
LT75	GGGTCCTCAAGCTGCTCTTGTGTTA	TAACACAAGCAGCTTGAGGACGC	LT158	GGATGATGGCGGAAGTTGTCATCTC	GAGATGACAACTTCCGCCATCATCC
LT76	CACTTCTAAGTGACGGCTGCATACT	AGTATGCACGCGTCACTTAGAAGTG	LT159	AGAACTTCCTGCCGGACAACACGAT	ATCGTGTTGTCCGGCAGGAAGTTCT
LT77	TCTTCTGAACCAGACTCTTGTCATT	AATGACAAAGAGTCTGGTTCAGAAGA	LT160	GTCGTGTATTCCGGACGTACGTG	CCACGTACTGCTCCGGAATACAGAC
LT78	AATGATTCGTCATCTGCGAGGCTGT	ACAGCCTCGCAGATGACGAATCATT	LT161	CAAGGGTGACAAGTCACGTATGACC	GGTCATACGTGGACAAGTCACGCTTG
LT79	CCTCATCAGTGCGCTCTATCTGAACG	CGTTCAGATAGAGCCACTGATGAGG	LT162	CTTCGATCCGGTTGAGGTGGATATG	CATATCCACCTCAACCGGATCGAAG
LT80	ATGGTTCCTGCATATGACATGACAATG	CATTGTCATCATATGCCAGGAACCAT	LT163	CACTGCTTCGCAGGCTGACGTTACT	AGTAACGTACGCCTGCGGAAGCAGTG
LT81	GGTATCATGTAGCCGCTTATGCTGA	TCCAGCATAAGCGGCTACAATGATACC	LT164	AAGAAGTTCAGGAAGCGGTGATGCT	AGCATCACCGCTTCCTGAACTTCTT
LT82	GCAATATATGAATGAACGATGCAGAG	CTCTGCAATCGTTCATTCATATATGC	LT165	AAGAGGAATGGTGCAGCAACCAACAA	TTGTTGGTTGCTGCACCATCTCTT
LT83	TTGGTAGGTGAGAGATCTGAATTGC	GCAATTCAGATCTCTCACCTACCAA	LT166	AAGTGAGAGGCACCTGTCAGATTGAG	CTCAATCTGACAGGTGCCTCTCACTT

Use LT1 as positive control normalize between spots. 5′-FAM label the reverse complement.
Attach 14 Ts to the 5′ end of all tags to be spotted on the microarray.

DESIGN AND USE OF SBE-TAGS

- **Tag oligonucleotide:** Unique sequence tags are generated from an irrelevant genome of known sequence that contains few repeated elements, for example, the bacteriophage λ genome. Primer picking software (e.g., PRIMER3.0; http://www.genome.wi.mit.edu) may be used to identify potential tag oligonucleotides. The design parameters of tag oligonucleotide include

  > length (between 25 and 27 bases),
  > T_m (~55°C at 50 mM salt concentration),
  > low self-similarity (fewer than 3 bases at primer ends, fewer than 8 internal bases),
  > G+C content (40–60%), and
  > no more than two consecutive identical bases.

  From this set, select oligonucleotides that have low sequence similarity to one another. Use BLAST (http://www.ncbi.nlm.nih.gov/blast/blast.cgi) to ensure that the sequences of the oligonucleotides are not homologous to those of the genome under study. A set of tags that work well for humans and mice are listed in Table 6-3.

- **Positive control oligonucleotide:** Design and synthesize a positive control nucleotide that is the reverse complement of one of the tags and attach a FAM label at its 5′ end. If using the tags in Table 6-3, use the sequence 5′-FAM-TACATAT-CACAACGTGCGTGGAGGC as the positive control oligonucleotide.

- **Addition of a linker sequence to the tag oligonucleotides:** 15 (dT) residues are added to the 5′ end of the tag sequence to facilitate hybridization to the attached oligonucleotide, once it has been attached to the array.

- **Design of PCR primers:** Primer sequences are selected using the program PRIMER3.0, available at www-genome.wi.mit.edu. The parameters should be set to T_m: 57–63°C; CG content: 20–80%, primer length of 15–30 nucleotides and a maximum product size of 120 nucleotides. It is important that amplicons be as short as possible so that the efficiency of amplification of all PCR products is approximately equal.

- **Selection of SBE sequences:** A sequence immediately 5′ to the SNP is chosen that is 15–30 nucleotides long and has a melting temperature of 50–60°C. The SBE primer sequence should not overlap any other SNPs. In the protocol described here, polymorphisms where adenine or cytosine would be the incorporated bases should not be selected, since both bases will result in the incorporation of a ddNTP bearing the same dye (TAMRA). For these SNPs, use the opposing strand, i.e., assay them as G/T rather than A/C polymorphisms.

- **Design of Tag-SBE primers:** An iterative process is used to select combinations of tag and SBE sequences. Each SBE sequence is randomly paired with the reverse complement of a tag sequence to generate a hybrid tag-SBE primer sequence containing the tag at the 5′ end. The total length of this primer is 41–52 bases. The algorithm given below is then used to predict whether the proposed primer will fold back onto itself in a way that would render it unsuitable for SNP genotyping. The algorithm calculates a score for each potential site of internal priming by comparing the sequence at the 3′ end of the primer with potential complementary sequences in the body of the primer. To qualify as a potential complementary sequence, the final base in the primer must be the complement of the final base of the complementary sequence, and a minimum of one base is required in the hairpin turn between the two complementary stretches of sequence. The two stretches of sequence are compared and the foldback score is calculated according to the algorithm:

  > Foldback score = (no. matching bases) – 1.7x (no. mismatched bases)
  > Subtract an additional 0.8 for a mismatch in the penultimate base

  Primers with foldback scores >3 should be redesigned by pairing the SBE primer with a different tag. If the foldback occurs within the SBE primer itself, the SBE primer should be designed on the opposite DNA strand, if possible.

- **Construction of compatible pools of SBE primer:** Tag-SBE primers are grouped into pools of ~30 loci. To prevent cross-priming in multiplex SBE reactions, the SBE primers are grouped so that no pair of primers within a single pool gives a foldback score of >8 using the algorithm described above. The cutoff score is higher for cross-priming than for foldback, because the degree of complementarity required to generate an intramolecular foldback is less than that required to generate a stable intermolecular hybrid. Cross-priming between the members of a group of oligonucleotides can be tested by performing multiplex SBE in the absence of template DNA (i.e., use an SBE reaction product [please see Step 14] in the absence of any PCR template). Primers giving a significant signal should be redesigned using an SBE primer on the opposite DNA strand. Alternatively, the pool composition can be changed, but it is usually simpler to redesign the offending primers.

MATERIALS

CAUTION: Please see Appendix 3 for appropriate handling of materials marked with <!>.

Buffers, Solutions, and Reagents

Please see Appendix 2 for components of stock solutions, buffers, and reagents.
Dilute stock solutions to the appropriate concentrations.

$MgCl_2$ (25 mM)
SBE buffer
    500 mM Tris (pH 9.5)
    20 mM $MgCl_2$
SDS (20%) <!>
20x SSC
Slide blocking buffers and reagents
    succinic anhydride (Aldrich) <!>
    1-methyl-2-pyrrolidinone (Aldrich) <!>
    sodium borate (1 M, pH 8.0)
    ethanol (95%)
Slide washing buffers
    2x SSC/0.1% SDS
    2x SSC
    0.2x SSC

Enzymes and Buffers

AmpliTaq Gold (5 units/µl) (Applied Biosystems)
Exonuclease I (Amersham Biosciences)
10x GeneAmp PCR Buffer II (4306894, Applied Biosystems)
SAP/Exo buffer
    500 mM Tris-HCl (pH 8.5)
    50 mM $MgCl_2$
Shrimp alkaline phosphatase (Roche)
Thermo Sequenase (32 units/µl) (Amersham Biosciences)

Nucleic Acids and Oligonucleotides

Bacteriophage λ DNA (500 µg/ml) (New England Biolabs)
dNTP solution containing all four dNTPs, each at a concentration of 10 mM (pH 8.0; Pharmacia)
Fluorescently labeled ddNTPs (custom, NEN Life Science Products)
    carboxytetramethylrhodamine (TAMRA)–ddATP
    carboxytetramethylrhodamine (TAMRA)–ddCTP
    cyanine 5 (Cy5)-ddGTP
    carboxy-X-rhodamine (ROX)–ddUTP
      The reason for using the same fluor for two bases is that the scanner used in this protocol (ScanArray 5000) can detect only four different wavelengths (four channels and four filters). One channel is used for the FAM control, leaving three channels/dyes to be used for the genotyping. The dye-base combinations that were most effective were determined empirically.
Genomic DNA
    Prepare as for standard PCR, diluted to 5 ng/µl.
    Extracted genomic DNA samples should be of high quality; the use of a commercial DNA extraction kit from Gentra Systems, Inc., is recommended.

Oligonucleotides (GIBCO Custom Primers, standard synthesis):
- Tags for microarray spotting (for examples of tag sequences used, please see Table 6-3) are dissolved in dH_2O at a concentration of 200 μM. A positive control oligonucleotide is dissolved in dH_2O at concentrations of 100 μM and 20 μM.
- 5-carboxyfluorescein (FAM)-labeled positive control oligonucleotide (e.g., from Table 6-3, reverse complement: 5′-FAM-TACATATCACAACGTGCGTGGAGGC), diluted to 5 μM in dH_2O.
- PCR primers, unmodified for single-plex PCR (please see the panel on DESIGN AND USE OF SBE-TAGS at the end of the protocol introduction). The forward and reverse primers for each SNP are paired in a solution to a final concentration of 1 μM each in dH_2O.
- Tag-SBE primers (please see the panel on DESIGN AND USE OF SBE-TAGS at the end of the protocol introduction). The primers are pooled in a solution sufficient for ~30 SNP assays, at a final concentration of 1 μM per primer.

Salmon testis DNA (10 μg/ml) (Sigma)

Special Equipment

Balance (for measuring and mixing slide blocking solution)

Coverslips (PMM-3, Lab Scientific, Livingston, New Jersey)

Desiccator cabinet (VWR Scientific Products)

Forceps (pointed and blunt-ended) for handling coverslips

Glass bottle (500 ml)

Glass-marking pen (diamond pen), for numbering slides (VWR Scientific Products)

Graduated cylinders (250 ml and 50 ml)

Heating block, set to 95ºC

Hybridization chamber (adapted from drawings on P.O. Brown's Web Site, http://cmgm.stanford.edu/pbrown/mguide/HybChamber.pdf, or custom-made by Eastern Tool, Cambridge, Massachusetts)

Hygrometer, for monitoring the humidity of the microarrayer chamber (VWR Scientific Products)

Microarray analysis software (e.g., ArrayVision, Imaging Research Inc., Ontario, Canada)

Microarray scanning system (e.g., ScanArray 5000 with an external argon laser, Packard Biochip Technologies, Billerica, Massachusetts)

Microarrayer (GMS417 Arrayer, Affymetrix)
> Attach a humidifier to the arrayer and place a hygrometer inside it for monitoring the humidity of the chamber.

Microtiter plates and plate sealers
> Use 96- or 384-deep-well plates for printing as recommended by Affymetrix (any 96- or 384-well V-bottom plates from Marsh or MJ Research or an equivalent supplier are appropriate); use plate sealers (available from Marsh) or microseal A film (from MJ Research).

Orbital shaker (VWR Scientific Products)

Oven set to 50ºC

Plate washer, for Dynabeads washing step in multiplex PCR (SLT Lab Instruments, custom modified with an attached 96-well magnetic doughnut base)

PRIMER3.0 Primer section software (http://www.genome.wi.mit.edu)

Slide drying bench (VWR Scientific Products)

Slide rack (Thermo Hybaid, Franklin, Massachusetts)
> Straighten out one bend of the metal slide holders' handles to fit into the centrifuge carrier trays.

Slide staining dish kit (VWR Scientific Products)

Slide storage boxes (light-resistant) (VWR Scientific Products)

Slides, poly-L-lysine-coated (Lab Scientific, Livingston, New Jersey) or silane-coated (Telechem, Sunnyvale, California)

> The two types of slides are comparable; however, silanated slides from Telechem are more consistent in the authors' experience.

Stratalinker UV cross-linker (Stratagene)
Tabletop centrifuge (VWR Scientific Products)
Thermal cycler

> The cycler should be programmed with desired amplification protocol (MJ Research DNA Engine or Tetrad or Perkin Elmer 2400, 9600, or 9700) preferably with heated lid.

Water bath preset to 55°C

METHOD

Preparation of Glass Slide Microarrays for SBE

Microarrays for SBE are prepared by depositing tag oligonucleotides on coated glass slides. Many of the issues discussed in Section 2, Protocol 2, such as the availability of various printing robots and microarray slide scanners, are relevant to this protocol.

1. Prepare the source plate for printing:

   a. Prepare a mixture for each well of the source plate as follows:

Source plate component	Volume/well (μl)
Positive control tag oligo (100 μM)	3.0
20x SSC	4.5
dH$_2$O	7.5
Total volume	15.0

   b. Transfer 15 μl of this mixture into each well of a 96-well microtiter plate (the Source Plate).

   c. Add 15 μl of a unique tag (200 μM) to each well, omitting six wells at diverse locations on the source plate.

   d. Into these six wells deliver a further 15 μl of the positive control tag (20 μM). These wells serve as positive control-only spots.

   > Each well of the source plate should now contain 30 μl. The Affymetrix 417 Arrayer can spot 168 slides from this volume of material, according to the specifications below.

2. Use a GMS417 microarrayer to spot each oligonucleotide in four adjacent locations on the slide, or in duplicate pairs if the spots are spatially well-separated on the array, onto poly-L-lysine-coated microscope slides (or silane-treated slides) at a rate of three hits per spot, in a humidified chamber (40% relative humidity).

3. Because the spotted microarrays are clearly visible on the slides at this point, prepare templates to facilitate visualization of the microarrays during hybridization (Steps 15–16). On a piece of paper, draw an outline of a slide and the position of the microarray within it. Make sure to mark the frosted end of the slide on each template.

Processing and Blocking the Printed Slides

4. Place the slides in a slide rack, and humidify them, spotted side facing down, over a 55°C water bath for ~30 seconds. Snap-dry the slides, spotted side facing up, on a slide-drying bench (preheated to 100°C) for ~2 seconds.

5. Place the slides in a UV cross-linker, spot side up, and cross-link the spotted oligonucleotides to the slide surface at 60 mJ.

6. Block the slides as follows:

   a. Prepare the blocking solution by dissolving 3.75 g of succinic anhydride in 236.25 ml of 1-methyl-2-pyrrolidinone. Place the slides in a removable glass tray from the slide staining kit and place the holder into a clean staining dish.

   b. Quickly add 26.25 ml of a 1 M sodium borate solution to the solution of 1-methyl-2-pyrrolidinone in succinic anhydride. Immediately mix the solution by swirling and, without delay, pour the blocking solution over the slides. Cover the staining dish and place it on an orbital shaker at a speed of ~75 rpm for 15 minutes.

   c. Fill a fresh staining dish with 95% ethanol. After 15 minutes on the orbital shaker (Step b), remove the glass tray from the blocking solution and transfer it into the staining dish filled with ethanol. Rinse the slides in the ethanol bath by dunking the tray gently up and down for 1 minute.

   d. Transfer the slides to a modified metal slide holder (the slide holders are modified by straightening one of the bends in its handle) and centrifuge them at 500 rpm (low speed) for ~5–10 minutes at room temperature to dry (be sure to balance the slide holders).

7. Number the slides with a glass-marking pen and place them in a light-shielded box.

   The slides can be stored in a desiccated atmosphere for at least 3 months.

Quality Control Check of Microarrays

8. Hybridize one slide (Steps 16–19) from each batch with the FAM-labeled reverse complement positive control. Follow the directions in Step 16, *except* replace the SBE product with 13.3 µl of H_2O (Step 16a).

   It does not seem to matter which slide in the series is tested, although some investigators prefer to discard the first slide or two.

9. Scan and analyze this slide (Steps 21–24). Use the remaining slides in the batch only if the positive control yields a good signal and if variation in the signal strength between spots is small.

Performing the PCR and SBE Reactions

PCRs can be performed singly and subsequently pooled together, or they can be performed in multiplex. The single-plex protocol is given here and a method for the multiplex amplification is provided in the panel on **ALTERNATIVE PROTOCOL: MULTIPLEX AMPLIFICATION REACTIONS FOR SBE** at the end of this protocol. Single-plex PCR has several advantages: It does not require compatible pools of PCR primers and is more robust, with a simpler cleanup protocol. However, multiplex PCR conserves template DNA and can be accomplished in a smaller number of amplification reactions.

10. Dilute the test genomic DNA to 5 ng per microliter in H$_2$O. Label a microfuge tube for each sample to be used in Step 11b.

11. Set up single-plex amplification reactions in microtiter plates as follows:

    a. Add pairs of PCR primers corresponding to given SNPs (1 μM of each primer in a total volume of 5 μl) to the wells of a PCR microtiter plate.

    b. Prepare a PCR master mix for each genomic DNA to be tested. Calculate mix for each well to be amplified plus an additional 10% of the total volume to compensate for losses during pipetting.

Reagent	Volume/reaction (μl)
10× PCR Buffer II	1.5
25 mM MgCl$_2$	0.9
10 mM dNTP solution	0.15
5 units/μl AmpliTaq Gold	0.15
5 ng/μl DNA	2.5
dH$_2$O	4.8
Total volume	10.00

    c. Add 10 μl of the master mix to each well plated to a particular genomic DNA.

      Some assays work better with other magnesium concentrations; however, magnesium is usually not optimized in this reaction. Probably a more important variable is the dNTP concentration, since excess dNTPs will inhibit the efficiency of the subsequent clean-up step with SAP/Exo.

      Because the master mix contains DNA, meaningful individual negative controls cannot be included; the only possible negative control is an entire plate's worth of primers, replacing the DNA in the master mix with H$_2$O.

12. Place the microtiter plate(s) in the thermal cycler and amplify the reactions using the denaturation, annealing, and polymerization times and temperatures listed below:

Number of cycles	Denaturation	Annealing	Polymerization (Extension)
1	10 minutes at 96°C		
35	30 seconds at 96°C	1 minute at 50°C	1 minute at 72°C

    These times are optimal for the specific equipment and reactions described in this protocol, but the conditions may need to be adapted to suit other types of equipment and reactions.

    The average size of resulting PCR products is 50–150 bases.

13. Remove the microtiter plates(s) from the thermal cycler and generate a pool containing a sample of the PCR products, typically 1 μl per reaction. Pool only the loci that were amplified from the same individual and only those products where the SBE primers are known to be compatible (please see the discussion on construction of compatible pools of SBE primers in the panel on **DESIGN AND USE OF SBE-TAGS** in the introduction to this protocol). Each pool should contain samples of ~30 PCR products. Reserve 10 μl of each pooled product for the clean-up (Step 14). The remaining PCR products can be stored at 4°C for several months.

14. Purify the PCR products: Remove excess dNTPs by digesting with shrimp alkaline phosphatase and excess primers by digesting with exonuclease I:

a. Prepare the following reaction mixture for each pool of PCR products:

Reagent	Volume/reaction (μl)
1 unit/μl shrimp alkaline phosphatase	2.0
20 units/μl exonuclease I	0.2
SAP/Exo buffer	1.5
PCR product (from Step 16)	10.0
dH$_2$O	6.3
Total volume	20.0

b. Incubate the reaction mixture(s) for 45 minutes at 37°C, followed by 15 minutes at 96°C to inactivate the enzymes. Reserve 10 μl of the cleaned-up product for use in the SBE reaction (Step 15). The remaining material can be stored for several months at 4°C.

15. Perform the SBE reactions:

a. Prepare the following SBE reaction mixture for each pool:

Reagent	Volume/reaction (μl)
SBE buffer	1.0
Tag-SBE primer pool (1 μM each)*	1.0
32 units/μl Thermo Sequenase	0.06
100 μM TAMRA–ddATP	0.05
100 μM TAMRA–ddCTP	0.05
100 μM Cy5–ddGTP	0.05
100 μM ROX–ddUTP	0.05
dH$_2$O	2.74
Purified PCR product (from Step 14 of this protocol or Step 4 of the alternative protocol)	10.00
Total volume	15.00

Include a negative control (no PCR product) for each SBE pool.

*The primer pool is selected as described in "Construction of compatible pools of SBE primer" in the panel on DESIGN AND USE OF SBE-TAGS in the introduction to this protocol.

b. Place the SBE reactions in a thermal cycler and perform SBE according to the conditions listed below:

Number of cycles	Denaturation	Annealing	Extension
30	30 seconds at 96°C	15 seconds at 50°C	1 minute at 60°C

The tag-SBE primer is in molar excess over the PCR template. In each cycling reaction, some primer is extended and competes with unmodified primer in the subsequent reactions. Amplification for 30 cycles provides a good level of signal intensity after hybridization to a microarray.

c. Remove the microtiter plates from the thermal cycler. If continuing the protocol the next day, store the SBE products overnight at 4°C, otherwise proceed to Step 16 (hybridization).

Microarray Hybridization of SBE-TAGS Products

Hybridization is performed by adding labeled SBE products from Step 15 to the microarray. Many of the steps are similar to those in Protocol 20 of Section 3, which also provides a step-by-step set of images to help first-time users.

16. Prepare the hybridization buffer in a microfuge tube by combining the following reagents:

Reagent	Volume/12 slides (µl)
20x SSC	18.0
20% SDS	0.9
Salmon testis DNA (10 µg/ml)	0.9
FAM-labeled positive control oligo (5 µM)	3.0
dH$_2$O	67.2
Total volume	90.0

Place the tube on a heating block at 95°C to prevent the SDS from precipitating. Remove the tube from the heating block before proceeding to the next step. Do not place the tube on ice.

a. To 6.7 µl of hybridization buffer, add 13.3 µl of SBE products from one individual (from Step 15). Pipette the entire volume of this mixture (20 µl) directly onto the microarray (to accurately determine the position of the microarray, place the slide over the template created in Step 3). Use forceps to remove the protective seal from a coverslip and place it over the hybridization mix, being careful to avoid trapping air bubbles underneath it. Push out the air bubbles through the edges of the coverslip by gently tapping the coverslips with forceps. Repeat this step for each genotyped DNA.

b. Place the slide(s) in a small, sealed hybridization chamber with 55 µl of H$_2$O on the frosted end of the slide to limit evaporation.

17. Hybridize the microarrays for 4 hours at 50°C.

18. Wash the microarrays:

a. Using a slide staining dish, wash the arrays in 2x SSC/0.1% SDS for 5 minutes at room temperature (with frequent agitation), followed by three brief rinses in 2x SSC and a final rinse in 0.2x SSC for 1 minute.

b. Centrifuge the slides at 500 rpm for 15 minutes at room temperature to remove residual wash solution.

19. Store the dry slides in a light-shielded slide box and scan them within a few days.

Scanning the Microarray

The multiple fluors used in this protocol have overlapping excitation and emission spectra, resulting in a small amount of "cross-talk," where the signal from one dye is detected in more than one channel. This problem can be corrected by applying a matrix that is determined empirically for each scanning protocol and is dependent on the equipment and settings used.

20. To determine a 3 x 3 correction matrix:

a. Using each of the three filter sets, scan a slide with three "pure dye" samples, each containing one of the three dyes (TAMRA, ROX, and Cy5).

b. For each pure dye sample, express the data from each filter set as the fraction of the signal intensity obtained using the filter set corresponding to the dye present in the sample.

c. Arrange these data as a 3 x 3 matrix with the diagonal elements equal to 1. The correction matrix is simply the inverse of this 3 x 3 matrix.

TABLE 6-4. Matrix Showing the Degree of Cross-talk between Dyes

	Channel		
Dye added	TAMRA	ROX	Cy5
TAMRA	1	0.26	0.29
ROX	0.06	1	0.02
Cy5	0.03	0.06	1

The degree of cross-talk is assessed by exciting slides with either TAMRA, ROX, or Cy5-labeled SBE products (rows); readings are made in the channels that are appropriate for each dye (columns). Values indicate strength of signal in the incorrect channel as a fraction of that in the correct channel for a given dye.

TABLE 6-5 Correction or Inverse Matrix for the Values in Table 6-4

	Channel		
Dye added	TAMRA	ROX	Cy5
TAMRA	1.023453086	−.253515888	−0.290777954
ROX	−.060654832	1.016085402	−0.001023174
Cy5	−0.02573221	−0.051794878	1.008371708

21. Scan the arrays at 20-μm resolution using a microarray scanning system such as the ScanArray 5000 with an external argon laser. For this particular instrument, use the following settings:

> FITC: laser 100%, PMT 90%
> TAMRA: laser 80%, PMT 80%
> ROX: laser 90%, PMT 90%
> Cy5: laser 80%, PMT 80%

The FITC laser is used to measure the FAM fluorescent signal of the positive control oligonucleotide.

Data Analysis

For a detailed discussion on data analysis, please see Section 7.

22. Determine the relative fractions of the total signal contributed by each of the two relevant dyes.

a. Subtract the local background in each of the channels by using a microarray analysis software package such as ArrayVision (Imaging Research Inc.). Normalize the signal to the intensity of the FAM-labeled positive control oligonucleotide at each spot. If the positive control signal is quite faint (<10% of the average for the slide), treat this spot as missing.

b. Multiply the normalized data from the TAMRA, ROX, and Cy5 by the correction matrix (from Step 20) to generate corrected "pure dye" values. To correct for the different brightness and efficiency of incorporation of the dye terminators, multiply the Cy5 matrix-corrected signal by 0.5 and the TAMRA matrix-corrected signal by 1.5 for

SNPs where a C is incorporated. These correction factors may need to be adjusted depending on the samples, instruments, and parameters used.

> The need for further adjustment may be determined by testing samples with known genotypes for various SNPs, expecting that the values for heterozygotes will, on average, be 50:50.

23. Determine whether the quality of the data is sufficient to carry on with genotyping. Exclude all slides with low overall hybridization signals.

    a. The average signal of the data points on the slide must exceed threshold, which is defined as 1/10 of the average signal of all spots containing both a positive control and an SNP assay.

    b. Make sure that the average signal over the four replicate spots is >25% of the average signal for those spots taken over all slides.

    c. Omit individual spots with low signal (such as might be caused by a small bubble during hybridization) and use the remaining replicate spots to determine the genotype.

    d. The genotypes at all replicate spots must agree.

24. Calculate the genotyping scores for each spot as follows:

> Genotype score = $\log_{10}[(\text{fraction allele A dye} + 0.01)/(\text{fraction allele B dye} + 0.01)]$

Cluster the genotype scores by SNP. For each SNP, the genotype scores should fall into clusters representing the three possible genotypes:

> Homozygous A (AA) individuals will generally have a score of less than –1.
> Homozygous B (BB) individuals will generally have a score of more than +1.
> Heterozygous (AB) individuals will always have scores that fall between –1 and +1.

> A score of ±1 corresponds to a ratio of the two dyes of 10:1.

> SNPs with poor separation of clusters cannot be genotyped. Note that clustering works best with many data points; therefore, it is advisable to genotype as many individuals together per SNP as possible.

TROUBLESHOOTING

As is appropriate with any genotyping methodology, including some fraction of duplicate genotypes or of related individuals (to check for inheritance errors) is strongly recommended to ensure that the error rate is not high. Visual or semiautomated inspection of the clustered data is recommended to screen for SNPs with poor clustering of data points.

ALTERNATIVE PROTOCOL: MULTIPLEX AMPLIFICATION REACTIONS FOR SBE

Multiplex rather than single-plex amplification of genomic DNA is generally performed if the source of template DNA is limited. The amount of DNA required to amplify and genotype one locus using single-plex PCR is sufficient to amplify and genotype 50 loci using multiplex PCR. The multiplex amplification and subsequent clean-up protocols, however, are more labor-intensive than those for single-plex PCR.

In the multiplex protocol, a primary amplification is performed with 5´-tailed primers. A second PCR is performed using biotin-labeled primers corresponding to the tail. This strategy is used to increase the yield of PCR products due to the competition of many loci in the reaction.

The high concentrations of both primer and dNTPs in the multiplex reaction necessitates the use of a more efficient clean-up step. Because the secondary PCR primers are biotinylated, streptavidin-coated magnetic beads can be used to bind biotinylated products resulting from the secondary amplification.

The multiplex protocol follows the sequence of the main protocol with the exceptions noted below in the corresponding steps.

Additional Materials

Biotinylated primers, modified for the second round of multiplex PCR

    T3 primer: 5´-biotin-AATTAACCCTCACTAAAGGGAGA
    T7 primer: 5´-biotin-TAATACGACTCACTATAGGGAGA

These primers, biotin-labeled at their 5´ ends, are identical to bacteriophage T3 and T7 sequences attached to the primers for the first-round amplification. The biotin-labeled primers are paired together in a solution containing each primer at a concentration of 20 µM in H_2O or 0.1x TE.

Dynabeads, M-280 Streptavidin (10 µg/ml) (Dynal Biotech Inc., Lake Success, New York)
Dynabeads binding buffer
    TE (pH 8.0)
    2 M NaCl
Dynabeads wash buffer
    70% ethanol
    3 mM Tris (pH 8.0)
    0.3 mM EDTA (pH 8.0)
Microarrays, printed with tag oligonucleotides, prepared for hybridization as described in Steps 1–9 of the main protocol
PCR primers, modified for the first round of multiplex PCR

    T3 "tail" sequence to attach to the 5´ end of the forward primers:
      5´-AATTAACCCTCACTAAAGGGAGA
    T7 "tail" sequence to attach to the 5´ end of the reverse primers:
      5´-TAATACGACTCACTATAGGGAGA

The primers are pooled in a solution containing ~30 SNP assays, at a final concentration of 1 µM per primer.

Method

Tag and Tag-SBE Primer Design for Multiplex Amplification

1. Design the tag oligonucleotides with additional linker sequences, following the recommendations given in the panel on DESIGN AND USE OF SBE-TAGS at the end of the introduction to the main protocol.

2. Design and modify the PCR primers for multiplex amplification:

   a. Select primer sequences using the program PRIMER3.0, available at www.genome.wi.mit.edu. The parameters should be set to T_m: 57–63°C; CG-content: 20–80%; primer length of 15–30 nucleotides and a maximum product size of 120 nucleotides. It is important that amplicons be as short as possible to facilitate equal amplification.

   b. Modify and assemble the multiplex PCR primers:

      i. Modify the primers for use in the primary amplification by attachment of a T3 (AATTAAC-CCTCACTAAAGGGAGA) tail to the 5´ end of each forward primer and a T7 (TAATAC-GACTCACTATAGGGAGA) tail to the 5´ end of each reverse primer.

      ii. For the secondary amplification step, prepare a 20 µM solution of 5´-biotinylated-T3 (5´-biotin-AATTAACCCTCACTAAAGGGAGA) and 5´-biotinylated-T7 (5´-biotin-TAATACGACT-CACTATAGGGAGA) oligonucleotides.

   c. Determine PCR pools of compatible loci by making sure that no large regions of homology exist among loci within a pool. Use the fold-back algorithm from the panel on DESIGN AND USE OF SBE-TAGS in the introduction to the main protocol, but compare the corresponding SBE primers to the whole PCR product, not only to the SBE primers within the pool.

3. Select the SBE sequences and design the tag-SBE primers for construction of compatible pools of SBE primers following the recommendations given in the panel on DESIGN AND USE OF SBE-TAGS at the end of the introduction to the main protocol.

Multiplex PCR and SBE Reactions

4. Perform multiplex PCR:

   a. Dilute the genomic DNA to 2 ng/µl.

   b. Set up the first amplification reactions in microtiter plates as follows:

      i. Deliver 1.25 µl of PCR primer pool into each well of the microtiter plate, keeping all of the pools for a particular genomic DNA next to one other.

      ii. Deliver 1.25 µl of genomic DNA (2 ng/µl) into *each* of the wells of the microtiter plate.

      iii. Prepare a master amplification mix for each PCR pool; calculate the total volume required based on the number of PCR pools, plus 10%.

Reagent	Volume/reaction (µl)
10x PCR Buffer II	1.25
25 mM MgCl$_2$	1.042
10 mM dNTP solution	0.625
5 units/µl AmpliTaq Gold	0.5
dH$_2$O	6.583
Total volume	10.0

      iv. Deliver 10 µl of the PCR mix into each well of the microtiter plate.

   c. Place the microtiter plate(s) in the thermal cycler and amplify the reactions using the denaturation, annealing, and polymerization times and temperatures listed below:

Number of cycles	Denaturation	Annealing	Extension
1	9 minutes at 95°C		
31	30 seconds at 95°C	30 seconds at 55°C	30 seconds at 72°C
1			5 minutes at 72°C

These times are optimal for the specific equipment and reactions described in this protocol, but the conditions may need to be adapted to suit other types of equipment and reactions.

   d. Set up the second-round amplification reactions:

      i. Transfer 3 µl of *each of* the first-round PCR products into a well of a fresh microtiter plate.

      ii. Prepare the secondary amplification mix; calculate the total volume required based on the number of primary amplification products, add 10%.

Reagent	Volume/reaction (µl)
10x PCR Buffer II	3.0
25 mM MgCl$_2$	4.8
10 mM dNTP solution	1.2
5 units/µl AmpliTaq Gold	0.6
20 mM each biotinylated T3 and T7 primers	1.2
dH$_2$O	16.2
Total volume	27.0

      iii. Dispense 27 µl of amplification mix into each well of a fresh microtiter plate.

   e. Place the microtiter plate(s) in the thermal cycler and amplify the reactions using the denaturation, annealing, and polymerization times and temperatures listed below:

Number of cycles	Denaturation	Annealing	Extension
1	8 minutes at 95°C		
32	30 seconds at 95°C	1 minute, 30 seconds at 55°C	30 seconds at 72°C
1			7 minutes at 72°C

These times are optimal for the specific equipment and reactions described in this protocol, but the conditions may need to be adapted to suit other types of equipment and reactions.

5. Purify the PCR products by removing excess dNTPs and primers from the amplification products using streptavidin-coated Dynabeads:

   a. For each secondary PCR product, mix the following reagents in a round bottomed plate:

Reagent	Volume/reaction (µl)
Dynabeads	5.0
Dynabeads binding buffer	12.0
second-round amplification product	7.0
Total volume	24.0

   b. Incubate the binding reactions for 30 minutes at room temperature on a magnetic plate.

   c. Wash the binding reactions three times in Dynabeads wash buffer using the SLT-modified plate washer, and then remove the wash buffer.

     The washing can also be done by hand pipetting the wash mixture up and down slowly. Take care to place the pipette tips in the middle of the well *without* touching the circle of beads at the side of the well.

   d. Allow the beads to dry in the air for a few minutes, and then resuspend each set of magnetic beads containing the PCR products in 10 µl of H$_2$O.

6. Return to the main protocol at Step 14 and use the products in the SBE reaction, making sure that the loci in the SBE pool corresponds to the loci in the PCR pool. Continue with hybridization, scanning, and analysis as described in the main protocol (Steps 16–24).

Protocol 7

SNP Genotyping by SBE Using Affymetrix Tag Arrays

Thomas Ryder, Xiaohua Huang, Nila Patil, and Jian-Bing Fan
Affymetrix, Inc., Santa Clara, California 95051

This protocol describes the use of Affymetrix arrays to genotype single-base polymorphisms (SNPs) using the Affymetrix GenFlex array. The human SNP (HuSNP) array described in Protocol 9 makes use of specific probes that are complementary to sequences flanking specific SNPs. The range of SNPs that can be measured on a HuSNP array is therefore governed by the composition of the array. By contrast, the GenFlex array makes use of generic 20-mer oligonucleotide *tag probes* that in principle can be used to detect any SNP, through the use of a bifunctional *tag primer* to perform a single-base extension (SBE) reaction. The 5′ half of each tag primer is the reverse complement of a tag probe on the array, and the 3′ half corresponds to a sequence immediately 5′ to a given SNP (Figure 6-9). The 3′ base of the tag primer terminates one base before the SNP site.

In an SBE reaction (Figure 6-9), each SNP locus is first amplified by PCR using primers that flank the SNP site. These reactions are typically multiplexed, so that 20–30 loci are amplified in a single reaction. An SBE is then performed using using *Taq* polymerase or Thermo Sequenase, also in multiplex. The tag primer is annealed to the PCR product and one of the two possible bases, corresponding to the biallelic SNP polymorphism, incorporated using dideoxynucleotide triphosphates. The identity of the added base can be determined, as the alternatives are labeled with a different fluorophore or hapten. The use of chain-terminating dideoxynucleotides ensures that only a single base is added. The SBE products are then pooled and hybridized to a tag array. A laser scanner collects data, and genotype results are determined from the relative signal intensities observed. A similar assay has been applied to spotted arrays using presynthesized oligonucleotides (please see Protocol 6) (Hirschhorn et al. 2000; Lindblad-Toh et al. 2000b).

The basic method used in this protocol was first described by Fan et al. (2000) and formed the prototype for the commercially available GenFlex tag array. Fan et al. describe an array with 32,000 distinct, perfect-match (PM) tag probes and a further 32,000 mismatch (MM) oligonucleotides, which differ with respect to the cognate PM probes at the middle base. At the time of writing, the GenFlex tag array comprises 2050 PM and 2050 MM tags that yield high PM/MM signal ratios when hybridized to labeled oligonucleotides. Of these, 50 representative tag probes have been selected as controls, leaving 2000 available for measuring SNP identities. A pool of 50 fluorescein-labeled oligonucleotides, which are the complement of the tag probe controls, is added to the hybridization mix of each experiment as a control for signal intensity.

The generation of the bifunctional tag oligonucleotides for use in SBE reactions requires careful consideration. The panel on DESIGN AND USE OF SBE-TAGS in the introduction to Protocol 6 describes some of the considerations in their design and also processes for determining which tags might be pooled for multiplex reactions.

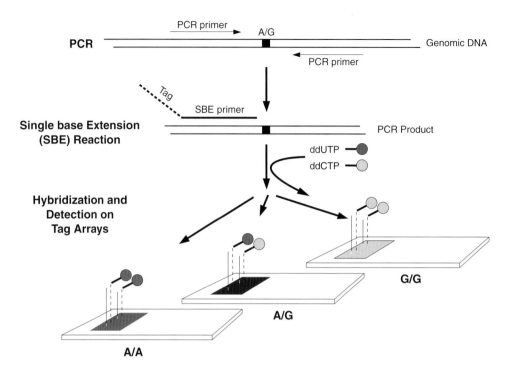

FIGURE 6-9. Tag-SBE genotyping assay. Marker-specific primers are designed for amplification of each SNP from genomic DNA (Wang et al. 1998). All SNPs with the same pair of variant bases (e.g., A/G SNPs) are pooled. Double-stranded PCR products serve as templates for the SBE reactions. Each SBE primer is chimeric with a 5′ end complementary to a unique tag synthesized on the array and a 3′ end complementary to the genomic sequence and terminating one base before a polymorphic SNP site. Thus, each SNP primer is uniquely associated with a specific tag on the array. SBE primers corresponding to multiple markers are added to a single reaction tube and extended in the presence of pairs of ddNTPs, labeled with different fluorophores; for example, an A/G biallelic marker is extended in the presence of biotin-labeled ddUTP and fluorescein-labeled ddCTP. The labeled multiplex SBE reaction products are pooled and hybridized to the tag array. Three resulting hybridization patterns are shown, corresponding to the three genotypes AA, AG, and GG. (Adapted from Fan et al. 2000.)

MATERIALS

CAUTION: Please see Appendix 3 for appropriate handling of materials marked with <!>.

Buffers, Solutions, and Reagents

Please see Appendix 2 for components of stock solutions, buffers, and reagents.
Dilute stock solutions to the appropriate concentrations.

Acetylated bovine serum albumin (BSA) (50 mg/ml) (15561020, Invitrogen)
BSA (20 mg/ml)
Ethanol, prechilled to –20ºC
Glycogen (100 μg/ml) (Boehringer Mannheim)
Lithium chloride (LiCl) (8 M)
MES buffer (0.5 M, pH 6.7)
$MgCl_2$ (5 mM)

1x SSPE-T
>   Prepare 1x SSPE with 0.001% Triton X-100. Filter the solution through a 0.2-μm filter.

6x SSPE-T
>   Prepare 6x SSPE with 0.005% Triton X-100. Filter the solution through a 0.2-μm filter.

Staining solution
>   2.2 μg/ml streptavidin R-phycoerythrin
>   0.5 mg/ml acetylated BSA
>   Dissolve the reagents in 6x SSPE-T.

Streptavidin R-phycoerythrin (1 mg/ml) (Molecular Probes)

Tetramethylammonium chloride (TMAC) (T 3411, Sigma) <!>

Triton X-100 (T 9284, Sigma)

Enzymes and Enzyme Buffers

AmpliTaq Gold (Applied Biosystems)

10x GeneAmp PCR buffer II (4306894, Applied Biosystems)

Exonuclease I (10 units/μl) (Amersham Biosciences)

Shrimp alkaline phosphatase (1 unit/μl) (Amersham Biosciences)

Thermo Sequenase (32 units/μl) (Amersham Biosciences)]

5x Thermo Sequenase buffer (provided with the enzyme)

Nucleic Acids and Oligonucleotides

Biotinylated dNTPs (New England Nuclear)
>   biotin-N6-ddUTP
>   biotin-11-acyclo-dCTP [(d)dCTP]
>   biotin-N6-ddATP

dNTP solution containing all four dNTPs, each at a concentration of 25 mM (stock dNTPs; 27-2035-01, Pharmacia Biotech)

Fluorescein-labeled control oligonucleotides (pool of 50) (900302, Affymetrix)

Fluorescein-labeled dNTPs (New England Nuclear)
>   fluorescein-N6-ddGTP
>   fluorescein-N6-ddCTP
>   fluorescein-N6-ddATP
>   fluorescein-N6-ddCTP

GenFlex Tag Arrays (5 pack) (900302, Affymetrix)

Genomic DNA samples, diluted to 20 ng/μl

PCR primer mix
>   Forward and reverse primers defining an amplicon spanning each SNP site. For each primer, the concentration is 1 μM.

Tag-SBE primer mix (TAG-SNP for each SNP locus)
>   For design considerations, please see the panel on DESIGN AND USE OF SBE-TAGS in the introduction to Protocol 6. For each primer, the concentration is 20 nM.

Special Equipment

Fluidic station (FS400, Affymetrix)

GeneChip software (Affymetrix) for analysis of microarrays

Hybridization chamber with rotisserie for rotary movement

Microfuge (5415C, Eppendorf)

S-300 Column (Pharmacia)

Scanning system (custom, Affymetrix)

> The system should have a resolution of 60–70 pixels per feature, and two filters designed to capture emissions for wavelengths of 530 nm and 570 nm.

Thermal cycler

> The cycler should be programmed with desired amplification protocol (MJ Research DNA Engine or Tetrad or Perkin Elmer 2400, 9600, or 9700) preferably with heated lid.

METHOD

Multiplex Amplification

Because SNPs are typically biallelic, two distinct labels should be sufficient to resolve most SNP alleles in an SBE reaction (Marth et al. 2001). To facilitate the subsequent SBE reaction, the locus amplification reactions are pooled on the basis of SNPs that have same base composition at the polymorphic site, for example, all SNPs that have an A or G. Multiplexed pools usually contain up to 30 locus amplification reactions.

1. Prepare the mix for multiplex locus specific amplification in a final volume of 25 µl per reaction according to the table below:

Stock solution	Volume/locus (µl)	Final concentration
10x buffer II	2.5	1x
25 mM $MgCl_2$	5.0	5 mM
25 mM dNTPs	1.0	1 mM
PCR primer mix (1 µM each)	2.5	0.1 µM
Genomic DNA (20 ng/µl)	2.5	50 ng
5 units/µl AmpliTaq Gold	0.4	2 units
ddH_2O	11.1	
Final volume (µl)	25.0	

2. Transfer the samples to a thermal cycler and amplify the reactions using the denaturation, annealing, and polymerization times and temperatures listed below:

Number of cycles	Denaturation	Annealing	Extension
1	10 minutes at 96°C		
40	30 seconds at 94°C	40 seconds at 57°C	90 seconds at 72°C
1			10 minutes at 72°C

Remove the reactions from the thermal cycler and transfer them to 4°C until needed for the next step.

3. To each of the PCR products from Step 1 (25 µl reactions), add 1 µl of exonuclease I and 1 µl of shrimp alkaline phosphatase; incubate the digestions for 1 hour at 37°C. Inactivate the enzyme activities for 15 minutes at 100°C.

> Enzymatic treatment of the PCR products is required to degrade and dephosphorylate the unused primers and dNTPs, respectively, because they may interfere with the SBE step.

4. To purify the products, apply each sample to an S-300 column, prepared according to the manufacturer's (Pharmacia) instructions.

> A volume equal to that of the sample applied (~25 µl) will be displaced into the collecting tube and will consist of the PCR amplicons dissolved in ddH_2O, purified away from residual fragments of PCR primers and nucleotides. The samples are ready for the SBE reaction.

SBE Reaction

5. Perform the SBE reactions:

   a. Prepare the SBE reaction mixture as outlined in the table below. Set up six reactions, one for each combination of labeled and unlabeled nucleotide pair.

      The SBE reaction follows the same multiplexing set up at the PCR level and contains up to a 25-plex SNP mixture to be extended. For a discussion of primer design and determination of which primers should be multiplexed together, please see the panel on DESIGN AND USE OF SBE-TAGS in the introduction to Protocol 6.

Stock solution	Volume (µl)/sample	Final concentration
Amplified template (Step 2)	6.0	
Tag-SBE primer mix (20 nM each)	2.5	1.5 nM each
5x Thermo Sequenase buffer	6.6	1x
Flu-ddNTP (1 nmole/µl)	0.8	24 µM
Bio-ddNTP (X nmole/µl)*	0.5	7.6 or 3.8 µM
Other two unlabeled ddNTPs (1 nmole/µl)	0.3 each	10 mM each
6.4 units/µl Thermo Sequenase Gold	0.4	2.56 units
ddH$_2$O	15.6	
Final volume (µl)	33.0	

      *The concentration of Bio-ddNTP is 0.5 nmole/µl for Bio-ddUTP or Bio-11-acyclo-dCTP (0.5 mM) and 0.25 nmole/µl for Bio-ddATP (0.25 mM). The choice of labeled and unlabeled ddNTPs is determined by knowledge of the possible allelotypes in a given SBE pool; e.g., all As or Gs will require Bio-ddATP, Flu-ddGTP, and unlabeled ddCTP and ddTTP.

   b. Transfer the reactions to a thermal cycler and perform SBE using the denaturation and annealing times and temperatures listed below:

Number of cycles	Denaturation	Annealing and Extension
1	3 minutes at 96ºC	
45	25 seconds at 94ºC	11 seconds at 58ºC

      These times are optimal for the specific equipment and reactions described in this protocol, but the conditions may need to be adapted to suit other types of equipment and reactions.

   c. Remove reactions from the thermal cycler and transfer them to 4ºC until the next step.

Purification

6. Combine all six of the separate SBE reactions (each 25 µl) and mix them with 30 µl of 100 µg/ml glycogen (Boehringer Mannheim). Precipitate the products of the SBE reactions with 18.75 µl of 8 M LiCl and 1125 µl of prechilled (–20ºC) absolute ethanol.

   Although the same fluors are used for different nucleotides, all six extension mixes (A/G, A/T, A/C, G/T, G/C, and T/C) can be pooled and the reactions hybridized to single array because both the identity of the tag sequence and the reaction conditions used for each SNP locus are known.

7. Mix the samples well, and recover the precipitates by centrifugation in a microfuge at maximum speed (16,000g) for 15 minutes at room temperature. Decant the supernatant and dry the pellets for 40 minutes at 40ºC. Resuspend the samples in 33 µl of ddH$_2$O.

The SBE products are now ready for hybridization. If not used right away, the samples can be stored frozen at this stage.

Microarray Hybridization of SBE Products

Hybridization is performed by adding labeled SBE products from Step 7 to the microarray. Please refer to the Troubleshooting Guide at the end of Section 3, which provides a step-by-step set of images to help first-time users.

8. Prehybridize the GenFlex Tag Array with a solution of 6x SSPE-T and 0.5 mg/ml of BSA for 15 minutes at 42°C.

9. Prepare the hybridization buffer by combining the following reagents:

Stock solution	Volume (µl)	Final Concentration
5 M TMAC	72.0	3 M
0.5 M MES buffer	12.0	50 mM
1% Triton X-100	1.2	0.01%
10 mg/ml herring sperm DNA	1.2	100 µg/ml
5 nM Flu-c213 control oligo	1.2	50 pM
20 mg/ml BSA	3.0	100 µg/ml
SBE products (Step 7)	29.4	
Final volume	120.0	

10. Denature the SBE sample in hybridization buffer (Step 9) for 10 minutes at 100°C, and then snap cool for 2–5 minutes on ice.

11. Remove the prehybridization solution from the Tag Array, and then pipette the entire volume of the hybridization buffer (120 µl) directly onto the Tag microarray.

12. Hybridize the Tag Array with SBE-labeled products in 120 µl of hybridization solution for 2 hours at 42°C on a rotisserie, rotating at 40–50 rpm.

Washing and Staining the Hybridized Arrays

13. Remove the hybridized Tag Arrays from the hybridization chamber, and wash them as follows:

    a. Rinse the arrays with 1x SSPE-T twice for 10 seconds.

    b. Wash the chip with 1x SSPE-T for 15–20 minutes at 40°C on a rotisserie, rotating at 40–50 rpm.

    c. Wash the arrays on a fluidic station 10 times with 6x SSPE-T at 22°C.

    Alternatively, wash the array directly on the GeneChip fluidics station using scripts provided with the GenFlex Array. Their use is described in the FS400 user manual.

14. Stain the array(s) with 120 µl of staining solution for 15 minutes at room temperature on a rotisserie, rotating at 40–50 rpm.

15. After staining, rinse the probe array on the fluidics station 10 times with 6x SSPE-T at 22°C.

Scanning the Arrays

16. Scan the chips using a custom scanning system with a resolution of 60–70 pixels per feature at 530 nm and 570 nm.

17. Use the GeneChip software to convert the image files into digitized files to give a list of intensity values for every probe on the array.

DATA ANALYSIS

The sequences selected for synthesis on the GenFlex array are deliberately enriched in probes with high intrinsic discrimination against hybridization to mismatched targets (see GenFlex Tech Note 1, Affymetrix 700482, Rev. 2). In samples of substantial sequence complexity, however, stray signals from concentration-driven binding of sequences similar but not identical to the complementary target may still occur. A single-base mismatch version of each capture probe is provided as a control to allow subtraction of such stray signal from the overall observed signal. The magnitude of stray signal will usually be about the same for the perfect match (PM) and the mismatch (MM) probes. Because the intrinsic discrimination of the GenFlex capture probes is so high, subtraction rarely causes more than a trivial loss of information. Raw versions of the signal for each captured target can therefore be reasonably approximated for each emission wavelength (530 nm and 570 nm) listed in the GeneChip Hybridization Analysis Window report as $S_{570} = PM_{570} - MM_{570}$ and $S_{530} = PM_{530} - MM_{530}$. Since there is some overlap of phycoerythrin signal into the fluorescein ("530") channel and vice versa, a crossover correction estimated from internal standards included in the hybridization reaction can be applied. For these two labels, a single iteration, channels-ratio subtraction is usually sufficient. For example, a panel of 20 fluorescein-labeled oligos (Genset) complementary to a subset of the GenFlex control probes (as described in the GenFlex Technical note) can be included in the hybridization reaction at 50 pM. An overlapping set of 20 biotin-labeled oligos (Genset) can also be included at 50 pM such that 10 of these are the same sequence as fluorescein-labeled oligos and 10 are complementary to a unique subset of the GenFlex control probes. For each of the features hybridized to fluorescein-only targets, the S_{570}/S_{530} intensity ratio should be calculated and averaged over all 10 to yield the $F_{570/530}$ correction factor. Conversely, for the features hybridized to biotin-only targets, the phycoerythrin correction factor, $P_{530/570}$, can be calculated by averaging the 10 corresponding S_{530}/S_{570} ratios. The corrected signal values can then be calculated as $C_{530} = S_{530} - S_{570} \times P_{530/570}$ and $C_{570} = S_{570} - C_{530} \times F_{570/530}$.

These corrections should also be applied to the 570-nm and 530-nm channel signals from each of the 10 features hybridized to equimolar mixtures of biotin- and fluorescein-labeled oligos and the C_{570}/C_{530} ratios averaged to obtain a normalization factor, $N_{570/530}$. This value, which need only be approximate, can normalize intrinsic intensity differences from two labels with different photon yields and balance their magnitude for the next step, calculation of the relative allele signal (RAS) at each feature reporting an SBE result: $RAS = N_{570/530} \times C_{530}/(N_{570/530} \times C_{530} + C_{570})$. The RAS reports essentially the fraction of total signal at a feature contributed by the SBE product labeled with fluorescein and tends toward zero if the genotype is homozygous for the allele yielding a biotin-labeled target and toward 1 if the genotype is homozygous for the fluorescein-nucleotide complement. Heterozygotes can be expected to yield intermediate values, which should cluster about a typical value for a particular locus, which may not be exactly 0.5 due to the influence of local sequence motifs or structure on primer binding and/or differences in incorporation efficiency of different nucleotides.

Evaluation of the discordance rate of the chip versus conventional SNP methods depends on intrinsic factors of the SNP loci, the size of the training set, the quality of reference genotypes extant for that training set, the sophistication of the algorithm, and so forth. Discordance rates also depend on the accuracies of the methods being compared. For a more detailed discussion of the accuracy rate of this technology, please see Protocol 8. Typically, the concordance rates for most flexible genotyping methods can be expressed as >98% x >98% = >96% (please also see the discussion in Fan et al. 2000). Note that assays highly refined for a particular marker set can certainly yield higher rates of accuracy.

TROUBLESHOOTING SINGLE-BASE EXTENSION

The overall assay performance of SBE is generally determined by the success of the amplification and SBE reactions. High pass rates (90%) and accuracy (98–99%) can be obtained with preselection of loci and careful optimization of primer designs to avoid secondary structures (J. Hirschhorn, pers. comm.). Parameters to consider include melting temperatures of PCR and SBE primers, length, foldback, and dimer formation potential. Mispriming at heterologous sites can occur at low but measurable rates which can be compounded depending on the total complexity of the DNA sample containing the analyte SNPs. Locus-specific amplification, as well as the SBE-tag oligonucleotides must be designed with the desired level of reaction multiplexing in mind. For locus-specific amplification, primers should be chosen to be as close to the polymorphic site as possible to maximize the success rate of the multiplex PCR, ideally yielding a uniform population of amplicon size less than ~120 bp. Generally only one strand is chosen for the SBE reaction, but including an independent reaction for the other strand builds in redundancy and may improve accuracy.

The fluorophore selection and associated spectral overlap are also critical considerations for the user. Once fluorophores have been selected, a matrix of label concentrations may be designed to sample and correct for the potential overlap in emission spectra. Given the biallelic nature of SNPs, there is a minimum of six (A/G, A/T, A/C, G/T, G/C, and T/C) reactions when using two fluorophores to distinguish the two alleles for all SNPs. The addition of unlabeled ddNTPs in this reaction increases the specificity of the assay.

Other parameters to be considered include analysis and clustering algorithms needed to assign a genotype call with a certain level of confidence from the signals obtained from the chip. For a sufficiently large sample population, the RAS scores for any one locus should cluster in up to three populations, corresponding to the three diploid genotypes possible for a biallelic marker. If the clusters are sufficiently distinct, this will often be enough information to bootstrap the genotypes of the constituent samples, as well as to provide training on boundaries that demarcate genotype calls that can be applied to subsequent samples. In some cases, additional cluster resolution might be achieved by two-dimensional graphing of the RAS scores derived from from SBE on both strands for a particular marker.

Sequence Variant Detection Using High-density Microarrays

Thomas Ryder, Hajime Matsuzaki, and Suzanne Dee

Affymetrix, Inc., Santa Clara, California 95051

Highly effective methods have been developed to interrogate successive nucleotides from continuous segments of genes or genomes using arrays of short oligonucleotides (Chee et al. 1996; Kozal et al. 1996). This strategy, often termed resequencing, involves the generation of a tiled array of oligonucleotides, typically 15–25 bases in length, that collectively span the entire sequence of a known gene. To determine the sequence of any given base, four oligonucleotide probes are generated that are complementary to a region of a gene of interest but differ from each other in that a base near the middle of the oligonucleotide is substituted with all four possible bases (A, G, C, T). A group of four oligonucleotides is referred to as a probe set and a typical array has thousands of such probe sets. The fluorescently labeled target, derived from the gene of interest, typically hybridizes most strongly to the correct oligonucleotide variant, allowing the sequence to be "read" at that position. Reading the hybridization pattern at all other features on the array allows the complete sequence of the target DNA to be determined. Increased precision and confidence are achieved by using complicated statistical and pattern-recognition algorithms, as well as by the redundant interrogation of target bases using multiple probe sets of different lengths and/or substitution positions. The method can also accommodate detection of well-characterized deletions or defined insertions in a gene by building features into the array that encompass the novel sequences generated by these mutations (please see Figure 6-10).

Resequencing technology is a powerful and rapid method for detecting novel spontaneous mutations or the identification of heritable single-nucleotide polymorphisms (SNPs) in specific regions of a genome (Hacia et al. 1996; Wang et al. 1998; Ahrendt et al. 1999; Hacia and Collins 1999; Wikman et al. 2000). Using current photolithographic synthesis technology, in conjunction with amplification of long PCR products, it is possible to partially resequence regions spanning >10 kb (Cutler et al. 2001) to >10,000 kb (Patil et al. 2001) in a single hybridization reaction; the latter scale relies upon incubation of the entire wafer with the hybridization sample.

This protocol describes an assay that can analyze the complete coding region of the human *p53* gene to detect spontaneous mutations, even in the presence of moderate amounts of contaminating wild-type sequences from normal tissue. The protocol illustrates the principles employed in analyzing millions of bases at a time using oligonucleotide arrays and can be performed using readily available commercial reagents.

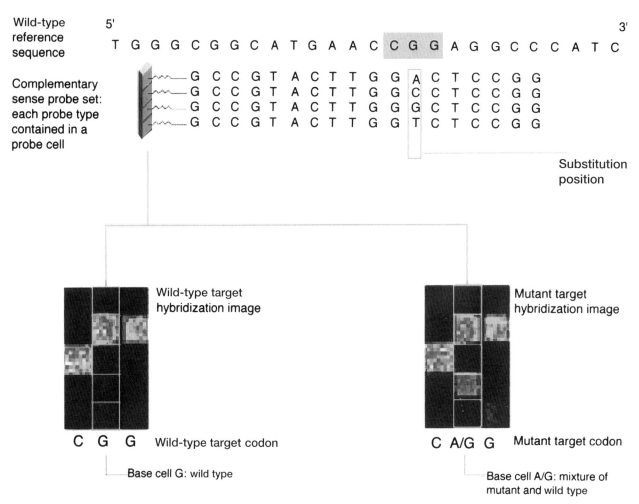

FIGURE 6-10. Schematic representation of the chip array system. Probes on the array are arranged in sets of four. Each probe in the set is complementary to the reference sequence except for a mismatch position, called the "substitution" position. At this position, each of the four possible nucleotides (A, C, G, T) is represented in the probe set. Assay conditions optimize hybridization of the fluorescently labeled DNA target to the probe that best matches its sequence. This perfect hybrid yields a higher fluorescence intensity relative to the other four target-probe hybrids in the set. There are probe sets complementary to every base in the *p53* gene. (Adapted from Ahrendt et al. 1999 [courtesy of Affymetrix].)

OVERVIEW OF THE *p53* MUTATION SCANNING PROCEDURE

DNA may be extracted from the samples under test using a variety of standard laboratory techniques. Reliable results have been obtained in the author's laboratory using the QIAGEN QIAamp tissue kit. Note that DNA from formaldehyde-fixed tissues is likely to be damaged and special handling may be required as described below (please also see Gall et al. 1993; Greer et al. 1995). All ten coding exons of the *p53* gene are amplified in a single reaction using the extracted DNA as template, after which the amplicons are fragmented and labeled at their 3′ ends with a fluoresceinated dideoxynucleotide. The labeled fragments are diluted into hybridization buffer. The buffer includes a fluoresceinated oligonucleotide complementary to probes distributed across the array, and thus serves as a hybridization control.

From this low-complexity PCR, sufficient quantities of labeled target are made to permit hybridization reactions that are as short as 30–60 minutes. Sample handling is facilitated by use of an automated fluidics station that controls sample and wash buffer introduction, removal and mixing, and incubation temperature. Labeled DNA is hybridized to the probes on the array for 30 minutes in a buffered salt solution using the fluidics station and then washed.

The hybridized probe array is scanned using a GeneArray Scanner. Scans take ~4 minutes, producing a data image file (*.dat). Data are analyzed using Affymetrix Microarray Suite. In the Image window, a grid is automatically placed over the image, and software calculates the intensity of each probe cell. Hybridization intensities obtained with the sample sequence are compared with those from a reference sequence. Intensity patterns that diverge from the reference standard are identified, and sites containing mutant bases are displayed. Further background information about the use of the fluidics station, scanner, and analysis software can be obtained from specific User's Guides and On-line Help (www.affymetrix.com).

MATERIALS

CAUTION: Please see Appendix 3 for appropriate handling of materials marked with <!>.
IMPORTANT: Use molecular biology grade (nuclease-free) H_2O in the preparations below.

Buffers and Solutions

Please see Appendix 2 for components of stock solutions, buffers, and reagents.
Dilute stock solutions to the appropriate concentrations.

Acetylated bovine serum albumin (BSA) (20 mg/ml) (B 8894, Sigma)
EDTA (0.5 M) (15575-012, GIBCO)
Ethanol (absolute)
H_2O, molecular biology grade (16-001Y, BioWhittaker)
Hybridization buffer concentrate (12x SSPE/0.1% Triton X-100)
> Combine 600 ml of 20x SSPE with 390 ml of H_2O and mix thoroughly. Add 10 ml of 10% Triton X-100. Mix thoroughly and filter the buffer through a 0.2-μm or 0.45-μm vacuum filter unit. Dispense 50-ml aliquots of the 1-liter bulk volume into 20 polypropylene centrifuge tubes. Store the solution at room temperature.

$MgCl_2$ (25 mM) (N808-0241, Applied Biosystems)
4x PCR reagents

10x GeneAmp PCR buffer II	5 ml
25 mM $MgCl_2$	5 ml
100 mM dNTPs	100 μl

> Add 2.1 ml of H_2O to a total volume of 12.5 ml. Mix the solution thoroughly and deliver 250-μl aliquots into 50 microfuge tubes. Store the tubes at –20ºC.
> **IMPORTANT:** Prepare and store the 4x PCR reagent in an area of the laboratory designated as template-free.

20x SSPE (16-010Y, BioWhittaker)
Tris-Acetate (400 mM, pH 8.2) (0279-IL-E, Teknova)
Triton X-100 (T 9284, Sigma)
Wash buffer A (3x SSPE/0.005% Triton X-100)
> Add 150 ml of 20x SSPE and 500 μl of 10% Triton X-100 to 850 ml of H_2O. Mix the solution thoroughly and filter through a 0.2-μm or 0.45-μm vacuum filter unit. Store the buffer at room temperature.

Enzymes and Enzyme Buffers

AmpliTaq Gold (N808-0241, Applied Biosystems)
> This protocol has been optimized for use with AmpliTaq Gold and use of this enzyme is recommended.

BioArray Terminal Labeling w/FL ddCTP kit (Enzo, distributed by Affymetrix, 900180), for labeling fragmented DNA amplicons

Calf intestine alkaline phosphatase (18009-027, GIBCO)

GeneAmp 10x PCR buffer II (N808-0241, Applied Biosystems)
> 10 mM Tris-HCl (pH 8.3)
> 50 mM KCl

Fragmentation reagent (supplied with GeneChip p53 reagent kit, 900132)
> Prepared DNase I in 10 mM Tris-HCl (pH 7.5), 10 mM $CaCl_2$, 10 mM $MgCl_2$, and 50% glycerol.

Nucleotides and Oligonucleotides

DNA ladder (50 bp) (10416-014, GIBCO)

dNTP stock solutions (100 mM each) (27-2035-1, Pharmacia Biotech)

GeneChip p53 reagent kit (900132, Affymetrix)

Kit Components
- p53 Primer Set (20 primers in 1 mM Tris-HCl [pH 7.4], 0.1 mM EDTA)

Exon 2:	5′-TCATGCTGGATCCCCACTTTTCCTCTTG-3′
	5′-TGGCCTGCCCTTCCAATGGATCCACTCA-3′
Exon 3:	5′-AATTCATGGGACTGACTTTCTGCTCTTGTC-3′
	5′-TCCAGGTCCCAGCCCAACCCTTGTCC-3′
Exon 4:	5′-GTCCTCTGACTGCTCTTTTCACCCATCTAC-3′
	5′-GGGATACGGCCAGGCATTGAAGTCTC-3′
Exon 5:	5′-CTTGTGCCCTGACTTTCAACTCTGTCTC-3′
	5′-TGGGCAACCAGCCCTGTCGTCTCTCCA-3′
Exon 6:	5′-CCAGGCCTCTGATTCCTCACTGATTGCTC-3′
	5′-GCCACTGACAACCACCCTTAACCCCTC-3′
Exon 7:	5′-GCCTCATCTTGGGCCTGTGTTATCTCC-3′
	5′-GGCCAGTGTGCAGGGTGGCAAGTGGCTC-3′
Exon 8:	5′-GTAGGACCTGATTTCCTTACTGCCTCTTGC-3′
	5′-ATAACTGCACCCTTGGTCTCCTCCACCGC-3′
Exon 9:	5′-CACTTTTATCACCTTTCCTTGCCTCTTTCC-3′
	5′-AACTTTCCACTTGATAAGAGGTCCCAAGAC-3′
Exon 10:	5′-ACTTACTTCTCCCCCTCCTCTGTTGCTGC-3′
	5′-ATGGAATCCTATGGCTTTCCAACCTAGGAAG-3′
Exon 11:	5′-CATCTCTCCTCCCTGCTTCTGTCTCCTAC-3′
	5′-CTGACGCACACCTATTGCAAGCAAGGGTTC-3′

- Control Oligonucleotide F1 (100 nM in 10 mM Tris-HCl, pH 7.4, 1 mM EDTA) Sequence
  5′-Fluorescein-CTGAACGGTAGCATCTTGAC-3′
- Fragmentation Reagent
  DNase I in 10 mM Tris-HCl (pH 7.5) in 10 mM $CaCl_2$, 10 mM $MgCl_2$, and 50% glycerol
- p53 Reference DNA
  Human placental DNA (50 ng/µl) in 10 mM Tris-HCl (pH 8.0), 0.1 mM EDTA (pH 8.0)
- p53 Probe Array
  We recommend that probe arrays from the same lot be used for the reference sample and that test samples be compared with a reference sample in each experiment.

Genomic DNA from tissue samples, isolated, e.g., with the QIAamp tissue kit (29304, QIAGEN)
> Dilute the isolated DNA in 10 mM Tris (pH 9) to a concentration of 5–50 ng/µl. Store the sample of genomic DNA at 4ºC.

Gels

Mini-agarose gel electrophoresis unit with appropriate buffers and ethidium bromide <!>
NuSieve agarose (3:1) (50092, FMC Corporation)

Special Equipment

Centrifuge tubes (conical, 50-ml capacity) (25325-50, Corning)
Eppendorf microfuge tubes (1.5 ml) (20901-641, VWR)
GeneArray Scanner (Affymetrix)
GeneChip Fluidics Station 400
MicroAmp (0.2 µl) PCR tubes with caps (N801-0612, Applied Biosystems)
Microarray Suite Analysis software (Affymetrix)
Micropipettors (P-2, P-20, P-200, P-1000) (Rainin Pipetman or equivalent)
Pipette tips (sterile-barrier)
Thermal cycler, with accessories (Applied Biosystems GeneAmp PCR System 2400 or 9600)
Vacuum filter units (1-liter capacity, 0.20 µm or 0.45 µm) (25988-1L, Corning)

METHOD

IMPORTANT: Separate and conduct the steps of the amplification protocol in three separate areas of the laboratory to minimize potential for carryover of PCR products from previous amplification reactions.

Setting Up the Amplification of Extracted Genomic DNA: Template-free Area

Perform the initial set up of the PCR master mix and reaction tubes in a designated template-free area. Use pipettes, pipette tips, and test tube racks dedicated to this procedure. Store the 4x PCR reagents, GeneChip p53 Primer Set, and *Taq* polymerase in a designated template-free −20ºC freezer.

1. Combine the components of the PCR master mix in the proportions shown below. Each reaction requires 50 µl of PCR master mix. The total number of reactions equals the number of tissue samples and the reference, plus two extra reactions—one for a control and the other to accommodate loss during handling.

Component	Volume (µl)
4x PCR reagents	25
p53 primer set	5
AmpliTaq Gold (5 units/µl)	2
H_2O, molecular biology grade	18
Volume of PCR master mix	50

   Allow the components to thaw completely. Take special care when pipetting the AmpliTaq polymerase as it is stored in 50% glycerol.

2. Transfer 50 µl of the PCR master mix into a series of PCR tubes. Close the caps of the tubes firmly.

Preparing the Amplification Reactions: Low-template Area

3. Add samples and GeneChip p53 reference DNA to the tubes containing the PCR master mix as follows.

    a. To prepare the no-template control reaction, add 50 μl of H_2O to 50 μl of PCR master mix in a reaction tube. Cap the tube firmly.

    b. To prepare the reference DNA reaction, add 5 μl of GeneChip p53 reference DNA and 45 μl of H_2O to 50 μl of PCR master mix in a reaction tube. Cap the tube firmly.

    c. To prepare the test sample, add 250 ng of the test sample of DNA and H_2O in a volume of 50 μl. Cap the tube firmly. The total volume of each PCR is 100 μl.

Amplification and Analysis of Products: High-template Area

Locate the thermal cycler(s) and gel electrophoresis equipment used for PCR in an area of the laboratory designated as High Template.

4. Transfer the tubes to a thermal cycler and amplify the reactions using the denaturation, annealing, and polymerization times and temperatures listed below:

Number of cycles	Denaturation	Annealing	Extension
1	10 minutes at 96°C		
35	30 seconds at 95°C	30 seconds at 60°C	45 seconds at 72°C
1			10 minutes at 72°C

Remove the reactions from the thermal cycler and transfer them to 4°C until needed for the next step.

> These times and temperatures are optimal for the specific equipment and reactions described in this protocol (Applied Biosystems GeneAmp PCR System 2400 or 9600 Thermal Cycler), but the conditions may need to be adapted to suit other types of equipment and reactions.

5. Resolve PCR products by electrophoresis through a 4% NuSieve agarose gel including a 50-bp ladder of DNA as a size marker.

    a. Load at least 5 μl of each PCR plus appropriate gel dye-loading buffer. For a size standard, load 1 μl of 50-bp DNA ladder plus gel-loading buffer.

    b. Run the gel at 125 V in 1× TBE for 60–90 minutes.

    c. Stain the gel in ethidium bromide (0.5 μg/ml in 1× TBE) to visualize the bands of DNA.

    > All bands may not always appear if only ≤5 μl of each PCR is loaded.

6. Examine the gel to confirm the quality and yields of the PCR products before proceeding to the next step (please see Figures 6-10 and 6-11). For recommendations in dealing with problems, please see the TROUBLESHOOTING panel at the end of the protocol.

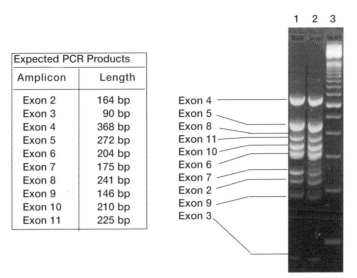

Expected PCR Products	
Amplicon	Length
Exon 2	164 bp
Exon 3	90 bp
Exon 4	368 bp
Exon 5	272 bp
Exon 6	204 bp
Exon 7	175 bp
Exon 8	241 bp
Exon 9	146 bp
Exon 10	210 bp
Exon 11	225 bp

FIGURE 6-11. Gel electrophoresis and ethidium bromide staining of fragments obtained following PCR amplification of coding exons of the *p53* gene from reference (lane *1*) DNA or test (lane *2*) DNA. A DNA ladder (lane *3*) is used to estimate fragment sizes and amplicon abundance. Note that discrete fragments, rather than a smear, have been obtained. Typical yields of 1–3 μg of DNA are obtained from a good-quality template. The table shows the expected PCR products.

Fragmenting DNA Amplicons

The optimal amount of GeneChip fragmentation reagent has been determined to be 0.15 units/μg of DNA. The following fragment reaction is appropriate for a range of 1–3 μg of DNA, which corresponds to a typical yield of PCR product from good-quality template. For recommendations on how to deal with issues such as uniformly low signal intensity or poor discrimination, please see the **TROUBLESHOOTING** panel at the end of the protocol.

7. Transfer 45 μl of the sample PCR and reference DNA PCRs to fresh MicroAmp reaction tubes. For more accurate results, transfer another 45 μl of each PCR to a second set of reaction tubes to obtain duplicate analysis of the sample. Otherwise, store the remaining 50 μl of each PCR at 4ºC for possible future use.

8. Prepare a working mix for fragmentation according to the following table:

Component	Mix sufficient for 24 reactions	Final concentration
Fragmentation reagent (check label for concentration)	6 units	0.25 units
EDTA (20 mM)*	X μl	variable
Alkaline phosphatase (1 unit/μl)	60 μl	2.5 units
Tris-acetate (10 mM)	60 μl minus the volume of fragmentation reagent added	0.5 mM
Volume of working mix	120 μl	

*When using Affymetrix Fragmentation Reagent, EDTA must in added in a volume proportional to the enzyme used to complex excess divalent cations included in the enzyme storage buffer by the particular supplier that Affymetrix uses as a source of DNase I.

The number of reactions is equal to the number of samples and the reference plus one extra reaction to compensate for loss during handling. Take special care when pipetting the fragmentation reagent and phosphatase as these enzymes are stored in glycerol.

IMPORTANT: The working mix must be prepared fresh and any remainder discarded after use.

9. Add 5 µl of the working mix to 45 µl of PCR for a reaction volume of 50 µl.

   Add the working mix as quickly as possible to minimize variations in incubation times between the first and last reactions. The use of a multiple dispensing pipette or a multi-channel pipette is recommended. Mix the samples well.

10. Transfer the reaction tubes to a thermal cycler, programmed with the times and temperatures listed below:

Number of cycles	Time	Temperature
1	15 minutes	25°C
1	10 minutes	95°C

Remove the reactions from the thermal cycler and transfer them to 4°C until ready to perform the end-labeling reaction. For long-term storage of the PCR amplicons, store the reactions at –20°C.

   This reaction has been optimized on a Applied Biosystems GeneAmp PCR System 2400 or 9600 Thermal Cycler. Because the incubation time and heat inactivation of this reaction are critical, the use of simple heating blocks is not recommended.

Labeling of Fragmented Products

The fragmented PCR products are ready substrates for addition of nucleotides labeled with fluorescein (or other fluors or haptens).

11. Label the fragmented amplicons at their 3′ ends with a fluoresceinated dideoxynucleotide using terminal transferase and components supplied with the Enzo BioArray Labeling kit.

    The use of the Enzo BioArray Terminal Labeling w/FL ddCTP kit is recommended for this step. The kit provides the enzyme and a labeled nucleotide. To perform the labeling reaction, please refer to the protocol included with the kit.

Hybridizing the Sample to the GeneChip p53 Array

The GeneChip p53 assay requires the use of a single probe array to analyze both sense and antisense strands of a DNA sample. The GeneChip assay reagents are designed for use on a GeneChip Fluidics Station 400 and a GeneArray Scanner.

12. Combine the following components of hybridization master mix in the proportions below. The number of hybridizations equals the number of samples and the reference plus one extra to allow for pipetting error. Allow the components to thaw completely.

Component	Volumes/sample	Final concentration or amount in hybridization
Hybridization buffer concentrate	250 µl	6× SSPE
Acetylated BSA (20 mg/ml)	50 µl	2 mg/ml
Control oligonucleotide F1 (100 nM)	10 µl	2 nM
H_2O	90 µl	–
Final volume of hybridization master mix	400 µl	

13. Aliquot 400 µl of the hybridization master mix into microfuge tubes.

14. Transfer the 100 μl of the labeling reactions (Step 12) to the microfuge tubes containing 400 μl of the hybridization master mix for a final hybridization volume of 500 μl. Mix the contents thoroughly.

    The hybridization target samples may be stored at –20ºC protected from light for up to 4 weeks. Avoid repeated freezing and thawing.

Target Hybridization and Wash

15. Set up the hybridization experiment and the fluidics station.

    The GeneChip Fluidics Station 400 is controlled by the Affymetrix Microarray Suite and performs hybridization, stain, and wash procedures on the probe array. Instrument control scripts are available for each GeneChip assay, directing the injection and agitation of hybrization and wash solutions within the cartridge, as well as the timing and temperature of these steps. Additional details and description of techniques for modifying assay conditions are described in the technical literature distributed with the GeneChip p53 array.

16. Hybridize the solution containing fluorescently labeled DNA fragments to the p53 probe array for 30 minutes at 45ºC. Follow the instructions in the Affymetrix GeneChip p53 manual to hybridize the sample to the array and to wash the array.

17. Purge the tubing of the GeneChip Fluidics Station 400 with Wash buffer A prior to the wash cycle.

18. For the wash routine, carry out 2 cycles with 10 mixes per cycle with Wash buffer A at 35ºC. The holding temperature is 20ºC.

    The probe array is ready to be scanned after the hybridization and wash protocols are complete.

19. Scan the hybridized arrays using the GeneArray Scanner.

    The scanner is controlled by the Affymetrix Microarray Suite. For further information on scanning, please refer to the Affymetrix Microarray Suite User's Guide and On-line Help and GeneArray Scanner User's Guide. After scanning the probe array, store the resulting image data on the hard drive of the GeneChip workstation as a .DAT file with the name of the scanned experiment.

ANALYSIS OF THE SAMPLES

Data analysis is based on a comparison of hybridization patterns of an unknown sample to a wild-type reference. The software calculates the average intensity of each probe cell using the intensities of the pixels contained in the cell. Pixels on the edges of each cell are not included, which prevents neighboring cell data from affecting a cell's calculated average intensity. The calculated average intensity is assigned an x/y coordinate position, which corresponds to the cell's position on the array. These data are stored as a .CEL file using the same name as the .EXP and .DAT files. The .CEL file is an intermediate data file and is not displayed in the Affymetrix Microarray Suite.

The software then applies the selected probe array algorithm to compare the cell intensities and determine a base call at each position. This is done with reference to the information contained in the .CDF file, the second library file for the probe array. A report with a summary of nucleotide changes in the sample is automatically displayed as a .CHP file in the Sequence Analysis window of Affymetrix Microarray Suite. The .CHP file has the same name as the .EXP, .DAT, and .CEL files.

TROUBLESHOOTING AND SPECIAL CONSIDERATIONS

- ***Assessing the quality of the amplification products.*** In principle, substantial deletions or other rearrangements might be evident in the gel-banding pattern, but they are infrequent in the Soussi p53 Mutations database (http://p53.curie.fr). It is therefore more likely that altered patterns represent problems with PCR (please see Figures 6-10 and 6-11). Such problems are most likely to reflect quality problems with the starting genomic DNA. When starting with genomic DNA extracted from formalin-fixed paraffin-embedded tissue, it may be problematic to obtain decent yields of amplification of products larger than ~200 bp. This can result in missing bands or bands of decreased intensity on the gel. If this is the case, it may be necessary to repeat the amplification.

- ***Fragmenting DNA amplicons.*** DNA amplicons are fragmented by digestion with DNase I in the presence of calf intestine alkaline phosphatase. Fragmentation serves to increase access of the target to the probe, shortens the required hybridization time, and improves perfect match/mismatch signal discrimination. The extent of fragmentation can be critical to the accuracy of array-based resequencing. The conditions for this assay have therefore been established in multifactorial titration experiments to maximize the quality of discrimination and overall accuracy (please also see Cutler et al. 2001). The optimal amount of GeneChip fragmentation reagent has been determined to be 0.15 unit/μg of DNA. The fragmentation reaction is appropriate for a range of 1–3 μg of DNA, which corresponds to a typical yield of PCR product from good-quality template. If uniformly low signal intensity or poor discrimination is observed upon hybridization (especially for the reference DNA), the amount of DNA present in the PCR volume should be measured, and the appropriate fragmentation reaction composition recalculated using 0.15 unit fragmentation reagent per microgram of DNA.

- ***Data analysis: Specificity of the assay.*** Typically, resequencing applications require very high accuracy to ensure the predictive value of any variant candidates reported. In general, the false positive rate per nucleotide x the resequencing target size in nucleotides must be substantially less than the expected occurrence rate of variants. For example, even a nominally high specificity rate of 99.9% would still yield a report of one or more mutations in almost 80% of the *p53* genes analyzed by resequencing 1.5 kb, far greater than the true spontaneous mutation rate.

The GeneChip p53 assay was designed to yield robust amplification of a 10-plex PCR and with hybridization conditions carefully optimized to yield reliable signal from the A/T-rich portion of the *p53* gene, yet provide high discrimination and freedom from cross-hybridization artifacts among the probes which interrogate the bulk of the gene that is G/C-rich. Accuracy was also enhanced by redundant interrogation. All positions are interrogated at least twice, once on each DNA strand. At the most critical sites, there are seven additional probe sets per strand, employing different substitution positions relative to the probe ends, for more than 300 of the most prevalent *p53* mutations (based on the compilation of Soussi et al.; please see http://p53.curie.fr). Finally, rather than relying on a priori assumptions of how intensities should be distributed among the five different substitution variants of each probe (i.e., T, G, C, A, and deletion of the interrogation base) for wild-type and mutant analytes, mutations are detected by comparing these to a wild-type reference sample included with each batch of samples run. The presence of a mutation is indicated by a shift in the pattern of intensities in a test sample to an empirically determined extent from the pattern yielded by the reference sample. The reference standard can be used in comparing hybridization patterns from two different arrays as described here, or it can also be achieved by mixing the test and standard samples, each of which has a different, distinguishable label, in a single hybridization (Hacia et al. 1996).

In studies at Affymetrix, overall accuracy of the GeneChip p53 assay was ~99.5% for samples run a single time (compared to dideoxy sequencing). Because false positives tended to occur at random, running a sample twice and requiring concordant mutation calls to define a detection event improved the accuracy to >99.94% with a specificity of >99.99%. Sensitivity for detecting mutations was most effective at sites with redundant interrogation. At these sites, mutants could be detected reliably in contrived mixtures with wild type at levels <25%, and often <15%. Overall mutation detection sensitivity on a panel of characterized true patient samples obtained from tumor tissue was 89% in a blinded study. These results compared very favorably with the sensitivity obtained by dideoxy sequencing (please also see Ahrendt et al. 1999; Wickman et al. 2000).

It is straightforward to tile single-base deletion mutations in resequencing by adding a fifth probe to each probe set with the interrogation base deleted as has been done for the GeneChip p53 array. Very few examples of these *mutations* were observed in the panels of samples available for training this algorithm, and thus, this potential functionality was not fully explored during development of this assay. It is also straightforward to add four additional probes for all single-base insertions at a point adjacent to the interrogated site of a probe set. Multiple-base deletions can likewise be tiled systematically if there is any reason to expect a particular deletion target size. However, multiple-base insertions become exponentially challenging to tile systematically. Electrophoresis-based sequencing can thus be more flexible than hybridization to defined probes for complex mutations of this type when analyzing pure targets, but in crude mixtures such as tumor sample, or even in a discrete diploid mixture with different alleles, sequence tracings of samples with insertions or deletions can also be uninterpretable.

Loss of Heterozygosity Analysis Using SNP Arrays

Kerstin Lindblad-Toh

Whitehead Institute/MIT Center for Genome Research, Cambridge, Massachusetts 02139

Human cancers arise by a combination of discrete mutations and gross chromosomal alterations. Knudson's "two-hit" hypothesis is applicable to the development of many types of tumors, where the first hit involves a discrete germ-line mutation in one copy of a tumor suppressor gene. The second hit involves the loss of the second copy of the gene, sometimes through loss of a larger part of the chromosome bearing the normal copy. As a tumor evolves, many more gross chromosomal alterations may follow. When large pieces of chromosomal material are lost, this can be seen as a loss of heterozygosity (LOH) (Dracopoli and Fogh 1983). LOH can also arise through mitotic recombination, break-induced replication, mitotic nondisjunction, gene conversion, or poorly defined structural changes in chromosomes involving interchromosomal recombinations and deletions (Thiagalingam et al. 2001).

Genetic markers, such as restriction-fragment-length polymorphisms (RFLPs) and simple-sequence-length polymorphisms (SSLPs), are frequently heterozygous in DNA from normal tissues and homozygous in DNA from tumors. Allelotyping using PCR amplification and gel electrophoresis of SSLPs has been a reliable method for LOH analysis in a multitude of different tumor types (Weissenbach et al. 1992). Other methods, such as comparative genomic hybridization (CGH) (Kallionemi et al. 1994) and spectral karyotyping (SKY) (Schrock et al. 1996), involve fluorescent painting of whole chromosomes and are used to systematically search whole genomes for changes in copy number. An advantage of using genetic markers to study LOH is that the allele status at a discrete position in the genome can be determined, whereas CGH and SKY provide regional information only. Coverage of the entire genome by large-scale allelotyping studies using genetic markers requires a dense marker set and therefore a high degree of genotyping efficiency. If the requirements of marker density and efficiency of genotyping can be met, small deletions might be ascertained by LOH and used to quickly identify genes involved in tumorigenesis.

The recent discovery of large numbers of single-nucleotide polymorphisms (SNPs) in human and other genomes has contributed immensely to the availability of markers to densely cover the genome. For example, the number of human SNPs in public databases already exceeds 1.6 million, which corresponds to an SNP approximately every 2 kb (Sachidanandam et al. 2001). Several large-scale genotyping methods are being developed to take advantage of SNP markers (for a review, please see Table 6-4 in the introduction to Part 2). In theory, many genotyping technologies can be used for LOH analysis. In practice, however, the method must be able to cope with a slight degree of contamination of tumor DNA with heterozygous normal tissue DNA. Due to their flexibility and capacity for large-scale genotyping, it is likely that both mass spectrometry (Haff and Smirnov 1997) and microarray-based methods will be used as the leading techniques for large-scale LOH analysis in the future.

Microarray-based LOH methods that use relatively small numbers of SNPs (600–1500 SNPs) have involved two similar types of microarrays (Lindblad-Toh et al. 2000a; Mei et al. 2000). This protocol describes one of these methods, namely, allele-specific hybridization to an Affymetrix HuSNP array for LOH detection (as described in Lindblad-Toh et al. 2000a). The Affymetrix HuSNP array contains 1494 SNPs that were originally identified in one of the first large-scale SNP discovery projects (Wang et al. 1998). Of the 1494 SNPs, ~1205 routinely amplify well from different human DNA samples, and the fraction of loci amplifying is termed the *call rate*. In any given DNA, ~30% of the SNPs will be heterozygous, and therefore ~350 are said to be *informative*. Although at the time of writing, the number of markers on HuSNP arrays is not very high, the use of these arrays provides proof-of-principle of the method. In addition, the HuSNP array achieves a marker density similar or higher than that achieved with a commonly used set of 350 SSLP markers, which have a heterozygosity rate of ~70% (Cooperative Human Linkage Center [CHLC] Screening set/version 6; CHLC http://gai.nci.nih.gov/ CHLC/).

To perform LOH on an HuSNP array for one individual, DNA (100 ng) from normal tissue is analyzed once and the tumor DNA (200 ng) is analyzed in duplicate. Each DNA sample is subjected to 24 multiplex PCRs, each involving a mixture of loci-specific, T3/T7-tailed primer pairs representing 50–100 loci. The products of this reaction are then amplified in 24 multiplex reactions using biotinylated-T3/T7 primers. The resulting PCR products are pooled, hybridized to the SNP array, stained with streptavidin-phycoerythrin, and assayed by fluorescence detection on a scanner. The detector for each SNP locus contains four rows of 25-mer oligonucleotides, two of which contain oligonucleotides that perfectly match either SNP allele A or SNP allele B, whereas the other two rows contain single-base mismatches at various positions. LOH is determined by comparing the results from normal and tumor DNAs. If DNA from the normal tissue is heterozygous (has both alleles A and B), it scores as "informative" and will be recorded as "LOH" if the tumor DNA is homozygous compared to normal or "retention" if the tumor DNA is also heterozygous (Figure 6-12). If the normal DNA is homozygous for a SNP, that SNP is recorded as "uninformative" and is excluded from the analysis. The use of multiplex PCR amplification for microarray-based LOH analysis results in the use of much smaller amounts of DNA than when conventional SSLP-based LOH is performed. The ability to use small amounts of DNA for LOH analysis is important when working with limiting amounts of tumor material.

Because the accuracy of genotyping on the HuSNP array lies somewhere between 95% and 99%, it is advisable to look for regions of LOH that involve several adjacent SNPs, rather than relying on the information derived from a single SNP. A simple algorithm is therefore used to determine the most probable regions of LOH, and the two most likely windows of LOH for each chromosome are calculated. Once two consecutive SNPs showing LOH have been identified, the maximum *window size* (affected chromosomal region) is calculated by adding up the number of SNPs that show LOH, and subtracting the number of interspersed SNPs showing retention. It is important to note that some false interspersed retentions can occur due to genotyping errors, inappropriate assignment of the position of the SNP in the genome, or due to contamination of tumor with normal DNA. The problem of correct SNP position assignment should be resolved when all SNPs are mapped directly on the human genome. Because all solid tumors have some level of contaminating normal tissue, however, it is important to consider whether the detection of loci in tumor cells that have undergone LOH is likely to be obscured by DNA from normal cells. Operationally, genotypes are deter-

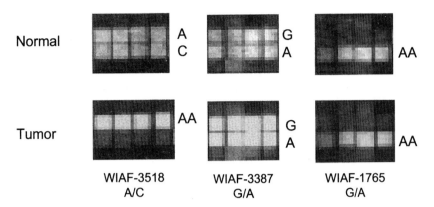

FIGURE 6-12. Representative images of fluorescence intensities for SNP array hybridization to normal and tumor DNA samples. The intensity fraction of allele A/(A+B) was used to determine the genotype based on predetermined values for each SNP (see the algorithms described in the "Experimental protocol"). For each sample pair calls of either LOH, retention or uninformative was made. WIAF-3518 is an SNP marker on chromosome 9, and WIAF-3387 and WIAF-1765 are SNPs on chromosome 3.

mined using the HuSNP array by identifying whether the relative signals from the two possible alleles fall within previously defined boundary values for all possible genotypes for that particular SNP. Because these boundaries were developed empirically for each SNP, some SNPs have very narrow boundaries and can tolerate very little contamination, whereas others are rather insensitive to contamination. If there is a substantial level of contamination, the relative allele signal value may fall outside the defined boundaries and become an ambiguous call. If the contamination level is higher still, the tumor DNA may be erroneously scored as being heterozygous at a given locus (the SNP scored as a retention, please see Figure 6-13). In practice, a tumor purity of >80% works well to correctly assign regions of LOH using the HuSNP array, whereas a lower degree of purity leads to results that are hard to interpret. With 200 ng of tumor DNA that has a purity of >80%, 100 ng of matching normal tissue DNA, and three HuSNP arrays, it is possible to obtain a reasonable assessment of the LOH distribution across the genome of a single tumor sample during a period of 2–3 days.

To increase the chance of detecting small deletions, it is advisable to choose an ideal set of several thousand highly heterozygous SNPs distributed across the genome. One way to achieve a dense microarray-based screen is the use of SBE-tag microarrays (please see Protocols 6 and 7). HuSNP chips can be used in conjunction with more flexible approaches, like SBE-tag microarrays. In this context, an HuSNP screen can provide an initial survey, and any critical regions that are identified can be further analyzed using higher-resolution techniques.

The following protocol is adapted directly from Lindblad-Toh et al. (2000a); the laboratory steps essentially follow the protocol supplied by Affymetrix for the GeneChip HuSNP chip. The main stages are listed below, and the scheme for SNP array design is shown in Figure 6-14.

- Multiplex Amplification of SNPs to be Assayed
- Pooling of Samples
- HuSNP Chip Hybridization
- Analysis of Data

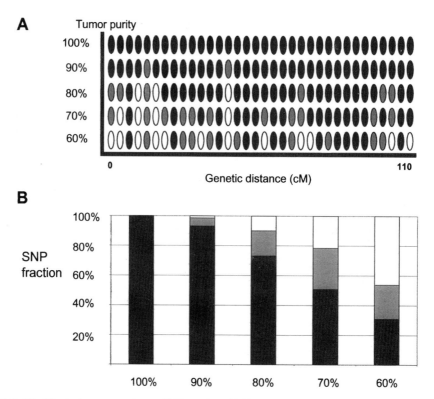

FIGURE 6-13. Effect of tumor purity on SNP scoring. (*A*) Tumor mixing experiment. SNPs on chromosome 3p showing LOH in a pure tumor cell line DNA (100%) were assayed in mixtures with corresponding normal DNA (90–60% tumor content). As the percentage of tumor DNA content drops, SNPs showing LOH progress from LOH to uncertain to false retention. (*Black*) LOH; (*gray*) uncertain LOH; (*white*) retention of heterozygosity. (*B*) Effect of tumor DNA content on accuracy of "true LOH" calls, considering all 130 informative samples in a tumor mixing experiment. (*Black*) LOH; (*gray*) uncertain LOH; (*white*) retention of heterozygosity. Note that samples with 80% or 90% tumor content give results very similar to those obtained with a 100% tumor sample, but below 80%, the quality of the results falls off steeply.

MATERIALS

CAUTION: Please see Appendix 3 for appropriate handling of materials marked with <!>.

Buffers, Solutions, and Reagents

Please see Appendix 2 for components of stock solutions, buffers, and reagents. Dilute stock solutions to the appropriate concentrations.

10x Buffer II (supplied with AmpliTaq Gold, Perkin Elmer)
ddH$_2$O
50x Denhart's solution (Sigma)
EDTA (0.5 M) (GIBCO)
MgCl$_2$ solution (25 mM)
Streptavidin-Phycoerythrin (SAPE) (Molecular Probes)
20x SSPE (BioWhittaker)
20x TBE (BioWhittaker)
TE
    10 mM Tris-HCl (pH 8.0)
    0.1 mM EDTA
TMACl (Sigma)

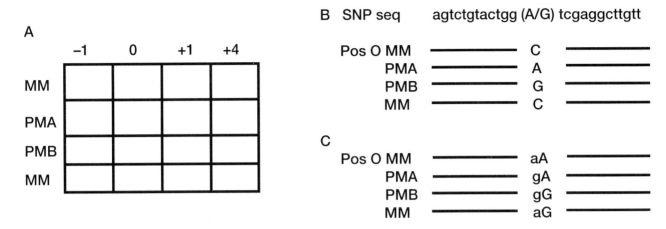

FIGURE 6-14. SNP array design. (*A*) Each SNP is queried at four positions, with the SNP residing in the middle of a 25-base oligonucleotide (0) or offset by −1, +1, or +4. Each of these columns has four rows: Mismatch (MM), perfect match A (PMA), perfect match B (PMB), or mismatch (MM). The row corresponding to allele A, allele B, or both (heterozygote) will light up. (*B*) In column 0, the base of the SNP will be either A, B, or a mismatched base for the two MM rows. (*C*) In the other positions (−1, +1, and +4), the SNP allele will be allele A in the top two rows and allele B in the lower two rows and the queried position will either be a match or mismatch that is the same for the two alleles.

Tris-HCl (1 M, pH 7.8)
Triton X-100 (Mallinkrodt)
Tween-20 (Pierce Chemical)
Wash solution A (6x SSPE-T)

30x SSPE	300 ml
100% Triton X-100	50 µl
ddH$_2$O	700 ml

> Mix thoroughly by swirling the bottle, and store at room temperature. Make sure that Wash solution A is prepared at least 1 day before scanning.

Wash solution B (4x SSPE-T)

30x SSPE	200 ml
100% Triton X-100	50 µl
ddH$_2$O	800 ml

> Mix thoroughly by swirling the bottle, and store at room temperature. Make sure that Wash solution B is prepared at least 1 day before scanning.

Enzymes and Buffers

AmpliTaq Gold (supplied with 10x Buffer II; Perkin Elmer)

Antibodies

Antibody (goat), anti-streptavidin, biotinylated (0.5 mg) (Vector Laboratories)
> Add 1000 µl of ddH$_2$O to the vial before use and mix. Store the solution at 4ºC.

Gels

Agarose gel (4%) (NuSieve 3:1 Plus as 24-well format; FMC Bioproducts)
Mini-agarose gel electrophoresis unit with appropriate buffers, ethidium bromide <!>, and loading dye, 1% agarose

Nucleic Acids and Oligonucleotides

DNA ladder (100 bp) (GIBCO)

dNTP solution containing all four dNTPs, each at a concentration of 10 mM (pH 8.0) (Pharmacia Biotech)

Genomic DNA from normal tissue (control DNA)

Genomic DNA from tumor tissue, isolated, for example, using a QiaQuick column

Herring sperm DNA (Promega)

Labeling primers

> The labeling primers consist of biotin-labeled primer pairs carrying the T3 and T7 sequences used to tail the multiplex primers. The labeling primers are used in the secondary amplification reaction and are supplied with the HuSNP Reagent kit.

Multiplex primer pools 1–24

> The primer pools consists of T3- and T7-tailed primer pairs, where each of the 24 pools represents a discrete set of 50–100 genetic loci. The multiplex primers are used in the primary amplification reaction and are supplied with the GeneChip HuSNP Reagent kit. Please see Table 6-7 in Part 4.

Oligonucleotide B1 control (from the GeneChip HuSNP Mapping Reagent kit)

Special Equipment

Caps

Centrifuges (swinging bucket and tabletop)

Film (Microseal "A") (MJ Research)

GeneChip Fluidics Station 400 (Affymetrix)

GeneChip HuSNP Probe Arrays (Affymetrix)

GeneChip HuSNP Reagent kit (Affymetrix)

GeneChip Hybridization Oven 320 (for arrays) (Affymetrix)

Heat block preset to 95ºC

Microconcentrators (Microcon YM-10) (Millipore)

Microplates for PCR (96-well polypropylene v-bottom) (MJ Research)

Microtube tough spot labels (US Scientific)

Pipettes (1–10 µl and 5–50 µl multichannel)

Pipettes (transfer; small bore)

Pipette tips (sterile barrier; RNase-free)

Pipette tips (sterile barrier and nonbarrier)

> Extra long pipette tips must be pointed, not rounded, to permit dispensing of liquid into the probe arrays (US Scientific).

Plate (1-ml deep-well titer) (Beckman)

Plates (1-ml deep-well round bottom)

Scanner (HP Gene Array or Agilent Scanner from Affymetrix)

Scanning software (Affymetrix GeneChip 3.1)

Thermal cycler

> The cycler should be programmed with desired amplification protocol (MJ Research DNA Engine or Tetrad; or Perkin Elmer 2400, 9600, or 9700).

Tubes with caps (0.2-ml thin-walled, strip of 8) (MJ Research)

Tubes (1.5-ml microfuge, RNase-free) (US Scientific)

Vacuum filter units (0.20 µm or 0.45 µm with 1-liter capacity) (Corning)

METHOD

Multiplex Amplification of SNPs to be Assayed

For each individual's DNA to be assayed for LOH, three samples are genotyped using the HuSNP chip: normal control tissue DNA and tumor DNA in duplicate. Each of these samples is assayed for 1494 SNP loci, divided into 24 pools of multiplexed PCR primers.

1. Perform the primary multiplex PCR.

   a. Dilute each of the genomic DNAs to 4 ng/µl in TE and label them as $N_{individual}$, $T_{individual}a$, and $T_{individual}b$ for the normal and tumor DNAs, respectively. Note that tumors a and b are duplicates of the same sample. Label a microfuge tube for each sample, and add 35 µl of the appropriate genomic DNA to each tube.

   b. Set up the multiplex amplification reactions in microtiter plates as follows:

      i. Mark one microtiter plate per individual according to the scheme below:

	1	2	3	4	5	6	7	8	9	10	11	12
A	1	9	17	1	9	17	1	9	17			
B	2	10	18	2	10	18	2	10	18			
C	3	11	19	3	11	19	3	11	19			
D	4	12	20	4	12	20	4	12	20			
E	5	13	21	5	13	21	5	13	21			
F	6	14	22	6	14	22	6	14	22			
G	7	15	23	7	15	23	7	15	23			
H	8	16	24	8	16	24	8	16	24			
Sample		Normal 1			Tumor 1a			Tumor 1b				

      ii. Deliver 3 µl of each of the multiplex primer pools 1–24 onto each quarter plate.

      iii. Prepare a master mix sufficient for 28 reactions for each DNA sample (24 wells and additional mix in case of small pipetting errors).

Reagents	1 Reaction (1x)	1 Sample (28x)
10x Buffer II	1.25	35.0
25 mM MgCl$_2$	2.5	70.0
10 mM dNTP solution	0.625	17.5
5 units/µl AmpliTaq Gold	0.25	7.0
H$_2$O	3.625	101.5
Total volume (µl)	8.25	231.0

      iv. Aliquot 231 µl of the master mix to each microfuge tube (Step 1a) and mix.

      v. For each quarter plate, deliver 9.5 µl of the master mix into each of the 24 wells containing primer pools. Seal plate with caps.

   c. Place the microtiter plate(s) in the thermal cycler and amplify the reactions using the denaturation, annealing, and polymerization times and temperatures listed below:

Number of cycles	Denaturation	Annealing	Extension (polymerization)
1	10 minutes at 95°C		
30	30 seconds at 95°C	1 minute at 55°C, auto +0.2°C/cycle	30 seconds at 72°C
5	30 seconds at 95°C	1 minute at 58°C	30 seconds at 72°C
1			7 minutes at 72°C

These times are optimal for the specific equipment and reactions described in this protocol, but the conditions may need to be adapted to suit other types of equipment and reactions.

2. Prepare 1:1000 dilutions of the multiplex products:

   a. Aliquot 1 ml of ddH$_2$O into each well of the 96-deep-well plates. Prepare as many plates as were used for the primary PCR, using a well layout similar to that described in Step 1. Seal the plates with Microseal plastic film until ready to proceed to Step b.

   b. Withdraw 1 μl of each multiplex product from the amplification reaction in Step 1 and suspend it in the corresponding well of the plate prepared in Step 2a, to give a 1:1000 multiplex dilution (continue until all products have been diluted). Seal the top of each 96-deep-well plate with Microseal plastic film, using a roller to seal the plastic tightly. Vortex samples lightly.

   c. Centrifuge the plates in the big swinging bucket centrifuge at 1000*g* for 2 minutes at room temperature to remove any liquid from the seal.

3. Perform the secondary multiplex PCR.

   a. Set up the secondary multiplex amplification reactions in microtiter plates as follows:

      i. Mark the secondary microtiter plates using the same pattern as the primary reaction plate described in Step 1.

      ii. Remove the film from the deep-well plate containing the diluted multiplex product and deliver 2.5 μl of the diluted samples to the corresponding spot on the newly prepared microtiter plate.

      iii. Prepare a master labeling mix sufficient for 28 reactions for each DNA sample by adding in the following order:

Reagents	Reaction (1x)	1 Sample (28x)
10x Buffer II	2.5	70
25 mM MgCl$_2$	4.0	112
10 mM dNTP solution	1.0	28
10 μM biotinylated T7 primer	2.0	56
10 μM biotinylated T3 primer	2.0	56
5 units/μl AmpliTaq Gold	0.5	14
ddH$_2$O	10.5	294
Total (μl)	22.5	630

      iv. Deliver 22.5 μl of the master labeling mix into each well on the microtiter plate. Seal the plate with caps.

   b. Place the microtiter plate(s) in the thermal cycler and amplify the reactions using the denaturation, annealing, and extension times and temperatures listed below:

Number of cycles	Denaturation	Annealing	Extension
1	10 minutes at 95°C		
40	30 seconds at 95°C	90 seconds at 55°C	30 seconds at 72°C
1			7 minutes at 72°C

These times are optimal for the specific equipment and reactions described in this protocol, but the conditions may need to be adapted to suit other types of equipment and reactions.

4. (*Optional*) Check the amplification products from each pool on a 1% agarose gel.

   a. Mix 2 µl of product from each well with agarose-loading dye and separate the products by electrophoresis through 1% agarose.

   b. Analyze the gel. Make sure that each pool has a smear of product of about the same size (50–100 bp) and staining intensity.

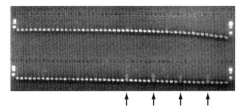

   c. If any sample lacks product, perform Steps 1–4 again for this particular sample/PCR pool combination. Calculate the amount of mix needed based on single reactions, not samples.

   In general, the PCR pools perform well, but the gel can provide useful information if troubleshooting array results becomes necessary later on (please see Figure 6-15).

FIGURE 6-15. Effect of tumor DNA purity on SNP scoring. Each pool shows up as a distinct band. Pools marked by arrows have a smear and may warrant reamplification, particularly when correctly sized products are absent (third arrow from left).

Pooling of Samples

IMPORTANT: The products from each DNA sample must be pooled and concentrated. Avoid contamination or sample mix up.

5. Centifuge the products briefly to remove any liquid from the caps. It is advisable to remove the caps *only* from the 24 pools belonging to a given DNA sample when pooling PCR products. Remove the product from each of the 24 wells and pool them in a clean, labeled microfuge tube.

6. Concentrate the samples.

   a. Label one Microcon YM-10 filter device for each sample. Make sure to label both the column and the secondary collection tube.

   b. Place the pooled sample into the green filter unit, which is positioned within a primary collection tube.

   c. Collect the samples by centrifugation in a tabletop centrifuge in a fixed-angle rotor at 13,000*g* for 26 minutes at room temperature.

   d. Carefully invert the green filter unit into the secondary labeled collection tube, and discard the primary collection tube. The approximate volume should be 60 µl at this stage. It is best not to measure this by pipetting because the tip can damage the filter membrane. Add 60 µl of sample to a blank filter unit for comparison.

   e. Collect the resulting sample by centrifugation in a tabletop centrifuge at 3000*g* for 3 minutes at room temperature.

   f. Measure the volume of the collected product. If it is 60–90 µl, proceed to Step g. If the volume is less than 60 µl, add ddH$_2$O to 60 µl. If the volume is larger than 90 µl, repeat

Steps c–f and centrifuge for 2 minutes only. It is very important that the sample not be spun to a dry residue on the membrane.

g. Once all of samples have the correct volume, store them at –20°C until ready to proceed to hybridization.

HuSNP Chip Hybridization

7. Carry out hybridization as described below:

a. Label one microfuge tube for each sample. To each tube, add 30 µl of concentrated pooled product (from Step 6).

b. Prepare the hybridization mix in a microfuge tube by adding the following in order (this recipe is sufficient for one sample):

Hybridization mix	1x (µl)
5 M TMACl	81
Control oligonucleotide B1	1.35
1 M Tris-HCl (pH 8.0)	1.35
1% Tween-20	1.35
0.5 M EDTA (pH 8.0)	1.35
10 mg/ml herring sperm DNA	1.35
50x Denhardt's solution	13.5
ddH$_2$O	3.75
Total volume (µl)	105

Note that the control oligonucleotide is necessary for the scanner to recognize the array type and to align the corners of the array.

c. Add 105 µl of hybridization mix to each microfuge tube containing a pooled sample (Step a), and centrifuge the tubes in a microfuge briefly to mix.

d. To denature samples, place the microfuge tubes in a heat block for 10 minutes at 95°C.

e. While the samples denature, label the GeneChip HuSNP Probe Arrays using tough-spots labels. Ensure that all of the chips are from the same lot and note the lot number. Place a P-10 (micropipette) tip into one of the two vents for each chip.

f. It is important to place the hybridization reactions in the hybridization chamber of the array without creating an excess of air bubbles. Use long thin 300-µl tips to deliver each denatured sample onto the correct chip: Slowly insert the pipette tip into the lower vent on the array. Then push fluid into the chip slowly while holding the chip vertically to allow air to rise up and observe the entry of the fluid through the window side.

g. Remove the P-10 pipette tip from top vent. Seal the array chamber tightly to avoid evaporation during the overnight hybridization step. If evaporation occurs, the salt in the hybridization mix will precipitate and render the array useless. Use tough spots to seal both of the air vents on the array.

h. Place the chips in the rotating holder in the hybridization oven, balance them, and set them to rotate overnight at a speed of 45 rpm.

i. Hybridize the arrays overnight (or for 16 hours) at 45°C.

8. Wash and stain the hybridized arrays:

   a. Prime the Affymetrix Fluidics Station with Wash solutions A and B.

   b. Mix the following staining solution in a 50-ml Falcon tube and centrifuge briefly to mix:

Staining solution	1x (μl)
20x SSPE	150
50x Denhardt's solution	10
1% Tween-20	5
1 mg/ml SAPE	25
ddH$_2$O	305
Total (μl)	495

   c. Aliquot 495 μl of the staining solution into a labeled microfuge tube for each sample. Keep the tubes on ice, covered with foil, as the streptavidin-phycoerythrin (SAPE) is light-sensitive.

   d. Remove the number of chips from the hybridization oven that will fit simultaneously in the wash station (usually four chips/station). Peel off the tough spots covering the air vents on the chips.

   e. Use one microfuge tube containing the staining mix for each sample (Step 8c). Add 5 μl of 0.5 mg/ml biotinylated anti-streptavidin antibody to each microfuge tube by placing a drop on the inside of the tube. Vortex quickly to mix and to prevent precipiation of the SAPE and antibody.

   > Including both SAPE and biotinylated anti-streptavidin antibody in the staining solution serves to enhance the signal from weak loci by amplifying the signal, as several SAPE and antibody molecules bind to each biotinylated PCR product.

   f. Immediately start the wash/stain protocol on the Affymetrix Fluidics Station. When indicated, add the chip and then the staining vial to the wash station. Set up the washing and staining protocol using the following conditions:

Solution	Temperature	Number of washes	Number of mixes per wash
Wash A	25°C	2	2
Wash B	35°C	6	5
Staining	25°C	1800 seconds	
Wash A	25°C	6	4

   g. When the wash protocol is completed, keep the chips in the dark and scan them as soon as possible.

   > The chips are stable for up to 12 hours at room temperature, but it is advisable to start scanning them as soon as the washing is completed.

   h. Continue to process the remaining chips by repeating Steps d–g as many times as necessary.

9. Scan the HuSNP chips on the Affymetrix Agilent Scanner using the Affymetrix GeneChip 3.1 software (or later version if available). To offset the amplification of signal arising from strong loci, scan the arrays at both 530 and 570 nm. Whereas 570 nm is at the optimal emission wavelength, the signal strength is only ~5% at 530 nm. Therefore, strong loci can be read at 530 nm and their signal extrapolated to 570 nm.

a. Prepare experiment files labeled with the date and sample name, for example, L010601N, L010601Ta, and L010601Tb. Make sure that the probe array type is set to HuSNP.

b. Scan the chips at wavelengths of 530 and 570 nm (check the option on the scanner).

c. Store the chips at room temperature in the dark until the initial analysis is complete.

> It is preferable to perform Step 10, a–c, on the same day that the scanning is done.

Analysis of the Data

Data analysis can be divided in two parts: (1) the genotyping of each sample and (2) the determination of LOH for individual loci and LOH for chromosomal regions for each individual screened. Genotyping is performed automatically using Affymetrix software, whereas the LOH determination requires custom-made software scripts.

10. Perform the genotyping of each sample:

a. Align the grid to fit the square outlined by the control oligonucleotide on the chip. Extract information from each tile by creating .cel files.

b. Run the analysis module, which will create a chip file containing genotypes for each marker.

c. Check the scan quality by running the report tool to check that the call rate is >75%, and the correlation coefficient for each wavelength is larger than 98% for each array.

> Any array falling below these numbers should not be used for the analysis. A discussion of the reasons why the array may fail is given in panel on TROUBLESHOOTING at the end of the protocol.

11. Perform the basic LOH analysis: For each sample, each SNP is scored as either loss of heterozygosity (L), retention of heterozygosity (R), or uninformative/uncertain (U), by comparing the calls for the normal control and the tumor duplicates. Score each sample by assigning the appropriate status:

- LOH = Any SNP showing both alleles (*AB*) in the normal and only one allele (*AA* or *BB*) in at least one of the tumor duplicates.

- Retention = Any SNP showing both alleles (*AB*) in the normal and either both alleles (*AB*) in both tumor duplicates or both alleles (*AB*) in one and "no signal" in the other tumor duplicate.

- Uncertain = Any SNP showing only one allele (*AA* or *BB*) or "no signal" in the normal or both alleles (*AB*) in the normal and "no signal" in both tumor duplicates.

12. Define the number of informative SNPs by summing the scores for LOHs and for the retentions. Calculate the LOH fraction by dividing the number of LOHs by the number of informative SNPs for each individual sampled.

13. Assign the regions of LOH: This procedure is intended to be robust against occasional errors in genotype or map position and is intended to provide only a rough estimate of the critical region (please see Figure 6-16).

a. Create a map of the SNP analyzed by taking the map position for each SNP from Table 6-8 (please see Part 4, SNP Sequences: Mapping Data). All 1081 SNPs contained in this

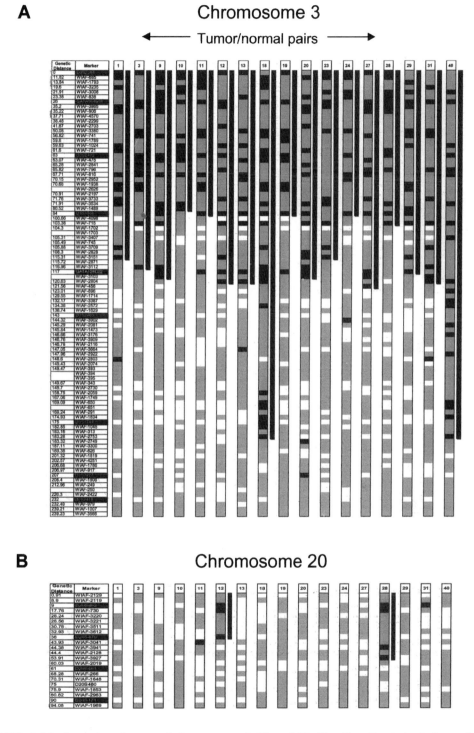

FIGURE 6-16. Examples of maps of chromosome 3 (*A*) and 20 (*B*) with estimated windows of LOH. "Genetic distance" is actual genetic distance for SSLPs and inferred genetic distance for SNPs, based on radiation hybrid map position. Markers in black are SSLPs. Each marker/sample pair is annotated as follows: (*black*) LOH; (*white*) retention; (*gray*) uninformative. Estimated windows of LOH, calculated as described in this protocol, are marked by black bars to the right of each sample.

file were mapped using the TNG radiation hybrid panel http://www-shgc.stanford.edu/ RH/index.html and were consistent with the Genebridge4 radiation (Walter et al. 1994) hybrid panel results, where the SNP had been mapped on both panels.

b. Define the approximate regions of LOH by ignoring all uninformative loci and proceeding as follows:

  i. Scan each chromosome, starting at the tip of the p-arm, to identify the first occurrence of two consecutive markers showing loss.

  ii. Initiate a running tally, denoted σ with an initial value of 2 (indicating two consecutive markers showing loss).

  iii. Increment this tally by +1 for each successive locus showing loss and by −1 for each successive locus showing retention.

  iv. Define the regions of LOH as the *two regions* corresponding to the largest value of σ.

If the informative SNP closest to either end of the chromosome is considered to be part of a window, then the remaining uninformative SNPs at that end of the chromosome are also considered part of the window. An example of the type of final data output from this analysis is shown in Figure 6-16.

TROUBLESHOOTING

Low Call Rate or Poor Correlation Factor from the Array

As noted above, it is important to check the correlation coefficient and the call rate of the individual arrays. If the correlation coefficient is <0.98, there is a risk that the genotype calls were not made correctly as the reads at 530 nm are extrapolated to the 570 wavelength based on the correlation coefficient. Low call rates or both a low call rate and low correlation coefficient are seen occasionally. In such cases, the array image shows features that appear either more or less brighter than the average. The problems of poor call rate or correlation coefficient are frequently associated with the array lot and may therefore be related to the synthesis quality of the array.

  If these problems are detected, assess the hybridization strength by comparing arrays with normal correlation coefficients and normal call rates with those with flawed values using visual inspection of the array image. When comparing arrays, make sure that the visual representations have the same degree of amplification of signal.

• If the hybridization signal is low and the call rate is low, hybridize the sample once again on a new array. If the sample still fails, repeat the amplification.

• If the call rate is low, correlation coefficient is low, but the signal strength is high (array very bright), try hybridizing only 5–15 μl of the sample (redo Steps 7–9). Adjust the sample volume in Step 5a by adding H_2O up to 30 μl.

• If several samples give poor results, and the amplification steps seem to have worked satisfactorily (Optional Step 4, gel electrophoresis of products), the batch of arrays may be defective and the samples should be tried on a new batch.

Part 3: Microarray-based Detection of DNA-Protein Interactions: Chromatin Immunoprecipitation on Microarrays

Vishwanath Iyer
University of Texas, Austin, Texas 78712-1095

INTRODUCTION

Cellular processes involving the genome, such as transcription, DNA replication, DNA repair, recombination, and chromosome segregation, involve the interaction of proteins with genomic DNA. The identification of the binding sites or loci for each DNA-binding protein is central to the investigation of these processes at the molecular level. There is an abundance of methods to identify target DNA sequences for a specific protein, but the method of chromatin immunoprecipitation has recently seen a surge in popularity. The method relies on the use of a specific antibody to immunoprecipitate the protein of interest together with its associated DNA sequences. Covalent cross-linking using formaldehyde allows specific in vivo interactions to be detected and has been used for mapping DNA-protein interactions in yeast (Strahl-Bolsinger et al. 1997), *Drosophila* (Orlando and Paro 1993), and mammalian cells (Boyd and Farnham 1999).

More recently, this approach has been combined with microarray hybridization to enable mapping of DNA-protein interactions in yeast on a genomic scale (Reid et al. 2000; Ren et al. 2000; Iyer et al. 2001; Lieb et al. 2001). The feasibility of making microarrays representing essentially every yeast promoter (please see Section 1, Protocol 6) makes this a particularly powerful approach. Like most experiments involving spotted DNA microarrays, the method uses a two-color fluorescence hybridization strategy. The specifically immunoprecipitated DNA (Protocol 9) is labeled using one fluorescent dye. The second dye is used to label a reference sample which can consist either simply of genomic DNA, amplified and labeled in parallel, or DNA derived from a parallel immunoprecipitation reaction that serves as the control. This immunoprecipitation is performed with a yeast strain bearing a deletion of the relevant gene, with an antibody lacking a fused epitope tag, with an irrelevant antibody, or with no antibody at all. In controls such as these, the DNAs recovered after carrying out the immunoprecipitation are likely to be largely representations of genomic DNA and may be interchangeable with each other and with reference samples. However, rather than taking this assumption at face value, microarray hybridizations should be carried out using various combinations of control or reference samples.

After the differentially labeled reference and immunoprecipitation samples have been simultaneously hybridized to a microarray representing all yeast intergenic sequences (Protocol 10), the ratio of fluorescence at an array element is proportional to the enrichment of that locus in the immunoprecipitation sample and hence indicative of the extent of binding of the protein to that locus.

Monoclonal and polyclonal antibodies to native proteins or to epitope tags fused to proteins have been successfully used in this approach. Epitope tagging has advantages in that the same immunoprecipitation conditions can be used for a variety of proteins, and high-affinity antibodies proven to work in immunoprecipitation reactions are available for the most popular epitope tags such as influenza virus hemagglutinin (HA) or Myc. However, for this approach to be successful, the epitope-tagged version of the protein must be functional in vivo, and the epitope must be exposed in the DNA-bound form of the protein after cross-linking.

Mapping DNA-Protein Interactions on the Yeast Genome Using Arrays

This protocol describes the steps involved in microarray-based mapping of the DNA-binding distribution of proteins in yeast. The entire procedure (except the manufacture of microarrays) can be performed in 3–4 days. Yeast cells can be grown overnight by inoculating cultures with appropriate numbers of cells and cross-linked and harvested on the morning of day 1. If the incubation with the antibody is carried out for a short time (4 hours), it is possible to perform the reversal of the cross-links overnight. Day 2 consists of purifying the immunoprecipitated DNA and performing the labeling with amino-allyl-conjugated nucleotides. Coupling to Cy dyes, microarray hybridization (6 hours), and scanning can be completed on day 3. Only a portion of the immunoprecipitated DNA is used for each microarray hybridization. A third of the material is used for amino-allyl labeling, and only half of the resulting DNA is used for each coupling reaction and microarray hybridization. Each immunoprecipitation (IP) reaction thus provides enough material for at least 6 microarray hybridizations.

MATERIALS

CAUTION: Please see Appendix 3 for appropriate handling of materials marked with <!>.

Buffers, Solutions, and Reagents

Please see Appendix 2 for components of stock solutions, buffers, and reagents.
Dilute stock solutions to the appropriate concentrations.

Benzamidine
Bovine serum albumin (BSA) (0.5 mg/ml stock)
Chloroform <!>
Dithiothreitol (DTT) (0.1 M) <!>
EDTA
Ethanol
Formaldehyde (37%) <!>
Glycerol
Glycine (2.5 M)
Glycogen (20 mg/ml)
HEPES-KOH (1 M, pH 7.5)
IP elution buffer
    50 mM Tris-HCl (pH 8.0)
    10 mM EDTA
    1% SDS <!>

IP wash buffer I
    50 mM HEPES-KOH (pH 7.5) <!>
    150 mM NaCl
    1 mM EDTA
    0.1% sodium deoxycholate
    1% Triton X-100
IP wash buffer II
    50 mM HEPES-KOH (pH 7.5)
    500 mM NaCl
    1 mM EDTA
    0.1% sodium deoxycholate
    1% Triton X-100
IP wash buffer III
    10 mM Tris-Cl (pH 8.0)
    250 mM LiCl
    1 mM EDTA
    0.5% sodium deoxycholate
    0.5% Nonidet P-40
KCl
Lithium chloride (LiCl)
Lysis buffer
    50 mM HEPES-KOH (pH 7.5)
    150 mM KCl
    1 mM EDTA
    10% glycerol
    0.1% Nonidet P-40
$MgCl_2$ (25 mM)
N-Hydroxysuccinimidyl ester-linked Cy3 and Cy5
Nonidet P-40 (10% w/v)
Phenol:chloroform (1:1) equilibriated <!>
Phenylmethylsufonyl fluoride (PMSF) <!> (100 mM stock in isopropanol)
Protease inhibitors (add just before use)
    1 mM benzamidine
    1 mM sodium metabisulfate
    0.2 mM PMSF
    1 μg/ml pepstatin
Protein G–Sepharose
SDS (10%) <!>
Sodium acetate (3 M, pH 5.2)
Sodium deoxycholate (10% w/v) in 10 mM HEPES-KOH (pH 8.0)
Sodium metabisulfate
TE (pH 8.0)
Triton X-100

Enzymes and Enzyme Buffers

Pepstatin
Proteinase K
RNase A

Antibodies

Primary antibody to epitope tag or protein of interest

Cells

Saccharomyces cerevisiae strain

Special Equipment

Glass beads (500 μm)
Microfuge tubes (screw-capped) fitted with O-rings
Mini-Beadbeater-8 (Biospec Products Inc.)
    Optional, please see Step 6.
Nutator (Clay Adams Inc.)
    Optional, please see Step 10.
QIAquick PCR purification kit (QIAGEN)
Syringe (6 ml with 25-gauge needles)
Ultrasonicator with fine tip

METHOD

Cross-linking and Immunoprecipitation

1. Grow 200 ml of yeast cells to an OD_{600} of ~0.6–0.8.

    A healthy yeast strain growing in complete medium should be in the logarithmic phase of growth. The volumes of reagents in this protocol are based on this assumption. A 200-ml culture will generally yield enough material for four immunoprecipitation reactions. The volumes of reagents can be adjusted accordingly for different strains, growth conditions, cell densities, and culture volumes.

2. Cross-link the DNA and proteins by adding 5.6 ml of 37% formaldehyde directly to the culture, to give a final formaldehyde concentration of 1%. Continue incubation for 15–30 minutes at room temperature (26ºC), shaking at 100 rpm.

    A 30-minute incubation with formaldehyde appears to be sufficient for completely cross-linking most DNA-binding proteins. It may be worthwhile to try a range of cross-linking times, especially for proteins whose mechanism of interaction with DNA is not well-characterized. However, too much cross-linking is possibly detrimental to the subsequent antibody binding and immunoprecipitation steps. The cross-linking time should be kept constant for a given series of experiments.

3. Quench the cross-linking reaction by adding 11 ml of 2.5 M glycine (to a final concentration of 125 mM). Continue shaking the culture for 5 minutes at room temperature.

4. Harvest the cells by centrifugation at 1500*g* for 5 minutes at 4ºC. Wash the cells twice in ice-cold PBS. During washing, consolidate the cell pellet into a single 15-ml conical tube.

5. Add 2 ml of ice-cold lysis buffer and resuspend the cells by pipetting up and down with a 1-ml pipettor. Add 1 ml of the cell suspension to each of two 2-ml screw-capped microfuge tubes, fitted with rubber O-rings. Add ~1 ml of glass beads (500 μm) to each tube and screw the cap on tightly.

Glass beads can be measured using a clean microfuge tube marked on the outside based at the level of 1 ml of H_2O in an identical tube.

Before screwing the cap to the tube containing the glass beads and the cell suspension, make sure there are no beads sticking to the lip of the tube or the O-ring.

6. Disrupt the cells to the fullest extent possible by vortexing at maximum speed at 4°C.

Because the quality of the extract depends on the extent of cell disruption, it is critical that this step be performed thoroughly. On an ordinary rotary vortexer, complete disruption will require 30 minutes of vortexing at 4°C. It is impractical to hold the tubes by hand on a vortexer for this length of time. A clamp holding several tubes in place will be required.

A better option is to invest in a Mini-BeadBeater-8 (BioSpec Products, Inc.), which agitates tubes much more violently and significantly reduces the time for disruption. If using a BeadBeater, agitate the tubes for four 1-minute sessions at maximum speed, returning the tubes to ice for 2 minutes between each agitation to prevent heating up of the contents.

7. Place a 6-ml syringe barrel fitted with a 25-gauge needle over a fresh 15-ml conical tube placed on ice. Pour the contents of the disruption tube, including the beads, into the syringe, and let the extract flow into the collection tube. Rinse the glass beads remaining in the syringe by adding 0.5 ml of lysis buffer, and use the syringe plunger to force the last of the liquid through. If the needle becomes clogged, raise the plunger a little, invert the syringe, and flick it a few times. The needle can be replaced if it becomes irretrievably blocked.

8. Shear the DNA in the cross-linked extract by ultrasonication. Use a sonicator with a fine tip immersed into the extract in the 15-ml tube. Sonicate for 3 cycles of 30 seconds each, at a power setting of 5 and duty cycle of 50%. Keep the extract cold by returning it to ice for 2 minutes between each sonication session.

The sonication step randomly shears the cross-linked DNA into fragments 300–1000 bp in length. The extent of sonication can be checked by agarose gel electrophoresis of a small aliquot (10 µl) of the extract after Step 9.

9. Transfer the sheared, cross-linked chromatin to microfuge tubes and centrifuge in a microfuge at maximum speed for 10 minutes at 4°C to remove the cell debris. Carefully transfer the supernatant to fresh microfuge tubes.

The volume of the extract should be just over 2 ml, which should be sufficient for at least four immunoprecipitation reactions.

If needed, dilute the extract for additional immunoprecipitation reactions, e.g., with different concentrations of antibody, for mock immunoprecipitation reactions without antibody or with preimmune serum, or for immunoprecipitation of a different target protein.

10. For each immunoprecipitation reaction, add the specific primary antibody to 500 µl of the sheared, cross-linked extract.

It is sometimes necessary to determine empirically the optimal antibody concentration for each protein being analyzed. Generally, however, antibodies can be used at a 1:100 or 1:50 dilution or between 2 and 5 µg of antibody per immunoprecipitation reaction. Incubate the immunoprecipitation reactions with slow rotation or rocking for 4 hours to overnight at 4°C. A Nutator (Clay Adams Inc.) is ideal for this and subsequent steps.

11. Add 50 µl of a 50% suspension of protein G–Sepharose beads, preequilibrated in lysis buffer, to the antibody complex. Use a 200-µl pipettor tip with a cut-off end to pipette the protein G beads. Incubate the suspension for 2 hours at 4°C with slow rotation or rocking.

12. Centrifuge the suspension at 1000*g* for 15 seconds at room temperature. Aspirate the supernatant carefully so as to not disturb the beads. A small amount of solution may be left together with the beads.

13. Wash the beads twice with 1 ml of IP wash buffer I for 5 minutes each at room temperature. Centrifuge the suspension at 1000*g* for 15 seconds at room temperature after each washing.

14. Wash the beads once with 1 ml of IP wash buffer II for 5 minutes at room temperature. Centrifuge the suspension at 1000*g* for 15 seconds at room temperature.

15. Wash the beads once with 1 ml of IP wash buffer III for 5 minutes at room temperature. Centrifuge the suspension at 1000*g* for 15 seconds at room temperature.

16. Wash the beads once with 1 ml of TE for 5 minutes at room temperature. After this final washing step, aspirate as much of the wash solution as possible without disturbing the beads.

    The preceding wash steps affect the quality of the immunoprecipitation reaction. The stringency of the washing steps can be optimized by varying the concentrations of salt and detergent in the wash buffers and assaying how they affect the specific enrichment of known target loci after the elution step. The stringency can be lowered if desired by using lower salt and/or detergent concentrations in IP wash buffers II and III. It is important, however, to work quickly and consistently through the wash and elution steps.

17. Elute the immunoprecipitated material by adding 100 µl of IP elution buffer to the pellet of beads. Mix and incubate the suspension for 15 minutes at 65°C. Centrifuge the suspension at maximum speed in a microfuge for 2 minutes and transfer the supernatant into a fresh tube. Add 50 µl of elution buffer to the beads and repeat the elution step. Combine the eluates (~150 µl).

18. Reverse the cross-linking by heating the eluate for at least 6 hours to overnight at 65°C in a heating block. Make sure that the tubes are tightly capped and sealed during this process.

19. Centrifuge the tube briefly and then add 150 µl of TE. Add 1 µl of 20 mg/ml glycogen and proteinase K to a concentration of 100 µg/ml. Incubate the solution for 2 hours at 37°C.

20. Add 300 µl of phenol:chloroform (1:1). Vortex the suspension for 10 seconds and then centrifuge it in a microfuge at maximum speed for 10 minutes at room temperature. Transfer the aqueous layer to a fresh tube. Add 100 µl of TE to the organic phase and vortex; recover the aqueous phase by centrifugation as before. Combine the aqueous extracts (~400 µl) and extract the solution once with an equal volume of chloroform.

21. Add 3 µl of 0.5 µg/µl DNase-free RNase A. Incubate the solution for 30 minutes at 37°C. Add sodium acetate (pH 5.2) to 0.3 M and 2 volumes of ethanol. Store the ethanolic solution for at least 1 hour at –20°C.

22. Recover the precipitated DNA by centrifugation at maximum speed in a microfuge for 30 minutes at 4°C. Wash the pellet once with 500 µl of 70% ethanol. Dry the pellet in the air and resuspend the pellet of DNA in 25 µl of TE. Store the immunoprecipitated DNA at –20°C.

Mapping DNA-Protein Interactions on the Yeast Genome: DNA Amplification and Labeling

This procedure is used to amplify the immunoprecipitated DNA prepared in Protocol 10. Amplification is carried out in two stages: In Round A, a partially degenerate primer is used to nonspecifically prime two cycles of DNA synthesis using the immunoprecipitated DNA as a template. The double-stranded product of Round A is exponentially amplified in Round B, using a specific PCR primer and amino-allyl-labeled nucleotides as substrates. Because Round A uses degenerate primers that have the capacity to amplify DNA from many sources, it is important to avoid contamination of the immunoprecipitated DNA with exogenous sequences. To avoid problems, use aerosol barrier tips, carry out manipulations with gloved hands in a laminar flow hood, and avoid making aerosols.

MATERIALS

Buffers and Solutions

Please see Appendix 2 for components of stock solutions, buffers, and reagents.
Dilute stock solutions to the appropriate concentrations.

Magnesium chloride (25 mM)
Phosphate-buffered saline (PBS)
Sodium bicarbonate buffer (1 M, pH 9.0)
    Dissolve 4.2 g of $NaHCO_3$ in 40 ml of H_2O, adjust the pH to 9.0 with 5 N NaOH, and bring the volume to 50 ml with H_2O.
20x SSC
TE (pH 8.0)

Enzymes and Enzyme Buffers

10x PCR buffer
    100 mM Tris-HCl (pH 8.3)
    500 mM KCl
Sequenase (13 units/µl) (US Biochemical)
Sequenase dilution buffer (US Biochemical)
5x Sequenase reaction buffer (US Biochemical)
Taq DNA polymerase (5 units/µl) (e.g., AmpliTaq Gold from Applied Biosystems)

Nucleic Acids and Oligonucleotides

100x Amino-allyl dNTP stock
    25 mM dATP
    25 mM dGTP
    25 mM dCTP
    10 mM dTTP
    15 mM amino-allyl-dUTP

Control DNA, sheared yeast genomic DNA (5 μg/ml)

dATP, dCTP, dGTP, dTTP (100 mM stock, ultrapure) (e.g., 27-2035-01, Amersham Biosciences)

Immunoprecipitated DNA, prepared as described in Protocol 10

Poly(A)/poly(dA) (5 μg/μl polyadenylic acid) (Sigma)

Primer A oligo 5′-GTT TCC CAG TCA CGA TCN NNN NNN NN (40 μM)

Primer B oligo 5′-GTT TCC CAG TCA CGA TC (500 μM)

Yeast intergenic microarrays (please see Section 1, Protocol 2)

Special Equipment

Aerosol barrier tips for micropipettors

> For all pipetting steps that do not involve a multichannel pipettor, use barrier pipette tips to avoid contamination.

Amplification tubes (0.2-ml thin-walled for PCR)

Microarray reader/scanner

Microcon YM-30 microconcentrator (Millipore)

Pipettors (adjustable single-channel) and barrier tips

Pipettors (2.5 μl and 200 μl capacities) (adjustable-volume 12-channel)

QIAquick PCR purification kit (QIAGEN)

Thermal cycler, programmable with heated lid (e.g., ABI 9700)

Additional Reagents and Equipment

Step 12 of this protocol requires reagents listed in Section 3, Protocol 14.

Step 18 of this protocol requires reagents and equipment listed in Section 3, Protocol 20.

METHOD

Round A: Amplification of Immunoprecipitated DNA

1. Prepare a sufficient volume of reaction mix to accommodate the total number of planned amplification reactions plus 1 (please see Step 2). For each amplification reaction, combine the following components in an 0.5-ml microfuge tube on ice. Add the Sequenase just before the reaction mix will be used (in Step 3):

5x Sequenase reaction buffer	1.0 μl
Round A dNTP mix (stock containing 3 mM of each of the 4 dNTPs)	1.5 μl
dithiothreitol (DTT) (0.1 M stock)	0.75 μl
bovine serum albumin (0.5 mg/ml stock)	1.5 μl
Sequenase (13 units/μl)	0.3 μl

2. For each amplification reaction, combine the following reagents in separate 0.2-ml thin-walled PCR tubes with caps.

immunoprecipitated DNA (or control sample)	7 μl
5x Sequenase reaction buffer	2 μl
Primer A (40 μM stock)	1 μl

   As controls, set up reaction mixtures containing:

- Sheared yeast genomic DNA (5 μg/ml) instead of the immunopreciptated DNA; the amplified products of this reaction will be used as the reference probe (if needed).

- No DNA (substitute 7 μl of TE in place of DNA).

3. Transfer the tubes containing the DNA/primer mixture prepared in Step 2 into a thermal cycler fitted with a heated lid. Carry out amplification using the following denaturation, annealing, and polymerization times and temperatures:

    a. 2 minutes at 94°C

    b. 2 minutes at 8°C

    > A pause may be programmed or entered after this step as needed.
    >
    > During the pause at 8°C, add 5 μl of the reaction mixture containing Sequenase (from Step 1) to each tube. Quickly remove each tube in turn from the thermal cycler, add the reaction mixture, pipette fluid up and down several times to ensure mixing, and replace the tubes in the machine. Set the instrument to "Pause" if more time is needed to finish the additions and mixing before the ramp to 37°C begins.

    c. Ramp to 37°C over the course of 8 minutes.

    > Not all thermal cyclers may permit ramping this slowly. On the ABI 9700, a ramp speed of 7% (of normal) achieves the desired ramp rate.

    d. Hold the reactions for 8 minutes at 37°C.

4. Repeat the amplification cycle described in Step 3 from a through d, with delivery of additional Sequenase at Step 3b:

    a. Prepare a reaction mixture containing 0.3 μl of Sequenase and 0.7 μl of Sequenase dilution buffer for each reaction.

    b. During the second pause at 8°C (Step 3b in the second cycle), add 1 μl of the freshly diluted Sequenase to each tube. Pipette the enzyme into the 15 μl of liquid inside each tube.

    c. Using another pipettor set at 8 μl, mix the reagents well by pipetting up and down, and return the tubes to the thermal cycler before next step (ramping to 37°C) begins.

5. Cool the reactions to 4°C.

6. After completion of Round A, dilute the product to 50 μl with TE. Use 15 μl of the diluted Round-A product for the next amplification step and store the remainder at –20°C. Transfer the 15-μl aliquots to 0.2-ml thin-walled PCR tubes.

Round B: Amplification and Amino-allyl Labeling of Immunoprecipitated DNA

7. For each of the reactions to be amplified in Round B and labeled, mix the following components:

double-distilled H_2O	63.0 μl
10x PCR buffer	10.0 μl
magnesium chloride (25 mM stock)	8.0 μl
Primer B (500 μM stock)	2.5 μl
100x amino-allyl-dNTP stock	1.0 μl
Taq DNA polymerase (5 units/μl)	1.0 μl

8. Add 85 μl of the reaction mix prepared in Step 7 to each of the thin-walled PCR tubes containing 15 μl of the amplified DNA produced in Round A.

9. Transfer the tubes to a thermal cycler and amplify the DNA templates using the denaturation, annealing, and polymerization times and temperatures listed below:

Number of cycles	Denaturation	Annealing	Polymerization
32	30 seconds at 92°C	30 seconds at 40°C, then 30 seconds at 50°C	1 minute at 72°C

Analyze 5 μl of the Round-B product by electrophoresis through an agarose gel. A smear of DNA should be seen ranging in size from 200 to 600 base pairs. No amplified DNA should be visible in the lane containing a sample of the "no DNA" control.

10. Add 400 μl of H_2O to a Microcon YM-30 device. Use a separate device for each amplification mixture. Concentrate each Round-B amplification reaction to ~20 μl. Add 500 μl of H_2O to the same Microcon device and concentrate the solution to a volume less than 19 μl. Adjust the volume of the recovered samples to 19 μl with H_2O. Avoid drying the samples as they will then be difficult to resuspend. Use 9 μl of each concentrated amino-allyl-labeled sample for coupling to Cy dyes. Store the remainder of the samples at –20°C in H_2O.

11. To 9 μl of the concentrated DNA sample in H_2O, add 1 μl of fresh 1 M sodium bicarbonate buffer (pH 9.0) and mix well.

12. Add the 10 μl of DNA sample in 0.1 M sodium bicarbonate to an aliquot of the appropriate succinimidyl (NHS)-ester-linked Cy dye. Mix the reagents thoroughly by pipetting up and down to ensure complete resuspension of the dried Cy dye aliquot. Allow coupling of the dye to the amino-allyl-labeled DNA to proceed for 1 hour at room temperature in the dark.

   For instructions on how to aliquot and store the monofunctional Cy dyes, please see Section 3, Protocol 14.

13. To each coupling reaction, add 70 μl of H_2O and 8 μl of 3 M sodium acetate (pH 5.2). Purify the labeled DNA from the uncoupled dye, separately for each coupling reaction, using a QIAquick PCR purification kit as follows:

   a. Add 700 μl of PBS buffer to each coupling reaction. Apply the mixture to the top of spin column. Centrifuge the samples at 10,000*g* in a standard microfuge for 1 minute. Discard the flow-through.

   b. Add 600 μl of PE buffer to each of the samples and centrifuge as in Step a. Repeat this step once more. After the last flow-through has been discarded, centrifuge the column at 13,800*g* for 30 seconds to dry the column. Transfer the column to a clean microfuge collection tube.

14. Add 60 μl of EB buffer (elution buffer) onto the center of the membrane in the column. Stand the column for 5 minutes at room temperature to ensure maximal recovery of DNA. Centrifuge the column at maximum speed for 1 minute, collecting the eluate in a standard microfuge tube. Repeat this step once more, collecting the eluate in the same tube.

15. Combine the appropriate Cy3- and Cy5-labeled purified probes, and adjust the volume to 500 μl with TE. Using a Microcon YM-30, concentrate the solution to ~10–15 μl. Add H_2O, poly(A)/poly(dA), and 20x SSC to bring up the volume as required for the microarray geometry and coverslip type, in a final concentration of 3.5x SSC.

16. Add 10% SDS to a final concentration of 0.1%, boil the probe, and apply the solution to the surface of the microarray containing yeast intergenic elements. Hybridize for 6 hours at 65°C and then wash and scan the microarray.

   For details of hybridization, washing, and scanning, please see Section 3, Protocol 20 and Table 3-9.

Part 4: SNP Sequences: Mapping Data

Kerstin Lindblad-Toh* and Thomas Ryder[†]

*Whitehead Institute/MIT Center for Genome Research, Cambridge, Massachusetts 02139;
[†]Affymetrix, Inc., Santa Clara, California 95051

Large-scale genotyping methods take advantage of SNP markers that were originally identified in one of the first large-scale SNP discovery projects (Wang et al. 1998). Protocol 9 describes the use of the Affymetrix HuSNP array and HuSNP mapping assay for detection of loss of heterozygosity (LOH), based on the method described by Lindblad-Toh et al. (2000).

Table 6-7 Multiplex Primer Pools: SNP Mapping Data

The table presents a collection of locus-specific primers used for the primary multiplex amplification reactions. The primer pools consist of T3- and T7-tailed primer pairs, and each of the 24 pools represents a discrete set of 50–100 genetic loci.

Table 6-8 Map Locations for SNPs on the Affymetrix HuSNP Chip

The table provides the map positions for 1081 SNPs. Many of the SNPs included in the table were discovered in conjunction with the Whitehead Institute/MIT Center for Genome Research (www-genome.wi.mit.edu/SNP/human/index.html). The SNPs were mapped using the comprehensive TNG radiation hybrid panel from the Stanford Human Genome Center (www-shgc.Stanford.edu/RH/index.html).

TABLE 6-7. Multiplex Primer Pools: SNP Mapping Data

WIAF Name	Alleles	Allele A	Allele B	Chipregion	primer up	primer down	ncbi SS	NwLib chrom
WIAF-1000	C/T	C	T	TCAAGATCCTCCTCAAACTT[C/T]AAGGGTGAAAAGCATACCAT	TAAAACATATCAAGATCCTCTCA	AATGGTATGCTTTTCACCCTT	3099	15
WIAF-1001	C/T	C	T	CATTCTGTTCTCCAGTCTTG[C/T]AGGTTACATAAGCCATTTCC	CACATTCTGTTCTCCAGTCTTG	TTATGGAAATGGCTTATGTAACC	3100	18
WIAF-1002	A/T	A	T	GTGCTATTCAAGCAACAATT[A/T]TCTTTTATGTTCCTAAGCTC	GGGTGCTATTCAAGCAACAA	TCATGATGAGCTTAGGAACAATAAA	3101	18
WIAF-1004	A/G	A	G	CCTTAAAATCACAGTACTGG[A/G]ATCAGGTGAAATTTGCTTTC	CCTTAAAATCACAGTACTGG	TTAGAAAGCAAATTTCACCTGAT	3103	2
WIAF-1007	C/T	C	T	GCTACCCAGGCTGGTCTCAT[C/T]TCAGGCTCATGCGATCCTCC	CTACCCAGGCTGGTCTCAT	GGATCGCATGAGCCTGA	3106	3
WIAF-1008	G/A	A	G	GAAATCGACTACCAGCTGAT[G/A]AAATACCTGCAAAGTGCTCT	GAGAAATCGACTACCAGCTGA	TTTAGAGCACTTTGCAGGTATTT	3107	5
WIAF-1009	T/C	C	T	TCACTTCATGTGAAAACTAC[T/C]CCAGTGGCTGACTGAATTGC	TTCTTCTCACTTCATGTGAAAACT	CAATTCAGTCAGCCACTGG	3108	6
WIAF-1012	T/A	A	T	GTTCCTGGTACCAATATCAAT[T/A]CAGTTTTCAAAGCCATTTGC	GTTCCTGGTACCAATATCAAT	GCAAATGGCTTTGAAAACTG	3111	15
WIAF-1013	G/C	C	G	TCCAGTGCTGTGTCCTGCA[G/C]GCTGTCCTCCAGGCAAGTTGC	TCCAGTGCTGTGTCCTGCA	CAACTTGCCTGAGGACAGC	3112	1
WIAF-1014	T/C	C	T	GCCCTTTCAATTAATAGTAG[T/C]TGAGCGCTGGTGAAGT	TCAATGCCCTTTCAATTAATAGTA	AGCCCCAGCGCTCA	3113	1
WIAF-1018	T/G	G	T	TAACCTCAATTCGTGAAAAC[T/G]AACATGCCTCAAAAAGAGG	TCTAATAAACCTCAATTCGTGAAAA	CAGCACAGTGTTCTGTTAAAGTTT	3117	1
WIAF-1021	C/G	C	G	TGAATCATAAATTATCAAAT[C/G]TGCGCCCAGTAATCTGTGTT	CCCACTGAATCATAAATTATCAAA	CACAGATTACTGGGCGCA	3120	17
WIAF-1023	A/G	A	G	GAGGCATTAACTGAGATTAT[A/G]GGAAACGCACAGCAAAATG	GAGGCATTAACTGAGATTAT	ATTTTGCTGTGCGTTTCC	3122	2
WIAF-1024	A/G	A	G	TCACCGAACAATATTTTAGG[A/G]ATTTGAAATTATTCTGTAC	CTTTCACCGAACAATATTTTAGG	CATATTCTGGGTGGTGAGAA	3123	3
WIAF-1026	T/C	C	T	TGAGTAAATGCATTTGAGCTG[T/C]CCCAGGCTCGTTCCTCCAG	CAGTGAGTAAATGCATTTGAGCT	GAGGAGACAGAGCCTGGG	3125	14
WIAF-1027	A/T	A	T	CGAAGATTTTGGCTAATTTG[A/T]TAGTCTTACAAAGGCAGTCT	TCGAAGATTTTGGCTAATTTG	GGTGAACTAGACTGCCTTTGTAAGA	3126	8
WIAF-1029	A/G	A	G	CCACCTGTCTTCTCTCCCAC[A/G]TGCACAGCTTCCTGAGTCAC	CCACCTGTCTTCTCTCCCA	TGACTCAGGAAGCTGTGCA	3128	8
WIAF-1031	G/C	C	G	AACACCAGGTCCCCCACCC[G/C]CGTGCGTGGTGTAGTCATAGA	CAGCGTCCCCACCC	GCTCTATGACTACACCACGACG	3130	2
WIAF-1032	C/T	C	T	CGATTTAATACGTTAG[C/T]TGGAATTATTCTATGTCAAT	CCACGCGATTTAATACGTTAG	TTTCATAGCTTAAAAATCATTGACA	3131	4
WIAF-1036	A/G	A	G	TTCTATTCCCACGTTAGCCA[A/G]TTGTTCTTGATGAATCTATA	TTCTATTCCCACGTTAGCCA	TGACTCATATAGATTCATCAAGAACA	3135	14
WIAF-1040	T/C	C	T	AGGTGCTACCAGAACTCATG[T/C]GATAGCGCTTTCTTTTAGGC	TAAGGTGCTACCAGAACTCATG	TGCCTAAAAGAAAGCGCTATC	3139	13
WIAF-1044	C/A	A	C	ATGATGCCGAGGTCACTGCT[C/A]TACAAAGATTAAAGAAACTT	TGCCGAGGTCACTGCT	GGAAGTGTTTGATGGTAAGTTTCT	3143	8
WIAF-1045	A/G	A	G	TGATACACTACGCATGCACA[A/G]ATAAAGTCACATCAAGACTA	TGATACACTACGCATGCACA	CATTTAGATTATTAGTCTTGATGTGACTT	3144	3
WIAF-1046	T/C	C	T	CATTGGGTCTAGGAGTAGAAA[T/C]GCACAACAAGGAATAAGGGAG	GCCATTGGGTCTAGGAGTAGAAA	CTCCCTTATTCCTTGTGTGC	3145	5
WIAF-1049	C/T	C	T	AGCTAAATTAGCCCTAAATG[C/T]GGGTAATATTTTTCCTCATG	TGACAGCTAAATTAGCCCTAAATG	TTTTAAAACATGAGGAAAAATATTACC	3148	5
WIAF-1051	A/G	A	G	GTCTCCCTGAGGTGATATGG[A/G]CCCTAAGTCCACGATGGTGA	TGTCTCCCTGAGGTGATATGG	TCACCATCGTGGACTTAAGG	3150	9
WIAF-1053	C/T	C	T	ATTGCGAAATCTGTTGTGCA[C/T]GCTCAAATGAAAACGGCCTTT	ATTGCGAAATCTGTTGTGCA	AAGGCGTTTTCATTTGAGC	3152	12
WIAF-1056	T/G	G	T	GTAGATAAGAGCATAATCT[T/G]AAACAAAATTCTTTCGAAA	CTCTCAAGTAGATAAGAGGCATAATCT	GCTAAATTTCGAAAAGAATTTTGTTT	3155	10
WIAF-1057	G/C	C	G	TGGAACCAACGATCATATCT[G/C]TATGCCCATTTTATTCTGT	AGTGGAACCAACGATCATATCT	CATTGACAGAATAAAATGAGGCA	3156	13
WIAF-1059	C/T	C	T	TTGTTCCTCCAGACCGCAGG[C/T]TCCCCCAGCCTCAGGTTGCT	TCCTCCAGACCGCAGG	ACCTGAGGCTGGGGG	3158	11
WIAF-1063	C/T	C	T	ACATGAATACTTGAAGACAA[C/T]ATAACTACAACCTTACAAAT	CTACATGAATACTTGAAGACAA	GGCATTTGTAAGGTTGTAGTT	859	13
WIAF-1082	C/T	C	T	AAAATTTTCCAGTTGGTAAG[C/T]CATTAAAGCAGAAGTTTCTT	ATATTGCCAGTTTGTAAG[C/T]CATTAAAGCAGAAGTTTCTTG	AAGATCACTGAAGAACTTCTGCTT	19381	6
WIAF-1084	C/T	C	T	ATATTGCCAGTTTGTAAG[C/T]CATTAAAGCAGAAGTTTCTTG	GGATTGTAATATTGCCAGAGG	AACGCTGTCCTTGTGGGTGAT	19368	6
WIAF-1085	A/G	A	G	TGAATGCTGTCCATGCCATGC[A/G]CAAGCAGCACAGTGATCATC	CACTGAATGCTGTCGCCATGA	TGAAAGATCATTGATAAGAATCTGG	19373	8
WIAF-1089	C/T	C	T	GCTTCCTTGACTGTTCTCCA[C/T]GCCAGATTCTTATCAATGAT	TGCTTCCTTGACTGTTCTCCA	GATCTAAGCAGCGGTTCCCAC	19480	8
WIAF-1091	A/C	A	C	ACCGGCGTATAGTAAGCTCTG[A/C]GGAACTCCAAGAATCTAGAG	AAGATTAGGACACAGACCGCGT	TTAATATATAGCCTGATGATGAGAG	19385	14
WIAF-1119	C/T	C	T	GGAGTTTTGTTTCTTGTAAC[C/T]CTCTCATCATCGAGGCTATA	TTTGGAGGTTTGTGTCTGGA	GGAAGTGAAGGAACTGTTGG	19435	18
WIAF-1121	C/T	C	T	CATCTGGGAAGATTTCTACC[C/T]GACCAACAGTTCTTCAGCT	TGCATCTGGGAAGATTTCTACC	ACTTGGTGTCCTTTCCCTCC	19361	1
WIAF-1133	A/G	A	G	CAGCAGCAGGTGGCACGGAAG[A/G]AGTGGAGGGAAAAGGACACCA	GTGCCCTGAAGATTAGCAGC	GAGCAGACTCGTGGGATCTG	19376	17
WIAF-1134	A/G	A	G	AAGTGGGCCCTCCCAGTC[A/G]TTCTCTGGGCACAGATCCCAC	AAGTGGGCCCTCCCAGTC	CTTGAGTGGGTGGGAGGAG	19436	17
WIAF-1138	A/G	A	G	CCACCGAATGACAGCA[A/G]CCTCTCTCCCACCCACTCAA	AGTGATTTTGGCTAGGCGTG	TCTTCTGCACAGAATGGCTC	19481	17
WIAF-1139	A/G	A	G	TAATTTTGCAGGCAGACTTC[A/G]TAGGAACCATTCTGTGCAGA	CGTAATTTTGCAGGCAGACTTC	TGGGAACTGAACACGGCT	892	16
WIAF-1145	C/T	C	T	TTTGTGAAGTCACATTGGC[C/T]GAGCGCGTGTTCAGTTCCCAG	TTTGTGAAGTCACATTGGC	GTGCTACACTGAGTTATTGAGAA	19437	10
WIAF-1146	C/T	C	T	AACTAAGTGTTATTGAACTG[C/T]AATTCTCTCAATAACTCAGT	TGAAGCCAACTAAGTGTTATTGAA	GTGCTACACTGAGTTATTGAGAGAA	897	2
WIAF-1148	A/G	A	G	CAAAATCAAATATTCATCAC[A/G]TTGGGTTGAAAAGTTGGAAG	AACAATTCACAGTCACAGGAAATC	TACCCGCGATAGGAAGGGC	19438	19
WIAF-1149	C/T	C	T	GAAACCAAGAGTTTCCCAGG[C/T]GAGCCCTTCCTACCCACCTCCAA	ATGATTTTCCTGTCCCATCG	TGGGTCAGGCTCTTTCTGTT	19186	9
WIAF-1154	C/G	C	G	GATGATGGGGTCTGAGATGT[C/G]TTCCTCAGGCTGCCATCAGCTG	TTTCAGATGATGGGGTCTGA	TGGGTCAGGCTCTTTCTGTT	19414	1
WIAF-1156	A/G	A	G	CTATACCAAGTTTCCATAAA[A/G]CTGTCTGCTGGTTGGGGAGG	TTTAGCTGCTATACCAAGTTTCCA	GCAAAGAATGTGGTCAGGCT	19378	16
WIAF-1162	A/G	A	G	TCTTGGCATTCGTCCTCCTC[A/G]GGGCAGTGCTCCACCCAAGT	CTGGTTCTCTTCGTCTTGGC	ATCATCGGGAAGGACACTTG	19439	19
WIAF-1164	A/T	A	T	TCAGTTCACAGTGGAGACTA[A/T]GGAAGTTCAGGGCAGGATCC	CTCCCCTCCTCCAGTTCACAG	GGATCCTGCCCTGAATCTC	19365	17
WIAF-1165	C/T	C	T	TTCTCCTCTTCCAGAAGTTG[C/T]AGAGCTGCTATTTAGTTTGAT	GCACGTTCTTTGTTCTCCTCTT	CGACAGATAATCAAACTAAATAGACG	19371	17

(Continued on following pages.)

TABLE 6-7. (*Continued*)

WIAF Name	Alleles	Allele A	Allele B	Chipregion	primer up	primer down	ncbi SS	NwLib chrom
WIAF-118	C/T	C	T	CTATTGTGGAGACAAACAG[C/T]TGGGAAGTAAAGGTTGATT	GCCTATTGTGGAGAACAAACAG	AAGTAATCAACCTTACTTCCCAA	2512	19
WIAF-1186	A/G	A	G	TGCAGATCTTCTATTCCTGG[A/G]GTTGATATGACAAGGAAACC	CACTGCAGATCTTCTATTCCTGG	CCAATAGGGTTTCCTTGTCA	742	8
WIAF-1218	C/T	C	T	GTTGCTGGGACCTGGAACA[C/T]TGGACTTCTTCTACTGCAG	TGCTGGGACCTGGAACA	CTGCTGCAGTAGAAAGAAGTCC	19482	7
WIAF-1242	A/T	A	T	AAGCCAGTATGTTGTGGCAA[A/T]AATTCGAGAAAACACACTGAA	GAAGCCAGTATGTTGTGGCA	TTTTTCAGTGTGTTTTCTCGAAT	19483	15
WIAF-1247	A/G	A	G	GAAGGGCAGGACTAATCCAA[A/G]TCTCTACCCGCAGCTTGCTC	GAAGGGCAGGACTAATCCAA	GAGCAAGCTGCGGGATAGG	19484	11
WIAF-1250	A/T	A	T	ATCTTCAGGAAAATGAAACA[A/T]GAGAAGCTGAAACAATCTAC	GCCTGCTCACAAGGTAGACA	CATTCAGGTGTAGATTGTTTCAGC	19380	5
WIAF-1251	A/T	A	T	AAATTACTGCCTTAGCAAAC[A/T]CTATGTTGTCAGGTTTTCT	GGTAAAGTCTAAATTACTGCCTTAGCA	TGCAGCAGAAAAACCTGACA	19440	5
WIAF-1252	C/T	C	T	CAGTTTGGCTTCGTCCTCA[C/T]AGTCTCTCTCCATGTGGCAA	CCAGTTTGGCTTCGTCCTC	TGTTTGCCACATGGAGAGAG	19362	1
WIAF-1258	C/T	C	T	CTTAAGTACTGTTGTCTACACAGACACTT[C/T]ATGCAGCGGCCTGTGGAGGC	CTTAAGTACTGTTGTCTACACAGACACTT	CTCAGGACACAGGCCAG	19417	1
WIAF-1262	A/G	A	G	TACATGCGTAACCTTCTAAC[A/G]CTTGAAAAATCAATTTCAAC	CCTTTACATGCGTAACCTTCTAAC	TCCCTTGAAAATGCATTTTTCAA	929	10
WIAF-1266	C/G	C	G	ACAGGAGAGCGCAAAACAAA[C/G]CCTGGCTGCCTCGGGATGGA	GCAGCATTTGTGACAGGAGA	ATGCAGTGGTGGTGAGGC	19441	22
WIAF-1274	C/T	C	T	CTCTGGTGTGCAGGGAATCA[C/T]TTTGCTGGATTAGAGGAAAG	GTCTCTGGTGTGCAGGGAAT	AAGTCATGGAAACAGACGGC	19375	17
WIAF-1283	A/G	A	G	TGATTGCCTCACACAAGCAT[A/G]ATCAATCGCCACGAGAGACT	ACCATGATTGCCTCACACAA	CCAGCCATACTCTTTGGCAT	19374	15
WIAF-1284	C/G	C	G	AAAGTACAATCCAGTATATGCAGAAAG[C/G]TACTCAGCATCACATCGTG	AAAGTACAATCCAGTATATGCAGAAAG	TGATCACGAGTGTCAGTGCTG	19366	17
WIAF-1290	C/T	C	T	ACCTATCTGAGTCTGTATCC[C/T]CATCTTTAAAATTTACAAATTT	ATCTCACCTATCTGAGTCTGTATCC	TGATAGGTGTCCTTAAAATTTACAAATTT	19431	X
WIAF-1291	C/G	C	G	TGTGTGGCAAAATAGAAAAT[C/G]TTTCAATTACATTAGGAAAT	CCAAGTGTGTGGCAAAATAGAAA	CCCGATTTCCTAATGTAATTGAA	934	8
WIAF-1302	A/G	A	G	TTCAGCCTCCTCTACCCTAC[A/G]AGATCTGGAGCAACAGCTAG	CCCTGTAGCAGTCTTCAGCC	TTTCCTAGCTGTTGCTCCAGA	19442	4
WIAF-1306	A/G	A	G	ATAGCTGTTCCTGAGTTGCA[A/G]GCACGGATGGAGATTTGGACA	AGATAGCTGTTCCTGAGTTGCA	CAGTGTCCAAATCTCCATCG	19443	6
WIAF-1307	A/G	A	G	CTCTGCCTGCAGGATGTGCG[A/G]GGTGCTGCGAGGTAGCCCC	TCTCTGCCTGCAGGATGTG	GGGCTACTCCAGGCACAC	19159	11
WIAF-1310	C/T	C	T	TTCCTCCACTTCATTTTTCC[C/T]TTGTCCTTTCTCTCTAATTC	TCTTCCTCCACTTCATTTTTCC	AAACACTGAATTAGAGAGAAAGGACA	946	1
WIAF-1318	C/T	C	T	AGCCATTTCTTTTTGAATGA[C/T]TGACAATAAAAATGATTTGAA	CAGCCATTTCTTTTTGAATGA	TTCCCAATTTCAAATCATTTTT	753	13
WIAF-1320	C/T	C	T	TTTATTTCTTCTTTCCCATT[C/T]TATGTTGGTAAATATAAAGA	TGTGTTACTTTTATTTCTTTCTTTCCA	TTGCACAATCATCTTTATATTTACCAA	755	8
WIAF-1325	G/C	C	G	CTGCAGTACAAGGATCTGCC[C/G]TCTCCCCTGCGTCGGGGGGC	CTGCAGTACAAGGATCTGCC	CCCGACGCAGGGAGA	19433	17
WIAF-1331	G/C	C	G	GTATTGAAGTCTTTGGGCAA[G/C]GTCGTAATGATCTGACTTC	GTATTGAAGTCTTTGGGCCA	GGGAGAAGTCAGATCATTACAGA	2285	5
WIAF-1353	C/G	C	G	TGACTAGCCATCTCAAGCAA[C/G]TTTCGACGTTTGACTAGCCA	TGACTAGCCATCTCAAGC	TGGCTAGTCAAACGTC	962	13
WIAF-1362	C/T	C	T	TGGTCATCGTGGCCATCGCC[C/T]GGACTCCGAGACTCCAGACC	ATCGTGGCCATCGCC	TGGTCTGGAGTCTCGGAGTC	19434	8
WIAF-1366	A/G	A	G	TTTTCAGTATGGTTCAGAAT[A/G]AGTATCTTAGTATTCTTTCT	GCTGCCACTTTTCAGTATGG	CCATAGCAAAATAGAAAGAATACTAAGA	965	6
WIAF-1412	A/G	A	G	CTGGTTTCTAGATGTACAC[A/G]TGTGGGACCTCGTCTCAAC	CACCCAACTGGTTTCTAGATG	AGGTTGAGACAGAGGTCCCA	777	9
WIAF-1417	C/T	C	T	TTAGCAAACATTTTTAAAA[C/T]CCCAATCCAACAGATTGGTT	TCTTACTTGGGTAGTTTAGCAAAACATT	AACCAATCTGTTGGATGTGG	19372	1
WIAF-1421	A/T	A	T	CTGATGAGGAAGCTCTAGTG[A/T]AGAAATTCAGGACGCGGTCT	GGGTAACCTGATGAGGAAGC	GACTTGAACCAAGCCCTCTG	19444	17
WIAF-1430	A/G	A	G	CACAGCAGCTTACTCCAGAG[A/G]TCAAGTCCAAGGCCATTGGC	ACACAGCAGCTTACTCCAGAG	CCAATGGCCTTGGACTTG	674	12
WIAF-1450	C/T	C	T	AAGCAGCCCTGCAAGTGG[C/T]GCTGGATACCACTGAGAAGT	CAGCCCTGCAAGTGG	TCAGTAGACTTCTTAGTGGTATCCA	993	9
WIAF-1461	T/A	T	A	CCATAGGACAGTTGTTTGAG[T/A]TTGGTTGCCACCTTATTGGCC	ATTCCATAGGACAGTTGTTTGAG	TCTACACCCAGTTTCCTTATC	2004	6
WIAF-1463	A/T	A	T	CCAATGAAGCAGGCTATGGA[A/T]TTAAAAGAAACAACAAATGGG	CCAATGAAGCAGGCTATGG	AATGAACCCATTTGTTGTTTCT	1090	11
WIAF-1464	T/C	C	T	GAATGCCTACATCTGGAATT[T/C]CAATACATCAACGTAAATT	GGGAATGCCTACATCTGGAA	GGACAAAATTTAACGTTGATGTAATG	3161	
WIAF-1465	G/T	G	T	GAAACTGCATGGGTACAAAT[G/T]TTCCAATTCATACTTAACAAG	GGAAACTGCATGGGTACAAA	TCCCCACCTTGTTAAGTATGAA	3162	11
WIAF-1466	A/G	A	G	GAACTTGATGGAAAATTGGC[A/G]TCTGTTGAATGATTCTAA	GAACTTGATGGAAAATTGGC	AAAGCTTTAGAATCATTCTACACAGA	3163	4
WIAF-1468	G/A	A	G	AGGCCTGAGGTGGGCGTTAC[G/A]AATTAGTATTTCGAAATACCT	GCCTGAGGTGGGCGTTAC	TTAGGAAGGTCTTCGAAATACTAATT	3164	18
WIAF-1469	A/G	A	G	TAAACACACATAAAGACACC[A/G]GGTTCTCAGTAATGCTCTAG	ACACATTCATTTTTATAAACACACATAA	CCTGGACTAGAGCATTACTGAGA	3165	4
WIAF-1470	A/G	A	G	TGGCTGTGCCAACTCAAGGC[A/G]GCTACCTTGACATTATAAGG	GCTGTGCCAACTCAAGGC	CAGCCTTATAATGTCAAGGTAGC	2006	1
WIAF-1473	G/A	A	G	GTCAAAAACCAATGTTCTC[G/A]TAAGTGGGAGATAAACAATG	TAATGATACAGAAAGTCAAAAACCA	CACGTCCAGGTGTACACATTG	1092	3
WIAF-1474	A/G	A	G	AATTAGTTTTCGTAATATT[A/G]TTCTAGTCCATTTAGATTGT	CCAACTAACAAATTAGTTTTCGT	CATTTACAAATCGTAAATGGACTAGAA	3166	16
WIAF-1475	A/G	A	G	CAACTACAATTAATTTTCTTG[A/G]TGAACAACAGTAGACATATGA	GGCACCAACTACAATTAATTTTCTT	AGTACATTTCATATGTCACTGCTGTTCA	1093	4
WIAF-1476	T/C	C	T	CACCTGTTTGTATAAACATAT[T/C]GTCGGGGTAAGCCCTTCTTTG	CCAATGCACCTGTTTGTATAAA	AAAGAAGGGCTTACCCAC	3167	6
WIAF-1477	C/T	C	T	ACCTGCTGCCTGCCTGCTCA[C/T]GACTGATTACTTTCAATCCC	CCTGCCTGCCTGCTCA	GCTGGGATTGAAAGTAATCAGTC	3168	7
WIAF-1479	C/T	C	T	TAAAATGACCTTGATGCCGT[C/T]GGAATTATATTTCAGACACAG	AAAATGACCTTGATGCCGT	AAGCCTGTTGTGAATATAATTCC	1094	17
WIAF-1482	A/T	A	T	AATGTCTTAACATACCAAAG[A/T]AGTGGAATCAATAGAATAAA	TTTAAAGAAATGTCTTAACATACCAAAG	CGTACCGTTTGTTGAAGACTTAAATATTT	3171	8
WIAF-1488	G/A	A	G	CACAGGTAGTCCACAGAATA[G/A]GACACAAGAAACCTCAAGCT	GAGCACAGGTAGTCCACAGAA	CAGCTTGAGGTTTCTTGTGTC	3174	19
WIAF-1489	G/A	A	G	ATTCATTCTTTTCTTCACCA[G/A]TAAAGGCTGTTCTTGGGCTT	CGCCTACAAAGAGAATCATTCATTC	AGCCCAAGACAGCCTTTA	826	3
WIAF-1490	T/C	C	T	GGTCTGGGCTTCTGAGGTCC[T/C]GGTAGAAGGAGGGCAGGTGG	TCTGGGCTTCTGAGGTCC	CACCTGCCCTCCTTCTACC	3175	15
WIAF-1500	C/T	C	T	ACCTGACCTCGACATGTGG[C/T]CTCTGGTGCCCCCATTTGTCTC	CCTGACCTCGACATGTGG	AGCAAATGGGGACCAGAG	3184	21
WIAF-1504	G/A	A	G	GCTGTGTGGGGGCCAGTAT[G/A]AGCCCAGGGACTCCCTTCCCA	GGAGCTGTGGTGGGGG	GAAGGGAGTCCCTGGCT	3188	1

WIAF	SNP			Sequence (with SNP)	Flank 1	Flank 2	No.	No.
WIAF-1505	T/A	A	T	ATTATTAAAAGAGCAAAGTT[T/A]CCCCTCCCTTTCTTACTTTC	CTGAACATAATTATTAAAAGAGCAAAGT	TGAAAGTAAGAAAGGGAGGGG	2011	18
WIAF-1506	T/C	C	T	TTTGGACAACTTAAAACTTA[T/C]TAGTGACATTGCGTCTAAT	CAATTAACTTGGACAACTTAAAACTT	TTGATTATTAGACAGCAATGTCACT	2012	18
WIAF-1509	C/T	C	T	TCCTCGTCAAAAGAAAACCA[C/T]CCCGGGACCCACTGTTCTAT	TCCTCGTCAAAAGAAAACCA	ACAGTGGGTCCCGGG	2015	15
WIAF-1511	G/C	C	G	GCTTGAATTTTAGATGCAGA[G/C]ATCATTTTATATATATCTGT	CTGCTTGAATTTTAGATGCAGA	TGTAATTTTCTGTATTACATTGCAGA	2016	10
WIAF-1514	G/A	A	G	GGCAGGGAGGGGCGAGAAAC[G/A]CACTAGCTTGGGGGTGGGCA	GGCAGGGAGGGGCGAGAAAC	CCACCCCAAGCTAGTG	3191	16
WIAF-1516	C/T	C	T	TCCCTCTAAAGTTTCAGTTT[C/T]TTCACCAGTAAAGGAAAAGG	GCTCATTCCCTCTAAAGTTTCA	CAACCTTTCCTTACTTGGTGAA	3192	8
WIAF-1517	C/A	A	C	AAGATGCCCCATTCCTTGCG[C/A]CTCAGCCCTCAGTTCCTTCA	GCCCCATTCCTTGCG	GAAGGAACTGAGGCGTGAG	1100	8
WIAF-1519	G/A	A	G	GAGGGTACTGGAAGTGGGAG[G/A]AGGCAAGGTCTGCTATCAGG	GAGGGTACTGGAAGTGGGAG	CCTGATAGCAGACCTTGCCT	2018	17
WIAF-1520	A/G	A	G	ATCTTTTACAAAATTTCATT[A/G]GAACTGACAAATGTTATGGTG	ATCTTTTACAAAATTTCATT	GACTCACCATAACATTGTCAGTTC	1101	12
WIAF-1524	C/T	C	T	TTTCCCCAACTACGATAAGT[C/T]CATTGCCGGATGCTGAATTA	TTTCCCCAACTACGATAAG	TCAGCATCCGGCAATG	2019	4
WIAF-1525	G/A	A	G	GGGATGACTGTAGAGGATTA[G/A]ATGATCCCTGAATTACTTTTC	GGGATGACTGTAGAGGATTA	GCTGAAAGTATTCAGGGATCA	1103	11
WIAF-1529	A/G	A	G	GCCAATGTCTTTTCCCAGTC[T/A]GTCATATTTTTGTCCATGGT	GCCAATGTCTTTTCCCAGTC	GGGCATCATTTTGTTTTGTC	2022	11
WIAF-1533	T/A	A	T	TCTTTTACAATGCAGTTTC[A/G]ACATAACATTGTCCAATGTT	TCTTTTACAATGCAGTTTC	ACAACCATGGACAAAAATATGAC	1106	19
WIAF-1538	A/G	A	G	TTTACAAACCCATTTAAGTA[T/C]GGAATGATTTATATGGGGTC	TTTACAAACCCATTTAAGTA	GGTTTGTTGTTTACTCTACCAATGTT	3201	21
WIAF-1540	T/C	C	T	AAAGTACAGCAGGCTCTAC[C/G]CATTCTCTCTCTTCTTGCTCT	AAAGTACAGCAGGCTCTAC	CTGACCCCATATAAATCATTCC	1108	17
WIAF-1541	C/G	C	G	CTTGTTCATAAATAAGGA[T/A]TTCAATCAAGATTCATGAAA	CTTGTTCATAAATAAGGA	TGTGTTGTGAGCAAGGAGAGA	1109	6
WIAF-1542	T/A	A	T	AACATTAATCATTACTATTT[G/T]CAACTCCGTATTTTCAAAAC	AACATTAATCATTACTATTT	CATTCATGGATCTTGATTGAA	3202	11
WIAF-1543	G/T	G	T	TGGCTAGTCAAACGTCGAAA[G/C]TTGCTTGAGATGCCTGTCA	TGGCTAGTCAAACGTCGAAA	GTTTAGTTTTGAAAATACGGAGTTG	1110	1
WIAF-1544	G/C	C	G	AGAACCAGGGAGACACCTCA[C/T]GTGAGATGACCTGCACACAA	AGAACCAGGGAGACACCTCA	TGACTAGCCATGTCTCAAGCAA	1111	13
WIAF-1549	C/T	C	T	ACCCTCCCCATTTTGAGTCT[G/C]CATAGTCCAATTATACCACTC	ACCCTCCCCATTTTGAGTCT	TTGTTGTGGAGGTCATCTCAC	1114	19
WIAF-1556	G/C	C	G	TTTCCCACTGAGCCTGG[C/T]TGAACTACAGCTGCCAGCAT	TTTCCCACTGAGCCTGG	TGCAAAGGCATACAGAGTGG	3205	2
WIAF-1559	C/T	C	T	GGTTCTCCCCAGAGTAAAG[C/G]GTTTTCTCTGGGGATTGGCA	GGTTCTCCCCAGAGTAAAG	TGCTGGCAGCTGTAGTTCA	1122	11
WIAF-1564	C/G	C	G	CCCTGCCCAACGTGCTGATCC[A/G]GTGCCCTGCCTCTCGAGTTAGAG	CCCTGCCCAACGTGCTGATCC	GGGTTTCTCCCAGAGAAAC	2024	8
WIAF-1565	A/G	A	G	AAAGAAAATACTTGGTTAAA[G/A]TTGAAAGGACCTAGTTAGAG	AAAGAAAATACTTGGTTAAA	GGTAACTCCAGGCAGGGCAC	1124	6
WIAF-1567	G/A	A	G	GCCACGAGGAGTAGCCAGGT[A/G]GGGCGAGACACAAAAGGCCT	GCCACGAGGAGTAGCCAGGT	TCTAACCTCTAACTAGGTCCTTTCAA	1130	1
WIAF-1577	A/G	A	G	TTGCTCATTTGCTACATGAA[A/G]CAGAGGCAGAGTATTCTGTG	TTGCTCATTTGCTACATGAA	GCCTTTTTGTGTCTCCGCC	1133	8
WIAF-1580	A/G	A	G	ACAGTTTTTATCCTGAAATT[G/C]TTTTTAGAAGCCCTGCCCAA	ACAGTTTTTATCCTGAAATT	CCACACAGAATACTCTGCCTCT	2027	9
WIAF-1582	G/C	C	G	TCTGTAATGCCATTTTGATG[G/A]TTAACATTACGTGTCCACTT	TCTGTAATGCCATTTTGATG	GGGCAGGGCTTCTAAAA	2029	8
WIAF-1584	G/A	A	G	GGGCAGAGTGAGGGGCAGAC[A/G]GGATGAGGCTCTTCTGTAAA	GGGCAGAGTGAGGGGCAGAC	GGCTTCCTTCCATTCCATTCA	3213	10
WIAF-1585	A/G	A	G	GGAAAGCTGAGGCAGCTAAT[G/A]GGGCTCATACAAAGTTTTGA	GGAAAGCTGAGGCAGCTAAT	GACTTTACAGAGAGCCTCATCC	3214	11
WIAF-1588	G/A	A	G	GCACTTTACTCTGCACTTAC[G/A]GCAGCTCAGCTAAT	GCACTTTACTCTGCACTTAC	TCCAAACCTTTGTATGAGCC	3217	4
WIAF-1593	G/A	A	G	CTTAATTGCTTGAGAACATG[G/C]CAAATTGGAATTGGACAAAATC	CTTAATTGCTTGAGAACATG	CAGCAAAATGAGGGAGCTCTTC	2033	5
WIAF-1594	G/C	C	G	TGGGTCTCTTTCAAGTGAAT[T/G]TTTCCTTTCGTTCCTGTTCTA	TGGGTCTCTTTCAAGTGAAT	CAGTGATTTTTGTCCAATTCATT	3218	8
WIAF-1596	T/G	G	T	AACTCCCCAGGTAAACACC[C/T]TGTAATTTACCTTGAAGCTC	AACTCCCCAGGTAAACACC	TTTAGAACAGGAACGAAAGGATAA	2035	17
WIAF-1598	C/T	C	T	ACTGAGTTACAGCCCCCTCC[T/C]CACTCGTGTATCTGCTCAGG	ACTGAGTTACAGCCCCCTCC	TACCACCCTGAGCAGATAC	1139	14
WIAF-1602	T/C	C	T	TCTGCCCCTTCCGTGAAT[T/C]ACCTGCCCCAGCAGTCA	TCTGCCCCTTCCGTGAAT	CAGTGATTTTTGTCCAATTCATT	1143	22
WIAF-1606	T/C	C	T	AGGCTTGCCCTTCCGTGAAT[G/C]TGCCTTCTTGTTGGCTTTAAC	AGGCTTGCCCTTCCGTGAAT	TGGGGTGGGGCAGGT	1144	22
WIAF-1607	G/C	C	G	ATAATGAAGTGAATAAACGC[G/A]TGTGAACTAATGTTTAAAA	ATAATGAAGTGAATAAACGC	GCTAAAGCCACAAGAGGCA	3222	1
WIAF-1610	G/A	A	G	TCTCTCACGCTGCATCCAGCC[G/A]GGCACCCTGCTTAAGTCAGT	AAGCTTAATGAACATAATGAAGTGAAT	GCTCTAACTTTTTAAACATTAGTTCACA	1146	16
WIAF-1614	G/A	A	G	ACAGGCCAGTTTTACTGTACA[T/C]CACTCCTGTATCTGCTCAGG	TCTCTCACGCTGCATCCAGCC	TGACTTAAGCAGGGTGCC	2039	7
WIAF-1620	T/C	C	T	CAAAGCAGTTTTACTGTACA[C/A]AGAGGCAAGGTACTACATTA	ACAGGCCAGTTTTACTGTACA	GCCCTTCTTTTTCAGGCAC	2040	20
WIAF-1621	C/A	A	C	CTTCTGGGCATGGCCGTGA[G/A]CACCCTGTGTGGGCGAGGTGC	CAAAGCAGTTTTACTGTACA	GACTTAATGTAGCATTGCACTTC	1149	8
WIAF-1622	G/A	A	G	TATTACATTCAGAATTATGC[A/G]AAACAATTAGTTATATTGCA	CTTCTGGGCATGGCCGTGA	CTCGCCACACAGGCGTG	1150	6
WIAF-1623	A/G	A	G	GTCATGGGAGATTGGATAGA[T/C]GCCTAACCTATCTCAATTTT	GCTGATTATTCATATCTATTACATTCAGAA	CAGCTTTGCAATATAACTAATTGTTT	3226	18
WIAF-1626	T/C	C	T	GCATCTATACCTTGAAACC[T/G]CCCTTAACCTCTCCCAGGC	GTCATGGGAGATTGGATAGA	AATAGCATCTAAATTGAGATAGGTTTAGGC	3227	7
WIAF-1627	T/G	G	T	GGCAAGAGAGGCATCACTGA[C/G]GCTGCATGCCATGCGGCTC	GCATCTATACCTTGAAACC	GCTGGGAGAGGTTAAGAGG	1151	16
WIAF-1628	C/G	C	G	AAAGGAGGCAACTCTTTAAT[A/G]AAGGAAATGTTACCAAATCC	GGCAAGAGAGGCATCACTGA	GCATGGCAGATGCAGC	3228	3
WIAF-1629	A/G	A	G	ATCTTCAGCACAGGAATTGT[T/C]AATCTTCTCCACTTCACCTGT	AAAGGAGGCAACTCTTTAAT	CTATGGATTTGGTAACATTTCCTT	2043	9
WIAF-1634	T/C	C	T	CTACGCAATTTTCATGCAGA[C/T]CTGTTGGCTGCAACAAGATC	ATCTTCAGCACAGGAATTGT	AAGAACAGGTGAAGTGAGAAGATT	3232	15
WIAF-1635	C/T	C	T	AGACATTAGAAAAGGACGC[C/T]CTGTTGCGTCGAACAAAGATC	CTACGCAATTTTCATGCAGA	TGATCTTGTTCAGCCAACAG	1154	9
WIAF-1638	C/T	C	T	TGAACCCAATATCATTGAGGC[A/T]AACAGTTTGGATATTTATGCAGG	AGACATTAGAAAAGGACGC	GGAAAACAGCCCAAACTGT	1157	1
WIAF-1642	A/T	A	T	AGTATCAACTTGAGTACCTC[A/G]TTATGGATATTTATGCTAGG	TGAACCCAATATCATTGAGGC	TGTCATTCCTAGCATAAATATCCA	3234	12
WIAF-1643	A/G	A	G	ATACAACAGTGCACACACA[A/G]AGAGGCAAGTACAAAAATGT	AGTATCAACTTGAGTACCTC	GGGTTACATTTTGTACTTGCC	3238	20
WIAF-1648	A/G	A	G	GCTAAAGGAACTAATACA[T/C]GTACAAGCACCTCAGCACAAA	ATACAACAGTGCACACACA	TTTGTGTGGAGGTGCTGTAC	3242	17
WIAF-1652	T/C	C	T	TCATACCCCTCCAGCTTCCCA[C/T]TGACAGAGCCAGTGTCCTCT	GCTAAAGGAACTAATACA	GAGGACACTGGCTGTCA	3245	
WIAF-1655	C/T	C	T	TCATACCCCTCCAGCTTCCCA[C/T]TGACAGAGCCAGTGTCCTCT	ACCCTCCAGCTTCCCA	GAGGACACTGGCTGTCA	3245	17

(Continued on following pages.)

TABLE 6-7. (*Continued*)

WIAF Name	Alleles	Allele A	Allele B	Chipregion	primer up	primer down	ncbi SS	NwLib chrom
WIAF-1660	A/G	A	G	AGATCCCACTTTATTTTTTA[A/G]CTCCAATAAATGTAATTATC	CTCCTTAAGATCCCACTTTATTTTT	GCAGCTGATAATTACATTTATTTGGA	1160	1
WIAF-1665	G/A	A	G	AAAAGTAACTATGACTAGAA[G/A]AGGCAGGAGGAGTGGGTTGAG	GCACTTAAGGAAAAGTAACTATGACTAGAA	CAACCCACTCTCTGCCT	1162	2
WIAF-1667	C/G	C	G	CCAGTGGGATGTGGCTTCCC[C/G]AGGTTGCAACCCCAAGGAAG	TGGGATGTGGCTTCCC	CCTTGGGGTTGCAACCT	3249	
WIAF-1670	G/A	A	G	CTGAAAATATCTGCTAGTGGG[G/A]AATTTACAACCCACTGACCA	CCCTGAAATATCTGCTAGTGGG	GATGGTCAGTGGGTTGTAAATT	3252	6
WIAF-1671	G/A	A	G	ACAGAGACAAGACATCAATC[G/A]TCTGTTAGCAGCGAGAGAGA	GGTCACAGAGACAAGACATCAA	GTCTCTCGCTGCTAACAGA	3253	19
WIAF-1672	G/C	C	G	AGGCCCAGCCCCAGAACCTG[G/C]AGTGCTTCTTTGACGGGGGC	CCAGCCCCAGAACCTG	CCCCGTCAAAGAAGCACT	19250	22
WIAF-1673	C/T	C	T	AAGTGGAGCCCAGAGGTTTG[C/T]TGGGACTCCCAGCCAGGGGA	TGGGACCCAGAGGTTTG	CCTGGCTGGGAGTCCC	19251	22
WIAF-1674	T/C	C	T	CAGGATTAGTCTTCTCTGTT[T/C]CTTGGTGCAAGTTTGAACCA	GGTTGCATGACAGGATTAGTC	CACTGGTTCAAACTTGCACC	3254	6
WIAF-1676	G/A	A	G	GCAGATCAACAGCTGCTACC[G/A]TTCACCCAGAGGTGGCTGC	GCAGATCAACAGCTGCTACC	GCCACCTCTGGGGTGAA	1165	10
WIAF-1677	T/G	G	T	TCATGGTCCTTTGTGATCTG[T/G]ACCTCACCCATGTCCCCAC	ATCATGGTCCTTTGTGATCTG	GGGAGACATGGTTGAGG	3255	1
WIAF-1680	T/C	C	T	CTCATAGAAAATCACGGATAG[T/C]ATCACCAGTCTACAGCCACT	CTCATAGAAAATCACGGATAG	AAATTCTGTGATAGATGGCTGT	1168	7
WIAF-1682	G/A	A	G	ACACACTGGCAGGGATTTGC[G/A]TATCTAAACATAGAAAAGT	CACTGGCAGGGATTTGC	TGGCCCCATAATACCGTAT	1170	21
WIAF-1689	T/C	C	T	ATAAACTCTCTTATGACAAG[T/C]AGTGATTGAAACTCTAGTAA	CCTTTCAGTATAAACTCTCTTATGACAAG	CAAAACCTTACTGAGTTCAATCACT	1172	19
WIAF-1690	A/C	A	C	TCTTCCTTTCCCCTTGATCA[A/C]AGTGAAGATATGATAGGAA	CTTCCTTTCCCCTTGATCA	CTGAATTCCTATCATATCTTCACT	1173	6
WIAF-1693	G/C	C	G	TTTCCTCCCCATGACC[G/C]GCCTTCCCGGGCCACCTGT	CCTCCCCCATGACC	ACGGACAGGTGCCG	1174	8
WIAF-1694	C/G	C	G	CCTTACAAAATATTTCTGT[C/G]TAGAGAGGGAAAGAGCTGGT	CCCAGAACCTTACAAAATATTTC	CACCAGCTCTTTCCCTCTCT	3258	11
WIAF-1696	C/G	C	G	ATTTGCCATCTGTCTGACTC[C/G]CGTCTTCCCGGGGCGTGGGG	CAATTTGCCATCTGTCTGACTC	ACGCCCGGGAAGAC	3260	6
WIAF-1697	A/C	A	C	AGACCCTTTCCAAGGGAATA[A/C]TACTACACTAAGCCTACACT	AGACCCTTTCCAAGGGAATA	CACAGTACAGTGGCTTAGTGTAGT	3261	16
WIAF-1698	G/A	A	G	AAGATAAAGAGGCAGGCTTA[G/A]AGTAGTATTTGTGGTATGTAA	CATTTTAAGATAAAGAGGCAGGCTTA	GCATCATTGTATACTGTGGTATGTAGA	3262	12
WIAF-1700	G/A	A	G	CAGGTATGGACTATGTACAT[G/A]ACAATACAAGAGGGGTTTGT	GCACTCAGGTATGGACTATGTACA	AAACAAAGCGCCTTGTATTG	2052	2
WIAF-1702	A/G	A	G	TCAACATTACAAAACCCCCA[A/G]TCTTCAAGGAAAAGGAGCACA	TCAACATTACAAAACCCCCA	TGTGCTCCTTTCCTTGAAGA	3263	3
WIAF-1703	C/T	C	T	GGAGCACATTACCATGGAGC[C/T]ACAGGACTCCAAAGGAGCTC	GGAGCACATTACCATGGAGC	GAGGTCCTTTGGGAGTCCTGT	3264	3
WIAF-1706	G/T	G	T	CAGGCCCACTTTGGAGAAAG[G/T]AAGGAAATGCTATTAATCAA	CAGGCCCACTTTGGAGAAAG	TTCCTATATTCCCAAACATAGTGTC	3266	22
WIAF-1709	A/G	A	G	TTTGTAACAGAAAGCCTTA[A/G]GACACTATGTTTGGGAATAT	TGTTTGTAACAGAAAGCCTTA	CGAAAGCAGAAAGTTTGCC	2053	8
WIAF-1714	C/T	C	T	AATGTTGTCTTTTTTTTTCC[C/T]GGCAAACTTTCTGCTTCGG	TCGATGGTAATAATGTTGTCTTTT	GGTAATTGTAGGAAGATGGGCT	1182	3
WIAF-1717	G/C	C	G	TGAAAGCCCTCGGCTCGGTC[G/C]TTAGCCCCATCTTCCTACATT	GCCCTGGCTCGGTC	GAGCCGAGGCTTTCA	2054	16
WIAF-1718	C/A	A	C	ACCTGTGTGTCAGGATGCAC[C/A]TGAAAGCCCTCGGCTCGGTC	CTGTGTGTCAGGATGCAC	GGTAATTGTAGGAAGATGGGCT	2055	16
WIAF-1721	T/C	C	T	TCCATCAAGGACCTTTGTTT[T/C]GTCTTCCACTCTGCTATTT	TTTCCATCAAGGACCTTTGTTT	TTGTATTATAAATAGCAGAGTGAAGAGAC	3269	5
WIAF-1741	C/T	C	T	AACCTCCATTCCTATAAA[C/T]CTTTAAACAAAACAGTTAGC	CCAAACCTCCTCATTCCTATAAA	TGTAAACAGCTAACTGTTTTTGTTAAA	3288	17
WIAF-1742	T/C	C	T	GAAAGGAAAAGCAATAAACTT[T/C]AGGATTTCATTGTCTCTTGG	CCAGAAAGGAAAAGCAATAAACTT	CCCAAGAGACAATGAAATCCT	3289	10
WIAF-1743	T/C	C	T	GCGTGGAAACCAATTGTCA[T/C]GTGTATGAACTACAAAAGGA	CGTGGAAACCAATTGTCA	CCGATCCTTTTGTAGTTCATACA	3290	X
WIAF-1745	T/C	C	T	GATGATCACTGTCGTGCTTG[T/C]GGCTCATGGCGAGCATTCA	GATGATCACTGTCGTGCTTG	TGCTCTGCCATGAGCC	3292	8
WIAF-1748	A/G	A	G	TCGTAGACATCTAACATTAG[A/G]TAGCCTTCAAGATTGAACCAG	TCCTGAGATGTCTTTTACCTGAG	CTGCTTGGTTCAATCCTTATTAG	3295	1
WIAF-1749	G/A	A	G	AAGGGATTGCTTTATTTAAC[G/A]TGAAAAGCGTGATAGGAGGAA	TTTGAAGGGATTGCTTTATTTAA	GTTCCTCTATCACGCTTTTCA	3296	3
WIAF-1753	G/A	A	G	AAGGGAGTGGGGGAGTAAAA[G/A]TGGAAGCAGGGTGACGCATG	GGGGAGTGGGGGAGTAAAA	CGTCACCCTGCTTCCA	3300	4
WIAF-1762	T/G	G	T	AATGAAAATAGTCTGGGCCATT[T/G]GACTAACCAGTTCTACAAAT	AATTAATGAAAATAGTCTGGGCCATT	TGTGAAATTTGTAGAACTGGTTAGTC	3309	2
WIAF-1763	G/A	A	G	TTAAGTACAAAATGCTAAAC[G/A]GGAGCCGAGCTCTTCCGCAT	TTATTTCCTTAAGTACAAAATGCTAAAC	CGGAAGACTCGGCTCC	3310	9
WIAF-1764	A/C	A	C	TACAACACCCTTCAAGATC[A/C]ACAAAAGCTTAACAAAGTA	AAATATATCAACACTCCCTTCAGATC	CGTTTTACCATTTGTTAAGCTTTTG	3311	3
WIAF-1765	G/A	A	G	AATGTTAATCGTAACATACT[G/A]GAAAGCTGTTACAGTAGAAG	CCCCAAATGTTAATCGTAACA	GCTAACAGTTCTACTGTAACAGCTTTC	3312	11
WIAF-1767	T/G	G	T	TATAATGGGGATTTTCTGCT[T/G]AACTGCCCACTGATTCTTAC	CATTTTTATAATGGGGATTTTTCTG	TGTAAGAATCAGTGGGCAGTT	3314	1
WIAF-1768	A/G	A	G	CTGTAGACATCTAACATTAG[A/G]TAGCCTTCAAGAATTGCAAGT	AAAGATTCCTGTAGACATCTAACATTAG	CACTTGCAATTGCAAGGCT	3315	7
WIAF-1772	A/G	A	G	GTTTGATTTGGCTTCCCTAT[A/G]GATTCGAGGACCCATAACTCT	TGTTTGATTTGGCTTCCCTA	CAAGAGTTATGCGTCCTGAATC	3319	2
WIAF-1774	A/G	A	G	AATAAGCATAATGGCAAT[G/A]CTAGTGGGTCTTCCCAATTCA	CAAATAAGCATAATGGCAA	TGTGAATTGGGAAGACCACT	3321	18
WIAF-1775	T/C	C	T	TCCTAGTCACCAAGCATACTT[T/C]TCCTGGCTCCCCAAGTACTT	TTCTCCTAGTCACCAAGCATACTT	ACTTGGGGAGCCAGGA	3322	14
WIAF-1778	A/G	A	G	CACCTGACTCGGGTACTGCTTTAC[A/G]TACATTACCTCACAGCCAGG	CACCTGACTCGGGTGCTTTAC	CCCTGGCTGTGAGGTAATGT	3325	1
WIAF-1779	C/T	C	T	GGGTGGGGTACTGCATTTATC[C/T]TTAGATCCAAATAAAGCATGC	GGGTGGGGTACTGCATTTATC	CTGCATGCTTTATTTGGATCT	3326	6
WIAF-1780	A/C	A	C	TACAGCCAACATCACTGTTT[A/C]ATTCCAGAACATTTCAACA	TGTACAGCCAACATCACTGTTT	GAGATGTTGAAAATGTTCTGGAA	3327	7
WIAF-1781	C/G	C	G	CTTCCTCTGTCGATTTTCCAA[C/G]ACTATGTTTAATGTATGACT	TCATCTGAGAATAAAGTTCCTGTCT	CATTATTAGGTACTGAGTCATACATTAAACA	3328	7
WIAF-1785	C/T	C	T	GACCTAGCTGGCTTTGTAGT[C/T]GTTCAGGCCCATTGAAATAG	CAGACCTAGCTGGCTTTGTAGT	CTATTTCAATGCCCTGAAC	3332	3
WIAF-1786	A/G	A	G	CCAACTACTTTGGAGCCCT[A/G]AGGAGTTTTTAGAAAAGCT	CCAACCTACTTTGGAGCCCT	CAAGAGTTATGCGTCCTGAATC	3333	3
WIAF-1789	A/G	A	G	AATACACTGCAGATAAATAGGTAGC[A/G]TATAACATTAGAAAAGCAA	TGCAGTAATACACTGACAGGTAAAT	GTTAAAGAAATTTGCTTTTCTAATTGTT	3336	
WIAF-1793	G/A	A	G	AGTTTCACAATATAGGTAGC[G/A]ATAACCAGGTCTCACTTTCC	CCCAGAGTTTCACAATATAGGTAGC	GGGAAAGTGAGACCTGGTTAT	3340	

WIAF	SNP			Sequence 1	Sequence 2	Sequence 3	No.	Chr
WIAF-1796	A/T	A	T	CCACACATTTCAGTCCAAGA[A/T]AACCTTCCTCAAATTTTCCA	CCACACATTTCAGTCCAAGA	GATGGAAAATTTGAGGAAGGTT	3343	5
WIAF-1799	T/C	C	T	GGACATTTGGATGGTGACTT[T/C]CCTGGGTGGTTCCCCATAGA	GGACATTTGGATGGTGACTT	GGGGAACCACCCAGG	3346	10
WIAF-1804	A/G	A	G	AITCACATCTTCAGGATAGGT[A/G]ATAACAGTGTGAAGGGTGTG	AGTGTATCACATCTTCAGGATAGGT	GCACACCTTCACACTGTTA	3351	5
WIAF-1805	T/C	C	T	ACTCTGGTTTTATAAAGCTA[T/C]AGGACAGAGCAGAGATGGAA	CCACACACTCTGGTTTTATAAAGC	TTCCATCTCTGCTCTGTCCT	3352	12
WIAF-1810	G/A	A	G	GAGTAAAGATGGCGCTAGAA[G/A]GTATCTGTTATAGAAACGAT	AAGAGTAAAGATGCGCTAGAA	CAAAATGAAGTATCGTTTCTATAACAGA	3357	7
WIAF-1811	G/T	G	T	CCAAGGGGATTAAACGTATAGG[G/T]TTCTTAAACAAGGGATCCCC	GCCAAGGGGATTAAACGTATAGG	GGGGATCCCCTTGTTTAAGA	3358	18
WIAF-1812	G/A	A	G	CAGCTTTCGTTAGGCTAGTT[G/A]GCTGAGCCATTGTATGCGGA	AAACAGCTTTCGTTAGGCTAGTT	CGCATACAATGGCTCAGC	3359	16
WIAF-1816	A/G	A	G	CGTCCCGTCCCGCCAGCCCT[A/G]TCGGCCTCGTCACTGGCCTT	GTCCCGTCCCGCCAG	CCAGTGACGAGGCCGA	3363	22
WIAF-1819	A/G	A	G	GACCTGCGAACTTAAAACAC[A/G]GAGCATTTATTGTTAGAAAG	GACCTGCGAACTTAAAACA	GCCCTTTCTAACAATAAATGCTC	3366	3
WIAF-1827	A/G	A	G	TGTAAAATAACAATAACGTT[A/G]AAGGCAAAAGCAAGATTCTG	CATTTCTTTGTAAAATAACAATAACGTT	CAGAAATCTTGCTTTTGCCTT	3374	5
WIAF-1834	G/A	A	G	ATTCATAAACATATCAACCA[G/A]TAGCATTAAACCCATTTTATT	GAGTGATTCATAAACATATCAACCA	AGGAAATAAAATGGGTTAATGCT	3381	3
WIAF-1842	G/A	A	G	TAGTCACTTTGAAATGTAAC[G/A]AAATGGTACTACAACCAATTC	CAGCATTAGTCACTTTGAAATGTAA	TTGGAATTGGTTGTAGTACCATT	3388	1
WIAF-1846	A/G	A	G	TGCACAGCATGGCTAAAACG[A/G]TAAAGATGGAATCAACAAAA	GCACAGCATGGCTAAAACG	GGTATTTGTTGATTCCCATCTTT	3391	8
WIAF-1847	C/T	C	T	AITATTTCAGGCCAATGTGT[C/T]TGTTGGGTCTGAGATTTGAT	AITATTTCAGGCCAATGTGT	AATCAAATCTCAGACCCAACA	3392	8
WIAF-1849	C/T	C	T	CCCAAACATCCTCTGCCA[C/T]ACACAACAAAAGTAAGTTT	CCCAAACATCCTCTGCCA	CCAACAACATTCCTCGCCA	3394	11
WIAF-1851	G/A	A	G	AACTTTGGGAAAAGGTGTAA[G/A]ACAGTAGCCCCATCAACATTT	AAATAAACTTTGGGAAAAGGTGT	CAAATGTGATGGGCTACTG	3396	X
WIAF-1853	C/T	C	T	AGTCTTCAGGACTGGACTC[C/T]GGTCCCTTTATTGAGACTGA	AAGCTGTTCAGGACTGGACTC	TGTCAGTCTCAATAAAGGGACC	3398	20
WIAF-1854	G/A	A	G	CATTAAGCATCACTGTCACT[G/A]GCTAACTCCTCAAATCAACA	GGAACAAACACATTAAGCATCA	GGTATTGTTGATTTGAGGAGTTAGC	3399	1
WIAF-1856	C/T	C	T	TTTTACAGAGGTAGCACAA[C/T]TGAATTCCAACACAAAACCCC	TTCATTTTACAGAGGTAGCACAA	GGGGTTTTGTGTTGAAATCA	3401	21
WIAF-1857	T/C	C	T	TTTCAACAGGAAAAACACCATG[T/C]TCAACAATTCAAACAACCATCA	TTCAACAGGAAAAACCATG	AATAATAGCGTGTTTTGAAATGTCA	3402	21
WIAF-1858	C/G	C	G	CTGAGTCACGCTGAGGAGAG[C/G]CTTCACTCAGGAGTTCATGC	TGAGTCACGCTGAGGAGAG	AGCATGAACTCCTGAGTGAAG	3403	13
WIAF-1861	C/T	C	T	AITCGGGTTGTCCAGCCAACA[C/T]GGAGGTGATTTTGGTGGGGA	GGGTTGTCCAGCCAACA	CCCACCAAAATCACCTCC	3406	15
WIAF-1862	A/G	A	G	TCCTCAGAACTTCTCAGCCT[A/G]GTAGCACAAGTGGATGCTTG	TCCTCAGAACTTCTCAGCCT	TCAAGCATCCACTTGTGCTA	3407	11
WIAF-1866	C/T	C	T	AGTAAAAGAAACTCATGAC[C/T]TTTCTCCTTGGACTGGCTCCT	AGTAAAAGAAACTCATGAC	GGAGGCGAGTCCAAGGAGAA	3411	11
WIAF-1869	C/T	C	T	TACAACAGGAGATAATCT[C/T]CAGGAGGAGATAATCT	AGGAGGAGAATCTCAACAGGAGATAATCT	TTTCTTCACAGGCGATCCTG	3414	5
WIAF-1870	T/A	A	T	TGATGAGACTAGAGTGACAG[T/A]GTTTTCAGAACCCAAATGTCC	TTTTCTGATGAGACTAGAGTGACAG	AGGACATTTGGGTTCTGAAA	3415	16
WIAF-1871	G/A	A	G	CTGCTAAGCTGTATTTCAGA[G/A]GAAATGTCACAATCATACCAC	GTAGCTGCTAAGCTGTATTTCAGA	CCAGTGGTATGATTGTGACATTC	3416	10
WIAF-1872	G/A	A	G	TGCTCTCGGAGGATGCCTAG[A/G]AGATGTTGGGAACAGAAGAA	TGATATGGACAGAAAGCATACTTC	ACCGTGTAACAAAGCCA	3417	X
WIAF-1883	A/G	A	G	ATTACTAGCTAGATCCTAAT[T/C]TGAGGACATGAGATTTATTG	GCTCTCGGAGGATGCCTAG	TCCCCTTAAACTCAGTTTATTT	3428	1
WIAF-1885	T/C	C	T	AAAGTCTGGGATGACTTTCC[T/G]ATTCTACATCAAGTAGAACC	AAACATCATTACTAGCTAGATCC	CCTTCAATAAATCTCATGTCCTCA	3430	8
WIAF-1886	T/G	G	T	GATACAGGCCATATTTCCCA[C/T]ATAGGACTCTAGTTCTAGAA	CCTAAAGTCTGGGATGACTTTCC	TTGGCTTAGGTTCTACTTGATGT	3431	2
WIAF-1895	C/T	C	T	GTTGGGCCAGACAACACTAG[C/A]AITTTTCACGGGTGTGGGCAC	GATACAGGCCATATTTCCCA	CAAGGCTTTCTAGAACTAGAGTCC	3440	14
WIAF-1897	C/A	A	C	TGTATTTACACGGATAGA[C/T]GGCAGAGGGTAGA	GGTGGCAGACAACACACTAG	CCCACCCGTGAAAT	3442	8
WIAF-1898	C/T	C	T	AAGAATTTGCATGGCGATT[A/C]AAATAGAAAAACCTATAAATG	AGGTGTATTTACACGAGGGTAGA	CTCTGTCAGGCATCTGCC	3443	8
WIAF-1899	A/C	A	C	AGATAAACCAAAATGATTGA[G/A]TATGATAAAGAATTTTGCAT	GAATTTGCATGGCGATT	AGACCTGCTTTTTCTACAITTTATAGG	3444	9
WIAF-1900	G/A	A	G	AGTCTGGTCACTTTGGGGCC[C/T]GGCCGTGGGCCAGAGCCCACTG	GGAAGATAAACCAAAATGATTGA	GCCATGCAAAAATTCTTTATCA	3445	9
WIAF-1904	C/T	C	T	TTTCTGGTCACTGCAGCCCC[A/G]TCTGTATTAGGGAGCACCCC	TGGTCACTTTGGGGCC	GGCTCTGCCCACGCC	3449	22
WIAF-1906	A/G	A	G	AACCACTTCTGTAATGGT[A/C]TCTGCTGAGAGTCCACATTTT	GGTCACTGCAGCCCC	GGGGTGCTCCCTAATACAGA	3451	3
WIAF-1909	A/C	A	C	CTTTTGTTTTCTACCCCTAT[T/C]CATTACAGTCAAATTAACAG	AACCAGATTTTCTCAGGCCTT	CAAAATGTGGACTCCGACAG	3454	16
WIAF-1910	T/C	C	T	AACCAGATTTTCTCAGGCCT[T/C]TTTGGATACCTTTAGTAGT	CTTTTGTTTTCTACCCCTAT	TTGCCTGTTAAITTGACTGTAATG	3455	5
WIAF-1918	T/C	C	T	CTTAAACTCAGTTTCCGTG[G/A]TTGCTATGTAAAGCATCCACG	AACCAGATTTTCTCAGGCCT	ACAAGAGGGTTTGACAAAAGAG	3463	12
WIAF-1919	G/A	A	G	GAAAATGCCACGTCTCTGAC[A/G]GCGATTTAACCTGAATGATGTGT	CTTAAACTCAGTTTCCGTG	CCATCGTGGATGCTTTACAT	3464	9
WIAF-1923	A/G	A	G	AAACTACATTTGGGTTTTGG[G/T]AAGTCCCCTGTAATGATGAA	GAAAATGCCACGTCTCTGAC	GACAATGCCACGTCTGTGAC	3468	9
WIAF-1925	G/T	G	T	AITACCAAGTGTACATACTGT[T/C]CACATGATTTATGGCTGTTG	AAACTACATTTGGGTTTTGG	GATTCATCATTACAGGGGACTT	3470	4
WIAF-1928	T/C	C	T	AAGGGAAAGCAGAGCCTGGGG[A/C]CCACGGGCAATCACATGAGA	GCTATTAGTTACATCACCAAGTGTACA	TCAACAGCCATAAATCAITGTG	3473	3
WIAF-1929	A/C	A	C	TCATGGAAATAGGCCTGGAG[C/G]ACAGGATTTGGCTGGAGCTT	GGAAAGCAGACCTGGGG	AITGTGATTGCGCGTGG	3474	2
WIAF-1930	C/G	C	G	CACAGGAATCAGCAGCCTGA[C/T]TTCCTTGTCCAAACAAC	CATGGAAATAGGCCTGGAG	GCCTCAGCCAAAITCCTGT	3475	2
WIAF-1934	C/T	C	T	TGTCTCACCTGGACTTAAGC[G/A]TCTGGCTCTAAITTCACAGTG	CACAGGAATCAGCAGCCTGA	TGTTTGGACAAGTGCAACA	3479	1
WIAF-1938	G/A	A	G	CAAAAGGACTCTGCATTTG[A/G]ATTAAGTTTATTAATCAGCT	TGTCTCACCTGGACTTAAGC	GCACTGTGAATTAGAGCCAGA	3483	3
WIAF-1940	A/G	A	G	AGCAGCTCATTTTGATTAC[G/A]GGTATACATGAAGTAAAATT	CAATAAGCAGACTCTGCATTG	GCTAAAGTCAGCTGATTAATAAAACTTAA	3485	19
WIAF-1942	G/A	A	G	TGTCCTAGCTAATGAATCA[G/A]CTGAGCAAAAGAACCACAAACA	AGCAGCTCATTTTGATTAC	AITTATTATTTTGCAGGCAATACTC	3487	2
WIAF-1943	T/C	C	T	GTAAGAAAATCAGGGATAAGA[G/A]CTGAGGAACAAGAGGGATAT	GTTGTCCTAGCTAATGAATCA	AGTCCTGAAGATCTCAGTCCTACA	3488	21
WIAF-1945	G/A	A	G	TTAGCAGCAGAAGTGCAC[T/C]TTTGCAGAAACACCACAAACA	GTAAGAAAATCAGGGATAAGA	GTGTTTGTGTGTTTCTGCAAA	3490	15
WIAF-1946	T/C	C	T	TGCTCCCCACAITTTGATT[C/T]GGTGGCTTCATAAGGGACCC	TTAGCAGCAGAAGTGCAC	GGTCCCTATGAAGGCACC	3491	3
WIAF-1947	C/T	C	T	GTTGGGGGAGGTAGGAGACT[C/T]GGACCGGCAGCCCTGGCTCC	TGCTCCCCACAITTTGATT	CAGGGCGTGCCGGTCC	3492	5
WIAF-1948	C/T	C	T	GTTGGGGGAGGTAGGAGACT[C/T]GGACCGGCAGCCCTGGCTCC			3493	19

(Continued on following pages.)

TABLE 6-7. (Continued)

WIAF Name	Alleles	Allele A	Allele B	Chipregion	primer up	primer down	ncbi SS	NwLib chrom
WIAF-1949	A/G	A	G	AGACCCTTAGCTGATCTCAT[A/G]AAGTCCACCTCATGAAGGAG	TGAGACCCTTAGCTGATCTCA	TCTCCTTCATGAGGTGGACTT	3494	11
WIAF-1950	C/G	C	G	ACACCATGTCCCTAAAATGT[C/G]ATTCAACATIATGCACACC	AAACACCATGTCCCTAAAATGT	CGAAGGTGTGCATIATIGTTGAA	3495	11
WIAF-1955	G/A	A	G	TCAGAAGCTGATAAACGTGG[G/A]CTTACACCTTTAGCACGGAT	GTCAGAAGCTGATAAACGTGG	AAACTATCCGTGCTAAAGGTGT	3500	6
WIAF-1956	C/T	C	T	TTTCTGCCAGCTTACAGGCT[C/T]ACAGAAGAATGAGACACTTA	TCTGCCAGCTTACAGGCT	GCGTAAGTGTCTCATTCTTCTGT	3501	1
WIAF-1958	A/G	A	G	AGGGAAACTTATAACCTCAC[A/G]CGCCTGTGTTCACAAAACAAC	GTTGAGGGAAACTTATAACCTCAC	TGTTGTTTTGTGAAACAAGCG	3503	4
WIAF-1959	T/C	C	T	AACCACCTTCAGAAAATTCTA[T/C]AAAACACTAGCAACTTCCTT	AACCACCTTCAGAAAATTCTA	TGATAAAGGAAGTTGCTAGTGTTT	3504	6
WIAF-1960	C/T	C	T	ATAGGGACTTCAGATAATA[C/T]GGTTTATGTCAGTTTTCCAG	CTACTGACATAGGGACTTCAGAGTAA	TCCTGGAAAACTGACATAAACC	3505	7
WIAF-1964	T/C	C	T	TCAGAGCCAGGGCTAGAGGA[T/C]GCACGGTGGCTAGAGCCCGC	AGAGCCAGGGCTAGAGGA	GGCTCTAGCCACCGTGC	3509	2
WIAF-1969	C/A	A	C	CCTGGGCACATTATCCCCCT[C/A]GGGTAAACCAGGACTATTGC	CCTGGGCACATTATCCCCCT	TGCAATAGTCCTGGTTTACCC	3514	20
WIAF-1970	G/A	A	G	GGAAGGAAGCGGCGGTCATT[G/A]GGTGATGGCCTTCTGGCCTC	GGAAGGAAGCGGCGGTCATT	AGCCAGAAGCCATCACC	3515	1
WIAF-1971	A/G	A	G	AGGAGCCATTGTTGGGGTTA[A/G]ACTGTCCTGAACAAAATCTA	GGAGCCATTGTTGGGGTTA	GCCTAGATTTTGTTCAGGACAG	3516	16
WIAF-1974	A/G	A	G	CAGAAATGCAGGAGGGTGGC[A/G]AGAGGGGCCGAGATTGGGTG	AATGCAGGAGGGTGGC	CAATCTCGGCCCCTCT	3519	22
WIAF-1977	A/G	A	G	CAGCTTCTACATTCTGAATA[A/G]AGTACATAATGGGATTTAAG	CAAGTCAGCTTCTACATTCTGAATA	TAAAGATTTACTTAAATCCCATTATGTACT	3522	7
WIAF-198	C/T	C	T	GAGGCCTAAAGGAATGGGAA[C/T]GTGTTGGTGCGCTTGTGATA	GGCCTAAAGGAATGGGAA	TCAAGCGACCACCAACAC	19249	1
WIAF-1980	T/C	C	T	TGCAGGTGCACCGAAAGGAC[T/C]TGGGAGATAAAATTCAAAAA	CAGGTGCACCGAAAGGAC	GAGCAGCACATCACACTTTTT	3525	12
WIAF-1988	A/G	A	G	AACCATAGGAGCCAAAAGTC[A/G]GACAAACAGAAGAAGGCACA	GAACCATAGGAGCCAAAAGTC	GTGTGCCTTCTTCTGTTTGTC	3533	12
WIAF-1991	A/G	A	G	AGCCATCTTTCCGGAAGCTC[A/G]TTGGAGCACAAGCAGAACTCG	CCATCTTTCCGGAAGCTC	GAGTTCTGCTTGTGTCTCCA	3536	7
WIAF-1992	G/A	A	G	TTGTGATGAAGAACATGATG[G/A]TTCACTAGTAGGTAACTTTCT	ACATTGTGATGAAGAACATGATG	AATGACACGAAAGTTACCTACTAGTGA	3537	8
WIAF-1996	A/G	A	G	CTTCTCTTTAGGTAATTTGC[A/G]TAAGAACAATAAAAGCATTT	GGATTAATCTTCTTTAGGTAATTTGC	GACTTTTAAAATGCTTTATTGTTTCTT	3541	17
WIAF-1997	G/C	C	G	AAACTTTAGATATCTCCCAT[G/C]TTCCACAGAATCAAATATAT	TGTTCTCTAAACTTTAGATATCTCCCA	CAAGAAATATATTTGATTCTGTGGAA	3542	14
WIAF-1999	A/G	A	G	AATGGATCCTTATCTGCACA[A/G]CCATTGAAGAAAAAAAAAAA	AAATGGATCCTTATCTGCACA	AGTTTCAGTTTGCATGAATTTTT	3544	1
WIAF-200	A/G	A	G	CCTAGTTGGCATTAAGGATGC[A/G]GTAGGATGTCCACTTTTAGT	CCTAGTGGCATTAAGGATGC	TTGCTACTAAAAGTGGACATCCT	2570	7
WIAF-2006	A/G	A	G	TCAAGCACAGCCCTCGCCCCC[A/G]TCTTGAGATTCAGAATCCAG	CACAGCCCTGCCCCC	CCCTGTCAAGTTCTGAATCTCAA	3551	20
WIAF-2007	T/C	C	T	TGTCACTCTAGCATCTGGAA[T/C]GCTCCGTTGTATATTCAGGA	GCTGTCACTCTAGCATCTGGAA	CCTCCTGAATATCAACGGAGC	3552	1
WIAF-201	C/T	C	T	TGAGAGCTTAAAACAAACACT[C/T]ATTTGTTATTTCACAGTTCA	AGACTTGAGAGCTTAAAACAAACACT	GCCTACTGGACCTCTAAACTACTGA	2571	3
WIAF-2012	C/T	C	T	AAAACCACAGGGATTCCGGA[C/T]GCCAGACCCCATTTTATACT	CCACAGGGATTCCGGA	AAGTATAAAATGGGGTCTGGC	3557	15
WIAF-2013	T/A	A	T	ATCAATAGGAGAGGATTGGC[T/A]TTTGAATTCAGCAAAGCC	AATCAATAGGAGAGGATTGGC	GGCTTTGCTCTGAATTCAAA	3558	10
WIAF-2014	T/C	C	T	AGATCTCTGCCATTCTTT[T/C]GTGAGGCTGTTTTTCCAAGG	GAAGATCTCTGCCATTCTTT	TGGAAAAACAGCCCCAC	3559	1
WIAF-2016	G/A	A	G	GAGTCCTGCCCAGCAGCCTC[G/A]GTGGCCCAAGCCCAGACACTC	CCTGCCCAGCAGCCT	TCTGGGCTTGGCCAC	3561	10
WIAF-2019	G/A	A	G	AGAGCAGAGTTCCTGCCCTC[G/A]GTGTGCGGGGGGGAGAGGG	AGCAGAGTTCCTGCCCTC	CCTCCCTCTCCCCC	3564	20
WIAF-2021	T/C	C	T	AATAITAGAGAATCCTGCACT[T/C]CCCAAGTCTCGTCGCAGG	CACAAAATATAGAGAATCCTGCA	TGCGACGAGCTTGGG	3566	6
WIAF-2023	T/C	C	T	TGTAGAATTTGTCAGAG[T/C]CTGTCCTCCGCTCCTTCCC	GCTGTAGAATTTGTCGTGATGC	GGAAGGACGGAGGACACAG	3568	5
WIAF-2029	C/A	A	C	ACAAAGGCAACTATGTGCAG[C/A]AACAATCTGATGGGCAGTCC	ATACAAAGGCAACTATGTGCAG	CAAGAAGTTGGACTGCCC	3574	15
WIAF-2041	C/T	C	T	AAAAATCCAAGCTTACAACT[C/T]GTCCTTTAACCTGATACATTT	GCTAGACCTAAAAATCCAAGCTT	TGGAATAAATGTATCAGGTAAAGGA	3583	14
WIAF-2043	C/T	C	T	AICTTATGTCTGCCTCTATT[C/T]ATCCCTATTCTCTGATCTTA	GATCTTATGTCTGCCTCT	ATAAGATCAGAGAATAGGGA	784	11
WIAF-205	A/C/G	A	G	GTGATTTTCCACAATTGTA[A/C]AGTGAAAGCTCTTCAGCTTG	TGGTGATTTTCCACAATTG	TCCAAGCTGAAGAGCTTTCA	3585	11
WIAF-2057	G/A	A	G	AGTGGAACCCTGAGACTTTA[G/A]ATCTGCAAAGGGGTTTAATA	CTAATAGTGGAACCCTGAGACTTTA	CATTATTAAACCCCTTTGCAGA	2575	5
WIAF-2059	C/G	C	G	AACACACAAATACAGAGATT[C/G]AATTCAGGAGCCAGTTTCTA	TCCCCCACAACACACAAATA	CCTAGAAAGCTGGCTCCTGAA	1081	22
WIAF-2061	C/T	C	T	TGGCACCGTTTGGCTCATTC[C/T]ACTCCTCCCTGGGTCTTATTG	GCACCGTTTGGCTCATTC	GTCAATAAGACCCAGGGAGAG	3590	3
WIAF-2062	A/G	A	G	GCTTCTAACTGAGGAACTAC[A/G]TTATTACTGGAATCATGTGAA	GGCTCCACCTTTAATCTGTTT	TTTAGAATGTCTTCACATGATTCC	789	19
WIAF-2063	C/G	C	G	GTCTCCTGAGTGTCTGAATG[C/G]GCCAGGTGGCTAAGTGCTGG	GGTCTCCTGAGTGTCTGAATG	CAGCACTTAGCCACCTGG	1083	13
WIAF-2064	C/T	C	T	CAGGTGGCTAAGTGCTGGGG[C/T]TCTGGGGTCAGCGTGCCTGG	CCAGGTGGCTAAGTGCTGG	GGCAGCCTGACCCCA	1084	19
WIAF-2067	A/G	A	G	TTGTGTATTGGCATTTTAAA[A/G]GTACCATTCCATTTTCTTCT	CAATTATTGTGTATTGGCATTTTAAA	GCCAGAAGAAAATGGAATGG	1085	19
WIAF-207	G/A	A	G	ATGAGCTTGTGCACCATTAG[A/G]TTCCTGGTGTTCTCAGT	GACAGACTTCAAAAGCAATTCA	AGGTTTGAAAATATGTATTAAGTACTTTGT	19227	8
WIAF-2072	A/G	A	G	AATGAGCTTGTGCACCATTAG[A/G]TTCCTGCAGAATAAACAAAA	AATGAGCTTGTGCACCATTAG	TGAACACCCAGCAGGA	1185	6
WIAF-2074	C/T	C	T	CCCTCCTCCAAAACAAA[C/T]GAACAAAAATAAAGAAAGAA	CCCTCCTCCAAAACAAA	ATGGGTTTTTCTTTCTTTATTTTTG	1187	3
WIAF-2077	G/T	G	T	CAAACTGTCACCTTTGTAGC[G/T]CTGGGTCAAAGTCTAAAGAG	CCAAACTGTCACCTTTGTAGC	TCCTCTTTAGACTTTGACCCAG	1190	15
WIAF-2078	G/T	G	T	GGAGTTTGGGTGTGCACTGG[G/T]TGTCTTTCAACTGGGTGGAA	AGTTTGGGTGTGCACTGG	TCCACCCAGTTGAAAGACA	1191	1
WIAF-2079	C/T	C	T	GAGTGCTCAGTGATGTGAAG[C/T]ACACGAGGAGTCCCTCAGGGC	CTAAATGAGTGCTCAGTGATGTG	CCCTGAGGGACTCCTGTGT	1192	9
WIAF-2080	G/A	A	G	CAGCCAACAGCAAACAGCCC[G/A]ATGCAGGAGAATGCGCACATAGT	CCAACAGCAAACAGCCC	TGTGCCGATTCCTGCT	1193	2
WIAF-2081	C/T	C	T	GCTAGGCAGTGAACAACATCA[C/T]GTATGCAATGAGAAAATAAC	GCTAGGCAGTGAACAACATCA	CCTACCAGTTGGTTATTTTCTCA	1194	3

WIAF	SNP			Sequence	Flanking	No.	Chr
WIAF-2084	G/C	G	C	GAATTCAGAAAATTGTGT[G/C]TGGGAGGCAGGGTAGCAAGA	CCAAAGAATTCAGAAAATTGTGTG	1197	8
WIAF-2086	G/A	G	A	GTGTCCCAAGGGAGGACGGGCC[G/A]GGCTCACACATCCCATCAAA	CCAAGGGAGACGGCC	1199	7
WIAF-2087	G/A	G	A	GTGCACATCCACCAGGCAC[G/A]TAACATACACAGTACTGTCT	GCACATCCACACAGGCAC	1200	5
WIAF-209	G/A	G	A	GGTTTTCACCCTATTCTTC[G/A]TAGACCGTGGGAGAAAAA	TGAGGTTTTCACCCTATTCTTC	2577	5
WIAF-2091	T/C	T	C	GGCACAAAAACCCCAATGA[T/C]CCTATTTCCAAGAATGTATC	CCACCTGGCACAAAAA	1204	4
WIAF-2092	G/A	G	A	AAGAGAGACGGATATGGTCCC[G/A]TTGCTGACTCCATGTGTTGC	GGAAAGAGAGGATATGGTCC	1205	8
WIAF-2094	C/A	C	A	CGGGAGGCTTCACGTCCTCG[C/A]CCGTGGTCCCTGGGTGGCCT	GAGGCTTCACGTCCTCG	1207	9
WIAF-2095	G/C	C	C	TGGCTCTTCCTTCTGTGGCGT[G/C]TTCGGGCATGGGAAATACATCT	GGCTCTTCCTTCTGTGGT	1208	9
WIAF-210	C/T	T	C	ACACATATGAGTGAAATTTC[C/T]GGGGCATTGCACATATGAGT	TTTGTTAGTCTATATTCACACATATGAGT	2109	18
WIAF-2100	A/G	G	A	CCCTCAGGCTGTCCTACTCA[A/G]TGTGGTTTGCTAGCCTCACT	GTGAGGCTAGCAAACCACA	1213	8
WIAF-2101	C/T	T	C	GGCCGGAGGAGGAAGGGGCTC[C/T]GTGCACTTGCAGGCCACGTC	TGGCCTGCAAGTGCAC	1214	19
WIAF-2103	A/G	G	A	TGCCCTGGGACTGGAGCAG[A/G]CTTGGGTGAGCTCTAGGTGG	CCACCTAGAGCTCACCCAAG	1216	6
WIAF-2104	A/G	G	A	GACCACGACTACGCTCTGCC[G/A]GTGGGAAGCAGAAGCAGGA	CTGCTTCGTTTCCCAC	1217	11
WIAF-2105	A/G	G	A	AGAATCATGGGCAAAAGTC[A/G]CTATGGGCCAGAGTCGAGGT	CCTCAGTCTGGCCCCATAG	1218	2
WIAF-2106	C/T	T	C	GGGGGCTGGGCACCTTTTCT[C/T]CAGCCACAGGCCCTCGAGGA	AGGGGCCTGTGGCTG	1219	6
WIAF-2108	A/G	G	A	AGGGGCTCCACAGAGAGAGC[A/G]TAAGGGGAAGACTTTTATAG	TGTCCTATAAAGTCTTCCCTT	1221	5
WIAF-2112	T/C	T	C	TTTCTGTGGTCAGCAAA[T/C]GCCCCTTTATTTTAAATGAT	GGAATCATTTAAAATAAAGGGGC	1225	20
WIAF-2114	C/T	C	C	CAGAATGGCAGCCACCACTGG[C/T]ATGGCGATGGTGGCACGTGGG	CCTGCACCATCGCCAT	1227	4
WIAF-2116	A/G	G	A	ATTTTTTAGACCGTGATTTC[A/G]AAAGAAACAATAAATGTGGA	CTTTCTAATCACATTTATTGTTTCTT	1229	3
WIAF-2119	G/A	G	A	TGATTGAAAAAGTCAAAAC[G/A]TGAAGAGCATCAAAGCCAA	TGGCTTTGATGCTTCTTCA	1232	20
WIAF-2120	A/G	C	A	AGAGGTTGAAGAAGTGCTGA[A/G]AAATATATTTAAGATTTCCT	TCTCCCAAGGAAATCTTAAA	1233	8
WIAF-2122	C/T	G	C	CTACAAAATCTGTTGGTTGCT[C/T]GCCGCGTGACTCAGCTAATG	GCTGAGTCACGCGGC	1235	1
WIAF-2128	A/G	G	A	TTTCCTTTGTGTACATTTCT[A/G]TATATTATTTTACTTCTCT	GGCATTTTCAGAAGAAGTAAAATAA	1241	20
WIAF-2129	C/T	T	C	TGAGCCTGATATTCACACTA[C/T]CTACATTCCCTCCAGTATAA	TCCTATTATACTGGAGGGAATGTAG	1242	20
WIAF-2130	G/C	C	C	AGTACCTACCTGGGAGGTTG[G/C]TGTACTTGGCTTAAGTACTT	GCATGAAGTACTTAAGCCAAGTACA	1243	2
WIAF-2133	A/G	G	A	AAAATAATAAATGAACGTGC[T/A]GATAAACATTCTTCTTATGG	CACATTTCATGCAAGGGAG	1246	9
WIAF-2134	T/G	T	G	GAGTAAAGGATGCAATCACG[A/G]CTCCCTTAGCCTGCCACTC	TGGAACCATAAGAAGAATGTTTATC	1247	22
WIAF-2135	A/G	G	A	CGCACAGCACTTTGTGTCT[T/C]GCTTTGAGCACTTGCCACTC	GAGGTCCAGGCTACAGTGAG	1248	2
WIAF-2136	T/C	T	C	TCTTTGCTGGGTAACACTGA[T/A]CAAGTTGCTTAACCTTTGTG	GTGGCAAGTGCTCAAAGC	1249	16
WIAF-2137	T/A	A	T	ATATTACTATTTAGTCTAAG[T/C]TTTAATTCAAAGGTTGAAGAA	GGTTTCACAAAGGTTAAGCAAC	1250	18
WIAF-2138	T/C	C	T	TTTATGAACCTACGCCCCA[G/A]AGTCACTCAGCGTTTGCGGG	CGTCATTCTCAACCTTTGAATT	1251	13
WIAF-2142	G/A	G	A	TTAGCACTCAGACTTCCCCA[C/T]TCCCTAACTTTTGTTAATTG	GAACTGTCCGGCCCCC	1255	16
WIAF-2145	C/T	T	C	CATATACGCTTCTGTCATTT[A/C]AACAAACTTCCAGAGAAAAC	CAGCAATTAACAAAAGTTAGGGA	1258	17
WIAF-2149	A/C	C	A	TACACAGCTCAATGGGTCAC[C/T]TGGAACAAAACTTGCTTGACT	CCAGTTTTCTCTGGAAGTTTGTT	1262	1
WIAF-2150	C/T	T	C	AATAAAACAAGTAGAGACC[G/A]TTTACTTACATCCAGTCGGT	ATATAGTCAAGCAACGTTTGTTCCA	1263	1
WIAF-2152	G/A	G	A	GGGGATAAACTCATCTTTTGC[A/C]CCTTCACACTAGAAACGAC	GTCTATAAACCGAACTGATGTAAGTAAA	1265	7
WIAF-2155	A/C	C	A	AAATGTTCCGACCTAGATA[C/G]TGACGAAGGTAGCACGACAC	TGAGTGCTTACCTTCGTCA	1268	9
WIAF-2158	T/C	T	C	TAGCCATATTTAGGATGAGA[T/C]GGATTGAGAGGCATGAACCA	GGTTCATGCCTCTCAATCC	1271	10
WIAF-2162	A/G	G	A	CTTCTCCAAGGGGAGAACAG[A/G]CTGGAAACTGCGGCGTCTGCAA	CAGAGCCGCAGTTCCAG	1275	1
WIAF-2165	A/G	G	A	GTCTAGGCCTGAGAATATTC[A/G]TTTCTAACAAGTTCCCAGGT	CTCAGGGTCACCTGGGA	1278	9
WIAF-2167	G/A	G	A	GAACAAGGACGCTTTGAAGA[G/A]GTGGCAATTACTGTGCAAGGA	CTCCTTGCCACAGTAATTCCAC	1280	2
WIAF-2173	C/G	G	C	GAATGGAGGGAAATAAATGA[C/G]TGGATGGTCGCTGCTTTTTA	AAGCAGGCGACCATCCA	1286	2
WIAF-2177	G/C	G	G	TCCAATGAGCACTGTATGTA[G/C]AGAAAAGGAAGGAGCAGGA	CCTGCTCCTTCCCTTTTCT	1290	6
WIAF-2180	C/T	T	C	AACATTCCCGTGGTCTCC[C/T]TCTGAAAGCCGATGACCATC	TGGTCATCGGCTTTCAGA	1293	X
WIAF-2182	G/A	G	A	GGCTCTAAGTCTTTATTGGGG[G/A]AGAATACCACCCACCTTCC	GGAAGGTGGGTGGGTATTCT	1295	1
WIAF-2184	C/G	G	C	AAATGTTCCGACCTAGATA[C/G]TGAGGAAGGTAGCACGACAC	TGTCGTGCTACCTTCGTCA	1297	19
WIAF-2186	A/G	G	A	CAACAAAAGCTCTTCTGCAC[A/G]ATGGGAGGGAGACACCATTG	TGGTGTCTCCCTCCAT	1299	6
WIAF-2189	G/A	G	A	AGTGCCGATGGTTACACAAT[G/A]TTGTAAATGTATTTAATCCC	TTCGTAAGTGGGATTAAATACATTT	1300	7
WIAF-2190	G/C	G	G	TCCTCTGGGGAGCAGGTCTA[G/C]GGCACGGAGGATGGAGGGCT	TGCATCCTCCGTGCC	1301	9
WIAF-2194	A/G	G	A	GACTCCAGGAAAAGGTCCTTA[A/G]TCTTAGCTTCCTCCTCCTTA	AGTAGGGAGGGAGAAGCTAAGA	1305	3
WIAF-2195	G/A	G	A	AAGGAGGATTCATGAGCCCC[G/A]GTGACACAGATGGGGCCCT	GCCCCATCTGTGTCAC	1306	11
WIAF-2196	C/T	T	C	AGTAGATGAAAAGGAAAGTA[C/T]AGAGAGCGCATTCAGGCCAA	GGCCTGAATGCCCTCTCT	1307	4
WIAF-2197	A/G	G	A	TGATGATTGAAATGCGGGCCTTC[A/G]TACTCTTTACGGTCTTACAC	TGTCTAGCTCCGGGGGTA	1308	3
WIAF-2206	A/G	C	A	GGATGCTTCCGCAGGCTC[C/T]TTAAATTGTGCGTAAACCTG	CCCAGGTTACAGCACAATTT	1316	19
WIAF-2207	C/T	C	C	GGATGCTTCTTGCCAGGCTC[C/T]TTAAATTGTGCGTAAACCTG	TGCTTCTTGCCAGGCTC	1317	13
WIAF-221	T/C	T	T	CAGAAACTCTTTTTGGGCTC[T/C]TTTTTCTCCCTCTGGATCAA	CTACTTTGATCCAGGGGAGAA	2586	1

(Continued on following pages.)

TABLE 6-7. (Continued)

WIAF Name	Alleles	Allele A	Allele B	Chipregion	primer up	primer down	ncbi SS	NwLib chrom
WIAF-2214	G/A	A	G	CAAACATCCACATGGACAA[G/A]CAGGGCCGGCCACTCCAGGC	AAACATCCACATGGCACAA	GAGTGGCGCGCCCTG	1324	21
WIAF-2216	T/C	C	T	ATAAGAATTGTTCTTCTGTT[T/C]GACAGTGAAGTGGGTGTGA	TCACTGTTAATAAGAATTGTTCTTCTGT	CTCACACCACTTCAACTGTC	1326	8
WIAF-2218	T/G	G	T	AGGGGAGACTTGGTATTTTG[T/G]TCAATCATTAAGAAGACAAA	GAGGGGAGACTTGGTATTTTG	CCCTTGTCTTCTTAATGATTGA	1328	14
WIAF-222	T/C	C	T	AGCTTTGATTCTCCCCTTTT[T/C]TTGCATAAAGGCTGGGAAGG	AAGCTTTGATTCTCCCCTTT	TTCCCAGCCTTTATGCAA	2587	18
WIAF-2220	C/T	C	T	ACCTCAAAATGCAGAAACCA[C/T]TACAGATTAAAAGAGAAACA	CCTCAAAATGCAGAAACCA	GAGTTTCTCAAAGTGTGTGCGTG	1330	11
WIAF-2221	A/G	A	G	CTTAACCATTCAAACACCGC[A/G]TGACAACGAACCCAGTGGAC	TTAACCATTCAAACACCGC	TCCACTGGGTTGCTTGTC	1331	9
WIAF-2225	C/A	A	C	TGCAGAGATGATTCTTCTCA[C/A]CCCTTCTCTCAGGGTCGTGG	GGTTGCAGAGATGATTCTTCTCA	ACGACCCTGAGAGAAGGG	1335	17
WIAF-2226	T/C	C	T	GGAAAGCTAAAGGAACAAAA[T/C]GGTTTTAGTTTTGCTGAAGA	CTAGGAAAGCTAAACGAACAAAA	CAGTCTTCAGCAAAACTAAAACC	1336	8
WIAF-2227	C/T	C	T	AGTTCAGGAACTGCCTTTTA[C/T]GTCTCGCAAATAAACTCCAA	GAGTTCAGGAACTGCCTT	TTGGGAGTTTATTTGC	19263	15
WIAF-2228	G/A	A	G	ATTTTTGTTCAATGCCCACC[G/A]AGACATATGAATTGGGAAC	AAACAATTTTGTTCAATG	ATGTATCAGTTCCAATTCTATAT	19445	8
WIAF-223	G/C	C	G	CTTCCTATTTTCTTTGCTT[G/C]TTTTTCTTTCACCTCAGAA	CTTCCTATTTTCTTTGCTT	GGGTTCTGAGGTGAAAGAAAAA	19485	2
WIAF-2233	A/G	A	G	TATTCATTCAATGAAGATTA[A/G]CACTGAAGATCCAGAGAGCT	CACTATTCATTCAATGAAGA	AGCGCTCTGGATCTC	19402	14
WIAF-224	C/T	C	T	TAGAATTGTATAGGCATGAC[C/T]TCTTAATTATAATTGATTT	ACTGAATAGAATTGTATAGGCATGAC	TTGCAGTCAAATCAAATTATAATTAAG	2588	6
WIAF-2264	T/C	C	T	AAATCCAGCTGTAACTTTTT[T/C]GGACTTGTCTTTTATTTCTT	GCAAATCCAGCTGTAACTTTTT	GCTTTTACTAAGCAAGAAATAAAAGAC	2286	7
WIAF-2265	T/C	C	T	TCAGCTCAAACTGCCTCCTT[T/C]AGTGAGCCTGAGAAGTTCTT	CAGCTCAACACTGCCTCCT	GGTGGTTCACAGGCTCACT	2287	2
WIAF-2268	A/G	A	G	TACAGTTGCTGGAAGTTGT[A/G]TGAACTGAGCAAGTTCTCA	GGCTTACAGTTGCTGGAAGTTG	TTAAGACACTTGCTCAAGTTCA	2289	8
WIAF-2275	A/G	A	G	ACTGTGTGTTTGCTTGATTT[A/G]GGAGATAAAACCTGATCTCT	CCACTGTGTGTTTGCTTGATTT	TTTCTTAGAGATCAGGTTTTATCTCC	2292	9
WIAF-2278	A/C	A	C	TTGGCTCAAAGGAAACTGTAG[A/C]AAATTCTTTTTTTATTTT	TTGGCTCAAAGGAAACTGTAG	CAAACTCCACTCTTTGAGTTAAAAA	2294	X
WIAF-228	C/G	C	G	GAGGTACAGAGTGCTGCCAA[A/G]CACCTTAGAAAAGTGACATG	AGTGAGGTGACACAATCAAGACT	CATAGGAGGTTGAGGCTACTGT	2592	11
WIAF-2286	A/G	A	G	TCTGCTTGCATTTTCAAGAT[T/C]CAATATATCCAGATTGTT	GGGTACAGAGTGCTGCCAA	CGTGTCATGTAATTTTCTAAGGTG	3607	13
WIAF-2287	T/C	C	T	TGTAACAAGAATTGATCCTA[T/C]ACTGGGACTACAGCCATGA	GTCTGCTTGCATTTTCAAGAT	GGGAAAACAATCTGGATATATATTG	2299	7
WIAF-2288	T/C	C	T	TAGCAACAATATCAACAGAA[A/G]GGCTATTAGAAAATTCTA	CACAAATGTAACAAGAATTGATCC	CCATGGCTGTAGTCCCAGT	2300	4
WIAF-2291	A/G	A	G	TGTGTTACTCTATTTTGTTC[C/T]AGCCACCTGTGGCATTTCA	CCTATAATTTAGCAACAATATCAACAGAA	TGCAGGTAGAATTTTCTAATATAGCC	2303	4
WIAF-2292	C/T	C	T	CCTGGAATGCTCTTTCCCTC[T/A]GAGCTTTGCTTGGCTTACTT	GCATGTCTGTTACTCTATTTTGTTC	AAATGCCACAGGGTGGCT	2304	1
WIAF-2293	T/A	A	T	TCCATTATACAACAGAAAAG[G/C]GGGCTGGAAAAGAAAGGTCA	CTGGAATGCTCTTTCCCTC	AAAGTAAGGCAAGCAAAGCTC	2305	17
WIAF-2295	G/C	C	G	ATGCTAGAAAATTATGCCTA[A/G]CCAAGTAGACAACTTAAGCA	ACATACATATCCATTATACAACAGAAAAG	GACCTTTCTTTTCCAGCCC	2307	X
WIAF-2298	A/G	A	G	GTGCTAGAACTAATCCCTCA[T/C]GGAGAACGTGGAACCACTGA	GCAATGCTAGAAAATTATGCCT	TTAGGTGCTTAAGTTGTCTACTTGG	2310	5
WIAF-2299	T/C	C	T	AGTGGTGAGATGCTCTGAGT[T/G]CAAGGCTGCTGACAGTGTCA	GGGTGCTAGAACTAATCCCTCA	CAGTGGTTCCACGTTCTCC	2311	3
WIAF-230	A/C	A	C	AATAAATGAATGCCATAATC[T/C]CTGTGTTTTTGTCCCCACC	TGAGCACATATGGGTGCC	CCTCGTCTCGGGCC	2594	22
WIAF-2301	T/G	G	T	CATTGAGGAAGTGTTTAAAG[G/C]AGAAGATGACCCATCCATT	CAGTGGTGAGATGCTCTGAGT	CCATGTCAGCAGCCTTG	2313	14
WIAF-2302	T/C	C	T	GCAGAGTCTGGGGGAGAAGA[C/T]AAACGAACATAAAGCATGGCAA	GAGTGAATAAATGAATGCCATAATC	TGGAGGTGGGGACAAAAA	2314	14
WIAF-2303	G/C	C	G	AGTTGTAGCATTGCAGAAGTC[C/T]CTCTTAGAGGTAGTTGTGACT	GCCATTGAGGAAGTGTTTAAAG	GAATGGATGGGTCATCTCT	2315	10
WIAF-2305	C/A	A	C	AAGCCAGAACAACACGAAAGT[A/G]TATAAAGAAAAACAAGTTAGTA	CAGAGTCTGGGGGAGAAGA	TTGCCATGCTTTATCTCGTT	2317	4
WIAF-2308	C/T	C	T	TTCTTAGGCCCATCAGAGAT[C/T]GAAGTCATGGGGAAAATTGA	CCAAGTTGTAGCATTGCAAGAGTC	ACGAGCACAACTACCTCTAAGAG	2319	7
WIAF-2311	A/G	A	G	TGCACTATGGAACACCACAC[G/A]CAACTGAATGCAGATTCCAT	AAGCCAGAACAACACGAAAGT	GGTGAAAGATTACTAACTGTTTTCTTT	2322	11
WIAF-2312	C/T	C	T	GAGGTCTTAGTCATTGCATG[A/T]TGTATAACAATATTGTCACT	TTCTTAGGCCCATCAGAGAA	TCAATTTTCCCCATGGACTTC	2323	8
WIAF-2313	G/A	A	G	CCTCCTTCACAACCTCACCA[A/G]ACTGGCCTATTAGGCAAGGCA	TGCACTATGGAACACCACAC	AATATGGAATCTGCATTCAGTTG	2324	11
WIAF-2318	A/T	A	T	AATTATTATTAACATGGTACA[G/A]ACAACTTCAGTTTAACATTG	GAGGTCTTAGTCATTGCATG	TGAGTTCCTATTAAGTGACAATATTGTT	2328	2
WIAF-2319	A/G	A	G	TTCTCCCTTGTTTTCTTTTG[G/C]ATTGAAAAATACTGGTTTTC	CTCCTTCACAACCTCACCA	CTTCCGGTAAGCCAAGT	2329	X
WIAF-2320	G/A	A	G	AATGCTATGTTAGCAAATCTA[A/T]TTCCCTAAGCACAGTAATCA	GCATTGAATTAACTATAGATGGTACA	CACTAGCAATGTTAAACTGAAGTTG	2330	12
WIAF-2321	G/C	C	G	AGATCCCAAGTTCGTGGGG[G/T]CTTCCACGTGCAGATGGTAA	TTTATTCTCCCTGTTTTCTTTTG	ACTGTTAGAAAACCAGTATTTTTCAAT	2331	15
WIAF-2325	A/T	A	T	AAAAGTAGAGATAATAATCA[G/A]TTCTTTACAAGCGATGGTAA	TGATGTAATGCTATGTAGCAAATCT	TTGATTACTGTGTTAGGGGA	2334	4
WIAF-233	G/T	G	T	ATCTCCAGGAGACTTTCATG[T/C]AGCCCAAAGTAACGATAGCCTGGA	CCCCAAAGTGGTGGGG	TTAGTCAACTGCAGCGTGAA	2595	9
WIAF-2333	G/A	A	G	AAATTTCAGCATATGTATTAT[C/T]TGAACTAAATTTACAAAAGT	GCCAGGAATAAAAAGAAAAGTAGAG	TTAATTACCATGCGGTTGTAAAGAA	3614	2
WIAF-234	T/C	C	T	ATCAAAGAAAAGAATCTGAAT[A/G]TGAGGGAACTGCAGAAATTA	CATCTCCAGGAGACTTTCATG	CCAGGCTGTACTTTGGGCT	2596	1
WIAF-2343	C/T	C	T	AGTTAACATCAAACAATACAAC[C/T]GAGAACCCACTAATACAAC	GGATATAGGAATTTCAGCATATGTATTA	TGTTCCACTTTTGTAAATTTAGTTCA	19324	16
WIAF-2351	A/G	A	G	TGATGTAGTTACCCCACTATAGCAAC[A/G]TACCGACTTCAAAT	TGTTTATAACATCAAAGAAAGAAATCTGAA	TTAATTTTCGAGTTCCCTCA	3626	18
WIAF-2359	C/T	C	T	TCCCTTATGTTGGCATTGCAA[A/G]AGACACTGCCACTTATCTGAG	TGATGTAGTTACCCCACTAATACAAC	CATAATATTTGAAGTCAGGTGTTCTC	3631	12
WIAF-2362	A/G	A	G	CCCTTATGTTGGCATTGCA[T/C]...	CCCTTATGTTGGCATTGCA	AACCTCAGATAAGTGCAGTGTCT	3634	X
WIAF-2363	G/A	A	G	AAGGGCTATATGTAACTACACA[G/A]TATGCACCACCAGCCATGT	TGGAAGGGCTATGTAACTGAAC	CATGGCTGGTGTGCATA	3635	12
WIAF-2364	A/G	A	G	TTGAACCATGTGTAGACTGC[A/G]GGGCACTTTAGAAAGAAGCTG	CTTGAACCATGTGTAGACTGC	TTCAGCTTCTTTTCTAAAGTGCC	3636	7
WIAF-2365	T/C	C	T	CATGTACCGCACTAAAAAAAA[T/C]GTGTGCTTGCTGCTGCTGTG	CCAGTATCATTGTACGCACTAAAAA	AGCAGCAGCAAGCACAC	3637	18

ID	SNP	A1	A2	Sequence (5')	Sequence (mid)	Sequence (3')	Pos	Chr
WIAF-2372	T/C	C	T	TAATTAATGTGGGCACATT[T/C]GCATGTGCTTACTGGGTCAT	CATATAATTAATGGTGGCACA	TGACCCAGTAAGCACATGC	3644	9
WIAF-2374	T/C	C	T	AGACTGAGGTAAATAGTATT[T/C]ACGGCTGGAAATCAACATGC	GAGCAGTAGAGACTGAGGTAAATAGTATT	CATGTGATTTCCAGCCGT	3646	8
WIAF-2375	A/C	A	C	CTCCCCCTTGTCCCTAGTTT[A/C]TTAATTTCTCAGTGGACAAAT	TCCCCCTTGTCCCTAGTTT	TCCATTTGTCCACTGAGAAATT	3647	17
WIAF-2376	C/T	C	T	GCAGCCATTAACACCAGCAC[C/T]GATGCCACTTCGTATCAGG	CAGCCATTAACACCAGCAC	TCCTGATACGAAGTGGCATC	3648	2
WIAF-2377	T/A	A	T	CTTTGCCAGCAAAGCAAATA[T/A]CCGACTGACTGCTCTCTTAGT	TTTGCCAGCAAAGCAAATA	ACTAAGGAGCAGTCAGTCGG	3649	8
WIAF-2382	A/C	A	C	CAGAGGAATAACTGATGTTC[A/C]CAATACCCGACCCCTGACC	GGCAGAGGAATAACTGATGTTC	CAGGGGTCGGGGTATTG	3654	19
WIAF-2385	A/G	A	G	TATGCATTATCTTCACATGA[A/G]AAGGTTTCAGTTTATAAATG	GGTAAAATATGCATTATCTTCACATG	GTATTTAAGCATTTATAAACTGAAACCTT	3657	13
WIAF-2399	C/G	C	G	TAATGACTTTCTTGAACAAA[C/G]TGATTACGAAAGTGAAAGGC	ACAAAGTAATGACTTTCTTGAACAAA	GTAGCCTTTCACTTTCGTAATCA	3671	16
WIAF-2402	T/C	C	C	ACTGAATTCCTAAAATCTAT[T/C]ACACTGAGGAGAAAATGGAA	TCAGAATCTGCAGAATTCCTAAAA	AAAGCTTTATGCAAACATTTTCTT	3674	8
WIAF-2405	C/T	C	T	CTCCAAATACGAACAGTGCA[C/T]GCTGATGGCCTGCAGTCCTC	CTCCAAATACGAACAGTGCA	GACTGCAGGGCATCAGC	3677	17
WIAF-2407	G/A	A	G	CGTGCTTGGCTCTCTGGACG[G/A]TTCATTCTACATGGCGTGCTG	GCTTGGCTCTCTGGACG	CAGCAGCCATCTAGAATGAA	3679	17
WIAF-2413	A/G	A	G	ACCATCTGTAACCCGAGCCC[A/G]CAGTGACCGGGACTTGCTGC	CATCTGTAACCCGAGCCC	GCAAGTCCCGGTCACTG	3685	17
WIAF-2420	A/G	A	G	TCAAGTCCCAGGCCCCAGGC[A/G]TCTTTGCCGCCTGCCCTTGC	GTCCCAGGCCCCAGG	GGCAGGGCAGGAAAGA	3692	12
WIAF-2422	C/G	C	G	GACTATTCTGTGAAGAACAAC[C/G]AAGAGAAAATTGCAAAAAGA	GCAAATGCTCAGCTACTTCTCCT	TTGTCTTTTGCAATTTTCTCTT	3694	
WIAF-2423	G/C	C	G	AGTGCTCAGCTACTTCTCCT[G/C]CACTTTGAAAGACCCCTCCC	CAAGTGCTCAGCTACTTCTCCT	GGAGGGGTCTTTCAAAGTG	3695	12
WIAF-2426	T/G	G	T	CTTGATTGTATAAGATAA[T/G]TCATACTGGAGAAAACTCCC	CGGTTGTCACACTTGATTGTA	TCTGGGAGTTTCTCCAGTATG	3698	
WIAF-243	C/T	C	T	GTACTTGCTCTGTGCCGTAT[C/T]TTGCTCCAATCACCCATTCCA	CTTGCTCTGTGCCGTAT	GAATGGGTGATTGGAGCA	2115	15
WIAF-2434	C/T	C	T	AAATATGGACTATCTTCAAA[C/T]TTGCACAAATGAATGCATGAAT	AAATATGGACTATCTTCAAA	TTCATGCATCATTTGTGCA	3706	
WIAF-2436	A/G	A	G	AAGGATTGTAATTTGGGTAA[A/G]CTGAGTCACGTGGCCCTGA	GGGCACCGTGACTCA	GGGCACTCAAAGACTGAAGATGA	3708	21
WIAF-2438	C/G	C	G	ATCCCAGCCCTTAGCATCAA[C/G]TCATCTTCAGTCTTTGAGTC	CCCAGCCCTTAGCATCAA	CCAAGATTTGCTTTAATTTCACTC	3710	10
WIAF-2441	C/T	C	T	ATAAGGGAAAATGGGAAGAA[C/T]AGAGTGAAATAAAGCAAAT	GAATAAGGGAAAATGGGAAGAA	GAATTTTCCCATTTGAAGGAT	3713	1
WIAF-2445	G/A	A	G	TACTACTTGCAAITTTAGC[G/A]ATCCTTCAAATGGGAAAATT	ATACTTCCTACTACTGTGACAATTTAGC	GTCAGAGCCTACTCCCCAG	3717	17
WIAF-2449	G/A	A	G	GGAGGGACAGAAACATGA[G/A]CTGAGAGAAGTAGGCTCTGACA	GGAGGGACAGAAAACATGA	GGAGCAGAGGCAAAGGAG	3721	2
WIAF-2450	T/C	C	T	TCAGCTGCAACTTCTGCTTT[T/C]CTCCTTTGCCTCTGCTCCTT	TCAGCTGCAACTTCTGCTTT	TTTGTAATCTAGGAGGCGACAGTT	3722	17
WIAF-246	G/A	A	G	ACACTGAATAAACATCTCAC[G/A]AACTGTCGCCTCCTAGATTAC	ACACTGAATAAACATCTCAC[G/A]AAACTGTCGCTTT	GCCCCAAAGTCAATAGTGTT	2602	14
WIAF-2460	C/T	C	T	AACCTTAGAATACATAGCCGA[C/T]TTGTATACAGAGGTTCATCTC	TGAAAACCTTAGAATACATAGCCGA	AGCCATAATCACCTCCCC	3732	X
WIAF-2467	G/T	G	T	GCTGTAAGCCAGCATGGGT[G/T]GGGGAGGTGATTATGGCTGG	GCTGTCAGCTATTGTTATTTCAAA	GGAGAAAAGGGAGCAGAAGA	3739	12
WIAF-2477	A/G	A	G	CAGCTATTGTTATTTCAAAT[A/G]TATCTTCTGCTCCCTTTTCT	GCTGTCAGCTATTGTTATTTCAAA	CTGCAGCACATTGTCAGG	3749	21
WIAF-2482	C/T	C	T	TCCTTACTTCCCCCATAGAT[C/T]CCTGACAAITGTGCTGCAGAA	CTTCCTTACTTCCCCCATAGA	GGGTGGCATGCAGCT	3754	5
WIAF-2488	C/T	C	T	ACCAGCCCTGGCCCTGCCCTT[C/T]AGCTGCAITGCCACCCTCATA	CAGCCCTGGCCCTGC	CGTGCTCAGTTCAGAATCACTT	3760	11
WIAF-2489	A/G	A	G	AGCATTAGGGATGAGGTCTC[A/G]GAAGTGAITTCTGAACTGAGC	GCAGCATTAGGGATGAGGTCTC	GCCAGTGTAGAAAAGAAA	3761	15
WIAF-249	C/G	C	G	TGAGACTGAAGGGAAAITCCC[C/G]CITTTCTTTTCTTACCACCCTG	TGAGACTGAAGGGAAATCCC	GTCAGTTCCCATTGTGTATTTTT	2604	3
WIAF-2490	T/C	C	T	TCCGAATACAGTACTTCTTT[T/C]GAAAAAATACACAATGGGAA	TCCGAATACAGTACTTCTTT	AAGGATTATGCTCTGAGAGCC	3762	5
WIAF-250	C/T	C	T	ACCAGCCCTGGCCCTGCCCT[C/T]AGCTGCATGCCACCCTCATA	TACAGACAAAAACGGCCTC	GTTGTGTTCTGTACCAGTGCA	2605	3
WIAF-2501	A/C	A	A	TTGATTGAGCAAITCTAGGGG[A/C]TATGTGACAGGGGTTTCATG	TTGATTGAGCAATCTAGGGG	CCATACTCGGTCTTTTATCCC	3773	5
WIAF-2513	T/G	G	T	GGTCTTTTATCCTCGCCCCTG[T/G]CTCCCACTTTCCCCTCAAG	GGTCTTTTATCCTCGCCCC	TGCAGAGCTGAAAAGTGGGAG	3785	21
WIAF-2514	A/C	A	A	TTGCTTAAGCCACTTGGGTA[A/C]CTCCAGGCTCCACCCTCACCT	TTGCTTAAGCCACTTGGGTA	TGCAGAGCTGGGTA	3786	2
WIAF-2515	C/G	C	G	ATGTTGCAGTGCGGATGAAT[C/G]TTATCATGAITGCTAAGTGAA	GTTGCAGTGCGGATGAAT	ACAGGTAGAATGATACATTTGGATT	3787	19
WIAF-2525	G/A	A	G	GTATTTACTTGAGGGCAACA[G/A]AAITTACGGCTTAACAACACA	TCGTATTTACTTGAGGGCAACA	TTTAGTGTTGTTGTTAAGCCGTAAT	3796	8
WIAF-2528	G/A	A	G	CAACTGGAAAGCTTTTACAC[G/A]TGCTTCAGAATGCGGCAGTA	CCCAACTGGAAAGCTTTTACA	GCCGCATTCTGAAGCA	3799	5
WIAF-2531	G/A	A	G	AATTAITGGACTTTAAAGCTC[G/A]ACATAAAAITAGTAGCTTCA	AGATAACAATTATGGACTTTAAAGCTC	CCCTTTGAAGCTACTAATTTTATGT	3802	12
WIAF-2534	G/A	A	G	ACAITTTGAATATAGCTATC[G/A]TTTTAACAAACCTCATATG	TCCAAATAAACAATATAGACATTTTGAA	AGTGATCATAATGAGCATTTTGAA	3805	13
WIAF-2538	A/C	A	C	CTGAATTAGTCAAGCAGGTC[A/C]GATACTATTGTCTGCTAGAT	GGCTGAATTAGTCAAGCAGGTC	TTAAAGTATTACAGAAGCAAACTTTTT	1340	22
WIAF-2541	T/C	C	T	CAAAGCAGCTAAAGGAAITAT[T/C]TACACCACCCACCCCCCTTTT	TGCAAAGCAGCTAAAGGAAT	GGGGGTGGGTGGTGTA	1343	17
WIAF-2544	G/A	A	G	TGAGATATTTCTCACAATCA[G/A]ACAAGAGCCAAGGGCCCAG	TGAGATATTTCTCACAATCA	CCTGCTGAGATATTTCTCACAATC	1345	22
WIAF-2546	A/C	A	C	GGAGAAAGTGAAAITTAAITC[A/C]TTCCTAAATTTAAGTCAGAT	CATGGGAGAAAGTGAAAGTTAAATC	GATTTCTTTCTATCTGACTTAAATTTAGG	2060	6
WIAF-2555	G/A	A	G	CGTCTATCTGGCGAGGAGGC[G/A]ACGGCATGGAGTCCAGGGTGG	TCTATCTGGCGAGGAGGC	CCTGGACTCCATGCCG	2068	13
WIAF-2560	T/C	C	T	GAACTGGCCTGGACGGGGAITT[T/C]GAGGGCAGCTGGCGGGGGCT	GAGCACAAGCCAAAGATACA	CCGCCAGCTGCCCTC	3808	17
WIAF-2563	G/C	C	G	GAGCACAAGCCAAAGATACA[G/C]AGAAAATAAAGAGTGTACAAT	GAGCACAAGCCAAAGATACA	ACTGTGCTCTTATTGTACACTCTTTATT	3811	3
WIAF-2567	C/T	C	T	TGTCTAAAITTCCACTAAAGC[C/T]GCTTCTCCAAITCGTCCCAGT	TGTCTAAATTCCACTAAAGC	CACTGAGAACACTGAGAAGC	2341	9
WIAF-2569	T/C	C	T	TGGCAITTTCCCATGCTTCTT[T/C]AGAITTTAGGAGAAAACCACG	GCATTTTCCCATGCTTCTT	CCGTGGGTTTCTCCTAAATC	3815	11
WIAF-2572	T/C	C	T	TAAAGTTCAAAGTGGTAAITG[T/C]GCTTTTCTCCCAAGTACCTATG	AGAAGAATCTAAAGTTCAAAGTGGTAAT	CTTAACATAGGTACTTGGAGAAAGC	2342	3
WIAF-2573	G/C	G	G	TGGCCGCCAGAGGAAGCTG[G/C]CTGCCGGAGGACCCCCACTT	CGCCACAGAGGAAGCTG	GGGGTCTCCGGCAG	3818	17
WIAF-2574	C/G	C	G	CTCGGCTTGAAGATCCCTAA[C/G]GCTCATAGGTTTTGCGAAITT	TCGGCTTGAAGATCCCTAA	TTTAATTCCAAAAACCTATGCAG	2343	19
WIAF-2576	C/G	C	G	TCAACTGAAAITAAAATAT[C/G]AAAGGAGAAAAITAT	TCAACTGAAATAAAATAT	TTTAATTTTCCCATCCTCCTTT	2345	15
WIAF-258	A/C	A	C	TCCTCATGGGTTTGTGACAG[A/C]CCCTGCCGGTGCTCAGTGCCT	CCTCATGGGTTTGTGACAG	CACTGAGCACGGCAGGG	2612	6

(Continued on following pages.)

TABLE 6-7. (Continued)

WIAF Name	Alleles	Allele A	Allele B	Chipregion	primer up	primer down	ncbi SS	NwLib chrom
WIAF-2581	A/C	A	C	CATAACCACCAGTCAGAG[A/C]TACTCTGCTCCACCATCACA	GCATAACCACCAGTCAGA	TGTGATGGTGGAGCAGAGTA	2347	10
WIAF-2588	T/C	C	T	AACTGTTGCCCATACTGATAG[T/C]CATGGCCAGGAGAATTTTGA	GCAACTGTGCCCATACTGAT	CAAAATTCTCCTGCCATGC	2351	10
WIAF-2589	G/A	A	G	GCAGTTGTTACCCATTAAAT[G/A]ATCAAATTTCTATCCCTCAAT	TCAGCAGTTGTTACCCATTAAA	TGAAGACTGTATTGTATTGAGGGAT	3824	X
WIAF-2590	A/G	A	G	CTTACTGTGTCATCCTATCC[A/G]TTCCCTTCCCTGAGCCTCGGG	TCTGTACTTACTGTGTCATCCTATCC	AGGCTCAGGGAAGGGAA	3825	2
WIAF-2592	C/T	C	T	GTGCAAATGCCTTAAGATAG[C/T]GTAAGTCTAGGGAGTGTGAG	CAAGTGCAAATGCCTTAAGAT	CAAATCTCACACTCCCTAGACTTAC	2352	4
WIAF-2597	C/T	C	T	CAATCACACTAAATAGAAAC[C/T]TTGTGCCATGTACAAGCACT	GTACAATCACACTAAATAGAAAC	AGTGGTTGTCATGGCACAA	3828	6
WIAF-2601	G/C	C	G	TCCTTCCAGAGCTGAGCGGA[G/C]AGAAATGCGTTTTCTTTGCCTT	TTCCAGAGGCTGAGGGA	CGCTTCTGGAAAGCTGG	3832	7
WIAF-2612	C/T	C	T	TCAGCCTGCACCCTCTTCTC[C/T]TTCTGGCTTCCCTCTCTGAAA	AGCCTGCACCCTCTTCTC	TTCAGAGAGGGAAGCCAGA	3839	3
WIAF-2616	T/G	G	T	AGGTTGGACTCTGCAGAAAC[T/G]TGACTCAGTGTTGTTGGG	CAGGTTGGACTCTGCAGAAA	ACCAAACAACACTGAGTCAC	2362	7
WIAF-2618	C/A	A	C	TCCTCTTTCTCTAGGCTGAC[C/A]CAGGTCGTTTTACTGACCGA	TCCTCTTTCTCTAGGCTGA	TCGGTCAGTAAAACGACCTG	2363	16
WIAF-2626	C/T	C	T	CACTGTGAATTAGAGCCAGA[C/T]GCTTAAGTTGCCCAAGTTGGAC	GACTGTGAATTAGAGCCAGA	TGTCTCACCCTGGACTTAAGC	3847	3
WIAF-2627	A/G	A	G	CAGAACCACTTGCCATCAAC[A/G]GCTGGGGAATCCTAGCCAGT	CAGAACCACTTGCCATCAAC	GGCTAGGGATTCCCCAGC	2366	6
WIAF-263	A/C	A	C	CCCTTCCTCCCTGTCTCTGC[A/C]TCTGACTCTCTTTTGAGGTC	CCCTTCCTCCCTGTCTCTGC	GGGACCTCAAAAGAGAGTCAGA	2616	7
WIAF-2630	C/G	C	G	GCAAGACCAGAACACTCTG[C/G]CCTATGGTAGATCTACAAAA	GGCAAGACCAGAACACTCTG	GGCCTCTTTTGTAGATCTACCAT	2369	15
WIAF-2633	A/T	A	T	CTGCTGGAATCAAGCATAA[A/T]CACATCCATCGATACAAAG	TGCTGGAATCAAGCATAA	AAGATACTTTGTATCAGATGGATGTG	2370	8
WIAF-2635	C/G	C	G	CTAGTGATAACTATACAAAT[C/G]TGGACATGGAATGAACAG	CTAGTGATAACTATACAAAT	CCTGTTCATTATCCATGTCCA	3849	2
WIAF-2636	G/A	A	G	TCGAGTCTCATGTTCCAACC[G/A]ACCGTCTGGCTCAGTGACTG	TCGAGTCTCATGTTCCAACC	GTCACTGAGCCAGACGGT	3850	1
WIAF-2637	C/T	C	T	ATGTTGTGTGAGTTTAACA[C/T]ATTTGGGCTTGCATTTGTTC	GCAACCTTTAATATATATCATGTTGTG	GCTGATAAACTTTTCATATTACACATTG	3851	19
WIAF-2638	A/G	A	G	GTCCTCATCAGTGAAACCAG[A/G]GTAAGAGAAAACACCAAAGGC	GGTCCTCATCAGTGAAACCAG	TGCCTTTGGTGTTCTCTTAC	2372	2
WIAF-2639	T/A	A	T	TTTATCTCCCATATTTCAAA[T/A]AACAGTGTCTGCCAAGTTTGGCT	TTTATCTCCCATATTTCAAA	AGCCAAACTTGCAGACATG	3852	19
WIAF-2640	A/C	A	C	TAAAAATAGCTCCAGATGAC[A/C]GAACAGTATTGCATACACAG	CATCTTAAAAATAGCTCCAGATGAC	GGAACCTGTGATGCAATACTGTTC	3853	10
WIAF-2641	C/A	A	C	CAGTGGACACAAATCCCTCC[C/A]TCATTATCCAGGCATGGATG	GCAGTGGACACAAATCCC	CATCCATGCCTGGATAATGA	3854	19
WIAF-2642	A/G	A	G	GAGTACCAGTCGCTAAATGT[A/G]CAGTAAAAGAAGCAGGCAAC	CGAGTACCAGTCGCTAAATGT	TGTTGCCTGCTTCTTTTACTG	2373	18
WIAF-2643	G/C	C	G	GGGAAAGACAGAATAAATA[G/C]AACAGTAGAAATGTTACT	TGGGAGGAGAAAGACAGAATAA	CCCATCTGTGATCCATTCTACTGTT	3855	21
WIAF-2644	T/A	A	T	CTTTTCAGCATTCAGTTTTG[T/A]GGCTCATGGGAAATGTTACT	GCTTTTCAGCATTCAGTTTTG	AAGTAACATTTCCCATGAGCC	3856	1
WIAF-2649	T/C	C	T	TTCCGGGACCACGATCGGC[T/C]GCTTGTCTGCTACCCAGCAT	GGGACCACGATCGGC	GCTGGGTAGCAGACAAGC	19486	2
WIAF-2650	A/G	A	G	TGTTGGGTGGAACAGCAGAG[A/G]TTAATAGGTTTCCACAAGCC	TTGGGTGGAACAGCAGAG	TGGCTTGTGGAAAGCTATTAA	3860	16
WIAF-2651	C/G	C	G	TGCTCCCACAGGGGCCATGT[C/G]CTCTCTTAATAGGTGGCACT	CCCACAGGGGCCATGT	GGGTAGTGCCACCTATTAAGAGA	3861	7
WIAF-2652	A/C	A	C	CTTGGGCTTGATCTTGGCTG[A/G]GTCCTGGGAATCTCATCGT	GGGCTTGATCTTGGCTG	GATGACATTCGCCACCTC	2375	16
WIAF-2654	A/G	A	G	GTATTGCAATCCCAGTTGAA[A/G]GTCCTGGGGAGGTGTTTGTA	GGTATTGCAATCCCAGTTGAA	CAAACACCTCCCAGGAC	2376	17
WIAF-2658	G/A	A	G	CATACTATAACTTCTATTCT[G/A]ACTTAAACTCTGTTCTATTC	TGTCAAAGCCATACTATAACTTCTATTC	TGACACAAGAAATAGAACACAGAGTTTAAG	2377	12
WIAF-266	A/C	A	C	AGGCCAGGCAATTTTATTTG[A/C]GCCCTAGGAGGGTTACTATA	GGCCAGGCAATTTTATTTG	AAATTATAGTAACCTCCTAGGGC	19446	20
WIAF-2661	A/T	A	T	GTGCCCAAAGATGCCTCAA[A/T]GCCTAGAAAAGTGCCTTCCC	CCCCAAAGATGCCTCAA	TGGGGAAGGCACTTTTCTAG	2378	12
WIAF-2662	T/C	C	T	GATGTTGCAAATCTCAGAG[T/C]TGGATAGTTCCAGGAAGCTG	GGATGTTGCAAATCTCAGAG	CAGCTTCCTGCAAGTATCCA	3867	19
WIAF-2665	A/G	A	G	GGAGGGAGGGAGGCAGCCAAA[A/G]GTGAATAGCACAAGATGAGC	GAGGGAGGGAGCCAAA	CTGCTCATCTTGTGCTATTCAC	2380	3
WIAF-2667	G/A	A	G	CAATAGAGTTTATAGTCTTA[G/A]GGGCAACAATAGGGAATGAG	AAAGGCTGATGTGCTAACACA	TCATTCCCTATTGTTGCCC	2381	1
WIAF-2669	T/G	G	T	CAATAAAAAAACCAACAC[T/G]TTGCTCTATGTGGTCGTTCCAA	TCCTACATTTCATTAAGTGCTAAGTA	TGGAACGACCACATAGCAA	3870	X
WIAF-2670	C/T	C	T	TTTCATTAAGTGCTAAGTAT[C/T]GTCTGCCAACTGATTTTCCTG	TCCTACATTTCATTAAGTGCTAAGTA	TCAGGAAAATCAGTTGCAGAC	3871	2
WIAF-2671	C/T	C	T	AAGCAAATTATGTTTAAAAG[C/T]TGGCGTCGCCATCATTATCC	CACATTTCTGTTGAAGCAAATTATG	ATGGATGGCAGCCCA	3872	2
WIAF-2672	G/A	A	G	ACATTTCTAAATACACTAAAC[G/A]TTATCTAATGAAGTCACACT	GCACAAATTTACACATTCTAAATACAC	GAAGACCAGTGTGACTTCATTAGA	3873	8
WIAF-2674	T/C	C	T	TAACTTCATGCAGAACATTC[T/C]GGCTGTGTTGGGAATGAGAA	CGTAACTTCATGCAGAACATTC	CTCATTCCCAACACAGCC	2383	1
WIAF-2676	A/C	A	C	TCAGAAGACCAGGAAGGCGG[A/C]ATAGGGATGCCAGAGCCCCA	AAGCACGGGAAGGCG	GGGCCTAAAAATCATAAATCCA	3875	1
WIAF-2677	A/C	A	C	GACTAGGAGGAGAAAGGGGG[A/C]GTGGATTTATGATTTTATTCG	ACTAGGAGGAGAAAGGGGG	TTGCCATAAAATCATAAATCCA	3876	14
WIAF-2679	G/A	A	G	CTTTTGTATTTGCCTTTAGA[G/A]AGGAGGATAACAGTAACTTAT	TTGCTTTTGTATTTGCCTTTAGA	CTTCTACAAATAAGTTACTGTTATCCTCC	2385	12
WIAF-268	C/T	C	T	GTGGGACAAAAGGCTTGTCA[C/T]CTGTCAGAAACATTGAAAAC	GGGACAAAAGGCTTGTCA	GCTGTTTTCAATGTTTCTGACAG	19487	10
WIAF-2686	G/A	A	G	CCAAACAATGCCGTGGAAGA[G/A]GTGATCAAAGCAGAAGGGGC	AAACAATGCCGTGGAAGA	CCCCTTCTGCTTTGATCAC	19488	2
WIAF-2689	T/C	C	T	GAGAATGGCTATTGGTTC[T/C]TTTGTAGTTCTCTCACATTTA	GAGAATGGCTATTGGTTCTC	CTTGATGTGATAAATGTGAGAGACTAC	19266	12
WIAF-2690	G/C	C	G	AAGAAGTAGCAGACGTCCA[G/C]ATGCTTTTATCTTCCCTAG	CTGAAAAGAAGTAGCAGACGCTC	GATCTAGGGGAAGATAAAAGCAT	19222	6
WIAF-2692	T/C	C	T	CGTTCCAGGTTTAAAGATTA[T/C]AGCTAAACACTTTGAGGGAC	TGAACGTTCCAGGTTTAAAGA	GCAGTCCCTCAAAGTGTTTAGC	19331	9
WIAF-2693	G/A	A	G	GATCATTCACCACTTTGCTG[G/A]GATTTTGCCTTAGTGCCACC	GGATCATTCACCACTTTGCTG	GGTGGCACTAAGGCAAAATC	19489	7
WIAF-2696	A/G	A	G	TTGCCAAGGAAGTAGTTGTC[A/G]AGATCCAGGTCAAAAGGAAA	TTTGCCAAGGAAGTAGTTGTC	CTTTCCTTTTGACCTGGATCT	19490	2
WIAF-2699	T/C	C	T	TGTGGATTTCCTACATGATG[T/C]CATGGAAAAACACTGGTTTTG	CTAGTGTGGATTTCCTACATGATG	CCAAAACCAGTGTTTTCCATG	19491	11

WIAF	Allele	a1	a2	Sequence [SNP]	Flank 5′	Flank 3′	ID	n
WIAF-270	A/G	A	G	CCAGAAGACTCAGCTGCTTG[A/G]GGCATGTTCCCACCCTGGAC	CCAGAAGACTCAGCTGCTTG	AGGTGGGAACATGCC	2619	1
WIAF-2701	T/C	C	T	AGTGGGGTCCTCCCCTGAAA[T/C]AGGTAAATGAGAACTGGGAG	GGGGTCCTCCCCTGAAA	CACTCCCAGTTCTCATTTACCT	19492	2
WIAF-2703	G/T	G	T	TGTTCCAATTAGTTTAATG[G/T]AGACTCATTGTTTGAAAGGC	TGTATCATTTTCTAATATTGTTCCAATT	CATGTGAGGCCTTTCAAAGT	19173	3
WIAF-2705	G/A	A	G	GGACCTGTCAAATGATCT[G/A]AGACTCATTGTTTGAAAGGC	GGACCTGTCAAATGATCT	TTCTTCTCGTGCTCCCC	19223	5
WIAF-2706	A/G	A	G	GTGTGAATAAAGAAATGAAA[A/G]GGCATTTAGAGGAGAGGTGA	GTGTGAATAAAGAAATGAAA	CATTCACCTCTCTCTCTAAATGC	19259	13
WIAF-2709	C/T	C	T	TGCAGTGGAGAGCTAAGG[C/T]TGGGAGTAAAGGCAGAGCT	AGGCTGAGAGCTGGCACCAC	CAGCTCTGCCTTACTCTCCA	19493	6
WIAF-271	G/A	A	G	AGGCTGAGAGCTGGCACCAC[G/A]CACTGGTTTCTAAATCTCTG	AGGCTGAGAGCTGGCACCAC	AAGCCAGAGATTTAGAAACCAGT	2620	10
WIAF-2713	T/C	C	T	GCTCACATTTTGAATCTTG[T/C]CCTCAATACCTGAACCTGAG	CTGCTCACATTTTGAATCTTG	CCTCAGGTTCAGGTATTGAGG	19494	13
WIAF-2714	C/T	C	T	ATGAAGCTTTCCTAGGACCA[C/T]TAAACAATTGTAGTTCATTA	ATGAAGCTTTCCTAGGACCA	GGATCAGTAATGAACTACAATTGTTTA	19279	9
WIAF-2716	C/A	A	C	CTCAACAGAACAAGCCTGCT[C/A]CTGCCCTCAGGGCCTCTGTCC	TCAACAGAACAAGCCTGCT	AGAGGCCCTGAGGCAG	19295	12
WIAF-2718	C/A	A	C	CTCTCCATAGCTAGGTCCTG[C/A]TTATTCTTCCTCTTCCCAGG	GCCTCAGGGCCTCTGTC	CCTGGGAAGGAGGAAGAATAA	19296	12
WIAF-272	G/C	G	C	CTCTCCATAGCTAGGTCCTG[G/C]TCTCCTCATCAATTGCCACG	GTCTCCCATACGTAGGTCCTG	CGTGGCAATTGTATAGGAGA	19197	10
WIAF-2721	G/A	A	G	ATGAGAGCAGTCCTGCCTG[G/A]TAGGGCAAGACAGAAAGGCT	CTCTCCATAGCTAGGTCCTG	CCTTTCTTCTTGCCCCA	19495	9
WIAF-2723	A/G	A	G	TTTGTATCAGAAAAACCTGC[A/G]TTCAAGTTCCAGCTCTCCCA	TTTGTATCAGAAAAACCTGC	GGGAGAGCTGGAACTTGAA	19176	5
WIAF-2724	T/C	C	T	AGACCCAAGATGTCAATACA[T/C]AGTGCTGCATTGAGAGACCA	CAGAATAGCCTCTGACCAAAA	TGGTCTCTCCAATTGCAGCACT	19317	8
WIAF-2728	G/T	G	T	GTCTGGAGAGATTTGCTGTG[G/T]AATATATTTCTAAGGAAGAA	AGTGTCGGAGAGATTGCTGTG	CCACTGCAGTTTCCTTAGAAAATATATT	19496	7
WIAF-2729	T/G	G	T	TCAAGTCTGATAATGAAATA[T/G]ATGTCGCAAAATCTGGAGAG	GGATACATTTTCAAGTCGATAATGA	CCACTGTCAGTTTTGCACAT	19497	10
WIAF-2730	A/G	A	G	TTAGTATTTCCTAGGGCTGC[A/G]ATGTCACGTTTCTTCCTCAC	CTGATTACGATATTTTCTGGAAGCT	GTGGAAGGAAAAACGTGACAT	19310	3
WIAF-2735	C/T	C	T	TATTAGTTCCTAGGGCTGC[C/T]GGAGCAGAGTACCTTAAGCT	AAAGTAACATTGTGTATTAGTTCCTTAGG	CAGCTTAAGGTACTCTGCTCC	19307	4
WIAF-2736	G/C	C	G	AACAGACATTCATTCTCTCA[G/C]CAGGTCTGCAGGCCAGAAGTC	CCTTAAGCTGGTGACTTAAAACAA	TTGTTTTAGACTTCTCTGGCCTG	19308	4
WIAF-2737	A/G	A	G	CTGCAGGGGAACCAACCTAG[A/G]AGCCTGAACTGGGGGCCTGG	CTGCAGGGGAACCAACCTAG	GCCCCCAGTTCAGGCT	19264	8
WIAF-2738	G/T	G	T	ATGATTCTAGATTACAGAGA[G/T]TTTTTCAAACCAATGCACT	TCTAGTGCGTTGTTTGAAAAA	TCTAGTGCGTTGTTTGAAAAA	19265	8
WIAF-2739	C/T	C	T	AGATTGTATAATCACTTATCA[C/T]GTTTTTGCGTCATCATGTG	CAAGGCTAGATGTATAATCA	CACATGATGCAAGCAAAAAC	19498	2
WIAF-2741	G/A	A	G	AAGGAGCAGATTACAGCAAA[G/A]AACATTATCCACCCAGCACC	GAAGGAGCAGATTACAGCAAA	GGTGCTGGGTGGATAATGTT	19166	11
WIAF-2749	C/T	C	T	TGTGGGTAGATAATAGATT[C/T]AACTCAAAATTCCTCCCCA	AATTGAATCCTTGTGGGTAGATAA	GGGGGAGGAATTTTGAGTT	19292	3
WIAF-2750	G/A	A	G	CCAGTATGTGAGTTTGCAG[G/A]CATCATCCTCCCAAAGCAGG	CCAGTATGTGAGTTTGCAG	TCTCTGTGGAGTCTCTAAATCTACTG	19499	16
WIAF-2752	A/T	A	T	CAAAGCAGGAAGTAGAATAA[A/T]GACATAGGTTAGCAGTCC	CCAAGACAGGAAGTAGAATAA	CCCAAGACAGGAAGTAGAATAA	19323	3
WIAF-2753	A/C	A	C	TCACAGGCAGAGGGGATAC[A/C]CTTGCAGATCAGCTCCATGG	TCACAGGCAGAGGGGATAC	CATGGAGGGTGATCTGCAAG	19293	13
WIAF-2754	T/C	C	T	AGTCACTATCTCCCTGACTC[T/C]AGTTATAAGGTAAATTCTGT	AGTCACTATCTCCCTGACTC	GTATTTTAGTCAACACAGAATTTACCTTA	19500	11
WIAF-2758	C/G	C	G	CCCTCAGCAGTCCTTTGCTT[C/G]TTTTTTGCCTCACTCCCTC	GGATCCAGGATCCTTTGCTT	GGGGAGTGAGGCAAAAA	19154	11
WIAF-2759	A/G	A	G	TCTGATACCTCCACTTCAAC[A/G]TTACGATGTGTAATTCCAGT	CCTCAGCAGTTGCTGCTTTGC	GGTGGAAGACCGTAGCA	19212	9
WIAF-2760	C/T	C	T	AGATTCCTGGGGTGTGCTAT[C/T]TACGATGTACCTCCAGCT	TGAATGTTATTCTGATACCTCCAC	GTAAACTGGAGAATTACACATCGT	19318	17
WIAF-2763	G/A	A	G	TAAATGGCGTGATATTACTA[G/A]GAAGTACTTTGCCCAAATTT	GATTCCTGGGGTGTGCTAT	GAAAATTTGGGCAAAGTACTTC	19291	8
WIAF-2765	G/A	A	G	TAAATGGCGTGATATTACTA[G/A]GCATCACCAAATTGCAGAAT	GAAGCTAAATGGGTGATATTAC	TTCTGCAATTTGGTGATGC	19501	4
WIAF-2766	A/G	A	G	AGTCCTTCAAGTGTCTT[A/G]GATCTTCTTTTCTCGTTTTC	GAGTCCTTCAAGTGTCTT	CCCAAGACAGGAAAAGAAGAT	19230	6
WIAF-2767	A/G	A	G	AGAGCCGCTCGACTTCTTAC[A/G]GTGGTGTTTGTTCTGCCTTTTTC	CATTAGAGCCGTCCTTTAC	GCCACCCCTCTATTCACAC	19231	6
WIAF-2768	C/T	C	T	CTCCTGGTTATGATGCCAAG[C/T]GTGTGAATAGAGGGTGGCA	TCCTGGTTATGATGCCAAG	AAACAGGCCTGATGGCA	19198	11
WIAF-2769	A/G	A	G	ATCATGTCATTTAATCACCC[A/G]TGCCATCAGGCCTGTTTAT	CGTATCATGTCATTTAATCACCC	CATCTAAGCATCCAGTTCCCT	19502	11
WIAF-2780	G/C	C	G	TGCTGCTGTCTATACCCACA[G/C]ATAGGGAACTGGATGCTTAG	TGCTGCTGTCTATACCCACA	GGTGTGACTCCAACAGCAT	19503	18
WIAF-2781	A/G	A	G	TCTCTAAAACTCAATG[A/G]ATGCTGTTGGAGTCACCACC	GATTTTCTCCAGTAAAACTCAATG	GAATAATTACAAGCTATTGCAGTAG	19206	13
WIAF-2782	T/C	C	T	CTATTCCATCACTTCTTAC[T/C]GGGCTACTGCAATAGCCTTG	CTATTCCATCACTTCTTAC	TCTGAAACTTCTTCAGTAGAAATCATT	19506	14
WIAF-2783	G/A	A	G	ATATTCACACTTCCTTCTAC[G/A]GTGAATCTCAATCTGACAC	TCTCCATATTCACACTTCCTTCTA	GTGTGTCAGGATTGAGATTCAC	19169	9
WIAF-2785	G/A	A	G	ATGGTCCACTGGGTGCCATG[G/A]CTGCAGTAACTGGTTCAGGG	ATGGTCCACTGGGTGCCATG	CCTGAACCAGTTACTGCAG	19504	9
WIAF-2787	A/G	A	G	ACTGGTTTCAGGGATGGTCC[A/G]TGACCTTAGATTATCCAATC	TTTGGCCTCTATACCCACATG	CCGATTGGATAATCTAAGGTCA	19281	12
WIAF-2788	T/C	C	T	TTTGGCCTCTATACTATAAA[T/C]CACAGACTACGAAGTGAGA	TTTGGGCCTCTATACTATAAA	AACTCTTGAGCCTCTAGTCTGTG	19505	12
WIAF-2789	C/A	A	C	TTATATGTCACAAAACTTTT[C/A]AATGATTCTACTGAAGAAGT	TTATAGTCACAAAACTTTT	TCTGAAACTTCTTCAGTAGAAATCATT	19240	4
WIAF-2791	C/T	C	T	TTAAGACAGTAGCAGTGGGG[C/T]AAATGATGGAGGGCTGATT	TTAAGACAGTAGCAGTGGGG	CAAATCAGCCCTCCATCTATTT	19185	14
WIAF-2802	G/A	A	G	AGTGCTCCTGTTTCTAGAG[G/A]TTGCCTCTATTTTCTTTAC	AGTGCTCCTGTTTCTAGAG	AGTGAGTAAAGAGAAAATAGAGGCA	19507	15
WIAF-2803	G/C	C	G	AAAGGAGTACCACTGGAGAT[G/C]CCTGAGGCCATGGAAGGAGAGA	CTAAAGGAGTCCACTGGAGAGA	CTCTCCATGGCCTCAGG	19252	3
WIAF-2804	A/G	A	G	TTCTTTCTAAAAATAAGCA[A/G]CTAAATTGACCCAGGAAAG	TGAGACCCAATATTTTCTTTCTAAAA	GCTTTCCTGGGTCAATTTAAG	19283	3
WIAF-2805	C/T	C	T	AGCTTCTCTCGCCTTGGCA[C/T]TTACGTCTCAGGCTCTGAAC	AGCTTCTCTCGCCTTGGCA	TGTTCAGAGCCTGAACGTAA	19508	10
WIAF-2809	G/A	A	G	AGAAAGCTTGTGGATGCTG[G/A]AGTTTGTCGACAAAGTGACTA	AGAAAGCTTGTGGATGCTG	TCAATTAGTCACTATAGGATGGTGC	19509	8
WIAF-2810	G/A	A	G	TTTAGGTTACAGTAAATGA[G/A]AGTTTGCTGCAAGTGAGA	TTTAGGTTACAGTAAATGA	CACCGTTTCTCCAGTTTTCTCACT	19268	6
WIAF-2813	T/C	C	T	AAGGGACAGTGTAAGAAGCA[T/C]TTTTTCCTTTAACAACCTT	AAGGGACAGTGTAAGAAGCA	TGTGTTAGATGTTTTAAGGAAAAA	19325	18
WIAF-2815	G/T	G	T	GTAAACTTCTTATTTGGGTT[G/T]ATTTTGACTCTTACAGGTGT	GTAAACTTCTTATTTGGGTT	GAAAGACACCTGTAAGACTCTT	19510	7
WIAF-2816	A/G	A	G	GCAGGAAGTTCAGAGAGCAC[A/G]GCAGACCACCTTGCAAATCAC	GCAGGAAGTTCAGAGAGCAC	TGATTTGCAAGTGGTCTGC	19152	2

(Continued on following pages.)

TABLE 6-7. (Continued)

WIAF Name	Alleles	Allele A	Allele B	Chipregion	primer up	primer down	ncbi SS	NwLib chrom
WIAF-2817	C/T	C	T	ACTGCCTGGCTGCTCTGCTCGA[C/T]GCACGGTGATGGGGACCTCA	CCTGGCTGTGGCTCGA	TCCCCATCACCGTGC	19275	7
WIAF-2818	G/A	A	G	TAGATTCAGGAAATAAGGGT[G/A]AAAATGTAGGTGAAGTTAGG	GCCTAGATTCAGGAAATAAGGG	CATGACCTAACTTCACCTACATTTT	19511	1
WIAF-2820	C/A	A	C	TTTACAGCAAATTCTTTAGA[C/A]CAACTACCTAAAAIGTTTTC	TCATATCTAATTTACAGCAAATTCTTTAG	CAGAAGAGAAAACATTTTAGGTAGTTG	19512	1
WIAF-2822	C/A	A	C	CTCTCATGGGAGTGGAGAGC[C/A]ATTAGCATATAATCTAAAAT	TCTCATGGGAGTGGAGAGC	CCAGATTCATGATTTTAGATTATATGC	19513	11
WIAF-2823	G/C	C	G	GCAATTGCCCCAGGACCTAG[G/C]CTAGTCCAGCAGAGGCCACT	AATTGCCCCAGGACCTAG	TGGCCTCTGCTGGACTAG	19514	11
WIAF-2824	C/T	C	T	ATTAATACTGCCATGTGAAT[C/T]GTAAACACTTGGACTTGCCT	ATAAACATTAATACTGCCATGTGAAT	TGAGGCAAGTCCAAGTGTTT	19515	18
WIAF-2827	A/G	A	G	AGTTAAATGGTTGTTAAACT[A/G]ACAAACAAGAAGGGAAAC	AGTTAAATGGTTGTTAAACT	CGTTTCCCTTCTTGTTTG	19516	2
WIAF-2828	A/G	A	G	GAAAAGGTGAGGGCCTTTAT[A/G]TATCACCAGAGCCTTGAGCT	GAAAAGGTGAGGGCCTTTAT	AGCTCAAGGCTCTGTGATA	19517	3
WIAF-283	C/T	C	T	TTGGCATTCAATAGCCTATC[C/T]AACTCCATGTGGGAGTTTCA	TTGGCATTCAATAGCCTATC	TGAAACTCCCACATGGAGTT	2624	8
WIAF-2832	G/A	A	G	GATTTATTGTAGAGATATGC[G/A]TTAAGAAGTCCACGTGTCCA	CATTAAGTCTGATTTATTGTAGAGATATGC	GTGGACACGTGGACTTCTTAA	19229	X
WIAF-2834	C/T	C	T	TGCTGGGCCATCCTGCCT[C/T]AACTCACATGCCCAGCAGCC	TGCTGGGCCATCCTGCCT	GTGCTGGGCATGTGAGT	19274	
WIAF-2837	G/C	C	G	GCCTCTGAGATTTTGAGATT[G/C]TGTTACATGCCAGTTGATCTT	TGAAGCCTCTGAGATTTTGAGA	TTGTAAGATCAACTGCATGTAACA	19289	
WIAF-2839	T/A	A	T	ATTTGGCAGTGATTTAAAGA[T/A]AACAGCTAAAGGGCAAATCT	GATATAGATTTGGCAGTGATTTAAAGA	GAGATTTGCCCTTTAGCTGTT	19518	
WIAF-2841	T/C	C	T	AAGGAAGATTGGACAGATGA[T/C]AGGCAGAGGGGCAGGTAGGT	GGTTAAGTAACGGAAGATTGGACAG	CCTGCCCCTCTGCCT	19215	3
WIAF-2847	G/T	G	T	GGTGGGGCTCTTCTAAATGG[G/T]CTGGGATAATTCAGACATTA	GTGGGGCTCTTCTAAATGG	TCATTAATGTCTGAATTATCCCAG	19213	1
WIAF-2848	T/G	G	T	GACTTTTCTTTCTTCTTCAAAA[T/G]AGCATAGCTGAGCAATAAAG	GCAATGACTTTTCTTTCTTCAAAA	CCTCTTTATTGTCCAGCTATGC	19334	8
WIAF-2849	C/T	C	T	AGCTATATGACTGTAGGCAA[C/T]ATGGAGGAATATTACTTCGCA	AGCTATATGACTGTAGGCAA	TTTCCCAAGTAATATTCCTCCA	19314	2
WIAF-2853	C/T	C	T	CTTGTCCCTCCCCTTCCTG[C/T]GCTGGAGCAGCTCTCTCTCTG	CCCTCCCCCTTCCTG	CAGAGAGAGCTGCTCCAGC	19260	2
WIAF-2857	G/C	C	G	AAGCTTTGGAAAAGCCATCT[G/C]CTCAATTCCCAGTGGCTTAT	AAGCTTTGGAAAAGCCATCT	CATAAGCCACTGGGAATTGAG	19519	19
WIAF-2858	C/A	A	C	GCTTACCCTTGAACACGGAA[C/A]CTTCACTGTTCCCAGCTGGGC	GCTTACCCTTGAACACGGAA	CCAGCTGGGACAGTGAAG	19253	17
WIAF-2859	T/C	C	T	TGCATGACAAATCATAGCTC[T/C]GTTCTCCATTTCTTCTTTT	TGCATGACAAATCATAGTC	CCCCTCATAAAAGAAAGAATATGA	19155	5
WIAF-2860	G/A	A	G	TGCCTTCTACCCCAGGCTGT[G/A]CAATGACGAGTTATCTTGA	TGCCTTCTACCCCAGGCTGT	TGTCCAAGAGTACTCGTCATTG	19520	16
WIAF-2861	C/T	C	T	CGAGGACATCATGGTCCAGC[C/T]CGAGGGAGATTTATCTTTGA	GAGGACATCATGGTCCAGC	CAATCAAAGATAAATCTCCCTCG	19343	16
WIAF-2866	A/C	A	C	CAGACATGGATTTTGAATTC[A/C]GTTTTTCTTGTTCCAGTTTT	AATTACAGACATGGATTTTGAATTC	CCAAAACTGGAACAAGAAAAAC	19203	1
WIAF-2867	C/T	C	T	ATAAGGAAATTAGGGTCCTT[C/T]TTGGACTTCTAGAGGATACTG	AAAGATAAGGAAATTAGGGTCCTT	TTCCAGTATCCTCTAGAAGTCCA	19162	14
WIAF-2868	A/G	A	G	TGAAACAGTATTAAAACAGCA[A/G]ATTCAAGGCAGACAGT	TTCCTTTGAAATAAATTGAAACAGT	GGGCTAACTCTGCCTTGAAT	19521	14
WIAF-2869	C/G	C	G	CATGGGATTGTTAACTGCTTT[C/G]CGATGTTGACAGCACTGCTG	AGCATGGATTGTTAACTGCTTT	GCAGTGCGTGCAACATCG	19522	2
WIAF-287	T/G	G	T	AAGGTATTTTCTAAGCTTTT[T/G]GTTTTATTAGTATATAAAAT	CATGAAGAGTGGGCAGTTCA	TCCTGTAAAGCCAATTTTATATACTAATAA	2627	5
WIAF-2871	G/A	A	G	AAGTATTTTCTAAGCTTTT[G/A]GATTGAAGGACAATCAAGCA	AAGGTATTTTCTAAGCTTTT	CTATGCTTGATTGTCCTTCAATC	19523	3
WIAF-2874	G/A	A	G	AAGAATAATTAAACATTTT[G/A]AGCACATATTAAGCACCAGG	AAGCAAGATCACCAGAGAAAAA	GCCTGGTTGTTAATATGTGC	19524	17
WIAF-2876	G/C	C	G	TGGGAGTCATTAACAGTTAA[G/C]AACTTTTTACCAGTAAACAGTT	CACCTGGAGTCATTAACAGTT	GCTCTTTTTACCACTGAAAAAGTT	19525	11
WIAF-2877	A/G	A	G	AGAGTCAACAGGGCTGCCAA[A/G]GTCCCAAAGGGTCTGGAATT	TCAACAGGGCTGCCAA	TTCCAGACCCTTTGGGAC	19225	6
WIAF-2878	C/T	C	T	TATCAGATTATTCTTTATTG[C/T]TTCCAGAATACTGGGAGGCT	CACCTTTGTTTGTATATCAGATTATTCTT	GCCTCCCAGTATTCTGGAA	19236	11
WIAF-2887	C/T	C	T	ACAAAAAAGTATTTTACTC[C/T]ATACAAATTTAAAAATAAA	AAAACTCAGTTGTGCAACAAAA	TCATCCCCATTGTTTTATTTTT	19526	15
WIAF-2889	C/T	C	T	TCCAACAAGACCTAAGTGCA[C/T]TTCAAGCAAGATAATTAA	CACCTCCAACAAGGCTAAG	TGGATACTTTTAAATAGTCTTGCTGA	19328	15
WIAF-2891	A/C	A	C	ATGAAGGCTTCGGGCTTCGA[A/C]TTTCTCTCAAGTCCTAGCCTT	GGCTTCGGGCTTCGA	ACAAGGCTAGGACTTGAGAGAA	19527	3
WIAF-2892	A/G	A	G	GAAACACAGTTTATTACAGT[A/G]GGGATTAGAGTACACAAACTC	CAACTTCAGAAACACAGTTTATTACAG	AGAATATAGGAGTTTGTGTACTCTAATCC	19528	6
WIAF-2894	A/G	A	G	CTTATCCTGCTGCTGCTGA[A/G]TTACAATGCAGGCTGAACTC	TCTTATCCTGCTGCTGA	GGAGTTCAGCCTGCATTGTA	19529	11
WIAF-2897	T/A	A	T	TCTTCAGTCACCCTCATTTGA[T/A]TTCTTAGTTCTTGCCCTTTG	CCTCTTCAGTCACCCTCATTTGA	GCAAAGGGCAAGAACTAAGA	19157	11
WIAF-2907	T/C	C	T	TTTTTAATGAGTACCCATTT[T/C]AGGAGCACGAACAATTCTTC	AACAAATTGAGAACTTTTAATGAGTAC	GGTGAGAATTTCGTGGTCTCTC	19530	4
WIAF-291	C/T	C	T	CAAACTGAACATTTAAATGT[C/T]ATCCATGTGAGGGCTCTAGA	GCTATTAGGCAAACTGAACATTTAAA	TCTAGAGCCCTCACATGGAT	2631	3
WIAF-2911	A/C	A	C	GGGCCTAGGCACTTAATCAG[A/C]GAACCTAAATTTAGATCTCA	GGGCCTAGGCACTTAATCAG	GGCAACAGTGAGATCTAAATTTAGG	19277	10
WIAF-2912	A/G	A	G	AAAGCCCCTTCCTTGCCAT[A/G]GGGGCTGGAACCTAGGCCTGG	CCCCCTTCCTTGCCAT	GGCTAGGTTCCAGCC	19278	1
WIAF-2914	C/T	C	T	GCAAGTGGATATTTTGATGA[C/T]GGTGAGTCTCCAAGCTATTGT	GGCAAGTGGATATTTTGATGA	GAACAATAGCCTTGGAGATCACC	19531	8
WIAF-2919	A/G	A	G	GGTGTTGCCCAAGCAAATTC[A/G]TTGGAGTGTAAGGGAGAAAAACA	TGTTGCCCAAGCAAATTC	GATGTTTTTCTCCTTTACTCCA	19532	14
WIAF-2920	G/C	C	G	TCTTCTGCTTTAATTTATTT[G/C]TTGCTTTAGCTATATTAACAAT	GAACAGTTTCTTCTGCTTTAATTTATTT	ACACAAATCTTATTGTTAATATAGCTAAGC	19533	4
WIAF-2921	G/T	G	T	ACTTACCTGCATTGCTTTTT[G/T]AAAATCTTCAATCTCTGCT	CATTACTTACCTGCATTGCTTTTT	CCCAGCCAGAGTATGAAAGATTTT	19315	1
WIAF-2922	C/T	C	T	TCCACTTCTTCTTCTTCTACAAA[C/T]AGGCATGATCATTCCTTGTC	TCCACTTCTTCTTCTTCTACAAA	GGTAGACAAGGAATGATCATGC	19534	3
WIAF-2924	C/T	C	T	TTATTGCTGCTAATTCTGTC[C/T]GAACCACACGATTTTCTGTC	CTTAAATTATTGCTGCTAATTCTGTC	CAGACAAAAATCGTGTGGTTC	19535	7
WIAF-2925	G/A	A	G	AGAAAACTGTGCTCAGTCCC[G/A]GGAAGGAGGGCAGCCTGATG	GAGAAAACTGTGCTCAGTCC	GGCTGCCCTCCTTCC	19536	8
WIAF-2927	A/G	A	G	ATTCCTTCCTCTCTCATCCA[A/G]TTTTCAATCACATAGCAAAA	TCAATTCCTTCCTCTCTCATCCA	TGGTTTTGCTATGTGATTGAAAA	19537	8
WIAF-2930	C/G	C	G	GGTGCAAGGCCCAGTGAGGT[C/G]TAGGTCCAGGGTCTCTCCAC	GCAAGGCCCAGTGAGGT	TGGAGAGACCCCTGGACCTA	19199	2

WIAF ID	Allele	Assay sequence (5′ flank [SNP] 3′ flank)	Flank B	Flank C	Contig	n
WIAF-2931	G/A	TCTCATGAGGACAGCACTCT[G/A]CAGTGACATCCTATTTGTT	TTCTCATGAGGACAGCACTCT	GCAACAAAATAGGATGTCACTG	19248	15
WIAF-2935	C/A	TTTTTTCCTAAGAGTAAA[C/A]AACAAAAATTATCCCTGGGA	GGATGGAAGAATGTACAGCTTAA	TTCCAGGGATAATTTTTGTT	19538	5
WIAF-2936	C/G	TAACCAATACCATCATTACA[C/G]TCAAGCCATAGAGATCTAAT	TGTTTAACCAATACCATCATTACA	AGATTCAACATTTCATTAGATCTCTATG	19255	4
WIAF-2937	A/G	GTTTTAAATGAGGGAGGAGG[A/G]CAATAACAGCAGCCATTTTCA	CAGTTTAAATGAGGGAGGAGG	TGTGAAATGGTGCTGTTATTG	19539	19
WIAF-2938	G/C	TCATTAATCAAACCCGACCA[G/C]AGTATAGCCAATATACAAAA	TCATTAATCAAACCCGACCA	CTCTCTTGATTTTGTATATTGGCT	19302	12
WIAF-294	T/C	TTGGTTATTTGACTCCAAAA[T/C]TGAATAAGTATTGGGGAAGA	GCTTGGTTATTTGACTCCAAAA	GGATTCTTCCCCAATACTTATTCA	2634	14
WIAF-2941	T/C	TGAGCCACCCAAGGCGATCA[T/C]AAAAGCCAAAGTTACAGATG	CCAGGAAAAATGAGCCACC	TCTTACATCGTAACTTTGGCTTTT	19303	5
WIAF-2943	A/G	ATAAACTCAATGATTTCACA[A/G]TATCTCAGCACTTTCCTCGA	CCTACTTTATAAACTCAATGATTTCACA	TGCAGGAAAGTGCTGAGATA	19540	5
WIAF-2945	T/C	TATTGAATATAAGTGCCATG[T/C]GACGTGGGAGCCTTCATTAA	AAAATTTATTGAATATAAGTGCCATG	TTAATGAAGGCTCCCAGT	19297	9
WIAF-2948	G/A	CCTTCCTGACTCAAGCCCAT[G/A]CTGAGTGCCTTCTCCTATGTA	CTTCCTGACTCAAGCCCAT	CAGAGTACATAGGAGAAGCACTCA	19541	5
WIAF-2949	T/C	ACTGAGTGTCCGATTTGTGC[T/C]TATGCAACTAAGTGAATGGAA	ACTGAGTGTCCGATTTGTGC	TTAAACCTTCCTATCAAGAGTTTCA	19542	15
WIAF-295	G/T	TTGGTGCCTGCACACCCACA[G/T]TGGCAACTAAGGTAATCTC	TGCCTGCACACCCACA	CCATATTTAGAGATTACACTTAGTTGCC	2635	14
WIAF-2950	G/T	CTTCTGCCAGTGACTGATG[G/T]TTCTATTTTCAGTTCCATGAA	CTTCTGCCAGTGACTGATG	AACCTTCATGAACTGAAAATAGA	19543	9
WIAF-2952	C/T	TCTGCCATGAACTTAGGAAT[C/T]TAATTAGCTCAAAGGTCAGA	TCTGCCATGAACTTAGGAAT	TGACTCTGACCTTTGAGCTAATT	19544	3
WIAF-2953	A/G	GACTAGTTTTTCTTAAAGGC[A/G]GTGCATTCCACTTTGTAATGA	GACTAGTTTTTCTTAAAGGC	TTATTTCATTACAAAGTGAATGCAC	19257	9
WIAF-2956	C/T	GGGAAACTTAATCTGTATGA[C/T]GGAAAAGAAGATAAGAAATAA	GGGAAACTTAATCTGTATGA	CCACATGAGAATTGTTTTTATTTCTT	19178	6
WIAF-2957	T/C	GTAGGAGAACTTTTTAGCAA[T/C]GGCCATCATGAGCTGTGTAA	GTAGGAGAACTTTTAGCAA	ACACAGCTCATGATGGCC	19545	10
WIAF-2963	T/C	GTGATCCCCTTCTTGAGATG[T/C]CTTCTCCAGACCCTCACGAG	GTGATCCCCTTCTTGAGATG	CTCTCGTAGGGTCTGAGAGAAG	19546	20
WIAF-2964	G/A	GAGGACACGTGGGTGGGAAC[G/A]GGTGAAGATTCTCTCTGCTC	GAGGACACGTGGGTGGGAAC	TGAGCAGAGAATTCTTCACC	19547	4
WIAF-2967	A/G	GAACAGTGCTGGAAATCCCC[A/G]AGACAGCTGGATAGACGCCC	GAACAGTGCTGGAAATCCCC	GGCGTCTATCCAGCTGTCT	19287	16
WIAF-2970	A/G	AGGGTCATTGCTTTCCAAGT[A/G]GCCTAAGATGAGAACAAACT	AGGGTCATTGCTTTCCAAGT	CTTCTCCCATGCATCTGATAC	19182	5
WIAF-2971	A/G	TGTGGCTTAGGAAAACTCAT[A/G]GCAGAGCAGCAGTGAGGCC	TGTGGCTTAGGAAAACTCAT	GGAATAGTTTGTTCTCATCTTAGGC	19160	18
WIAF-2975	T/C	CTTGAAAGAGTTTCTGACAC[T/C]ATATTTTAATTTCTATATGA	CTTGAAAGAGTTTCTGACAC	GCCTCACTGTCTGCTCTGC	19548	4
WIAF-2977	G/A	GAATGAAGAGTCAGGTCAGC[G/A]GGCAGGGATTGGGGGGGTGG	GAATGAAGAGTCAGGTCAGC	TCTTAGCATCATCGAGAGGTCATAT	19284	6
WIAF-2978	G/A	TTTATTCTTCAGGAGATCAG[G/A]TTCACATGCCACTCTCGTGA	TTTATTCTTCAGGAGATCAG	CCCCAATCCCTGCC	19218	4
WIAF-298	A/T	TCTCTTCTCCATAATCCCA[A/T]CTGAAGGTTCCACTTGTTTT	TCTCTTCTCCATAATCCCA	CACGAGAGTGGCATGTGAA	2123	1
WIAF-2980	T/C	GTACTGTGCTCCTCCGTGTA[T/C]CTCCCCGTGAGGCTGGGGTG	GTACTGTGCTCCTCCGTGTA	GAAAACAATGGGAAGCTTCAG	19321	8
WIAF-2983	A/G	CTACATCTGTTTAGCTGGATC[A/G]GTGAATAATAGAAATGTGATT	CTACATCTGTTTAGCTGGATC	CCAGCCTCACGGGGA	19338	11
WIAF-2984	G/C	TGGATTTAGCTGGAGTTGTG[G/C]GCCAGCTCTTCTACAGAATT	TGGATTTAGCTGGAGTTGTG	CTTTCAAAATCAATCACATTCTATTATT	19180	2
WIAF-2987	C/T	CGCAGAGGGAATTTTATGTT[C/T]AGAACAGGAAGACTGACCTG	CGCAGAGGGAATTTTATGTT	TCAATTCTGTAGAAGAGCTGGC	19164	6
WIAF-2989	G/A	GGAAGGAAGGAGGCTTGCTT[G/A]GGGTCTGCGATCTGTAAAGCAC	GGAAGGAAGGAGGCTTGCTT	GCTCTGAAGACCATGGAAATATC	19549	16
WIAF-2997	A/T	ACACATGTGCTCATCCACA[A/T]CAGCGAGGTATTTTGTGTA	ACACATGTGCTCATCCACA	TGTGCTTTACAGATCAGACCC	19267	5
WIAF-2999	T/C	TCCTGGGTAAGAGGAGGACAA[T/C]GATATTTCCATGGTCTTCAG	TCCTGGGTAAGAGGAGGACAA	CACTTTACACAAAATACCTCTGCTG	19179	5
WIAF-3000	A/G	TAATTTTTCTTTGAAATCAC[A/G]GAGCTCCAGTAACTGCCGGTC	TAATTTTCTTTGAAATCAC	GCTCTGAAGACCATGGAAATATC	19226	2
WIAF-3001	A/G	GTAATGCCATTTTAAACAT[A/G]TTCCATCCATCCCCTTTACTC	GTAATGCCATTTTAAACAT	CCGCAGTTACTGGAGCTC	19550	2
WIAF-3005	T/G	TCTGAGAAAGCAAGAAGAAG[T/G]TTAGGAAGGAGCGTGATTCAGA	TCTGAGAAAGCAAGAAGAAG	AGTAAAGGGGATGGCATCA	19332	9
WIAF-3006	T/C	AGACTTGACTTGCTTTGTTT[T/C]TTTTCCATTCGTCTCCCAAA	AGACTTGACTTGCTTTGTTT	TTTGGGAGACAGAATGGAAA	19327	11
WIAF-3007	T/C	ACCATTGGTTAGCTCTGACC[C/T]GATGCATGGACCTCCCTGGG	ACCATTGGTTAGCTCTGACC	CAGGGAGGTCCATGCATC	19447	3
WIAF-3008	G/A	TAGATTTTCTTTTTCTTGCCA[T/C]GAAAAATATATTCTCTAGCT	TAGATTTTCTTTTTCTTGCCA	GGCCAAGAGCTAGAGAATATATTTTT	19210	2
WIAF-301	A/T	TTCACATAGGAATGGCGTAA[A/T]TATACTTCTCTCGGGCTA	TTCACATAGGAATGGCGTAA	GGCTGATTGAGTTTGCGTAA	2126	11
WIAF-3012	C/T	TCTGAGAAAGCAAGAAGAAG[C/T]TGATGCCATCCCCTTACTC	TCTGAGAAAGCAAGAAGAAG	CAAGCACTGTACACAAAGCCT	19326	18
WIAF-3013	C/T	AGACTTGACTTGCTTTGTTT[C/T]TTTTCCATTCGTCTCCCAAA	AGACTTGACTTGCTTTGTTT	TCCTGATCAGCTCCTTCCTA	19551	18
WIAF-3015	C/T	ACCATTGGTTAGCTCTGACC[C/T]GATGCATGGACCTCCCTGGG	ACCATTGGTTAGCTCTGACC	GAGGATCTGCGGGGCC	19214	8
WIAF-3016	T/C	TAGATTTTCTTTTTCTTGCCA[T/C]GAAAAATATTCTCTAGCT	TAGATTTTCTTTTTCTTGCCA	GCCAAGAGACCAGATGTG	19329	11
WIAF-3019	G/C	TTCACATAGGAATGGCGTAA[G/C]TATACTTCTCTCGGGCTG	TTCACATAGGAATGGCGTAA	CCAGCCCCAGGATAGCGTAT	19341	4
WIAF-302	C/T	TGGCTTATATTCTATTTCTA[C/T]TTGACACAGTTCTTCAC	TGGCTTATATTCTATTTCTA	CAATTTTCAGATTGGTATTAGCGAAAC	19335	15
WIAF-3022	G/T	CCTGAAGATGATGAGCTCCTC[G/T]ATCACCTTCATCTTTGAAACC	CCTGAAGATGATGAGCTCCTC	GGGTTCAAAGATGAAGGTGA	19552	11
WIAF-3023	C/T	GCCTGGGCATTGAGTCCTGT[C/T]GTCTAGGCTTTGTGTACAGT	GCCTGGGCATTGAGTCCTGT	CAAGCACTGTACACAAAGCCT	19175	19
WIAF-3024	G/T	TAAAGAAATGAGGTTATAGAA[G/T]TTAGGAAGGAGCTGATCAGGA	TAAAGAAATGAGGTTATAGAA	TCCTGATCAGCTCCTTCCTA	19553	9
WIAF-3025	A/C	GGAGTTTGCCCCACCTGAAG[A/C]GGCGAACAGCATCCTCCCCTC	GGAGTTTGCCCCACCTGAAG	GAGGATCTGCGGGGCC	19168	10
WIAF-3029	C/T	CTGCAGCAGTCTTTAATAAA[C/T]CACATCCTGGTCCTCTGGCCA	CTGCAGCAGTCTTTAATAAA	GCCAGAGGACCAGATGTG	19554	10
WIAF-303	G/A	CATAGTATTTCCCAATTAGA[G/A]CCATGCATCATCTTTCAGAAAA	CATAGTATTTCCCAATTAGA	GCTTTTCTGAAAAATGACATGG	2127	10
WIAF-3030	A/G	AGAAATGAGGTGTGGCCCC[A/G]CCATTGGTTAGGCTATTCAC	AGAAATGAGGTGTGGCCCC	GGGCCTTCAAGCATGATC	19555	17
WIAF-3033	A/C	TGTGCTGGGTACTTAGGAAC[A/C]AACTGGGTATTCCCCA	TGTGCTGGGTACTTAGGAAC	GGGTGAATAGCCCCACAGTT	19276	8
WIAF-3035	G/A	AGGGATTTTCTGAGAAGCGGC[G/A]TGTGCCTGGTGTCCTCTGT	AGGGATTTTCTGAGAAGCGGC	GAGGGACCACCAGGCACA	19224	9

(Continued on following pages.)

TABLE 6-7. (Continued)

WIAF Name	Alleles	Allele A	Allele B	Chipregion	primer up	primer down	ncbi SS	NwLib chrom
WIAF-3036	G/T	G	T	TAATAAAGTGACCCGAGAT[G/T]TAGAGGGGCAGAAAAGTAT	AGATAATAAAGTGACCCGAGAT	TCATACTTTTCTGCCCCTCT	19556	9
WIAF-3038	C/T	C	T	GTGTCTTACTAGGCTCACAG[C/T]AAGGCAAAGCTGAATGTGAA	GATCAGTGTCTTACTAGGCTCACA	TTCACATTCAGCTTTGCCTT	19163	1
WIAF-3041	A/G	A	G	CCACAGTCGTCACATGATCA[A/G]TCCTGGTCTTTATACCATTA	GGAGCCTTAGTCGCCAC	GGAAGTAATGGTATAAAGACCAGGA	19228	20
WIAF-3042	C/T	C	T	TGGTACTTGAGAGTATCATC[C/T]GAAATATGTAGAAGAGAAAT	AAAGATGATGGTACTTGAGAGTATCA	GGGCTTATTTCTCTTCTACATATTTC	19313	1
WIAF-3046	A/G	A	G	AGGACTTGGAAATCACCAAC[A/G]ATGGTCATAATCACGGTTAG	CAGGACTTGGAAATCACCAA	TGCTAACCGTGATTATGACCA	19204	2
WIAF-3047	T/G	G	T	GTTCTACATATCACAGGAAG[T/G]CACTGCCAGGTCTTAGGCAG	CAGATATTGTTCTACATATCACAGGAAG	TGCCTAAGACCTGGCAGTG	19238	4
WIAF-3049	T/G	G	T	AGGGAGAGAAGGGGGTGGAAA[T/G]GAATTAAGTGTAGTCAAGGG	GGAGAGAAGGGGGTGGAAA	CATTTCCCTGACTACACATTAATTC	19244	12
WIAF-305	T/C	C	T	TGAACTGTCTAGCAGTATTA[T/C]GCTATTAGCTATGTTTACAA	GCATCATATGAACTGTCTAGCAGT	GGACAAATTGTAAACATAGCTAATAGC	2639	2
WIAF-3051	T/C	C	T	GAAGGTACTGGGGTCAATAC[T/C]GGAGATAGAATCAACCAAAC	GTGAAGGTACTGGGGTCAATAC	TGTACTTCAGTTTGGTTGATTCTATC	19557	17
WIAF-3053	T/C	C	T	CTTACCATCTAATTCAAAAA[T/C]GCACTTAAGTACATAGACCA	AAACACTCTTACCATCTAATTCAAAAA	TGTCACTGGTCTATGTACTTAAGTGC	19190	11
WIAF-3054	G/C	C	G	GAAAACTTACAAAGTATTTC[G/C]TTTATCACATGCCTATCTGT	CCGGTATGAAAACTTACAAAGTATTT	AAGATAACAGATAGGCATGTGATAAA	19211	8
WIAF-3055	T/C	C	T	GGGTTTGGCGTAGCGAAAGA[T/C]GAAAATATACACTAGATTGTT	GGTTTGGCGTAGCGAAAGA	GATCCATGAAAGTTAATAATTCTCTTATT	19298	11
WIAF-3058	T/G	G	T	TGTTTTGTGACTTAAGGAC[T/G]GTCATCAAGAAACCTTAAC	TGGTATGTTTTTGTGACTTAAGGA	CTGGTTAAGGTTCTCTTGATGAC	19232	10
WIAF-3059	C/T	C	T	TCATGCAAAATTCGAGATTA[C/T]TTTAATGTCTGTGACTTAGT	CTTCATTGCAAAATTCGAGATT	AAAATACACTAAGTCACAGACATTAAA	19299	11
WIAF-3063	C/A	A	C	ACTATCTGTCTGTTCCACTATTATTGTC[C/A]TTGGAAACAGGGCCTGAATT	ACTATCTGTCTGTTCCACTATTATTGTC	TCAGGCCCTGTTTCAA	19558	12
WIAF-3064	C/T	C	T	ACAGTCCAGATTTCCATAAC[C/T]GCTTTCTCTTACTAGGCGAA	CAAAACAGTCCAGATTTCCATAA	TCTTCGCCTAGTAGAGAAAGC	19559	X
WIAF-3065	A/G	A	G	TGAGTGTCCTTCACAAAGGC[A/G]CAGCTGTCTCCACAGCCCTG	TGAGTGTCCTTCACAAAGGC	GGGCTGTGGAGCAGCTG	19273	22
WIAF-3067	A/G	A	G	ATTTATTTAAGGTTCTATTT[A/G]CACTGGTCGGATATTACTGA	GACAACTATGTTTGATTTATTTTAAGGTTC	CCCCACAGTGTATTCAGTAA	19560	22
WIAF-3068	G/A	A	G	CACCTGAACAGCTCCTGGTC[G/A]TTCTGCAGACACAACTTTGA	ACCTGAACAGCTCCTGGTC	TCTCAAAGTTGTGTCTGCAGAA	19340	16
WIAF-3070	G/A	A	G	CCATTAGGGAAGGGCGATGC[G/A]GGGCAAGAAGGTAAAGG	AGGGAAGGGCGATGC	TCTGCCCTTTAACCTTCTTCTCT	19170	13
WIAF-3071	A/G	A	G	TGCAAGCCCCTCTGTCTTCC[A/G]GTAGCTTGTGATGAGCGGTC	CAAGCCCCTCTGTCTTCC	GACCCGTCATCACAAGCTAC	19239	11
WIAF-3072	G/A	A	G	CATCCCAGAATGCATTCTTGG[G/A]AAAGGATTATTCTTATTCAGGCT	TCCCAGAATGCATTCTTGG	GTCAAGCCTGATAAGATATCCTTT	19561	1
WIAF-3073	A/T	A	T	GGCCCTGGGCAGCTCTAAGG[A/T]AGTTTTGCTGGAGGAGGAGA	CCCTGGGCAGCTCTAAGG	CTCCTCCTCCAGCAAAACT	19562	17
WIAF-3074	T/A	A	T	TTTCAGGGACTAGGTTTTTG[T/A]GGTGTTCCCTGTTTGTCAAC	CGTTTCAGGGACTAGGTTTTTG	GTTGACAAACAGGGAACACC	19312	17
WIAF-3078	A/C	A	C	AAGACCTGAGCCAATAAGGA[A/C]CACCCCTCTTTGTGTTTAAT	AAAGACCTGAGCCAATAAGGA	CAATTAAACACAAAGAGGGGTG	19322	14
WIAF-308	G/C	C	G	CCTTAAAACAACTATCAACA[G/C]CTGCAACACAAACCACAGGC	AACAATCCTTAAAACAACTATCAACA	CCTGTGGTTTGTTGTTGCAG	2641	10
WIAF-3081	G/T	G	T	GGGGGAGGATTCATTCTCCAG[G/T]TTTTAAAAATAAACACGCTTA	GGGGAGGATTCATTCTCCAG	AGATAGTGTAAGCGTGTTATTTTTTAAAA	19563	6
WIAF-3084	T/G	G	T	TTTCTCTTACAAAGGTGACT[T/G]TGGATATCCCCTTCTAGCCA	CATGTTTTCTCTTACAAAGGTGAC	TGGCTAGAAGGGGATATCCA	19337	13
WIAF-3086	C/T	C	T	TATTCTTGCCCACAGAATGTC[C/T]ACCTGAAGGTGGGTAGTTGA	CTATTCTTGCCCACAGAATGTC	TCAACTACCCACCTTCAGT	19301	4
WIAF-3093	T/C	C	T	GGAATATAGAAGAAATTCAAGT[T/C]GCCCTCTTCTGAAGGAGGTC	AAAAGGAATATAGAAGAAATTCAAG	TGACTCTCCTTCGAAGAGGC	19448	9
WIAF-3095	G/A	A	G	TGCTCAAATTTCATTCATTTC[G/A]GAGACATTCTCCTAATTCAC	TCTTTGCTCAAATTTCATTCATTT	TATATGGTGATTAGGAGAGATGCTCTC	19316	1
WIAF-3096	T/A	A	T	TTCGCACTGCCTGCAGGTAC[T/A]GCTGCCACCTCACCCTCGAAT	CGCACTGCCTGCAGGTAC	TCAGAGGTGAGTGGCAGC	19285	13
WIAF-3097	G/A	A	G	AAGTTGGGTGGTGATTTAGCT[G/A]CAAGATCAGTTTCTCAAATG	TTTAAGTTGGGTGGTGATTTAGCT	TCTTATCATTTGAGAAAACTGATCTTG	19311	6
WIAF-3098	G/A	A	G	CCAACAGGTCCCTTCCACCC[G/A]CTGTGGCCTTGGCGTCCTTC	CAGGTCCCTTCCACCC	ACGCCAAGGCCACAG	19205	9
WIAF-310	C/T	C	T	TGTGGGCAGGGACTGTGTCT[C/T]GTTCCCTGTTGGGTCCCCGG	TGGGCAGGGACTGTGTC	GGGACCCAACAGGGAAC	2128	10
WIAF-3103	A/G	A	G	ATCAGACAGCAGGAAATA[A/G]GGAATAAGGAGGATATGTCA	TGATATCAGACAGCAGGAAATA	TGAGTGACATATCCTCCTTATTCC	19233	3
WIAF-3106	C/G	C	G	CACCACTTCAAATCACAAGA[C/G]TAGCTAACATATACTGAATG	CCACCACTTCAAATCACAAGA	TGTGATAAGCATTCAGTATATGTTAGC	19220	15
WIAF-3110	T/A	A	T	CCACCACGCAAATCATTCTA[T/A]TAACAATTCAAGCCAGGTGT	CCACCACGCAAATCATTCTA	GACACCTGGCTTGAATTGTT	19191	8
WIAF-3111	C/T	C	T	CAAGGTCATTTGACCTTCTC[C/T]AGGAGTCCGGAGTCTTTTAA	GGATTATTTGCTCATTTGACCTTCTC	AGTTCAAGGATAGTTTTATTCTTTAGAAGA	19564	15
WIAF-3112	T/C	C	T	CAGGACAGGTCCTGAGGGTC[T/C]TGTAGAGCTGAGCCTCTTTAA	GGACAGGTCCTGAGGGTC	CCTCTTAAAAGAGGCTCAGCTC	19234	3
WIAF-3114	G/A	A	G	CCTTGAAGAGCTCAATGAAT[G/A]CTGCCCACTAAGTGCCCTCA	GGAATCCTTGAAGAGCTCAA	GGGCACTTAGTGGGCAG	19221	15
WIAF-3118	C/G	C	G	AAGAGGGTGGTAAGAAGTTT[C/G]AGATTCTGCATATTTTGTTA	GCAGAAGAGGGTGGTAAGAAGTG	CATTCTATTAACAAAATATGCAGAATCT	19565	4
WIAF-3119	G/A	A	G	ACTGAAAAAAAAAAAATCCTATA[G/A]CATGTAAAAATCCTATA	CTGTTTTCAAGTGCATGACTGAA	AGTTTCCAAATACACAGATCAACTT	19566	12
WIAF-3120	T/A	A	T	GGAGGCATGACATCTATTA[T/A]TAAGTTGATCTGGTATTTG	TGTTGGAGGCATGACATCTATT	GACACGGCGGCAGCGAGGA	19286	18
WIAF-3122	G/A	A	G	CCTGGGTGTGTTCACTGC[G/A]TCCTCTGCTGCCCTGTCTTG	TGGGGTGTGTTCACTGC	GACAGGCGGCAGCGAGGA	19342	1
WIAF-3123	G/T	G	T	GTTGATAAGTTGTTCATAAA[G/T]CCAAATAAACCATGCCGCGAA	GGGGTTGATAAGTTGTTCATAAA	CGGGCATGTTTATTTGG	19567	7
WIAF-3124	A/C	A	C	TATAAGAAAAGCCTGGAATT[A/C]GATACTCTAAAATGTCAACA	TGTGTATTTTATGTATAAGAAAAGCCTG	CCTTAAAATAACTGTTGACATTTTTAGAG	19568	6
WIAF-3125	C/A	A	C	TTGGCCACTCCACTTAAACCT[C/A]TTCTGGGCTTCTTTGCTCATC	TGGCCACTCCACTTAAACCT	TGAGCAAAGAAGCCCAGA	19269	11
WIAF-3126	A/C	A	C	CTTTTTCAAAAATAATCTATT[A/C]GGCCGCGGGCGAGGTCGTCA	GGATATTGGCTTTTTCAAAA	CTCGTGATGCGCCCC	19192	15
WIAF-3129	G/T	G	T	GTAGCTACTATCTTTCTATA[G/T]ATTTTTACCTCCTGCCCATC	AGTTTGAGTGGTAGCTACTATCTTTCTA	TGGGGCAGGAGGTAAAT	19569	11
WIAF-313	C/T	C	T	ACTTTATGCCATGGCTGCTTT[C/T]AGTTTAATGCTGTGTCTCTG	ACTTTATGCCATGGCTGCTTT	TTTGAGAGTTTATCTGCAGAGGACA	2644	
WIAF-3130	T/C	C	T	CAGCAGGAGCACTCAACTT[T/C]CACTTGTTGCCCCGGTCAGT	GCAGCAGGAGCACTCAACTT	GAACGGGCAACAAGTG	19570	10

WIAF ID	SNP Sequence	Allele	A1	A2	Probe Sequence	Flank Sequence	ID	Chr
WIAF-3133	GCAGTCATCTTTCTCTGCA[T/A]AAATACCTATGCCTTTACAG	T/A	A	T	AGCAGTCATCTTTCTCTGCA	CACAGTCTGTAAAGGCATAGGTATTT	19571	5
WIAF-3136	GCCCGGTTCAGTAAAAGCAA[G/C]ATCCTAAATGAAAAACTGAC	G/C	C	G	CCCCGGTTCAGTAAAAGCAA	CGTTGGTCAGTTTTCATTTAGG	19572	10
WIAF-3137	TAGTTAGGGTGCCATTTACC[T/C]GAAGAGGTATCTGGGATTGT	T/C	C	T	CCTAGTTAGGGTGCCATTTACC	AGAACAATCCCAGATACCTCTTC	19188	5
WIAF-3139	GTCTCCCACTCTCCCA[C/A]AGACATCACTAGTCAAAGG	C/A	A	C	CCCTCCCACTCTCCCA	TTGGCTTTTGACTAGTGATGTC	19270	11
WIAF-314	TCTGCCCAATGCCTAGAATA[C/T]AGTAATACTATTAGGGACCCA	C/T	C	T	TCTGCCCAATGCCTAGAATA	GGAACTAATAACTATTAGGGACCCA	19262	9
WIAF-3140	AGTTGGCAGCAGTTGTAGAAC[T/G]TGGTATATGCATGTGCTTCT	T/G	G	T	ACTAGTGGCCAGCAGTTGTAGAAC	AGAGAAGCACATGCATATACCA	19261	12
WIAF-3143	TAAAGATGGGCAAAGAAATA[T/C]CAGGATAGTGCTGGTAATGG	T/C	C	T	GGGAAATAAAGATGGGCAAAG	TCCATTACCAGCACTATCCTG	19573	2
WIAF-3144	AAAGAAAGAACACATTTGT[A/G]TAAGTAAATGATTCCCAAAT	A/G	A	G	AAAGAAAGAACACATTTGT	AGTTGATATTTGGGAATCATTTACTT	19258	4
WIAF-3145	TTCTCCTATTTAAAAGCCA[C/G]ATAAATTTAAACATAAATAT	C/G	C	G	TTCTCCTATTTAAAAGCCA	GCTGTGTGGGGATATTTATGTTTAA	19319	X
WIAF-3148	CAGCTAGTGTAGGCATTTT[C/G]TGCTTTTCTAGTTGCTTTTT	C/G	C	G	CAGCTAGTGTAGGCATTTT	GCAGATATAAAAGCAACTAGAAAAGC	19574	6
WIAF-315	ATATATCAAGGTAAAGTCCA[A/G]TACAAAAAAACAGCATTTCC	A/G	A	G	ATATATCAAGGTAAAGTCCA	GCCATAGGAAATGCTGTTTT	2645	8
WIAF-3151	TAATGTTTAGTAGGCGTTAG[A/C]TCTCAGATTCTGAAGTTCAG	A/C	A	C	TAATGTTTAGTAGGCGTTAG	CCCTGAACTTCAGAATCTGAGA	19304	3
WIAF-3153	GTCCTTCCTCAGCAGCACTC[A/G]AGAGGAAACCCAGCAAGAAA	A/G	A	G	GTCCTTCCTCAGCAGCACTC	TTCTTGCTGGGTTTCCTCT	19208	9
WIAF-3156	ACCTATGTGGGGGAGTTTGGC[T/C]GATACGGTTTGGCTGGAGCCC	T/C	C	T	ACCTATGTGGGGGAGTTTGGC	GGGCCTCATAAAACCGTATC	19247	8
WIAF-3157	ATGTAATCAAGTTCCTTTAC[C/T]GGGCCTCGGAGGAGAAAATA	C/T	C	T	ATGTAATCAAGTTCCTTTAC	TCTCCTCCGAGAGCCC	19575	8
WIAF-3158	AAACTAAGATAAGATTCTAG[G/T]AAATGATTGCTGCTACCCAC	G/T	G	T	AAACTAAGATAAGATTCTAG	GTGGGTAGCAGCAATCATTT	19576	6
WIAF-316	GTCAGGGTAAAGCATTATGA[C/T]TTGAGCCAAACAGCAGTTTA	C/T	C	T	GTCAGGGTAAAGCATTATGA	GCAACTTTACCTCTTTGTCTTTG	2129	4
WIAF-3161	GAGCCTGTTTTCTAAAA[A/T]CATGCTTTGTCGTTATAA	T/C	C	T	GAGCCTGTTTTCTAAAA	AAACTGCTGTTTGGGTCAA	19165	6
WIAF-3164	CTAATCACTGGGAACAAA[G/C]AGTAACATTTTAGGTACTGT	A/T	A	T	CTAATCACTGGGAACAAA	CAGAATTATTCAAGAAAGCATCATG	19158	6
WIAF-3166	GACAATACAGCAAAATTGTT[C/A]CCCTTCACTGTTCAACAAA	G/C	C	G	GACAATACAGCAAAATTGTT	TGAAAATTCACAGTACCTAAAATGTT	19577	6
WIAF-3168	TAAAAAGATCTGCTTATCCT[A/G]TATATCCACATAACTCTAGT	C/A	A	C	TAAAAAGATCTGCTTATCCT	GATGGGTGCATATTTGTTGAA	19578	2
WIAF-317	ATGAAGTCACAGTAGAGCA[G/A]GACAAGGGGATAAAACCGTA	A/G	A	G	ATGAAGTCACAGTAGAGCA	AGAAACTTGCTAAATATTTATGTAACACT	2646	15
WIAF-3172	GTCTGCTCATCTCGTTGAGT[A/G]TGTAGGATGGATGCAGCTTC	G/A	A	G	GTCTGCTCATCTCGTTGAGT	CTACGGTTTATCCCCTTGTC	19579	
WIAF-3176	ATGAACTTGTCAAGTTTGAT[C/T]ATGTTGTCCCTTACCTTTAA	A/G	A	G	ATGAACTTGTCAAGTTTGAT	AAGCTGCATCCTCCTCACA	19580	3
WIAF-3178	ATTGAGCTAGAAGGAGTACA[G/A]CCCATTAGCAATCATTAACA	C/T	C	T	ATTGAGCTAGAAGGAGTACA	GAATTTAAAGGTAAGGGAACACA	19330	18
WIAF-3180	TGGACTTTTGTAGTTCATGA[A/G]TTTTGATTGTATTGTTACAA	G/A	A	G	TGGACTTTTGTAGTTCATGA	GGTGTTAATGATTGCTAATGGG	19195	18
WIAF-3184	ACATTGTCCAATTATGAAAT[A/G]TGAGGTGAGGCCTGAAATAC	A/G	A	G	ACATTGTCCAATTATGAAAT	TTGCTTTGTAACATACAATCAAAA	19196	14
WIAF-3185	GGACAATACAGCAAAATTGTT[T/C]GATAAGGCCACAGAAAATAC	A/G	A	G	GGACAATACAGCAAAATTGTT	GTATTTCAGGCTCCAACCTCA	19581	14
WIAF-3186	TACGAGGCAGGGCTAGACCC[G/A]GAAGCCTTGTCTGTGTGATT	T/C	C	T	TACGAGGCAGGGCTAGACCC	GGCATTTCTGTCTGGCCTTATC	19272	11
WIAF-3187	GAGAAACAGGTTGCACGAT[G/T]GTGGAGAAACAACAGGTTGC	G/A	A	G	GAGAAACAGGTTGCACGAT	GAATCACACAAGACAAGGCTTC	19582	7
WIAF-3188	CTCACTGAGGTGTTAAAAT[G/T]GAAACAGAATCAAGTAGCCA	G/T	G	T	CTCACTGAGGTGTTAAAAT	GCAACCTGTCTTTCTCCAC	19583	20
WIAF-3189	CTCGAGGTGTTTAAAAT[G/T]GTAAATGATTGCTTTTCC	G/T	G	T	CTCGAGGTGTTTAAAAT	CCATGCCAAGTTTATTCTGTTTC	19167	13
WIAF-3190	AAAAGGGAGTAATCTCAA[G/A]TCTAATGAAGGTCATGAGAAGC	G/A	A	G	AAAAGGGAGTAATCTCAA	CCACATTCCAAGTTTATTTATTACC	19254	6
WIAF-3191	GACAAAAGGAGTGTTTGGAA[G/T]GATGAAAAGGTCATGAGAAGC	G/T	G	T	GACAAAAGGAGTGTTTGGAA	GGCTTCTCATGACCTTTCATC	19584	7
WIAF-3194	TTGGTACATTTATTCTTAAATC[T/C]CTGCAATCTTTGAACCAGGTT	T/C	C	T	TTGGTACATTTATTCTTAAATC	AACCTGGTTCAAAGATGCAG	19339	17
WIAF-3197	GTCTCTGTATCCTGGGGAGT[A/G]GGATTTGCTGTTATCCTCAG	A/G	A	G	GTCTCTGTATCCTGGGGAGT	GCTGAGGATAAACAGCAAATCC	19235	5
WIAF-3198	AACTCCTAGTAATTCTCAA[G/C]AATCCAGCTCAAATGTGGCTT	G/C	C	G	AACTCCTAGTAATTCTCAA	GCCACATTTGAGCTGGAT	19585	5
WIAF-3199	CTCCTTTCCTCCCTTGCATC[T/G]ACCTTTGCTTGTCTCATC	T/G	G	T	CTCCTTTCCTCCCTTGCATC	TGATGAGACAACGAAAGG	19586	11
WIAF-3203	AATTAAGCCTCTTCAATAT[G/A]GGGAAAGTCAGAACACTGA	G/A	A	G	AATTAAGCCTCTTCAATAT	TCCAGTGTTCTGACTTTCCC	19587	18
WIAF-3204	TGGCTGGATACAAAGGTCTC[G/C]AAGGCCTAGACTTCCACAGT	G/C	C	G	TGGCTGGATACAAAGGTCTC	CACTGTGGAAGTCTAGGCCTT	19588	9
WIAF-3206	AGTGATGGTTCTGAGGAGTGC[T/C]CCTTGTATGGTGTTGAAG	T/C	C	T	AGTGATGGTTCTGAGGAGTGC	TTCTTCAACACCATACAAGG	19194	7
WIAF-3208	GATTGTTGAGGAGTGC[C/A]TTAGATTGTTCAGAGGTC	C/A	A	C	GATTGTTGAGGAGTGC	CAGTCCTTAGCATTCTCCAATATATATTT	19589	7
WIAF-3209	TAAAGAAAAGGGTGATTAG[T/G]TGTATCAAATGTTGCTAATC	T/G	G	T	TAAAGAAAAGGGTGATTAG	GCCTGATTAGCAACATTTGATACA	19309	5
WIAF-3210	AATGGCATCTGATTTCACAT[A/G]TTAGATATTAGACAATTGTGT	A/G	A	G	AATGGCATCTGATTTCACAT	AAAATTGTAGCATCACACAATGTC	19171	7
WIAF-3212	AGAAACCAGGTGAGTAAGGG[A/T]CAGGCTCCAGAGACTTCTGG	A/T	A	T	AGAAACCAGGTGAGTAAGGG	CCAGAGTCTCTGGAGCCT	19590	7
WIAF-3213	GGGTCCGCTGGCTGACTCAG[G/A]GAGGGCCCCGGCTCGGGTCTGC	G/A	A	G	GGGTCCGCTGGCTGACTCAG	CAGACCGAGCCGGC	19209	10
WIAF-3214	GTGAGATTTCATCAGCCTG[T/C]GGGTAAACATGGCTTTTGC	T/C	C	T	GTGAGATTTCATCAGCCTG	GCAAACAGCCATGTTTACCC	19181	1
WIAF-3215	TTCTTCCTTTACTAGGGCT[C/T]TAGTCCCCATAGTTTCTGAG	C/T	C	T	TTCTTCCTTTACTAGGGCT	AGAACTCAGAAACTATGGGGACT	19280	1
WIAF-3216	ACCCGGGTGTCTCATCCAGG[A/C]CTGGACACGTGGTGAGAGCT	A/C	A	C	ACCCGGGTGTCTCATCCAGG	GCTCTCACCACGGTCCAG	19200	2
WIAF-3218	AATGGACTTGGAGGTAGGAACA[G/A]TATAGCTTAACATAAGAGCA	G/A	A	G	AATGGACTTGGAGGTAGGAACA	GTACAAGTTCTGCTCTTATGTTAAGCTATA	19320	8
WIAF-3219	TTAAAGGACTTGCAGGCTC[G/A]CTACTTACTAGTAAGTGCTAA	G/A	A	G	TTAAAGGACTTGCAGGCTC	GGAATTCATTACTTTACTTAGTAAGTGCTAA	19202	6
WIAF-3220	TTGGGGTAAATGCTGTGGTT[A/G]AATATCAGTAGAGGAACTGG	A/G	A	G	TTGGGGTAAATGCTGTGGTT	GAAACCAGTTCCTCTCACTGATAT	19216	20
WIAF-3221	AGGAACTGGTTGCAGGGCTT[G/A]GAGGCTTTGCCAGGATGTTAG	G/A	A	G	AGGAACTGGTTGCAGGGCTT	CTAACATCCTGCCAAAGCCTC	19217	20
WIAF-3223	TTAAAGGGGATAACCCGGC[G/A]TACTTGGTGATTGTCGATC	G/A	A	G	TTAAAGGGGATAACCCGGC	TTTGATCAGCAATCACCAAGT	19591	2
WIAF-3224	GAATGAATGACATACAGGGAGCTAG[G/T]TTCTATTTCGAAAGAAAGGT	G/T	G	T	GAATGAATGACATACAGGGAGCTAG	ACTCAACCTTTCTTTTCGAAATAG	19305	2
WIAF-3225	TGGACTCTTACATTCCTTCA[T/C]GTACACTGCTATTAAATGAG	T/C	C	T	TGGACTCTTACATTCCTTCA	CATGGCTCATTTAATAGCAGTG	19592	4

(Continued on following pages.)

TABLE 6-7. (Continued)

WIAF Name	Alleles	Allele A	Allele B	Chipregion	primer up	primer down	ncbi SS	NwLib chrom
WIAF-3227	A/G	A	G	GGTTGCAACTTGGCAGCATC[A/G]CCTTCCAAACAAGAAACAAT	TGCAACTTGGCAGCATC	CAATTGTTTCTTGTTTGGAAGG	19593	14
WIAF-3228	G/C	C	G	GAGTAAGTTTGACACAGTTT[G/C]ACTTTAACATGTCAGTGAAA	AGGTTGAGTAAGTTTGACACAGTTT	CCTTCAACTTTCCACTGACATGTT	19306	2
WIAF-3231	T/C	C	T	CTGTTGTCCTATAGAGAGTCA[T/C]GGTCCCATCCCTGGAACCA	TTGTTCTGTGTCCTATAGAGAGTCA	CCAGGGGATGGGACC	19594	8
WIAF-3232	G/A	A	G	ATCAGATTTTACGTGTAGCA[G/A]AGCCACAGATGTGATGATGG	AATTCAATCAGATTTTACGTGTAGC	CCATCATCACATCTGTGGCT	19333	1
WIAF-3233	C/G	C	G	TGAAGCAACATAAGCCAAAT[C/G]TTTGTGTTTATCTTACACGA	CTGAAGCAACATAAGCCAAAT	TCTCTTTCGTGTAAGATAAACACAAA	19153	1
WIAF-3235	C/A	A	C	GAACACAGCTTCTTACTACAA[C/A]CTGTACAGCCAGCCTCAT	TGGAGAACAAGCTTCTTACTACAA	TGAGGCTGGTGCTGTACA	19595	3
WIAF-3236	G/C	C	G	AGCACATGTCTTAAAGCTTC[G/C]TCTCTGAGTAGGATCTCTGT	GCAGCACATGTCTTAAAGCTTC	CCCACACAGTCTACTACCAGAG	19596	11
WIAF-3237	C/T	C	T	ATTAATTATCTCTAAGCTTC[C/T]TTAAATTCCTAAGATTTTAA	GAGATTGGATTAATTATCTCTAAGCTTC	ACAGAGAATATTTTAAAATCTTAGGAATTT	19597	14
WIAF-3238	T/C	C	T	GTCATCGCTGTCACAGAGCT[T/C]GCAATCTGTCTGTCTCCGCT	TCATCGCGTCACAGAGCT	TGATGTATAATAGCGGGACAGACAGAC	19174	7
WIAF-3241	C/A	A	C	TACAAAGAATTCAGACGA[C/A]ATCAGCAAGATGTGGGATA	TACAAAGAATTCAGACGA	TCCCACCATCTTGCTGAT	19242	
WIAF-3245	G/A	A	G	TCTATCCTCAAGCCTAGGG[G/A]TGGTGAAAATTTCATCACTA	CTCTATCCTCAAGCCTAGGG	CCCTGTTGTAGTGATGAAATTTTC	19598	6
WIAF-3246	T/G	G	T	TAGACAAACTGAAATGCACT[T/G]AAATAAATGGATGAAGGAAGT	CAATTTAGACAAACTGAAATGCACT	AGAAACTTATACTTCCTCATCCATTT	19189	5
WIAF-3247	C/G	C	G	TGGTGGCGTGCTGCCTGA[C/G]GACAGCTGGGTATGACTCTC	GGGCTGTGCTGCCTGA	GAGAGAGTCATACCCAGCTGTC	19599	1
WIAF-3249	C/T	C	T	ATGATGCAAACTAGTGACCA[C/T]CACTTACTCCTTTCTGTACC	CATGATGCAAACTAGTGACCA	CGTGGTACAGAAAGGAGTAAGTG	19600	14
WIAF-3250	C/T	C	T	TCCAAGCCAGCTGACCA[C/T]GTCAAAAAAGAAGGCGTGTG	GACTCACCCACCATCAGTAGACC	AAACCACGACCCTTCTTTTT	1347	2
WIAF-3253	G/A	A	G	TTCCAAGCCAGCTGCCTGA[G/A]TATCACTTAAACCTAGAGTG	TTCCAAGCCAGCTGCCTGA	TTTGGATGATAAATTGTACAGTCAC	1350	8
WIAF-3256	T/G	G	T	GGTTCCCGGAAGAAAAATTT[T/G]AAGCACATGGGTTAATGCA	GGTTCCCGGAAGAAAAATTT	CTGCATTAACCCATGTGTCTT	1353	4
WIAF-3257	T/C	C	T	GTTGTAAGCAGTTATTTTTT[T/C]TGGGGACTGTTCTGTCTGA	CCCTCGTTGTAAGCAGTTATTTTTT	CCAGACAGAACAGTCCCCA	1354	4
WIAF-3260	A/T	A	T	TAGAACCAGAGAGGACAATG[A/T]TTCTTGATTCCCAGGTTTCCC	CAATATCTTATTAAAAGGCCCG	GAAACCCGGGAATCAAGA	1357	X
WIAF-3262	C/T	C	T	ATCTTATTAAAAGGCCCGTA[C/T]TGAAAGAAGAAATCAGTAAAC	CAATATCTTATTAAAAGGCCCG	AAGAAGAGTTTACTGATTCTTCTTTCA	1359	5
WIAF-3263	G/A	A	G	TGTGCCAGATGCCTTCAAGG[G/A]TGACTAGATTGCCCATTTGA	GCCAGATGCCTTCAAGG	TTCAAATGGGCAATCTAGTCA	1360	1
WIAF-3265	G/C	C	G	CTGGATTGGCTTCGTTATTT[G/C]GTGGCCTGGCAACCTGTGGT	CCTGGATTGGCTTCGTTATT	CAGGTTGCCAGGCCAC	1362	4
WIAF-3268	A/T	A	T	ACTCTCCTTACCTAGGGTA[A/T]GTCAATGCGAGCTGAGTTGC	CACTCCTGCCAGCTGAAAGG	CAACTCAGCTCGCATTGAC	1365	13
WIAF-3270	C/T	C	T	ATCTCCTTACCTAGGGTA[C/T]GTTGCTTTCCAAACCAAGAG	CAGAAATCTCCTTACCTAGGG	CTCTTGGTTTGGAAAGCAAC	1367	16
WIAF-3271	T/C	C	T	GTATCAATGAAATAGCTGATA[T/C]GCATTGTTGGGAGAATCATT	CCACTCTAAGTATCAATGAAATAGCTGA	AATGATTCTCCCAACAATGC	1368	2
WIAF-3272	G/A	A	G	TGAGTTTGAGAGCAGAGTGC[G/A]TGGTATTTTTCTGGGCTTAA	CTGAGTTTGAGAGCAGAGTGC	CCTTAAGCCCAGAAAAATACCA	1369	1
WIAF-3276	G/A	A	G	AAAACCCACACATGGGAGA[G/A]CCTCGGTAGGGAACCCAGCC	AAACCCACACATGGGAGA	TGGGTTCCCTACCGAGG	19201	19
WIAF-3277	A/G	A	G	AACTCTCTGTCCACTGGAGA[A/G]AAGTGCTTGCCACAGAAAAC	CCGAACTCTCTGTCCACTGG	TTTTCTGTGGCAAGCACTT	1373	6
WIAF-3279	A/C	A	C	CAAATAAAGTGGGCAGCCTG[A/C]GACCTGGCCTATGACCTAGGG	AAATAAAGTGGGCAGCCTG	CCCTAGGTCATAGCCCAGTC	1375	8
WIAF-3280	C/T	C	T	CATCAGAAAATCCATACTGG[C/T]GAGAAACCTTATGAATGTAA	CAACATCAGAAAATCCATACTGG	ACATTCTTTACATTCATAAGGTTTCTC	1376	19
WIAF-3281	T/C	C	T	TGAGAGTTGTTATCCATGGA[T/C]CAGAAAAGAGCTCCCATGAA	AAGTGAGAGTTGTTATCCATGGA	TTCATGGAGCTCTTTTCTG	1377	10
WIAF-3283	G/A	A	G	AGGTAGAAGCGGGTCTCC[G/A]AACCTAGGGTAATCTGGGCT	GGTAGAAGCGGGTCTCC	AAGCCCAGATTACCCTAGGTT	1379	14
WIAF-3285	C/T	C	T	AAAAAAGCTTCTCAGGTGAT[C/T]CTAAAGTATAACTAGATTTG	AAAAAGCTTCTCAGGTGAT	TCTTCTGGTTCTCAAATCTAGTTATACTT	1381	7
WIAF-3287	C/T	C	T	CTTCTATGATGACTATGAT[C/T]TTATCCATGGGAAGCTTAGT	GATTGACCCTATGATGACTATGTAT	AACTAAGCTTCCCATGGAT	1382	15
WIAF-3289	A/G	A	G	CAATGAAAAGGGCTGAGGAA[A/G]TCCTCCAAAATGTGGAGACA	AATGAAAAGGGCTGAGGAA	TGTCTCCACATTTTGGAGGA	1384	2
WIAF-3291	C/A	A	C	TGTCCACATCATTCCATCTG[C/A]ATCGTCTTCCTACAAACAGT	TGTCCACATCATTCCATCTG	AAAAACTGTTTGTAGGAAGACGA	1386	11
WIAF-3292	T/C	C	T	AAGCACATTAAATTAATTCA[T/C]GAGTGAACATACAAGTATGA	GAAAATGTAAGCACATTAAATTAATTCA	GCATAGCTGTGATCATACTTGTATG	1387	7
WIAF-3293	T/C	C	T	AAGATATATTTTCCAAAACC[T/C]GAAAGAGGATAAATGGATGA	CGCAAAGATATATTTTCCAAAACC	TGAGAAATCATCCATTTATCCTC	1388	1
WIAF-3294	A/G	A	G	TTTCTGAATATTTTAAAGAA[A/G]TACTGTCCTCCTTATGCTC	GCTCCTTTTCTGAATATTTTAAAGAA	AGTTAGAGCATAAGGAGGCAAGT	1389	10
WIAF-3296	T/C	C	T	TTTTGCCATTGCAGTGGACA[T/C]TTCTAAAAGCAAATGCCTA	TGCCATTGCAGTGGACA	CCATAGGCATTTGCTTTTTGAA	1391	12
WIAF-3297	T/C	C	T	ACCCTATAGCGAGACATTTG[T/C]ATTGAGTGGCACGTGGGCTG	CCAACCCTATAGCGAGACATTTG	CCCACGTGCCACTCAAT	1392	11
WIAF-3299	C/A	A	C	TGATAATCCCTCATGGAACC[C/A]AATTTCTGTATTTTAAAAC	TGATAATCCCTCATGGAACC	AAGGTGCGGTTTTAAAATACAG	1394	10
WIAF-3300	G/C	C	G	TACAGAAAGAAATTTTAGA[G/C]TAAACTTTGGAACTTTGGATA	CAAATGGTAAATTCACGAAAGAA	TCTAGTTATATCCAAAGTTCCAAGTTT	1395	3
WIAF-3302	G/C	C	G	TTTTCTGCACTGTAGGCACA[G/C]TCTCTCAAGCATATCCTGAT	TTTTCTGCACTGTAGGCACA	TGATCAGGATATGCTTGAGAGA	1397	12
WIAF-3305	G/A	A	G	AGCCGGGCGCGGTGGATTCT[G/A]CCACACGCCACGCTCTACTA	GGGCGCGGTGGATTCT	AGAGCGTGGCGTGTGG	1399	17
WIAF-3307	A/G	A	G	TATTTAAAAACTTGTTAAGA[A/G]GTACAAGCCAGTCTTCTGCT	GAGGTCCACATATTTAAAAACTTGTT	CAGCAGAAGACTGGCTTGTAC	19245	13
WIAF-3308	A/G	A	G	CTTCAAAGAAAATAGGCCTA[A/G]AACAGCTATCAAATCAAAC	CTTCAAAGAAAATAGGCCTA	GGATTTGGATTTGATAGCTGT	19246	13
WIAF-331	C/T	C	T	CATAGATTTTTATGGACTA[C/T]GTGGGCCATGAAATTTCGTTG	GGTTTGACCTGCATAGATTTTT	GGAATGGCCATGGCCAC	2657	18
WIAF-3310	G/A	A	G	CAGGGCCCGGCAGCCGGGGTC[G/A]TGGGAGCTGGAGGTGTCACGG	TGTTGGACATGCAGGCC	GGAAACCCAGCTCCCA	19172	9
WIAF-3312	G/A	A	G	CAAGGAAGAACAATAAAGTC[G/A]TAGGTTCAAATGTAAGAAGC	GGTAACCAAGGAAGAACAATAAAGTC	CATTGCTTCTTACATTTGAACCT	19601	6
WIAF-3321	T/A	A	T	CCCTAGTACTTGGGCCCTCA[T/A]CCTTCTCGTAGTACCTCTTG	CCTGGCTTTTGTTTTAGACCCT	CGCAAGAGGTACTACGAGAAGG	1401	7
WIAF-3323	G/A	A	G	ATCCCCATTCTGAAAGACCG[G/A]GAGCCTGGAGGTGTCACCC	CCCCATTCTGAAAGACCG	TCACACCTCCCAGGCTC	1403	9

WIAF ID	Alleles	A1	A2	Sequence (with [SNP])	Flanking read	ID	n
WIAF-3324	A/G	A	G	TTACCTAGCAGAACATCCCC[A/G]TGGTTTGGGTGATTCTGAAT	GCTAATTACCTAGCAGAACATCCC	1404	16
WIAF-3325	C/T	C	T	TCTTACTTTATAAGGAATAA[C/T]TGTATGAATCAATAAAAGAAGA	AGGAAAACAAAGTTCTTACTTTATAAGG	1405	9
WIAF-3328	T/C	A	C	TTAAAAATATAATCTGGGTT[T/C]GGCTTAAGTATIAGTGGGCC	AACAATGTTTAAAAATATAATCTGGGTT	19602	6
WIAF-3330	G/A	A	G	TAGAAAGAAACACACTTTAA[G/A]AAATCAAAATTCAATTCA	AGCAATTAGAAAGAAACACACTTTAA	1409	12
WIAF-3336	T/C	C	T	GCATAGACTGTCTTATTTAT[T/C]GAAATACTCACAGAATGTAT	TGAGGGCATAGACTGTCTTATTT	19256	10
WIAF-3338	C/T	C	T	CATATGGTCCACTTGATAGA[C/T]GTTCAGGAGGAAGAAATGC	AATTTCATATGGTCCACTTGATAGA	19271	2
WIAF-3339	A/G	A	G	TGAAGATACTTTATCTTAGG[A/G]TGACCTCTGTCTTTCCAC	CAGTGGAAAGAGACAGAGGTCA	19184	5
WIAF-3340	T/C	C	T	AAAATGCATTATGTCTAATA[C/T]TTCATGTCAAACAGCAGTAG	TGTCTACTGCTGTTTGACATGAA	19603	13
WIAF-3341	T/C	C	T	TGAAGCTATGAAGACTGGGG[T/C]GTAGTGTCCACCTTGCTGGATC	TCCAGCAAGGTGGACATC	19241	8
WIAF-3342	A/G	A	G	TGAGTGTCTTCCTAGAGTCC[A/G]TGGCTTTGGGTGTGAGAG	AAACTGAGTGTCTTCCTAGAGTCC	1415	5
WIAF-3343	T/C	C	T	ATTGAATCTACAGCAAATCA[T/C]GATAATTTATTCCAAAAGTG	CATCATCACTTTTGGAATAAATTATC	1416	17
WIAF-3344	C/T	C	T	CTCTCAGGCTAGAGAGG[C/T]GGGAATTTTATTTATTTTG	AGGGAGCAGTGAACAAAATAA	1417	6
WIAF-3345	C/G	C	G	GGGAATTGCTCTCCTCTATT[C/G]AGATCTTGTGATTCTGCTATT	TGCACCAGAATCACAAGATCT	1418	8
WIAF-3346	C/T	C	T	GCACCTTGCTCCACTTCTGG[C/T]TAATCATCACACTCTATCTG	TTCTGCAGATAGAGTGTGATGATT	1419	8
WIAF-3348	G/A	A	G	AGGGAGAGGGTGGCATGCTG[G/A]AGCCCATGCTCGGTCACGATG	CGTGACCAGCATGGGC	1420	2
WIAF-3354	T/C	G	T	GCAGAGAAACGGAGTAACT[T/C]CAAGGCGCCATCCATCCTCT	TCAGCTCACCCCAGGG	1426	6
WIAF-3355	T/G	C	T	TAATAACCCTTAAACTCCAT[T/G]GTCTTCTTCTTATACACCACT	ATGGATGGCGCCTTG	1427	6
WIAF-3358	T/C	C	T	TTGAGTATTCTTGCTTTGAT[T/C]GTCTACGTAAGCATGTAAGA	GAGGAGTGTGTTATAGAAGAGAGC	1430	9
WIAF-336	T/C	C	T	CAGATGGCCATTAGAAGTTA[T/C]TAAACAAATATTTCTCCCAA	GTTGTAGTCTTACATGCTTACGTAGAC	2660	15
WIAF-3361	T/C	C	T	CAAGCATGTGACAGTCTGAG[G/T]TTCCCTCCAAGAGCCAGGGGA	CTTTGAGTTTTGGGAGAAATATT	1433	4
WIAF-3365	G/T	G	T	GATTTCACTGAGGAGCTGA[C/A]TTGGTGAGAGACTGTACTCC	CTGGCTCTTGGAGGGA	19604	1
WIAF-3367	C/A	C	C	TCTTCTAATTTAAGTGAGA[A/C]TCTTTTAAACACCTGTTAAA	GGAGTTCACTGAGGAGCTGA	1438	13
WIAF-337	A/C	A	C	ATCTTCTAGGTCTTTCCCCA[C/A]TTGGTGAGAGACCTGTTAAA	GCTACATTAAATTTAACAGGTGTTTAAAA	2661	2
WIAF-3372	C/T	C	T	TGTCATTTCTGCTCACACTT[A/G]CCTCACTTATTAAATGGTAA	TGCACCTGTTACATGACACAC	19288	4
WIAF-3380	A/G	A	G	TGCATGACAATGGAATGTCT[C/G]TTTAGTTACTTAGGTCTA	GCCCTTACCATTAATAAGTGAGG	1449	3
WIAF-3383	C/G	C	G	CCATTCTCTCGCCCTAATCTC[C/T]TCAAGAGGCATTTCAAC	GAGAGAGAAAGTGAGACCTAAGGTAAC	19605	14
WIAF-3384	C/T	C	T	AATCTCTAGGGGAACCCTCA[C/A]AACACTACTGGGAGGAAATGTA	GCAGCTTTTCATTCAGCTGA	1451	13
WIAF-3385	C/A	C	A	TTTCTTAACAGCTTTAAAAT[T/G]CAGTATTTTATTTTATTAACA	GGGAAACCTCCATACTGCTC	1452	3
WIAF-3386	T/G	G	T	CTTAACCTTTAGTTGTTGAA[C/T]GCCTACTTCGAGTAAGAGAT	TCTAGCGGCCATTTAATGTTAATAAATAAA	1453	13
WIAF-3387	C/T	C	T	GACCAGCTGTCAATTGACA[G/A]TCATCCTGCAGGGGATCTG	CACAATCTCTTACCTTAACCTTTAGTTGTTGA	1454	3
WIAF-3390	G/A	A	G	ACTGTCCCATGCTTGGTCACA[G/A]TGGATAGAACTTAGGGAGTT	CCCCTGCCAGGATGA	1457	7
WIAF-3392	G/A	A	G	CAGGTTTGAAATTCTTGGTT[G/T]GAGTTTCCTCTTCAAGAATG	TCAGAACTCCCTAAGTTCTATCCA	19219	19
WIAF-3393	G/T	G	T	CCCTTTGTACCTGAATGTGCC[G/A]TTTCCTCCTAGGCTGCCTTTA	ATTTTCATTCATTCTTGAAGAGGA	1459	19
WIAF-3394	G/A	A	G	GCATGGTGGTCCGTCAGC[G/A]TTTATGTCACACTCATTCAAT	CCTTAAAGGCAGCGCCTAGAGGA	1460	10
WIAF-3396	T/C	C	T	GCATGGTGGTCCGTCAGC[T/C]CTGACTCCTGTTTCCCACTC	GAGTGGGAAACAGGAGTCAG	1462	5
WIAF-3402	C/G	C	G	GCATGGTGGTCCCAGCCCTTC[C/G]AGCCGGACGCAGTTCACAGT	TTTAAAAATGTTATAGGCCACTCTAAGTTT	1467	3
WIAF-3404	A/G	A	G	GCTTCCAGCCCCAGCCCTTC[A/G]AGCCGGACGCAGTTCACAGT	AAAAGAAGAAAGGTATAGGTACAAAAAGT	19294	8
WIAF-3407	C/A	A	A	AGTTCTTCTTGGTGTCTAAT[C/A]TAACTCTTTCTTGCTATTGC	AAGGGAATCAAAATCAGAAGG	2664	17
WIAF-341	G/C	C	G	CCATGTTCTTCACTCATCA[G/C]CCTTCTGATTTTGATTCCCT	GCCATTGAATGAGTGTGACA	1473	1
WIAF-3410	G/A	A	G	CAGGGAAAATGGTAAATCA[G/A]TTATGTCACACTCATTCAAT	CCTGGGATGTTTAATGCAAAC	1475	4
WIAF-3412	C/T	C	T	CTGGGATGTTTAATGCAAAC[C/T]GTACATTCTCAGCAGGAC	GCAGAAGGTCATTTCAGTTTTT	1477	8
WIAF-3415	A/G	A	G	AAAGGAGATCCAACATTAGG[A/G]CTAATAAAAACTGAAATGACC	CAGGGCACCACGCTG	19237	16
WIAF-3416	A/G	A	G	CAAGGAGATGGACCCTCCTCC[A/G]CAGCGTGGTGCCCTGCCCTCG	TGGAAGTTCTTCTTGGTGTCTTCTAA	1479	19
WIAF-3418	T/C	C	T	GAGGTTGAACTGGGGACCAA[T/C]TGCTTGGCTGGCAAGGAAGTA	GCCATGTTCTTCACTCATCA	1481	16
WIAF-3420	A/G	A	G	AAGGTCGAGACTGGGGACCGG[A/G]GCTAAATCATCAGGAGTGGA	AGGGAATCAAAATCAGAAGG	1482	3
WIAF-3421	C/T	C	G	CTTGTGCTCAGCTTATGCCC[C/T]GCATTTATAAAAGAGATTGTC	TGTGTGCTCTGCTGAGAATGT	1483	1
WIAF-3422	G/A	C	T	AGTGAAAAGACAACCAATCC[G/A]CTGAAATAAGAGAGACTATTT	AGGAAAGAAATCTCTTTATAAATGC	1486	2
WIAF-3425	T/C	G	A	CTTTCCTAACCATTCGAGGG[T/C]TTTGTGCCATTTCCCAAAGGA	GTCCCTAATCAGATCTATAAATTTGTAAATA	2665	2
WIAF-343	G/C	C	G	TCCCATGCTTGGATGTCACA[G/C]TTATGTCAAGTTAATATAAA	CCTTTGGGAAATGGACAAA	1491	6
WIAF-3430	G/A	A	G	TAATAAGTGCATGTTGCCAT[G/A]TCTGTGGCATGTGTCGTGT	CACACACTTGCATGTCACA	1498	6
WIAF-3437	G/A	A	G	AAACAAAACAATATAAAGTC[G/A]TAAGAGATAAACCCTGATAGG	AAAATAATAAGTGCATGTGTGCAT	1503	3
WIAF-3442	G/T	A	T	CAGAGGCCAAAGTCTGGGGG[G/T]TTAGAAAGAAGGAAGCTTGAC	GGGTCAAGCTTCCTTCTTTCT	1504	1
WIAF-3443	G/T	C	T	AAGGTCGAGACTGGGGACCGG[G/T]ACCTATTATATACAGTTATAC	GGCCCAAAGTCTGGGGG	1505	2
WIAF-3444	G/A	A	G	CAATACCTTTATGCCC[G/A]CAGCCTGTGAGGATTTCA	CCAAGGCCTGACTGTATATAC	1510	2
WIAF-3449	T/C	C	T	AGCTGCCTGGGTTCTTGAGT[T/C]TGAATCCGTCTTAAAGG	TGTGTTATAACCTTACCATGCAGGCTG	1513	6
WIAF-3452	T/C	C	T	ATTAAAAACAAGGTATGGGA[T/C]GCCTGATAAACACTACAACTT	AAAAGAAGTTGTAGTGTTATCAGGC		

(Continued on following pages.)

TABLE 6-7. (Continued)

WIAF Name	Alleles	Allele A	Allele B	Chipregion	primer up	primer down	ncbi SS	NwLib chrom
WIAF-3455	T/G	G	T	CACTTTGAAGCAACCAGATG[T/G]GATGAGGACTCAATATCAGG	CACCACACTTTGAAGCAA	TCTCCTGATATTGAGTCCTCATC	1516	3
WIAF-3459	C/T	C	T	ACCACTCTGGCCCTTTTGAA[C/T]GAACTTGGTCTGTGCAATCT	CACTCTGGCCCTTTTGA	GAGATTGCACAGACCAAGTTC	1520	4
WIAF-3460	C/T	C	T	CTCATGACATTATAATGGAG[C/T]TTGAAAAATTGCTATTGGCAG	CCATGATGTCTCATGACATT	GAACTGCCAATAGCAATTTTC	1521	1
WIAF-3462	A/G	A	G	CCTTGCTATGAAGCGGAAAT[A/G]AAATTAGGGTTCTGTTGGCA	CCTTGCTATGAAGCGGAAAT	TGCCAACAGAACCCTAATT	1523	2
WIAF-3464	C/G	C	G	GCATCCATTCCTGCGCCTTT[C/G]GTGCTCCTGTATGTGGAAGT	CATCCATTCCTGCGCCTTT		1525	5
WIAF-3467	G/T	G	T	GGGCTCCTTACTTGTATTCT[G/T]TTATCAGCTGATTTTGAAAC	AATATGGGGTCCTTACTTGTTATTCT	ATTATTATIGTTCAAAATCAGCTGATA	1528	6
WIAF-3468	G/T	G	T	TCAGATGCAGAAGACGTACA[G/T]GATCCCATTTATTTAAAGCA	TGTGAGATGCAGAAGACGTACA	AGTTTGCTTTAAATAAATGGGATC	1529	2
WIAF-3469	G/C	C	G	AGAAACATAGGGAAATGATT[G/C]AGAGAGATAATAGAAGAGAA	GGTGATAGAAACATAGGGAAATGAT	TGTAATACTCATTTCCACTTTCTTTC	1530	10
WIAF-3472	G/A	A	G	TCTCTAAAGATGGCTCTTAT[G/A]TTTGAGGAAACTGAGACTCA	GAACAATTCTCTAAAGATGGCTCTT	GCAAGTAAACCTCTTGAGTCTCA	1533	9
WIAF-3473	C/A	A	C	AGACCACCAGATATCATGAG[C/A]CCCCTGGCAGAAATGCATGC	CAAAGACACCACCAGATATCATG	GCATTTCTGCCAGGGG	1534	2
WIAF-3474	G/C	C	G	TCACTTTGCCATCTTATCT[G/C]TTTAAAACTCTTGGGGAAAA	CAGTCACTTTGCCATCTTATCT	CCTTTCTTTCTTTTCTTGAAAGAG	1535	6
WIAF-3477	T/G	G	T	CGTACACTGTACCACCAAA[T/G]GTTGCAACACCGAGATGGGG	TCTCACTGTGTTTAAGAGACG	CCCCAACGATGCAAC	1538	9
WIAF-3479	C/A	A	C	GGGTGGTGGAGCTCCAGGGG[C/A]CTGCCCATGAAAGGGCTGGG	GCTGAGCTGCAAGCAGAC	CCATCTCGGTGCGTGG	1540	21
WIAF-3483	G/C	C	G	CTGGTGTGAATGATTCTCAG[G/C]TTCAGGATTTCACGAAGCTGT	GGTGGAGCTCCAGGG	GCCCTTTCATGGGCAG	1544	11
WIAF-3485	T/C	C	T	ACATGAAGGTATGCATAAAC[T/C]GTCTTCACATTTAATTTTGT	GCACATGAAGGTATGCATAAAC	CAGCTTCGTGAAATCCTGA	1546	6
WIAF-3486	T/G	G	T	TCTCTCTTTGTCCATGGCTT[T/C]CTGAGAATTCAGTGTCCTCGA	TCTCTCTTTGTCCATGGCTT	CGAATCATACAAAATTAAATGTGAAGA	1547	21
WIAF-3492	T/C	C	T	TGCCAAAATTCTCTAGAAGA[A/C]AGAATTATTATGGCTTCCCA	TTTTGCCAAAATTCTCTAGAAGA	CATCGAGGACACTGAATCTCAG	1553	11
WIAF-3494	A/C	A	C	ATGGATGGAACATTAACTGA[T/C]GTTTTGTTGTGTGGTAGGAA	GCATGGATGGAACATTAACTGA	GAGTTACTGGGAAGCCATAATAAT	1555	16
WIAF-3496	T/C	C	T	AGGAGAGGTAGGTTAGGGA[A/G]AAGACTGAGCTCATTAAAGT	AATAGTAGGAGAGGTAGGTTAGGGA	TTCCTACGGCACAACACAAAC	1557	21
WIAF-3497	A/G	A	G	CATTAAAGTTTTGGTTGTCTTCAG[G/A]TCATCGAATCAAAATAT	CATTAAAGTTTTGGTTGTCTTCAG	CCAAAACTTAATGACCTCAGTCTT	1558	21
WIAF-3498	G/A	A	G	AAAGTTTGGTTGTCTTCAG[G/A]TCATCGAATCAAAATAT	CCTTCTCGTTAAGTGCTGA	TGACATTAATATATTTTGATTCGATG	1559	21
WIAF-350	T/C	C	T	TCGTTAAGTGCTGGATATAC[T/C]TTGGCTTGCACCGGACACCTT	CACATGAAATAATAACTCGATGAGTTTTT	CCCTCCGTAAAAGGTGTCC	2670	7
WIAF-3500	A/G	A	G	GTTTTTTCATCTAAGAAAT[A/G]AGAAACTCTGAGCAGCAAAT	TGACGCAATTGTGTGACCTA	CAACTATTTGCTGCTCAGAGTTT	1561	14
WIAF-3501	C/G	C	G	TGACGCAATTGTGTGACCTA[C/G]CTCTAAGTCCTCTACCAGA	AGACACTGTTGACCTTGGCTTG	CTAACTTTCTGGTAGAGGACTCTAGAG	1562	12
WIAF-3504	G/C	C	G	GACACTGTTGACCTTGGCTTG[G/C]GTAAAGGTACACATGAAAAC	GGTGCTATTGCTCAGGGTTA	AAGCACGTTTTCATGTGTACCTTT	1565	16
WIAF-3505	T/C	C	T	GGTGCTATTGCTCAGGGTTA[T/C]GCTAAACGTTTTAATCAGCAT	TGATTTTCCACAATAATTTGTTAGAA	GCAATGCTGATTAAAACGTTAGC	1566	1
WIAF-3508	G/A	A	G	CAATAATTTGTTAGAATAAC[G/A]GTAAGTGCACAGGCTCAATA	TGGCACAAATGGACGAC	TTATTATTGAGCCTGTGCACTTAC	1569	21
WIAF-3511	G/A	A	G	TTGTGGCACAAATGGACGAC[G/A]TGTGCTTCTTAAGAAAGACC	TGAGGCCAGTTTCTCAGTG	ACTGGTCTTTCTTAAGAAGCACA	1572	20
WIAF-3512	T/G	G	T	TTGAGGCCAGTTTCTCAGTG[T/G]TTAACTGAGAACCTTAAAGAT	GCTGCCAAATACTGAGC	GGAGTTAAACATCTTTAAGGTTCTIAGTTAA	1573	12
WIAF-3518	G/A	A	G	ACAGCTGCCAAATACTGAGC[G/A]CGGGCCAGACTCTTCAGGCA	GATACCCACATAGCTGTGTAGACA	CTGAAGAGTCTGGCCCG	1579	9
WIAF-3520	T/C	C	T	CCCACATAGCTGTGTAGACA[T/C]TGATATGTCAGCAGAAACCT	GGCTACTATTACGGTCTTACAGAATACC	CAAAGGTTTCTGCTGACATATCA	1581	9
WIAF-3527	T/C	C	T	ACGTCTTACAGAATACCTAT[T/C]GAGATATTACACCTATTTTA	CCTGTCCAATGGAATACAACA	CCTAGCTCTTTAAGATAAAATAGGTGTAA	1588	9
WIAF-3529	T/G	G	T	GTCCAAGTGTGGGCATTTAT[C/T]CAGAAACAGGTAAGCTGGGG	GGAGGTGTGGCGATTC	CCCAGTTACCCTGTTCTG	1590	1
WIAF-3531	T/C	C	T	CTGGAAGGTGGGCATTTAT[G/C]AGCTGGGACTGGGAAAA	CAATCACAGATAGTTATCAGCAGTC	ATTTTAAGGCAGTCGAATTTCA	1592	6
WIAF-3533	A/T	A	T	AGATAGTTATCAGCAGTCTT[T/C]GTGAAATCAGGACTTCCAACTAATA	GGTGGAAAGGAAGGAACAGCTATG	AATGAAATATTAGTTGGAAGACTTCAC	1594	2
WIAF-3534	G/A	A	G	TGGAAAGGAAGGAACAGCTATG[A/T]CCCAACCACCAAAAGAC	GATTCTGCGCTAAGTGCTCT	TTTTGGTGGGTTGTTGGG	1595	3
WIAF-3537	G/A	A	G	GATTCTGCGCTAAGTGCTCT[G/A]CTGTGAGACATCACAGGTTG	CCTTCTCCAGGGAATCCC	TGACAACCTGTGATGTCTCACA	1598	10
WIAF-3538	G/C	C	G	CTCCTTCCAGGGAATCCC[G/A]CTGGAGGACTGGGAAAA	CTGCTCCATCTGGGGATTG	ACCTTTTCCCAGTCCCTG	1599	2
WIAF-3540	G/A	A	G	AGCTGCTCATCTGGGGATTG[G/C]AGCTGAGCATCTGTCAAGG	AGGCCTGAGAACCAAGAGA	CCTTGCAGCAGTGCTCCAGCT	1601	6
WIAF-3542	A/G	A	G	AAGGCCTGAGAACCAAGAGA[G/A]AGAGAGGGTTAGCCATCCTG	TCTTCTGGTCTAGTACAAGATGGTAG	GGACTTAGACTAGAATTTACACCATTGA	1603	10
WIAF-3543	A/C	A	C	GGTCTAGTACAAGATGGTAG[A/G]AGAGAGGGTTAGCCATCCTG	AAACATTGTTTATCAGTTTGTACTGATAT	CAGGATGGCTAAACCCTCTCT	1604	13
WIAF-3546	T/A	A	T	ATCAGTTTGTACTGATATTT[A/C]AAGTGCACACATGGTACAT	GAATAATCTGACTGATGGAC	TATATGTACCCATGTGTGCACTT	1607	19
WIAF-3547	T/C	C	T	GAATAATCTGACTGATGGAC[T/A]ATGCTCACAAACAGATTTTA	CCAATTATGGAAGGTCTTAAACA	TGTCTAAAATCTGTTTTGTGAGCA	1608	5
WIAF-3549	G/A	A	G	ATTATGGAAGGTCTTAAACA[T/C]TTCACTGGAGGTCTTAAACA	AAGAAAGAAGAGCCTGGGAA	CAAACTCCTAAAAACATGGCTG	1610	12
WIAF-355	C/T	C	T	AAGAAAGAAGAGCCTGGGAA[G/A]AGGGAATGAGAAAAGCACAA	ACGTATGTTCACAAAAGCC	TTGTGCTTTTCTCATTCCCT	2134	8
WIAF-3553	A/C	A	C	ACGTATGTTCACAAAAGCCC[C/T]AAGTGATTTTGAAGCAGCTG	GGTCCATCATGCCCCA	CCAGCTGCTTCAAAATCACTT	1614	5
WIAF-3554	C/A	A	C	GACAGGTCCATCATGCCCCA[A/C]TGGAAGCACCCACACCCTAA	GCCAAAATAAAAGAAAATGTCA	GGGGTGTGGTCTTCCA	1615	9
WIAF-3556	A/T	A	T	AAGAAAATGTCATTATAAAAC[C/A]TAGAAAATGTCTTTTAGG	TTTTCATGAAGAAAACTAGGAGTACT	GATTGTCCAGGAACTACAATTCTCT	1617	2
WIAF-3557	T/C	C	T	TGAAGAAAACTAGGAGTAC[T/A]TTTATAGAAAATGTCTTTTAGG	GCACTGCAGGTACAGGGA	TGAACCCCTAAAAGACATTTCTA	1618	4
WIAF-3558	A/T	A	T	AGGCACTGCAGGTACAGGGA[T/C]GGTGAGCTGTGACACTGCTC	ACAGTTTAGAAATCATCTTCAAATCTC	GAGCAGTCTCACAGCTCACC	1619	2
WIAF-3559	C/T	C	T	AGAAATCATCTTCAAATCTC[A/T]TTCACTGGAGGAAGGCCAAGA	ACACTGAGGTGGTTGTTTTAGATACT	TGGCCTCCTCCAGTGAA	1620	5
WIAF-3562	C/T	C	T	AGGTGGTGTTTTTAGATACTA[C/T]ACAGTAAGAATATAACAATG	ACACTGAGGTGGTGTTTTAGATACT	TACTTGTTCTCTATGCATTGTTATATTCTTAC	1623	21

Marker	SNP			Sequence (bracketed)	Sequence	Sequence	Pos.	Count
WIAF-3564	C/G	C	G	ATCAAAGTTGTAGACCTCTG[C/G]CATGCCCTGATGTAGAGTTT	GTAATAAAATCAAAGTTGTAGACCTCTG	CAAAACTCTACATCAGGCATG	1625	12
WIAF-3565	A/G	A	G	ATGGAGGCTTCATTATGTAG[A/G]CATGATTGATTAAATTGTTG	CCTGAACTCAGCTCTTCTGG	AGTGCCAACAATTAATCAA	1626	1
WIAF-3566	T/C	C	T	CTCCAGTGAGACATGGATGA[T/C]ACCCACACTTCACTCTTGAT	CTGCAGTGAGACATGGATGA	GGATCAAGAGTGAAGTGTGG	1627	3
WIAF-3568	A/C	A	C	CACCTCCATATCGTCCCA[A/C]TGGAAGTCTTCAGGGGTAA	ACCTCCATATCGTCCCA	AGGCATTGTATTCATAGATGACAG	1629	8
WIAF-357	C/T	C	T	GAGGGTCTGTGTGAAGGAGC[C/T]GGCTTCTTCTTGGTGCTGCT	GGTCTGTGTGAAGGAGC	CAGGCACCAAGAGAAGCC	2675	22
WIAF-3572	G/A	A	G	CCGGCACATTACAGGTCTTC[G/A]CGGGAGGGCAGCTGTGTCGG	CCGGCACATTACAGGTCTTC	ACAGCTGCCTCCCG	1633	8
WIAF-3573	T/C	C	T	TTATTGTGGTCTTAATTCTA[T/C]ACATAATTACATTAATTACC	CTCCCTTATTGTGGTCTTAATTCTA	TTCTCTCATGGTAATTAATTGTAATTATTGT	1634	16
WIAF-3574	C/T	C	T	TCAGATTTATTGATTTCCAT[C/T]GTATTGACTTTAAAAATGGT	GGAATTCAGATTTATTGATTTCCA	GCTTCATACCATTTTTAAAGTCAAT	1635	5
WIAF-3575	G/A	A	G	GTTTCAATAGGACCAAGAAC[G/A]TTAGAGAATAAAGATCTTAG	CAATGTTTCAATAGGACCAAGAA	CATTTTCCATCTAAGATCTTTATTCTC	1636	1
WIAF-3580	T/G	G	T	TGGGTTAGGAAAAGTACAGG[T/G]ACAACCTTGACTTGCCTGAC	TTTGGGTTAGGAAAAGTACAGG	GTCAGGCAAGTCAAGGTTGT	1641	12
WIAF-3581	C/T	C	T	ACATGAAGTTGATATTGGTG[C/T]TTATAAATCACTCTCTCCCA	CCACATGAAGTTGATATTGGTG	GGACTGGGAGGAGAGTGATTTATAA	1642	1
WIAF-3583	T/C	C	T	CACAAAGACCTCCCATCCTC[T/C]TGTTCCATCCACCTCTTCCA	CACAAAGACCTCCCATCCTC	GGAAGAGGTGGATGGAACA	1644	7
WIAF-3585	A/G	A	G	TTCTGTGAATTTTGTGCTT[A/G]CTACTGTATAGTGCATGTGG	CATTCTGTGAATTTTGTGCT	CCTACCACATGCACTATACAGT	1646	5
WIAF-359	C/T	C	T	TGGTTGCTGAACAAAACTGAA[C/T]TGCTGCTTATCTTTCCTGA	TGGTTGCTGAACAAAACTGAA	AATCAGGAAAGATAAGCACAGC	2677	13
WIAF-3594	A/G	A	G	AGCCACACGCATTACCCGAC[A/G]CAGCCCTCCTGACATCGGCA	AGCCACACGCATTACCCGAC	CGATGTCAGGAGGGCTG	1655	9
WIAF-3600	A/C	A	C	TCCACAGTCCTTCCATTTCA[A/C]CTTAGAGATGAACCTTTAAT	TCCACAGTCCTTCCATTTCA	ACCTTCATTGTATATTTTATTAAAGGTTC	1661	2
WIAF-3602	A/G	A	G	CAGGAAGAAGCCAAATATAGC[A/G]CAAGGTGTGGAAGGAGGGAC	CCTCAGGAAGAAGCCAAATATAGC	CCCTCCTTCCACACCTTG	1663	7
WIAF-3603	T/G	C	G	CTCATCCCTCCTACTTCAGA[T/G]TTATTACTATGGCGATGTCC	CCTCATCCCTCCTACTTCAGA	TCCAGCCCCTACCTTAGTAATAA	1664	19
WIAF-3607	C/T	C	T	CTCTGGGTACCTGGGATTA[C/T]TAGGCACGTGCCACGATGCC	TCTGGGTACCTGGGATTA	TGGTGCACGTGCCT	1668	3
WIAF-3612	T/C	T	C	AGTTCTCTTACATAAAAAG[T/C]CTGAAGTTATGCAGGCTAGG	GAGGTATGCTTAGTTCTCTTACAATAA	TCCTAGCCTGCATAACTTCAG	1673	6
WIAF-3613	G/A	A	G	CAGGAAGCTATGCTAGGCAC[G/A]GCACGGGTTGACTGAAAATG	CAGGAAGCTATGCTAGGCAC	TTTCAGTCAACCGTGC	1674	10
WIAF-3614	C/T	C	T	TTTTTCAGGCTTTTTGAGTT[C/T]TTGTGGACAGCTCCATTACTC	CCGGCTCTTATTTTACTTAGTTTTTT	GGAGTAATGGAGCTGTCCACA	1675	2
WIAF-3616	C/T	C	T	CTGAATTGACTTTTCCTCTC[C/T]GCTTCACTCAGGGCAGCCCG	TGCCTGAATTGACTTTTCCTC	AGTTCGCCCACGAAGC	1677	22
WIAF-3618	G/C	C	G	TGTGCAAAATGCTAAGCAGG[G/C]GTTTCACTCAGGGCAGCCCG	GTGCAAAATGCTAAGCAGG	GGCTGCCCTGAGTGAAAC	1679	15
WIAF-3619	G/A	A	G	TGATGAGTTTGATTTGAAAC[G/A]CCCACTATTGAGCACTCAATC	GGAGATGATGAGTTTGATTTGAAAA	CAGATTGAGTGCTCAATAGTGG	1680	15
WIAF-362	G/A	A	G	ACTGCACCCACTGACGGAGAC[G/A]CAGAGACCTTGGACTACAGA	TGCACCCACTGACGGAGAC	TCATCTGAGTCCAAGGTCTCTG	2679	8
WIAF-3621	T/G	G	T	TGTTTAATTTTTAAATTATT[T/G]AITTGTTCTGTAGGACAAGG	GTTTTAATTTTTAAATTATT	CATGCTGGCTAATTTGTTTTT	1682	12
WIAF-3624	G/A	A	G	AAGACCAGGGTCATCGGAGT[G/A]AGCAGATGAGTAGGACAAGG	AAGACCAGGGTCATCGGAGT	GCGTGTCCTACTCATCTGCT	1685	7
WIAF-3627	A/G	A	G	TTACCTCATTAGAGGTTGCA[A/G]AAATGAATGATGAGTCAGCTAT	TTACCTCATTAGAGGTTGCA	GGATAGGCTGCATCTATCATTT	1688	10
WIAF-3630	A/C	A	C	TTTTTCCTTTCTTCTAATA[A/C]GGAGACTACACTCTAGATAA	AITTTCCTTTCTTCTAATA	CCTGTCTGTTTTGTTTATCATCAGAGTG	1691	12
WIAF-3631	G/A	A	G	AATTTGCAAGGCTTTGCTAT[G/A]GTAACCCACATGCTAAAAAC	AAITTTGCAAGGCTTTGCTAT	GGAGTTTTTAGCATGTGGGTAA	1692	1
WIAF-3632	T/C	C	T	GAGGAGCAGGGAGGTAGT[T/C]ACAGCCGGTCAATTATAATA	GAGGAGCAGGGAGGTAGT	CTGATTATAATTGAGCGGCTGT	1693	10
WIAF-3637	A/G	A	G	GGTTTGAATTGGTGATTAGA[A/G]TAAGAGATGCATATTCCCTT	AGGGTTTGAATTGGTGATTAGA	GAAAGGGAATATGCATCTTT	1698	12
WIAF-364	A/C	A	C	GGAAGTTAAATACTGATAGA[A/C]GATGCAAATTTGTCCTTTCA	GGAAGTTAAATACTGATAGA	CATGAAAGGACAAAATTTGCATC	2681	12
WIAF-3644	T/C	C	T	TATATACTTTGTCTTGTGAC[T/C]AACTAGAGCTTACAGGAGTA	GAAAATGTTACTTCATTACAAAGTGTAC	CAGTTGTTACTTGTTATACTCCGTAAGC	1705	6
WIAF-3645	C/A	A	C	TAAACATTTGTTGAACAG[C/A]TTTCTTTTCTAATATAATGA	CAAATTAAACAAAGTTTGTTGAACAG	CAGTTGTCCATGTACACATAGTCA	1706	11
WIAF-3649	T/C	C	T	CACATTAAAAAATGCACCA[T/C]GTCAACGGAGCACATTAAAGA	GACAGGTGCACAGGCACAITTAAAAA	ATTTTCTTCTTACATCTCCTGATC	1710	7
WIAF-3650	T/C	C	T	GTGGTGGTTATCTTTAAATA[C/T]GTCATGCTTTTTTTCTTAAC	TTACGGTGGTTATCTTTAAATA	TCCTCAAGACGTGATTATGTTG	1711	15
WIAF-3651	C/T	C	T	TACACCCATGTGCTTCATCC[A/G]TATCCAACCCAGATCACCCA	CACCCATGTGCTTCATCC	TTATCTAGAAAAATGTCATTGGCTAA	1712	11
WIAF-3653	C/T	C	T	TGACTGGCACCTACCCTGA[C/T]TTCCAGAACGTGTAGCCGTC	GTACACAAACAGGCCCAA	GGCTAGGGTATCCATCCA	1714	7
WIAF-3656	C/A	A	C	TTCTGAGATCTCATCACATA[C/A]CTGATCCCATTTAACTTCAC	TTCTGAGATCTCATCACATA	AACACTTCTGAGATCTCATCACATA	1717	11
WIAF-3659	A/G	A	G	AGGACCTCCGCTGCAAATAC[A/G]TCCTCCTCCATTTCACCAAC	AGGACCTCCGCTGCAAATAC	CATAGTTGGTAGATGAGGGAGGA	1720	11
WIAF-3660	C/T	C	T	GTGGTGGTTATCTTTAAATA[C/T]GTCATGCTTTTTTTCTTAAC	TTACGGTGGTTATCTTTAAATA	CCAACTAAAAAATGGTTAAGAAAAA	1721	17
WIAF-3661	A/G	A	G	TACACCCATGTGCTTCATCC[A/G]TATCCAACCCAGATCACCCA	CACCCATGTGCTTCATCC	GGGTGATCTGGGTTGGATA	1722	3
WIAF-3663	C/T	C	T	TGACTGGCACCTACCCTGA[C/T]TTCCAGAACGTGTAGCCGTC	CTGGCCCAGTACCTGA	GGCTACAGGTTCTGGAA	1724	2
WIAF-3664	G/A	A	G	TCTGGACCTCAGTTTCTCCA[G/A]TGAGCTGGTTAAGAATGCACT	TGGCCCTGTCTCTTCTTTTT	TTACTGCATTCTACCAGCTCA	1725	3
WIAF-3667	C/T	C	T	GCCTGGGCAGGGACAACTCA[C/T]TTGTTATGATCAGAGGGAAA	TGGGCAGGGACAACTCA	CCTTTCCCTCTGATCATAACAA	1728	
WIAF-3673	A/G	A	G	CTGAACTGTCATGAATTGGA[A/G]TTTTTCTAGTAAAACACAATG	AGTCTGAACTGTCATGAATTG	GCCAACATTGTTTTACTAGAAA	1734	
WIAF-3675	C/T	C	T	AGAGATGCCGACACCCTC[C/T]AAGGTTCTACAAGGTGACCA	GATGCCCTGACACCCTC	TTTGGTCACCTTGTAGAACCTT	1736	
WIAF-3676	C/T	C	T	AAGCTTTAGAAAGTGACAA[C/T]ACATTTAATAGACTCCAGAA	CTTGGAAATACACACAATGAA	GAAATATCAACTTCTGGAGTCTATTAAA	1737	6
WIAF-3677	C/T	C	T	TATCAATTGAGTAAGAGGAA[C/T]ATAAAATGTCTGACAACATTT	TGTTGGTATCAAATTGAGTAAGAGAGGA	CATCGTTATCAATTGAGTAAGAGGA	1738	6
WIAF-3679	T/C	C	T	TTAATCTGCTTTAGTTGAAA[T/C]AGCCAATACCAAAAGGGTAC	ATTTCAGGTTAATCTGCTTTAGTTGTTG	TGTACCCTTTTGGTATTGGCT	1740	19
WIAF-3681	C/G	G	C	AATTACTTCATATTTGACAT[C/G]TATTTTGAAATTCTGTTTTA	GGAAGTCTGAATTACTTCATATTTGA	CCCTGTAAAACAGAATTTCAAAA	1742	8
WIAF-3683	G/A	A	G	CACTACAGGTAGCCTCTGCA[G/A]ATCGTTAAATCTGGAGC	TGGCCCTGTCTCTGA	GCTCCGAGAGGTTAAACGAT	1744	15
WIAF-3684	G/A	A	G	GGAAATAAAATTGGAACGAA[G/A]AAAGGTTAGGAGAGTAGGGA	CAGGAAATAAAATTGGAACGAA	CCTTCCCTACTCTCCTAACCTTT	1745	20
WIAF-3688	T/C	C	T	ACACTGATCATGTCGTCATAA[T/C]CACGTTCTATGGTTGATTAAGCT	TCCACACTGATCATGTCTCAT	TGAGCTTAATCCATAGAACGTG	1749	9

(Continued on following pages.)

TABLE 6-7. (Continued)

WIAF Name	Alleles	A	B	Chipregion	primer up	primer down	ncbi SS	NwLib chrom
WIAF-3691	G/T	G	T	TTTTGGAAGTAATAATACTCTGC[G/T]TCTTCATACTGATCTGCTAG	TTCCTTTTGGAAGTAATAATACTCTGC	TGCTCTAGCAGATCAGTATGAAGA	1752	10
WIAF-3699	C/T	C	T	CAGAAAACCAAGGCTCAACC[C/T]AGTAGCGTCCTAGAGTAACG	CAGAAAACCAAGGCTCAACC	CCCGTTACTCTAGGACGCTA	1760	15
WIAF-370	A/G	A	G	GACACAACTGCCAATGCA[A/G]TTAGTATATAGAAATAATAC	CAATGCTGCCAATGCA	TAACACGCTGCGTATTATTTCTATATACTAA	2687	8
WIAF-3700	A/G	A	G	AACACACCTGAAGAAGACTT[A/G]GTTCCTGGTAACATTTCCTT	TTGAACACACCTGAAGAAGACTT	GCAAGGAAATGTTACCAGGAA	1761	6
WIAF-3704	C/T	C	T	ACCCCAAGTGAGTTCATTTA[C/T]GGCCCTGAGCCTTAGTTTCC	TGACCCCAAGTGAGTTCATT	CCACATGTTTGCTGCTCTACT	1765	6
WIAF-3705	C/G	C	G	ATGGTAACTTAGGGAAAAGT[C/G]GTAGTAGGACAGCAAACATG	TTTTGTGAATAAAATGTGTTTATGG	CCCATGAAAATCCCAAGACTT	1766	16
WIAF-3706	T/A	A	T	AGTCCCAGCGATGGGTTGGA[T/A]AAGTCTTGGGATTTCATGGG	CCAGCGATGGGGTTGGA	CCCATGGGACATACGTTC	1767	19
WIAF-3709	G/A	A	G	AGACGTTCACTGAGCGTCTT[G/A]GAACGTATGTCCCATGGGTA	GACGTTCACTGAGCGTCT	GCTGGTTCATTGTAGGTATAATTATATG	1770	3
WIAF-3711	T/C	C	T	TTCTTTCCTCGGATTCTTTGC[T/C]TTGCATAATTATACCTACAA	TTCTTTCCTCGGATTCTTTGC	CTCCAACCCCACCGA	1772	10
WIAF-3712	A/G	A	G	ATCCACTTGGAGGGGTAGAT[A/G]TCGGGTGGGGTTGGAGCGGCT	ATCCACTTGGAGGGGTAGAT	GAATGCCAAGGGAATCAAT	1773	
WIAF-3713	C/T	C	T	GATCAGGAGACTCGTTAAT[C/T]ATTGATTCCCTTGGCATTCA	AAGATTGATCAGGAGACTCTGTTAA	CAGAGCAGCCATGAGTCC	1774	14
WIAF-3714	G/A	A	G	AGGGCTTGGGTCACAGCCTC[G/A]GAGCTCTGTCTCTGTCTGTA	GCTTGGGTCACAGCCTC	TCCTGCCCACTGAGAA	1775	16
WIAF-3720	A/G	A	G	CTTGCGCGCTGCTCTCGCTCC[A/G]TTCTCAGTGTGGGCAGGAAC	CGCGTGCTCTCGCTCC	CTGATTATGTAATCCCTATTCCATC	1781	6
WIAF-3723	A/T	A	T	CCATAAGTGTAAGACTGGAT[A/T]GATGGAATAGGGATTACATA	CCAACCATAAGTGTAAGACTGGA	TTTGCAGTTTCTCACAAAATGA	1784	6
WIAF-3724	A/G	A	G	CAACACAGAGCAGCATGAAA[A/G]TTCATTTTGTGAGAAACTGCA	CAACACAGAGCAGCAGCATGA	CCCCAGCGACCTACA	1785	8
WIAF-3725	G/A	A	G	CTAGGGTCCCGATGAGCGTGC[G/A]TTCTAGGTCGCTGGGGGGTGA	GGTCCCGATGAGCTGC	TCACAGCATGCTTAATGGG	1786	20
WIAF-373	G/A	A	G	GCCAAAACTAGGCCTCAGGT[G/A]CCCATTAAGCATGCTGTGAA	GCCAAAACTAGGCCTCAGGT	CCACCACAAATTGTGCATAGTC	2688	4
WIAF-3733	A/G	A	G	AAAGGGGTGGTATCATCTGA[A/G]GACTATGTACACAATTTGTG	GAAAGGGGTGGTATCATCTGA	AGGCACTTTCAAAATATGTCAA	1794	3
WIAF-3736	G/A	A	G	GACGGGACTGGCTTTTGGAC[G/A]TTGACATATTTTGAAAAGTG	GGGGACGGGGACTGGCTTT	CGCTGGTAAGGACCATGA	1797	9
WIAF-3737	G/C	C	G	ATCCCTAACTTTATTATTC[G/C]TCATGGTCCTTACCAGCGGA	CACTCACTATCCCTAACTTTATTATTC	AATGAAAATGTACATGTGACCTGT	1798	X
WIAF-3738	T/C	C	T	CATAATATATAACATAC[T/C]ACAGGTCACATTACATTTT	GGCATTTAAACATTTACAGTACCATAATAA	GCAACTCTGTGCCATTCC	1799	12
WIAF-3745	T/C	C	T	TCCTCACTGTTAGCGATCTC[T/C]CGGAATGGCACAGAGTTGCTT	CCTCCTCACTGTTAGCGATCTC	GGTTTTAATGGAAGCAGTTGTT	1806	11
WIAF-3746	T/C	C	T	ATTGTCTTCAGAACAATCAG[T/C]ACTACACTGCTTCCCATTAA	CAATATTATTGTCTTCAGAACAATCAG	GCTCACTGAGGAGCTTTGTC	1807	6
WIAF-375	A/G	A	G	TGGGACTCTTGATCCAGAGA[A/G]GACAAAGCTCCTCAGTGAGC	TGGGACTCTTGATCCAGAGA	AATGTTTAGCCACAAACTTGTTC	2690	12
WIAF-3750	T/C	C	T	GACAAGGAACAGCAGAATAG[T/C]GAACAAGTTTGTGGCTAAAC	GCTGACAAGGAACAGCAGAA	CACACACAACACTGTCCCCT	1811	4
WIAF-3755	C/A	A	C	CTCATGGGTTGTAGAGCTGG[C/A]AGGGGACAGTGTTGTGTGTG	TCATGGGTTGTAGAGCTGG	CGCGGGGAGCAGAAA	1816	
WIAF-3756	T/C	C	T	TGTAAGTCCCTCCGATGCCT[T/C]CTTTCTGCTCCCGCGCAGT	AAGTCCCTCCGATGCCT	GTGTGAAGACGGCATTTGT	1817	13
WIAF-3761	T/C	C	T	CCTCAGTAATTAGAAAATGA[T/C]ACAAATGCCGTCTTCACACT	AACTGCGCTCAGTAATTAGAAAAATGA	TGTCTTATTCCGCTTGAAAATAG	1822	10
WIAF-3762	G/C	C	G	ATCCACACAGTAGACTTTTTG[G/C]CTATTTTCAAGCGGGAATAAG	GTTTATTACAAATACCACAGTAGACTTTTT	CAACTAACTGAATTCTCTAATTTAAACAA	1823	1
WIAF-3765	G/C	C	G	ACCTTTCACTTCCCTTCAAA[G/C]TTGTTTAAATTAGAGAATTC	AACCTTTCACTTCCCTTCAAA	TGGTGCATTCGGCACA	1826	4
WIAF-3766	T/C	C	T	TAATTTCTGCCCGCACCGCT[T/C]TGTGCCGAATGCACCAGTGC	TTTCTGCCGCACCG	GGCAGGGTGGATGAAGTC	1827	6
WIAF-3768	T/C	C	T	GAAAAACTCCCAGACATTCA[T/C]GACTTCATCCACCCTGCCTG	CAGAAAAACTCCCAGACATTCA	AAACTTGCTTCTTCGTGCTTT	1829	16
WIAF-3769	A/C	A	C	GTGAAGGGTATTTTACGGGA[A/C]CTCTATAAAGCAGGAAGAAG	GGTGAAGGGTATTTTACGGGA	CCCATAAAATATATGCAAAGTAACAC	1830	11
WIAF-377	C/T	C	T	AGTGATCTACTCTCTTTAC[C/T]AAGTGTTACTTTGCATATAT	AGTGATCTACTCTCTTTAC	CAACACATGTTGACCCATAAAT	2137	12
WIAF-3770	G/A	A	G	CTCTCAAACCATGATGTGTC[G/A]TATATTTATGGTCACAATG	CTCTCAAACCATGATGTGGT	CAAAGGGTCTTTCCATATTCC	1831	11
WIAF-3775	G/A	A	G	ACAGAAACCACGTGAATGTC[G/A]GGAATATGGAAAGACCCTTT	GACAGAAACCACGTGAATGTC	CATGGGGACTCAGTCTTTCTC	1836	19
WIAF-377	C/T	C	T	AAAATGCCTGGAAATGGATG[C/T]GAGAAAGACTGAGTCCCCAT	AAATGCCTGGAAATGGATG	AGAATTGAAGACTGAGAGACCCT	1838	14
WIAF-3779	A/G	A	G	CTTCAATTCTCACTTTTCCC[A/G]CTTCTAATTCAACGGGAATC	AGTCTTCAATTCTCACTTTTCCC	TGAGTAGCACTGGTGAATTAGAAG	1840	17
WIAF-3780	A/G	A	G	GGAACCTCCCCAAAACCTT[T/A]CCCGCAACACAATTCTCCTGT	AACCCTCCCCAAAACCTT	CAGGAGAATGTGTCTGGGG	1841	17
WIAF-3784	T/A	A	T	AGGAAGGAGCAGAAGTTTGGA[C/T]CTGAAGGCAGGAAGGCCAGCT	GGAAGGAGCAGAAGTTTGGA	TGGCTTCCTGCCTTCAG	1845	6
WIAF-3785	C/T	C	T	ATTTATACCCCAAAACAATT[A/G]TGACAGTTAATAGGAAATCC	TGTCTCTATTTATACCCCAAAACAA	AAAGTAAGGATTTCCTATTAACTGTCA	1846	2
WIAF-3788	A/G	A	G	TAAGAATGCAAACACACAGA[C/A]AAATGCAGCTATCACAGGGG	CAAATAAGAATGCAAACACACAGA	CCCCTTGTATAGCTGCATTT	1849	5
WIAF-3797	C/A	A	C	TCTGTCACTGCAGGGCAAGA[A/C]ACCAGTTGTACACCTGAGCCTA	TGTCACTGCAGGGCAAGA	TCTAGGCTCAGGTGTAACTGG	1858	10
WIAF-3798	A/C	A	C	CATAGACAACTGGGATTTCC[T/A]GATATTAGGGAAATAAATTA	CACATAGACAACTGGGATTTCC	TCAATACTAATGCTCTAATAATGTAAATTG	1859	1
WIAF-3799	T/A	A	T	GGGAAACCTCAGGTAGCTCC[C/T]GAAGATCTGTGCTTTCCAAC	GGGAAACCTCAGGTAGCTCC	TGTTCGGAAAGCACAGATCTTC	1860	6
WIAF-380	C/T	C	T	GTCTATTGATAGATAAACCC[G/A]CTGTGTCCTCACGGCTATCG	TTGGTGTCTATTGATAGATAAACCC	GGATAGCCGTGAGGACACAG	2694	11
WIAF-3800	G/A	A	G	TGGGATGGAGCAATCCTGTTA[C/T]AGTACATCCTGTAATAGT	TGGGATGGAGCAATCCTGTTA	GGTAGAAGGTCCAGATGT	1861	1
WIAF-3801	C/T	C	T	TTCTGTCGTCCATGGCAACA[C/T]AGTACATCTGTTA	TGGTGTCGTCCATGGCAACA	CCACTATTACAGCCATAAGGCC	1862	9
WIAF-3805	T/C	C	T	TCCTCTGTTCATGCGAACA[T/C]AGCCAGTGAAGTGGTGCCATT	TGGTTCCATGCGAACA	TGGCACCACTTCACTGCT	1866	6
WIAF-3806	T/C	C	T	GATTTATTTAAATCATTA[T/C]AGCCAGTGAAGTGGTGCCATT	GATGATAAGTCTGCTTGATTTATTATTTAAA	GCAGGGAGTGGTTCATTCC	1867	6
WIAF-381	A/T	A	T	TTTTCCAGCCCCTGAGGAAA[A/T]GGAATGAACCACTCCCTGCC	CCAGCCCCTGAGGAAA	GCAGGGAGTGGTTCATTCC	2695	11
WIAF-3813	G/T	G	T	ACCAACCAGATTGGTTTAGA[G/T]GCCCATTAATCAAATCAAGT	CACCAACCAGATTGGTTTAGA	TGACTTGATTTGATTAATGGGC	1874	9

ID	SNP			Sequence (5′ flank [SNP] 3′ flank)	Probe A	Probe B		
WIAF-3818	A/G	A	G	GCTGCTCAGCCAAACCATGG[A/G]GCAAGATTGGAAATAATAAT	GCTCAGGCAAACCATGG	GACCATTATTATTCCAATCTTGC	1879	4
WIAF-3819	G/A	A	G	CACCTTTTCCAGCTTCATAG[G/A]CCCCTTCCTCCAACTTCAAA	GGGGAAATCTGTTTCCTCA	CTAATCTGCTGCCTTTGAAGT	1880	20
WIAF-3821	G/T	G	T	ATTGGAAATAATAATGGTCT[G/T]CATACATCCTCCCATAGGGC	GCAAGATTGGAAATAATAATGGTC	GCCCTATGGGAGGATGTATG	1882	4
WIAF-3824	G/A	A	G	TCTTTCACAAAACAGCATTC[G/A]AAGGAGAAGGAAAGTTCGC	TTTCTTTCACAAAACAGCATTC	GGGAACTTTCCCTTCTCCT	1885	22
WIAF-3825	G/T	G	T	AGAGGAGGCACGGAATTCTG[G/T]ATGTGCTCAGGAGATGATA	GGAGGGCTCCAGGAGTCACA	AGTATCATCCTCCTGAGCACAT	1886	1
WIAF-3827	A/T	A	T	TGGGGGCTCCAGGAGTCACA[A/T]GTTTACATTGCAGAGAAGGA	CCAAGGACCAGAAGAAACTG	TCATTTCCTTCTCTGCAATGT	1888	3
WIAF-3828	T/C	C	T	CTCTATGGGTGACCTTGGCA[T/C]AGGTTCTTCTAAGAACTGGC	CTATGGGTGACCTTGGCA	AGAGCCAGTTCTTAGAAGAACCT	1889	16
WIAF-383	A/C	C	A	CAGATACAAGGAAATAAAAA[A/C]CACTTTTAGGAGATGAAAAC	AAAAGACTACAGATACAAGGAAATAAAAA	TTGTGTTTTCATCTCCTAAAAGTG	2697	2
WIAF-3831	G/A	A	C	CACCTGTTTCCAAACTTCAA[G/A]GTTAGGGCTTTGAAACATTC	CCAACTGTTTCCAAACTTCAA	GGAATGTTTCAAAGCCTAAC	1892	9
WIAF-3834	G/T	G	T	TCTTGCTTAATGTTTTTACT[G/T]TTAATAGAAATGAAACTGAT	GGTAGTCTTAATGTTTTTACT	GCCATAATCTTTATACCTATCAGTTCTA	1895	8
WIAF-3838	G/A	A	G	ATTGCCGAAGAAGGGGGAAA[G/A]AACTCCGAGTCCACTGTGGA	GCCGAAGAAGGGGGAAA	CCACAGTGGACTCGGAGTT	1899	11
WIAF-3839	C/T	C	T	GCTTCTTCATACATGCTGAG[C/T]GCCCTAGAAATGGAGCCTGT	ATGCTTCTTCATACATGCTGAG	CAGCCTCCATTTCTAGGGC	1900	11
WIAF-3840	A/G	A	G	TCGGCCTCCTATCTGGA[A/G]AGTGGGACTGAGGGAGGATT	TCGGCCTCCTATCTGGA	GGGTGAATCCTCCCTCAGTC	1901	11
WIAF-3843	C/T	C	T	CATTATCTGAGACAACATAT[C/T]AAGTGCAGCAGTACAAAG	AACCTTTCATTATCTGAGACAACA	CCTTTGTACTGCTGCTCACTT	1904	6
WIAF-3855	G/C	C	G	ACCCTGGCAAGGCAAGGGGC[G/C]CGCATAGCACTCTTACCTGA	TGGCAAGGCAAGGGG	GGTCAGGTAAGAGTGCTATGGC	1916	16
WIAF-3858	A/G	A	G	ATAGCTACAAAGTTACAAAT[A/G]TATATTATGAGATTATTACA	TCAAGTGATTTCAAAGATAGCTACA	TGAAACTGAAIATCATTGTAATAAATCTCA	1919	4
WIAF-3861	G/A	A	G	GCCTGGGAGGATCTGGTGAT[G/A]GCAGAGAAAAGCAGGTGGGT	CCTGGGAGGATCTGGTGAT	GGCTTAGAGAATTTCTGAGAATATAA	1922	2
WIAF-3863	A/G	A	G	TTGGTTCACAAATTGCTGC[A/G]TGGTACTTATATTCTCAGAA	TTGGTTCACAAATTGCTGC	GGCTTAGAGAATTTCTGAGAATATAA	1924	15
WIAF-3864	T/C	T	C	TATGCTAAACAGGGTGGAT[T/C]ATTCATGAGTTTTCCAAGAA	CCTATGCTAAACAGGGTGG	CCTTTGTAAAAACTCATG	1925	22
WIAF-3865	C/T	C	T	CCCACAAAGTAATCTGACGG[C/T]GGGGCAAACTCAGGATCTCT	CCCAAAAGTAATCTGACGG	AGATCCTGAGTTTGCCCC	1926	3
WIAF-3873	G/A	A	G	GTGCTTTGCTTGTTCCTTA[G/A]GAGGGGATTTAGTAGATGCT	GGTGCTTTGCTTGTTCCTT	AAAGTAGCAICTACTAAATCCCCTC	1934	19
WIAF-3876	A/G	A	G	GGAAGGATATAAATGAAGAT[A/G]GGCAGACTGACAGCTGGTGG	CAGAGGATATAAATGAAGAT	ACCAGCTGTCAGTCTGCC	1937	15
WIAF-3877	G/A	A	G	CATGTAAGATGTCATGGAAG[G/A]AGTGGAATTGCATGGAAG	CATGTAAGATGTCATGGAAG	CAGACTCAGATCCAATTCCACT	1938	6
WIAF-3880	G/C	C	G	CCAGAGAGGCCCACGGACGA[G/C]TCCGGAAGTGAGGGGAGGGAG	GAGGGCCACGGACGA	CCTCCCTACTTCCGGA	1941	22
WIAF-3881	A/G	A	G	AGCTGTAACAGGTTTGGAGA[A/G]GGCAGCGTGTGGATTCTCTTT	CAGCTGTAACAGGTTTGGAGA	AAGAGAATCCACAGCTGCC	1942	9
WIAF-3882	A/G	A	G	GGCGCTTTATGCCATGTAGAG[A/G]AGACACTGGGTAACCACAGC	GGCGCTTTATGCCATGTAGAG	GCTGTGGTTACCCAGTGTCT	1943	11
WIAF-3885	G/A	A	G	CAAATGCGACGAACCTCTGA[G/A]CATCCTGGTGAGGAATAACA	AATGCGACGAACCTCTGA	TGTTATTCCTCACCAGATG	1946	1
WIAF-3887	C/T	C	T	AATTTATGTTGCTGATATATA[G/A]CTCGAAGTACTCTTGGTGG	CAAATTTGATAAATTTATGTTGCTGA	TCTATTCATCCAAGAGTACTTCTGAG	1948	14
WIAF-3889	A/G	A	G	AGCCACCAGCACTCATGGGC[C/T]AGTCCCTGTCCAGGCTGCCC	AGCCACCAGCACTCATGGGC	CAGCCTGGACAGGGACT	1950	17
WIAF-3890	A/G	A	G	TCCTTATACAACGCACAAAT[A/G]ACATTAAGCATTATCCCTGA	CATTCCTTATACAACGCACAAAT	CTTTTCAGGGATAATGCTTAATG	1951	15
WIAF-3891	C/T	C	T	GTTAGTATACAGATATTACT[A/G]TACTGGTACCCATCTTGTAA	CAATACAAAGCCCTAGTTAGTATACAGAT	TCCTTACAAGATGGGTACCAGT	1952	1
WIAF-3894	C/T	C	T	ACTGATGGTGACGATACTGA[C/T]GATAGTAATAACACTTACTG	ACTGATGGTGACGATACTGA	GTGGGACGGCCAAG	1955	2
WIAF-3896	T/C	C	T	GCTGCTGGGAAAGACAGACTGA[T/C]CTTGGCGGCGTCCCACAATCC	TGCTGGGAAAGACAGCAG	AACTGGATCACACTTAATTTTCTTC	1957	19
WIAF-3899	C/G	C	G	ATACACGAGGATGAAGTAGA[C/G]GATATGGAAGAAAATTAAGT	TGAAGATACACGAGGATGAAGTAG	CCTTTGCAATTGTGGATCTT	1960	10
WIAF-39	T/C	C	T	AATCTGCTGAGAGCAGAGCT[T/C]AAGATCCACAATTGCAAAGG	AATCTGCTGAGAGCAGAGCT	CCTTTGCAATTGTGGATCTTC	2451	17
WIAF-3901	G/C	C	G	AAGCAATGTGGGCGGTGCTGA[G/C]TGCCCGTGGGAAGGTTCGGAG	AAGCATGTGGGGCGGTGCTGA	AGACCTTCCAGGGCA	1962	10
WIAF-3902	G/C	C	G	TAGAAACCTCGTAGTAACA[G/C]AGTTTATGGTTTTACAAAAG	GCATTATAGAAACCTCCTGAGTAACA	GGAGTTCTCTTTGTAAAACCATAAA	1963	3
WIAF-3906	G/C	C	G	CCCTACGCACGGCGCAATGA[G/C]ATCTGGCTGTTGAAGACAGA	CGGACGCGGCAATGA	TCATGTCTTCAACGCAGA	1967	12
WIAF-3907	T/C	C	T	AGTGATTATCAAGCAGTCAG[T/C]TTATCTCTTTTCAAACATTT	TGAGAGTGATTATCAAGCAGTCAG	GTCTTTATGAAATGTTGAAAAGAGA	1968	15
WIAF-3908	G/A	A	G	CTTTTAAATTTAACCTAAC[G/A]GAAAGCCATTAAAACATTTT	ACAAAGGACTTTTAAATTTTAACCTAAC	GCTTAAAAATGTTTTAATGGCTTTC	1969	10
WIAF-3909	C/T	C	T	AACATTCTTCTGAGAGGACT[C/T]TTTCCATGCTCACAGGCACAT	AACATTCTTCTGAGAGGACT	CCTGCCCACTTCCCTG	1970	3
WIAF-3911	G/T	G	T	TACAAGCAAGGGACCTTGGC[G/T]CGCTGACGACTGCTGCTGTG	GCCAGGAGGGCCAG	GGCAGCAGGGACCTTGGC	1972	12
WIAF-3915	C/T	C	T	GTTCCCCACCCGTCTTCAA[C/T]AGTAACTGCGGCAGTGGCTT	TAAAGCAAGGGACCTTGGC	TTGTTTGCGAAGGATTGC	1976	12
WIAF-3918	G/A	A	G	GCAACCTGGCCCCACACC[G/A]TGTGGACAGGCAGCACCAG	GGCTGTCGCCGTGTCCACA	GGGCAACTTCGGGAAAT	1979	22
WIAF-3921	T/C	C	T	TTGGTCAGAACATTGCCTA[T/C]CTACTTTCTGCATTTGTTTT	CATTTGGTCAGAACATTGTCC	TTCACCCGCTGCAGC	1982	1
WIAF-3923	T/C	C	T	TCTGTCAGCTAAACCTTTGCT[T/C]TGTCTATAACCTTGCATT	GTTCGTCGTAACCTTTGCT	TGCAAGTTTATGCAGGTTATGA	1984	4
WIAF-3924	G/A	A	G	AGCTTGATTTAGTTCATCTC[G/A]TTGTCTCTGGGACAGCACCA	GCTTTAGCTTGATTTAGTTCATCTC	GGTGCTGTCCCAGACACAA	1985	2
WIAF-3927	C/T	C	T	GAAAATCAGAGATGGTGCCA[C/T]CACCAGACAACACAAGTGCT	GAAAATCAGAGATGGTGCCA	AGCACTTGTGTTGTCTGGTG	1988	20
WIAF-3928	A/G	A	G	CCTGGGGCCAGGTTTGAGCC[A/G]CAGGGAGTGGGCAGGGGTG	GGGCCAGGTTTGAGCC	CCTGCCCACTTCCCTG	1989	9
WIAF-393	G/A	A	G	TAAAGCAAGGGACCTTGGC[G/T]CGCTGACGACTGCTGCTGTG	CCTGGGGCCAGGTTTGAGCC	GGCAGGGGACCTTGGC	2704	3
WIAF-3937	C/T	C	T	GGCCTGTCTGCGAGGCCCCA[C/T]GCAATCGTCGCAAACAGAT	GTCTGCGAGGCCCCA	TTGTTTGGCGAAGGATTGC	1998	20
WIAF-3938	A/C	A	C	GATGTATCTTCTGATTTTCC[A/C]AITTCCCGAAGTTGCCCACA	CCAGGATGTATCTTCTGATTTTCC	GGGCAACTTCGGGAAAT	1999	9
WIAF-3939	A/G	A	G	CCCTCGTTTGGGACGGAAC[A/G]GCTGCAGGCGGGTGAAGGAAG	CCTCGTTTGGGACGGGAA	TTCACCCGCTGCAGC	2000	20
WIAF-394	A/C	A	C	AGGGCTGGCCAGACAAGA[A/C]GCTGCGCAGACTGC	GGGGCCTGGCCAGACAAGA	TCCATTCCAAGATTGTCAGTT	2705	3
WIAF-3941	T/C	C	T	GGGCCTGACGTCACTAACGG[T/C]AACTGCACAATCTTGGAATCG	GCCTGACGTCACTAACGG	AGGCAGTAGCCATCACGC	2002	20
WIAF-395	T/C	C	T	TCTGAGTCCTGAGACTTTTC[T/C]GCGTGAICGCTATGCCTTGC	TTTATTGGTGTAGTTCTGAGTCCTG	AGGCAGTAGCCATCACGC	2706	3

(Continued on following pages.)

TABLE 6-7. (Continued)

WIAF Name	Alleles	Allele A	Allele B	Chipregion	primer up	primer down	ncbi SS	NwLib chrom
WIAF-402	A/G	A	G	CCAACTTACCAAACCTCTGT[A/G]GCTTAGCCTCGCCTACCGTA	CCCAACTTACCAAACCTCTG	CGGTAGGCGAGGCTAAGC	2709	14
WIAF-4024	A/G	A	G	CCTCCTCCGCATGCCAACGACC[G/A]GTTCATGTACAAGGCCCCTC	GATGTGTTGCCCCTC	AGAGGGGCCTTGTACA	1002	4
WIAF-4027	A/C	A	C	CTGCAACCCACTCTGAGCCTC[C/A]TCTCTCCTCTATTTTACTT	TCTGCAACCCACTCT	CAAGTAAAATAGGAGGAGAG	1004	1
WIAF-4028	A/T	A	T	TTGAAAGTCAGTACAAAT[A/T]TCCTCAAGTGGCATAAAAT	TTTGAAAGTCAGGTACAA	CATTTTTATGCCACTTG	1005	10
WIAF-4029	C/T	C	T	CAGCTCCTTGACCTATGAGC[C/T]TGGGCGCTGACTAGGAAAAGT	TCAGCTCCTTGACCTATG	AACTTTTCCTAGTCAGGCC	1006	1
WIAF-4035	A/T	A	T	AGATTCACGTGGAGATGT[C/T]TTGGCCAGGGCGGGCGATG	AGATTCACGTGGAGAG	GTGGGCTCACATCTG	837	8
WIAF-4045	A/T	A	T	AATGGGACGAGTGGCACTAGAA[A/T]AATCTTGAGCACAGTTAATG	ATCAATGGGCAGTGG	CATTCACGTGCTCCAAGAT	1010	12
WIAF-4050	C/G	C	G	CCTTTCATAAAACCAAACT[C/G]TAGCAAGATGCAAATGCATG	CCCTTTCATAAAAACCAAAC	CCATGCATTTGCATCT	1014	1
WIAF-4055	A/G	A	G	TTACCATAACATATTCATGG[A/G]TTCTGGGATAAGGGGTAGAC	TTGTCATTACCATAACATATTCATGG	TGTCTACCCCTTATCCCAGA	798	10
WIAF-4066	A/G	A	G	CGCTCTAGCCTCTAATTCCC[G/A]CTCTAGACAGCTGGCCCTG	CGCTCTAGCCTCTAATTCC	GTACTGACGACCAGGG	1017	1
WIAF-4070	C/T	C	T	AGAACTAATACCTGCTGTC[C/T]TCTGCCTCCCAGCACCTAT	CAGAACTAATACCTGCTGTC	GATAGGCGTCGTGGAG	840	10
WIAF-408	C/T	C	T	TTTAAAGCGAAGTTGAAACA[C/T]GAAGACGATAGTTAACGTCT	TTACTTTAAAGCGAAGTTGAAACA	TTACGAGAGGTTAACTATCGTCTTC	2140	17
WIAF-4080	A/C	A	C	GGGCAGCACCCTATAAATCA[A/C]CACCTTAATATGCTGCAACA	GGGCAGCACCCTATAA	TTGTTGCAGCATATTAAGGT	1028	18
WIAF-4082	A/G	A	G	CACCTGCTGCCTTGGTTC[A/G]AGCCCTCATCTTCTTTTACAG	TCACCTGCTGCCT	CCTGTAAAAGAGATGAGG	19300	14
WIAF-409	G/T	G	T	ATACGGTGTGCGAGGCAACA[G/T]GGAGAGGTACGGAAAATAGTT	GGTGTGCGAGGCAACA	GGAAGTAGAACTATTCCCGTACCTC	2141	17
WIAF-4095	C/T	C	T	ACGTTCTTCCACCAGAATT[T/C]CAGCCACCTTCTGCAGTGT	ACGTTCTTCCACCAGAA	GACATCGCAGAAGGTG	1033	2
WIAF-4098	C/T	C	T	GTTTCTTCATAAGATGGAAA[C/T]GCTATACCTTACCTACCTCG	TTCAGTTTCTTCATAAGATGGAAA	TCAGACTTTTACGAGGTAGGTAAGG	19449	3
WIAF-4117	A/G	A	G	ATCTTTCCCTTTCATCTCC[G/A]TTTGTGTGTTTGGCCAAATA	CAICTTTCCCTTTCA	TTATTTGGCCAAACA	843	7
WIAF-413	A/G	A	G	TGCCCTTCACATAACAGAAT[A/G]ACTTGCCATCTGCCTGCACC	TGGTGGTCACATAACAGAA	GCAGGCAGATGCCAAGT	2715	17
WIAF-4131	C/T	C	T	TGATAGAATTGCTAAATTGT[T/C]GTGAAATAGGTTAGAATTTT	CGGTGATAGAATGTTT	AGAAAAATTCTAACCTATTTCA	1042	9
WIAF-4138	T/G	G	T	AGTTAGGGTCTATGTATTTA[G/T]GATGTCTGCACCTTCTGCAG	GCAAGTTAGGGTCTATGTA	CTGCAGAAGGTGCAG	1043	13
WIAF-4139	C/T	C	T	CAGTGAAGGAAGGGATGGCA[C/T]AGCGTTATGTGTAAAAAACA	CAGTGAAGGAAGGGATG	TGTTTTTACACATAACGC	1044	1
WIAF-414	C/T	C	T	GGAAGACACCGTGCAAATGC[C/T]AAAGTGCACTGAGGAGGAGGG	AAGACACCGTGCAAATGC	CCCTCTCCTCAGTGCACTTT	19420	8
WIAF-4142	C/G	C	G	AGAGACAGCGATTGGCTAAC[C/G]CATGGCAGTAGTGGGCCCCA	AAAGAGACAGCGATTGGCTAA	GGGCCCACTACTGCCAT	806	4
WIAF-4147	C/T	C	T	TCAGAGGATACAGAGGCAAA[C/T]GTTGGTTATAGAAACTTCAGA	TGGGTAAATGTTATAGAAACTTCAGA	TGTCGTTGACTGCTATAACCAA	846	18
WIAF-4150	T/G	G	T	CATTCACACATCCCTTTCT[T/G]AGATGGTATTGGAAAGTAG	CATTCACACATCCCTT	TCTACTTCTCCAATACCATC	19187	8
WIAF-4164	T/G	G	T	CCTCTGTCGTCTTCTTCC[G/T]GTCGGATCTCTCCTCCTCT	CCTCTGTCGTCTTCTC	AGAGAGGAGAGAGATCCG	1055	17
WIAF-4186	C/T	C	T	CTCCCCACCTTTAAATCTGTTT[C/T]ATACCTTGCTTATTAAATGA	CCTCCCACCTTTAAATCTG	CGCTCATTTAATAAGCA	1062	19
WIAF-4187	T/G	G	T	GTTTTAGATAAAGGGACTT[G/T]GCAGGAGTGTTTAGGATGAA	CAtGTTTATCGTATAAAGGGCACTT	TCTCTTCATCCTAAACACTCCTG	19386	14
WIAF-4189	C/T	C	T	TTTATCGCTATAGATTTGCC[C/T]ACTTGACCATATCATACACAT	ACTCTTTATCGTATAGATTTGCC	GGCTCCATGTTGTATGATATGTCA	19450	14
WIAF-4216	A/G	A	G	AGCTACAAAACCTACCCTCA[A/G]TGAGCATGGTACTTGGCCTT	GGAGCTACAAAACCTACCCTCA	CAAAGGCCAAGTACCATGCT	19606	14
WIAF-422	A/C	A	C	CCTCCCCGCCCCCATCCCA[A/C]ATGATTCTTGAGATTTCTTTT	CCTGCCCCCATCCCA	CTTCTTTAAAGAAATCTCAAGATCAT	2718	17
WIAF-4222	A/C	A	C	ACAATTACCCTGTCAAGAGG[C/A]GAGTGCAAGGAAAC	AACAATTACCCTGTCAAG	AATCCACCTGAGCTG	1074	4
WIAF-423	T/A	A	T	GAGGTGGGAGCAAGGAAAC[T/A]CCGAAGAGGAAGAAGAAAG	GGTGGGAGCAAGGAAAC	TTTCTTGCTTCCTCTTCGG	2719	17
WIAF-4237	C/G	C	G	ACACCTTCCCCACTCTTA[C/G]GGTACAGAAAGGAGATGCAT	GTACACCTTCCCCACTCTCTT	TGCTGTTCATGCATCTCCTT	682	1
WIAF-4240	A/G	A	G	AAGCAGATCTTGAGGGTTAT[A/G]GTTAAGCCTGATAAACAGCCT	TGTCAAGCAGATCTTGAGGG	AAAGAGGCTGTTATCAGGCTTAAC	19363	11
WIAF-4242	C/G	C	G	AGTCACCATGCCCAGCCTAG[C/G]ATGAGTTTAGTAAGATTTGG	AGTCACCATGCCCAGCCTA	CTCCCAGCATAACCAAATC	19369	22
WIAF-4245	A/G	A	G	ATATTTTCTTGACATGAGGT[A/G]GCTTTTAGCAGCATTTCGG	AAATCCATATTTTCTTGACATGAGG	CCGAAATGTGCTAAAAAGC	19156	10
WIAF-425	C/G	C	G	ACACTGAAGACTCACCAGAA[C/G]AGGGTGGGGTGGGGAATACT	CCACACTGAAGACTCACCAGA	TCCCCACCCCACCCT	2721	15
WIAF-4251	A/G	A	G	GCCGACAATCAGCATTGTCTC[A/G]TGTACAGCTGCCCTTCCCTGC	TCAGACACTGCCGACATCA	TCTTGTCCAGTTGTCTCCCA	19415	3
WIAF-4253	C/T	C	T	GGGGTGAGCACAGCACAAA[C/T]GGGGTGGGACGTGCAGAGAG	GTACACATCCTGGGGGTGAG	GCTTCCTTTGCCTTTACCCT	19382	17
WIAF-4256	C/G	C	G	TGCACTTGTTACTCCCCAGAC[C/G]GAGAGCTTACATACCATATA	TGCACTTGTTACTCCCCAGAC	CGCTTCCAGAACCCTGTAT	19383	19
WIAF-4257	A/G	A	G	TTATTTCATATTCCCCACCAC[A/G]ATAACGACTCCTTTAATTTA	TTCTACTTTATTTCATATTCCCACCA	CCCATTCAGCATTCCTTCTGA	19384	6
WIAF-4259	A/C	A	C	CTGAATCACAACAATGGAC[A/C]AATCTCAAATCATTATGCTG	CCACTGAATCACAACAATGCTG	TCCATCAGCATAATGATTTGAGA	19607	14
WIAF-432	A/T	A	T	GAGGGTTGAGGTGTAGATAT[A/T]CTTCCTCTCTTCTCGTGGAG	CTAGGAGGGTTGAGGTGTAGATAT	GCTCCACGAGAAGAGAGGAA	2727	11
WIAF-433	A/G	A	G	GCTTGGACCTTGGATAGGTC[A/G]ACCGGCTGAAGGTTGGACAG	GCTTGGACCTTGGATAGGTC	CCAACCTTCAGCGCGGT	2145	9
WIAF-436	T/G	G	T	CAGATCTCGTTTATTTAA[T/G]ATCAAACATTCACCACGCTG	TGAAGATCACAGTTCTCGGTTTATTT	CAGCTGTGGTGAATGTTGAT	2730	14
WIAF-440	C/T	C	T	TTGAAAAGTCTTTCGACCAC[C/T]TTCGTGGCATCCGAATTTTAG	CAGGACAAAACTTTTGAAAAAGTC	CTAAAATTGCGGATCCGAA	2148	X
WIAF-444	T/C	C	T	AGCCTCCCTTTAGACACCTC[T/C]ACAGGTACAGCCGACCATGC	AGCCTCCCTTTAGACACCTC	CATGTCGGCGTACCTGT	2734	15
WIAF-4500	G/C	G	C	TGCAAAAGGGTCAGTATGG[G/C]TTAGGGAAAACATTCCATCC	TGCAAAAGGGTCAGTATGG	AGGATGGAATGTTTTCCCTAA	19421	2
WIAF-4501	C/T	C	T	TCTTCCTGCTTTATTTTGCC[C/T]ACAGTTTAGGTAAATAAAAG	TCTTCCTGCTTTATTTTGCC	TCTTGGGCATCTTTTATTTACC	19403	1
WIAF-4502	G/T	G	T	CACTTAAGCCATTACCAATA[G/T]TGAGATGTAATGGAGAATTT	GCTCTTTACACTTAAGCCATTACCA	CCACATTAAATTCTCCATTACATCTC	19387	2

WIAF ID				Sequence	Flank	Flank	Pos	Chr
WIAF-4503	C	T	C/T	CAAATGGTGCCATAGTATAA[C/T]AATAGCTATAACAATTATGG	CCAAATGGTGCCATAGTAT	CAATCCATAATTGTTATAGCT	19432	7
WIAF-4504	A	G	A/G	CCATAAATGGTGCCATAGTATT[A/G]TTATACTATGGCACCATTTG	CCATAAATGGTGCCATAGTATT	TCCAAATGGTGCCATAGTA	19389	7
WIAF-4505	A	G	G/A	ATGCTTCCTCCTTTGTCTCTT[G/A]TGGCGTATGGCAGTGAGCAGG	CATGCTTCCTCCTTTG	CACTGCAAAGCTGGTC	19404	11
WIAF-4506	A	G	A/G	TATTCCAGATGTGTTTGGTC[A/G]TGGCTATGGCAGTGAGCAGG	TATTCCAGATGTGTTTGGT	ATACCTGCTCACTGCC	19608	7
WIAF-4507	C	T	T/C	TATTTGTTCTGCTCATAATT[T/C]CCAATATGTACCAGACCTTC	TATTTGTTCTGCTCATAATT	TTAGTTGAGTATTGTTCTGCTCATAA	19422	1
WIAF-4508	C	T	C/T	CGGAGAAGCATTGTTTTCTT[C/T]GGGCCAAGAAGGTATCTACC	CGGAGAAGCATTGTTTTCTT	GGTAGATACCTTCTTGGC	19390	9
WIAF-4509	A	C	A/G	TGGGTAGGTCCAGTAATCCA[A/G]GGATTCAGGAAGGAGGCCAC	TGGGTAGGTCCAGTAATCCA	CTTCGATCCTCGTGG	19391	8
WIAF-4510	A	C	C/A	AGGGAGACAGAAGTGCTGATT[C/A]TCTGGTGGACAAACCAGAACT	AGGGAGACAGAAGTGCTGATT	AAGTTCTGTTCTCCACC	19344	19
WIAF-4511	A	T	A/T	TGTGGAGCTAGAATCCCCAG[A/T]GGCCAGCTGAGTGCTGGTCG	TGTGGAGCTAGAATCCCCAG	CCAGATGTGCTGGCTGACT	19377	9
WIAF-4512	A	G	A/G	GAAATAGGGACTGCAAGGGC[A/G]GGCGTGTATTGCAGAAGGATGG	GAAATAGGGACTGCAAGGGC	GGGCCATCCTTCTCAATACA	19364	17
WIAF-4513	C	T	C/T	TAACACATTTTCTGCAAAT[C/T]ACCTCTTTCATTTAACAGCC	TAACACATTTTCTGCAAAT	GGGCTGTTAAATGAA	19392	15
WIAF-4514	A	C	G/A	CAGAAATCCAGTTATTTTCC[G/A]CCCTCAAAATGACAGCCATG	CAGAAATCCAGTTATTTTCC	CATGGCTGTCATTTTGA	19393	21
WIAF-4515	A	C	A/C	ACATGGCTTCGAGAGTTG[A/C]ACAGATTCGTGGAATCACCCAG	ACATGGCTTCGAGAGTTG	GCTGTCTTCCAGGAATCT	19394	15
WIAF-4516	C	T	T/C	CTTGCCTCCTTCTGGTGCTC[T/C]TACTCCAAGTCTATTTCATT	CTTGCCTCCTTCTGGTGCTC	GGAAAAATGAAATAGACTTGGAGT	19451	8
WIAF-4517	A	G	A/G	TGTTTTCTATTACAGGACAC[A/G]TGGATGCTGGAATCACCCAG	TGTTTTCTATTACAGGACAC	CTGGGTGATTCCAGC	19345	7
WIAF-4518	C	C	C/T	CCAGTGACTCTGAGATGTCA[C/T]CAGACTGAGATGTC	CCAGTGACTCTGAGATGTCA	TAACGGTGGTTCTCA	19346	7
WIAF-4519	A	C	C/A	GAAAATATGATTTAAATAGAC[C/A]GTGATGTCATCTTAAAAATATA	GAAAATATGATTTAAATAGAC	GAAAGTATATTTAAGATGTACCA	19405	10
WIAF-452	A	G	G/A	CTTTTCATTTTTGCTTTTAAATAGAAC[G/A]CATTTGATTTTTAGTATATGA	TTTGCTTTTTAAATAGAACCA	TGATGTGTCAATATACTAAAAATCAAAG	2739	4
WIAF-4520	C	G	G/C	ATGAAATAAAAGTAAGACCA[G/C]ATAAAAATACCTATGATGCT	ATAATGGTATGAAATAAAAGTAAGACCA	AACAATGAGCATCATAGGTATTTT	19336	13
WIAF-4521	A	G	A/G	AATCTGAATATTCAGCACAT[A/G]CAAGTGTGACAACCACTTGT	GGAGAATCTGAATATTCAGCACA	TACTAAACAAGTGGTTGTCACACTT	19452	7
WIAF-4522	C	G	A/G	TGCCAGGAGGTAATACTAT[A/G]CATTACAAGAAAAGACAAC	TCATTGCCAGGAGGTAATACT	GTTTCAGTTGTCTTTTCTCTGTAATG	19453	4
WIAF-4523	C	C	C/G	CAGATCATTGGTTAGGCTAC[C/G]CTTCCGTAATTGCCTTGGTC	CAGATCATTGGTTAGGCTC	AACAGAAGCAATTACAGGAA	19406	9
WIAF-4524	C	T	C/T	CCCTACCAGATTATTAGGAGACAG[C/T]CATGCAAAGGAATTTCTAGC	ACCAGATTATTAGGAGACAG	TGCTAGAAATTCCTTTGCATG	19454	8
WIAF-4525	A	T	T/A	ACTCTAATTAGCATGACATGAGAGACAATTTAC[T/A]TTTTAAGAACTTTGTGATC	TAGCATGAGACAATTTAC	GGCTGATCACAAAGTTCTTAAAAA	19455	11
WIAF-4526	T	T	T/A	GTGTTTTCAGCAAAACTTG[C/T]ATAGATCATTCAGAGAGGGC	GAGTACTGACCCGGGAGATG	CACTGGTTTTCCTTTTCGAAG	19456	12
WIAF-4527	C	T	C/T	CTGTGTTTTCAGCAAAACTTG[C/T]ATAGATCATTCAGAGAGGGC	GTGTTTTCAGCAAAACTTG	CGTAGCCCTCTCTGAAATGATC	19457	4
WIAF-4528	A	G	G/A	GAGGAGTGTTTTTCTATCT[G/A]CAGCCAACAGAAATACTGT	ATACTGGGGCCATTGTAGG	TGTACTACAGTATTTCTGTTTGGCTG	19458	4
WIAF-4529	C	T	T/C	GTTTACGGATATTTATATTC[T/C]AGTCTCACTCTCTTGTCCCA	AGATGCGTGTTTACGGATATTTATATTC	GGTGGGACAAGAGAGTGAGACT	19407	1
WIAF-4530	C	T	C/T	TTACATGGTGAATAACTTTC[C/T]ATAGGACCCACAAGGCCTGC	TGCTAGATTACATGGTGAATAACTTTC	CAGGCCTTGTGGGTCCTAT	19459	11
WIAF-4531	G	G	T/G	TTCCATCCTTTCAACATCTT[T/G]TGTCACATTTTAGGTGATGC	TTTTTGGTTAGTGTATGTCTACTATACCTT	TTACAAGAGCATCACCTAAAATGT	19430	14
WIAF-4532	C	T	C/T	TTCCAGAAAATGGCGATT[C/T]CTGCAACGGCCCTCCCCCA	TTCCAGAAAATGGGAT	TTTGGTGAGGAAGGG	19290	6
WIAF-4533	A	G	A/G	TTATGTACAAGAAAATGGAA[A/G]TGATTTTAGATCCTCCCCA	TGCTTTATGTACAAGAAAATGGAA	CTGGGGGGAGGATCTAAAATC	19425	5
WIAF-4535	G	G	G/A	TAGTTGTGCTCCAGGACCTA[G/A]GCGTGCTCACTCTACCTTGT	CTAGTTGTGCTCCAGGAC	ACAAGGTAGAGTGAGCA	19460	2
WIAF-4536	C	T	C/T	ACATCCACTGCTTTCAATAA[C/T]TTCACTCCACTTATGTCTTAC	CCTCACATCCACTGCTTTCA	TGTAATTTTGTAAGACATAAGTGGAGTG	19395	8
WIAF-4537	C	T	G/T	AGGATCTTTCAGGTAGCACT[G/T]GAGAATCTGAATATTCAGCA	TCAGGATCTTTCAGGTAGCACT	AAAATGGGCTCTATTCATTTC	19424	7
WIAF-4538	C	T	C/T	AGGAAATAGACTGGATAATGA[C/T]AAGAATGAATAGAACAACCAT	TCAGGAAATAGACTGGATAATGA	TTCTGTTGTTGTTCTTGCTTGT	19426	2
WIAF-4539	C	T	C/T	ATGTCCATTACCTCTACTTA[C/T]GACAAGCAAGAACAAGCAACA	AAGGTCCATGTCCATTACCTCTACTTA	TGATGACACCACAAAACACTTG	19408	7
WIAF-4540	C	A	C/T	CGTTAACATGCATGTCTGTT[C/T]AACAAGTGTTGTGGTGTGTCA	ACGGTTAACATGCATGTCTGTT	CAAGTAATCCATCCCAATC	19429	9
WIAF-4541	A	G	A/G	GCCTATGTTACTGGTATGCTA[A/G]TGGTATTGGATTGGGATGGA	CCCAAGCCTATGTTACT	TTTGGAAGGTAAGATGTGAACC	19388	2
WIAF-4542	A	G	A/G	GTAAGATGTGAACCTATACA[A/G]TGGCCAAGGAAAGTAGAAATG	GTAAGATGTGAACCTATACA	CTGTCAGAAAACAGAGGTGTTG	19427	14
WIAF-4543	A	C	A/C	CACTGCGCCAATATCCTCC[A/C]CCAACACCCTCGTTTTCTGA	CACTGCGCCAATATCCTCC	TGCCGCCATATCTCCTC	19428	1
WIAF-4544	A	G	A/G	CAGGCCCACTGTTCCTATGC[A/G]CACTGGCTTTGTAGGCATTC	CAGGCCCACTGTTCCTATGC	TGAATGCCTACAAAGCCAGT	19409	9
WIAF-4545	C	T	C/T	CCTGGTGCTAGGTCAGCTAAAGG[C/T]AACTGTTCTATAAGGATGGG	GGAAAGGGGTCAGCTAAAGG	GGATACCTACCCATCCTTATAGAACA	19410	12
WIAF-4546	A	C	A/C	AGGAAAATAGACTGGATAATGA[C/T]GGAGAGTTGAGTGCCACAGG	AGGAAAATAGACTGGATAATGA	ACCTGTGGCACTCAACTCTC	19411	21
WIAF-4547	G	A	G/A	AGCAAAAGGTTGTTCCTAAA[G/A]TAAGGCGAGTCACAGCGGG	AGCAAAAGGTTGTTCCTAAA	TGTATCAGCTGCCC	19412	15
WIAF-4548	G	T	G/T	AAAGGTAGCTTTTCCCAAAC[G/T]GATCTTTTCATTTAGGTGAG	AAAGGTAGCTTTTCCCAAA	CCTCACCTAAATGAAAAG	19413	12
WIAF-4549	A	G	A/G	TACCTTCTGGGCATACAACAC[A/G]TGGCAGCAGGGCCTCGGGAA	GTACCTTCTGGGCATAC	CTACCCCTCTTCCCG	19396	2
WIAF-455	C	T	T/C	GAATCCCTATCCCATTCTG[T/C]GTATGAGTCCCATTTGCCTT	GAATCCCTATCCCATTCTG	CAAGGCAAAATGGGACTCATA	2741	1
WIAF-4550	C	G	C/G	GAGCACCCACCTACCTCATG[C/G]AACTGTTGAGAGAAATAAAT	GAGCACCCACCTACCTCATG	CAATGTTCATTTATTTCTCTCAACA	19357	X
WIAF-4551	C	T	C/T	TGGACAACAAAAAGGAATA[C/T]GATCCAGCCTCATGCAACAT	TGGACAACAAAAAGGAATA	TGTTGCATGAGCCTGGAT	19183	15
WIAF-4552	T	C	T/C	CTCATCATCTGCGCAAGAGA[T/C]CAAAGAGGTCAGCTTCTGTT	CTCATCATCTGCGCAAGAGA	CAACAGAAGCTGACCTCTT	19207	22
WIAF-4553	T	C	T/C	TAGAGAGTAGCAGTATTTCA[T/C]TTGGTACCTGGTACTGATTAT	ATCTGTAGAGAGTAGCAGTAGTATTT	CATAATCAGTACCAGGTACC	19347	17
WIAF-4554	A	G	A/G	TTTTAGCAAAGCTGCAAGTCA[G/A]AGGAGAGCTCAAGCAATATTA	TAGAGAGTAGCAGTATTTCA	TTAATATTGCTTGAGCTGG	19348	17
WIAF-4555	A	G	A/G	TTTTAGCAAAGCTGCAAGTCA[G/A]AGGAGAGCTCAAGCAATATTA	TTTTTGGAAGGATGCCCC	GGACTCCTGCTAAGC	19349	17
WIAF-4556	A	G	A/G	TTATTTTCCCAAAC[G/T]GTATGTCCGCACCACTTGC	TTATTTTGGAAGGATGCCCC	AGCAAGTGGTCGGAG	19350	17
WIAF-4557	C	T	C/T	AGCCAGAGTCTGCACAGTCA[C/T]AGGGCAAGCAGAAAATTCTT	GGTTGCCTGCGAGCCAGAGTC	GAAAGAATTTTCTGCTTGCCC	19461	11

(Continued on following pages.)

TABLE 6-7. (*Continued*)

WIAF Name	Alleles	Allele A	Allele B	Chipregion	primer up	primer down	ncbi SS	NwLib chrom
WIAF-4558	A/T	A	T	GCTTCCTTTGGCGAAAGGATI[A/T]AAGAAGTGAGTGACGGTGAC	GATGAAGTGGCTTCCTTTGG	CACAGGTCACCGTCACTCAC	19370	5
WIAF-4559	A/G	A	G	AGATGGAGACGAAGGCCAGCI[A/G]TGGCTCTCACAGGGCAGCGC	TCAACCAGAGATGGAGACGA	AGGCGTGCCCTGTGAGAG	19282	3
WIAF-456	G/C	C	G	GACTCCTGGGACAAAGGACI[G/C]AAAAACACTCTTCTGTCGAT	GACTCCTGGGACAAAGGAC	CAGATATCCACAGAAGAGTGTTTT	19161	3
WIAF-4560	G/T	G	T	AGGGCTCAGAAGATGTCGGGI[G/T]ACGATAATCAGTGTAGGC	AGAGGGCTCAGAAGATGTCG	CATCGATGGTGCCTACACTG	19367	3
WIAF-4561	C/T	C	T	ACAGACACAGCATCACACCAI[C/T]AGGGCCCACGGAGGGTCGG	ACAGACACAGCATCACACCA	GATTAGAGCTGCCTTTCCCA	19416	1
WIAF-4562	G/A	A	G	TGGGTGCTGTTCTCGCCTCI[G/A]GGAGCTCTCGTCAATTGCA	TTGGGTGCGTGTTCTCT	TGCAATTGACAGAGAGC	19351	2
WIAF-4563	C/T	C	T	GGTCTAAGTTGCTGATTACCI[C/T]GGATTTTTCTGACGATCTTT	GGTCTAAGTTGCTGATT	GAAAGATCGTCAGAAAAA	19352	7
WIAF-4564	G/A	A	G	ATCCACACTGCCACTGCCTI[G/A]GCCCAAAACGTCTTATGTG	TATCCACACTGCCACTG	CACAATAAGACGTTTTGG	19397	14
WIAF-4565	C/T	C	T	TTTAAGAAGCTTGATTTGGAI[C/T]AATTCTGGTTCTTTGAGTGT	TTTAAGAAGCTTGATTTGG	CACACTCAAAGAACCAGAA	19398	2
WIAF-4566	G/A	A	G	ATGCAGAAAGAGGGGAAAAAI[G/A]GAGCGAGCTGTGGTGGACAA	AATGCAGAAAGAGGG	CTTGTCCACCACAGCT	19353	1
WIAF-4567	G/C	C	G	TAGGATAAGTGTTATCCCAGI[G/C]TTCATAGGTATGGAGTCTCA	AATGAGTAGGATAAGTGTTATCCCAG	CATCTATGAGACTCCATACCTATGAA	19243	5
WIAF-4568	C/A	A	C	AATTTCATTTATCATCTGAI[C/A]AGCCCCTTCTTATAACGTAC	GGGGTGGTTTATTAATTTCATTT	GATGTACGTTATAAGAAGGGCT	19462	1
WIAF-4569	G/C	C	G	TACCGCTGCTATTCCCAGATI[G/C]AAGATTTTGGTGACGAGAC	CCCGCTGCTATTCCCAGAT	GGTCTCCTTCACCAAAATCTT	19419	9
WIAF-457	A/G	A	G	ACCTCTTGTGGATAAAAGGI[A/G]CATTGTTTTTCATTTAGCTTG	TTAATACCTCTTGTTGGATAAAAGG	GAAGACAAGCTAATGAAAAACAATG	2742	8
WIAF-4570	G/A	A	G	GAAAATACAAGAACCTGCCCI[G/A]AAATAAGGCAACTTTTGAA	AGAAATACAAGAACCTGCCC	TCTTCCAAAAGTTGCCTTATTT	19463	3
WIAF-4571	G/A	A	G	GAGTGGAGGCATAATAGGCTI[G/A]TGGTGTTAGAAGGCAGGAAT	GAGTGGAGGCATAATAGGCT	AAATAACCACATTCCTGCCTT	19464	2
WIAF-4572	A/G	A	G	AAAATTCTATCCACATCCAAI[A/G]GTGTCTCTGAGAGTCGGAG	AAAATTCTATCCACATCCAA	GCCTCGACTTCTCAGAGACA	19465	6
WIAF-4573	G/A	A	G	GGATAAAGGGACTGAGATGCI[G/A]AATGGGGATGGGCAATAACC	TGGATAAAGGGACTGAGATGC	TTATTGCCCATCCCATT	19466	7
WIAF-4574	T/C	C	T	CAAAATGTAAATCAAAACCAI[T/C]ACTTTTCTGCATGTACTAAG	CGTATTCCCAAAATGTAAATCAAA	TGACCTTAGTACATGCAGAAAAGT	19467	6
WIAF-4575	A/C	A	C	TACTTTCAGGAGCAAGCATCI[A/C]CATATATGTAGAAGTAAAAT	AATACTTTCAGGAGCAAGCATC	TGGCTTTTTCATTTTACTTCTCTACA	19468	13
WIAF-4576	C/T	C	T	GACTCATTTCTTCTTTTTGCAI[C/T]TATTTCTCAGTTATTTGCAG	TGGACTCATTTCTTCTTTTTGCA	GGGGCTGCAAATAACCTAGA	19469	7
WIAF-4577	C/T	C	T	TCCCCGAACTTGCCATTCAGI[C/T]AGATATTCTTTCATGGGTTA	GTTCCCCCAACTTCACATT	GCAAAATAACCCATGAAAGAATAT	19470	15
WIAF-4578	C/T	C	T	GAATGTACTTGAITGTACTTGI[C/T]CCTCACATCCATTTACCACC	CAGAGTGAAITGTACTTGAITGTACTTG	GGTGGTAAAITGGAITGTGAGG	19471	3
WIAF-4579	T/C	C	T	CGGACGGAAAGCGGGGCCTGI[T/C]GGGTCCTTGTGTCCCTGCCG	GGAAAGCGGGGCCTG	CAGGGACACAAGGACCC	19358	10
WIAF-4580	A/G	A	G	AGATGGGAAAGGTGACCAAAI[A/G]ACAATATAGAGGCAGAGGGC	GATGGGAAAGGTGACCAAA	TGGGCCTCTGCCTCTATITG	19472	21
WIAF-4581	A/T	A	T	AAGCAAACACTTACAGAATTI[A/T]ACCAAACCTACGGGGATCTAG	AAGTTAAAAGCAAACACTTACAGAATT	GGAAATGTIAAACAGAITACCTCTTCA	19473	7
WIAF-4582	C/T	C	T	GTTTTGAACCCTAGCTGTCAI[C/T]GTGCCACCTGCGGGATCTAG	CGTTTTGAACCCTAGCTGTCA	TCCCGCAGGTGGCAC	19474	11
WIAF-4583	C/T	C	T	TAGTCTGTCTCCATTTGCCAI[C/T]GTCTTCCTCCAGTAGAATAAG	ATAGTCTGTCTCCATTTGCCA	CCCTGTCTTATTCTACTGGAGAAGA	19475	6
WIAF-4584	C/T	C	T	GAGCCTTTAGTGCAAAAACAI[C/T]TATGCCATGCGGGGAAATAAA	TGAGCCTTTAGTGCAAAAACA	TTTCCCGCATGGCATA	19418	6
WIAF-4585	T/C	C	T	GCATTGGGCGTGTGTTCCI[T/C]CTCCCACTTCCCTCCCACTA	TGCTGGGCGTGTGTTCC	GGTGCAGAAGAGCCCG	19423	17
WIAF-4586	A/G	A	G	ACATTAAGAACAAGCTTTCCI[A/G]CTCCCACCTTCCCTCCCACTA	CAGACATTAAGAACAAGCTTTCC	TGGGAGGGAAGTGGGA	19359	2
WIAF-4587	G/A	A	G	CAGGTCAGCCACCACTATGCI[G/A]CAGGTTCTCATCATTGAAGC	AACAGGTCAGCCACC	GCTTCAATGATGAGAACCT	19354	22
WIAF-4588	T/C	C	T	CACTCAGGGCCGTCATGCTGI[T/C]ACACATCCAGGGGGCGCCCT	ATACACTCAGGGCCGT	TACAAAGGGTAGGGCG	19355	17
WIAF-4589	T/C	C	T	ATGTGGTGGTCTTGTGTAGAI[T/C]GGGGGGCTTTGGTTTCAGTTG	ATGTGGTGGTCTTGTGTAG	GCAACTGAAACCAAAGC	19356	17
WIAF-459	A/G	A	G	ATAACGTAGACCTATGTCI[A/G]TGCCATGTAGTTTTTTGGTT	CCCAAAAATAACGTAAGTACCTATGTC	TTGCAAGTAAATGAACCAAAAA	19609	9
WIAF-4590	C/T	C	T	CCATCAAAATTTCCTTCACAI[C/T]TCAATACTGTTGAACAACAA	GCCATCAAAATTTCCTTCACA	TTCAAGTGGATGAGCAAGA	19379	15
WIAF-4591	C/T	C	T	ATCTCAAGCATCGATGTCAAI[C/T]GGGGGCAACCGGAAGACCAT	CATCTCAAGCATCGATG	ATGGTCTTCCGGTTG	19399	
WIAF-4592	A/G	A	G	AAAATACCTCCATTTGCTTI[A/G]TCCTTTAGTGAAGATGATA	TAAAATACCTCCATTTGC	GGTATCATCTTCACTAAAGG	19400	11
WIAF-4593	T/C	C	T	GCATTGTTTTCTAGGAGAACCI[T/C]GCGTCATACCTTTATCTATA	TGCATTGTTTTCTAGGAG	GCTATAGATAAAGGTATGACG	19401	15
WIAF-4594	G/A	A	G	TGGAGACTGCCTGCATGGAGI[G/A]TTGGCTTATCGGGGATACAG	GAGACTGCCTGCATGAGG	TGTATCCCCGATAAGCCAA	19476	4
WIAF-4595	G/C	C	G	TAATTCCTTTGTGCAGGAAGI[G/C]AGGTTTTGTGGAAATGATGT	GATAATTCCTTTGTGCAGGAAG	CAACATCATTTCCAAAAACCT	19477	15
WIAF-4596	A/C	A	C	TTTTCCCTTTAAATGCTAI[A/C]ACAAGTGCCACTAATCCACA	GGAGTTTTTCCCTTTAAATGC	CTGTGGATTAGTGGCACTTGT	19478	2
WIAF-4597	G/A	A	G	TTATCTGGCCAAACTGATACI[G/A]GCATGACCCCAAGCCTCAGG	CTTATCTGGCCAAACTGATA	ATACCTGAGCGTGTGG	19360	15
WIAF-463	C/A	A	C	GCTGTGGGTGGTGATTTGGTI[C/A]AGCATATCTTAGGTATATAA	TGTGGGTGGTGATTTGGT	CAGTTAAAAGTTATGGCTTCAAAG	2744	12
WIAF-468	G/T	G	T	TCAGTTGCTTCCTTGGCCAGTI[G/T]CTACTCCTCAGGGTGCAGCAT	CAGTGTCCTTGGCAGTGT	TGCTGCACCTGCAGGAGTAG	2749	22
WIAF-472	T/C	C	T	GTGTAGGATAGAGTTTTAAAI[T/C]ATTGGTATGTGGTGCTAGAG	GTTTTTATGAAGTGTAGGATAGAGTTTTTAA	ACTAACTCTAGCACCACATACCAA	19610	8
WIAF-475	C/T	C	T	TGCAACTTCTCAGTTTATTI[C/T]TAACTTTAAITGAITCTCTGTG	GATAITTTTGCAACTTCTCAGTTTTATT	TCTTAAAGCTAGTATAAAGTCACAGAGA	2753	3
WIAF-478	A/G	A	G	CAGAAAGCCACGGAAGCCACI[A/G]GCCACTAGCCCTGAACCTTG	AAGCCACGGAAGCCAC	AGGTTCAGGGCTAGTGC	2150	14
WIAF-482	A/G	A	G	AAAGATGCTCTTAGACTGAI[A/G]AITCAITAAAGAGTGCCTCAG	GTCAAAAAGATGCTCTTAGACTGA	GACCTGAGGCACTCTTTATGAA	2152	4
WIAF-483	C/A	A	C	TAGAAAGCACAGCACTGAI[C/A]AAATCACTAAAGGATTCCAC	CTAGAAAGCACAGGGATGACA	GTCTTAGTGGAATTCCTTAGTGAITTT	2153	4
WIAF-484	T/C	C	T	CCTTTCCTTCCAITGTCCTCI[T/C]CTTGAGATGGGTTGCAAATG	CCTTTCCTTCCAITGTCCTC	CATTTGCAACCCATCTCAAG	2756	4
WIAF-487	C/T	C	T	GGAGACCCCACCTCTCACCAI[C/T]TTAGAAAAGGGCAITTCAAG	GACCCCACCTCTCACCA	GCTTGAAAITGCCCTTTTCTAA	2155	2

WIAF ID	Flanking Sequence (left)	Allele 1	Allele 2	SNP	Flanking Sequence (right)	Pos	Ct
WIAF-489	TGACTGTGGGACCAGAGAAAG[G/A]GATGTAGATTGTCACATTCA	A	G	G/A	TGACTGTGGGACCAGAGAAAG	2156	8
WIAF-490	TTTGGTTGTTCCATCCTA[G/C]ATGTTCTGCCTTATAATCTTT	C	G	G/C	TCTTTGGTGTTTCTCCATCCT	2157	8
WIAF-496	ACACAGAATCATCAAAGCAC[A/T]ATGTTGTTTGACAGAAATG	A	T	A/T	CAGACTACATCATTTATCTCAAACACAGA	19479	8
WIAF-505	AATCTCTGCCTTGTATCATG[G/C]TTATCACTGGACACAGCCAC	C	G	G/C	GTGGCTGTGTCCAGTGATAA	2765	13
WIAF-506	GGGCTGGACACTGCAGTGAT[T/C]AGGGGCAGGTGTGGGGCAGG	C	T	T/C	CCCACACCTGCCCCT	2766	16
WIAF-507	GAATCTGTGGTTTTCCGCTG[A/G]TAGACCACAGGGCCAATCAC	A	G	A/G	TGATTGGCCCTGTGTCTA	2767	17
WIAF-510	TTTATCACGCAGGGGACAGT[T/C]AAGGTTGGCTTCTCTAAATGC	C	T	T/C	GGCATTAGAGAGGCCAACCTT	2770	16
WIAF-511	CTAATAAGCAAAGACCTGCA[A/C]CCCTGGCTTCTGCAACTGCA	A	C	A/C	GGAGTCAGGAAGCCAGGG	2161	5
WIAF-512	TTTGGGTGTGAGCGGGATTAT[G/A]TCTGACGCCATGGGTGTTCA	A	G	G/A	CACCCATGGCGTCAGA	2771	7
WIAF-514	CTGTCTCATCCAATAAGCAC[T/G]CATGACCTCAGCCCCATACT	G	T	T/G	TGTCTGTCTCATCCAATAAGCA	2779	3
WIAF-523	TTGTTGGCACCAGAAAAGCT[C/T]ATGTTCTATGTTATGTCACT	C	T	C/T	CAGTATGTACAGTGACATAACATGAAACA	2782	1
WIAF-531	TCTTGAACTTAATAAATAC[T/G]CTGTTTTACAAAACAGTGAA	G	T	T/G	GTACATTCACGTGTTTGTAAAAAG	2783	12
WIAF-533	GCTTCAGCTTAACTGACAGA[T/C]GTTAAAGCTTTCTGGTTAGA	C	T	T/C	AAACAATCTAACCAGAAAGCTTTAA	2169	15
WIAF-534	ACCCAAAACACAGAGACCCC[G/A]TGAGTCTTAGTCAATCCTAT	A	G	G/A	GCCACTATAGGATTGACTAAGACTCA	2170	1
WIAF-537	GGCACAGAAGCCAGTCATAC[G/T]TGCTTTAAAATTGACCAAC	G	T	G/T	GGTTGGGTCAATTTTAAAGCA	2171	6
WIAF-538	TATTGTGATTGTTTTACATG[C/T]GAAATCTGGCTTCAGAAAGG	C	T	C/T	ACCTTTCGGAAGCCAGAATTTC	2790	4
WIAF-545	TGGACACCAACAGAAT[A/C]CTCCCCGTCCTTTGAAATTTC	A	C	A/C	GAAATTTCAAAGGACGGGAG	2792	5
WIAF-548	TTCTTCCAAAAACAAAGAAT[A/G]AACATTGGAATAGTCACTTA	A	G	A/G	CCTTGTAAGTGACTATTCCAATGTT	2793	7
WIAF-550	GGTCAGGTCCCCAGATTGA[G/C]GTCTGAGTGTGGGCAAGTGT	C	G	G/C	CACTTGCCCACACTCAGAC	2794	12
WIAF-552	CCTGCAAACATAATTGATTC[A/G]TATCTGCGAGACTTACACTC	A	G	A/G	GCTTGAGTGTAAGTCTGCAGA	2796	14
WIAF-554	AGGGGCCTTGCTGCTACTGG[G/A]TGTTAGTTTGCTACACTGCTG	A	G	G/A	CACACAGGACTGCAAACTAACA	2177	21
WIAF-559	CCTGCATGGTCTTTTCTCTG[C/T]TTTACATCATTGTCATAAAT	C	T	C/T	AGTTGAGATTTATGACAATGATGTAAA	2181	8
WIAF-563	GTAGAAAAATTACTATCCAA[A/C]CTGAAATTCAGAATAAATAGA	A	C	A/C	TCACCTTTCTATTTATTCTGAATTCA	2183	8
WIAF-565	CAAATAAAGATGGTAGTGAG[C/T]GAACAGAAGAAGGTTTCATTG	C	T	C/T	CAGTTTAGGAGTCAATGAAACCTC	2187	7
WIAF-570	AAGAGCGTCCTATGAATCAT[G/A]CATTTGTTCCTGTTTATGCT	A	G	G/A	AACAGCAATAACAGGAAACAAATG	2802	19
WIAF-571	ATCTACAGCTGCAGAATGGC[C/A]CTCTTCCCTTCCCCAGCTTTT	A	C	C/A	AAAAGCTGAAAGGAAGGAGAG	2805	5
WIAF-575	TATTCAGGGAAAACTTTAAT[C/T]TTCTTTGTCTTCTCCAAAAA	C	T	C/T	CTGTTTTTGGAGAAGACAAAGAA	2189	6
WIAF-577	AAAATGAGTTGAAATAAATG[T/C]AAGTTGAATAATGACACTGT	C	T	T/C	TTTCAACAGTGTCATTATTCAACTT	19612	3
WIAF-579	AAAATTGCTTTAAGTACTTTA[C/G]GAAGACCTTGACTGTTGGAT	C	G	C/G	CAAACCAAACAGTCAAGGTCTTC	2807	8
WIAF-583	CCCAGAGAAGCTCTGTCTGC[G/A]CTGCAAAGCCATGGCTGCAG	A	G	G/A	CAGCCATGGCGTTGCAC	2808	6
WIAF-584	AATAAACAATGCAACGTTCC[C/T]GATTTCTAATCTTGGTTCTG	C	T	T/C	GCTCTCAGAACCAAGATTAGAAATC	19193	11
WIAF-588	TTTGGCTCTGCTACTTGCCA[A/G]ATGAGATTTATTTATGTGGG	A	G	A/G	GAAACTCCCACATAAATAAATCTCA	2193	6
WIAF-592	TTTAACAGACTCAAAAATAT[A/G]GCGAAAACTATCTTTACAAA	A	G	A/G	AGATAATTTGTAAAGATAGTTTTCGC	2194	2
WIAF-594	CAAAGATTGGGAGTATATAA[T/G]AAAGAACCATGTAAAGATTT	G	T	T/G	AATTAAAGAAATCTTTACATGGTTCTTT	19613	21
WIAF-599	TCAAATTTGGAACTATGAACA[A/C]GACATAGTTGTAAGGATAT	A	C	A/C	GTGGAATATCCTTAGCAACTATGTC	2197	13
WIAF-600	CAAGGGAGGAAACATTTACAG[A/G]GTCCATCTCTGATGTCACCA	A	G	A/G	CTGGTGACATCAGAGATGGAC	2813	5
WIAF-601	TGTCCCTGGGAGACTATGG[C/T]AGTGAACACTAAAATCCTAA	C	T	C/T	GCGATTAGGATTTTAGTGTTCAC	2198	8
WIAF-603	ATTCAGAAAATTATAGTTCC[C/T]CAAGTTCATGCATAACAGGA	C	T	C/T	TTTCCTGTTATGCATGAACTTG	19614	16
WIAF-606	TGTGTTCTTCATTGGTTCACT[C/A]TTAAAGTTCATTTATGCATT	A	C	C/A	AAGAACAATGCATAACAGAACTTTAA	19615	19
WIAF-608	GTTTTTGCTACGTTGTTA[G/C]AGCAACCCCAGAAAAATTAA	A	T	A/T	GAGTGACAATCCTAATGGTTGG	2200	6
WIAF-613	GGTGATAATGGGCCCTGTT[G/T]CTCTGGCATACATATAAAAG	G	T	G/T	CCTTCCTTTATATGTATGCCAGA	2202	8
WIAF-615	ATGAATTCATCTTTCAGTTT[T/A]TAGATCGGATCATGAATTAG	A	T	T/A	GGACTAATTCATGATCCGATCT	2818	15
WIAF-618	TAACACTCCAGGCCGTTTCCC[A/G]TTTATATCCAGGTATGCTACA	A	G	A/G	AAGAACTTGTAGCATACCTGGATATAA	2203	3
WIAF-619	AACCATGGCTCAACTATGAT[C/A]GAAGACCCCAAAGCTTGATGA	A	C	C/A	TTAGACAACACTGCTGTTTTTGG	2819	18
WIAF-620	TGGATAAATCATGTGCCCCA[C/G]AGAGCCCCAAAGCTTGATGA	C	G	C/G	ATCAAGCTTTGGGGCTCT	2205	11
WIAF-623	TTTGTGCTACGTTGTTA[G/C]AGCAACCCCAGAAAAATTAAA	C	G	G/C	TTTTAATTTTCTCIGGGGTTGCT	2206	21
WIAF-624	ATTAAGAAAAGATAACAAGA[G/A]ATGAATAAATGAGGTAGTGG	A	G	G/A	GCAAGATAAAGATTAAGAAAAGATAACA	2208	3
WIAF-626	TGTCATTTATGCTGCAGTGG[A/G]AANTACTTGGAAGGCCTGGG	A	G	A/G	TTACTTCCAGGCCCAAGTATT	2821	16
WIAF-627	TGACAAGCAGCTCATTCAAG[C/T]GCCACCATGGCGCCTAAGGG	C	T	C/T	AGGGCCCATGGTGGGC	2214	7
WIAF-636	CATTTCTGGTAGCAGGTATA[T/C]CGGACTCATTTCTTCTTTGCA	C	T	T/C	GATGCAAAGAAGAAAATGAGTCC	2216	1
WIAF-638	CCCAGAGAAAAATCCAAGAG[C/T]CTTAAACCATATTTTGTGTT	C	T	C/T	TCCCAGAGAAAAATCCAAGAG	2825	1
WIAF-640	CCTGAGCCCTCAAGAAACTCA[C/T]GTCCAGCCTCAGCCCTACCACCA	C	T	C/T	GTGTAGGCGTGAGCTGGC	2826	12
WIAF-641	ATATTGTCTGCGTCTAAAGCA[G/A]TACCCCCCTACCACACAAC	A	G	G/A	GGTGTGTGTGTAGGGGG	2219	11
WIAF-645	ACCAGAAAACTTCTGCGGTG[C/G]TTGACCCAGCGAGGAGCCAAC	A	C	C/G	CAGCAGCATAACTACGTCCTTTCT	2829	14
WIAF-646	GGAGAAGGCACCCAGCCATC[C/G]TTGACCCAGCGAGGAGCCAAC	A	G	G/A	GCTCCTCGCTGGGTCA	2221	13
WIAF-648	TCCTAGTTCTTCTCTTATAGG[G/A]ACCCTGTGATTACACTTAGG	A	G	G/A	GCCCTAGTGTAATCACAGGG	2221	13

(Continued on following pages.)

TABLE 6-7. (*Continued*)

WIAF Name	Alleles	Allele A	Allele B	Chipregion	primer up	primer down	ncbi SS	NwLib chrom
WIAF-650	T/C	C	T	GAGAGGTCAGATCATATCCA[T/C]AGAAAAACAGCTCTCTTTA	CGAGAGGTCAGATCATATCCA	GCAAGTAAAAGAGAGCTGTTTTTC	2830	3
WIAF-651	T/C	C	T	GCACAGCACATAGTGGAAAG[T/C]GCTAAGTGTCCTACGAGAGG	AGCACAGCACATAGTGGAAAG	GACCTCTGTAGGACACTTAGC	2831	3
WIAF-653	C/T	C	T	GGCACCAGCCTTTTAGAGT[C/T]CCTGGGCAATTTGTGCACTA	GGCACCAGCCTTTTAGAGT	TGCACAAATTGCCCAGG	2224	1
WIAF-654	A/G	A	G	AGGGACTTAACCTTTGGCCT[A/G]CCTGCCTGGCGTGTTTGGCCTC	AGGGACTTAACCTTTGGCCT	CAAACAGCCAGGCAGG	2832	19
WIAF-657	T/A	A	T	CTCCCACCCTATATTTTAA[T/A]GCAACTGACAGTTTTGAAGG	CCTCCCACCCTATATTTTAA	TCCTTCAAAACTGTCAGTTGC	2834	9
WIAF-664	C/T	C	T	GGTTTTCCATCTGTCTTCCA[C/T]AGAGATCTAGGGTGTCTTTG	GGTTTTCCATCTGTCTTCCA	TCCAAAGACACCCTAGATCTCT	2231	4
WIAF-665	A/G	A	G	TTCTCACCATGGAATCTTG[A/G]TGCAAGTTAGATCCCACCCT	TTCTCACCATGGAATCTTG	GGGTGGGATCTAACTTGCA	2232	1
WIAF-666	C/T	C	T	AGAAGCCATTTATTTTGCAG[C/T]CTTCAGTCCAAGAAGTCA	TGAGAAGCCATTTATTTTGCAG	GTTTATTGTTATAAAATGACCTACAACTT	2835	12
WIAF-671	C/T	C	T	ACAGACTCTGGAGCCACAGC[C/T]GGCTAATACACTGCAATATT	CAGACTCTGGAGCCACAGC	ACATAAAATATTGCAGTGTATTAGCC	2837	7
WIAF-672	T/C	C	T	ACCACCATTATTAAGGAGAG[T/C]ACTAGGAAAAACTACCAAAC	AAACACCACCATTATTAAGGAGAG	GCTGTGTTTGGGTAGTTTTTCCT	2838	7
WIAF-673	T/C	C	T	TTTCTACCTCTATTCCTTA[T/C]TAAACTTTTGGATACATTCC	CTGTTGATTTTCTACCTCTATTCCTT	GCTTTGGAATGTATCCAAAAGTTT	2236	16
WIAF-678	A/G	A	G	CTTTTGTTATTATGCTCTTA[A/G]TGATTTACAGACTGATGCCA	AGAGTTCACTTTTGTTATTATGCTCTCT	TCTGGCATCAGTCTGTAAATCA	2840	7
WIAF-68	C/A	A	C	AGTGACCATGAACTGGCTG[C/A]GTTTTCAAACTGGCTGTGGG	TGAGCCATGAACCTGGCTG	CCCAAGAAAGGTTGAAAAC	2473	15
WIAF-685	T/C	C	T	AGCAGAGTACCTTTCTAACT[T/C]ATAAGATTGTGTAGAGGTTG	ATCACAGCAGAGTACCTTTCTAACT	CCTTCCAACCTCTACACAATCTT	2244	3
WIAF-692	G/A	A	G	GTGGAGTGGGCAGATAAAGA[G/A]CCAAGCCCTAGTTGAGTGA	GTGGAGTGGGCAGATAAAGA	TCACTCAAACTAGGGCTTGG	2247	10
WIAF-693	G/A	A	G	CCCTTCTTAAAGATAGTC[G/A]CCAGAGGCAATTCGACTTTC	TTTTCTCCCTTCTTAAAGATAGTC	AAAGTCGAATTGCCTCTGG	2248	18
WIAF-694	C/T	C	T	TCTGATGCCCCTGTCCAAAG[C/T]TGTGTCTACAACTGATTTA	TCTGATGCCCCTGTCCAAAG	CAATCTCTAAATTCATGTGTGACACA	2249	14
WIAF-696	A/G	A	G	CCCTGTATCTGTTCAGGCCC[A/G]GAATCGTCACGGCTCACAAC	CCTGTATCTGTTCAGGCCC	TGTGAGCCGTGACGATTC	2250	1
WIAF-700	A/G	A	G	TATTTAAAATTATCCTTCC[A/G]TGAAATTGGTGAAAGGTCAA	TCACTGTATTTTAAAATTATCCTTCC	TTTGACCTTTCACCAATTTCA	2252	18
WIAF-706	T/C	C	T	TCTTTATTCTCCTTCTTTCA[T/C]TAATTTTCTTTCACGTTATT	GGCTCTTTATTCTCCTTCTTTCA	CGTTCAGGGTGAGGGAATAA	2256	3
WIAF-712	G/C	C	G	TAACCTGGATAAACATCT[G/C]ATGGAAGGCTGCACTGGATG	TAACCTGGATAAACATCT	CCAGTGCAGCCTTCCAT	2259	11
WIAF-713	T/G	G	T	CCATGCCCCTGATAGTTCTG[T/G]GAGCCACCTAAACTCGTTC	CCATGCCCCTGATAGTTCTG	GGAAACGAGTTTAGGTGGCTC	2260	11
WIAF-715	T/C	C	T	TTTACGTTCCCGTCTCATC[T/C]TTCTAGGTAATTTGAGTTTC	TGTTTACGTTCCCGTCTCATC	GGTTGGAAACTCAAATTACCTAGAA	2261	3
WIAF-716	C/T	C	T	AAGAAATGGCTGATACCAAG[C/T]CTGCAGTGAAAATGCACAT	TGAAGAAATGGCTGATACCAA	ATGTGCATTTTCACTGCAG	2262	8
WIAF-718	T/C	C	T	CACCACAGTGCACCAAGGAC[T/C]GGACTTGCCACTCTATCTTTA	CCACAGTGCACCAAGGAC	GGGTAAAGATAGGTGCAGGTCC	2264	2
WIAF-721	A/C	A	C	CCAGAGTCTTCTAATAGCAA[A/C]AGCTACTGAAGGCGGCAAGA	GTTACCCAGAGTCTTCTAATAGCAA	TGCCGCTTCCAGTAGCT	19616	3
WIAF-723	G/C	C	G	ATCTGAAGTTTTGTCTCCA[G/C]AGAAGTCATTTTGTAGGTGT	CAGTATCTGAAGTTTTGTCTCCA	AGGAACACCTACAAAATGACTTCT	2266	10
WIAF-724	A/G	A	G	GGGAAGGATCCTGTAAAAG[A/G]TAAATATTGTTTTCCATAAT	GGGAAGGATCCTGTAAAAG	CATCTTCAATATTATGGAAAACAATATTT	2267	8
WIAF-725	G/T	G	T	TATGAGTCTTGTGAAACAGG[G/T]GTGGGAAGGATCGTGTAAAA	TCAATATGAGTCTTGTGAAACAGG	CTTTTACAGGATCCTTCCCAC	2268	8
WIAF-726	C/T	C	T	ATTAGATTTCTATTTTGATA[C/T]TGATGTTCTTTCAAGAGGA	ATTAGATTTCTATTTTGATA	ATTTCCTTTGAAAAGAAACATCA	2269	6
WIAF-729	C/T	C	T	AGAAGATAACTAGAAAAATGC[C/T]GACAGAAAAATAACCAGAA	GATGCAGAAGATAACTAGAAAAATGC	GAACTCTTCTGGTTATTTTTCTGTTC	2271	14
WIAF-730	A/C	A	C	CACTGAAAGACACCATTTAT[A/C]TACCCAAGGGCAGAAGTAG	CACTTCACTGAAAGACACCATTT	TCTACTTTCTGCCCTTGGGT	2851	20
WIAF-731	C/T	C	T	CATCTTCATGGCGCAGGAATT[C/T]CATTTCTGTTTCTTAGGG	CATCTTCATGGCGCAGGAATT	CAAACCCTAAGAAACACAGAAATG	2272	9
WIAF-736	C/G	C	G	AAGACTATTTGGATAAGTTT[C/G]ACAAAGATGGAACAGGTCC	AAAAGCAAGACTATTTGGATAAGTTT	TCTAGGACCTGTTCTCATCTTTG	2274	6
WIAF-737	G/A	A	G	AACAGGTCCTAGAACCTCAG[G/A]ATCGAAAGGAAGTTCATCTA	GAGAACAGGTCCTAGAACCTCAG	GACGATGAACTTCCTTTCGA	2275	6
WIAF-741	C/T	C	T	GCTTGGAGATTCTGATTCAG[C/T]GTGCTCAAGGGCGGGCGTGAC	CAGCTTGGAGATTCTGATTCAG	GCCCGCCTGAGCAC	2854	3
WIAF-742	C/T	C	T	CAGTGGAATCATTTACACTA[C/T]CGAAATCAGCAAATGCTAAA	GCCACAGTGGAATCATTTACA	TTTTAGCATTTGCTGATTTCG	19177	2
WIAF-744	T/C	C	T	TCCCAGAGACCACTTCATTC[T/C]TTTTTGGATTATGAAATAGA	TCCCAGAGACCACTTCATTC	CTACTCTTTCTATTTCATAATCCAAAAA	2277	10
WIAF-745	C/G	C	G	AAGTAGCCCAGCTACAGCCT[C/G]GGTGCATCTTAACCCCTCTC	AAGTAGCCCAGCTACAGCCT	GAGAGGGGTTAAGATGGACC	2855	3
WIAF-747	G/A	A	G	AGACACCAAAAATTCCCAAT[G/A]CTCTAAATATGAACTTTAGA	AATAGCAGACACCAAAAATTCCCAAT	GGGGTTGAGTCCCATCTATTTAGA	2279	17
WIAF-748	G/A	A	G	AATCGACGAACATCACAGTG[G/A]GCTGTGGTGCCAAGGACGGA	AATCGACGAACATCACAGTG	TCCTTGGCACCACAGC	2280	17
WIAF-750	A/G	A	G	TTTCTAAAATATAATTTGCT[A/G]TAGAGTTCACAGATGAGCAC	GCCTCACAAAGTATTTTCTAAAATATAA	AAAAGTGCTCATCTGTGAACTCT	2857	11
WIAF-751	T/C	C	T	CCAAACAGAATTACTTGGCA[T/C]AGGGTTTCTTAAAACTATTT	ACCAAACAGAATTACTTGGCA	TGCAGAAATAGTTTTAAGAAACCC	2281	2
WIAF-752	C/T	C	T	ACGAATTTGCTGGGGAATCT[C/T]GTTTTTCTTCTTAAGACTTT	CGCGTTTGACTTGTCGGG	TCCCAAAATGCTTAAGAAAGAAAAA	2858	17
WIAF-761	T/C	C	T	CTAGCGTTTGACCTTGTCGCGG[T/C]GCTACTCAAATGGGGGCAGT	GCGTTTGACTTGTCGCGG	TCCCACACTGCCCCC	2864	8
WIAF-762	C/G	C	G	ATGAGAGGATTCCCTCTCTC[C/G]TCCAAGGGAAAGAAGCTTTT	CATGAGAGGATTCCCTCTC	AAAAGCTTCTTTCCCTTGGA	2865	6
WIAF-768	C/T	C	T	CAAAGGAAAAGAACAAATTT[C/T]CAAAGACTTGGGGAGTGAA	GACTTCAAAGGAAAAGAACAAATTT	TCACTCCCCCAAGTCTTTG	2870	1
WIAF-774	A/G	A	G	GGGAGATTTTAGACTGAATC[A/G]TTCTAGATATTTGACGACT	GGAGGGAGATTTTAGACTGAATC	AGCTGTAGTCGGTCAAATACTCTAGAA	2876	1
WIAF-782	C/T	C	T	CACACAAACTTTTAAACTC[C/T]GTCAAAAACAACAAGAACAG	TTATATTGTATTGCACAAAACTTTTT	TCATCTTGTTCTTGTGACTCAGG	2884	12
WIAF-785	T/C	C	T	TTTGACAATAAACACCATCAT[T/C]CCTGACTCCACAGTAAGGT	CATTTGCAATAAACACCATCA	GGACCTTATCTGTGGACTCAGG	2887	20
WIAF-786	C/T	C	T	AACACAAACATATCAAGGAT[C/T]GGGCTGGAATCTTTTCCATT	ATGTTTAAACACAAACATATCAAGGAT	TGGAAAGATTCCAGCCC	2888	19
WIAF-791	C/T	C	T	ATTCAAGGCACAAAGCTAAG[C/T]ACATGCAACAATATAGATGA	CAATTCAAGGCACAAAGCTAAG	CCAAATCATCTATATTGTGCATG	2893	15

WIAF ID	Allele	A1	A2	Seq (5′)	SNP sequence	Seq (3′)	Pos	#
WIAF-796	T/G	G	T	CCCAATCAAACAGTACATGATTAC	ATCAAACAGTACATGATTAC[T/G]CGGTTTCCAGAAATCTGGAT	TCCAGATTTCTGGAAACCG	2898	3
WIAF-798	T/C	C	T	CGCAGAAAAAGGCATATTCA	GCAGAAAAAGGCATATTCAA[T/C]TGTCCCATACTAATTTTTGA	GGTTATTCAAAAATTAGTATGGGACA	2900	14
WIAF-801	G/C	C	G	TGTCAGTTTGAATGTATTCCTGA	AGTTTGAATGTATTCCTGAT[G/C]TTTTCCTTTGCCAACTATTC	TGAATAGTTGGCAAAGGAAAA	2903	18
WIAF-802	A/G	A	G	CCCACTTGAACTCAAGTCATCA	CACTTGAACTCAAGTCATCA[A/G]TTTAGGCACAAAGTTTTA	AAACTAAAACCTTTGTGCCTAAAA	2904	15
WIAF-806	G/C	C	G	CCAACAGGGAAAAAGTCA	TGGCTTTAGAATCAAATGGG[G/C]TGACTTTTCCCCTGTTGGT	CCAACAGGAAAAAGTCA	2908	7
WIAF-807	T/C	C	T	CAGACAAGTCTTGTGTCCAC	TGAAATGGCACTTAGCGAA[T/C]ACTTGTGGACCACAAGACTT	CAGACAAGTCTTGTGTCCAC	2909	7
WIAF-814	C/T	C	T	GCTGCCAATTACATTAACTTACAA	TGGTGATGCAATTGAAATAA[C/T]ATTGTAAGTTAATGTAATTG	GCTGCCAATTACATTAACTTACAA	2915	14
WIAF-815	C/T	C	T	CACAACCAACCAATACCGC	AGGAGGAGTCCTCATGGAT[C/T]GCCGTATTGGTTGGTTGTGG	CACAACCAACCAATACCGC	2916	1
WIAF-816	T/A	A	T	GAGGCATCACAATGTTAAGATTTT	TACCCACCACTACCCCTGT[T/A]AAAATCTTAACATTGTGATG	GAGGCATCACAATGTTAAGATTTT	2917	3
WIAF-818	G/A	A	G	CCGACCAAGATCCCTCAC	ACATTCCCATCTGTCTTGCA[G/A]GGAGGGATCTTGGTCGGCTT	CCGACCAAGATCCCTCAC	2919	12
WIAF-819	T/C	A	T	AAACCGAAACGAAAAATCAA	GGGATAGGAGGACAGATGTT[T/C]GTTGATTTTTCGTTTCGGTT	AAACCGAAACGAAAAATCAA	2920	8
WIAF-820	C/T	C	T	CTCTGGCTCAGACTTGTCTCT	TATAACCAAGAAGCCTTCAG[C/T]AGAGCAAGTCTGAGCCAGAG	CTCTGGCTCAGACTTGTCTCT	2921	11
WIAF-821	T/C	C	T	TGGGGCTGCAGACACTC	CATTCCAAGGCTCTCTAACA[T/C]CGAGTGTCTGCAGCCCATTC	TGGGGCTGCAGACACTC	2922	17
WIAF-823	C/A	A	C	AAGGTGCACGTGCGAGG	TAGTGATAGTAGGACTCA[C/A]CCTGCACGTGCACCTTTCAT	AAGGTGCACGTGCGAGG	2924	14
WIAF-827	G/A	A	G	GATGAGGTGATTCCCACACTT	TAATGAAACATCTGCGAAAA[G/A]AAGTGTGGAATCACCTCAT	GATGAGGTGATTCCCACACTT	2928	7
WIAF-828	G/A	A	G	TTTGAATAATGGTAGTCTTCCAAA	CAACTAGCTTGCTTTTGTC[G/A]TTTGGAAGACTACCATTATT	TTTGAATAATGGTAGTCTTCCAAA	2929	7
WIAF-829	A/T	A	T	GTCACCATGTTATATTTCTTTAAGAC	ATATAAAATTACTAAATTAA[A/T]GTCTTAAAGAAAAATATAAC	GTCACCATGTTATATTTCTTTAAGAC	2930	13
WIAF-832	C/A	C	A	GCATGGGTTAATCCAGCA	TGCACAACCAGGCAAAATA[C/A]TGCGATTAACCCATGCTA	GCATGGGTTAATCCAGCA	2933	8
WIAF-834	A/C	A	C	TGTACTTGCCAAGAGTTTTAAATT	AACCCTTTCATCCATTCCAGC[A/C]AATTTAAAACTCTTCAGC	TGTACTTGCCAAGAGTTTTAAATT	2935	1
WIAF-835	G/A	A	G	TCATTCAAGCCAATGAAAATG	TTATTCCAAGAATGGGAAGC[G/A]CATTTTCATTGGCTTGAATG	TCATTCAAGCCAATGAAAATG	2936	14
WIAF-838	T/C	C	T	ACTTATCCGTCAGGCAGAGTAG	CATGGCCCTTGGCACTATG[T/C]CTACTCTGCCTGACGGATAA	ACTTATCCGTCAGGCAGAGTAG	2939	3
WIAF-839	T/C	C	T	GGAAAGCCAGAGATTTTTAACAA	TTGACACAAAGTTCTAACTT[T/C]TTGTTAAAATCTCTGGCTT	GGAAAGCCAGAGATTTTTAACAA	2940	19
WIAF-841	T/A	A	T	GACTTCTCCACCCTCTTGC	GCTCTCTGTCCCTGGAGGTTA[T/A]CAAGAGGGTGGAGAAGTCT	GACTTCTCCACCCTCTTGC	2942	11
WIAF-842	G/A	A	G	GGCTTGGTGGTGGAACC	GAACAGACTGGAGTGAGAAC[G/A]GGTTCCACCACCAAGGAAAACT	GGCTTGGTGGTGGAACC	2943	11
WIAF-843	C/T	C	T	TCAAACTAAATCTTCCATTCTCAAGC	TTGATTTGCTTCGTTCAAAG[C/T]GCCTTAGAATGGAAGATTTAG	TCAAACTAAATCTTCCATTCTCAAGC	2944	22
WIAF-844	A/C	A	C	GCACAGCAGGCAGCTT	CTAAGGAAAACTTTCTCCAT[A/C]AAGCTGCCTGCGTGCACGT	GCACAGCAGGCAGCTT	2945	6
WIAF-845	A/C	A	C	AAGTTTTCCTTAGTGGCACCT	TACAGGAAGAGTTGTCTCAT[A/C]AGGTGCCACTAAGGAAAACT	AAGTTTTCCTTAGTGGCACCT	2946	6
WIAF-846	C/T	C	T	CCTGAATATGCAATTATTTATTGACA	GGGGAACCTAGTTGCAGTAA[C/T]GTGTCATAATAAATAATTGC	CCTGAATATGCAATTATTTATTGACA	2947	1
WIAF-847	C/G	C	G	GGAGATATTGATCTTTTTCTGACTCTTATTT	TCATTCTCATTTAAAATTGT[C/G]AAATAAGTCAGAAAAAGATC	GGAGATATTGATCTTTTTCTGACTCTTATTT	2948	3
WIAF-852	A/G	A	G	GATTGAACTAGGAAGAAATTAAATCC	CTAAGTTATTTAATATTCC[A/G]GGATTTAAATTTCTTCCTAGT	GATTGAACTAGGAAGAAATTAAATCC	2953	5
WIAF-856	T/C	C	T	GCCTGTAATCTTGCTATGCTCA	AACAAACAAAGCTGAAACTAA[T/C]GAGTGAGCATAGCAAGATTA	GCCTGTAATCTTGCTATGCTCA	2957	12
WIAF-858	T/G	G	T	GCAGTCCCCAGAAAGGAAAC	GATGATCCCGACAAAA[T/G]GTTTCCTTTCTGAGGCTGCC	GCAGTCCCCAGAAAGGAAAC	2959	1
WIAF-861	T/C	C	T	AGTTGCCCAGCTTTGACA	ATTCAAATGGTTTTTACTCTA[T/C]GTGTCAAACCAACTAT	AGTTGCCCAGCTTTGACA	2962	2
WIAF-865	A/C	A	C	CCTACTACAATGAAGTTAGTATGCAGTAT	ACACCGACATACATATCTCA[A/C]GTACAATTAGCTATACTGCA	CCTACTACAATGAAGTTAGTATGCAGTAT	2965	8
WIAF-866	G/A	A	G	GGCAGGTGTTCAGAAAGCAT	TATGGCCATTTAATAAGTG[G/A]TATGCTTTCTGAACACCTGC	GGCAGGTGTTCAGAAAGCAT	2966	1
WIAF-867	A/G	A	G	CCAGGCACAGTACACTCAAAA	TTAGGGGTGTTGACACACCA[A/G]TTTTGAGTGTACTGTGCCTG	CCAGGCACAGTACACTCAAAA	2967	8
WIAF-874	A/G	A	G	TGTGGTTTTAATGAATTCATGAC	TTTACAGTCATTTATTACC[A/G]GTCATGAATTCATTAAAAAC	TGTGGTTTTAATGAATTCATGAC	2974	14
WIAF-878	A/G	A	G	TGACTCTTCTTCAATATTGTATTCTCAA	ACCAACATTGTCCACCGGAC[A/G]TTGAGAATACAATATTGAAG	TGACTCTTCTTCAATATTGTATTCTCAA	2978	2
WIAF-879	G/A	A	G	CATGATTAGTGTCACTCCTGAGAA	TTATGAAAATATTAAAACCTCT[G/A]CTTCTCAGGAGTGACACTAA	CATGATTAGTGTCACTCCTGAGAA	2979	12
WIAF-88	A/G	A	G	TTGCATATGCGCGCA	CCGTCGATTCTGAATATCCC[A/G]TGGGCGCATATGCAAAGGAA	TTGCATATGCGCGCA	2490	15
WIAF-881	G/A	A	G	CACATTATTCCTTCTAGGCTGAGA	AAGAACTGAACTATGAAC[G/A]TCTCAGCCTAGAAGGATAAT	CACATTATTCCTTCTAGGCTGAGA	2981	6
WIAF-883	T/C	C	T	CCGAGTGCTTGCTGTCACA	AAGCTCAGGCAACATGAGA[T/C]GTGTGACCAACACTAGGA	CCGAGTGCTTGCTGTCACA	2983	1
WIAF-889	A/G	A	G	TTCTTGGAAGAAAGGCGTC	TCGCGTGGAAGCTGAAACAC[A/G]GACGCCTTTCTTCCAAGAAG	TTCTTGGAAGAAAGGCGTC	2989	16
WIAF-893	C/T	C	T	TTGAGGCAATAATCCAGCTC	GCGGAAGCAGTGAGCTGTT[C/T]GAGCTGGATTAGTGCCTCAA	TTGAGGCAATAATCCAGCTC	2993	19
WIAF-894	C/T	C	T	GAGGGTGGTTTCCACTTCA	ACTCATCATCCCAGATTATT[C/T]TGAAGTGGAAACCACCCTCC	GAGGGTGGTTTCCACTTCA	2994	19
WIAF-895	G/A	A	G	CTTATACTTGATGGGGTGAAATAAA	ATCTATATTGTACCAAGGACT[C/A]GGAATTTGGCTGTCTTCAAG	CTTATACTTGATGGGGTGAAATAAA	2995	4
WIAF-896	C/A	A	C	TGAAGCAGCCAAAATTCC	AATCATATAGCCAAGGGACT[C/A]GGAAGGGACTTTTTGTTCAC	TGAAGCAGCCAAAATTCC	2996	3
WIAF-899	C/T	C	T	AATTGTGAACAAAAAGTCCTCTTC	AGTGTATTTTTCCTGTTCCA[C/T]GAAGAGGAGCTTTTCATAGC	AATTGTGAACAAAAAGTCCTCTTC	2999	21
WIAF-901	T/C	C	T	GGGGTCCTTCTCCCTC	CCTGAGACATGTGTGGCTG[T/C]GAGGGAGGAGAAGGACCCCAAC	GGGGTCCTTCTCCCTC	3001	10
WIAF-902	C/G	C	G	AGGAAACATTGAGGTAATTTTTAAAGT	TTAAATGATTCAGCATTTA[C/G]ACTTTAAAAATTACCTCAAT	AGGAAACATTGAGGTAATTTTTAAAGT	3002	7
WIAF-903	T/G	G	T	AAGATTTTATCTTGGACCCGA	TAAGTGCAGAACCTGCATTG[T/G]TCGGGTGCCAAGATAAAATCT	AAGATTTTATCTTGGACCCGA	3003	4
WIAF-906	C/T	C	T	TGCCTTGAATTATTTACGTTCA	AAGGCCTAGAGGAGAGATTA[C/T]AATGAAACGTAAATAATTCAA	TGCCTTGAATTATTTACGTTCA	3006	3
WIAF-907	A/G	A	G	TCAATCTTATTTGATCCTCTCGTTCT	GTGCAAATGACAAAGCCCAA[A/G]AGAACAGAGGATCCAAATAAG	TCAATCTTATTTGATCCTCTCGTTCT	3007	18
WIAF-908	C/G	C	G	TTAGAATATGTGTGATATGTCCCC	AGGAAGTCTGGGGATTCCTA[C/G]AGGGCGACATATCACACATAT	TTAGAATATGTGTGATATGTCCCC	3008	17
WIAF-911	G/A	A	G	GGCTATGATAAACCATCCCTC	CAAGCGAGAGGAGCAAGC[G/A]GAGGGATGGTTTATCATAGC	GGCTATGATAAACCATCCCTC	3011	13
WIAF-914	T/C	C	T	GAGTGAATTTAAATGTCCAAACAA	ACTGAGCGATGACACCACAC[T/C]TTGTTTGGACATTTAAATTC	GAGTGAATTTAAATGTCCAAACAA	3014	2

(Continued on following pages.)

TABLE 6-7. (*Continued*)

WIAF Name	Alleles	Allele A	Allele B	Chipregion	primer up	primer down	ncbi SS	NwLib chrom
WIAF-915	G/A	A	G	CGCTCTCTTTTCTCCCAAGC[G/A]AAACCAAATGCGCCCTTCA	CGCTCTCTTTTCTCCCAAGC	GGGGCGCATTTGGTTT	3015	6
WIAF-916	T/C	C	T	TATTCTGCTATTCCTGCCCAT[T/C]ACCGCATCCTTCATGGTAGA	AATTATTCTGCTATTCCTGCCCA	ACCATGAAGGATGCGGT	3016	6
WIAF-917	A/G	A	G	GAGACACTACTCTTCCTTCA[A/G]GACTATTTCATTCTGACTAT	GCTGAGACACTACTCTTCCTTCA	TTCAATGTATTTATTCACTTATAGTCAGAA	3017	3
WIAF-918	T/C	C	T	ATCATTTTAGCGTAAATACC[T/C]GAATAACCCATAGTTACAGA	GCATTTTAACTATCATTTTAGCGTAAAT	CCAATTCTGTAACTATGGGTTATTC	3018	17
WIAF-919	A/G	A	G	CACTCCATCCTGATGCCCCA[A/G]GTTATCCACAGCCTCCTTCC	CCATCCTGATGCCCCA	GGAAGGAGGCTGTGGATAAC	3019	4
WIAF-922	A/C	A	C	GTCATTACACACTGAGCAAC[A/C]AAACAAAGGTGTTGAATCCT	TCATTACACACTGAGCAAC	AAGAGGATTCAACACCTTGTTT	3022	6
WIAF-923	C/T	C	T	CAGGGGTGACGTATGTAGAA[C/T]GCTTAGGGTGTCCTCCCAC	GCAGGGGTGACGTATGTAGAA	GGGGAGGCACCCTAAGC	3023	19
WIAF-924	G/T	G	T	CTACCTGAAACAGGGATGCC[G/T]TTCTCGGTACTATGTTTAAT	CCTGAAACAGGGATGCC	GCACAATTAAACATAGTACCGAGAA	3024	16
WIAF-931	T/C	C	T	CAGAGGAACAGCCAAGAGAT[T/C]TTACCGTGCGTCTTACTAAAG	CAGAGGAACAGCCAAGAGAT	GATATGTACTTTAGTAAGACCACGGTAA	3031	4
WIAF-933	G/A	A	G	GTGGTTTTCAATACTAAACA[G/A]TGTAAACAATGCAAATATTT	AGGGTGGTTTTCAATACTAAACA	CTGTATTTATTGTTAAATATTTGCATTGTT	3033	2
WIAF-939	A/T	A	T	CCTGAAGGAATCTGGGAATT[A/T]GCCCTGGCCTGAAAGTGGC	CCTGAAGGAATCTGGGAATT	ACTTTCAGGCCACGGC	3038	10
WIAF-944	A/G	A	G	AGGATGAAAACTGATACACC[A/G]GTTACTTACTTACTCCTTCACT	AACAGGATGAAAACTGATACACC	CAGTTTGAAGAGTGAAGAGTAAGTAGTAA	3043	1
WIAF-951	T/C	C	T	GCTGGGTAGTTCTAGAACTT[T/C]AGAAGCTCCATCTTTTAATG	TTCCAGCTGGGTAGTTCTAGAA	AAAAACATTAAAAGATGGAGCTTC	3050	9
WIAF-952	T/G	G	T	TACATGTTTTATATCACTTAT[T/G]TTATCTCAACAATCTTGAAA	CAGAACTAAGCTTTACATGTTTTATATCAC	CCCTTTCAAGATTGTTGAGATAA	3051	1
WIAF-953	G/A	A	G	GCTGCTGTCCCAGTGCCACA[G/A]TTGGTCTAGCCTCATGGCAGA	GCTGTCCCAGTGCCACA	TGCCATGAGGCTAGACCA	3052	20
WIAF-955	C/T	C	T	CTGCTTAGGTTTGTTCTTCC[C/T]AGCATATTCAGCTATAATCA	GCTGCTTAGGTTTGTTCTTCC	TGTAGGTGATTATAGCTGAATATGCT	3054	2
WIAF-960	G/A	A	G	GCTCTTGGCTTTCAAAATCA[G/A]TACAGACAGATAAGAGCTTT	GCTCTTGGCTTTCAAAATCA	CGAAATACTTAAAGCTCTTATCTGTCTGT	3059	9
WIAF-961	C/G	C	G	GGACTTTCAGTTGACAGATT[C/G]TCTCCTTACCTAACTCTAGT	AAGGGACTTTCAGTTGACAGATT	TCAGGAGAGTCTGACTAGAGTTAGGT	3060	7
WIAF-963	G/A	A	G	ACAGTACAACTTGCAAGCAC[G/A]GGGAGAAAACCTAGGTGAAA	TGTTACAGTACAACTTGCAAGCAC	TTTTCACCTAGGTTTTCTCCC	3062	17
WIAF-966	A/G	A	G	AGTGTGACCCTCGTGACCCC[A/G]TGAATGTGCCTCCAAGCGGC	CAGTGTGACCCTCGTGACCCC	CGCTGGAGGCACATTCA	3065	10
WIAF-967	T/C	C	T	TGGAAATGGAAAGAGTGACA[T/C]CCTTGTCCTGTTCTGAACTT	GTGGAAATGGAAAGAGTGACA	CAGTAAGTTCAGAACAGGACAAGG	3066	6
WIAF-971	G/A	A	G	CTCAAAGCTCTCAGGACTGG[G/A]GCTAGGGTTTAAGGAAGGCT	CTCAAAGCTCTCAGGACTGG	AAGCCTTCCTTAAACCCTAGC	3070	11
WIAF-973	A/G	A	G	ATGAATAGCAGCTTTTAGGG[A/G]TTATATCATGAGGTACAAAT	TCATGAATAGCAGCTTTTAGGG	GCCTCTTTATTTGTACCTCATGAT	3072	13
WIAF-974	C/G	C	G	TCCACAGGTCACACTTGTCA[C/G]CAGCAAGTATAAACAAAGTG	TCCACAGGTCACACTTGTCA	ACCCACTTTGTTTATACTTGCTG	3073	16
WIAF-975	G/C	C	G	AATTCCACAACCACCTTGAC[G/C]AATGCTTGCCAAGCTGTTTT	AATTCCACAACCACCTTGAC	AAACAGCTTGGCAAGCATT	3074	9
WIAF-977	T/C	C	T	GAAGTGTCATCCTGACTGAC[T/C]GTCCCTGCAGTGCCATGCG	CGAAGTGTCATCCTGACTGAC	TGGGCACTGCAGGGAC	3076	5
WIAF-978	A/G	A	G	AACTCTAACATCGTCTATAG[A/G]ACCATTTCCGTCTCCAGTT	CCATAGTTGAACTCTAACATCGTC	TGGAGACGGGAAATGGT	3077	19
WIAF-979	G/A	A	G	TCTGTGCTCTTCATTCTCAC[G/A]GGCCCGCAACCCCTCCTC	GCTCTGTGCTCTTCATTCTCA	AGGAGGGGTTGCGGG	3078	3
WIAF-980	G/T	G	T	AAAGACATGACTACCAACGC[G/T]GGCCCCTTCCACCCATACTG	CAAAGACATGACTACCAACGC	TGGGTGCAAGGGGCC	3079	X
WIAF-982	C/T	C	T	TTTAAAAATGATCATTTAAC[C/T]TCTTTGAACTACAGCCTGAA	CTTCCTATTGTTTAAAAATGATCATTTAA	GGATTCAGGCGTGAGTTCAAAGA	3081	6
WIAF-983	G/C	C	G	GCCATGGAAGGAAAGTATGC[G/C]GTGTTTTAGGGAGAGCTGGC	GCCATGGAAGGAAAGTATGC	GCCAGCTCCCTAAAACAC	3082	7
WIAF-984	C/T	C	T	CTTTCCTCATCTGCTGGTGT[C/T]TTCCTCAGAGCTTTAATGTC	CTTTCCTCATCTGCTGGTGT	CGGACATTAAAGCTCTGAGGA	3083	1
WIAF-985	T/A	A	T	TCTAGGCTGTGGGGAACCTC[T/A]GGTGCCTTACAAGTCCAACT	GGCGTGTGGGGAACCTC	GTAGTTGGAGTTGTAAGGCACC	3084	6
WIAF-988	C/T	C	T	AACAATTCAGTATCATTATG[C/T]TGTAGATTTCAGATAGT	TGATGTTTACATAACAATTCAGTATCAT	GACGACTACCATCTGAAATCTACA	3087	9
WIAF-989	A/G	A	G	AGGTTCTGATGGAAGCATCA[A/G]TGATGGATTTGGCTTTTCCA	GGTTCTGATGGAAGCATCA	GGAAAAGCCAAATCCATCA	3088	8
WIAF-991	A/G	A	G	CCATGGCCCTGAGCGTCCT[A/G]CCCGAAATTCACGAGGCTGA	GGCCCTGAGCGTCCT	CCTCGTGAATTCGGGG	3090	11
WIAF-992	A/G	A	G	GCAGCTGGTTCCTCCAGGGA[A/G]TTGGCCCCGAAGCTGGCTCA	GCTCGGTTCCTCCAGGGA	CAGCTTCGGGGCCAA	3091	11
WIAF-993	T/A	A	T	TGGAAAGTCCCTAGGTGTGT[T/A]TGAAACAATCTGGGTATTAC	TGGAAAGTCCCTAGGTGTGT	CCTGTAATACCCAGATTGTTTCA	3092	8
WIAF-996	C/G	C	G	TTCGAACCTACTTAGACCCT[C/G]GCCACAAAAGCTTGATCAAA	TGTTCGAACCTACTTAGACCC	TTTGATCAAACCTTTGTGTGC	3095	8
WIAF-999	C/T	C	T	AGCCCTTTGTCCATTGTTGA[C/T]TGTGAATAATTGGCAGCAGG	GCCCTTTGTCCATTGTTGA	CCTGCTGCCAATTATTCACA	3098	2

TABLE 6-8. Map Location for 1081 SNPs on the HuSNP Chip Mapped on the TNG Panel

SNP name	Chromosome	Genetic distance (cM)	SNP name	Chromosome	Genetic distance (cM)
WIAF-768	1	0	WIAF-4066	1	195.79
WIAF-984	1	0.32	WIAF-2818	1	211.3
WIAF-3800	1	6.49	WIAF-1121	1	213.43
WIAF-2674	1	9.55	WIAF-3460	1	213.64
WIAF-4507	1	28.87	WIAF-2644	1	213.73
WIAF-2292	1	39.96	WIAF-4543	1	219.17
WIAF-1577	1	59.56	WIAF-4237	1	219.55
WIAF-1677	1	64.45	WIAF-1018	1	219.64
WIAF-1970	1	68.96	WIAF-413	1	220.92
WIAF-944	1	71.08	WIAF-3263	1	222.12
WIAF-4027	1	76.62	WIAF-3215	1	223.18
WIAF-3095	1	80.12	WIAF-2441	1	226.74
WIAF-1504	1	80.13	WIAF-2122	1	227.43
WIAF-3825	1	82.31	WIAF-270	1	240.47
WIAF-4561	1	85.6	WIAF-3247	1	249.22
WIAF-1934	1	85.69	WIAF-2636	1	249.5
WIAF-774	1	88.26	WIAF-2078	1	252.69
WIAF-2162	1	89.36	WIAF-3122	1	254.33
WIAF-2912	1	89.68	WIAF-1470	1	255.33
WIAF-640	1	99.2	WIAF-3762	1	257.23
WIAF-1768	1	101.27	WIAF-3529	1	257.96
WIAF-638	1	103.93	WIAF-952	1	258.12
WIAF-3293	1	110.98	WIAF-2149	1	260.25
WIAF-846	1	113.86	WIAF-221	1	260.43
WIAF-653	1	115.56	WIAF-2847	1	260.59
WIAF-3233	1	122.36	WIAF-883	1	260.96
WIAF-2921	1	123.5	WIAF-234	1	263.39
WIAF-3891	1	136.07	WIAF-696	1	266.61
WIAF-1854	1	137.58	WIAF-1779	1	266.98
WIAF-3042	1	138.28	WIAF-4501	1	267.83
WIAF-1748	1	144.48	WIAF-3430	1	271.03
WIAF-4050	1	147.51	WIAF-1013	1	286.03
WIAF-3232	1	149.02	WIAF-1014	1	286.03
WIAF-4566	1	149.07	WIAF-2014	1	286.24
WIAF-1842	1	149.13	WIAF-815	1	287.55
WIAF-1642	1	149.41	WIAF-531	1	291.18
WIAF-2866	1	151.2	WIAF-4029	1	292.32
WIAF-1543	1	155.14	WIAF-200	1	293.8
WIAF-3565	1	158.36	WIAF-1610	1	293.82
WIAF-1417	1	158.57	WIAF-2072	1	293.83
WIAF-4568	1	158.59	WIAF-1660	1	299.35
WIAF-2007	1	165.68	WIAF-2930	2	6.44
WIAF-3798	1	167.52	WIAF-4535	2	10.08
WIAF-3632	1	169.21	WIAF-2853	2	12.83
WIAF-2676	1	170.43	WIAF-3001	2	15.91
WIAF-3038	1	172.82	WIAF-3168	2	16.31
WIAF-858	1	183.11	WIAF-933	2	37.58
WIAF-455	1	183.24	WIAF-1004	2	46.62
WIAF-2182	1	188.16	WIAF-3348	2	58.24
WIAF-3921	1	190.89	WIAF-2638	2	61.71

(Continued on following pages.)

TABLE 6-8. (*Continued*)

SNP name	Chromosome	Genetic distance (cM)	SNP name	Chromosome	Genetic distance (cM)
WIAF-955	2	65.3	WIAF-594	2	233.18
WIAF-3449	2	67.06	WIAF-1942	2	233.36
WIAF-2514	2	70.74	WIAF-1763	2	241.65
WIAF-2265	2	72.83	WIAF-2670	2	241.89
WIAF-3861	2	74.65	WIAF-2671	2	242
WIAF-3250	2	75.08	WIAF-878	2	242.63
WIAF-2649	2	83.34	WIAF-4538	2	246.79
WIAF-2318	2	88.76	WIAF-2686	2	247.66
WIAF-2167	2	98.79	WIAF-1031	2	250.33
WIAF-3538	2	101.69	WIAF-1023	2	251.2
WIAF-1146	2	105.58	WIAF-3216	2	258.47
WIAF-4565	2	105.63	WIAF-3785	2	261.67
WIAF-2635	2	106.02	WIAF-301	2	264.58
WIAF-487	2	108.66	WIAF-3462	2	265.61
WIAF-2130	2	111.41	WIAF-3602	2	271.47
WIAF-1665	2	113.53	WIAF-3143	2	273.32
WIAF-4500	2	113.83	WIAF-1930	2	273.48
WIAF-2449	2	114.03	WIAF-1929	2	273.95
WIAF-2739	2	116.92	WIAF-1700	2	274.68
WIAF-3894	2	123.09	WIAF-4596	2	282.25
WIAF-718	2	125.38	WIAF-3473	2	284.3
WIAF-4095	2	127.42	WIAF-1762	2	284.65
WIAF-4549	2	127.42	WIAF-685	3	11.82
WIAF-2173	2	130.39	WIAF-1793	3	13.84
WIAF-2105	2	131.25	WIAF-3235	3	19.6
WIAF-1964	2	133.35	WIAF-3008	3	21.91
WIAF-751	2	133.73	WIAF-838	3	23.38
WIAF-4562	2	145.18	WIAF-3865	3	35.2
WIAF-3442	2	145.24	WIAF-906	3	35.22
WIAF-3443	2	145.24	WIAF-4570	3	37.71
WIAF-305	2	157.43	WIAF-2299	3	38.48
WIAF-3663	2	157.53	WIAF-2703	3	41.67
WIAF-3556	2	167.83	WIAF-3380	3	50.08
WIAF-3667	2	171.72	WIAF-741	3	56.82
WIAF-1886	2	171.8	WIAF-1789	3	59.6
WIAF-4571	2	171.95	WIAF-1024	3	59.63
WIAF-4502	2	175.64	WIAF-721	3	61.6
WIAF-3616	2	192.65	WIAF-475	3	63.07
WIAF-2333	2	193.89	WIAF-2841	3	65.28
WIAF-861	2	196.04	WIAF-796	3	65.82
WIAF-3271	2	198.14	WIAF-816	3	67.71
WIAF-337	2	198.25	WIAF-2952	3	70.15
WIAF-2701	2	198.59	WIAF-1938	3	70.68
WIAF-2135	2	209.7	WIAF-2626	3	70.68
WIAF-223	2	210.13	WIAF-2197	3	70.91
WIAF-2376	2	215.78	WIAF-3733	3	71.76
WIAF-2080	2	216.56	WIAF-3534	3	71.91
WIAF-3338	2	217.67	WIAF-1489	3	80.52
WIAF-4541	2	223.88	WIAF-4098	3	100.66
WIAF-2827	2	225.63	WIAF-715	3	103.38
WIAF-2869	2	226.09	WIAF-1702	3	104.3

TABLE 6-8. (*Continued*)

SNP name	Chromosome	Genetic distance (cM)	SNP name	Chromosome	Genetic distance (cM)
WIAF-1703	3	104.3	WIAF-979	3	232.49
WIAF-3407	3	105.31	WIAF-1007	3	239.21
WIAF-745	3	105.49	WIAF-3566	3	239.23
WIAF-3709	3	105.88	WIAF-3858	4	0
WIAF-2828	3	108.3	WIAF-2091	4	0.81
WIAF-3151	3	115.31	WIAF-1593	4	2.33
WIAF-2871	3	115.72	WIAF-1958	4	2.33
WIAF-3112	3	116.96	WIAF-3225	4	3.05
WIAF-3103	3	117	WIAF-903	4	16.19
WIAF-2804	3	120.63	WIAF-2196	4	16.24
WIAF-456	3	121.56	WIAF-4142	4	17.08
WIAF-896	3	123.01	WIAF-3372	4	21.08
WIAF-1714	3	129.55	WIAF-316	4	25.1
WIAF-3387	3	132.17	WIAF-3750	4	25.18
WIAF-2572	3	134.38	WIAF-3885	4	34.14
WIAF-1629	3	138.74	WIAF-2788	4	38.37
WIAF-3902	3	144.32	WIAF-3459	4	39.06
WIAF-2081	3	145.29	WIAF-2325	4	48
WIAF-1473	3	145.84	WIAF-3923	4	54.82
WIAF-3176	3	146.66	WIAF-1925	4	57.8
WIAF-3909	3	146.76	WIAF-3412	4	57.85
WIAF-2116	3	146.78	WIAF-4522	4	59.56
WIAF-3664	3	147.05	WIAF-931	4	69.94
WIAF-2922	3	147.96	WIAF-4527	4	80.2
WIAF-2803	3	148.6	WIAF-1032	4	80.23
WIAF-2074	3	149.43	WIAF-482	4	82.65
WIAF-393	3	149.47	WIAF-483	4	82.65
WIAF-394	3	149.47	WIAF-919	4	82.72
WIAF-395	3	149.47	WIAF-2288	4	88.26
WIAF-343	3	149.67	WIAF-3047	4	94.02
WIAF-2730	3	149.7	WIAF-2114	4	97.93
WIAF-2059	3	158.75	WIAF-302	4	98.19
WIAF-1749	3	167.06	WIAF-3361	4	98.2
WIAF-650	3	169.09	WIAF-484	4	101.48
WIAF-651	3	169.09	WIAF-1302	4	107.23
WIAF-291	3	169.24	WIAF-2765	4	109.61
WIAF-1834	3	174.93	WIAF-2920	4	110.22
WIAF-1045	3	182.85	WIAF-2592	4	113.52
WIAF-313	3	183.16	WIAF-2791	4	114.57
WIAF-2753	3	183.28	WIAF-1753	4	117.5
WIAF-2749	3	183.32	WIAF-2964	4	120.29
WIAF-3300	3	187.11	WIAF-895	4	127.08
WIAF-626	3	189.38	WIAF-2305	4	129.28
WIAF-1819	3	201.32	WIAF-3818	4	132.94
WIAF-4251	3	202.57	WIAF-3821	4	133.02
WIAF-1786	3	206.68	WIAF-3086	4	135.86
WIAF-917	3	206.97	WIAF-664	4	145.01
WIAF-1906	3	208.4	WIAF-1475	4	154.06
WIAF-249	3	212.96	WIAF-4222	4	155.26
WIAF-250	3	212.96	WIAF-3265	4	160.82
WIAF-2422	3	226.3	WIAF-2936	4	169.1

(Continued on following pages.)

TABLE 6-8. (*Continued*)

SNP name	Chromosome	Genetic distance (cM)	SNP name	Chromosome	Genetic distance (cM)
WIAF-3144	4	172.39	WIAF-1690	6	2.47
WIAF-3418	4	185.32	WIAF-3766	6	3.69
WIAF-3118	4	187.49	WIAF-4574	6	6.24
WIAF-2907	4	193.08	WIAF-967	6	18.6
WIAF-3256	4	202.96	WIAF-1567	6	18.69
WIAF-2975	4	204.27	WIAF-2546	6	18.7
WIAF-3557	4	211.48	WIAF-881	6	19.02
WIAF-4594	4	221.12	WIAF-2892	6	26.63
WIAF-3262	5	21.03	WIAF-2597	6	39.36
WIAF-977	5	29.05	WIAF-2977	6	39.74
WIAF-852	5	29.06	WIAF-613	6	40.26
WIAF-4189	5	47.05	WIAF-3166	6	44.42
WIAF-3342	5	55.89	WIAF-3485	6	48.59
WIAF-1046	5	61.4	WIAF-3805	6	48.64
WIAF-3575	5	65.38	WIAF-4257	6	49.29
WIAF-2999	5	66.08	WIAF-1084	6	49.54
WIAF-601	5	66.4	WIAF-258	6	49.79
WIAF-2705	5	67.14	WIAF-1009	6	49.86
WIAF-1796	5	71.59	WIAF-2177	6	50.57
WIAF-1869	5	83.99	WIAF-2106	6	51.04
WIAF-1721	5	94.22	WIAF-2810	6	59.2
WIAF-205	5	95.04	WIAF-538	6	72.55
WIAF-2941	5	98.58	WIAF-4584	6	77.27
WIAF-512	5	99.89	WIAF-3700	6	79.56
WIAF-3553	5	100.29	WIAF-3444	6	82.12
WIAF-1594	5	106.6	WIAF-3843	6	85.55
WIAF-3198	5	107.18	WIAF-2690	6	87.39
WIAF-3199	5	107.18	WIAF-3097	6	88.06
WIAF-4558	5	111.13	WIAF-2877	6	91.42
WIAF-3339	5	112.7	WIAF-3161	6	94.14
WIAF-2723	5	118.43	WIAF-3158	6	94.16
WIAF-3210	5	128.24	WIAF-922	6	94.83
WIAF-1804	5	128.4	WIAF-4572	6	95.35
WIAF-287	5	129.3	WIAF-1670	6	95.54
WIAF-3133	5	130.14	WIAF-1541	6	96.83
WIAF-2108	5	132.9	WIAF-3799	6	97.3
WIAF-3547	5	135.31	WIAF-3746	6	97.51
WIAF-3246	5	136.75	WIAF-2956	6	102.94
WIAF-1331	5	140.75	WIAF-1476	6	109.88
WIAF-3559	5	146.07	WIAF-577	6	109.99
WIAF-209	5	152.09	WIAF-3344	6	111.27
WIAF-3402	5	154.16	WIAF-3245	6	117.81
WIAF-2087	5	169.7	WIAF-207	6	118.98
WIAF-3788	5	171.16	WIAF-3877	6	120.35
WIAF-1827	5	171.33	WIAF-985	6	127.12
WIAF-2023	5	173.82	WIAF-224	6	128.09
WIAF-3137	5	204.79	WIAF-3191	6	128.5
WIAF-3000	5	205.22	WIAF-3723	6	128.63
WIAF-2627	6	1.25	WIAF-3148	6	128.65
WIAF-3613	6	1.36	WIAF-726	6	128.65
WIAF-2709	6	2.41	WIAF-584	6	128.69

TABLE 6-8. (*Continued*)

SNP name	Chromosome	Genetic distance (cM)	SNP name	Chromosome	Genetic distance (cM)
WIAF-3081	6	129.72	WIAF-3187	7	135.26
WIAF-736	6	132.47	WIAF-1680	7	135.8
WIAF-737	6	132.48	WIAF-2364	7	137.25
WIAF-3531	6	132.85	WIAF-983	7	137.71
WIAF-1674	6	134.75	WIAF-671	7	139.85
WIAF-3474	6	141.01	WIAF-672	7	139.85
WIAF-3645	6	148.62	WIAF-2152	7	140.33
WIAF-3312	6	153.86	WIAF-3292	7	144.25
WIAF-2767	6	153.88	WIAF-3585	7	145.88
WIAF-592	6	162.59	WIAF-3285	7	145.92
WIAF-3676	6	164.85	WIAF-4573	7	150.32
WIAF-3677	6	164.91	WIAF-4518	7	151.36
WIAF-3806	6	172.8	WIAF-3650	7	155.99
WIAF-1955	6	176.79	WIAF-2651	7	156.67
WIAF-762	6	179.07	WIAF-2287	7	181.84
WIAF-982	6	179.16	WIAF-2264	7	181.85
WIAF-3452	6	180.76	WIAF-1627	7	184.82
WIAF-915	6	192.1	WIAF-3238	7	195.8
WIAF-3328	6	192.43	WIAF-1785	7	199.25
WIAF-3355	6	193.96	WIAF-1991	7	199.53
WIAF-3704	6	203.58	WIAF-3212	7	200.3
WIAF-3354	6	230.11	WIAF-2817	7	201.07
WIAF-3064	7	0	WIAF-2815	7	202
WIAF-350	7	8.12	WIAF-1977	7	215.34
WIAF-2601	7	8.43	WIAF-3834	8	3.61
WIAF-3390	7	21.69	WIAF-1992	8	9.51
WIAF-4506	7	25.7	WIAF-283	8	12.21
WIAF-4539	7	25.89	WIAF-2927	8	12.9
WIAF-514	7	55.89	WIAF-1897	8	13.4
WIAF-263	7	55.9	WIAF-1898	8	13.4
WIAF-4504	7	60.54	WIAF-3345	8	15.69
WIAF-2616	7	60.57	WIAF-3346	8	15.72
WIAF-3123	7	65.85	WIAF-1085	8	24.81
WIAF-678	7	65.89	WIAF-1745	8	24.83
WIAF-902	7	68.5	WIAF-496	8	32.68
WIAF-827	7	76.47	WIAF-2120	8	38.13
WIAF-828	7	76.7	WIAF-865	8	40.63
WIAF-1810	7	82.03	WIAF-1517	8	44.31
WIAF-636	7	83.18	WIAF-3157	8	44.47
WIAF-4576	7	83.19	WIAF-3156	8	44.48
WIAF-3321	7	101.5	WIAF-414	8	46.25
WIAF-806	7	112.47	WIAF-3420	8	46.28
WIAF-1218	7	119.48	WIAF-357	8	46.42
WIAF-4521	7	121.01	WIAF-996	8	46.73
WIAF-4537	7	121.04	WIAF-2809	8	48.14
WIAF-3603	7	124.82	WIAF-867	8	48.15
WIAF-3422	7	126.04	WIAF-819	8	49
WIAF-1772	7	127.21	WIAF-2525	8	50.3
WIAF-4117	7	129.95	WIAF-832	8	51.56
WIAF-2086	7	130.26	WIAF-2737	8	54
WIAF-807	7	132.59	WIAF-2738	8	54.02

(Continued on following pages.)

TABLE 6-8. (*Continued*)

SNP name	Chromosome	Genetic Distance (cM)	SNP name	Chromosome	Genetic Distance (cM)
WIAF-716	8	56.54	WIAF-3206	9	23.75
WIAF-2980	8	60.11	WIAF-2945	9	26.33
WIAF-370	8	60.28	WIAF-3688	9	26.54
WIAF-3218	8	65.62	WIAF-3600	9	27.71
WIAF-1693	8	67.76	WIAF-3093	9	44.7
WIAF-3573	8	68.18	WIAF-459	9	44.77
WIAF-3054	8	69.3	WIAF-2759	9	46.97
WIAF-2374	8	69.81	WIAF-1919	9	48.24
WIAF-3621	8	69.82	WIAF-1899	9	49.39
WIAF-2377	8	70.91	WIAF-1900	9	49.42
WIAF-472	8	72.47	WIAF-2372	9	56.14
WIAF-355	8	72.84	WIAF-4131	9	56.88
WIAF-1482	8	76.96	WIAF-4569	9	58.69
WIAF-2925	8	79.1	WIAF-3323	9	58.93
WIAF-1565	8	84.07	WIAF-975	9	61.82
WIAF-1580	8	89.27	WIAF-4540	9	64.81
WIAF-1885	8	90.82	WIAF-1634	9	64.89
WIAF-2084	8	91.39	WIAF-1450	9	68.06
WIAF-4516	8	98.32	WIAF-2782	9	69.99
WIAF-4509	8	98.35	WIAF-2783	9	69.99
WIAF-2268	8	99.23	WIAF-3813	9	70.8
WIAF-1846	8	100.28	WIAF-2165	9	86.46
WIAF-3341	8	102.27	WIAF-2133	9	90.92
WIAF-2312	8	104.31	WIAF-2275	9	91.58
WIAF-1320	8	104.33	WIAF-2567	9	94.45
WIAF-4536	8	104.34	WIAF-3520	9	94.64
WIAF-490	8	104.37	WIAF-3518	9	94.74
WIAF-2633	8	110.2	WIAF-960	9	94.74
WIAF-2226	8	113.99	WIAF-3831	9	96.74
WIAF-4035	8	114.47	WIAF-4544	9	104.33
WIAF-315	8	114.6	WIAF-3928	9	105.76
WIAF-3253	8	121.4	WIAF-1764	9	106.56
WIAF-341	8	130.9	WIAF-433	9	107.15
WIAF-3681	8	137.33	WIAF-3554	9	110.29
WIAF-761	8	137.79	WIAF-4508	9	111.39
WIAF-3231	8	143.76	WIAF-1412	9	114.09
WIAF-989	8	147.66	WIAF-4523	9	114.09
WIAF-1516	8	155.54	WIAF-2155	9	128.42
WIAF-583	8	155.82	WIAF-3477	9	129.27
WIAF-3033	8	163.14	WIAF-3358	9	129.84
WIAF-4524	8	164.32	WIAF-233	9	129.92
WIAF-1584	8	166.68	WIAF-951	9	130.48
WIAF-1027	8	168.85	WIAF-3036	9	136.95
WIAF-1186	8	169.13	WIAF-3801	9	139.77
WIAF-2402	8	170.79	WIAF-2953	9	140.48
WIAF-1029	8	178.66	WIAF-2721	9	140.6
WIAF-3881	9	0.34	WIAF-3938	9	141.15
WIAF-988	9	10.02	WIAF-3472	9	141.33
WIAF-3527	9	14.17	WIAF-2950	9	142.35
WIAF-2714	9	19.16	WIAF-2095	9	148.41
WIAF-1582	9	19.9	WIAF-2094	9	148.42

TABLE 6-8. (*Continued*)

SNP name	Chromosome	Genetic distance (cM)	SNP name	Chromosome	Genetic distance (cM)
WIAF-3153	9	156.98	WIAF-3019	11	18.77
WIAF-3035	9	157.02	WIAF-3129	11	18.86
WIAF-3025	9	157.08	WIAF-3125	11	18.9
WIAF-3310	9	157.08	WIAF-3139	11	18.9
WIAF-3736	9	164.96	WIAF-4592	11	19.89
WIAF-3006	9	166.96	WIAF-3023	11	25.18
WIAF-1742	10	10.09	WIAF-4530	11	37.24
WIAF-2581	10	15.49	WIAF-2046	11	40.22
WIAF-3537	10	16.5	WIAF-2311	11	40.27
WIAF-1511	10	27.68	WIAF-588	11	43.69
WIAF-272	10	31.56	WIAF-1949	11	43.98
WIAF-3614	10	42.47	WIAF-1307	11	48.25
WIAF-3908	10	45.56	WIAF-3007	11	49.68
WIAF-966	10	61.17	WIAF-2983	11	66.6
WIAF-2158	10	65.17	WIAF-2768	11	66.68
WIAF-3281	10	67.18	WIAF-2769	11	66.68
WIAF-4055	10	70.34	WIAF-2822	11	67.19
WIAF-3797	10	70.39	WIAF-2823	11	67.19
WIAF-1145	10	70.42	WIAF-4525	11	74.78
WIAF-3058	10	71.81	WIAF-2220	11	76.36
WIAF-2729	10	71.92	WIAF-1862	11	77.28
WIAF-3130	10	72.28	WIAF-1059	11	78.73
WIAF-3136	10	72.28	WIAF-3659	11	78.79
WIAF-303	10	76.37	WIAF-1529	11	79.13
WIAF-3110	10	79.84	WIAF-1866	11	79.84
WIAF-3899	10	88.16	WIAF-381	11	80.75
WIAF-3637	10	94.3	WIAF-4557	11	80.84
WIAF-3711	10	96.06	WIAF-380	11	80.87
WIAF-310	10	96.91	WIAF-2195	11	81.01
WIAF-308	10	97.37	WIAF-228	11	85.13
WIAF-744	10	98.09	WIAF-842	11	89
WIAF-2805	10	102.28	WIAF-2569	11	95.09
WIAF-1799	10	103.56	WIAF-2897	11	102.07
WIAF-1585	10	103.77	WIAF-2313	11	102.23
WIAF-2438	10	104.9	WIAF-3203	11	103.01
WIAF-4519	10	108.83	WIAF-3071	11	103.81
WIAF-3691	10	129.98	WIAF-1564	11	105.35
WIAF-2303	10	131.44	WIAF-3059	11	109.71
WIAF-2588	10	132.26	WIAF-3055	11	109.73
WIAF-2911	10	137.24	WIAF-1950	11	110.58
WIAF-4070	10	138.88	WIAF-1542	11	112.64
WIAF-901	10	144.51	WIAF-3012	11	119.75
WIAF-271	10	151.85	WIAF-1525	11	121.02
WIAF-1676	10	152.45	WIAF-3653	11	124.86
WIAF-3761	10	156.49	WIAF-2758	11	124.88
WIAF-3299	10	156.6	WIAF-1588	11	126.3
WIAF-3213	10	164.91	WIAF-3186	11	127.96
WIAF-3630	10	179.07	WIAF-3770	11	129
WIAF-991	11	16	WIAF-3769	11	129.01
WIAF-3297	11	16.23	WIAF-1247	11	130.7
WIAF-2043	11	16.47	WIAF-3882	11	131.06

(*Continued on following pages.*)

TABLE 6-8. (*Continued*)

SNP name	Chromosome	Genetic Distance (cM)	SNP name	Chromosome	Genetic distance (cM)
WIAF-1694	11	132.16	WIAF-1520	12	129.46
WIAF-712	11	134.86	WIAF-3911	12	132.8
WIAF-713	11	134.95	WIAF-1918	12	136.13
WIAF-3291	11	135.29	WIAF-2467	12	154.19
WIAF-971	11	141.63	WIAF-3624	12	154.59
WIAF-432	11	142.66	WIAF-3594	13	11.14
WIAF-3838	11	143.48	WIAF-2385	13	12.09
WIAF-3745	11	147.24	WIAF-973	13	12.15
WIAF-1463	11	161	WIAF-3070	13	15.6
WIAF-1767	11	161	WIAF-4575	13	19.03
WIAF-2696	11	161	WIAF-2781	13	36.92
WIAF-3053	11	161	WIAF-2138	13	42.48
WIAF-3049	12	18.22	WIAF-3367	13	44.52
WIAF-2689	12	21.69	WIAF-1544	13	47.86
WIAF-1430	12	21.79	WIAF-1353	13	47.88
WIAF-1805	12	22.02	WIAF-2713	13	50.28
WIAF-3906	12	31.77	WIAF-3543	13	50.99
WIAF-4548	12	32.95	WIAF-1858	13	51.57
WIAF-879	12	35.59	WIAF-505	13	51.78
WIAF-3296	12	44.8	WIAF-3384	13	70.17
WIAF-2679	12	50.83	WIAF-2754	13	70.31
WIAF-4045	12	55.17	WIAF-3084	13	71.41
WIAF-641	12	55.51	WIAF-1318	13	72.63
WIAF-4526	12	57.04	WIAF-2207	13	77.24
WIAF-3915	12	57.94	WIAF-3756	13	94.06
WIAF-2363	12	59.7	WIAF-2706	13	121.67
WIAF-1988	12	63.03	WIAF-2555	13	161
WIAF-2787	12	63.98	WIAF-1026	14	0
WIAF-2785	12	64.14	WIAF-436	14	0
WIAF-533	12	69.3	WIAF-3887	14	3.41
WIAF-1980	12	70.53	WIAF-3227	14	7.57
WIAF-463	12	71.53	WIAF-4082	14	10.31
WIAF-2420	12	71.75	WIAF-2867	14	18.14
WIAF-2423	12	71.75	WIAF-2868	14	18.25
WIAF-2661	12	74.34	WIAF-729	14	19.02
WIAF-2658	12	74.35	WIAF-3249	14	37.74
WIAF-3738	12	83.07	WIAF-3383	14	40.64
WIAF-3140	12	83.18	WIAF-2789	14	40.97
WIAF-818	12	85.81	WIAF-2919	14	43.31
WIAF-3644	12	86.93	WIAF-4542	14	43.59
WIAF-3330	12	87.52	WIAF-694	14	45.71
WIAF-1643	12	88.98	WIAF-1997	14	48.12
WIAF-1053	12	104.84	WIAF-3078	14	65.07
WIAF-377	12	105.33	WIAF-3777	14	69.24
WIAF-3063	12	105.54	WIAF-3713	14	69.46
WIAF-3549	12	110.7	WIAF-402	14	70.49
WIAF-4545	12	113.53	WIAF-1778	14	71.08
WIAF-3302	12	124.31	WIAF-1036	14	72.47
WIAF-552	12	124.7	WIAF-823	14	72.99
WIAF-2718	12	129.31	WIAF-295	14	73
WIAF-2716	12	129.42	WIAF-294	14	73.06

TABLE 6-8. (*Continued*)

SNP name	Chromosome	Genetic distance (cM)	SNP name	Chromosome	Genetic distance (cM)
WIAF-2677	14	73.23	WIAF-1945	15	82.62
WIAF-246	14	76.73	WIAF-2012	15	85.37
WIAF-3500	14	80.65	WIAF-1490	15	90.11
WIAF-478	14	85.18	WIAF-2489	15	94.47
WIAF-2735	14	85.2	WIAF-4547	15	94.54
WIAF-3237	14	85.62	WIAF-3876	15	97.14
WIAF-4259	14	95.72	WIAF-3683	15	97.37
WIAF-835	14	108.95	WIAF-2321	15	97.77
WIAF-1602	14	110.53	WIAF-2630	15	97.88
WIAF-646	14	110.53	WIAF-3106	15	98.11
WIAF-2218	14	111.62	WIAF-3111	15	98.12
WIAF-2233	14	112.18	WIAF-3114	15	98.12
WIAF-2301	14	122.02	WIAF-3022	15	98.41
WIAF-2302	14	122.04	WIAF-3699	15	103.31
WIAF-874	14	124.91	WIAF-444	15	105.08
WIAF-3184	14	132.99	WIAF-2849	15	117.87
WIAF-3185	14	132.99	WIAF-2931	15	161
WIAF-1895	14	134.41	WIAF-1514	16	7.68
WIAF-2041	14	161	WIAF-627	16	12
WIAF-4531	14	161	WIAF-924	16	12
WIAF-4513	15	5.77	WIAF-3828	16	16.36
WIAF-4593	15	5.77	WIAF-510	16	27.76
WIAF-4595	15	7.41	WIAF-1614	16	27.96
WIAF-4597	15	7.77	WIAF-3705	16	27.96
WIAF-4551	15	20.87	WIAF-1909	16	29.48
WIAF-4590	15	27.31	WIAF-2343	16	29.54
WIAF-802	15	27.32	WIAF-1156	16	43.32
WIAF-2802	15	28.71	WIAF-2652	16	44.07
WIAF-1283	15	32.13	WIAF-3574	16	46.49
WIAF-791	15	33.37	WIAF-1870	16	46.98
WIAF-2889	15	36.75	WIAF-606	16	49.9
WIAF-2887	15	39.42	WIAF-2136	16	58.74
WIAF-3863	15	42.99	WIAF-1971	16	68.82
WIAF-3907	15	43.02	WIAF-2618	16	68.92
WIAF-317	15	43.22	WIAF-1697	16	75.43
WIAF-618	15	44.65	WIAF-889	16	83.68
WIAF-2949	15	46.11	WIAF-2752	16	85.96
WIAF-2227	15	46.42	WIAF-2750	16	85.98
WIAF-1861	15	46.66	WIAF-2997	16	90.35
WIAF-336	15	51.19	WIAF-3421	16	92
WIAF-88	15	52.39	WIAF-3425	16	92
WIAF-3287	15	52.43	WIAF-3855	16	92
WIAF-3890	15	54.74	WIAF-3714	16	92.35
WIAF-1635	15	56.58	WIAF-1812	16	97.74
WIAF-4515	15	61.97	WIAF-2399	16	99.18
WIAF-534	15	64.15	WIAF-1474	16	99.23
WIAF-425	15	65.45	WIAF-3504	16	99.38
WIAF-1000	15	65.84	WIAF-3494	16	106.59
WIAF-362	15	68.25	WIAF-3270	16	106.94
WIAF-2576	15	68.46	WIAF-1139	16	107.59
WIAF-3619	15	69.03	WIAF-2650	16	110.63

(Continued on following pages.)

TABLE 6-8. (*Continued*)

SNP name	Chromosome	Genetic distance (cM)	SNP name	Chromosome	Genetic distance (cM)
WIAF-673	16	111.13	WIAF-2858	17	116.98
WIAF-1628	16	161	WIAF-3305	17	121.36
WIAF-2142	16	161	WIAF-1505	18	4.04
WIAF-2860	16	161	WIAF-1626	18	12.3
WIAF-2861	16	161	WIAF-1001	18	32.16
WIAF-3068	16	161	WIAF-1002	18	32.32
WIAF-974	16	161	WIAF-2971	18	41.64
WIAF-408	17	0	WIAF-2824	18	41.66
WIAF-409	17	0	WIAF-2137	18	43.18
WIAF-821	17	9.84	WIAF-2780	18	50.45
WIAF-918	17	14.07	WIAF-1468	18	61.19
WIAF-39	17	14.12	WIAF-3204	18	61.71
WIAF-3660	17	17.52	WIAF-907	18	61.84
WIAF-4585	17	18.25	WIAF-4147	18	66.09
WIAF-748	17	28.86	WIAF-1811	18	66.99
WIAF-747	17	29.15	WIAF-3013	18	67.69
WIAF-1274	17	34.78	WIAF-1775	18	74
WIAF-3197	17	41.14	WIAF-700	18	92.74
WIAF-2573	17	43.43	WIAF-210	18	93.21
WIAF-3889	17	43.57	WIAF-4080	18	97.49
WIAF-1519	17	52.83	WIAF-3180	18	99.36
WIAF-2293	17	55.65	WIAF-331	18	101.74
WIAF-3030	17	58.17	WIAF-801	18	115.85
WIAF-908	17	61.54	WIAF-693	18	119.26
WIAF-1996	17	61.85	WIAF-1119	18	123.8
WIAF-423	17	64.85	WIAF-2351	18	161
WIAF-422	17	64.92	WIAF-923	19	15.27
WIAF-3051	17	65.14	WIAF-894	19	21.73
WIAF-1741	17	67.04	WIAF-893	19	21.79
WIAF-1598	17	67.73	WIAF-3393	19	32.89
WIAF-752	17	68.02	WIAF-3706	19	39.09
WIAF-4164	17	70.3	WIAF-118	19	41.19
WIAF-1164	17	71.18	WIAF-608	19	47.96
WIAF-4554	17	71.3	WIAF-2857	19	49.63
WIAF-1133	17	73.82	WIAF-3276	19	51.57
WIAF-1134	17	73.86	WIAF-839	19	52.82
WIAF-1021	17	74.25	WIAF-1533	19	52.96
WIAF-3780	17	74.29	WIAF-2574	19	59.66
WIAF-3779	17	74.3	WIAF-1948	19	60.55
WIAF-507	17	76.22	WIAF-786	19	61.06
WIAF-1652	17	76.28	WIAF-2206	19	62.58
WIAF-2874	17	81.74	WIAF-2641	19	69.21
WIAF-511	17	86.09	WIAF-978	19	69.3
WIAF-1138	17	93.4	WIAF-2063	19	69.68
WIAF-1325	17	94.5	WIAF-2064	19	69.68
WIAF-2375	17	95.11	WIAF-3873	19	69.84
WIAF-2760	17	101.89	WIAF-4510	19	73.34
WIAF-2560	17	107.06	WIAF-3546	19	75.2
WIAF-2450	17	112.69	WIAF-3607	19	88.94
WIAF-2445	17	113.15	WIAF-2639	19	95.43
WIAF-2413	17	116.26	WIAF-2637	19	97.8

TABLE 6-8. (*Continued*)

SNP name	Chromosome	Genetic distance (cM)	SNP name	Chromosome	Genetic distance (cM)
WIAF-2101	19	103.18	WIAF-624	21	34.81
WIAF-4517	19	104.93	WIAF-1500	21	35.02
WIAF-3024	19	105.19	WIAF-3496	21	35.39
WIAF-1488	19	105.71	WIAF-1943	21	37.13
WIAF-2662	19	109.51	WIAF-2477	21	50.92
WIAF-2129	20	0.91	WIAF-2436	21	161
WIAF-2119	20	8.9	WIAF-4514	21	161
WIAF-730	20	17.76	WIAF-3618	22	0
WIAF-3220	20	28.24	WIAF-843	22	2.79
WIAF-3221	20	28.56	WIAF-2544	22	5.54
WIAF-3511	20	30.78	WIAF-3824	22	9
WIAF-3612	20	32.93	WIAF-1706	22	21.16
WIAF-3041	20	43.93	WIAF-2057	22	22.83
WIAF-3941	20	44.38	WIAF-3880	22	25.23
WIAF-2128	20	44.4	WIAF-2538	22	36.66
WIAF-3927	20	53.91	WIAF-230	22	37.28
WIAF-2019	20	60.03	WIAF-1974	22	37.91
WIAF-266	20	68.28	WIAF-1672	22	38.19
WIAF-1648	20	70.31	WIAF-1673	22	38.25
WIAF-1853	20	75.9	WIAF-3864	22	38.94
WIAF-2963	20	80.82	WIAF-1266	22	44.06
WIAF-1969	20	94.08	WIAF-1816	22	50.86
WIAF-3497	21	8.08	WIAF-1904	22	50.89
WIAF-3498	21	8.36	WIAF-3065	22	161
WIAF-599	21	17.53	WIAF-3067	22	161
WIAF-3562	21	18.91	WIAF-2669	X	18.97
WIAF-1682	21	23.86	WIAF-4550	X	73.33
WIAF-559	21	24.14	WIAF-1290	X	111.15
WIAF-4546	21	26.04	WIAF-1872	X	124.12
WIAF-3508	21	32.05	WIAF-3737	X	124.19
WIAF-2643	21	33.99	WIAF-2589	X	160.92

REFERENCES

Ahrendt S.A., Halachmi S., Chow J.T., Wu L., Halachmi N., Yang S.C., Wehage S., Jen J., and Sidransky D. 1999. Rapid p53 sequence analysis in primary lung cancer using an oligonucleotide probe array. *Proc. Natl. Acad. Sci.* **96:** 7382–7387.

Albertson D.G., Ylstra B., Segraves R., Collins C., Dairkee S.H., Kowbel D., Kuo W.L., Gray J.W., and Pinkel D. 2000. Quantitative mapping of amplicon structure by array CGH identifies CYP24 as a candidate oncogene. *Nat. Genet.* **25:** 144–146.

Alizadeh A.A., Eisen M.B., Davis R.E., Ma C., Lossos I.S., Rosenwald A., Boldrick J.C., Sabet H., Tran T., Yu X., Powell J.I., Yang L., Marti G.E., Moore T., Hudson J. Jr., Lu L., Lewis D.B., Tibshirani R., Sherlock G., Chan W.C., Greiner T.C., Weisenburger D.D., Armitage J.O., Warnke R., Staudt L.M., et al. 2000. Distinct types of diffuse large B-cell lymphoma identified by gene expression profiling. *Nature* **403:** 503–511.

Boyd K.E. and Farnham P.J. 1999. Coexamination of site-specific transcription factor binding and promoter activity in living cells. *Mol. Cell. Biol.* **19:** 8393–8399.

Chakravarti A. 1998. It's raining SNPs, hallelujah? *Nat. Genet.* **19:** 216–217.

Chee M., Yang R., Hubbell E., Berno A., Huang X.C., Stern D., Winkler J., Lockhart D.J., Morris M.S., and Fodor S.P. 1996. Accessing genetic information with high-density DNA arrays. *Science* **274:** 610–614.

Chen J., Iannone M.A., Li M.S., Taylor J.D., Rivers P., Nelsen A.J., Slentz-Kesler K.A., Roses A., and Weiner M.P. 2000. A microsphere-based assay for multiplexed single nucleotide polymorphism analysis using single base chain extension. *Genome Res.* **10:** 549–557.

Chen X. and Kwok P.Y. 1999. Homogeneous genotyping assays for single nucleotide polymorphisms with fluorescence resonance energy transfer detection. *Genet. Anal.* **14:** 157–163.

Chen X., Levine L., and Kwok P.Y. 1999. Fluorescence polarization in homogeneous nucleic acid analysis. *Genome Res.* **9:** 492–498.

Cheung V.G., Nowak N., Jang W., Kirsch I.R., Zhao S., Chen X.N., Furey T.S., Kim U.J., Kuo WL, Olivier M., Conroy J., Kasprzyk A., Massa H., Yonescu R., Sait S., Thoreen C., Snijders A., Lemyre E., Bailey J.A., Bruzel A., Burrill W.D., Clegg S.M., Collins S., Dhami P., Friedman C, Han C.S., Herrick S., Lee J., Ligon A.H., Lowry S., Morley M., Narasimhan S., Osoegawa K., Peng Z., Plajzer-Frick I., Quade B.J., Scott D., Sirotkin K., Thorpe A.A., Gray J.W., Hudson J, Pinkel D., Ried T., Rowen L., Shen-Ong G.L., Strausberg R.L., Birney E., Callen D.F., Cheng J.F., Cox D.R., Doggett N.A., Carter N.P., Eichler E.E., Haussler D., Korenberg J.R., Morton C.C., Albertson D., Schuler G., de Jong P.J., Trask B.J.; The BAC Resource Consortium. 2001. Integration of cytogenetic landmarks into the draft sequence of the human genome. *Nature* **409:** 953–958.

Collins F.S., Patrinos A., Jordan E., Chakravarti A., Gesteland R., and Walters L. 1998. New goals for the U.S. Human Genome Project: 1998–2003. *Science* **282:** 682–689.

Cutler D.J., Zwick M.E., Carrasquillo M.M., Yohn C.T., Tobin K.P., Kashuk C., Mathews D.J., Shah N.A., Eichler E.E., Warrington J.A., and Chrakravarti A. 2001. High-throughput variation detection and genotyping using microarrays. *Genome Res.* **11:** 1913–1925.

Deloukas P., Schuler G.D., Gyapay G., Beasley E.M., Soderlund C., Rodriguez-Tome P., Hui L., Matise T.C., McKusick K.B., Beckmann J.S., Bentolila S., Bihoreau M., Birren B.B., Browne J., Butler A., Castle A.B., Chiannilkulchai N., Clee C., Day P.J., Dehejia A., Dibling T., Drouot N., Duprat S., Fizames C., Bentley D.R., et al. 1998. A physical map of 30,000 human genes. *Science* **282:** 744–746.

DeRisi J., Penland L., Brown P.O., Bittner M.L., Meltzer P.S., Ray M., Chen Y., Su Y.A., Trent J.M., et al. 1996. Use of a cDNA microarray to analyse gene expression patterns in human cancer. *Nat. Genet.* **14:** 457–460.

du Manoir S., Speicher M.R., Joos S., Schrock E., Popp S., Dohner H., Kovacs G., Robert-Nicoud M., Lichter P., and Cremer T. 1993. Detection of complete and partial chromosome gains and losses by comparative genomic in situ hybridization. *Hum. Genet.* **90:** 590–610.

Dracopoli N.C. and Fogh J. 1983. Loss of heterozygosity in cultured human tumor cell lines. *J. Natl. Cancer Inst.* **70:** 83–87.

Eggerding F.A. 1995. A one-step coupled amplification and oligonucleotide ligation procedure for multiplex genetic typing. *PCR Methods Appl.* **4:** 337–345.

Fan J.B., Chen X., Halushka M.K., Berno A., Huang X., Ryder T., Lipshutz R.J., Lockhart D.J., and Chakravarti A. 2000. Parallel genotyping of human SNPs using generic high-density oligonucleotide tag arrays. *Genome Res.* **10:** 853–860.

Fortina P., Conant R., Monokian G., Dotti G., Parrella T., Hitchcock W., Kant J., Scanlin T., Rappaport E. Schwartz E., et al. 1992. Non-radioactive detection of the most common mutations in the cystic fibrosis transmembrane conductance regulator gene by multiplex allele-specific polymerase chain reaction. *Hum. Genet.* **90:** 375–378.

Gall K., Pavelic J., Fadro-Santel D., Poljak M., and Pavelic K. 1993. DNA amplification by polymerase chain reaction from brain tissues embedded in paraffin. *Int. J. Exp. Pathol.* **74:** 333–337.

Geschwind D.H., Gregg J., Boone K., Karrim J., Pawlikowska-Haddal A., Rao E., Ellison J., Ciccodicola A., D'Urso M., Woods R., Rappold G.A., Swerdloff R., and Nelson S.F. 1998. Klinefelter's syndrome as a model of anomalous cerebral laterality: Testing gene dosage in the X chromosome pseudoautosomal region using a DNA microarray. *Dev. Genet.* **23:** 215–229.

Greer C.E., Wheeler C.M., and Manos M.M. 1995. PCR amplification from paraffin-embedded tissues: Sample preparation and the effects of fixation. In *PCR primer: A laboratory manual* (ed. C.W. Dieffenbach and G.S. Dveksler), pp. 99–112. Cold Spring Harbor Laboratory Press, Cold Spring Harbor, New York.

Hacia J.G. and Collins F.S. 1999. Mutational analysis using oligonucleotide microarrays. *J. Med. Genet.* **36:** 730–736.

Hacia J.G., Brody L.C., Chee M.S., Fodor S.P., and Collins F.S. 1996. Detection of heterozygous mutations in BRCA1 using high density oligonucleotide arrays and two-color fluorescence analysis. *Nat. Genet.* **14:** 441–447.

Haff L.A. and Smirnov I.P. 1997. Single-nucleotide polymorphism identification assays using a thermostable DNA polymerase and delayed extraction MALDI-TOF mass spectrometry. *Genome Res.* **7:** 378–388.

Hemminki A., Tomlinson I., Markie D., Jarvinen H., Sistonen P., Bjorkqvist A.M., Knuutila S., Salovaara R., Bodmer W., Shibata D., de la Chapelle A., and Aaltonen L.A. 1997. Localization of a susceptibility locus for Peutz-Jeghers syndrome to 19p using comparative genomic hybridization and targeted linkage analysis. *Nat. Genet.* **15:** 87–90.

Hirschhorn J.N., Sklar P., Lindblad-Toh K., Lim Y.M., Ruiz-Gutierrez M., Bolk S., Langhorst B., Schaffner S., Winchester E., and Lander E.S. 2000. SBE-TAGS: An array-based method for efficient single-nucleotide polymorphism genotyping. *Proc. Natl. Acad. Sci.* **97:** 12164–12169.

Hodgson G., Hager J.H., Volik S., Hariono S., Wernick M., Moore D., Albertson D.G., Pinkel D., Collins C., Hanahan D., and Gray J.W. 2001. Genome scanning with array CGH delineates regional alterations in mouse islet carcinomas. *Nat. Genet.* **29:** 459–464.

Iyer V.R., Horak C.E., Scafe C.S., Botstein D., Snyder M., and Brown P.O. 2001. Genomic binding sites of the yeast cell-cycle transcription factors SBF and MBF. *Nature* **409:** 533–538.

Jain A.N., Tokuyasu T.A., Snijders A.M., Segraves R., Albertson D.G., and Pinkel D. 2002. Fully automatic quantification of microarray image data. *Genome Res.* **12:** 325–332.

Kallioniemi A., Kallioniemi O.P., Sudar D., Rutovitz D., Gray J.W., Waldman F., and Pinkel D. 1992. Comparative genomic hybridization for molecular cytogenetic analysis of solid tumors. *Science* **258:** 818–821.

———. 1993. Comparative genomic hybridization: A rapid new method for detecting and mapping DNA amplification in tumors. *Semin. Cancer Biol.* **4:** 41–46.

Kiko H., Niggemann E., and Ruger W. 1979. Physical mapping of the restriction fragments obtained from bacteriophage T4 dC-DNA with the restriction endonucleases *Sma*I, *Kpn*I and *Bgl*II. *Mol. Gen. Genet.* **172:** 303–312.

Klein C.A., Schmidt-Kittler O., Schardt J.A., Pantel K., Speicher M.R., and Riethmuller G. 1999. Comparative genomic hybridization, loss of heterozygosity, and DNA sequence analysis of single cells. *Proc. Natl. Acad. Sci.* **96:** 4494–4499.

Kozal M.J., Shah N., Shen N., Yang R., Fucini R., Merigan T.C., Richman D.D., Morris D., Hubbell E., Chee M., and Gingeras T.R. 1996. Extensive polymorphisms observed in HIV-1 clade B protease gene using high-density oligonucleotide arrays. *Nat. Med.* **2:** 753–759.

Kwok P.Y. 2000. High-throughput genotyping assay approaches. *Pharmacogenomics* **1:** 95–100.

Lander E.S., Linton L.M., Birren B., Nusbaum C., Zody M.C., Baldwin J., Devon K., Dewar K., Doyle M., FitzHugh W., et al. 2001. Initial sequencing and analysis of the human genome. *Nature* **409:** 860–921.

Lieb J.D., Liu X., Botstein D., and Brown P.O. 2001. Promoter-specific binding of Rap1 revealed by genome-wide maps of protein-DNA association. *Nat. Genet.* **28:** 327–334.

Lindblad-Toh K., Tanenbaum D.M., Daly M.J., Winchester E., Liu W.O., Villapakkam A., Stanton S.E., Larsson C., Hudson T.J., Johnson B.E., Lander E.S., and Meyerson M. 2000a. Loss-of-heterozygosity analysis of small cell lung carcinoma using single nucleotide polymorphism arrays. *Nat. Biotechnol.* **18:** 1001–1005.

Lindblad-Toh K., Winchester E., Daly M.J., Wang D.G., Hirschhorn J.N., Laviolette J.P., Ardlie K., Reich D.E., Robinson E., Sklar P., Shah N., Thomas D., Fan J.B., Gingeras T., Warrington J., Patil N., Hudson T.J., and Lander E.S. 2000b. Large-scale discovery and genotyping of single-nucleotide polymorphisms in the mouse. *Nat. Genet.* **24:** 381–386.

Lisitsyn N. and Wigler M. 1993. Cloning the differences between two complex genomes. *Science* **259:** 946–951.

Lisitsyn N.A., Rosenberg M.V., Launer G.A., Wagner L.L., Potapov V.K., Kolesnik T.B., and Sverdlov E.D. 1993. A method for isolation of sequences missing in one of two related genomes. *Mol. Gen. Mikrobiol.*

Virusol. **3:** 26–29.

Lisitsyn N.A., Lisitsina N.M., Dalbagni G., Barker P., Sanchez C.A., Gnarra J., Linehan W.M., Reid B.J., and Wigler M.H. 1995. Comparative genomic analysis of tumors: Detection of DNA losses and amplification. *Proc. Natl. Acad. Sci.* **92:** 151–155.

Livak K.J., Flood S.J., Marmaro J., Giusti W., and Deetz K. 1995. Oligonucleotides with fluorescent dyes at opposite ends provide a quenched probe system useful for detecting PCR product and nucleic acid hybridization. *PCR Methods Appl.* **4:** 357–362.

Lucito R., Nakimura M., West J.A., Han Y., Chin K., Jensen K., McCombie R., Gray J.W., and Wigler M. 1998. Genetic analysis using genomic representations. *Proc. Natl. Acad. Sci.* **95:** 4487–4492.

Lucito R., West J., Reiner A., Alexander J., Esposito D., Mishra B., Powers S., Norton L., and Wigler M. 2000. Detecting gene copy number fluctuations in tumor cells by microarray analysis of genomic representations. *Genome Res.* **10:** 1726–1736.

Marth G., Yeh R., Minton M., Donaldson R., Li Q., Duan S., Davenport R., Miller R.D., and Kwok P.Y. 2001. Single-nucleotide polymorphisms in the public domain: How useful are they? *Nat. Genet.* **27:** 371–372.

Mei R., Galipeau P.C., Prass C., Berno A., Ghandour G., Patil N., Wolff R.K., Chee M.S., Reid B.J., and Lockhart D.J. 2000. Genome-wide detection of allelic imbalance using human SNPs and high-density DNA arrays. *Genome Res.* **10:** 1126–1137.

Monni O., Joensuu H., Franssila K., and Knuutila S. 1996. DNA copy number changes in diffuse large B-cell lymphoma—Comparative genomic hybridization study. *Blood* **87:** 5269–5278.

Orlando V. and Paro R. 1993. Mapping polycomb-repressed domains in the bithorax complex using in vivo formaldehyde cross-linked chromatin. *Cell* **75:** 1187–1198.

Pastinen T., Raitio M., Lindroos K., Tainola P., Peltonen L., and Syvanen A.C. 2000. A system for specific, high-throughput genotyping by allele-specific primer extension on microarrays. *Genome Res.* **10:** 1031–1042.

Patil N., Berno A.J., Hinds D.A., Barrett W.A., Doshi J.M., Hacker C.R., Kautzer C.R., Lee D.H., Marjoribanks C., McDonough D.P., Nguyen B.T.N., Norris M.C., Sheehan J.B., Shen N., Stern D., Stokowski R.P., Thomas D.J., Trulson M.O., Vyas K.R., Frazer K.A., Fodor S.P.A., Cox D.R. 2001. Blocks of limited haplotype diversity revealed by high-resolution scanning of human chromosome 21. *Science* **294:** 1719–1723.

Perou C.M., Sorlie T., Eisen M.B., van de Rijn M., Jeffrey S.S., Rees C.A., Pollack J.R., Ross D.T., Johnsen H., Akslen L.A., Fluge O., Pergamenschikov A., Williams C., Zhu S.X., Lonning P.E., Borresen-Dale A.L., Brown P.O., and Botstein D. 2000. Molecular portraits of human breast tumours. *Nature* **406:** 747–752.

Pinkel D., Segraves R., Sudar D., Clark S., Poole I., Kowbel D., Collins C., Kuo W.L., Chen C., Zhai Y., Dairkee S.H., Ljung B.M., Gray J.W., and Albertson D.G. 1998. High resolution analysis of DNA copy number variation using comparative genomic hybridization to microarrays. *Nat. Genet.* **20:** 207–211.

Pollack J.R., Perou C.M., Alizadeh A.A., Eisen M.B., Pergamenschikov A., Williams C.F., Jeffrey S.S., Botstein D., and Brown P.O. 1999. Genome-wide analysis of DNA copy-number changes using cDNA microarrays. *Nat. Genet.* **23:** 41–46.

Prince J.A. Feuk L., Howell W.M., Jobs M., Emahazion T., Blennow K., and Brookes A.J. 2001. Robust and accurate single nucleotide polymorphism genotyping by dynamic allele-specific hybridization (DASH): Design criteria and assay validation. *Genome Res.* **11:** 152–162.

Reid J.L., Iyer V.R., Brown P.O., and Struhl K. 2000. Coordinate regulation of yeast ribosomal protein genes is associated with targeted recruitment of Esa1 histone acetylase. *Mol. Cell* **6:** 1297–1307.

Ren B., Robert F., Wyrick J.J., Aparicio O., Jennings E.G., Simon I., Zeitlinger J., Schreiber J., Hannett N., Kanin E., Volkert T.L., Wilson C.J., Bell S.P., and Young R.A. 2000. Genome-wide location and function of DNA binding proteins. *Science* **290:** 2306–2309.

Ronaghi M., Nygren M., Lundeberg J., and Nyren P. 1999. Analyses of secondary structures in DNA by pyrosequencing. *Anal. Biochem.* **267:** 65–71.

Ryan D., Nuccie B., and Arvan D. 1999. Non-PCR-dependent detection of the factor V Leiden mutation from genomic DNA using a homogeneous invader microtiter plate assay. *Mol. Diagn.* **4:** 135–144.

Sachidanandam R., Weissman D., Schmidt S.C., Kakol J.M., Stein L.D., Marth G., Sherry S., Mullikin J.C., Mortimore B.J., Willey D.L., Hunt S.E., Cole C.G., Coggill P.C., Rice C.M., Ning Z., Rogers J., Bentley D.R., Kwok P.Y., Mardis E.R, Yeh R.T., Schultz B., Cook L., Davenport R., Dante M., Fulton L., Hillier L., Waterston R.H., McPherson J.D., Gilman B., Schaffner S., Van Etten W.J., Reich D., Higgins J., Daly M.J., Blumenstiel B., Baldwin J., Stange-Thomann N., Zody M.C., Linton L., Lander E.S., and Atshuler D. 2001. A map of human genome sequence variation containing 1.42 million single nucleotide polymorphisms. *Nature* **409:** 928–933.

Sambrook J. and Russell D. 2001. *Molecular cloning: A laboratory manual*, third edition. Cold Spring Harbor Laboratory Press, Cold Spring Harbor, New York.

Sapolsky R.J., Hsie L., Berno A., Ghandour G., Mittmann M., and Fan J.B. 1999. High-throughput polymorphism screening and genotyping with high-density oligonucleotide arrays. *Genet. Anal.* **14:** 187–192.

Schrock E., du Manoir S., Veldman T., Schoell B., Wienberg J., Ferguson-Smith M.A., Ning Y., Ledbetter D.H., Bar-Am I., Soenksen D., Garini Y., and Ried T. 1996. Multicolor spectral karyotyping of human chromosomes. *Science* **273:** 494–497.

Schuler G.D. 1997. Pieces of the puzzle: Expressed sequence tags and the catalog of human genes. *J. Mol. Med.* **75:** 694–698.

Shi M.M. 2001. Enabling large-scale pharmacogenetic studies by high-throughput mutation detection and genotyping technologies. *Clin. Chem.* **47:** 164–172.

Snijders A.M., Segraves R., Blackwood S., Pinkel D., and Albertson D.G. 2002. BAC microarray-based comparative genomic hybridization. *Methods Mol. Biol.* (in press).

Snijders A.M., Nowak N., Segraves R., Blackwood S., Brown N., Conroy J., Hamilton G., Hindle A.K., Huey B., Kimura K., Law S., Myambo K., Palmer J., Ylstra B., Yue J.P., Gray J.W., Jain A.N., Pinkel D., and Albertson D.G. 2001. Assembly of microarrays for genome-wide measurement of DNA copy number. *Nat. Genet.* **29:** 263–264.

Solinas-Toldo S., Lampel S., Stilgenbauer S., Nickolenko J., Benner A., Dohner H., Cremer T., and Lichter P. 1997. Matrix-based comparative genomic hybridization: Biochips to screen for genomic imbalances. *Genes Chromosomes Cancer* **20:** 399–407.

Strahl-Bolsinger S., Hecht A., Luo K., and Grunstein M. 1997. *SIR2* and *SIR4* interactions differ in core and extended telomeric heterochromatin in yeast. *Genes Dev.* **11:** 83–93.

Syvanen A.C. 2001. Accessing genetic variation: Genotyping single nucleotide polymorphisms. *Nat. Rev. Genet.* **2:** 930–942.

Thiagalingam S., Laken S., Willson J.K., Markowitz S.D., Kinzler K.W., Vogelstein B., and Lengauer C. 2001. Mechanisms underlying losses of heterozygosity in human colorectal cancers. *Proc. Natl. Acad. Sci.* **98:** 2698–2702.

Tyagi S., Bratu D.P., and Kramer F.R. 1998. Multicolor molecular beacons for allele discrimination. *Nat. Biotechnol.* **16:** 49–53.

Visakorpi T., Kallioniemi A.H., Syvanen A.C., Hyytinen E.R., Karhu R., Tammela T., Isola J.J., and Kallioniemi O.P. 1995. Genetic changes in primary and recurrent prostate cancer by comparative genomic hybridization. *Cancer Res.* **55:** 342–347.

Visakorpi T., Hyytinen E., Koivisto P., Tanner M., Keinanen R., Palmberg C., Palotie A., Tammela T., Isola J., and Kallioniemi O.P. 1995. In vivo amplification of the androgen receptor gene and progression of human prostate cancer. *Nat. Genet.* **9:** 401–406.

Walter M., Spillett D., Thomas P., Weissenbach J., and Goodfellow P. 1994. A method for constructing radiation hybrid maps of whole genomes. *Nat. Genet.* **7:** 22–28.

Wang D.G., Fan J.-B., Siao C.J., Berno A., Young P., Sapolsky R., Ghandour G., Perkins N., Winchester E., Spencer J., Kruglyak L., Stein L., Hsie L., Topaloglou T., Hubell E., Robinson E., Mittman M., Morris M.S., Shen N., Kilburn D., Rioux J., Nusbaum C., Rozen S., Hudson T.J., Lipshutz R., Chee M., and Lander E.S. 1998. Large-scale identification, mapping and genotyping of single-nucleotide polymorphisms in the human genome. *Science* **280:** 1077–1082.

Weissenbach J., Gyapay G., Dib C., Vignal A., Morissette J., Millasseau P., Vaysseix G., and Lathrop M. 1992. A second-generation linkage map of the human genome. *Nature* **359:** 794–801.

Wickman F.P., Lu M.L., Thykjaer T., Olesen S.H., Andersen L.D., Cordon-Cardo C., and Orntoft T.F. 2000. Evaluation of the performance of a p53 sequencing microarray chip using 140 previously sequenced bladder tumor samples. *Clin. Chem.* **46:** 1555–1561.

WWW RESOURCES

http://cmgm.stanford.edu/pbrown/mguide/HybChamber.pdf Hybridization chamber drawings, P. Brown Web Site, Stanford University

http://gai.nci.nih.gov/CHLC/ The Cooperative Human Linkage Center (CHLC)

http://genome.ucsc.edu/ The UCSC Human Genome Project Working Draft

http://genome-www.stanford.edu/~rees/ CaryoScope, Christian A. Rees, Stanford University

http://p53.curie.fr. p53 Web Site at the Institute Curie

http://www.corning.com/CMT/ Corning Microarray Technology

http://www.genome.wi.mit.edu Whitehead Institute/MIT Center for Genome Research

http://www.ncbi.nlm.nih.gov/blast/Blast.cgi Protein-protein BLAST search

http://www.progenetix.net Progenetix-Comparative Genomic Hybridization (CGH) database

http://www-shgc.stanford.edu/RH/index.html The Stanford Human Genome Center RH Server

7 / An Introduction to Microarray Bioinformatics

INTRODUCTION

Confronted by "data deluge," the microarray community is scrambling to develop techniques that effectively address the analysis, systematic archiving, and sharing of microarray data. This section provides an introduction to some of the approaches in current use to manage the vast swell of information.

Design

Optimal design is particularly important with microarray experiments, which are expensive to perform and can cost prodigious amounts of money if they are approached in an unstructured way. Part 1 discusses four aspects of experimental design.

Part 1: Design of Microarray Expression Experiments

This part deals with general design issues such as the availability of slides, the amounts of RNA required for labeling, and the number of samples to be tested. More specific design considerations arise from the comparative nature of two-color competitive hybridization to glass slide microarrays (Schena et al. 1995, 1996), specifically, whether samples should be compared directly with one another or with a common reference or via a combination of these options. Further discussion is focused on issues of experimental design that arise when probing the interaction of multiple factors, such as treatment of cells with combinations of cytokines. Because microarrays typically test thousands of genes simultaneously, even a small amount of noise can yield large numbers of false positives. Replication, including dye swapping, allows averaging of results, which increases precision and facilitates statistical assessment of data quality and significance (Lee et al. 2000; Kerr and Churchill 2001; Tseng et al. 2001). Finally, this part discusses different approaches to replication of microarray data and the importance of obtaining independent replicate measures of gene expression.

Image Analysis, Presenting Slide Data, and Normalization

Three related parts—Image Analysis, Normalization, and Representing and Evaluating Slide Data—deal with the capture and treatment of data from individual microarray experiments. Although concerned primarily with data obtained from experiments using two-color glass slide microarrays, many of the concepts are also relevant to data obtained from Affymetrix arrays or from nylon filter macroarrays.

Part 2: Image Analysis

Various approaches are used to distinguish signal from noise and to correct background, a factor that has substantial impact on data output. Automated programs are described that appropriately subtract background readings and attempt to recognize "spots" on the microarray, as opposed to junk.

Part 3: Normalization

Approaches to detect and remove systematic bias from microarray data are described in Part 3. Differences in the amounts of RNA used and systematic variation in the efficiency of incorporation of fluorescent dyes frequently result in bias in data captured from competitively hybridized microarrays (Tseng et al. 2001; Yang et al. 2002).

Part 4: Representing and Evaluating Slide Data

This part discusses the use of graphical displays to review and evaluate results of microarray experiments and shows how data from individual slides can be depicted to facilitate rapid assessment of data quality.

Databases for Microarrays

A single microarray experiment in which 20,000 probes are scanned at 10 μm generates 30 million discrete data points, which, if stored in a Tiff file, would occupy ~60 MB of disc space. Even the casual user of microarrays must therefore find effective ways to store and analyze data.

Part 5: LIMS, Databases, and Data Management

This part deals with specifications for microarray databases and describes three prominent publicly available databases: AMAD, SMD, and GeneX. AMAD and SMD are tasked to address small- and large-scale projects, respectively, and their characteristics underscore the need to plan for expected need and capacity when choosing a database.

Analysis and Visualization of the Data from Multiple Slides

Microarray experiments have the power to reveal patterns of coordinate gene expression that reflect an unexpected degree of biological complexity. Good examples are wound healing and tissue remodeling in serum-stimulated fibroblasts (Iyer et al. 1999) and molecular subtyping of cancers (Golub et al. 1999; Alizadeh et al. 2000; Dhanasekaran et al. 2001; Hedenfalk et al. 2001; Kihara et al. 2001). In both cases, recognition of complex patterns of coordinated gene expression relied on methods to identify higher-order structure in the data sets.

Part 6: Cluster Analysis and Display

Two programs, Cluster and Tree View, have become mainstays of microarray analysis (Eisen et al. 1998). This part includes information to help the investigator access and implement these programs.

Part 7: Multidimensional Scaling and Self-organizing Maps

Two other unsupervised methods—multidimensional scaling (MDS) and self-organizing maps (SOM)—are used to order and visualize microarray data. Information is included to help the investigator access and implement these programs. These programs are now available at http://arrayanalysis.nih.gov.

Where data exist to guide initial analysis, computational methods that "train" an algorithm to recognize patterns in the data, so-called supervised learning programs (Brown et al. 2000; Khan et al. 2001; Pomeroy et al. 2002), can be more effective than unsupervised approaches for analyzing certain data sets. However, the application of such methods to the complex data sets obtained from microarray experiments was at an early stage at the time of writing this book and is not covered here.

Approaches to Annotating Genes and Public Storage of Microarray Information

A key part of mining microarray data is the ability to efficiently link to databases that contain information about individual genes of interest. Options for annotating gene lists that quickly relate biological information to differentially regulated genes of interest are discussed in the information panel on GENE ANNOTATION. The panel also describes the efforts of the Gene Ontology (GO) Consortium to facilitate gene annotation.

The microarray community has taken the first steps toward creating repositories of expression data that may be shared between investigators. The information panel on SHARING MICROARRAY DATA AMONG INVESTIGATORS describes the efforts of the Microarray Gene Expression Database (MGED) Consortium to provide a structured approach to recording and sharing microarray data. The goal of the MIAME (Minimal Information About a Microarray Experiment) protocol is to provide a consistent approach to recording the "Materials and Methods" of microarray experiments.

Although the development of bioinformatics tools for storing and mining microarray data is occurring very rapidly, investigators should recognize that there is currently no "best solution" for handling microarray data. Underestimating the scale of the problem is a common trap for facilities that have focused on the mechanics of making and using microarrays. However, once a facility can generate microarrays and protocols that "work," investigators at the host site are quickly keen to use them. Comparing the expression patterns of hundreds of diverse tissue samples requires vastly more sophisticated tools than are required to simply identify a few differentially expressed genes in a small number of samples.

One solution is to take an incremental approach to data storage and implementation of analysis programs. Although this approach runs the risk of putting the facility in a position of constantly playing "catch up" with data problems, it can be an effective way to deal at the outset with a daunting challenge. It is critical to develop a plan that adopts a first-version solution to address the most pressing problems while recognizing there will be second- and third-version solutions, and so on, as the facility scales up and as experience grows. The data must be stored in a durable way and key experimental details must be recorded with the knowledge that the systematic description of these details will become a prerequisite of publication in the very near future.

Finally, do not despair! Just as the pioneering efforts of the first builders of microarray hardware have given way, in part, to more accessible commercial solutions, the development of comprehensive, user-friendly microarray bioinformatics software will occur rapidly. It is important to remember, however, that analysis of complex patterns of gene expression is in its infancy and that investigators should be prepared to move quickly beyond a "point and click" attitude to data analysis.

Part 1: Design of Microarray Expression Experiments

Yee Hwa Yang and Terry Speed
Department of Statistics, University of California, Berkeley, California 94720

INTRODUCTION

Good experimental design simplifies analysis and empowers interpretation of data. Design must balance these aims against the constraints of microarray cost and availability, and the amount of RNAs available for testing and replication. In cDNA microarray experiments, the major design choice is whether two samples will be compared directly on one slide or indirectly via a third sample, such as a common reference.

Microarray-based expression analysis is inherently comparative. Samples are compared by hybridization to probes arrayed either on a single slide or on different slides. Because the principles of design for comparative experiments of this kind are not novel (Kerr and Churchill 2001a), design and analysis of comparative experiments can be accommodated within a classical statistical framework.

The choice of an experimental approach may be straightforward when a single issue is to be addressed, but investigators often want to explore more than one question in a single experiment. Because each question has implications for experimental design, priorities must be set and decisions must be made about the best way to achieve diverse outcomes. Insight into the ways in which experimental design impacts on the discriminating ability of a microarray analysis can be gained both from theoretical treatment of the problem and by comparing data from earlier experiments performed using different designs.

The choice of design is influenced by the priorities of the experiment. For example, suppose that a large number of tumor samples have been collected from patients (P) and corresponding normal tissue has been obtained (N). If the major goal is to find genes that are up- or down-regulated in tumors, then the best approach may be direct comparisons on the same slide of RNAs extracted from tumors versus normal cells. By contrast, if the aim is to classify tumor subtypes (Alizadeh et al. 2001), experiments based on the comparison of a series of tumors with a common reference RNA may be better.

When designing a cDNA microarray experiment, certain general issues must be addressed (please see box panel below) to help translate sometimes nebulous biological questions into an appropriate statistical framework. As discussed above, it is important to define the primary goal of the experiments. Results from previous experiments should be analyzed as they may indicate the likely number of genes that are differentially expressed and may therefore influence the number of slides needed to achieve statistical significance. The method used to verify the microarray experiments (e.g., northern or western blot analysis, reverse transcriptase–polymerase chain reaction [RT-PCR], or in situ hybridization) is also important since it can influence statistical methods used in analysis as well as the determination of sample size. For example, if relatively low-throughput techniques are used for verification, a high degree of certainty about the microarray results is required. Conversely, high-throughput validation techniques can more easily deal with noise in the microarray experiments. The source of RNA (e.g., tissue samples or cell lines) affects the amount of RNA available, and in turn the number of replicate slides possible. Methods of sample isolation, mRNA extraction, and probe labeling also influence the nature and amount of replication (please see the discussion on General Design Issues below). Control spots can be used simply for checking that the hybridization was successful, or may be useful in analyses such as normalization.

GENERAL CONSIDERATIONS FOR DESIGNING AN EFFECTIVE MICROARRAY EXPERIMENT

- ***What is the aim of the experiment?*** How will these microarray experiments contribute to the overall research plan? Can the experiments effectively address the question posed?

- ***What are the specific questions being asked and, subsequently, the most important comparisons?*** Specify the priority of the different scientific questions being asked with the types and numbers of samples available.

- ***What controls are planned?*** Is normalization necessary? Or desirable?

- ***What methods will be used to verify results obtained from microarrays?*** Is sufficient material available for northern hybridization? Is RT-PCR a better option than, for example, immunohistochemistry or in situ hybridization?

- ***What resources are available and in what quantity?*** Factors to be considered here include the types of samples and number of slides available, the amounts of mRNA required, including controls such as replication and dye swapping.

- ***Additional information*** is the experimental process prior to hybridization (i.e., sample isolation, mRNA extraction, labeling, and hybridization) running smoothly. Can the upstream process generate in a timely fashion all the reagents and biological materials required for microarray analysis?

- ***Downstream analysis.*** What type(s) of data analysis is appropriate/desirable? What types are available?

DESIGN CHOICE

Given the nature of the experiment and the material available, one design in some cases stands out as preferable to all others. For example, if cells treated with different drugs are to be compared with untreated cells, then the appropriate design is clearly one where the untreated cells become a de facto reference, and all hybridizations involve comparison of treated sets of cells with untreated cells. However, with most experiments, a number of designs can be devised that seem to be suitable for use, and thus some principles are needed for choosing one from the set of possibilities.

The heart of the design issue with cDNA microarrays is the decision between using *direct* rather than *indirect* comparisons, i.e., comparisons *within* slides rather than *between* slides. The simplest case involves treatment T versus control C. For the purposes of the following discussion, the terms "test" and "control" are used broadly to include comparisons between the cells or tissues under study and the normal or untreated cells or tissues, for example, drug versus untreated, wild-type versus mutant (including knock-out or transgenic), or two different tissues (tumor versus normal).

Suppose that two hybridizations are planned and that the quantity of RNA is not a limiting factor. In a direct comparison, T is labeled with Cy5 and C is labeled with Cy3, and the two samples are hybridized together (T-C) on two slides. For any particular gene, two independent estimates of the log–ratio log(T/C) for that gene would be obtained. If the variance for one such measurement is σ^2, then the variance of the *average* of two independent measurements is $\sigma^2/2$. (Note that variance represents the spread of individual measurements or data points around the mean and is thus an indication of the variability in the data.) On the

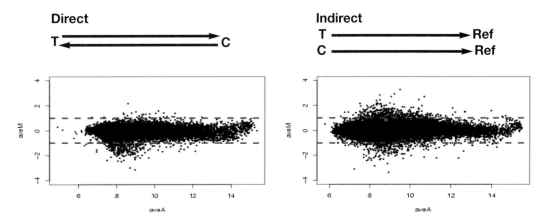

FIGURE 7-1. Comparison of estimates of relative gene expression in treatment and control samples obtained by direct and indirect methods. The measure of relative expression (aveM = averaged log$_2$ ratio) is plotted against the average intensity of each gene in both samples (A). Although two slides were used in both designs, the averaged log ratios obtained from the direct comparison (*left panel*) are clearly more narrowly spread than those obtained from the indirect comparison (*right panel*). The red dot is a gene known to be differentially expressed. It is evidently lost in the noise in the common reference plot (*right*), but it stands out more clearly in direct comparisons.

other hand, if a common reference is used, then the two hybridizations would be T-Ref and C-Ref. In this case, the log–ratio log(T/C) for any gene would be obtained as the difference of two independent log ratios via the equation: log(T/C) = log(T/Ref) – log(C/Ref). As before, if the variance for a single log-ratio is σ^2, then the variance of the *difference* of two independent log ratios is $2\sigma^2$. As described below, if the reference RNA is from the same extraction or labeling, the two denominators will be correlated and thus the variance may be smaller than $2\sigma^2$. In summary, with two hybridizations, a measure of the log ratio of a gene with variance $\sigma^2/2$ is obtained by doing two direct comparisons, and with variance $2\sigma^2$ by proceeding indirectly, the latter being greater than the former by a factor of 4. The higher precision of direct comparisons is the key difference between direct and indirect measurement (please see Figure 7-1). In practice, a factor of 4 is rarely observed, but for simplicity, we assume in the calculations that all samples are independent. This independence assumption is often not satisfied as target mRNAs may be technical replicates rather than biological replicates (please see discussion of Replication below).

For a proposed design to be acceptable, the experiment must be practically achievable given the number of slides and the amount of mRNA available for use. It should be clear that the scientific questions motivating the experiment can be answered by the chosen design, with the important questions being answered more precisely than less important ones. The illustrations that follow show that a combination of direct and indirect comparisons is often a practical solution to a design problem.

ILLUSTRATIONS OF DESIGN PRINCIPLES

Example 1: Comparisons among Multiple Sources of mRNAs

Consider three sources of mRNAs, and suppose that all pairwise comparisons are of equal interest. An example of this type of experiment would arise in investigating the differences in expression between different regions (A, B, C) of the brain. Table 7-1 shows a few design

TABLE 7-1. Design Choices for Comparison of Multiple Sources of mRNA

	(I) Common reference	(II) Direct comparison	(III) Common reference
	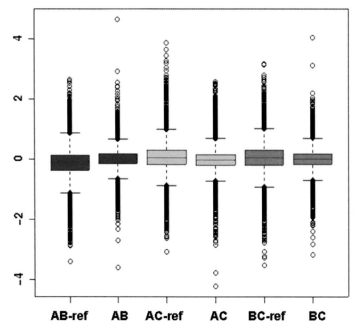		
Number of slides	$N = 3$	$N = 3$	$N = 6$
Average variance	$2v$	$2v/3$	
Units of material	$A = B = C = 1$	$A = B = C = 2$	$A = B = C = 2$
Average variance		$2v/3$	v

Average variances have been calculated twice: once (*light gray*) to compare Designs 1 and II which use the same number of slides; a second time (*dark gray*) to compare Designs II and III which use the same amount of material.

choices, where "Ref" denotes a common reference source of mRNA. Note that because all pairwise comparisons are of equal interest, the main scientific constraint is that they are estimable. Depending on different physical constraints, such as the number of slides or the amount of samples available, different design choices will be made. Although the same number of slides is used in Designs I and II, twice as much of each sample is used in Design II. The same amount of material is used in Designs II and III, but the precision is less in Design III even though the experiment is replicated. Direct comparison of all pairwise combinations of samples, Design II, will lead to the most precise estimates of transcriptional differences among the three regions and, in addition, save on the number of slides required. If there is only one sample of RNA from each of A, B, and C, then Design I is the only possible choice. The relative precision of each of these approaches (direct and indirect) is shown in Figure 7-2.

FIGURE 7-2. Box plot demonstrating the higher precision of direct versus indirect comparisons between samples. The $\log_2$ of the expression ratios of each sample pair is plotted, with the colored boxes indicating the interquartile range (IQR), which is defined as the difference between the 75th percentile (the upper quartile) and the 25th percentile (the lower quartile). For a description of box plots, please see Part 4.

When more than three sources of mRNAs are compared, the experimental design becomes a more complex issue. *Reference* designs (please see Table 7-1, Design I) are suited to the cross-comparison of a large number of samples. An *all-pairs* design (Design II) becomes progressively more challenging in terms of cost and materials for more than four comparisons. With four sources of mRNAs, there are six pairwise comparisons, for five there are ten, and so on. When the logistics of the experiment become difficult, it may be necessary to consider alternative classes of designs that involve fewer slides, including *loop* designs (please see discussion below) (Kerr and Churchill 2001).

Example 2: Time-course Experiments

In time-course experiments, the best design can depend critically on the number of time points. Table 7-2 demonstrates a range of experimental design choices for microarray time-course experiments. Design II involves hybridizations between consecutive time points, whereas Design I uses T1 as a common reference. When the main focus of the experiment is on the relative changes between T2, T3, T4, and the initial time point T1, Design I is the better choice. However, it is possible that the more subtle variations from one time point to another will be detected more readily using Design II.

TABLE 7-2. Six Possible Experimental Designs in a Time-course Experiment

		t vs. $t+1$			t vs. $t+2$		t vs. $t+3$	
Design choices in time-course experiments		$t1t2$	$t2t3$	$t3t4$	$t1t3$	$t2t4$	$t1t4$	Ave
$N=3$	(I) T1 as common reference	1	2	2	1	2	1	1.5
	(II) Direct hybridization	1	1	1	2	2	3	1.67
$N=4$	(III) Common reference	2	2	2	2	2	2	2
	(IV) T1 as common ref + more	.67	.67	1.67	.67	1.67	1	1.06
	(V) Loop design	.75	.75	.75	1	1	.75	.83
	(VI) T1, T2 as common references	1	.75	1	.75	.75	.75	.83

The table shows the corresponding estimated variance for all pairwise comparisons and the average variance for each design.

Choices among various experimental designs become more difficult when one is not limited by the number of hybridizations that can be performed. Design III shows a common reference approach where the common reference is not a time point. Design IV is similarly a common reference design using T1 as a common reference and with additional direct hybridization between T2 and T3 and T3 and T4. Designs V and VI each offer a different mix of direct and indirect comparisons, leading to higher precision for some comparisons and lower precision for others. To choose between Designs V and VI clearly depends on the sample comparisons of interest, as the average variance of comparisons is the same for both designs. Design V, a loop design, is preferable to Design VI if comparisons between consecutive times are more of interest than those two time units apart. Design VI is preferable if this priority of interest is reversed.

Example 3: 2 x 2 Factorial Experiments

The previous examples involve *single-factor* or *one-way* designs, where the single factor (tissue in Example 1, time in Example 2) has three or more levels. A more complex class of designs arises when two or more factors are considered jointly, each factor having two or more levels. These are called *factorial* experiments and are used to study both the expression differences caused by single factors and those resulting from the *joint effect* of two or more factors. Any discussion of factorial experiments necessarily includes a study of the notion of interaction among the factors. Factorial experiments were introduced by R.A. Fisher in 1926, and studied extensively with his collaborator Yates (1937). For a more modern treatment, please see Box et al. (1978). An example of 2 x 2 factorial is described below.

Example 3a (Figure 7-3): Cytokine Combinations

Suppose that there are two ways of treating a cell line, for example, by adding different growth factors to the growth medium. If C denotes mRNA derived from the untreated (control) cells, A and B denote mRNA derived from the cells treated by the first and second growth factor *separately*, then AB denotes cells treated with *both* factors simultaneously (Figure 7-3 depicts the interactions). The impact on gene expression of treatment A can be assessed by studying the relative expression of a given gene in sources A and C in the *absence* of the second treatment, where the effect of treatment A can be estimated by $\log(A/C)$. In addition, the effect of factor A in the presence of B is measured by the $\log(AB/B)$. The difference $\log(AB/B) - \log(A/C) = \log(AB \times C/A \times B)$ is called the *interaction* of the two treatments on the log scale. We can think

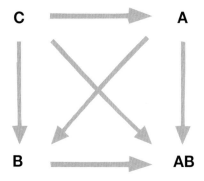

FIGURE 7-3. Possible comparisons in a 2 x 2 factorial design.

of the interaction as measuring the extent to which the differential expression of a gene induced by A is dependent on whether B is present. The measurement used is symmetric in A and B.

Example 3b: Cell-type-treatment Interaction

Suppose that there are two classes of cells, a special class T (e.g., tumor cells) and a control class C (e.g., normal cells from the same organ) and both cell types are treated with radiation (RT and RC). In this situation, it would be of interest to determine which genes are differently differentially expressed in irradiated tumor cells log(RT/T) compared with irradiated normal cells log(RC/C), expressed as log(RT/T) – log(RC/C).

Example 3c. Tissue-developmental Stage Interaction

Gene expression between two tissue types L and M, say at two times, for example, Te (embryonic) and Tp (postnatal), is compared. There are four possible mRNA samples in this experiment (please see Figure 7-3): C = region L at the embryonic state Te; A = region L at the postnatal stage Tp; B = region M at the embryonic stage Te; and AB = region M at the postnatal stage Tp. It might be expected that the differentially expressed genes in the A-C comparison are largely similar to those in the AB-B comparison, and thus for a particular gene, interest might then focus on the difference log(AB/B) – log(A/C).

How do these differences in scenarios influence experimental design? Suppose there are four sources of mRNAs and that the primary interest is in identifying genes for which the *difference* of the log–ratios log(AB/B) and log(A/C) is large, i.e., the main goal is to identify genes with large interaction. This can be done in several ways; a few designs are illustrated in Table 7-3 (Glonek and Solomon 2002). Note that all designs involve six slides. Designs II and IV give the smallest variance for the interaction term, whereas the main effect for A is not even estimable in Design IV. Design I is by far the worst for estimating the interaction, but it uses less mRNA: 2 units from each source, compared to 3 units in all of the other designs. The favored design will depend on the level of interest in the main effects with respect to the interaction, assuming any physical constraints are satisfied. In general, Design II (or its complement; with dye swaps horizontally rather than vertically) will probably be the design of choice, offering good precision for all comparisons, although more for one main effect than the other.

TABLE 7-3. Four Possible Designs for a 2 × 2 Factorial Experiment

Design choices	Indirect	A balance of direct and indirect		
	(I)	(II)	(III)	(IV)
Number of slides	N = 6			
Main effect A	0.5	0.67	0.5	n.a.
Main effect B	0.5	0.43	0.5	0.3
Interaction A,B	1.5	0.67	1	0.67

After Glonek and Solomon (2002).

GENERAL DESIGN ISSUES

Replication

Why replicate slides? The short answer here is (1) to reduce variability in summary statistics and (2) to permit the use of formal statistical methods. In essence, replication permits averaging, and averages typically have less variability than their component terms. The cDNA microarray system is rather noisy at the individual gene level. A gene that seems to be 4-fold differentially expressed in one hybridization may appear to be 1.3-fold changed in a second independent hybridization and 2-fold in a third. To determine which genes are differentially expressed between two samples of mRNA and have some assurance that the determinations are not false positives, replication is essential (Lee et al. 2000). Lack of replication greatly restricts the use of inferential statistics to decide whether or not a given intensity log ratio is significantly different from zero. In particular, replication is essential to estimate the variance of the log ratios across slides. Attempts to assess the significance of log ratios using data from only a single slide depend on unverifiable modeling assumptions and in general fail to take into account the most important source of variation: between-slide variability. With replicate slides, suitably defined, standard statistical methods become applicable (Dudoit et al. 2001). Replication usually involves a statistically random sample of mRNA preparations, and under these circumstances, extrapolation from samples to a population of the same becomes valid. In this sense, replication is intimately connected to the ability to generalize conclusions.

Figure 7-4 shows plots of log ratios $\log_2(KO/WT)$ averaged across replicates slides, against overall intensity $\log_2(\sqrt{KO \cdot WT})$, similarly averaged. Each of the replicate slides involves mRNA from a different experimental animal, cohybridized with the same reference mRNA (Callow et al. 2000). The green spots correspond to eight genes that are known to be differentially expressed in the two mRNA sources. As the sample size (in this case, the number of mice) increases, the cloud of points about the horizontal axis shrinks. This makes it easier to distinguish real change and random variation about zero. Note that with a single replicate, the cloud extends beyond ± 1 on the $\log_2$ scale, or 2-fold in either direction. By contrast, with $n = 8$ replicates, the cloud is largely contained within the range ± 0.7 on the log scale, ~1.6-fold in either direction.

If the eight replicate data sets had been genuinely independent, which they are not here because the reference RNA is shared across all eight mice, then a much greater reduction in the size of the cloud would be expected: to ± 0.35 on the log scale, or a fold change of 1.3 in either direction.

Different Forms of Replication

As explained above, and consistent with statistical tradition (Fisher 1926), replication is a highly desirable feature of comparative microarray experiments. There are a number of ways to replicate an experiment differing in the degree to which the data may be regarded as independent and in the populations the experimental samples represent. Given that the same investigator, using the same equipment and protocols, almost invariably carries out replicate hybridizations and frequently at about the same time, it is inevitable that replicate data will share many features. Most methods of replication listed below concern the target mRNA samples.

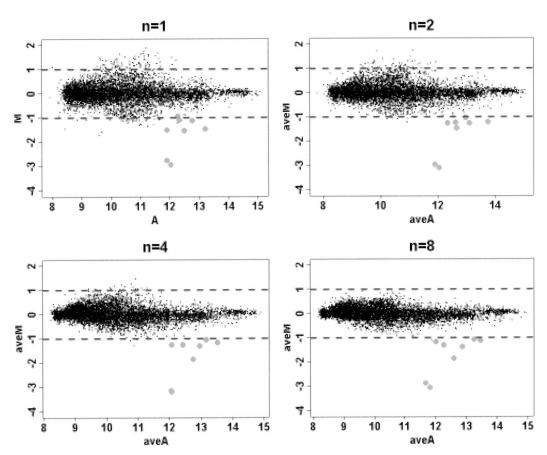

FIGURE 7-4. <u>Plots</u> of log ratios $M = \log_2(KO/WT)$, averaged across replicate slides, against overall intensity $A = \log_2\sqrt{(KO \cdot WT)}$, similarly averaged. The green spots correspond to eight genes that were known to be differentially expressed between the two mRNA sources. The number of replicate slides shown are $n = 1, 2, 4,$ and 8.

- ***Replicate spots.*** Many investigators spot cDNAs in duplicate on every slide, frequently in adjacent positions. This practice provides valuable quality information, as the degree of concordance between duplicate spot intensities or relative intensities is an excellent indicator of quality. However, because replicate spots on the same slide, particularly adjacent spots, will share most if not all experimental conditions, the data from the pairs cannot be regarded as independent. Typically, the overall degree of concordance between duplicate spots is noticeably greater than that observed between the same spot across replicate slides. Although the averaging of log ratios from duplicate spots is appropriate, physical juxtaposition causes the resulting information to be less useful than that from pairs of truly independent pairs. Therefore, if duplicate spots are to be printed on a slide, it is preferable to have them well spaced and not adjacent, as this provides a better view of the variability across the slide.

- ***Replicate slides: Technical replicates.*** The term technical replicate is used to denote replicate slides made with target RNA from the same preparation. Figure 7-5 shows examples of bias introduced when using the same RNA preparation (M1 vs. M2) compared with independent RNA preparations (M1 vs. M3). Findings such as these demonstrate that technical replicates do not provide the independence that results in

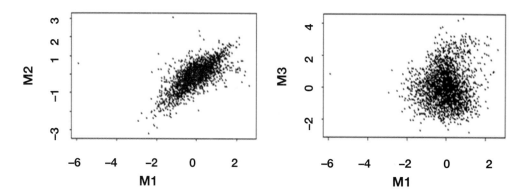

FIGURE 7-5. Scatter plots of log ratios from replicate slides using the same preparation (*left* panel) and using different RNA preparations (*right* panel). All three experiments (M1, M2, and M3) involved self versus self-hybridizations. Note that the genes which are apparently differentially expressed are consistently so (correlated) in both M1 and M2, as they tend to lie along the diagonal. By contrast, in M1 versus M3, differentially expressed genes are randomly distributed, demonstrating the independence of separately prepared RNA samples.

the full benefits of averaging: Shared systematic features (biases) of technical replicate samples will remain after averaging.

- ***Replicate slides: Biological replicates, same source.*** The term biological replicate refers to hybridizations involving RNA from independent preparations of different samples from the same tissue or cell line. In many cases, this is the most convenient form of replication. Provided the labeling is carried out separately for RNA from the different extractions, this approach will generate experimental results that are as close to independent as is feasible in this context. However, if a common reference design is being used, then logs of ratios whose numerators come from independent, biological replicates will still exhibit a measure of correlation due to their sharing of the unique features of a single batch of reference mRNAs in their denominators.

- ***Replicate slides: Biological replicates, different source.*** The term biological replicate may also refer to replicate slides using target RNA from preparations of different organisms or different versions of a cell line. This form of biological replication is clearly different in nature from the biological replication discussed above and typically involves a much greater degree of variation in measurements. For example, experiments dealing with a population of mice are subject to the inevitability of different mice having hormonal and immune systems in differing (fluctuating) states, or having tissues that exhibit different degrees of inflammatory activity, and so on. The greater amount of variation inherent in this form of replicate may seem unnecessary and make real expression differences harder to discern. However, from the perspective of the generalizability of conclusions, this may be the appropriate form of replication for some experiments.

The type of replication to be used in a given experiment affects the *precision* and impacts on the *generalizability* of the experimental results obtained. In most cases, an investigator will want to use biological replicates to validate generalizations of conclusions and technical replicates to reduce the variability in these conclusions. Given that there are usually several possible forms of technical and biological replications, the investigator will need to exercise judgment on the question of how much replication of a given kind is desirable, subject to experimental and cost constraints. For example, if a conclusion applicable to all mice of a certain inbred strain is sought, experiments involving multiple mice, preferably a random sample of such mice, must be performed. Extrapolating to all mice of that strain from results on a single mouse, even using multiple mRNA extractions, has well-known dangers associated with it (see Freedman et al. 1998).

Pooled mRNA versus Unpooled mRNA

In many situations, it is necessary to pool mRNA from a number of similar sources (e.g., mouse embryos) in order to have sufficient amounts to carry out a single hybridization. However, suppose that pooling of mRNA is not necessary: Is it nevertheless desirable? Suppose that four treated mice and four control mice are to be used in an experiment and that each mouse would provide sufficient mRNA for a single hybridization. Should the investigator pool RNA from the four treated mice, do likewise with the control mice, and then carry out the experiment four times using subsamples of the pools of mRNA? Alternatively, should the investigator make four separate treatment-control comparisons and then average the resulting log ratios? It may not matter greatly either way, but in the absence of data, there does not seem to be any strong argument in favor of pooling when it is not necessary. Not pooling permits a greater range of variation to be exhibited, and hence strengthens the case for averaging.

Power and Sample Size Determination: Differential Expression

Given the importance of replication, and having chosen a form of replication suited for the experiment under consideration, an important practical issue is to determine the sample size, or the number of slides to use. In general, a power calculation requires the investigator to state:

- The variance of individual measurements.
- The magnitude of the effect to be detected.
- The acceptable false positive rate.
- The desired power or the probability of detecting an effect of the specified magnitude (or greater).

An investigator might ask: How many hybridizations are needed in order to have a 90% chance of detecting a twofold differential in gene expression? Optimal sample size is difficult to determine in the context of microarray experiments, as the variance of the relative expression levels across hybridizations varies greatly from gene to gene. Even if gene-specific variances are known in advance, which they could not be in any detail, the investigators would usually be unable to nominate in advance the genes whose changes are of interest. Finding such genes is frequently the point of the microarray experiment. Thus, two vital components of the standard power calculations are absent:

- The variance σ^2 of the individual log-ratio measurements at the gene level.
- The magnitude of the effects of interest at that same level.

What can be done? This question could be answered provided we knew the variance σ^2 for the differentially expressed genes. An approach to surmount this impasse is to specify a value of σ^2 that is not too small, based on past experience with that experimental system (specifying this value is always necessary for power calculations), say, the median or upper quartile of the variances across genes. Doing a power calculation with the upper quartile variance, investigators would be able to assert that their number of replicates gives them a certain power for detecting differential expression of greater than a stated value, for all but the 25% most variable genes.

One difficulty that prevents us from giving a simple illustrative example remains. Investigators are generally not asking about the possible differential expression of one specific gene, in isolation, but of one gene, perhaps from a class of genes, against a background of thousands of genes that are not differentially expressed. The other genes provide a formidable level of background variation against which we seek evidence of differential expression, and their presence makes the power calculation still harder.

Discussion of power and sample size raises the issue of the trading of power against false positive rate. Although a standard statistical issue in microarray experiments, where validation of results is routine, there is a special twist because of the very large number of genes being tested. In situations where RNA samples for microarray experiments are scarce, but the verification method is straightforward and relatively inexpensive, an investigator may well be willing to accept a higher false positive rate on the grounds that sorting out true from false positives during validation is not so difficult. In such cases, the number of microarray replicates can be reduced.

Sample Size Determination for Observing All Subtypes

Another question to consider when determining sample size is: How many samples of a particular type (e.g., tumors) must be examined in order to detect all molecular subtypes? The answer depends in part on how a subtype is defined. In a trivial sense, each sample can represent a subtype and hence the number of samples to be tested is unbounded. However, in the same way that pathologists agree on histological categories of disease, descriptive and inferential expression analysis techniques can be used to define molecular subtypes despite individual sample variation. Another determinant when detecting subtypes is chance sampling. For example, consider a set of ovarian cancer samples where the distribution of histological subtypes is as follows: serous (~70% of cases), mucinous (~20%), endometrioid (~6%), clear cell (2.5%), and transitional cell (~1.5%). If repeated random sampling of a large population of cases is simulated, the number of pools that contain all five of these subtypes is heavily dependent on the size of the pool and is driven to a large extent by the frequency of the rarest subtype: 50 case pool sizes = 36% of sets containing all five subtypes, 100 cases = 72%, 150 cases = 88%, 200 cases = 95%, 250 cases = 98%, and 300 cases = 99%. If the goal is to achieve a subtyping more substantial than currently exists and further division of these sets is sought, then in excess of 500 samples are likely to be required.

Dye-swap Replications

Dye-swap replications, in which hybridization conditions are repeated with the dye assignments reversed in the second hybridization, are useful for reducing systematic bias (Tseng et al. 2001; Yang et al. 2001b). Most cDNA microarray experiments exhibit systematic differences in the red and green intensities that require correction at the normalization step. It is very unlikely that this normalization can be done perfectly for every spot on every slide, leaving no residual color bias. To the extent that color bias is repeatable across slides, averaging over dye-swap pairs will leave an experiment less prone to these biases. Accordingly, dye-swap pairs are recommended whenever possible. Alternatively, random dye assignments may be used, in effect including the bias in random error. What should be avoided is carrying out replicates of slides involving direct comparisons, all with the same labeling. Indirect comparisons, such as those involving a common reference sample, are based on differences between slides. For this reason, repeatable residual color bias should be removed in much the same way that it is with dye swaps.

Extensibility and Linking

Investigators often want to compare *essentially arbitrarily* many sources of mRNAs over long periods of time. One method is to use a common reference design for all experiments, with the common reference being a "universal" reference RNA that is derived from a combination of cell lines and tissues (please see Section 3, Protocol 12). Some companies provide universal reference mRNA (http://www.stratagene.com/gc/universal_mouse_reference_rna.html), although many individual labs create their own common reference pool (please see Section 6, Part 1, Protocol 1). Common references provide *extensibility* of the series of experiments within and between laboratories. When an investigator is forced to turn to a new reference source, it may be difficult to compare new experiments with previous ones that were performed on the basis of a different reference source. The ideal common reference is therefore widely accessible, available in unlimited amounts, and provides a signal over a wide range of genes. In practice, these goals can be difficult to achieve.

When a universal reference RNA is no longer available, it might be necessary to carry out additional hybridizations, conducting what we term a *linking* experiment (D. Lin et al., in prep.) to connect otherwise unrelated data. More generally, linking experiments allow unrelated experiments to be connected, with the number of additional hybridizations depending on the precision of conclusions desired. Suppose that in one series of experiments, reference R was used, and then in another series, reference R′ was used. The linking experiment compares R and R′, thus permitting comparisons between two sources, one of which has been cohybridized with R and the other with R′. However, this ability comes at a price. Log ratios for source A cohybridized with reference R can be compared with those from source Z cohybridized with reference R′, only by combining A-R and Z-R′ together with R-R′ through the identity $\log(A/Z) = \log(A/R) + \log(R/R′) - \log(Z/R′)$. In other words, cross-reference comparisons involve combining three log ratios, with corresponding loss of precision, as the variance of $\log(A/Z)$ here is three times that of the individual log ratios. Nevertheless, there will be times when cross-referencing is worthwhile, particularly when one notices that the variance of the linking term $\log(R/R′)$ can be reduced to an extent thought desirable simply by replicating that experiment. The linking term in the identity would be replaced by the average of all such terms across replicates.

Part 2: Image Analysis

Yee Hwa Yang and Terry Speed

Department of Statistics, University of California, Berkeley, California 94720

INTRODUCTION

The way in which the image of a microarray experiment is extracted from a scanned slide can have a substantial impact on subsequent analyses. In a microarray experiment, hybridized microarrays are imaged in a microarray scanner to produce red and green fluorescence intensity measurements over a large collection of pixels that collectively cover the array (for a description of some commercially available microarray reader/scanners, please see Section 3, Table 3-9). Fluorescence intensities correspond to the levels of hybridization of the two *targets* to the *probes* spotted on the slide. These fluorescence intensity values are stored as 16-bit images that are typically described as "raw" data.

During the last few years, a number of image analysis packages for glass slide cDNA microarrays, both commercial software and freeware, have become available. Some of these packages are variants of those that are used to analyze radioactive signals from arrays spotted onto nylon membranes (for a discussion of imaging filter arrays, please see Section 4). Other software packages are designed specifically for glass slide microarrays. These specifically designed packages take advantage of the rigid layout of the spots in their spot finding algorithm, utilize the information from the two fluorescent channels, and deal with characteristics of fluorescent signals that are different from signals generated by radioactivity. Table 7-4 lists some of the available image processing software for microarrays. The processing of scanned microarray images can be separated into three major tasks:

- ***Addressing or gridding*** is the process of assigning coordinates to each of the spots. Automating this part of the procedure permits high-throughput analysis.

- ***Segmentation*** allows the classification of pixels either as foreground, i.e., within a printed DNA spot, or as background.

- ***Intensity extraction*** involves calculating, for each spot on the array, red and green foreground fluorescence intensity pairs (R,G), background intensities, and possibly, quality measures.

It is important to note that in microarray image analysis, the higher the quality of slide printing, target hybridization, and image scanning, the easier it is for image analysis programs to correctly measure spot intensities at each of these stages. Frequently, the last slides of a print run are the most highly variable in terms of spot morphology.

A commonly used imaging system for microarrays involves a scanning confocal laser in which the laser excites fluorophor-labeled *targets*. Emitted photons are amplified by a photomultiplier tube (PMT), resulting in the release of a shower of electrons that are collected at a detector as signal. Depending on the scanner, a number of settings can be adjusted, including scan rate, laser power, and PMT voltage. Increasing either the PMT or laser settings can increase both signal and noise, and increased laser power can damage the hybridized samples by photobleaching. Setting a very high PMT level may saturate pixels, i.e., because the detec-

TABLE 7-4. Examples of Available Image Analysis Packages for cDNA Microarrays

Name	Institution/Company	Web Address
ArrayVision	Imaging Research Inc.	http://imaging.brocku.ca/products/ARV.asp
Array-Pro Analyzer	MediaCybernetics	http://www.mediacy.com
AlphaArray	Alpha Innotech Cooperation	http://www.alphainnotech.com/bio/lsmaster.html
arrayWoRx	Applied Precision	http://www.api.com/products/bio/arrayworxe.html
AutoGene 2.5 ImaGene 4.0	BioDiscovery	http://www.biodiscovery.com
DeArray	ScanAlytics	http://www.scanalytics.com/product/hts/microarray.html
GenePix 3.0	Axon Instruments	http://www.axon.com
GLEAM	Center for Behavioral Neuroscience, Atlanta	http://www.cbn-atl.org/research/molcore.html
P-Scan/F-Scan	Analytical Biostatistics	http://abs.cit.nih.gov/
QuantArray	Packard Bioscience	http://www.packardbioscience.com/
ScanAlyze	Eisen Lab, LBNL	http://rana.lbl.gov/EisenSoftware.htm
Spot	CSIRO	http://www.cmis.csiro.au/iap/spot.htm
Visage HDG	Genomic Solutions	http://www.genomicsolutions.com
Virtek ChipReader	Virtek Vision International Inc.	http://www.virtekvision.com/ http://www.virtekvision.com/pdf/imageanalysis.pdf

tor registers a signal of $2^{16} -1$ (a 16-bit image), the maximum signal that can be recorded is 65,535. In practice, the level of PMT is adjusted so that the brightest pixels are just below the level of saturation. If this does not occur, very strong signals may be underestimated. Comparison of scanned images produced at a range of PMT settings suggests that with appropriate normalization, the log ratios and ranks for the majority of genes remain the same (J. Rahnenfuhrer et al., unpubl.).

ADDRESSING

The basic layout or structure of a microarray image is known as it is determined by the spot deposition by the arrayer. This information is used to help the microarray image analysis software define the spots. Figure 7-6 depicts a typical microarray layout. To *address* the spots in an image, i.e., to match an idealized model of the microarray with the scanned image data, a number of parameters must be estimated, including

- displacement of grids or spots (translation) from the expected position caused by slight variations in print-tip positions,
- small individual translations of spots,
- separation between rows and columns of grids,
- separation between rows and columns of spots within each grid, and
- overall position of the microarray in the scanned image.

Other parameters that may need to be considered are misregistration of the red and green channels, rotation of the array in the image, or *deviation from symmetry* due to printer or scanning artifacts. The last two parameters are important issues for automated gridding algorithms.

It is important that the addressing procedure be both accurate, to ensure precision with subsequent steps of image analysis, and efficient, to allow rapid slide throughput. Allowing

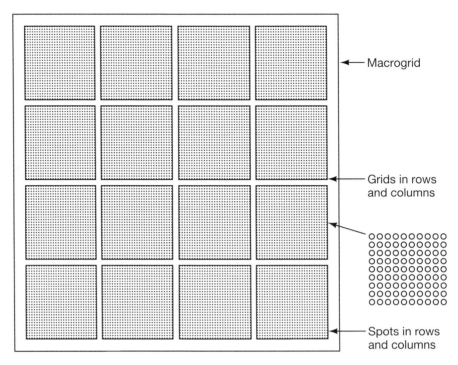

FIGURE 7-6. Layout of a typical microarray slide where there are four rows and four columns of grids comprising a macrogrid, and within each grid are nine rows and ten columns of spots.

user intervention can increase reliability of the addressing stage, although this has the potential to make the process very slow. The addressing steps are often referred to as "gridding" in the microarray literature. Most software systems now provide both manual and automatic gridding procedures. Addressing procedures are very varied and have not been well documented.

SEGMENTATION

Segmentation of an image can generally be defined as the process of partitioning the image into different regions, each having certain properties (Soille 1999). In a microarray experiment, segmentation is the classification of pixels as *foreground* (i.e., within a spot) or *background*. Segmentation of microarray images allows fluorescence intensities to be calculated for each spotted DNA sequence as measures of relative transcript abundance in the two samples tested on the microarray. Each segmentation method produces a *spot mask*, which consists of the set of foreground pixels for each given spot. Existing segmentation methods for microarray images can be categorized into four groups, according to the geometry of the spots they produce:

- Fixed-circle segmentation.
- Adaptive circle segmentation.
- Adaptive shape segmentation.
- Histogram segmentation.

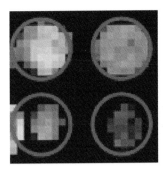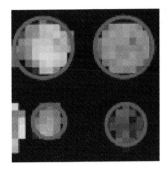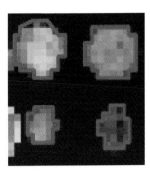

FIGURE 7-7. Schematic of the segmentation effect of fixed circle (*left*), adaptive circle (*middle*), and adaptive shape (*right*) segmentation. All three of these produce a spot mask where pixels inside the spot mask are considered as foreground, i.e., a measure of gene expression levels.

Fixed-circle Segmentation

Fixed-circle segmentation fits a circle with a constant diameter to all the spots in the image (Figure 7-7, left). This method is easy to implement and works nicely when all of the spots are circular and of the same size. It was first implemented in the ScanAlyze software written by M.B. Eisen (http://rana.lbl.gov/EisenSoftware.htm), and it is typically provided as a standard option in most software. However, for microarrays with spots of varying size, fixed-diameter segmentation may not be satisfactory.

Adaptive Circle Segmentation

In adaptive circle segmentation, the diameter of the circle that defines the foreground is estimated independently for each spot (Figure 7-7, middle). The software GenePix (Axon Instruments http://axon.com/GN_Genomics.htm/#Software) for the Axon scanner implements such an algorithm. Note that ScanAlyze and other similar software packages provide the user with the option to manually adjust the circle diameter spot by spot. In practice, this can be very time-consuming, as each array contains thousands of spots. Another example of adaptive circle segmentation is the software Dapple (Buhler et al. 2000), which finds spots by detecting edges of spots. Briefly, Dapple calculates the negative second derivative of the image (Laplacian). Pixels with high values in the Laplacian image correspond to edges of a spot. In addition, Dapple enforces a circularity constraint by finding the brightest ring (circle) in the Laplacian images.

Adaptive circle segmentation methods work quite well with well-produced microarrays but are less effective with oval- or doughnut-shaped spots. Common sources of noncircularity include the printing process (e.g., features of the print tips, uneven solute deposition) and effects of postprocessing of the slides after printing (Eisen and Brown 1999). Segmentation algorithms that do not place restrictions on the shape of the spots are then more desirable.

Adaptive Shape Segmentation

Two commonly used methods of adaptive shape segmentation (Figure 7-7, right) in image analysis are the *watershed* (Vincent and Soille 1991; Beucher and Meyer 1993), and the *seeded region growing* (SRG) (Figure 7-8) (Adams and Bischof 1994). At the time of writing, adaptive shape segmentation methods are not incorporated into the most widely used microarray analysis software packages. Both watershed and SRG segmentation require the specification

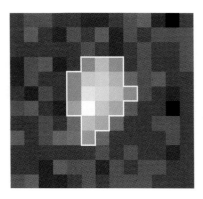

FIGURE 7-8. The thick white line shows the result of the SRG (seeded region growing) segmentation to image a noncircular shaped spot. The pixels inside the thick white line are classified as foreground and the other pixels are classified as background.

of starting points, or *seeds*, and the weak points of image segmentation procedures using these methods are typically the selection of the number and the location of the seed points. In microarray image analysis, however, the number of features (spots) is known exactly a priori, and the approximate locations of the spot centers are determined at the addressing stage. Microarray images are therefore well-suited to such methods. The SRG algorithm is implemented in the software Spot (Buckley 2000 http://www.cmis.csiro.au/iap/Spot/Spotmanual. htm) and AlphaArray (B.-H. Wang, unpubl.). These programs have the advantage of being able to cope with spot shapes that deviate from circles.

Histogram Segmentation

Histogram segmentation methods do not explicitly classify pixels into foreground or background. Instead, these methods analyze pixels within designated regions and estimate foreground intensity from the distribution of the pixels. This type of method uses a *target mask* that is chosen to be larger than any given spot. For each spot, foreground and background intensity estimates are determined from a histogram of pixel values for the pixels within the masked area. These methods therefore do not use any local spatial information. An example of the histogram segmentation is implemented in the QuantArray software, where the foreground and background are defined as mean intensities between some predefined percentile values. The default values are the 5th and 20th percentile for the background and the 80th and 95th percentiles for the foreground. Figure 7-9 shows the distribution of pixels within the cyan-colored square and the shaded region marks the pixel values that fall within the 80th and 95th percentiles. Another example of implementation of the histogram segmentation method is described by Chen et al. (1997). These authors use a circular target mask and compute a threshold value based on a Mann-Whitney test. Pixels are classified as foreground if their value is greater than the threshold and as background otherwise. This method is implemented in the QuantArray software for the GSI Lumonics scanner and DeArray by Scanalytics. The main advantage of the histogram method is simplicity. However, a major disadvantage is that quan-

TABLE 7-5. Segmentation Methods and Examples of Algorithms and Software Implementation

Fixed circle	ScanAlyze, GenePix, QuantArray
Adaptive circle	GenePix, Dapple
Adaptive shape	Spot, region growing, and watershed
Histogram	ImaGene, QuantArray, DeArray, and adaptive thresholding

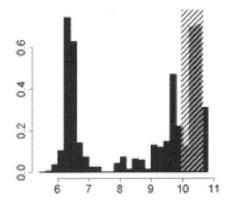

FIGURE 7-9. Histogram method of spot delineation. Shown is a histogram method used in QuantArray. The target mask is represented by the square drawn around each spot. The histogram represents the distribution of pixels within the cyan-colored square (*upper left*). The x axis of the histogram is the log transform of pixel intensities. By default, the foreground intensity estimate is the mean intensities between the 80th and 95th percentiles (*shaded region*) of the pixel values.

tification is unstable when a large target mask has been set to compensate for spot size variation. Furthermore, the resulting spot masks are not necessarily connected.

Figure 7-10 shows a comparison of the SRG and histogram segmentation methods on three kinds of anomalous spots. The first are the so-called *ghost* spots, spots with higher background values than foreground values. The second are frequently known as *comets*, spots whose signal has been contaminated by experimental artifacts, and which frequently exhibit very little difference between their foreground and background pixel intensities. The third class of spots are called doughnuts. The central pixel intensity values of doughnuts are lower than the intensity values for pixels in the periphery. These categories of spots present a challenge to segmentation algorithms. Figure 7-10 shows that SRG satisfactorily identifies a connected "spot-shaped" region for all three classes of spots, although in the case of comets, this region is probably too large and will contain signal beyond the region covered by DNA. By contrast, the histogram method picks out pixels with appropriately low and high intensities for background and foreground, respectively, but these pixels do not connect into spot-shaped regions. The spot intensity estimates obtained by adding the foreground pixel intensities are therefore probably reasonable in the case of comets and doughnuts, but are inadequate in the case of ghost spots.

INTENSITY EXTRACTION

Spot Intensity

Each pixel value in a scanned image represents the level of hybridization at a specific location on the slide. The total amount of hybridization for a particular spotted DNA sequence is proportional to the *total fluorescence* at the spot. The natural measure of spot intensity is therefore the *sum* of pixel intensities within the spot mask. Later calculations are based on ratios of fluorescence intensities, and as the ratio of averages is equal to the ratio of sums, the *average* pixel value over the spot mask is computed. Likewise, a ratio of medians may be substituted; thus, the median pixel value over the spot mask is computed.

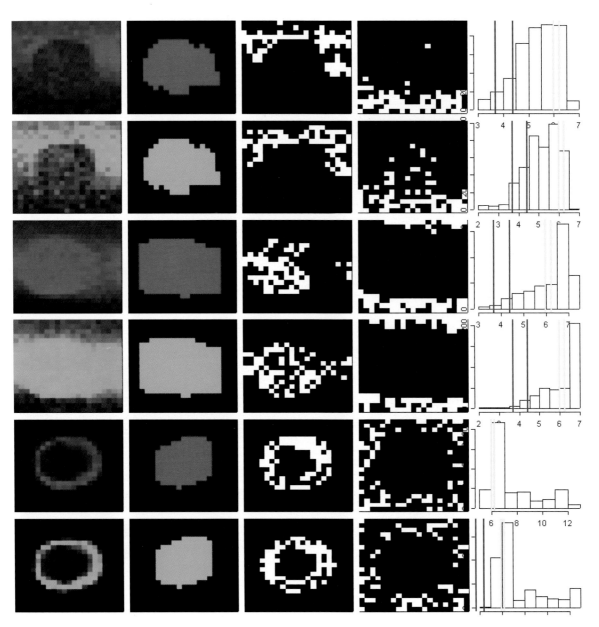

FIGURE 7-10. Identification of spots using SRG in areas of poor image quality. Three commonly observed poor-quality spots are shown in pairs, representing red and green channels. The first column is the color overlay of a spot, and the second column represents the spot mask obtained from the seeded region growing (SRG) algorithm. The white pixels shown in the third and fourth columns represent the pixels involved in the foreground and background, respectively, as estimated by the histogram method. The fifth column shows the histogram representing the distribution of pixels from the image in the first column. The foreground and background histograms, with the ranges of values used, are depicted in the fifth column.

Background Intensity

It is important in microarray image analysis to adjust for background, as the measured intensity of each spot includes a contribution of nonspecific hybridization and fluorescence emitted from other chemicals on the glass. Apart from histogram-based methods, the segmentation procedures described above identify local background regions for this calculation. The various background methods implemented in software packages can be divided into four categories as described below.

Local Background Intensities

These intensities are estimated by focusing on small regions surrounding the spot mask. Usually, the background estimate is the median of pixel values within these specific regions. Most software packages currently use this approach. Figure 7-11 illustrates different local background adjustment methods. One approach (used in ScanAlyze) is to include all pixels within a square centered at the spot center and exclude all those that are within the spot mask (Figure 7-11, blue square).

An alternate approach employed in QuantArray and ArrayVision is to estimate the area between two concentric circles (Figure 7-11, green circles). By not considering the pixels immediately surrounding the spots, the background estimate is less sensitive to the performance of the segmentation procedure. Finally, local background may be estimated in the regions having the furthest distance from all four surrounding spots, also known as the *valley* regions (Figure 7-11, pink diamond-shaped areas). The local background for each spot can be estimated by the median of values from the four surrounding valleys. Depending on the software, the shapes of the local valley regions are different, but this method of background estimation is somewhat independent of segmentation results. GenePix implements this method for background estimation. Using valley pixels that are distant from all spots ensures, to a large degree, that the background estimate is not corrupted by pixels belonging to a spot. Corruption by bright pixels may occur in the other methods, particularly the ScanAlyze method, introducing an upward bias into the background estimate. Using remote pixels reduces this bias effectively but entails the use of a smaller number of pixels and therefore increases the variance of the estimate, an example of a bias-variance trade-off.

Morphological Opening

A second approach to background adjustment relies on a nonlinear filter called a *morphological opening*. This filter is obtained by computing a local minimum filter (*erosion*) followed by

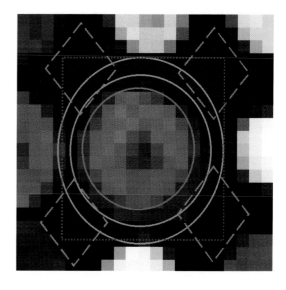

FIGURE 7-11. Image illustrating different local background adjustment methods. The region inside the red circle represents the spot mask, and the other regions bounded by colored lines represent regions used for local background calculation by different methods. (*Green*) Used in QuantArray; (*blue*) used in ScanAlyze; (*pink*) used in Spot. (Reprinted, with permission, from Yang et al. 2002a.)

a local maximum filter (*dilation*) with the same window. In a microarray image, the effect of using a window that is larger than any spot is to replace all spots with nearby background values (for a detailed description of such filters, please see Soille 1999). In Spot, the morphological opening is applied to the original images using a square structuring element with a side length at least twice as large as the spot separation distance. This operation removes all of the spots and generates an image that is an estimate of the background for the entire slide. For individual spots, background is estimated by sampling this background image at the nominal center of the spot. Because a large window is used to create the morphological background image, spatial variation is expected to be low. Morphological opening results in smaller background estimates than those of other simpler methods. More importantly though, morphological background estimation is expected to be less variable than the other methods, because spot background estimates are based on pixel values in a large local window, yet are not biased upward by brighter pixels belonging to or on the edge of spots.

Constant Background

A global method that subtracts a constant background for all spots is yet another alternative to estimate background noise. The approaches previously described assume that the nonspecific contribution to a spot signal can be estimated from the area surrounding the spot. However, some findings (X.J. Lou, unpubl.) suggest that the binding of fluorescent dyes to negative control spots, for example, spots corresponding to plant genes that will not hybridize with human mRNA samples, is lower than the binding to the glass slide. If this is the case, it may be more meaningful to estimate background on the basis of a set of negative control spots. This approach is limited in value if background across the slide is unevenly distributed due to inadequate washing, for example.

No Adjustment

Finally, we also consider the possibility of no background adjustment at all. A comparison of different methods (Yang et al. 2000) found that the choice of background correction method has a larger impact on the log ratio of intensities than the segmentation method used. Thus, finding better segmentation methods may not be as important as choosing a stable background adjustment method. In the estimation of background contribution, Yang et al. (2000) suggest that the morphological opening provides a better estimate of background compared to other methods. The log ratios $\log_2$ R/G computed after morphological background correction tended to exhibit low within and between slide variability. In addition, this method did not seem to compromise accuracy. Figure 7-12 displays four MA plots where the log ratio of intensities, $M = \log_2$ R/G, is plotted against the mean log intensity $A = \log_2\sqrt{R \cdot G}$. The different panels in Figure 7-12 show the MA plots from the same image quantified by different image analysis methods. A good image analysis method should permit a clear distinction to be made between differentially expressed genes and noise. Note that methods using local background adjustment (panels c and d) show greater variability around the low-intensity spots than methods not using any background subtraction (panel a) or the morphological background adjustment (panel b). Local background adjustment tends to blur the distinction between differentially expressed genes and noise.

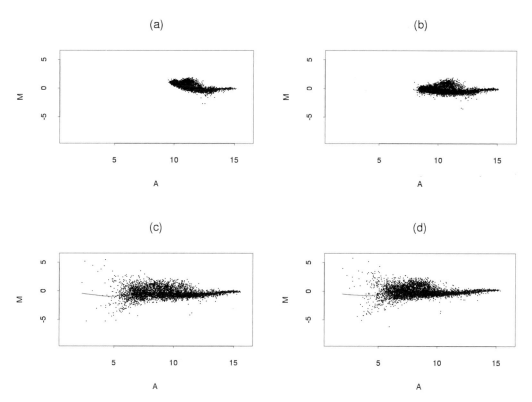

FIGURE 7-12. Four MA plots where the log ratio of intensities $M = \log_2 R/G$ is plotted against the mean log intensity $A = \log_2 \sqrt{R \cdot G}$. (a) Spot with no background subtraction; (b) spot with morphological opening; (c) GenePix; (d) ScanAlyze. (Reprinted, with permission, from Yang et al. 2001a.)

The comparison of different background correction methods indicates that estimates based on means or medians over local neighborhoods tend to be quite noisy and can potentially double the standard deviation of the log ratios. At the other extreme, no background adjustment seems to reduce the ability of identifying differentially expressed genes (Yang et al. 2001b).

A widely accepted way to correct spot intensities for background has yet to emerge. It seems possible that use of large numbers of negative control spots across a slide may lead to better background adjustments, which differ from those obtained by measuring fluorescence on nonspot regions of the slide in ways that have been discussed above. Any advice must necessarily be tentative, but for the moment, our recommendation is to adjust the background by using a method that varies the background more slowly than do local background methods.

Part 3: Normalization

Yee Hwa Yang and Terry Speed

Department of Statistics, University of California, Berkeley, California 94720

INTRODUCTION

Image analysis of microarrays provides measures of foreground and background values in both the red and the green channels and a range of quality metrics for each spot on the array. The next step in utilizing this information is to adjust for systematic differences in the relative intensity of each channel, a process known as *normalization*. Normalization also aims to correct for other differences in intensities between samples on the same slide, or between slides, which do not represent true biological variation between samples.

The need for normalization can be seen most clearly in self-self experiments, in which two identical mRNA samples are labeled with different dyes and hybridized to the same slide (Figure 7-13). Because there is no true differential expression in a self-self hybridization, the red and green intensities should be equal. However, red intensities often tend to be lower than the green intensities, due to the relatively lower incorporation of Cy5 nucleotides, and the imbalance in the red and green intensities is usually not constant across spots within and between arrays. Furthermore, overall spot intensities can vary as a result of differences in the location on the array, the sample plate origin, the arraying pins used, and the slide-scanning parameters. Dye biases can stem from a variety of factors, including physical properties of the dyes (heat and light sensitivity, relative half-life), efficiency of dye incorporation, experimental variability in the hybridization and processing procedures, differences in the amount of input RNA in each sample, or scanner-specific excitation and collection processes. It is necessary to normalize fluorescence intensities both within and between slides before performing further analysis of data to minimize false positives and to identify genes that are truly differentially expressed between two samples.

NORMALIZATION WITHIN SLIDES

Discussed below are a number of approaches for normalizing the data from each fluorescence channel.

Normalization Based on a Global Adjustment of Intensity Values

This approach assumes that red and green intensities are related by a constant factor for the entire slide. For example, let $R = kG$, and shift the center of the distribution of log ratios to zero:

$$\log_2 R/G \rightarrow \log_2 R/G - c = \log_2 R/(kG)$$

Two common choices for the constant c are expressed as $c = \log_2 k$ or $k = 2^c$. The first choice ($c = \log_2 k$) is often referred to as normalization based on *ratio statistics* and involves the

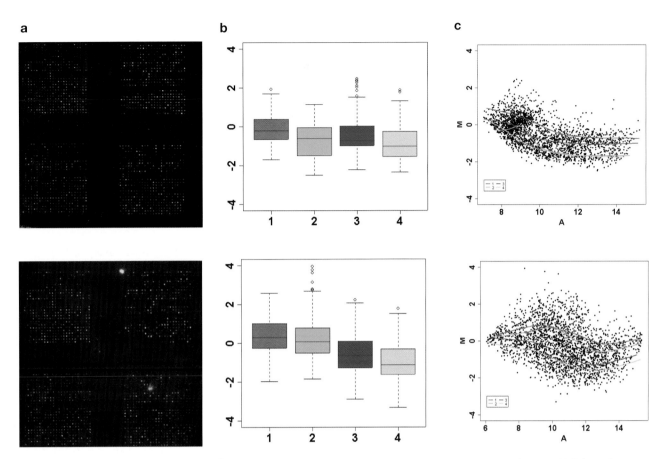

FIGURE 7-13. Self-self hybridizations, illustrating systematic variations seen in many microarray experiments. (a) False color overlay; (b) box plot representation of the data obtained from each of the four grids comprising each array in a. Note that the mean log₂ R/G ratio differs as a function of the grid. (c) Scatter (*M-A*) plot where colored lines indicate best-fit lines through the data derived from each grid. Note that the log₂ R/G ratio (*M*) varies in relationship to the intensity of the signal, *A*. For a further explanation of data representation with box plot and M-A plots, please see Part 1. Examples of the variation that occurs within slides are also illustrated in Part 3.

median or mean of the log intensity ratios for a particular gene set. This method usually assumes that among a particular subset of genes, such as housekeeping genes, the log ratios average zero. Possible gene sets that may be used for this method are discussed below. In one of the first normalization procedures, Chen et al. (1997) proposed an iterative method based on ratio statistics for estimating normalization constants. An alternate approach, known as *total intensity normalization*, is to estimate $k = 2^c$ by the ratio between the total intensity of red and total intensity of green, $k = \Sigma R_i / \Sigma G_i$, where i denotes the specific gene index. This approach assumes that although some genes are truly differentially expressed between two samples, the majority of the thousands of genes represented on a typical microarray are equivalently expressed and, furthermore, that those genes which are up- or down-regulated genes will balance each other out. If this is the case, the summed intensity values for each channel should be equal, and where they differ, a normalization value can be calculated and used to rescale the intensity values for each gene on the microarray. Kerr et al. (2000) proposed using the ANOVA model for the analysis of gene expression data and performed normalization by including the effects of dye bias in the model. Wolfinger et al. (2001) also proposed an ANOVA model for normalization, which takes into account the effects of treatments and microarray bias, where every gene on the microarray is then adjusted by the same fitted value defined by the ANOVA model. Fitting such models to unnormalized data essentially performs a global normalization but does not account for intensity or spatial differences, or other types of dye biases often present in microarray experiments.

Global normalization methods are widely used and are implemented in expression software such as Genepix and GeneSpring. At the time of writing, these methods treat the slide as a whole and as such, they do not correct for spatial differences, nor do they allow for intensity-dependent biases (Figure 7-13c).

Intensity-dependent Normalization

Variation between the red and green channels is not always constant, but can change as a function of the intensity of the signal. Intensity-dependent variation can be corrected by generating a best-fit curve through the middle of an MA plot, and this becomes the new zero line for the vertical axis (Figure 7-13c) (Yang et al. 2002b). In this analysis, the M value of the pair (A, M) is shifted by a quantity $c = c(A)$ depending on the A value:

$$M = \log_2 R/G \rightarrow \log_2 R/G - c(A) = \log_2 R/(k(A)G)$$

One estimate of $c(A)$ is made using the LOWESS (*lo*cally *we*ighted *s*catterplot *s*moothing) function (Cleveland 1979) within the software package R (Ihaka and Gentleman 1996) to perform a local scatter plot smoothing to the MA plot. The scatter-plot smoother, a type of regression analysis, performs robust locally linear fits by calculating a moving average along the A axis, using data from an unselected set of genes on the microarray. Robust in this context means that the curve is not affected by a small to moderate percentage of differentially expressed genes that appear as outliers in the MA plot. A user-defined parameter f is the fraction of the data used for smoothing at each point; the larger the f value, the smoother the fit. Typically, a value of $f = 30\%$ is used. It is important to note that this approach implicitly assumes that (1) relatively few genes are differentially expressed or (2) no systematic relationship exists between differential gene expression and intensity or location of the spots. LOWESS smoothing can also make use of designated gene subsets or controls that are not differentially expressed between samples (please see below). This approach may be most appropriate when comparing samples with widely divergent gene expression patterns.

Several other intensity-dependent methods have been proposed for location normalization. Finkelstein et al. (2000) present an iterative linear normalization, also known as a robust linear regression. This linear normalization can be viewed as a more constrained version of the above intensity-dependent normalization. Kepler et al. (2000) propose a more general intensity-dependent normalization approach, which uses a local regression method different from that of LOWESS, but otherwise very similar.

Software implementations of various smoothers are available at http://cm.bell-labs.com/cm/ms/departments/sia/wsc/smoothsoft.html, and some commercially available microarray packages such as GeneSpring have incorporated LOWESS normalization. Publicly available packages, including SMA (*s*tatistics for *m*icroarray *a*nalysis) (Yang et al. 2001b) and NOMAD (*n*ormalization *o*f *m*icroarray *d*ata) (C. Colantuoni et al., in prep.; details at http://pevsnerlab.kennedykrieger.org/snomad.htm), also incorporate intensity-dependent normalization. Both of these packages are based on R, a freely available statistical software package that can be downloaded from http://www.r-project.org/.

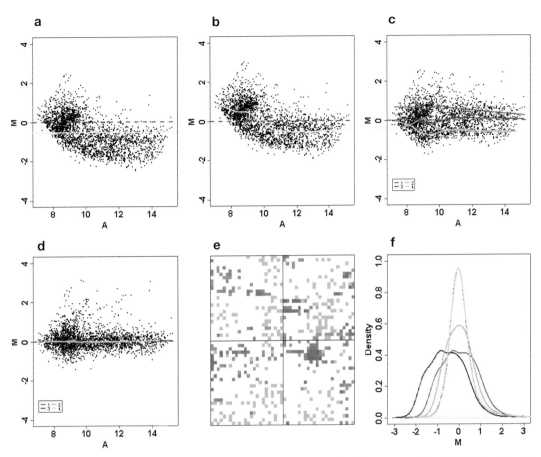

FIGURE 7-14. Effects of different types of normalization on data distribution in a self-self hybridization. (*a*) Scatter plot prior to normalization. The yellow line represents the median of the *M* values and is displaced from a median of zero (*broken blue line*). (*b*) Scatter plot following median normalization. The yellow line indicates a global LOWESS line through all the points. (*c*) Scatter plot following global LOWESS normalization. The solid blue, red, turquoise, and green lines indicate LOWESS smoothers through the points for each of the four print-tip groups. (*d*) Scatter plot after print-tip group LOWESS normalization. (*e*) Spatial plot of the data depicted in *d*. (*f*) Smoothed histograms of *M* values before any normalization (*black*), after median normalization (*red*), after a global LOWESS normalization (*green*), and after pin group LOWESS normalization (*turquoise*). Global median normalization shifts the center of the log ratio distribution to zero but does not affect the spread or affect intensity-dependent bias. Intensity-dependent normalization reduces the spread of the log ratios compared to a global.

Within Print-Tip Group Normalization

In addition to intensity-dependent variation, spatial bias can also be a significant source of systematic error. Most normalization methods do not correct for spatial effects produced by hybridization artifacts or print-tip or plate effects occurring during the construction of the microarray (for examples, please see Figure 7-14). The microarray shown in Figure 7-14 was printed with a 2 × 2 print head, and thus each LOWESS line corresponds to the spots printed with an individual print-tip (print-tip group). It is clear that the four curves are very different from one another (Figure 7-14c). The source of such variation is not always apparent, but it may arise from differences in the amount of wear of individual pin tips. It is possible to correct for both print tip and intensity-dependent bias by performing LOWESS fits for the data within individual print-tip groups:

$$\log_2 R/G \rightarrow \log_2 R/G - c_i(A) = \log_2 R/(k_i(A)G)$$

where $c_i(A)$ is the LOWESS fit to the MA plot for the ith grid only, $i = 1,..., I$, and I represents the number of print tips.

The extent to which normalization improves the precision of an experiment can be seen quite clearly in Figure 7-14. Because these data are from a self-self hybridization, the different spreads of the density plots in Figure 7-14f are good measures of the precision achieved following normalization. To identify a gene as differentially expressed, the corresponding log ratio (M value) must stand out from the noise, and the spreads of these curves describe the extent of the noise after different normalizations.

Scale Normalization between Slides

The preceding approaches to normalization aim to balance intensity values for the two dyes, but may not equalize the distributions of log ratios, for example, between slides. Figure 7-15 shows the reduction in the spread of M values for three replicate slides, after normalization (compare a and b in Figure 7-15). However, the degree of variation between slide data sets is not equal as shown as interquartile ranges (box sizes) that differ by more than a factor of 2 between slides. Such differences can lead to different replicate slides having unequal roles when they are combined, i.e., the slide whose M values have the greatest spread will tend to contribute most to averages and this is undesirable. It is a statistical principle that when combining estimates of the same quantity, data should be weighted such that its value is inversely proportional to the estimates' variances. Thus, one option is to weight the M values from the three slides differently than when combining them. An equivalent outcome can be achieved by scaling the M values from each slide so that the resulting scaled log ratios for each slide have the same interquartile ranges. The authors recommend that when the differences in interquartile ranges amount to a factor of 2 or more, corresponding to a variance difference of 4 or more, *scale* normalization should be performed according to these methods. Scale normalization can also be performed *within* slides, where the spread of data obtained from individual pin groups differs significantly (Yang et al. 2002b).

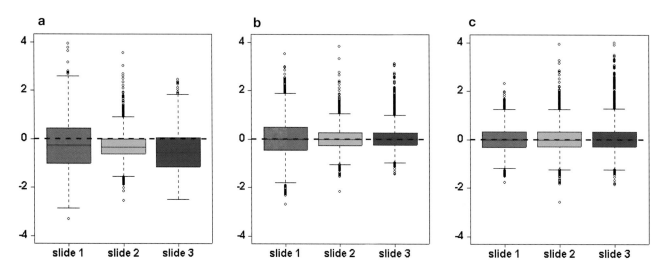

FIGURE 7-15. Multiple slide normalization. Box plots displaying the log ratio (M values) distribution from three replicate slides of a self-self experiment, before normalization (a), after within print-tip group normalization (b), and after between-slides scale normalization (c).

WHICH SET OF GENES TO USE FOR NORMALIZATION?

For most of the methods described above, a decision must be made as to which set of genes to use for the normalization. In general, the set of genes most appropriate for normalization depends on the nature of the experiment, the amount of variation in gene expression observed, and, probably, on the normalization method applied to the data.

All Genes on the Array

Frequently, biological comparisons made on microarrays are of a very specific nature, and the expected differences in gene expression are limited to a small proportion of genes. In such cases, the vast majority of the remaining invariant genes can be used as an index of relative intensity between the two channels. This is because it is considered reasonable to assume that

- only a relatively small proportion of the genes will vary significantly in expression between the two mRNA samples (see exception with self-normalization) or
- there is symmetry in the expression levels of the up-regulated versus down-regulated genes.

The use of "all genes" on the microarray can be applied to a variety of normalization methods (Table 7-6), but is less appropriate when the expression patterns between two samples differ widely, as the assumptions listed above may not hold.

TABLE 7-6. Summary of Various Normalization Methods

		Within slide				Between slide scale
		global $c(\bullet)$ is a constant $a(\bullet) = 1$	intensity-dependent $c(\bullet) = c(A)$ $a(\bullet) = 1$	print-tip-dependent $c(\bullet) = c(A, pins)$ $a(\bullet) = 1$	print-tip scale $c(\bullet) = c(A, pins)$ $a(\bullet) = a(pins)$	
All Genes	Assumes that the majority of genes in the two mRNA samples have similar overall expression levels.	yes	yes	yes	yes	yes
Housekeeping	Usually highly expressed and does not capture intensity-dependent structure.	yes	no	no	no	no
MSP Titration	Does not require any prior biological assumption; however, estimating the $c(A, pins)$ based on a small percentage of genes may not be very stable.	yes	yes	no	no	no
Rank Invariant Set	May not span the whole intensity range.	yes	yes	no	no	no

Columns refer to different normalization methods and rows correspond to a different set of genes used. For within-slide normalization, log ratios are adjusted by $\log_2 R/G \rightarrow (\log_2 R/G - c(\bullet)/a(\bullet))$, where $c(\bullet)$ and $a(\bullet)$ correspond to location and scale adjustment. yes or no refers to the practicality of performing the normalization procedure with the corresponding gene set. For example, it is possible to perform global normalization on the basis of housekeeping genes only, but it is not advisable to perform intensity-dependent normalization on housekeeping genes only.

Housekeeping Genes

Housekeeping genes are a set of predefined genes required for fundamental cellular process-es in a wide range of cell types and tissues and whose expression is not generally dependent on the developmental stage or physiological or pathological state of the tissue. Operationally, few if any genes truly fit such stringent criteria for invariant expression, although genes such as actin or GAPDH are frequently used in this context. Global methods of normalization based on intensity values of housekeeping genes may show sample-specific bias and do not address the issue of intensity-dependent dye biases. Designated housekeeping genes tend to be highly expressed and may not be representative of genes of interest that are expressed at lower levels and may be subject to an intensity-dependent bias.

Spiked Controls

This method consists of using RNA targets not from the organism being studied or synthetic genes with no substantial homologous regions on the microarray slide that would cross-hybridize to the hybridization probes. These "genes" are spotted on the microarray and their corresponding RNA transcript is included in the two target *samples* in equal amounts. Investigators can print a series of spots containing different quantities of spiked controls, which are expected to exhibit equal red and green fluorescence intensities across the range of con-centrations. Several companies (Stratagene and others) sell kits containing spike mixes and housekeeping genes for validation and normalization of microarray experiments.

Microarray Sample Pool (Titration Series)

Yang et al. (2002b) have proposed the use of a titration series of probes that are a pool of the cDNAs used to construct the microarray. Theoretically, all cDNA sequences should hybridize to this mixed probe sample, and it is assumed that the summed signal would be minimally subject to any sample-specific bias. However, inclusion of very highly expressed genes leads to some sequences contributing disproportionately to the probe signal from the pool. This signal may thus be derived from a less complex mixture of labeled targets than expected. Another disadvantage of this approach is that the normalization values are calculated on the basis of relatively few spots in the titration series. A related approach is the use of a concen-tration series of genomic DNA, for example, in yeast, whose genome contains a low degree of noncoding sequences.

Spiked controls or a microarray sample pool (MSP) series can be used with a range of normalization approaches; however, the number of individual spiked or MSP probes pres-ent on a microarray is important when considering their use. The use of "all genes" for nor-malization (please see All Genes on the Array above) provides the most stability for esti-mating intensity- or spatial-dependent trends in log ratios, because data are gleaned from a very large number of genes. By contrast, spiked controls or an MSP series may be only rep-resented by a few probes on the microarray and are less appropriate for spatial normaliza-tion (Yang et al. 2002b). MSP or spiked controls are likely to be most useful when there are substantial differences in gene expression between two samples, as the value of an "all genes" approach is more limited in this setting. For example, Figure 7-16 shows the concordance between MSP- and all-genes-based LOWESS curves when the data are obtained from sam-ples with similar expression patterns but the curves differ when the samples are biological-

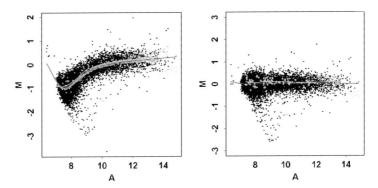

FIGURE 7-16. Within-slide normalization: MA plot for comparison of the anterior versus posterior portion of the olfactory bulb. These samples are very similar, and thus, there is no expectation that many genes will change. (*Cyan dots*) MSP titration series; (*cyan curve*) corresponding LOWESS fit. The red curve corresponds to the LOWESS fit for the entire data set. Control genes: (*Yellow*) tubulin and GADPH; (*green*) mouse genomic DNA; (*orange*) an approximate rank invariant set of genes with $P = 0.01$ and $l = 25$. (*Left*) MA plot before normalization; (*right*) MA plot after within-print-tip group location normalization. (Reprinted, with permission, from Yang et al. 2002b [© Oxford University Press].)

ly divergent (please see Figure 7-17). Yang et al. (2002b) propose a composite normalization approach, where normalization is based on "all genes" of a low-intensity value, and normalization is based on an MSP titration series for the higher-intensity range and divergent biological samples.

Other Sets of Genes

Microarray normalization can also be performed using genes that are selected because they are constant across a range of samples in a particular set of experiments. One such approach is to select a rank invariant set of genes. A set of genes is said to be rank invariant if their ranks are the same for the red and green intensities; i.e., for two genes to be rank invariant, the intensity values for gene *A* are larger than for gene *B* across a range of samples in a given experiment, in both the red and the green channels. In practice, a maximal invariant set tends to be too small to be useful for normalization. Schadt et al. (2000 [also http://preprints.stat. ucla.edu/303/]) and Tseng et al. (2001) proposed an iterative procedure to find an approximately invariant set of genes.

In conclusion, although it is important to adjust for the artifactual bias inherent in microarray experiments, it is likewise critical to understand that each approach to correcting for bias involves assumptions about its source. Investigators should be aware of these assumptions if normalization algorithms are to be applied intelligently and should check that, after normalization, systematic errors are reduced and that any gene expression differences observed are meaningful and valid.

FIGURE 7-17. Within-slide normalization: MA plot for comparison of the medial versus lateral portion of the olfactory bulb. (*Cyan dots*) MSP titration series; (*cyan curve*) the corresponding LOWESS fit. The red curve corresponds to the LOWESS fit for the entire data set. The green curve represents the composite normalization curve. Control genes: (*Yellow*) tubulin and GADPH; (*green*) mouse genomic DNA; (*orange*) an approximate rank invariant set of genes. The figure shows the MA plot before normalization. (Reprinted, with permission, from Yang et al. 2002b [© Oxford University Press].)

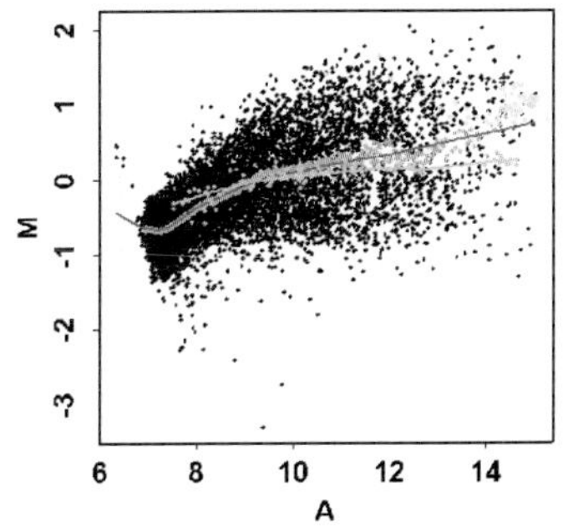

Part 4: Representing and Evaluating Slide Data

Yee Hwa Yang and Terry Speed

Department of Statistics, University of California, Berkeley, California 94720

INTRODUCTION

The routine use of a variety of graphical displays is recommended to examine the results of microarray experiments. Such displays can assist in deciding whether the experiment was successful, help in choosing appropriate analysis tools, and highlight specific experimental problems. Various representations of slide data can therefore facilitate better experimental outcomes in the future.

FALSE COLOR OVERLAY IMAGE

The peak emission for 5′ phosphoramidite conjugates of Cy3 is 570 nm and 667 nm for those of Cy5, and therefore the scanned microarray output images of the Cy3 and Cy5 channels are typically false-colored green and red, respectively. When combined, the two images result in yellow spots if a given gene is equally expressed in the two samples or shades of red or green if differentially expressed. For display purposes, the two 16-bit Tiff images (scanned output from the Cy3 and Cy5 channels) are compressed into 8-bit images using a square root transformation. This transformation is required in order to display the fluorescence intensities for both wavelengths using a 24-bit composite RGB overlay image. In this RGB image, blue values (B) are set to zero, red values (R) are used for the Cy5 intensities, and green values (G) are used for the Cy3 intensities. Coregistration and overlay of each channel offers a quick visualization of a microarray experiment, revealing information on color balance, uniformity of hybridization, spot uniformity, background, and artifacts such as dust or scratches. Overlay images also provide a rough impression of the number of genes that are differentially expressed between the two samples. Figure 7-18 shows two overlay images of differing qualities.

Overlay images provide a valuable qualitative impression of a microarray experiment, but they can be misleading, especially if the data have been enhanced with programs such as Adobe Photoshop. Therefore, it is essential that quantitative quality scores are obtained from and subtle expression differences detected by data extracted with image analysis software.

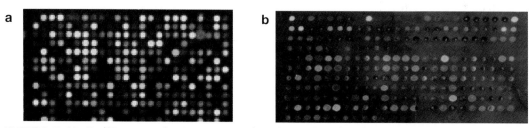

FIGURE 7-18. Red/Green overlay images. (a) Relatively good-quality slide, with low background and a large proportion of differentially expressed genes. (b) An array experiment with high background, including a number of ghost spots on the third row and few differentially expressed genes. For diagnostic information that can be obtained from overlay images, please see Section 3, Troubleshooting.

LOG TRANSFORMATION OF SPOT INTENSITIES

It is highly desirable, for several reasons, to take logs of the raw intensities obtained from an image analysis program before plotting or carrying out further analysis. First, the intensities in a successful microarray experiment typically span the full 16-bit range from 0 to 65,535 units, with the vast majority in the lower range of values, less than 1000. If data are not transformed, they must by necessity be presented in a very compressed form in the low range. Calculating a log spreads the values more evenly across the range and provides readier visualization of the data. Second, the random variation (as measured by the standard deviation of the intensities) typically increases approximately linearly with the average signal strength. Taking logs tends to make the variability more constant. Third, $\log_2(R/G)$ is the difference $\log_2 R - \log_2 G$. It is convenient to express values to the log base 2. Thus, log (base 2) ratios of 1, 2, and 3 correspond to fold changes of 2, 4, and 8, respectively.

SCATTER PLOTS: DIAGONAL AND MA PLOTS

A scatter plot, the most common graphical display following a cDNA microarray experiment, is a $\log_2$ plot of the two channel intensities, $\log_2 R$ versus $\log_2 G$ (Figure 7-19, left). Interest is typically focused on the points away from the diagonal, representing differentially expressed genes. The "cloud" of data represents the distribution of spot intensities.

An alternative type of scatter plot is an MA plot (Dudoit et al. 2002) where ratio information is rotated by 45º and the axes scaled. In an MA plot scatter plot, the log ratios ($M = \log_2 R/G$) are plotted on the y axis against the log of the geometric mean of the signal strengths ($A = \log_2 \sqrt{R \cdot G}$) for each spot on the slide (Figure 7-19, right). An MA plot serves to increase the room available to represent the range of differential expression. Having the geometric mean (A) of the two intensities visible as an overall measure of abundance of the transcripts provides a useful tool for later analyses. For example, it is helpful to know that a twofold change arose from a ratio of 20,000 over 10,000, rather than 200 over 100; the former is less likely to be chance variation.

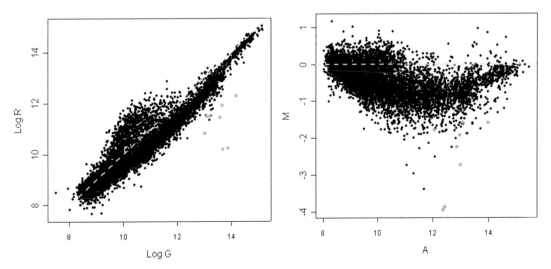

FIGURE 7-19. (*Left*) Scatter plot of log *R* versus log *G*. (*Right*) MA plot. (Data from Callow et al. 2000.) The central dip in the plot at the right is an artifact and is more evident than in the plot at the left.

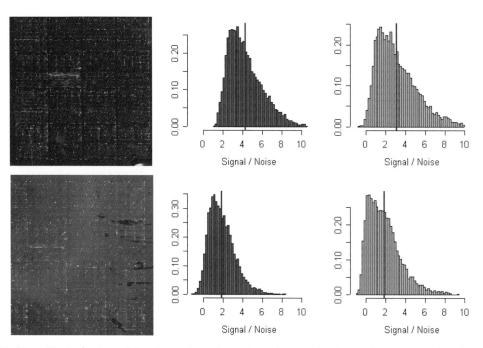

FIGURE 7-20. Evaluation of signal-to-noise (S/N) ratio at the spot level using histograms. The S/N ratio is plotted on the x axis and is a measure of the $\log_2$ (spot intensity/background adjacent to the spot). The frequency of spots with a given value is plotted on the y axis. The lower image has red haze in the top right-hand corner and this is seen as a lower average S/N ratio for this image compared with the upper image. By contrast, the average differences in the Cy3 channel are less striking.

HISTOGRAMS

Histograms provide a useful snapshot of the shape of the distribution of the data and provide information about quality statistics. For example, Figure 7-20 shows the signal-to-noise (S/N) ratio of each channel plotted against the proportion of spots with that value for two different images. The higher Cy5 background in the lower image is seen as mean S/N ratio of 2 compared with 4 for the upper image, whereas the Cy3 channels are comparable with similar mean S/N values.

BOX PLOTS

In conjunction with the MA plot, it can be helpful to perform a box plot of M values. Box plots (Tukey 1977), also called "box-and-whisker" plots, are simple graphical summaries of the distribution of a data set. This plot displays a statistical summary consisting of the median, upper, and lower quartiles; the range; and possibly individual extreme values. The central "box" in a plot represents the interquartile range (IQR), which is defined as the difference between the 75th percentile and 25th percentile, or the upper and lower quartiles. The line in the middle of the "box" represents the median; a measure of central location of the data. Extreme values >1.5 × IQR above the 75th percentile and <1.5 × IQR below the 25th percentile are typically plotted individually. Spots with extreme log ratios represent genes that

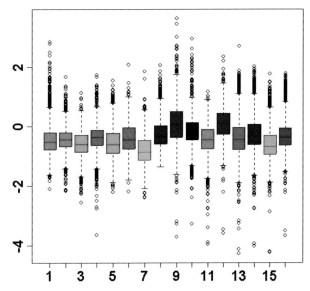

FIGURE 7-21. Box plots displaying the log ratio distribution for a large number of replicate experiments investigating a mutant mouse phenotype. (Data from Callow et al. 2000.) The plot shows that the different experiments have log ratios with different centers and somewhat different scales (IQR = box size).

appear to be strongly differentially expressed. The size of the box provides a measure of the spread of the experiment. A narrow box (i.e., a small IQR) is desirable as it often indicates less noise in the experiment. Figure 7-21 shows an example of a microarray experiment in which the range of values and the spread, as measured by the IQR, of 16 slides are depicted.

SPATIAL PLOTS

Depicting Background

Background often varies systematically across slides. Using a colored image representing measured background values provides a simple method to better visualize background variation and identify possible artifacts. Figure 7-22 shows a red-green overlay image and the corresponding background representations from the separate channels.

Highlighting Extreme Ratios

It is not infrequent that striking spatial effects are visible in the log ratio values across a slide. An easy way to check for this is to have a schematic spatial representation of the spots on a slide, and color-code spots with the top 5% or bottom 5% of *M* values (Figure 7-23). Nonrandom distribution of signals may result from a systematic ordering of probes on the microarray that tend to be highly expressed. For example, positive controls are often placed in the top row or rows of each pin group, and in such cases, they will stand out as an unusually bright point in the spatial plot. Alternatively, nonrandom distribution of signals may be a hybridization artifact (please see Part 3). Typical patterns of artifacts observed include pronounced gradients across the slide or regions with clusters of high or low log ratio values, often along edges of the slide.

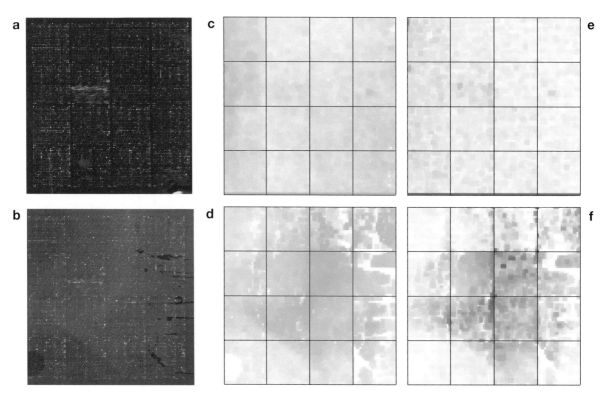

FIGURE 7-22. Spatial plots of background from two different microarrays. (*a,b*) Overlay images for the two microarrays; (*c–f*) false color representation of areas of high background. White areas represent low background, and bright green (*c,d*) or red (*e,f*) areas represent high background for Cy3 and Cy5 channels, respectively.

UNDERLYING ARTIFACTS REVEALED BY GRAPHICAL TOOLS

Pin (Subarray) Effects

The spots on a slide are arranged in a pattern corresponding to the print head used to spot out the probes. For example, if the print head has 16 pins in a 4 × 4 array, and each is used 25 × 25 times in a square array, then the spots on the slide will appear in the form of 16 subarrays of 625 spots each. The particular subarray to which a spot belongs is referred to as its pin group. All spots in a pin group are put down by the same pin in the arrayer print head.

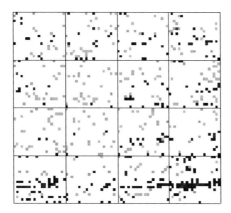

FIGURE 7-23. Spatial plot showing the extreme values, such as the top (*black*) and bottom (*green*) 5% of the $\log_2$ ratios. An area of nonrandom distribution of high-intensity signals is seen toward the lower right.

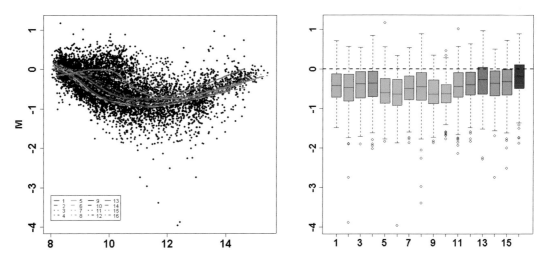

FIGURE 7-24. (*Left*) The 16 colored lines are smooth LOWESS lines through the points from the 16 pin groups. (*Right*) Box plots of log ratios by pin group. The plots demonstrate pin-group differences.

The pin group to which a spot belongs contains information that can be useful, either directly, because it reflects the pin that spotted down the DNA, or indirectly, as a surrogate for the position of the spot on the slide. For example, with a 4 × 4 array of pins on the head, pin groups 4, 8, 12, and 16 correspond to one edge of the slide, as do groups 1, 2, 3, and 4, and 13, 14, 15, and 16. It is frequently useful to depict data by pin group and to make adjustments for biases within pin groups.

Two plots that are valuable for depicting pin-group effects are MA plots and box plots of *M* values, as described in the previous section, but done within the pin group, rather than for the whole slide (Figure 7-24). LOWESS lines, for data obtained with each pin group (Figure 7-24, left), show that intensity-dependent variation in the red/green ratios differ, indicating pin-group bias. For a further description of LOWESS lines, please see Part 3.

Plate Effects

The printing of cDNA microarrays typically begins by polymerase chain reaction (PCR) amplification of the (probe) cDNA in 96-well microtiter plates, commonly four plates at a time. The cDNA arrays are then transferred to 384-well plates, and printing is carried out plate-by-plate from them. Thus, if a slide consists of a 12 × 4 array of 24 × 24-spot pin groups, then each 384-well plate will provide cDNA for 384/12 × 4 = 8 spots in each pin group. Furthermore, each set of 8 are assignable back to particular 96-well microtiter plates. Printing proceeds through 384-well plates until complete.

As described above in Highlighting Extreme Ratios, plate effects may be the result of systematic ordering of probes within plates or as a result of differences in probe preparation. The quality of the cDNA probe may differ markedly from plate to plate, depending on whether the PCR template is plasmid DNA or bacterial culture and on variation associated with any of the many steps taken in preparing the DNA. Sometimes, probes from very different original sources are put together on the same slide. Whatever the reason, there can be observable

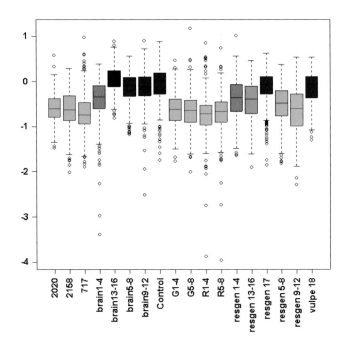

FIGURE 7-25. Each box plot represents log ratios from 1 of 18 384-well plates, spotted on the same microarray slide. The plot shows that median ratios differ markedly between plate groups. This type of variation should be removed before proceeding with analysis.

differences in spot signal characteristics across plate groups. Although competitive hybridization is designed to remove the effects of variation in probe quantity or quality, systematic differences based on plate effects may at times remain. The simplest way to detect plate effects is to perform parallel box plots of log intensities or log ratios, placing the set all on one page (Figure 7-25).

Time of Printing Effects

Printing (e.g., a batch of 1–200 slides) can be spread over several days. During that time, conditions such as temperature and humidity may change markedly in the lab and dust can accumulate. Due to these and other factors, marked differences can sometimes be seen in the shape or signal intensity or in the quality of spots printed over different days. Much of this variation disappears, however, when the ratios of intensities are taken, but at times what remains is noticeable (Figure 7-26).

SUMMARY

In summary, exploratory graphical tools such as scatter plots, box plots, and spatial plots provide quick and simple visual inspection of microarray data. These techniques provide an indication of the quality of the slides and the experiments and thereby help to identify possible systematic variations. Variations can include imbalance between dyes, spatial variation across slides, pin variation, plate effects, or time of print effects. Normalization of data (please see Part 3) provides approaches to remove such systematic effects so that real biological differences can be more easily distinguished.

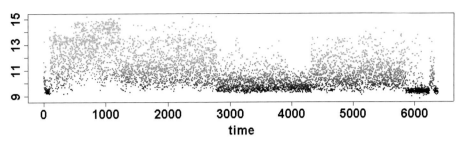

FIGURE 7-26. Green channel intensities of spots on an array printed over 4.5 days. The x axis shows the spot number, which accumulated on the slide over the printing period, and the y axis is $\log_2 G$. Note that the distribution of intensity is nonrandomly distributed over the 4.5 days. Especially low values of signal intensity were obtained from spots printed on day 3.

MAKING USE OF QUALITY MEASURES

Many image analysis programs collect a wide range of quantitative measurements associated with each spot. These include morphological measures such as area and perimeter (in pixels) as well as uniformity measures such as the standard deviation of the foreground and background intensities in each channel and of the ratios of intensities (with or without background adjustment) across the pixels in a spot. Other quantitative measurements include spot brightness indicators such as the ratio of spot foreground to background intensity and the fraction of pixels in the foreground with intensity greater than the background, or a given multiple thereof. From these initial measures, further derived measures can be calculated, such as one of shape (e.g., area/perimeter^2), and other signal-to-noise measures such as coefficients of variation (standard deviation/mean) and other quantities. Wang et al. (2001) describe a composite quality (q_{com}) measure based on parameters of spot size, signal to noise, variability in local background, excessively high local background, and signal saturation. These authors show that q_{com} is an effective indicator of slide variability. The implementation of this approach, Matarray, is publicly available and includes image analysis software for gridding, segmentation, and intensity extraction.

Quality assessment of microarray data encompasses not only measurement and use of information on individual spot properties, but also global measures of quality assessment. This is found in the distribution of log intensity values in each of the two channels across the spots on the slide (Figure 7-20). Pixel intensities are usually scaled to be between 1 and $2^{16} = 65,536$, i.e., to be between 0 and 16 on the $\log_2$ scale. Failure of the observed intensities to make use of the full scale, or almost the full scale, is usually an indication that something is wrong, possibly that the hybridization failed.

How should we make use of various quality measures? Most image analysis programs include procedures for flagging spots on the basis of one of more of the quality indicators, usually those involving a measure of signal to noise and/or of area. Users typically omit flagged spots from the primary analysis. Similarly, Wang et al. (2001) suggest that q_{com} can be used to decide whether to set threshold values for exclusion of spots with poor composite values. Data filtering of this kind clearly improves the appearance of the data, as indicated by a range of visual diagnostics. However, there are difficulties from a statistical viewpoint in rejecting data as unsatisfactory when the cutoffs used to set a threshold for inclusion of data may be somewhat arbitrary. Ideally, thresholds and weighting of quality measures should be done using values that are functions of validated quality measures that predict precision, for example, the between-slide variance of log ratios. Rather than setting a sharp boundary for inclusion of the data, it may be preferable to give less weight to lower-quality spots in a graduated way.

Part 5: LIMS, Databases, and Data Management

Catherine A. Ball and Gavin Sherlock

Stanford Microarray Database, Stanford University School of Medicine, California 94305-5120

INTRODUCTION

The ability to conduct a comprehensive expression survey of a genome (Lockhart et al. 1996; Schena et al. 1996; DeRisi et al. 1997; Lashkari et al. 1997; Wodicka et al. 1997; Spellman et al. 1998) has generated enthusiasm for microarray technology in many biologists; yet there are many steps that can be daunting to a first-time user. Warehousing of data produced by such studies and their associated analyses present particular challenges. Meaningful interpretation of results, and the detection of data artifacts, is greatly facilitated by the appropriate recording of microarray experiments and the ability to objectively identify high-quality data sets. As data are accumulated, the ability to store and track information becomes essential. Part 5 addresses data management for results generated from glass slide microarrays that have been spotted with DNA molecules. However, much of the information can easily be applied to data from microarrays spotted with proteins, or to other platforms, such as Affymetrix chips or nylon filter arrays.

Microarray experiments produce a great deal of data, not just in terms of the data output from a scanned slide, but also in terms of recording how the experiment was performed in the first place: information about the identity of probes[1] used on the microarray, methods in slide fabrication, and the hybridization conditions of each experiment. Successful use of the DNA microarray technology requires that the investigator be able to efficiently retrieve and make sense of this information. Without good data management, it is almost impossible to track down and troubleshoot problems, such as contamination of samples and incorrect recording of print information. In addition, unless essential information is comprehensively cataloged, it is impossible for other investigators to replicate the work or assess its quality. Although many microarray users wish to perform only a limited series of experiments, there are lessons to be learned from those who have been tracking and storing the data for large-scale projects.

Most large-scale microarray efforts use both an LIM (*laboratory information management*) system for tracking how the microarrays were fabricated and a database to store the results of individual array hybridizations. Databases of results hold raw data, but must also contain enough biological annotation to make analysis of the results possible. Although the distinction between LIM systems and results databases seems quite natural, in reality, there is significant overlap in the types of information each requires, and it is important that these two separate systems have an interface through which data from one can be connected to data in the other (please see Figure 7-27). Because of the considerable duplication of information in LIM systems and results databases, smaller-scale projects could reasonably make use of a

---

[1]The authors prefer the use of the term "reporter" to refer to the nucleic acid that is spotted on a microarray, and this term is also used in the MIAME protocol (please see the information panel on **SHARING MICROARRAY DATA AMONG INVESTIGATORS**). For consistency with other sections of this manual, the term "probes" is retained here (please see the panel on **NOMENCLATURE OF PROBES AND TARGETS** in the Introduction to Section 1).

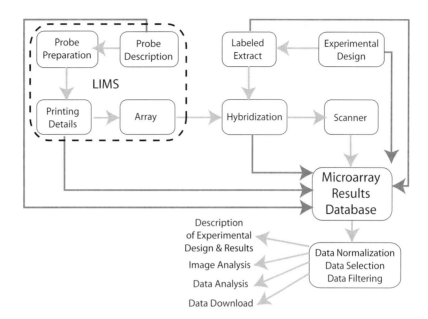

FIGURE 7-27. Data flowchart for microarray fabrication and experiments. Black arrows indicate the flow of information during the fabrication of microarrays and the design and implementation of microarray experiments. The information usually stored in a LIM system includes details about the description and preparation of DNA molecules spotted on the microarrays, information about the printing of those molecules on the microarrays and the fate of each array fabricated. Microarray results databases should contain information about the experimental design, description of the probes and conditions used during hybridization, and the results of scanning the hybridized microarray. Gray arrows indicate important information from each step of the process that should be stored in the microarray results database to enable interpretation of results and troubleshooting.

single database that combines their functions. A list of some of the many publicly and commercially available LIM systems can be obtained from pubs.acs.org/subscribe/journalsancham/72/supmat/files/ac57A.fil/LIMStabl.html.

INFORMATION TO BE CAPTURED BY A LIM SYSTEM

Tracking data that describe how a microarray is manufactured is essential both for future interpretation of the data generated and for troubleshooting during the course of the experiment. For example, when one copy of a sequence on a microarray behaves differently from another copy of the same sequence, there may possibly be contamination or mistracking of one of the samples. Given the number of spots on a typical array, automated approaches are required for detection. Conversely, the expression pattern of a given sequence may show close similarity to that of an unrelated sequence. Probe tracking enables an investigator to detect instances where sequences in adjacent wells in a microtiter plate show similar expression patterns. In the absence of tracking information, such falsely coincident expression patterns would be interpreted as biologically meaningful. The ability to detect likely contamination and other procedural problems allows the microarray spots generated from suspect samples to be flagged as unreliable. Given the number of spots on a typical array, automated approaches are needed to make such scenarios easy to detect.

An effective microarray LIM system should track procedures that were used to generate sequences spotted on microarrays, map samples as they are transferred from one microtiter plate to another, record the identity of the sequences spotted on microarrays as well as their position on the microarray, and, finally, store the details of the microarray printing process.

Tracking and Preparation of Samples

It is essential that information about the sequence identity of probes and their preparation be stored. Probes are most often PCR products or oligonucleotides. PCR products can be generated from a variety of templates, such as genomic DNA or cDNAs inserted into vectors. A microarray LIM system must be able to record each step of a sample preparation as well as the sources of templates and primers and their locations in relevant microtiter plates. For example, producing a PCR product from a vector insert requires that the LIM system record the following information:

- Source of clones/bacteria (whether commercial or homegrown).
- Bacterial strains containing plasmids.
- Identity of the plasmid.
- Storage location of the isolated plasmid.
- Any relevant accession numbers, clone identifiers, or other identifiers pertaining to the insert in the plasmid.
- Identity and source of each primer (typically a common pair of vector primers are used for amplification).
- Storage locations of each primer.
- Sequences of each primer.
- Expected size of the PCR product.
- Identity or biological name of the PCR product.
- Storage location of the PCR product.
- Images of any gels used to evaluate the quality of the PCR product.
- Quality of the PCR product, with respect to whether it is close to the expected size and/or whether a single or multiple bands are seen, or indeed no bands are seen.
- Transfer of samples from plate to plate, including mapping between plates, techniques used to transfer samples, and the dates that transfers are performed.
- Protocols followed at each step of the production of the microarray.

Being able to reconstruct the methods used to generate spots on a microarray is beneficial for troubleshooting. Suspected contamination can be verified only if all of the original samples can be readily tested.

Sequence on Arrays

An obvious use of an LIM system is to keep track of what is spotted where on each array. One component is recording what the probe is supposed to be. In the case of oligonucleotides spotted on a microarray, it could be as simple as recording its sequence. However, if a PCR product is to be spotted, its uniqueness should be based on both the template and the primers, and both components must be properly tracked as part of the probe's identity. The coordinates on the microarray where the probe has been placed must also accompany its identity.

Microarray Printing

The procedural details of microarray fabrication should include the type of array machine used (if more than one was available), the type of tip configuration employed, and the wash and dry times between each loading of the tips with sample. Most projects record the number of microarrays made, the order of each microarray within the batch (often glass slide microarrays printed at the beginning of a batch may have larger spots than microarrays printed later), the type of slide or surface used, and any pretreatments that might have been applied to the surface before printing. In addition, date, time, and names of individuals responsible for the print are often useful. Large-scale facilities will also track the fates of each microarray (whether given to another investigator or simply dropped and broken) and may have to track billing and payment records.

REQUIREMENTS OF RESULTS DATABASES

When a microarray database is selected or developed, it is important to make sure that each of the following issues is adequately addressed.

Data Storage

Data must be securely stored and easily loaded. When choosing a results database, it is important to consider that not all available databases will gracefully accept data from all array platforms. Some database packages are sufficient for storing data from glass slide microarrays, but they may be unable to store data from Affymetrix oligonucleotide arrays or nylon filter arrays, because each of these technologies provides a different type of data and different kinds and numbers of associated images. Additionally, it is essential that the database chosen to store microarray data be compatible with image analysis. Free or commercial packages available for extracting data from scanned images include Scanalyze, GenePix, and Imagene. Software packages such as these produce different data formats, as well as different types and quantities of data points. Ideally, data from different software packages should be able to be reconciled in the results database, so that when different packages provide the same type of measurement, this can be recorded.

Also related to the issue of data storage in a results database is the sheer magnitude of data. Considering that a single microarray of 20,000 spots generates approximately 1 million discrete data points, it is clear that handling data for even a modest experimental series is not a trivial undertaking. Most image analysis programs produce dozens of measurements per spot, such as intensity of each channel, background of each channel, and regression correlation. Relative expression levels can simply be expressed as the normalized ratio of background-subtracted signal intensities. However, other values can be used as filtering criteria for determining which data are reliable (such as regression correlation) and are therefore critical for subsequent data analysis. Storing all of the measurements for each spot will allow the quality of the data to be evaluated at a later time or allow the user to make use of yet-to-be developed analysis tools (e.g., a new approach to normalization of slide data). These issues also relate to the storage of microarray data on publicly accessible databases and are discussed further in the information panel on **SHARING MICROARRAY DATA AMONG INVESTIGATORS.**

Data Retrieval and Filtering

Data Retrieval

It is the ability of the database to effectively and efficiently query and retrieve data that makes it so powerful. A microarray database must be able to provide a single file for querying that contains all of the stored information for the microarray, as well as the associated biological information for the probes on the microarray. Annotation of the elements on the array is essential for interpretation of the results. Furthermore, a microarray database must allow retrieval of the data from multiple arrays, so that results from experimentally related arrays (e.g., arrays that are part of a time series or a study of related tissue samples) can be compared and analyzed as one data set.

Data Filtering

When retrieving data, it should be possible to filter out data from spots of dubious quality. Measurements of quality may be decided by the experimenter and will depend on the data stored within the database. Additionally, quality measurements from the manufacture of the microarray (whether a PCR product showed an anomaly or whether the sample might be contaminated) should be communicated from the LIM system that tracked the array synthesis to the selected results database. Examples of desirable database filtering metrics include the strength of signal to background, the regression correlation, and the flag status (an indication that either a user, or the software, has identified a spot as being unreliable).

A results database should have the capacity to filter data on a gene-by-gene basis. For example, an investigator might want to retrieve all of the data for a set of genes in a group of arrays or select data associated only with those genes that varied by a given amount over a set of arrays. Another option would be to filter data on the basis of the percentage of microarrays that provide "good" data for a given gene. A powerful results database will offer many filtering permutations.

Data Modeling of Biological Samples

To interpret the results of microarray experiments, the sequences spotted on the microarrays must be represented in a biologically meaningful manner. A simple model would assume that every sequence spotted on the array is a gene and store it as such. Although this is a convenient method of representing sequences, there are obvious shortcomings to such an approach. For example, this method would not enable a database to represent noncoding sequences such as intergenic regions or introns. In addition, a one-to-one, sequence-to-gene data model would not permit a microarray to contain distinct probe sequences that represent the same gene. A more sophisticated model is necessary to allow greater flexibility and analysis of data quality.

A more complex representation of data would require each sequence to have its own identifier. If a gene is represented by more than one sequence on a microarray, each sequence will be mapped to that gene. A database of this type allows results from sequences mapping to the same gene to be treated independently, or collapsed into a composite value during data selection. Using multiple sequences to represent a single gene allows an investigator to detect potential artifacts. An even more cautious strategy is to track not only every sequence placed on a microarray, but also each instance of that sequence. For example, using information from an LIM system, the product of each PCR can be given a unique identifier. With this information, the contamination of a well or failure of a PCR during the generation of one instance of a sequence would not cause other experimentally unrelated instances of the sequence to be regarded as a "bad" sequence. Transfer of information between the LIM system used to track the manufacture of microarrays and the database that stores the results of hybridized microarrays is therefore an important consideration in selecting or designing a database model.

Ideally, unique sequences could be mapped not just to the genes they represent, but also to exons. These exons could then be mapped to transcripts, and in such a manner, the database would allow comparison of expression patterns of alternative transcripts. Although this strategy is not terribly effective without detailed knowledge of both exons and splice forms, its value to the biologist is obvious.

Biological Annotation

The ultimate goal of microarray studies is to be able to draw conclusions about biological systems. This is impossible without associating a sequence on a microarray with a gene and in turn associating the gene with current annotation from the scientific literature. To be most valuable, biological annotations should be accurate, reflect the most current understanding of the gene product, be pertinent to the studies being undertaken, and be concise. When surveying hundreds, even thousands, of genes, making sense of lengthy descriptions or requiring access to external Web Sites is quite impractical. Storage of gene annotations in a database is therefore desirable.

It is essential to understand that biological annotation should be dynamic. New information can result from experimental discovery or a better understanding of a genome. For example, the UniGene project at NCBI assembles ESTs into clusters. New sequence data will result in a new build of the UniGene clusters and can result in EST clones being associated with different gene clusters from build to build. For annotation of sequences in a microarray database to be dynamic, a highly desirable feature in a database package would allow the investigator to make frequent updates of biological information. Issues associated with annotation of genes on microarrays are discussed further in the information panel on **GENE ANNOTATION**.

Recording of Experimental Information: MIAME

A community of microarray investigators has developed a set of standards to systematically define the minimal information necessary to allow other investigators to repeat an experiment or to correctly re-analyze published data (Brazma et al. 2001). The MIAME (Minimal Information About Microarray Experiments) standards are designed to facilitate data sharing, as described in the information panel on **SHARING MICROARRAY DATA AMONG INVESTIGATORS**. Public data can then be analyzed in new ways that can shed light on studies that are under way. Conversely, creative analysis of one investigator's data by other investigators can also be beneficial.

Data Must Be Retrievable in Formats Used by Software Analysis Programs

Interfacing Analysis Tools

It is often convenient or even necessary that analysis tools be connected directly to a results database. Tools for data analysis, such as hierarchical clustering, self-organizing maps, and principle components analysis, may come as part of a database package. Certainly, when using any one of the many commercial and free stand-alone tools, an obvious requirement is that the database be able to produce data in the correct format to interface with the desired tools.

Interfacing between the LIM System and the Results Database

For the information within the LIM system to be useful when retrieving and filtering microarray data, there should be a certain amount of redundant storage between the two databases. Obviously, the more redundancy, the harder the problem becomes when data need updating, and thus only those data required for on-the-fly filtering and analysis of the microarray results should be duplicated. Typically, this will be the information pertaining to the plates that were used in a microarray print and the samples they contain, and a unique identifier produced by the LIM system, which tracks each instance of a piece of DNA. Interfacing between the two systems can be accomplished by the LIM system feeding a print file into the results database. As experiments are entered into the results database, they become associated with the correct microarray print.

Computing Issues Associated with Results Databases

The storage capacity of a microarray database is a function of the number of experiments it can hold, the size of the individual arrays, and the depth of information that is held for each microarray. In particular, the required storage is greatly increased if raw data Tiff images from the scanning of the arrays are to be stored. For example, as of March 2002, the Stanford Microarray Database (SMD) had more than 22,250 experiments, whose results are recorded in ~440,000,000 rows (averaging 19,750 rows per experiment). Physically, these data occupied ~100 gigabytes (GB) of disc space, with an additional 50 GB needed for the indexes on the result table. Storage of original Tiff images produced upon the scanning of a microarray requires ~40 megabytes (MB) for each experiment totaling almost 1 terabyte (TB) of storage. At the time of writing, images in SMD were stored on RAID disc arrays for up to 3 months, before being redundantly archived to tape. Although many projects will not be generating thousands of microarrays a year, investigators must anticipate future demands and plan accordingly for projects of all sizes.

Maintaining a large microarray database is potentially an expensive proposition. The main factors to consider in the cost are:

- machine(s) on which to install and house the database,
- database back-end software, and
- staff to maintain the database.

The scale of the project and the preferences of the database manufacturer are the prime considerations when selecting the type of machine to house the database. Unix usually provides superior stability over other platforms and could be anything from a Sun server running Solaris to an inexpensive PC running Linux or a PowerMac running MacOSX.

The type of machine on which to install a microarray database is partly dependent on the total number of concurrent users of the database. If the database is a multiple user system, and many users may be entering, retrieving, and analyzing data simultaneously, then a multiprocessor machine is strongly recommended if the database management system (DBMS) supports it.

SELECTING DATABASE SOFTWARE

Commercial as well as free alternatives are available for the database software itself. Well-known commercial database management systems, such as Oracle and Sybase, have more features, as well as access to technical support, compared to a free alternative such as mySQL. The high price of commercial database software must be considered in light of the limited availability of front-end software for publicly available solutions.

Freely Available Databases

Commercial microarray databases are supplied with extensive documentation. For an excellent review of many of these microarray databases, please see Gardiner-Garden and Littlejohn (2001). Described below are three databases that are freely available, at least to academics, and for which the full source code and schema are distributed, allowing customization (or improvement) by enterprising labs. Some of the more important features or drawbacks of each are summarized in Table 7-7.

AMAD (Another Microarray Database)

AMAD is a flat-file database that evolved from a database used internally at Stanford in the Brown and Botstein laboratories. It was written by Mike Eisen, Paul Spellman, Joe DeRisi, and Max Diehn. AMAD is available from http://microarrays.org/software.html.

TABLE 7-7. Comparisons of Freely Available Microarray Database Packages

	Advantages	Disadvantages
AMAD: microarrays.org/software.html	Simple, easy to use. Inexpensive to support.	Not a relational database. Not easily scalable.
SMD: genome-www.stanford.edu/microarray	Scales to large data sets. Automated annotation updates of probes. Sophisticated analysis tools for data interpretations and quality control. Actively being developed; has been successfully used.	Requires Oracle RDBMS. Requires effort to install and maintain.
GENEX: www.ncgr.org/genex	Does not require commercial RDBMS. Accepts data from multiple platforms. Good tool for data analysis and interpretation. Actively being developed.	Not widely used and still relatively untried. No ability to view proxy images of scanned arrays.

- **Requirements and Installation:** AMAD requires a machine that can run a Web server and has Perl running on it. Typically, as stated in the installation documentation, a PC running Linux or an Apple running MacOSX are sufficient. Installation of AMAD requires little effort, and a detailed document explains how this can be achieved.

- **Features:** AMAD allows uploading of flat files on the file system. Data can be viewed on an experiment-by-experiment basis or can be retrieved for multiple experiments simultaneously into a single file that may then be used in subsequent analyses. Output files are compatible with the Cluster program, described in Section 6. When retrieving data from AMAD, any column of data that is present in the files may be used for filtering the data. In addition, the user can add additional columns of data when defining the contents of a microarray print, and AMAD will transfer that data to the experiment data files. AMAD is compatible with data either from Scanalyze (http://rana.lbl.gov/Eisen Software.htm) or from GenePix (http://www.axon.com/GN_GenePixSoftware.html), which are commonly used software packages for analyzing scanned microarray images. Selected screen shots showing some of the data selection features of AMAD are provided in Figure 7-28.

- **Advantages:** AMAD is a simple and effective database for a lab with a modest budget, and with a few dozen to a few hundred microarrays worth of data. It is easy to install and has a clean interface that is intuitive to use.

- **Disadvantages:** AMAD is not a relational database and, consequently, does not have the convenient features that a robust relational database provides. There is a large amount of redundancy within the database (e.g., every experiment coming from a given print reproduces all the same print information), making information updates intensive. The limitations of the AMAD flat-file system make this package impractical for any project that will house a significant number of microarray results. In addition, there is no simple way to update an experiment if an error in the print list is made, other than re-entering the experiment with a corrected print list. AMAD is no longer under active development.

Stanford Microarray Database

The Stanford Microarray Database (SMD) (Sherlock et al. 2001) is a relational database, which uses Oracle as its database management system. SMD was developed at Stanford, to replace the original flat-file system that was the model for AMAD. SMD is available from http://genome-www.stanford.edu/microarray. The road map illustrating some of the data flow and tools in SMD is shown in Figure 7-29.

- **Requirements and Installation:** SMD could be installed on a lower-end system, but, at this time, the Stanford installation is on a Sun E4500 server, running Solaris 8, with 8 processors, and 8 GB of RAM. Although there is no specific reason to use a Solaris system, it has been noted that Oracle updates and bug fixes usually first appear on this platform. SMD installation also requires a copy of the Oracle Enterprise Edition server software, a Web server, Perl, and several Perl modules. Installation is currently not a simple process, although an installer script distributed with the software does take care of most of the details of getting the software running. However, for complete installation, many additional details must be addressed, such as setting up the Oracle instance

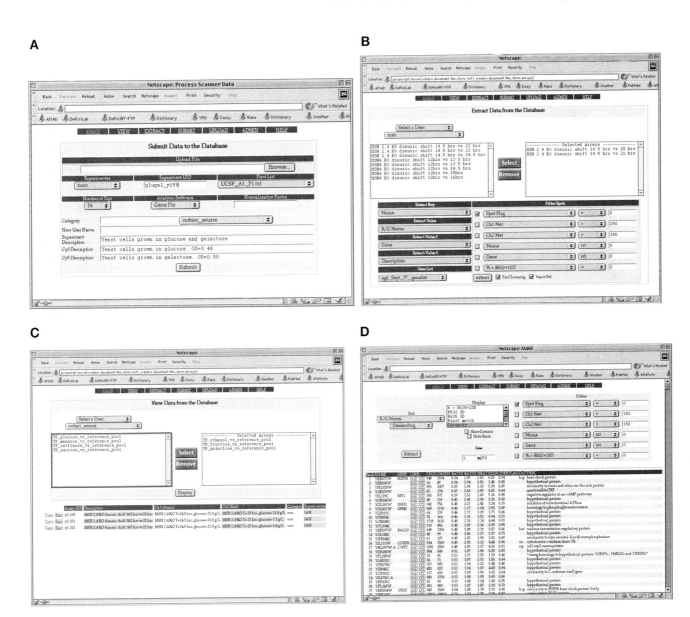

FIGURE 7-28. (*A*) Data submission tools in AMAD. AMAD's tool for submitting data allows the user to upload files from the computer and select from lists of options for experimenter, print list, tip geometry, analysis software, and experiment category. (*B*) Data selection in AMAD. AMAD allows users to browse lists of microarray results, select a subset, and specify which data to retrieve for further analysis. (*C*) Viewing descriptions of microarray data in AMAD. Users of AMAD can view the descriptions of microarray experiments and use this tool to view the results or simply download raw data. (*D*) Viewing microarray results in AMAD. AMAD allows users to filter results, define data displays, and sort the results from microarray experiments.

of the database and creating all of the tables and the relationships between them. Although all of the SQL scripts required to do this are distributed, their use requires a trained database administrator.

- *Features:* SMD allows entry of either GenePix or Scanalyze data (in either single or batch mode), and subsequent retrieval of data in either one experiment or many experiments with complex filtering, in much the same way as AMAD. In addition, SMD has many tools built on top of the database that may be used for assessing array quality and experiment reproducibility, as well as visualizing a representation of the original

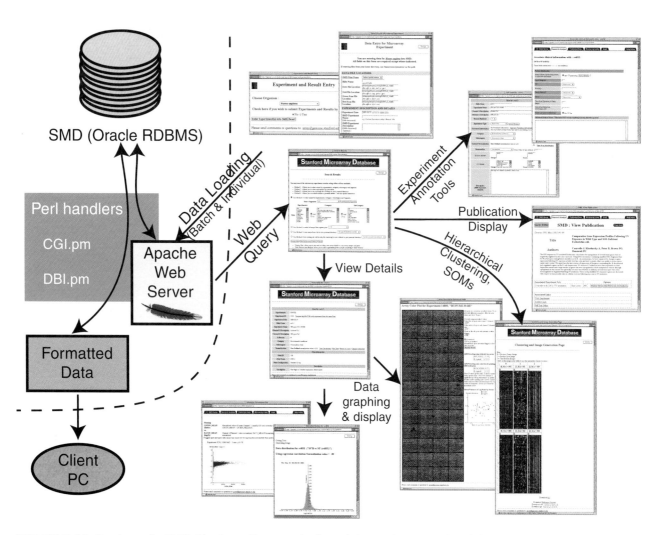

FIGURE 7-29. Road map for SMD. The figure illustrates the flow of data and associated tools for assessing quality and for graphical display of the data, as well as for downstream analysis.

microarray. SMD also has tools for downstream analyses. This is currently limited to hierarchical clustering (Eisen et al. 1998) and Self-Organizing Maps (Tamayo et al. 1999; Toronen et al. 1999). Future releases are to encompass *k*-means clustering (Tavazoie et al. 1999), Singular Value Decomposition (Alter et al. 2000), and imputation of missing data (Troyanskaya et al. 2001). Some of the features for data selection, analysis, quality control, and biological annotation are illustrated in Figures 7-29 to 7-35.

- *Advantages:* SMD is a scaleable solution for storing microarray data. The Stanford installation currently has greater than 22,250 experiments, constituting data from more than 440,000,000 spots. In addition, SMD has a flexible security model, to allow fine-grained access control to both data and tools. Many useful tools are available with the database, and the software allows users to view proxy images of the microarray scans to evaluate the quality of the results visually. Furthermore, SMD dynamically updates annotation of the human, mouse, and yeast genes that are represented on the microarrays. SMD is under active development, so that new features and improved schema and software will be available.

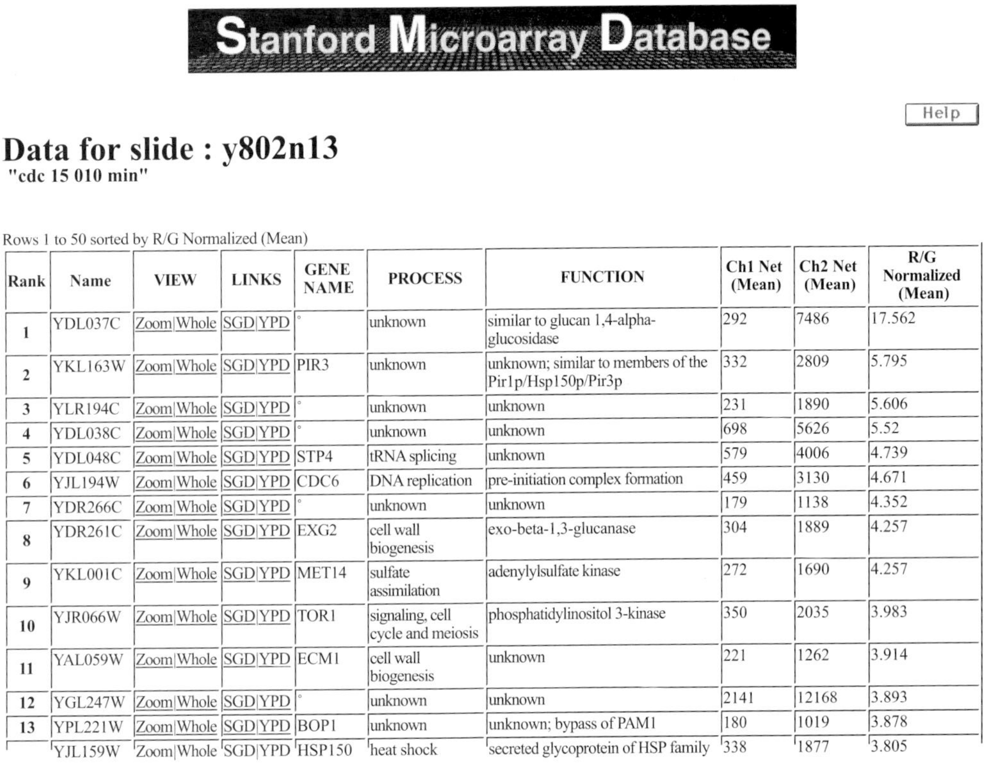

Stanford Microarray Database

Help

Data for slide : y802n13
"cdc 15 010 min"

Rows 1 to 50 sorted by R/G Normalized (Mean)

Rank	Name	VIEW	LINKS	GENE NAME	PROCESS	FUNCTION	Ch1 Net (Mean)	Ch2 Net (Mean)	R/G Normalized (Mean)
1	YDL037C	Zoom|Whole	SGD|YPD	°	unknown	similar to glucan 1,4-alpha-glucosidase	292	7486	17.562
2	YKL163W	Zoom|Whole	SGD|YPD	PIR3	unknown	unknown; similar to members of the Pir1p/Hsp150p/Pir3p	332	2809	5.795
3	YLR194C	Zoom|Whole	SGD|YPD	°	unknown	unknown	231	1890	5.606
4	YDL038C	Zoom|Whole	SGD|YPD	°	unknown	unknown	698	5626	5.52
5	YDL048C	Zoom|Whole	SGD|YPD	STP4	tRNA splicing	unknown	579	4006	4.739
6	YJL194W	Zoom|Whole	SGD|YPD	CDC6	DNA replication	pre-initiation complex formation	459	3130	4.671
7	YDR266C	Zoom|Whole	SGD|YPD	°	unknown	unknown	179	1138	4.352
8	YDR261C	Zoom|Whole	SGD|YPD	EXG2	cell wall biogenesis	exo-beta-1,3-glucanase	304	1889	4.257
9	YKL001C	Zoom|Whole	SGD|YPD	MET14	sulfate assimilation	adenylylsulfate kinase	272	1690	4.257
10	YJR066W	Zoom|Whole	SGD|YPD	TOR1	signaling, cell cycle and meiosis	phosphatidylinositol 3-kinase	350	2035	3.983
11	YAL059W	Zoom|Whole	SGD|YPD	ECM1	cell wall biogenesis	unknown	221	1262	3.914
12	YGL247W	Zoom|Whole	SGD|YPD	°	unknown	unknown	2141	12168	3.893
13	YPL221W	Zoom|Whole	SGD|YPD	BOP1	unknown	unknown; bypass of PAM1	180	1019	3.878
	YJL159W	Zoom|Whole	SGD|YPD	HSP150	heat shock	secreted glycoprotein of HSP family	338	1877	3.805

FIGURE 7-30. Viewing microarray results in SMD. Results for each spot as well as a description of the DNA molecule spotted can be viewed with SMD. Links from the page allow viewing of the image of the spot, the entire microarray as well as reports from outside databases.

Stanford Microarray Database

Help

Net Intensities for Experiment 78 (8832 spots total)

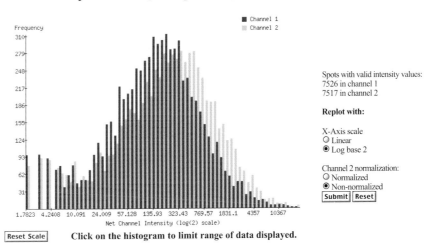

FIGURE 7-31. Expression history in SMD. SMD users can view expression for a single gene across all microarrays in the database. The distribution of intensities is plotted. Users can click on a point on the histogram to view experiments with a given intensity range for that gene.

Stanford **M**icroarray **D**atabase

Array Color Plot for Experiment 78, "cdc 15 010 min"

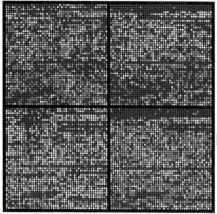

All spots are colored as specified below. To re-plot with different parameters, fill in the new values and click "Replot."

Currently using normalized values.
Color blue all spots with channel 2/channel 1 ratio
< 0.67
Color amber all spots with channel 2/channel 1 ratio
> 1.5
Show as dim all spots with intensity in either channel
< 300

◉ Normalized
○ Non-normalized
Absent/black spots are either flagged, or have no ratio recorded.
Replot Reset

ANOVA of log ratio (ch2/ch1) by sector

F(3, 7263)	7.2249
R-squared	0.00298

ANOVA of log ratio (ch2/ch1) by printing (384-well) plate

F(22, 7244)	7.185
R-squared	0.0214

Note: F values greater than ~5 and R-squared values greater than ~5% (0.05) indicate a significant and strong dependence on spatial location and/or printing plate. Low R-squared values may not reflect problems limited to one or a few sectors/plates.

FIGURE 7-32. Array color plot in SMD. SMD users can detect spatial bias in their results using a tool that displays spot intensities across an entire microarray.

S.O.U.R.C.E. Search   Switch to GeneReport   Help

IMAGE:1542757

cDNA Clone ID	IMAGE:1542757
Clone Source	NCI
Organism	Homo sapiens
dbEST Library Number/ Name	1042 [Unigene Lib ID = 600] / Soares_NFL_T_GBC_S1
Insert Length	1024
Vector	pT7T3D-Pac (Pharmacia) with a modified polylinker
	3' EST Information
dbEST ID	1637193
GenBank Accession	AA909121
GenBank GI History	3048526
High Quality Seqence	stops at base:`345
Putative ID	gb:M81590 5-HYDROXYTRYPTAMINE 1B RECEPTOR (HUMAN);
dbEST Entry Created	1998-05-20
dbEST Last Updated	1998-06-17
Perform a NCBI BLASTN	NR ````HTGS ````dbEST
Perform a NCBI BLASTX	NR ````SwissProt
UCSC Genome Viewer	Genome Viewer

| Search | GeneReport | Help |

Feedback for: array@genome.stanford.edu

FIGURE 7-33. SMD's SOURCE display for clones. SMD provides users with compiled annotations about cDNA sequences for human, mouse, and rat. Information comes from a variety of sources, including dbEST and GenBank.

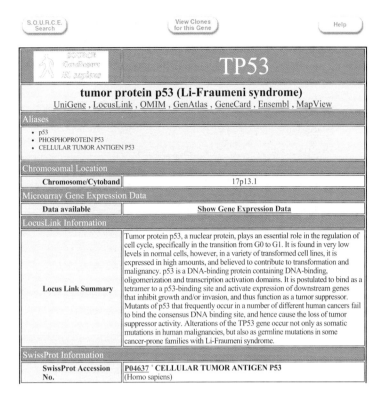

FIGURE 7-34. SMD's SOURCE display for genes. SMD users can obtain information about genes from SOURCE (Stanford Online Universal Resource for Clones and ESTs). Information is compiled from many sources, such as UniGene, LocusLink, and OMIM.

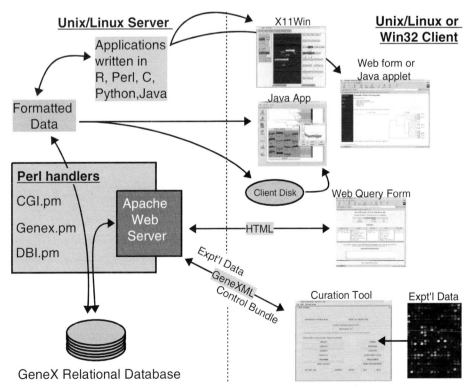

FIGURE 7-35. Road map for GeneX. GeneX requires a Unix or Linux server and Unix or Linux clients. Data can be loaded into GeneX via a web interface. The database can output data for web forms or for sending to applications outside the database, such as clustering programs.

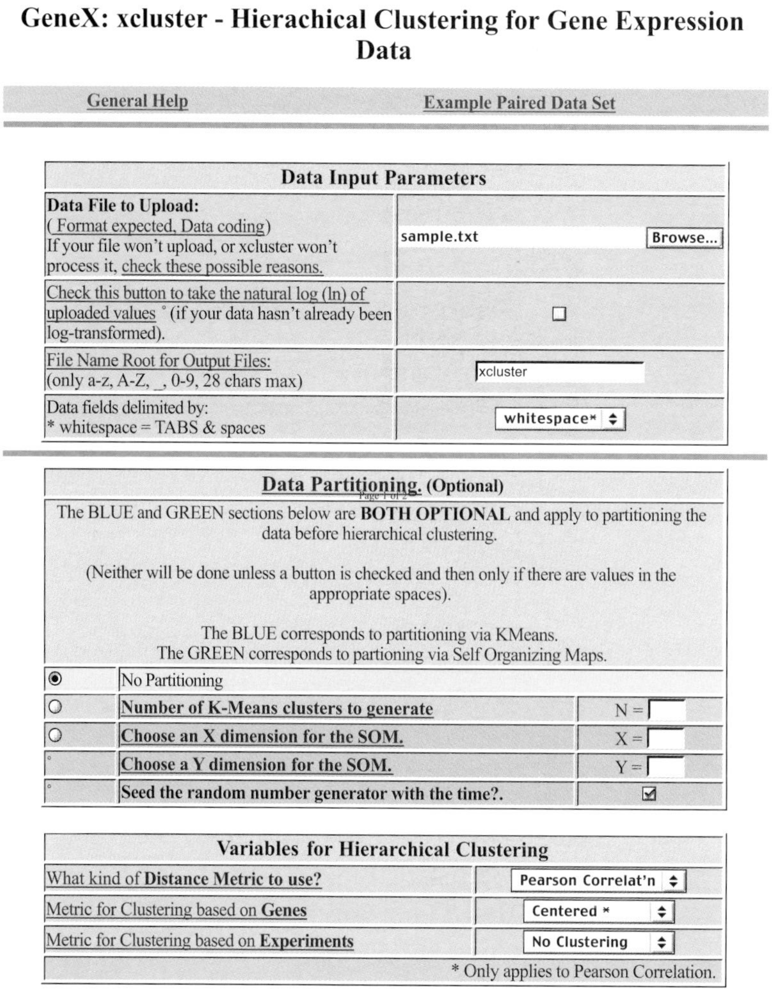

GeneX: xcluster - Hierachical Clustering for Gene Expression Data

General Help	Example Paired Data Set

Data Input Parameters	
Data File to Upload: (Format expected, Data coding) If your file won't upload, or xcluster won't process it, <u>check these possible reasons.</u>	sample.txt [Browse...]
Check this button to take the natural log (ln) of uploaded values ° (if your data hasn't already been log-transformed).	☐
File Name Root for Output Files: (only a-z, A-Z, _, 0-9, 28 chars max)	xcluster
Data fields delimited by: * whitespace = TABS & spaces	whitespace* ◆

Data Partitioning. (Optional)
The BLUE and GREEN sections below are **BOTH OPTIONAL** and apply to partitioning the data before hierarchical clustering. (Neither will be done unless a button is checked and then only if there are values in the appropriate spaces). The BLUE corresponds to partitioning via KMeans. The GREEN corresponds to partioning via Self Organizing Maps.

⦿	No Partitioning	
◯	**Number of K-Means clusters to generate**	N = ⬚
◯	**Choose an X dimension for the SOM.**	X = ⬚
°	**Choose a Y dimension for the SOM.**	Y = ⬚
°	**Seed the random number generator with the time?.**	☑

Variables for Hierarchical Clustering	
What kind of **Distance Metric to use?**	Pearson Correlat'n ◆
Metric for Clustering based on **Genes**	Centered * ◆
Metric for Clustering based on **Experiments**	No Clustering ◆
	* Only applies to Pearson Correlation.

FIGURE 7-36. Clustering options in GeneX. Using a file output by the database, GeneX users can select a variety of options to the hierarchical clustering, including self-organizing maps and *k*-means clustering. Results can be clustered by genes and/or by experiments.

- *Disadvantages:* SMD is not easy to install or maintain, and it requires expensive hardware and software, as well as trained staff (at least a database administrator and a programmer/curator) to keep it running. Currently, SMD does not store enough experimental or sample annotation to comply with the MIAME specifications, although this is a stated future goal. In addition, some modifications of the schema used by SMD are needed to better model the concept of a gene/locus and the sequence of the nucleic acid on a microarray and the mapping between them. SMD does not currently store single-channel microarray data, including data derived from Affymetrix GeneChips or from radiolabeled macroarrays.

GeneX

GeneX is a freely available database (released under the GNU public license) that uses the free database system, PostgreSQL, to store the data. For further details about GeneX, please see http://genex.sourceforge.net/.

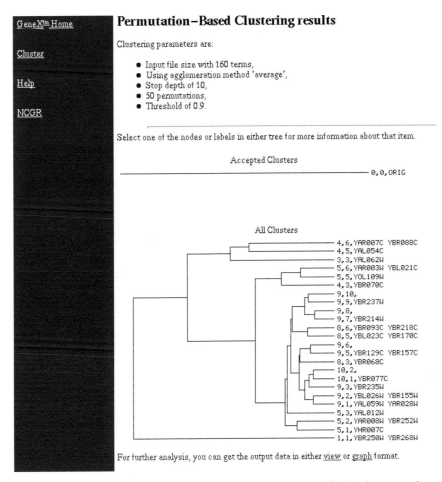

Permutation–Based Clustering results

Clustering parameters are:

- Input file size with 160 terms,
- Using agglomeration method 'average',
- Stop depth of 10,
- 50 permutations,
- Threshold of 0.9.

Select one of the nodes or labels in either tree for more information about that item.

Accepted Clusters

For further analysis, you can get the output data in either view or graph format.

FIGURE 7-37. r-Cluster from GeneX. Data output from GeneX can be submitted to a number of analysis tools, such as R-cluster, a tool for displaying and navigating clustered microarray results.

- ***Requirements and Installation:*** GeneX can be set up on a Linux machine, running an Apache Web server with Perl installed. An installation script is used to configure the components of the system. The general architecture of the package is detailed in Figure 7-35.

- ***Features:*** GeneX provides a client-side curation tool, written in Java, that can be used for formatting data sets for secure upload into the database; it also has simple html interfaces for retrieving data, either across data sets or for a single experiment. The software could permit more complex queries if an experienced programmer made extensions to the interface. A number of analytical routines can be run against the retrieved data, such as clustering, multidimensional scaling, cluster validation, and Principle Components Analysis. Figures 7-36 through 7-38 illustrate some of the data analysis features of GeneX.

- ***Advantages:*** Like AMAD, GeneX is fairly simple to install and does not require expensive hardware or software to install or maintain. Its software is a fully open source, and uses other open source tools. It has a well-considered data model and is also able to store data from different array platforms, such as two-color microarray data and sin-

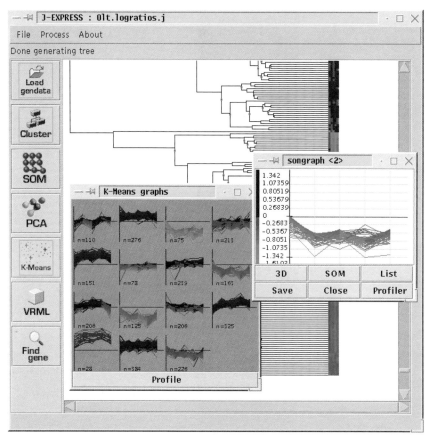

FIGURE 7-38. J-Express from GeneX. GeneX users can visualize graphs of expression patterns for nodes within clustered data using J-Express. J-Express provides a number of tools to assist experimenters in navigating their clustered data, such as a gene name search and generation of SOMS or *k*-means clusters.

gle-channel Affymetrix data. GeneX has a number of tools available to analyze data, and is under active development so that improvements to the software, data modeling, and analysis tools can be expected.

- **Disadvantages:** GeneX has not yet been demonstrated to be scaleable to many thousands of experiments, although, of course, that does not mean it cannot be scaled. Currently, GeneX does not store Tiff images and does not allow viewing of proxy images for characterization of microarray quality.

ACKNOWLEDGMENTS

Many thanks to John C. Matese and Harry Mangalam, both of whom contributed some figures and also provided helpful discussion. Thanks also to Tina Hernandez-Boussard and Janos Demeter for careful reading of the manuscript.

Part 6: Cluster Analysis and Display

Paul T. Spellman

University of California, Berkeley, California 94720-3200

INTRODUCTION

The production of microarrays and the generation of numeric information are only the first steps in understanding genome-scale data obtained by gene expression profiling. Simple comparisons—for example, the identification of genes that are expressed more highly in one experimental sample than another—can be easily analyzed using tools such as a spreadsheet. Unfortunately, most data sets are not easily explored and therefore require more powerful analytical techniques. Part 6 focuses on the use of two freely available tools: Cluster, which organizes related gene expression data, and Tree View, which allows clustered microarray data to be easily visualized (Eisen et al. 1998). Much of the information provided here is also relevant to other modes of analysis of microarray information.

Although not perfectly suited to all analyses, clustering tools are a simple, yet powerful method of organizing microarray-based gene expression data. In certain situations, a priori expectations of the results or the objectives of the experiment might suggest alternative analytical methods. In general, if an experiment was designed to be exploratory, rather than to answer a particular question, clustering is an excellent choice for initial data analysis. Examples of exploratory surveys include identification of genes transcriptionally regulated by some event, such as growth factor stimulation (Iyer et al. 1999), or the search for commonalities between biological treatments, such as comparing environmental stresses (Gasch et al. 2000) or genotypes (Hughes et al. 2000). More focused (supervised) methods may be appropriate when the goal is to find genes whose expression is correlated with a particular disease state or clinical outcome.

SUPERVISED AND UNSUPERVISED METHODS

Supervised methods typically make use of existing information to help guide associations between data. By contrast, unsupervised methods make use of gene expression information to reveal patterns in the data. In supervised learning, a group of samples are identified as belonging to one subtype or another, and this information is then used to help define gene sets that discriminate between subtypes. Once defined, the discriminating sets are tested for their ability to classify samples, where the subtype is not revealed to the algorithm. For example, an investigator may wish to use gene expression data to classify leukemia samples into their known subtypes.

Unsupervised methods, such as unsupervised hierarchical clustering, are useful for exploring data sets to find the unexpected, or when additional information is not available about samples. Other common unsupervised methods include k-means clustering, self-organizing maps, and principle component analysis. Although unsupervised methods may seem to be less biased than supervised techniques, the ability to identify useful molecular classes may be enhanced if all of the available information is used. To provide robust and reliable conclusions, training and test sets should be largely independent.

The goal of clustering is to organize microarray data so that the underlying structures can be recognized and explored. Many papers have shown that clusters based on gene expression data are enriched for genes known to be involved in similar biological processes, implying that genes of unknown function may be involved in those same processes (Eisen et al. 1998; Tavazoie et al. 1999). Another major use of clustering is to group biological samples, with the goal of identifying distinct subsets. Good examples of this type of analysis are classification of tumor samples (Alizadeh et al. 2000; Perou et al. 2000) and transcriptional changes that accompany specific genomic mutations (Hughes et al. 2000). Both supervised and unsupervised approaches can be used for clustering data.

Four aspects of clustering gene expression data are presented here: (1) microarray data structure, (2) the Cluster and Tree View software packages, (3) types of clustering and mathematical principles, and (4) adjusting and filtering data.

OVERVIEW OF MICROARRAY DATA STRUCTURE

Expression Space

Just as an object's position in three-dimensional space can be expressed as *x-y-z* coordinates, a *vector* for a gene can be expressed as coordinates, based on expression values that provide a position for the gene in *expression space*. For example, imagine an experiment using three arrays. Each array feature would have three log ratios, one from each array. One could easily represent a gene in three-dimensional space by plotting the expression value of the gene from the first array on the *x* axis, the value from the second array on the *y* axis, and the value from the third array on the *z* axis. This would result in a vector in three-dimensional space to represent the gene's overall expression pattern. Along the same lines, an experiment with *n* arrays would have its gene expression vectors plotted in *n* dimensions. This space is referred to as expression space. Genes with similar expression patterns would have similar vectors in expression space. *Samples* can also be represented as vectors, with a dimension for every feature on the array. Samples with a similar origin (such as tissues or cell lines of similar origin) would be expected to show similar gene expression patterns, and their vectors would refer to points in *n*-dimensional space that are relatively close.

Clustering is a broad term that can be applied to many methods for organizing a data set on the basis of underlying similarities. There are many different types of clustering. Commonly used techniques include hierarchical, *k*-means clustering, and self-organizing maps. These share many features, particularly the *distance metric* that measures the relationship between samples or genes in expression space. A distance metric is a method for calculating the "distance" between genes in expression space. The output from different clustering algorithms usually depends more on the type of distance metric used than on any other factor. The nature of different distance metrics is explored in detail below.

Gene Expression Maps

Given the huge volume of data in a typical microarray experiment, it is necessary to achieve a compact display of the output in order to readily visualize the implications of the data. Gene expression maps have many names in the literature, but their fundamentals were described by Eisen et al. (1998). These maps typically represent the data as an image where each gene is a row and each experiment is a column (Figure 7-39). Gene expression ratios are displayed by assigning progressively brighter shades of color to log ratios that increasingly deviate from zero. One useful convention is to color increasing gene expression red and decreasing gene expression green (a modified heat map), although a scheme of blue (decreasing) and yellow (increasing) is also common.

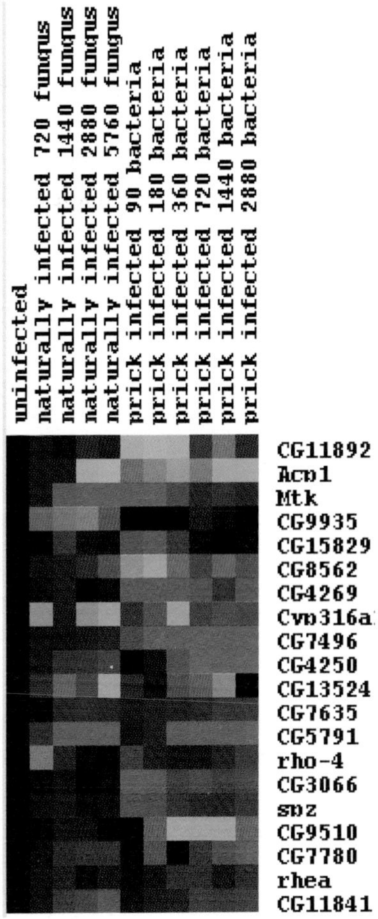

FIGURE 7-39. A gene expression map. The expression of 22 genes measured under 11 experimental conditions are represented. Descriptions of each experiment appear above each column, whereas gene identifiers (either *Drosophila* CGs or gene names) appear to the right of each row. (*Red*) Increased expression compared to the uninfected sample; (*green*) decreased expression. The intensity of the color corresponds to the magnitude of the change with brighter colors showing larger differences from the uninfected sample.

CLUSTERING AND VISUALIZATION TOOLS

Two of the original software applications for analyzing microarray data (Cluster and Tree View) were written by Dr. Michael B. Eisen. Both tools are available from Eisen's Web Site (http://rana.lbl.gov) and run under the Windows NT/2000/XP operating systems after a straightforward installation process. Several other freely available software packages with different capabilities can be obtained but are not reviewed here.

A small subset (400 genes) of the gene expression data from De Gregorio et al. (2001) is used to illustrate techniques involved in clustering microarray data. The data were obtained by infecting *Drosophila* with either fungal or bacterial pathogens and assaying gene expression on a microarray and can be retrieved on-line from http://www.fruitfly.org/expression/ immunity. All comparisons in the Web Site table are made to the uninfected (time zero) sample.

Cluster

Cluster is a Windows-based application for clustering microarray-based data. It has the ability to load, filter, and process microarray data so that it can be hierarchically clustered and *k*-means clustered and used to generate self-organizing maps (SOMs), and to perform princi-

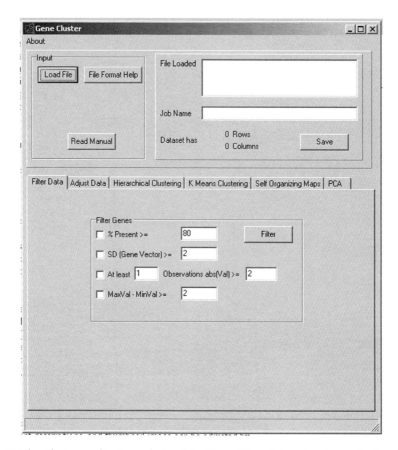

FIGURE 7-40. The Cluster application. Cluster (http://rana.lbl.gov/) is a simple application for organizing gene expression data. The "load file" button allows the user to choose a data file, and the "save" button, the current data set to a file, including modifications that have been performed in Cluster. Six tabs organize the analysis functions of Cluster: Filter Data (shown), Adjust Data, Hierarchical Clustering, K Means Clustering, Self Organizing Maps, and PCA. The text discusses the first three, and the remainder are documented in the Cluster manual.

pal component analysis (PCA). All of these functions are controlled by menu, which is accessible from the main window (shown in Figure 7-40). Cluster has an excellent manual (available at http://rana.lbl.gov/manuals/ClusterTreeView.pdf) that explains how its various options may be applied. Many relevant features are also described below in Type of Clustering and Data Issues.

Tree View

At this time, the documentation for Tree View is less developed than that for Cluster, and its features are therefore described in more detail here. Primarily, Tree View is a visualization package for microarray data that plots gene expression maps, produces exportable figures, and provides connectivity to external databases of genomic information.

Tree View has two main components: the thumbnail view and the zoomed view, each of which shows a gene expression map (Figure 7-41). In addition, the zoomed view shows gene and experiment descriptions, whereas the thumbnail view shows a *dendrogram*. A dendrogram is a tree structure that associates individual nodes, where the length of the individual branchpoints indicates the degree of similarity between two nodes. Dendrograms have been used extensively to display phylogenetic relationships. The thumbnail view in Tree View is a useful

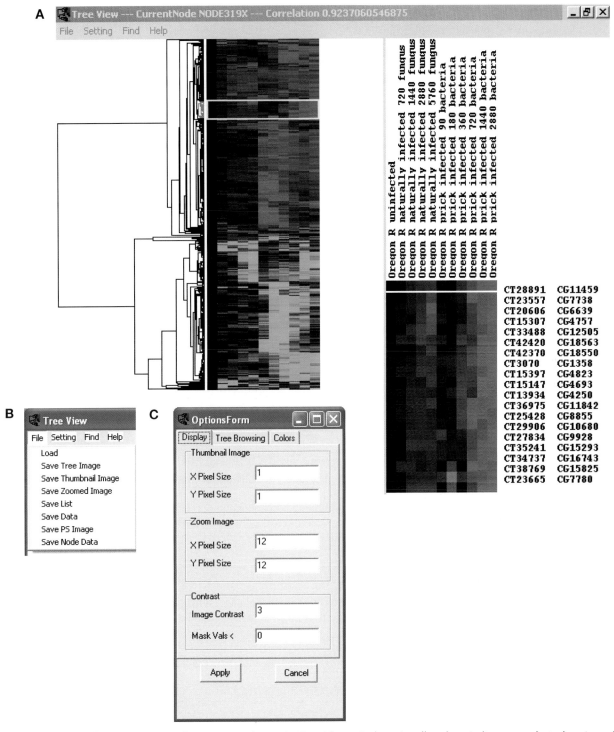

FIGURE 7-41. The Tree View application. (*A*) The main Tree View window. A yellow box indicates a selected region of the thumbnail, and the corresponding section of the tree (when available) is highlighted in purple. The left side of the screen shows the thumbnail view of the data currently loaded, and the right-hand side shows the zoomed image of the data currently selected. The divider between the two views is resizable, as is the areas allocated for the tree display, gene descriptions, and experiment descriptions. (*B*) The File Tree View menu. "Load" allows the user to select a data set (.cdt or .txt). The other options are for saving either PostScript (.ps) or Windows Bitmaps (.bmp) of trees, thumbnails, or zoomed images. (*C*) Settings menu. Options opens a panel that allows the user to change the display properties: column and row sizes for the zoomed and thumbnail images, as well as the contrast (the value at which the brightest color is used; e.g., a value of 2 with a palate of *red/green* would make any measurement with a log ratio greater than 2 the brightest red, whereas log ratios less than -2 would be the brightest green). The Colors panel allows the palate to be adjusted from the default *red/green* to the users choice.

tool for exploring the structure of gene expression clusters. Because the dendrogram is clickable, the user can select individual branches, which are then displayed in the zoomed view.

Tree View can open two types of files, namely, plain text files and clustered data files, which are identified by the suffixes .txt and .cdt, respectively. The file structures are well-documented in the manual for Cluster. In brief, Tree View expects the first two columns to be gene descriptors (a unique identifier and a descriptive string) and the first row to be experiment descriptors. Several other rows and columns are added by Cluster, the purpose of which is explained in the relevant documentation. Provided array tree (.atr) files and gene tree (.gtr) are in the same directory as the .cdt file, Tree View will generate tree structures for experiments and genes. If a regular text file is used, no trees are drawn, but all other functions are available.

Several general control mechanisms exist in Tree View. Clicking and dragging the border between panels can adjust the width of the tree, gene descriptions, experiment descriptions, or thumbnail image. However, if part of the display is too big or too small, resizing may not work properly in the current implementation of the program (Version 1.5, April 2000). The Options form in the Settings menu allows the user to adjust the image size, color intensity, and color scale. Finally, individual genes in a cluster can be easily identified by using the "Find" command to search for a particular word in the gene descriptions.

One of the most useful features of Tree View is its ability to allow easy access to external Web-enabled databases. When the application is started, it searches in the directory where it is installed for a file named URLstrings.txt. This file contains a set of canonical URLs for various data types. By default, it provides association from yeast ORF designators to the Stanford Genome Database, from mouse RIKEN clones to the RIKEN database, and image and general accession numbers to the Stanford SOURCE pages. To achieve this, the first column of the .cdt file must be designated with a string that is a starting entry in the URLstrings.txt file, and the remainder of the line should contain an "=" followed by the URL. The unique ID should be inserted at the point where the database would expect its query. Two examples that are defaults for Tree View are shown below:

YORF=http://genome-www.stanford.edu/cgi-bin/dbrun/SacchDB?find+Locus+%22UNIQID%22
MCLID=http://genome.rtc.riken.go.jp/cgi-bin/getseq?g+R+UNIQID

YORF designates a Yeast Open Reading Frame with an association to the *Saccharomyces* Genome Database (SGD). The second example is for a RIKEN clone. The UNIQID term in these examples will be replaced when the gene is clicked with the string present in the column designated YORF in the .cdt file for that gene. For example, if a yeast gene *SST2* whose YORF is YLR452C was selected, the query would be replaced with:

http://genome-www.stanford.edu/cgi-bin/dbrun/SacchDB?find+Locus+%22YLR452C%22

This output provides the results for *SST2* in SGD. Unfortunately, this tool is limited by the fact that databases have different syntaxes. However, performing test Web searches with different genes in a database of interest should reveal the structure of an appropriate database query for translation into the URLstrings.txt file. It is essential to make use of an identifier that the database understands (e.g., for SGD an ORF name such as YAL034W).

Tree View can output images that serve as the basis for journal-quality figures. The user saves postscript or bitmap images of their clusters using the corresponding save commands in the file menu. Saving the images as postscript and modifying them in an application such as Adobe Illustrator provides the greatest control over the quality of the images.

TYPES OF CLUSTERING

Cluster allows four types of analysis: hierarchical clustering, *k*-means clustering, self organizing maps (SOMs), and principal component analysis (PCA). Part 6 focuses on hierarchical clustering. In hierarchical clustering, a relationship between every gene (or experiment) is established whether or not biologically meaningful ones exist. In this approach, a tree is constructed where genes that show a similar pattern of expression across a range of samples are located near each other, whereas genes that have different patterns are far apart. Clustering algorithms are commonly used in biology to construct phylogenetic trees. Most clustering methods are agglomerative, i.e., trees are built from the bottom, by putting the most similar genes together first and working upward until all branches have been joined. Other hierarchical clustering tools provide for divisive clustering, where the data are continually divided into smaller groups (Alon et al. 1999). Hierarchical clustering tools are usually deterministic, i.e., they will always generate the same trees from the same input data, although it should be noted that slightly changing the input data set might create substantial differences in the output. Agglomerative hierarchical clustering is a step-wise process that begins with the calculation of all pair-wise distance relationships between genes and/or experiments. Pairs of values that are most similar are merged to form a *node* and then the process is repeated, comparing genes (or new clusters) until all clusters are joined.

Many hierarchical methods are hampered by computational limits, as data sets grow in complexity. Computing times scale with the square of the number of genes and linearly with the number of experiments. For example, if using a 1 GHz desktop computer, a small data set (~1000 genes × ~50 experiments) will take a few minutes, but a large data set (~14,000 genes × ~300 experiments) might take 2 hours, and a very large data set (~40,000 genes × ~1,000 experiments) will take ~50 hours. A final stumbling block that may be encountered is a lack of random access memory, depending on the implementation of the program, which may prevent the user from clustering a large data set.

Distance Metrics

A distance metric is a formula used to determine the similarity of the expression patterns for a pair of genes (or experiments). Although Cluster and other tools offer many distance metrics, it is generally best to use the Pearson correlation because this metric is not sensitive to the actual ratio values, only the relative magnitude of change between genes. The Pearson correlation is calculated by dividing the covariance of the two data series by the product of the standard deviation of each series (Equation 1). The uncentered Pearson correlation (Equation 2), where the mean gene expression is assumed to be zero, is useful when the reference sample is biologically related to the test samples, such as the use of a time zero reference for all other samples in a time point series.

$$r = \frac{1}{N} \sum_{i=1}^{N} \left[\frac{X_i - \bar{X}}{\sigma_x} \right] \left[\frac{Y_i - \bar{Y}}{\sigma_y} \right] \tag{1}$$

$$r = \frac{1}{N} \sum_{i=1}^{N} \left[\frac{X_i}{\sqrt{\frac{1}{N} \sum_{i=1}^{N}(X_i)^2}} \right] \left[\frac{Y_i}{\sqrt{\frac{1}{N} \sum_{i=1}^{N}(Y_i)^2}} \right] \tag{2}$$

Many other distance metrics have been used in the literature and are available in Cluster. Euclidian distance, a generalization of the Pythagorean theorem, is equal to the square root of the sum of the squares of the difference between each of the coordinates of a pair of genes (Equation 3).

$$\text{Distance} = \sqrt{(\sum_{i=1}^{N})(X_i - Y_i)^2} \tag{3}$$

The Spearman rank correlation (*rho*) and Kendall's *tau* ignore the actual gene expression values, but instead use their ranked order to determine the similarity. Several other metrics have been proposed and used for analyzing microarray data. One example, from Heyer et al. (1999), is the "jackknife correlation" which removes extreme values that are likely to represent errors. At this time, the jackknife correlation is not available in Cluster, although it may be included in a future version.

Another variable under the user's control is linkage, which is a set of rules describing how nodes are to be joined. *Average linkage clustering*, an option within Cluster, is recommended because it is the least sensitive to noise.

Figure 7-42 shows four "genes" of data measured on six "arrays" as line graphs, and Table 7-8 shows the similarity scores for each pair of series based on each of the correlation metrics described above. For the first three distance metrics in the table (Centered Pearson, Uncentered Pearson, and Spearman's rank), all values will lie between −1 and 1 (large values indicating stronger similarity), whereas for the Euclidian, distance values range from zero to infinity (smaller values indicating stronger similarity). Several very large differences can be observed in this data set, particularly between the centered and uncentered Pearson correlation where "genes" A and B go from perfect correlation to modest negative correlation. This is an excellent example of centering in calculating correlations. If these data were a time course compared to time zero, A and B would not be considered similar, but if these were cancers compared to a biologically unrelated sample, then the behavior of these genes would probably be considered similar.

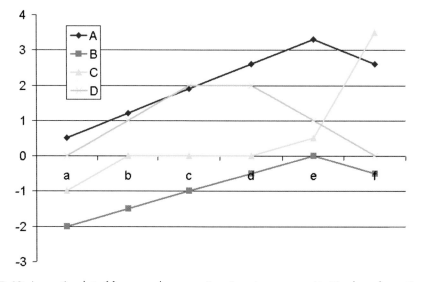

FIGURE 7-42. Log ratio plot of four sample genes. Four imaginary genes (A–D) whose log ratio expression in six experimental conditions (a–f) are plotted as a line graph. Note that the shape of curves for genes A and B are similar and that these are correlated when a centered Pearson correlation value is calculated but not when an uncentred metric is used (please see Table 7-8 and text).

TABLE 7-8. Distances for "Gene" Pairs by Different Metrics

	Centered Pearson[a]	Uncentered Pearson[a]	Spearman's rank[a]	Euclidian[b]
AB	1.00	−0.48	1.00	7.22
AC	0.53	0.51	0.75	4.77
AD	0.30	0.78	0.30	3.57
BC	0.53	0.02	0.75	4.56
BD	0.30	−0.44	0.30	5.17
CD	−0.36	0.04	−0.22	4.74

[a]Higher numbers indicate closer gene pairs (scale is −1 to 1).
[b]Lower numbers indicate closer gene pairs (scale is 0 to ∞).

DATA ISSUES

Ratios

Glass slide microarrays are typically used to measure the relative abundances of RNA in two samples by competitive hybridization of labeled cDNA to a single microarray. The standard output from such an experiment is a ratio of the signals in each channel for each element on the microarray. The fact that the output is not symmetric, i.e., a twofold change has a ratio of either 2 (up-regulation) or 0.5 (down-regulation), presents a problem for analysis because most distance metrics treat a ratio change differently depending on direction. Thus, it is essential that ratio <u>data</u> be converted into a form that is not sensitive to the direction of change.

There are two common solutions to this problem: (1) Transform all of the ratios to log ratios (log base 2 is convenient, but all bases are equivalent) and (2) instead of calculating the ratio of the two values, calculate the fold change compared to a baseline condition, expressed as (I1 − I2)/(smaller of I1 or I2), where I1 is the intensity of the first measurement and I2 is the intensity of the second measurement.

The main difference between expressing the data as log ratios compared with fold change is that high values are compressed using the log ratio, but not with fold change. The log ratio compression incurs a cost of increasing the importance of smaller ratios by relatively inflating them. An advantage of the log ratio is that the distribution of log ratios in microarray experiments usually approximates a normal distribution, as a general property of most types of data is that log transformation makes them normal even if they do not begin that way. This property is not critical for clustering, although it can come into play in other types of analysis and data processing. The practical implications of using log ratios or fold change rely more on the properties of the data set than any other factor. Clusters generated with the data of log ratios or fold change are shown in Figure 7-43.

Data Centering and Normalization

In most situations, the data obtained after scanning must be transformed and normalized before they can be analyzed. Even after the data have been transformed into log ratios (or some equivalent factor), additional data processing might be needed. When the reference sample has an expression pattern that is not expected to be vastly different from the expression pattern of the test sample, the average log ratio can be assumed to be close to zero and the data for one of the samples can be adjusted by a normalization factor that brings that ratio to zero. If the data set was created by using a biologically unrelated reference that has a

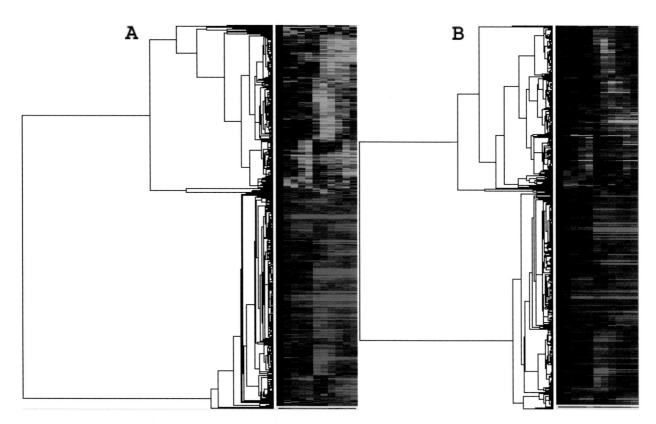

FIGURE 7-43. Comparison of log ratio and fold change. Immune response data are hierarchically clustered with the data in log ratio form (*A*) and that of fold change form (*B*). The color intensity of cell (each rectangle in the map) is proportional to its value. Note that far fewer cells have the maximum intensity when plotted by fold change. however, there are only minor differences in the way the data are clustered. The data are divided along two main branches (repressed and induced genes), with relatively little structure beyond the root branch.

very different expression profile from that of the test samples, the average log ratio (or equivalent) for each gene across the experiment set is unlikely to be zero, and may indeed be very far from zero. If the uncentered Pearson correlation metric is used, two genes whose expression patterns are identical to each other across a range of samples, but different in the reference sample, will not cluster together if a simple log ratio of intensity is used. This problem can be solved by subtracting the average log ratio for a gene from the log ratio value for each data point for that gene ("mean centering"). In the data set used as an example here, the data are most reasonably displayed "zero centered," where the time zero log ratio value is subtracted from the log ratio for each time point. Cluster outputs, when the data are zero centered compared with mean centered for each gene, are shown in Figure 7-44, A and B, respectively. The centered Pearson correlation can also be used for this type of analysis, but so doing will cause unusual visualization patterns, in which genes that are predominantly red (above zero log ratios) will lie adjacent in the tree to genes that are green. As can be seen from Table 7-8, genes *A* and *B* have a centered Pearson correlation of 1, but an uncentered Pearson correlation of –0.48. If these genes were plotted "mean centered," they would be identical, but "uncentered," they are clearly very different. A very similar transformation using the median log ratio may also be used ("median centering"). Centering can be applied to the "experiment" axis as well.

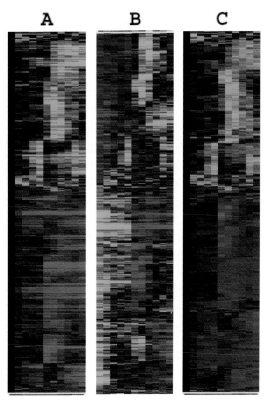

FIGURE 7-44. Centered and normalized data. Immune response log ratio data are represented when time zero-centered (*A*), mean-centered (*B*), and normalized time zero-centered (*C*). Each data series is hierarchically clustered (trees removed). The mean-centered data (*B*) have a completely different look from the time zero-centered data, although the cluster structures are reasonably similar (although far from identical). The normalized data show a similar look but intensities are more muted, allowing more variation to be visualized, whereas many of the genes in *A* show the highest values across all experiments, thereby masking their variation.

In some situations, it can be appropriate to normalize the expression of a gene. Normalization is distinct from centering because it adjusts the relative magnitude of a gene's expression vector to one, but does not alter the shape of the data. Normalization is frequently employed in self-organizing maps or *k*-means clusters to prevent genes that have large changes in expression from dominating the output patterns. Normalization of the data can also facilitate visualization of variation in gene expression for genes whose extreme values cannot be easily be displayed when the data are not normalized. Normalization in this context is setting the magnitude of a gene's expression vector to one (a unit vector), which is done by dividing the vector by its magnitude (the length of the vector). The output of the test data set following normalization and clustering is shown in Figure 7-44C.

DATA REDUNDANCY

Data sets are often generated that are partially redundant for either intentional or unforeseen reasons. Data redundancies are often a good thing, providing independent validation of results. However, partial redundancies can alter (sometimes profoundly) the results of clustering methods by exaggerating the value of some measurements. Redundancies in array feature contents might lead to unwanted biases during experiment clustering, whereas redundancies in samples might lead to biases during gene clustering. For example, if a fungal infection time series was assayed three times but a septic injury time series was assayed just once, the data would be partially redundant and potentially skewed by the more frequently assayed fungal series.

There are two approaches to addressing problems associated with data redundancy, although both require some effort to ensure that the method used is objective. Cluster has an auto-weighting feature that is designed to decrease the importance of data series that are very similar. However, this feature is not nearly as automatic as its name might imply. In reality, users must enter a correlation value, which they expect reflects the bias of the acquisition, and a power function to weight by. For a more complete explanation, please see the Cluster manual. Alternatively, the user can indicate the relative weights of genes and experiments in the data file. Typically, the information content of fully redundant data is proportional to the square root of the number of observations; thus, nine redundant experiments have the informational content of three nonredundant experiments. Each of the nine repeated experiments might thus be weighted to one third of a nonredundant experiment. Partially redundant data are more difficult to deal with because they should not be averaged, in which case it might be best to use the auto-weighting features.

Noise

Microarray data measurements can be quite prone to noise (defined as differences observed in repeated measurements of the same object). There are two main solutions to this problem, neither of which are available from within Cluster at the present time. Since empirical evidence shows that low-intensity spots are more likely to be noisy, eliminating those spots is a fairly safe option. Another option to decrease the effects of noise is to average replicated measurements. A variation of this method is to smooth data, averaging adjacent points in an experimental time series or dose response. Both experimental averaging and data smoothing can be done easily in a spreadsheet program such as Excel.

Reducing Data Complexity (Filtering Genes)

There are two main situations where it is desirable to reduce data complexity: the removal of noisy data and the elimination of "uninteresting data." As described above, Cluster relies on the data already having been filtered for individual measurements to remove noisy data. If a substantial fraction of the observations for a single gene have been filtered, it is likely that all of the measurements for that gene are unreliable or that the observed profile is not representative. Certainly, if less than half of a gene's data points are present, it is probably a good idea to remove them from the data set.

It is often advantageous to reduce the number of genes being clustered. Some of the reasons to decrease the size of the data set are poor excuses (e.g., large numbers of genes can be unwieldy and difficult to interpret), but removing genes that vary little can be justified by reasons other than convenience alone. First, invariant genes, if large in number, can negatively affect the clustering results. Second, biological signals that demonstrate small fluctuations will frequently be obscured by the random noise associated with the measurements. Cluster provides three separate parameters for including only those genes that have substantial changes: (1) a minimum standard deviation, (2) at least n measurements with a change greater than a minimum value, and (3) a minimum difference (maximum value–minimum value). It is usually best to set just one of these parameters, rather than combining them, which may be unpredictable.

SUMMARY

Hierarchical clustering and gene expression maps are now staple analytical tools in microarray analysis. By no means should one consider them to be the definitive answer. Clustering in particular should be used as a starting point, one that can be used to provoke thoughts, whereas expression maps are simply a means of visualizing the data. Users should also search for new applications that allow exploratory discovery and structured queries simultaneously. That said, however, Cluster and Tree View are staples for a reason; they are powerful tools when used in the correct setting.

Part 7: Multidimensional Scaling and Self-organizing Map

Sujatha Panavally and Yidong Chen

National Human Genome Research Institute, National Institutes of Health,
Bethesda, Maryland

MULTIDIMENSIONAL SCALING

Study of the gene expression profiles derived from a collection of experiments requires a matrix of similarity measures between all pairs of experiments. Although popular clustering algorithms, such as those described in Part 6, may be used to investigate relationships between genes and samples, other models for visual representation of such data are needed (Khan et al. 1998; Bittner et al. 2000; Hendenfalk et al. 2001). Particularly in the case of a limited collection of samples, correlation coefficients have wide confidence intervals (Dougherty 2001). The multidimensional scaling (MDS) technique is one method that can convert the structure of a similarity matrix to a simple geometrical picture. This program is publicly available at http://arrayanalysis.nih/gov. In MDS analysis, the larger the dissimilarity between two samples (evaluated through gene expression profiling), the further apart the points representing the experiments in the picture (Green and Rao 1972; Schiffman et al. 1981; Young 1987; Green et al. 1989; Borg and Groenen 1997; Cox and Cox 2000).

A gene expression data set is typically presented in a matrix form, $\mathbf{X} = \{\mathbf{x}_1, \mathbf{x}_2, ..., \mathbf{x}_M\}$, where vector $\mathbf{x}_i$ represents the ith gene expression experiment, with a total of M experiments in the data set. Each experiment consists of n gene expression levels or ratios, denoted by $\mathbf{x}_i = \{\mathbf{x}_{i1}, \mathbf{x}_{i2}, ..., \mathbf{x}_{in}\}^T$, where T denotes the matrix transposase. The matrix $\mathbf{X}$ can also be viewed in row direction, which provides profiles of genes across all samples. Samples may be ordered according to time or dosage or they may be unordered collections. Part 7 presents MDS concepts and algorithms by exploring the relationship of experimental samples.

The most commonly used similarity measure is the Pearson correlation coefficient. Given a matrix $\mathbf{X}$, a similarity matrix, $\mathbf{S} = \{s_{ij}\}$, is defined as

$$s_{ij} = \frac{\sigma_{ij}}{\sigma_i \sigma_j} = \frac{\sum_{k=1}^{n} (x_{ik} - \mu_i)(x_{jk} - \mu_j)}{\sqrt{\sum_{k=1}^{n} (x_{ik} - \mu_i)^2 \sum_{k=1}^{n} (x_{jk} - \mu_j)^2}} \tag{1}$$

where μ_i and σ_i are the mean and standard deviation, respectively, of gene expression ratios (typically log-transformed) for sample i.

Some other similarity measures, such as Spearman's correlation coefficient or normalized Euclidean distance, can also be applied here. The similarity matrix can be converted to distance matrix, $\mathbf{D} = \{d_{ij}\}$, by $\mathbf{D} = 1 - \mathbf{S}$. A typical similarity matrix is shown in Table 7-9, where the diagonal elements are all zeros, and the upper triangle region is symmetrical to the lower triangle, and each element takes value from 0 to 2. The size of the distance matrix is $M \times M$, since there are total of M samples under consideration. Therefore, by using distance matrix

TABLE 7-9. Partial Similarity Matrix, **S**, Generated from the Provided Data Sample

	UACC 383	UACC 457	UACC 3093	UACC 2534	M92 –001	A-375	UACC 502	M91 –054	UACC 1256	UACC 091
UACC383	1									
UACC457	0.60	1								
UACC3093	0.63	0.68	1							
UACC2534	0.56	0.51	0.59	1						
M92-001	0.53	0.46	0.54	0.59	1					
A-375	0.54	0.54	0.55	0.53	0.64	1				
UACC502	0.43	0.43	0.48	0.46	0.58	0.50	1			
M91-054	0.51	0.48	0.53	0.46	0.58	0.50	0.57	1		
UACC1256	0.49	0.51	0.51	0.52	0.59	0.53	0.60	0.54	1	
UACC091	0.52	0.44	0.50	0.47	0.53	0.52	0.51	0.59	0.58	1

Bittner et al. (2000). Note that the distance matrix **D** equals 1 – **S**.

D, we effectively reduce the dimension of the system from N (the total number of genes in each sample) to M, which is considerably smaller than N. The objective of multidimensional scaling is to further reduce the dimensionality of the matrix such that a graphic model is obtained with a minimum error. The challenge is to accurately represent the higher-order dimensionality of expression space in three-dimensional space. Typically, a Cartesian coordinate system is used for the graphic model, with Euclidean distance measuring the between-point distance.

To achieve the mapping of a distance matrix to a graphical model, it is necessary to find a target matrix $\hat{X} = \{\hat{x}_{ij}\}$ in one-, two-, or three-dimensional spaces. The accompanying distance matrix $\hat{D} = \{\hat{d}_{ij}\}$ is derived from Euclidean distance in p-dimensional space,

$$\hat{d}_{ij} = \sqrt{\sum_{k=1}^{p} (\hat{x}_{ik} - \hat{x}_{jk})^2} \qquad (2)$$

such that the stress T, a measure of the *goodness-of-fit*, is minimized. Here, we use the stress T defined by

$$T = \sqrt{\frac{\sum_{i=1}^{n-1}\sum_{j=i+1}^{n} (d_{ij} - \hat{d}_{ij})^2}{\sum_{k=1}^{n-1}\sum_{j=i+1}^{n} d_{ij}^2}} \qquad (3)$$

If an acceptably accurate representation, ranging from $T = 20\%$ (Poor), 5% (Good) to 2.5% (Excellent), as suggested by Everitt and Dunn (1992), can be found in three-dimensional space or less, the visualization via MDS will be an accurate and valuable way to gain an insight into the structure of data.

Implementation and Applications

The implementation of MDS follows the method proposed by Everitt and Dunn (1992). In the classical MDS setting, given the pairwise distance d_{ij} between all M experiments, the coordinates of M points in M-dimensional Euclidean space, $\mathbf{X} = (x_{ij})$, can be obtained by finding the eigenvectors of $\mathbf{B} = \mathbf{XX'}$, and the matrix elements of $\mathbf{B}$, $\{b_{ij}\}$, can be estimated by

$$b_{ij} = -(d_{ij}^2 - d_{i.}^2 - d_{.j}^2 + d_{..}^2)/2 \qquad (4)$$

where $d_{i.}$, $d_{.j}$, and d_{ij} are the results of summation of d_{ij}^2 over i, j, and both i and j, respectively. By selecting first k principal components of $\mathbf{X}$ to form a target matrix $\hat{\mathbf{X}} = \{\hat{x}_{ij}\}$, for $i = 1, ..., M$ and $j = 1, ..., k$, and then optimizing against Equation 3 via some optimization procedure (e.g., Steepest-Descend method), an MDS model is obtained. For further information on MDS, please consult the literature at the end of the section.

MATLAB is a mathematical analysis and visualization program, which the author's laboratory used to generate an implementation of MDS (Bittner et al. 2000). The Statistics Toolbox for MATLAB is required for this implementation. The current MDS program was tested for MATLAB v5.2 for a PowerPC Macintosh computer, and additional machine support is specified in a README file along with the distribution. The following packages are required for MDS:

MATLAB 5.2 (Macintosh): http://www.mathworks.com/products/matlab/

Statistics Toolbox: http://www.mathworks.com/products/statistics/

The Statistics Toolbox can be installed from the same CD as MATLAB; however, a different access code must be purchased before this option can be available in the installation process. After both packages are installed, extract the compressed MDS file into a new folder (name it "MicroarrayTools") in the MATLAB application folder. The path should therefore resemble ...Matlab5.3\MicroarrayTools\MDS\.

Now load the MATLAB application and select "add path" from the file menu. Locate the MDS folder icon and click the "Append" button. To run MDS, type mds_dialog at the prompt in the main MATLAB window. A dialog window should be seen as shown in Figure 7-45. To use the program, users must prepare the following input data:

- **Data Matrix** (choice of either Ratio Matrix or Intensity Matrix). The expression ratios (e.g., normalized ratio of mean intensity of Sample 1 to Sample 2) or intensities of each experiment are organized in columns, and each row provides expressions data for each gene. A typical data table is given in Figure 7-46.

- **Quality Matrix** (optional). The organization of this matrix is similar to that of the data matrix. However, each element of the quality matrix takes value from 0 to 1, indicating the lowest measurement quality (0) to highest measurement quality (1). The MATLAB Quality Matrix does not handle missing entries in the data matrix, and therefore it is necessary to convert missing entries into 0 in the quality matrix and set the remaining elements to 1 if the image analysis software package provides an incomplete data matrix format.

- **Color Assignment File** (optional). This is a simple text file (Figure 7-47), in which each sample is assigned to a color code to assist in viewing the data output. At the time of writing, the program is only capable of taking the colors r, g, b, c, m, y, k, and w, representing red, green, blue, cyan, magenta, yellow, black, and white, respectively.

Users may select some preprocessing steps, such as ratio rounding (all ratios greater than 50 or less than 1/50 will be rounded to 50 or 1/50, respectively) and log-transforming of the data. Several distance metrics are given as a drop-down menu, and the user can select the final view as a two-dimensional or three-dimensional graph, with or without the experiment

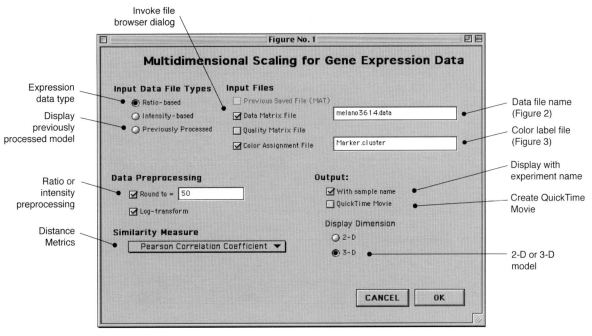

FIGURE 7-45. The dialog window.

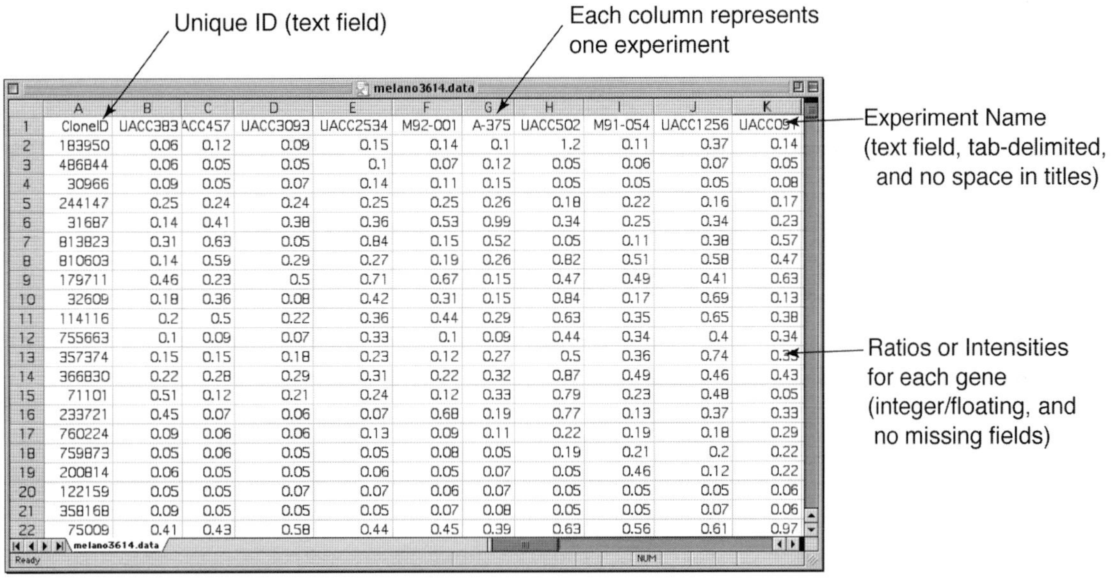

FIGURE 7-46. Data file format.

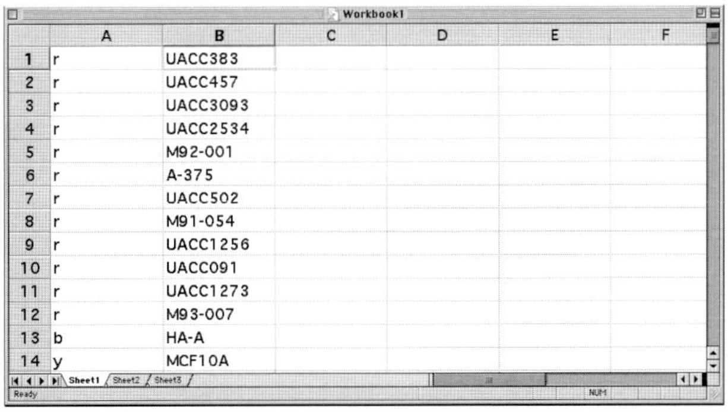

FIGURE 7-47. Color assignment format. The first column must be a color code.

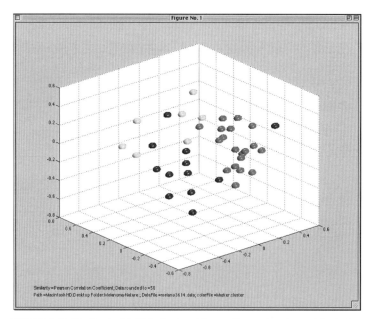

FIGURE 7-48. Typical MDS display: Three-dimensional graphical view.

names, or as a QuickTime movie. A typical MDS display is shown in Figure 7-48. The user can rotate the coordinate system by holding the mouse button down while moving the data set around.

THE SELF-ORGANIZING MAP

The self-organizing map (SOM), sometimes called a topologically ordered map or a Kohonen self-organizing feature map (Kohonen 1995; Oja and Kaski 1999), is a method closely related to multidimensional scaling. This program is publicly available at http://arrayanalysis.nih/gov. The goal is to represent all data points in the source space (the original multidimensional space spanned the gene expression profiles) by points in a target space, such that distance and proximity relationships are preserved as much as possible. The target space could be a one-dimensional line or a two-dimensional grid. SOM can also be interpreted as a special case of a neural network, which uses an unsupervised competitive learning algorithm to perform visualization and interpretation of high-dimensional data sets. The map consists of a layer of nodes or "neurons," where a multidimensional model vector consisting of features is associated with each node. The map attempts to represent all of the observations using the restricted set of nodes as models, and the nodes are ordered in such a way that similar nodes are close to each other and dissimilar nodes are far away from each other in the grid space.

An SOM is trained through competitive learning. When an input vector is presented to the network, the node in the SOM, whose underlying vector bears the closest resemblance to the input pattern, is declared the winner. The model vector that is represented by the winning neuron, as well as the model vectors of the winner's neighbors that lie within a defined radius around the winner, is changed in such a way as to make it more representative of the input pattern. The process is iterated over all available samples, and the completed map becomes representative of the space occupied by all the input vectors.

The SOM Algorithm

The fitting of model vectors is carried out by a sequential regression process. If t is the index of the samples, the input vectors described by a real vector are $\mathbf{x}(t) \in \mathbf{R}^n$, and each node in the map contains a model vector $\mathbf{m}(t) \in \mathbf{R}^n$, which is the same size as the input vector. $\mathbf{m}(t)$ may be initialized at random or in some orderly fashion, for example, along a two-dimensional subspace spanned by the two principal eigenvectors of the input data vectors. The self-organizing algorithm can be explained by the following steps, which create the ordered mapping (assuming a grid of $N_1 \times N_2$) through a competitive learning process:

1. Randomly or orderly pick an input vector $\mathbf{x}(t)$, and then compare it with all of the model vectors $\mathbf{m}_k(t)$ for $k = 1...N_1 \times N_2$. The best-matching node on the map, i.e., the node where the model vector is most similar to the input vector in some metric (e.g., Euclidean distance or Pearson correlation coefficient), is identified. This best matching node, i, is declared the *winner*.

2. The model vectors of the winner, $\mathbf{m}_i(t)$ and a number of its neighboring nodes in the target grid are updated toward the input vector according to the learning principle. The basic task in the SOM learning process is: for each sample input vector $\mathbf{x}(t)$, the winner and the nodes in its neighborhood in the target space are adjusted closer to $\mathbf{x}(t)$ in the source space (input data space). If the number of available input samples is restricted, the samples must be presented repeatedly to the SOM algorithm. Adaptation of model vectors in the learning process may take place according to the following equations:

$$\mathbf{m}_k(t + 1) = \mathbf{m}_k(t) + \alpha \left[\rho (i,k),t\right]\left[\mathbf{x}(t) - \mathbf{m}_i(t)\right] \tag{5}$$

where t is the discrete iteration index of the variables, the learn rate $\alpha (\rho, t) \in [0,1]$ is a scalar factor that defines the relative size of the learning step and depends on the iteration index t and the neighborhood function ρ. Function ρ specifies the neighborhood around the winner node i in the map grid. One may choose to have the radius of the neighborhood be fairly large at the beginning of the learning process, but shrink during learning. This ensures that a global order is obtained at the beginning, whereas toward the end, as the radius becomes smaller, the local corrections of the model vectors in the map will be more specific. It is here that the topological information is supplied. Nearby nodes receive similar updates and thus end up responding to nearby input patterns. An example of the neighborhood function may be

$$\rho(i,k) = e^{d_{i,k}^2 / (2\sigma^2)} \tag{6}$$

where $d_{i,k}^2$ is the distance between node i and k (grid), and σ is the width parameter that can gradually be decreased over time. And $\alpha(\rho, i)$ may be,

$$\alpha(\rho, i) = \rho(i,k) \, (a/[1 - bt])$$

where parameter a controls the step size and b controls the decreasing rate over the iteration index t.

SOM-based clustering algorithms utilize the mapping from target grid to source space (input data space). Input data points are assigned to the nearest (for a given distance definition) mapped target grid, thus achieving the required clustering results.

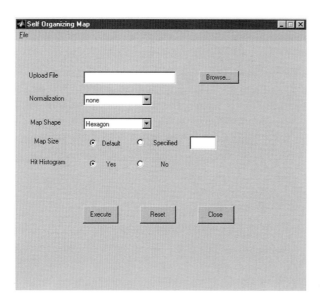

FIGURE 7-49. SOM: Graphical user interface (GUI).

Implementation

A number of gene expression profiling experiments have used SOMs to perform a clustering function (Tamayo et al. 1999; Toronen et al. 1999). A MATLAB implementation of the SOM, originally developed by the Laboratory of Computer and Information Science at the Helsinki University of Technology, has been modified by the addition of a graphical user interface (GUI) for performing the basic functions of the program. This SOM implementation is presented here, along with a data set discussed by Bittner et al. (2000). The original SOM program maintained at the Helsinki University of Technology, which can be freely downloaded along with all documentation, can be obtained from http://www.cis.hut.fi/research/ (Vesantao et al. 1999). The program has been tested for MATLAB v5.3 on a Windows NT 4.0 platform, and it is highly recommended that the system have a fast processor and a minimum of 64 Mb of RAM. Because the GUI has been developed on a Windows platform, it may function differently in other environments. To install the package, the folder (named SOM) is moved to a location of the user's choice and the MATLAB path is set to include the SOM folder. Launch the MATLAB environment, and type

>> som_launch ↵

This command brings up a GUI, which is shown in Figure 7-49. The GUI enables users to select normalization methods for their data (none, variance, and natural log) and the shape of the map lattice. Optionally, the user can specify the preferred number of map units, which influences the eventual size of the final map.

The program requires input in the form of tab delimited text, which must be formatted as shown in Figure 7-50, where the rows represent expression data for each gene and the columns represent the ratio or intensity measurement for each experiment. The first row contains only the number of experiments or the input space dimensions and is followed by a row that begins with #n and contains the labels for the experiments. Please note that the names of the genes are given as the last column, which does not have a column label associated with it.

The user can also opt to use a hit histogram, which shows the distribution of data within the map, or omit it. The results generated by the SOM are shown in Figures 7-51 and 7-52. Figure 7-51 shows the U-matrix visualization, which depicts the distances between neighboring nodes and thus the cluster structure within the map. Given that clusters are uniform

4				
#n	UACC383	UACC457	UACC3093	UACC253ᵃ
0.06	0.12	0.09	0.15	183950
0.06	0.05	0.05	0.1	486844
0.09	0.05	0.07	0.14	30966
0.25	0.24	0.24	0.25	244147
0.14	0.41	0.38	0.36	31687
0.31	0.63	0.05	0.84	813823
0.14	0.59	0.29	0.27	810603
0.46	0.23	0.5	0.71	179711
0.18	0.36	0.08	0.42	32609
0.2	0.5	0.22	0.36	114116
0.1	0.09	0.07	0.33	755663
0.15	0.15	0.18	0.23	357374
0.22	0.28	0.29	0.31	366830
0.51	0.12	0.21	0.24	71101
0.45	0.07	0.06	0.07	233721
0.09	0.06	0.06	0.13	760224

FIGURE 7-50. SOM data input: Tab-delimited text. The rows represent expression data for each gene, and the columns represent the ratio or intensity measurement for each experiment.

areas of low values, high values on the U-matrix indicate large distances between neighboring map units, and thus the borders between clusters. Figure 7-52 shows the average profile of the data points contained in each of the nodes. In addition, a list of all the gene names, along with their position (node number), is printed out in a file called som_nodes.txt in order to enable the user to identify the underlying components of each of the nodes.

If users so choose, they can learn about the extensive capabilities of the SOM package through the four demonstrations that are contained therein as som_demo1-4. More exhaustive analysis of the data can then be performed through the MATLAB command line, along with a rich collection of data analysis functions provided by the SOM ToolBox (http://www.cis.hut.fi/projects/somtoolbox/documentation/).

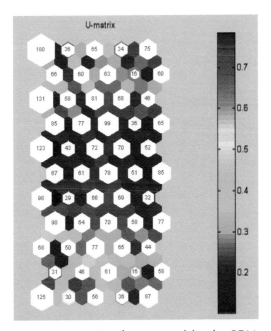

FIGURE 7-51. Results generated by the SOM: U-matrix visualization.

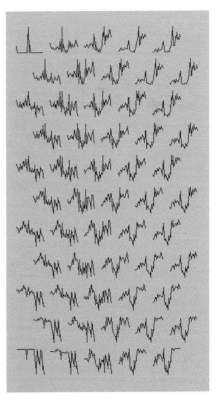

FIGURE 7-52. Results generated by the SOM: Average profile of the data points.

GENE ANNOTATION

The ability to obtain appropriate and readily understandable information about individual genes is critical to the efficient interpretation of microarray experiments. In a perfect world, every gene would have a unique identifier and complete molecular information would be available, including an annotated sequence that described promoter elements, intron/exon structure, splice variants, and related genes. Biological information associated with that gene would be readily available through links to other databases, ranging from PubMed to protein structure databases. Comprehensive annotation of the genes populating a microarray can be extremely useful in assigning potential functions to genes that are coregulated. This is especially useful when information is available about known genes that informs analyses of less well-characterized genes, particularly EST sequences (Figure 7-53).

GO Consortium

An essential part of synthesizing information from diverse sources is the use of structured, controlled vocabularies. Such vocabularies allow automated searches to filter information and draw meaningful inferences about possible associations between the data obtained in a microarray experiment and information that already exists. One attempt to address some of these issues has been made by the Gene Ontology Consortium (2001; Ashburner et al. 2000). The goal of the GO project is to produce a comprehensive controlled set of terms that can be used to describe genes in all organisms. The use of MeSH headings for the description of scientific literature via MEDLINE is a familiar example of this concept (Delozier and Lingle 1992; Lowe and Barnett 1994). The GO project began with the development of shared vocabularies for model organism databases FlyBase, the Mouse Genome Informatics (MGI) database, and the *Saccharomyces* Genome Database (SGD), and uses terms that describe:

- *Molecular Function:* The elemental tasks performed by individual gene products; examples are *calcium-activated potassium channel* and *ATP-dependent DNA helicase.*

- *Biological Process:* Broad biological goals that are accomplished by ordered assemblies of molecular functions, such as *mitosis* or *purine metabolism.*

- *Cellular Component:* Subcellular structures, locations, and macromolecular complexes; examples include *nucleus, telomere,* and *origin recognition complex.*

The GO project has expanded to include *Arabidopsis* (TAIR), *Caenorhabditis elegans* (WormBase), and *Schizosaccharomyces pombe* (PomBase). In addition, TIGR, Proteome, EBI, Compugen, and Celera have used GO to annotate bacterial and human genes. Annotations of some human genes performed by Proteome are available through LocusLink at NCBI.

A series of microarray experiments will often uncover groups of genes that have related patterns of expression. Information derived from the functional annotation of named genes within a group can suggest possible functions for members of the group for which little or no biological information exists. This is particularly valuable in ascribing potential roles to EST sequences. In addition, the observation of common biological purposes for multiple members of a coregulated group strengthens the conclusion that specific biological processes are being uncovered by microarray analysis. A good example of how annotation can pro-

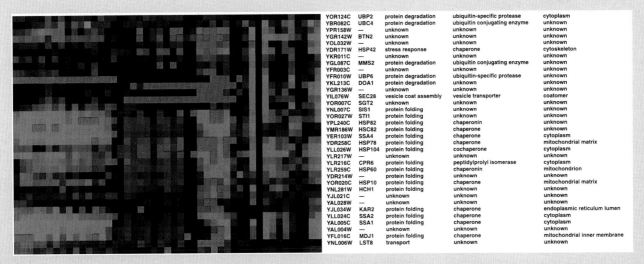

FIGURE 7-53. Output of a microarray experiment where GO descriptors provide information that helps assign potential functions to coregulated genes. (Reprinted, with permission, from Ashburner et al. 2000.)

vide information about EST sequences and also reveal unexpectedly complex responses was provided by a time-course experiment describing serum stimulation of fibroblasts (Iyer et al. 1999). Although the cells had been maintained in vitro, groups of genes were expressed that reflected complex biological responses indicative of wound healing and tissue remodeling reactions following stimulation. Many of the coregulated groups contained EST sequences that were implicated in the processes ascribed to the named members of the group.

Annotations to GO terms are generally made to the most specific term possible, but many situations exist when a more general term might provide more information about what a group of genes may have in common. For example, a gene cluster associated with terms such as *DNA damage checkpoint, cytokinesis*, and *DNA replication initiation* might be more easily interpreted if each gene were instead annotated to *mitotic cell cycle*. The GO consortium is planning to create and distribute a "GO Slim" ontology with annotations transferred to high-level terms. A more dynamic method of adjusting the specificity of GO annotations would be very advantageous for microarray research, so that the high-level terms used could be tailored to the study at hand.

Annotating cDNA Sequences

cDNA clones can be annotated several ways, using information from several sources. By far, the greatest challenge is reconciling information from multiple sources. Most laboratories identify cDNA clones by GenBank accession number or IMAGE clone ID, but this practice is not standardized. There are several files available at NCBI that show how IDs from different projects map to each other (e.g., please see the LocusLink ftp site at ftp://ncbi.nlm.nih.gov/refseq/LocusLink/).

Gene annotation updates can cause confusion when analyzing microarray data. Particularly in genomes where the precise location of all genes is not completely determined, each week may bring a new representation of the mapping between clones and their genes.

It is important to work with annotation systems that provide the most current and up-to-date information possible. Some sources of data that are kept reasonably current are listed below.

dBEST (Database of Expressed Sequence Tags): http://www.ncbi.nlm.nih.gov/dbEST/index.html

dBEST provides sequence information about ESTs from hundreds of organisms.

Swiss-Prot: http://www.expasy.ch/sprot/

Swiss-Prot provides curated protein data sets. The quality and level of detail of protein annotation are very high, and the data they produce are well-integrated with other databases. Swiss-Prot keywords are handy short annotations that can provide a quick idea of what a protein does in a cell.

GeneCards: http://bioinformatics.weizmann.ac.il/cards/ or http://genome-www.stanford.edu/genecards/

GeneCards is produced by the Weizmann Institute of Science. It provides a very concise set of information about human genes and their roles in human disease. GeneCards can be searched by keyword or by approved gene names. The information is extracted in an automated fashion from several external sources.

SOURCE: http://genome-www.stanford.edu/source

The Stanford Online Universal Resource for Clones and ESTs (SOURCE) combines information about human, mouse, and rat genes. Like GeneCards, the information is extracted in an automated fashion from several external sources. Searches can be performed using gene names or clone identifiers, and information about the clones or about their associated genes can be retrieved. SOURCE permits batch queries (simultaneous retrieval of data using many identifiers), which can be extremely convenient when analyzing a group of coexpressed genes.

UniGene: http://www.ncbi.nlm.nih.gov/UniGene/

UniGene partitions GenBank sequences (including ESTs) into nonredundant sets of gene-oriented clusters. UniGene is updated on a regular basis with the advantage of having up-to-date information, but with the disadvantage of having some very unstable relationships between clones and clusters. UniGene cluster IDs can be reassigned with every UniGene build. Tables that relate UniGene IDs to other IDs can be found at NCBI's LocusLink ftp site (ftp://ncbi.nlm.nih.gov/refseq/LocusLink/). UniGene currently builds clusters for human, rat, mouse, cow, zebrafish, frog, wheat, rice, barley, maize, and cress.

TABLE 7-10. Sources of Gene Annotation

Resource	URL	Type of Information
Unigene	www.ncbi.nlm.nih.gov/UniGene	Groups ESTs into unique gene-oriented clusters (human, mouse, rat, cow, and zebrafish).
LocusLink (Pruitt and Maglott 2001)	www.ncbi.nlm.nih.gov/LocusLink	Curated sequences and information about genes (human, fruit fly, mouse, rat, and zebrafish).
dBEST (Boguski et al. 1993)	www.ncbi.nlm.nih.gov/dbEST	Sequences of ESTs from many organisms.
GeneMap99	www.ncbi.nlm.nih.gov/genemap	Mapping information for human genes.
RHdb (Rodriguez-Tome and Lijnzaad 2001)	corba.ebi.ac.uk/RHdb	Mapping information for human, mouse, and rat.
GeneCards (Rebhan et al. 1998)	bioinformatics.weizmann.ac.il/cards	Functions of human genes and their roles in disease.
SwissProt (Bairoch and Apweiler 2000)	www.expasy.ch/sprot	Annotated protein sequences for many organisms.
SOURCE	genome-www.stanford.edu/source	Compiled information about genes and cDNAs for human, mouse, and rat.
Mouse Genome Informatics (Blake et al. 2001)	www.informatics.jax.org	Annotation of mouse genes and sequences.
FlyBase (FlyBase Consortium 1999)	flybase.bio.indiana.edu	Annotation of *Drosophila melanogaster* genes and sequences.
TAIR (Huala et al. 2001)	www.arabidopsis.org	Biological information about *Arabidopsis thaliana* genes.
WormBase (Stein et al. 2001)	www.wormbase.org	Biological information about *Caenorhabditis elegans* genes.
Saccharomyces Genome Database (Ball et al. 2001)	genome-www.stanford.edu/Saccharomyces	Annotated information about *Saccharomyces cerevisiae* genes and sequences.
Gene Ontology Consortium (Ashburner et al. 2000)	www.geneontology.org	Structured controlled vocabulary describing gene product processes, functions, and locations.
Proteome	www.proteome.com	Annotation of proteins from *S. cerevisiae*, *Schizosaccharomyces pombe*, and *C. elegans*.

SHARING MICROARRAY DATA AMONG INVESTIGATORS

Laboratories engaged in microarray research often experience data overload in the early stages of their research programs (Mills and Gordon 2001; Mills et al. 2001). As microarray technology becomes more accessible and pervasive, this problem will only get worse. If the information that is generated in thousands of labs worldwide is to be disseminated, there must be agreement on archiving formats and standards for data annotation. There are substantial incentives to improve the current situation, in which data are stored in nonstandard formats, often on dispersed Web Sites as supplementary information, with variable experimental detail provided (Becker 2001; Brazma et al. 2001).

Dissemination of microarray data is important because it allows other investigators to assess and validate the quality and analysis of the data, and enables further mining of the data beyond what might be presented in a publication. In addition, it facilitates the development of new tools for analysis by providing bodies of data that can be used for testing. By contrast to the data produced by DNA sequencing projects, certain aspects of microarray experiments create substantial problems for sharing results, both in the description of the experiment itself and in the description of the sequences present on spotted arrays (Brazma et al. 2001). From a technical standpoint, aspects of the hybridization (array manufacture and labeling approach, including amplification steps and scanner platform, among others) and the method of data analysis used (e.g., a normalization approach) greatly affect results and conclusions. Data from competitively hybridized microarrays are comparative, and relative expression levels are measured rather than absolute transcript numbers determined. This problem requires the development of common expression standards or references to facilitate the widespread comparison of data (see Section 3, Protocol 12). Alternatively, an increased focus on absolute measurement of RNA abundance, rather than comparative measures of gene expression, would allow a more robust description of the transcriptome (Velculescu et al. 1997) of specific cellular lineages and developmental stages. Finally, cellular or tissue context is all-important when measuring gene expression patterns. Variables that can have a major impact on expression patterns include the developmental stage or the physiological state of the organism from which it was removed, the site from which the tissue is taken, the growth conditions of cell lines used, and so on.

MGED

A consortium has been established to address some of the issues posed by microarray data sharing. The MGED group is an open discussion group initially established at the first Microarray Gene Expression Database meeting, held in Cambridge, England (http://www.mged.org/). The goal of the group is to facilitate the adoption of standards for DNA array experiment annotation and data representation, as well as to introduce standard experimental controls and data normalization methods. The underlying goal is to facilitate the establishment of gene expression data repositories, to create standards for the comparability of gene expression data from different sources, and to enable interoperability of different gene expression databases and data analysis software. MGED is composed of investigators and developers from many academic and private institutions (e.g., EBI, TIGR, Rosetta, Stanford, and Harvard).

Two parallel, but complementary, projects within MGED are focusing on the content, format, and exchange of stored microarray data. The first is MIAME, a project to define the

Minimal Information About a Microarray Experiment (Brazma et al. 2001). The second project is MAGEML (MicroArray Gene Expression Markup Language), whose goal is to define a structure for reporting microarray information that will allow communication and computation of the data and its associated annotation. The markup language is being defined by a large, collaborative group and uses XML.

MIAME

MIAME 1.0 was approved at the MGED 3 meeting at Stanford University in March 2001 (Kellam 2001). The document (http://www.mged.org/Annotations-wg/index.html) seeks to capture all the information required to interpret and reproduce the results (Brazma et al. 2001). A challenge is designating a mandatory set of information that captures the essential features of an experiment without placing an unnecessary burden on users. Although MIAME does not specify format, a key goal is to structure the information in such a way as to enable useful querying as well as automated data analysis and mining. This requires the use of controlled vocabularies rather than free-format text. The MIAME standards describe experimental annotations that fall into six categories:

- ***Experimental design: Description of the set of hybridizations as a whole.*** The MIAME specifications allow a group of related microarray results to be grouped together and described as a unit. The type of experiment can be described (e.g., a time series or comparison of diseased tissue with healthy tissue) and the relationships of one array to another can be detailed.

- ***Array design.*** In addition to information about the sequences spotted on the arrays, the intent of this category is to record details about the platform of the microarray and production protocols. Recording this type of information is discussed in Part 5, dealing with LIM systems and modeling of sequences.

- ***Samples.*** The description of the samples used for hybridization should include topics such as the primary source of the biological sample, the organism from which it was derived, and the protocols used for its preparation and labeling.

- ***Hybridization.*** The hybridization section of MIAME describes the standard technical parameters of the hybridization reaction such as concentration of buffer, temperature, and concentration.

- ***Measurements.*** Data from scans of each hybridization should include the hardware and software used to generate the results, as well as a complete set of results and information about replicates.

- ***Normalization and controls.*** Strategies and algorithms for normalizing data should be described. In addition, the locations of any control spots on the array are recorded in this section.

One of the most difficult issues addressed by the MGED group was whether raw image data should be stored. Storage of the raw image files retains maximum information, allowing the use of different normalization, image extraction, and quality metrics to be used subsequently. As reviewed recently by Geschwind (2001) and summarized in Table 7-11, a number of options exist for storing the output from a microarray experiment. The interim recommendation is to store the raw data files; however, the very large size of these files have practical implications for long-term storage capacity. At this time, no software integrates

TABLE 7-11. Sharing Paradigm Advantages and Disadvantages

	Raw image	Raw spot and background data	Normalized, processed data (ratio)	Gene list
Advantages				
Overall flexibility	+++	++	+	
Least biased	+++	++	+	
Allows re-analysis	+++	++	+	
Comparison of analytical methods	+++	++	++	
Image segmentation	+++			
Image analysis	+++			
Statistical flexibility	+++	+++	++	
Data mining flexibility	+++	+++	++	
Easy to use (least analytical demands)		+	++	+++
Disadvantages				
Requires large storage	+++	+		
Requires image analysis time and software	+++			
Requires data analysis time	+++	++	+	
Potential cross-platform incompatibility	+++	+		
Bias due to normalization			+++	+++
Not usable for some statistical methods			++	+++
Less useful for re-analysis of data			+/−	+++
Less useful for combining of data sets			+	++
Not quantitative				+++

Reprinted, with permission, from Geschwind (2001 [©Macmillan Magazines Ltd.]).

MIAME, although this is likely to change rapidly as MIAME, or a variant of it, becomes accepted by the research community. As structured recording of microarray data becomes the norm, the submission of this information will no doubt become a requirement of journals and funding agencies.

Public Databases for Deposition and Retrieval

Several databases are being developed for large-scale public storage and querying of microarray data, including the Gene Expression Omnibus (GEO, http://www.ncbi.nlm.nih.gov/geo/), ArrayExpress (http://www.ebi.ac.uk/arrayexpress/), the Gene Expression Database (GXD, http://www.informatics.jax.org/mgihome/GXD/aboutGXD.shtml), and GeneX (http://www.ncgr.org/genex) (Brazma and Vilo 2000; Brazma et al. 2000; Gardiner-Garden and Littlejohn 2001). It is envisaged that GEO and ArrayExpress will store information from diverse sources. GXD, which is based at the Jackson Laboratories, is focused on expression data obtained from *Mus musculus*. At the time of writing, all databases were at an early stage of development and acceptance of data. The features of these databases are surveyed in a review by Gardiner-Garden and Littlejohn (2001).

REFERENCES

Adams R. and Bischof L. 1994. Seeded region growing. *IEEE Trans. Pattern Anal. Machine Intell.* **16:** 641–647.

Alizadeh A.A., Ross D.T., Perou C.M., and van de Rijn M. 2001. Towards a novel classification of human malignancies based on gene expression patterns. *J. Pathol.* **195:** 41–52.

Alizadeh A.A., Eisen M.B., Davis R.E., Ma C., Lossos I.S., Rosenwald A., Boldrick J.C., Sabet H., Tran T., Yu X., Powell J.I., Yang L., Marti G.E., Moore T., Hudson Jr., J., Lu L., Lewis D.B., Tibshirani R., Sherlock G., Chan W.C., Greiner T.C., Weisenburger D.D., Armitage J.O., Warnke R., Staudt L.M., et al. 2000. Distinct types of diffuse large B-cell lymphoma identified by gene expression profiling. *Nature* **403:** 503–511.

Alon U., Barkai N., Notterman D.A., Gish K., Ybarra S., Mack D., and Levine A.J. 1999. Broad patterns of gene expression revealed by clustering analysis of tumor and normal colon tissues probed by oligonucleotide arrays. *Proc. Natl. Acad. Sci.* **96:** 6745–6750.

Alter O., Brown P.O., and Botstein D. 2000. Singular value decomposition for genome-wide expression data processing and modeling. *Proc. Natl. Acad. Sci.* **97:** 10101–10106.

Ashburner M., Ball C.A., Blake J.A., Botstein D., Butler H., Cherry J.M., Davis A.P., Dolinski K., Dwight S.S., Eppig J.T., Harris M.A., Hill D.P., Issel-Tarver L., Kasarskis A., Lewis S., Matese J.C., Richardson J.E., Ringwald M., Rubin G.M., and Sherlock G. 2000. Gene ontology: Tool for the unification of biology. The Gene Ontology Consortium, *Nat. Genet.* **25:** 25–29.

Bairoch A. and Apweiler R. 2000. The SWISS-PROT protein sequence database and its supplement TrEMBL in 2000. *Nucleic Acids Res.* **28:** 45–48.

Ball C.A., Jin H., Sherlock G., Weng S., Matese J.C., Andrada R., Binkley G., Dolinski K., Dwight S.S., Harris M.A., Issel-Tarver L., Schroeder M., Botstein D., and Cherry J.M. 2001. *Saccharomyces* Genome Database provides tools to survey gene expression and functional analysis data. *Nucleic Acids Res.* **29:** 80–81.

Becker K.G. 2001. The sharing of cDNA microarray data. *Nat. Rev. Neurosci.* **2:** 438–440.

Beucher S. and Meyer F. 1993. The morphological approach to segmentation: The watershed transformation. In *Mathematical morphology in image processing: Optical engineering* (ed. E. Dougherty), vol. 34, pp. 433–481. Marcel Dekker, New York.

Bittner M., Meltzer P., Chen Y., Jiang Y., Sefton E., Hendrix M., Radmacher M., Simon R., Yakhini Z., Ben-Dor A., Sampas N., Dougherty E., Wang E., Marincola F., Gooden C., Leuders J., Gatfelter A., Pollock P., Carpten J., Gillanders E., Leja D., Dietrich K., Beaudry C., Berens M., Alberts D., and Sondak V. 2000. Molecular classification of cutaneous malignant melanoma by gene expression profiling. *Nature* **406:** 536–540.

Blake J.A., Eppig J.T., Richardson J.E., Bult C.J., and Kadin J.A. 2001. The Mouse Genome Database (MGD): Integration nexus for the laboratory mouse. *Nucleic Acids Res.* **29:** 91–94.

Boguski M.S., Lowe T.M., and Tolstoshev C.M. 1993. dbEST-database for "expressed sequence tags." *Nat. Genet.* **4:** 332–333.

Borg I. and Groenen P. 1997. *Modern multidimensional scaling: Theory and applications.* Springer, New York.

Box G.E.P., Hunter W.G., and Hunter J.S. 1978. *Statistics for experimenters: An introduction to design, data analysis, and model building.* Wiley, New York.

Brazma A. and Vilo J. 2000. Gene expression data analysis. *FEBS Lett.* **480:** 17–24.

Brazma A., Robinson A., Cameron G., and Ashburner M. 2000. One-stop shop for microarray data. *Nature* **403:** 699–700.

Brazma A., Hingamp P., Quackenbush J., Sherlock G., Spellman P., Stoeckert C., Aach J., Ansorge W., Ball C.A., Causton H.C., Gaasterland T., Glenisson P., Holstege F.C., Kim I.F., Markowitz V., Matese J.C., Parkinson H., Robinson A., Sarkans U., Schulze-Kremer S., Stewart J., Taylor R., Vilo J., and Vingron M. 2001. Minimum information about a microarray experiment (MIAME)—Toward standards for microarray data. *Nat. Genet.* **29:** 365–371.

Brown M.P., Grundy W.N., Lin D., Cristianini N., Sugnet C.W., Furey T.S., Ares Jr., M., and Haussler D. 2000. Knowledge-based analysis of microarray gene expression data by using support vector machines, *Proc. Natl. Acad. Sci.* **97:** 262–267.

Buhler J., Ideker T., and Haynor D. 2000. Dapple: Improved techniques for finding spots on DNA microarrays. University of Washington, Tech. Rep. UW-CSE-00-08-05 (http://bio.cs.washington.edu/online.html).

Callow M.J., Dudoit S., Gong E.L., Speed T.P., and Rubin E.M. 2000. Microarray expression profiling identifies genes with altered expression in HDL-deficient mice. *Genome Res.* **10:** 2022–2029.

Chen Y., Dougherty E.R., and Bittner M.L. 1997. Ratio-based decisions and the quantitative analysis of cDNA microarray images. *J. Biomed. Optics* **2:** 364–374.

Cleveland W.S. 1979. Robust locally weighted regression and smoothing scatterplots. *J. Am. Stat. Assoc.* **74:** 829–836.

Cox T.F. and Cox M.A.A. 2000. *Multidimensional scaling,* 2nd edition. CRC Press, Boca Raton, Florida.

De Gregorio E., Spellman P.T., Rubin G.M., and Lemaitre B. 2001. Genome-wide analysis of the *Drosophila* immune response by using oligonucleotide microarrays. *Proc. Natl. Acad. Sci.* **98:** 12590–12595.

Delozier E.P. and Lingle V.A. 1992. MEDLINE and MeSH: Challenges for end users. *Med. Ref. Serv. Q.* **11:** 29–46.

DeRisi J.L., Iyer V.R., and Brown P.O. 1997. Exploring the metabolic and genetic control of gene expression on a genomic scale. *Science* **278:** 680–686.

Dhanasekaran S.M., Barrette T.R., Ghosh D., Shah R., Varambally S., Kurachi K., Pienta K.J., Rubin M.A., and Chinnaiyan A.M. 2001. Delineation of prognostic biomarkers in prostate cancer. *Nature* **412:** 822–826.

Dougherty E.R. 2001. Small sample issues for microarray-based classification. *Comp. Funct. Genomics* **2:** 28–34.

Dudoit S., Yang Y.H., Callow M.J., and Speed T.P. 2002. Statistical methods for identifying genes with differential expression in replicated cDNA microarray experiments. *Statistical Sinica* **12:** 111–139.

Eisen M.B. and Brown P.O. 1999. DNA arrays for analysis of gene expression. *Methods Enzymol.* **303:** 179–205.

Eisen M.B., Spellman P.T., Brown P.O., and Botstein D. 1998. Cluster analysis and display of genome-wide expression patterns. *Proc. Natl. Acad. Sci.* **95:** 14863–14868.

Everitt B.S. and Dunn G. 1992. *Applied multivariate data analysis.* Oxford University Press, New York.

Finkelstein D.B., Gollub J., Ewing R., Sterky F., Somerville S., and Cherry J.M. 2000. Iterative linear regression by sector: Renormalization of cDNA microarray data and cluster analysis weighted by cross homology. CAMDA'00 (Critical Assessment of Microarray Data Analysis Techniques), Duke Bioinformatics Shared Resource (http://bioinformatics.duke.edu/CAMDA/CAMDA00/Abstracts).

Fisher R.A. 1926. The arrangement of field experiments. *J. Min. Agric. Gr. Br.* **33:** 505–513.

FlyBase Consortium. 1999. The FlyBase database of the *Drosophila* genome projects and community literature. *Nucleic Acids Res.* **27:** 85–88.

Freedman D., Pisani R., and Purves R. 1998. *Statistics*, 3rd edition. Norton, New York.

Gardiner-Garden M. and Littlejohn T.G. 2001. A comparison of microarray databases. *Brief Bioinform.* **2:** 143–158.

Gasch A.P., Spellman P.T., Kao C.M., Carmel-Harel O., Eisen M.B., Storz G., Botstein D., and Brown P.O. 2000. Genomic expression programs in the response of yeast cells to environmental changes. *Mol. Biol. Cell* **11:** 4241–4257.

The Gene Ontology Consortium. 2001. Creating the gene ontology resource: Design and implementation. *Genome Res.* **11:** 1425–1433.

Geschwind D.H. 2001. Sharing gene expression data: An array of options. *Nat. Rev. Neurosci.* **2:** 435–438.

Glonek G.F.V. and Solomon P.J. 2002. Factorial designs for microarray experiments. Technical Report, Department of Applied Mathematics, University of Adelaide.

Golub T.R., Slonim D.K., Tamayo P., Huard C., Gaasenbeek M., Mesirov J.P., Coller H., Loh M.L., Downing J.R., Caligiuri M.A., et al. 1999. Molecular classification of cancer: Class discovery and class prediction by gene expression monitoring, *Science* **286:** 531–537.

Green P.E. and Rao V.R. 1972. *Applied multidimensional scaling.* Dryden Press, Hinsdale, Illinois.

Green P.E., Carmone F.J., and Smith S.M. 1989. *Multidimensional scaling: Concepts and applications.* Allyn and Bacon, Needham Heights, Massachusetts.

Hedenfalk I., Duggan D., Chen Y., Radmacher M., Bittner M., Simon R., Meltzer P., Gusterson B., Esteller M., Kallioniemi O.P., Wilfond B., Borg A., and Trent J. 2001. Gene-expression profiles in hereditary breast cancer. *N. Engl. J. Med.* **344:** 539–548.

Heyer L.J., Kruglyak S., and Yooseph S. 1999 Exploring expression data: Identification and analysis of coexpressed genes. *Genome Res.* **9:** 1106–1115.

Huala E., Dickerman A.W., Garcia-Hernandez M., Weems D., Reiser L., LaFond F., Hanley D., Kiphart D., Zhuang M., Huang W., Mueller L.A., Bhattacharyya D., Bhaya D., Sobral B.W., Beavis W., Meinke D.W., Town C.D., Somerville C., and Rhee S.Y. 2001. The *Arabidopsis* Information Resource (TAIR): A comprehensive database and web-based information retrieval, analysis, and visualization system for a model plant. *Nucleic Acids Res.* **29:** 102–105.

Hughes J.D., Estep P.W., Tavazoie S., and Church G.M. 2000. Computational identification of *cis*-regulatory elements associated with groups of functionally related genes in *Saccharomyces cerevisiae. J. Mol. Biol.* **296:** 1205–1214.

Ihaka R. and Gentleman R. 1996. R: A language for data analysis and graphics. *J. Comput. Graph. Stat.* **5:** 299–314.

Iyer V.R., Eisen M.B., Ross D.T., Schuler G., Moore T., Lee J.C., Trent J.M., Staudt L.M., Hudson Jr., J., Boguski M.S., Lashkari D., Shalon D., Botstein D., and Brown P.O. 1999. The transcriptional program in the response of human fibroblasts to serum. *Science* **283:** 83–87.

Kellam P. 2001. Microarray gene expression database: Progress towards an international repository of gene expression data. *Genome Biol.* **2**: 4011.1–4011.3.

Kepler T.B., Crosby L., and Morgan K.T. 2000. Normalization and analysis of DNA microarray data by self-consistency and local regression. Santa Fe Institute (http://www.santafe.edu/sfi/publications/Abstracts/00-09-55abs.html).

Kerr M.K. and Churchill G.A. 2001a. Experimental design for gene expression microarrays. *Biostatistics* **2**: 183–201.

———. 2001b. Statistical design and the analysis of gene expression microarray data. *Genet. Res.* **77**: 123–128.

Kerr M.K., Martin M., and Churchill G.A. 2000. Analysis of variance for gene expression microarray data. *J. Computat. Biol.* **7**: 819–837.

Khan J., Simon R., Bittner M., Chen Y., Leighton S.B., Pohida T., Smith P.D., Jiang Y., Gooden G.C., Trent J.M., and Meltzer P.S. 1998. Gene expression profiling of alveolar rhabdomyosarcoma with cDNA microarrays. *Cancer Res.* **58**: 5009–5013.

Khan J., Wei J.S., Ringner M., Saal L.H., Ladanyi M., Westermann F., Berthold F., Schwab M., Antonescu C.R., Peterson C., and Meltzer P.S. 2001. Classification and diagnostic prediction of cancers using gene expression profiling and artificial neural networks. *Nat. Med.* **7**: 673–679.

Kihara C., Tsunoda T., Tanaka T., Yamana H., Furukawa Y., Ono K., Kitahara O., Zembutsu H., Yanagawa R., Hirata K., Takagi T., and Nakamura Y. 2001. Prediction of sensitivity of esophageal tumors to adjuvant chemotherapy by cDNA microarray analysis of gene-expression profiles. *Cancer Res.* **61**: 6474–6479.

Kohonen T. 1995. *Self-organizing maps.* Springer, Berlin, Heidelberg.

Lashkari D.A., DeRisi J.L., McCusker J.H., Namath A.F., Gentile C., Hwang S.Y., Brown P.O., and Davis R.W. 1997. Yeast microarrays for genome wide parallel genetic and gene expression analysis. *Proc. Natl. Acad. Sci.* **94**: 13057–13062.

Lee M.L., Kuo F.C., Whitmore G.A., and Sklar J. 2000. Importance of replication in microarray gene expression studies: Statistical methods and evidence from repetitive cDNA hybridizations. *Proc. Natl. Acad. Sci.* **97**: 9834–9839.

Lockhart D.J., Dong H., Byrne M.C., Follettie M.T., Gallo M.V., Chee M.S., Mittmann M., Wang C., Kobayashi M., Horton H., and Brown E.L. 1996. Expression monitoring by hybridization to high-density oligonucleotide arrays. *Nat. Biotechnol.* **14**: 1675–1680.

Lowe H.J. and Barnett G.O. 1994. Understanding and using the medical subject headings (MeSH) vocabulary to perform literature searches. *J. Am. Med. Assoc.* **271**: 1103–1108.

Mills J.C. and Gordon J.I. 2001. A new approach for filtering noise from high-density oligonucleotide microarray datasets. *Nucleic Acids Res.* **29**: E72.

Mills J.C., Roth K.A., Cagan R.L., and Gordon J.I. 2001. DNA microarrays and beyond: Completing the journey from tissue to cell. *Nat. Cell Biol.* **3**: E175–E178.

Oja E. and Kaski S., eds. 1999. *Kohonen maps.* Elsevier, The Netherlands.

Perou C.M., Sorlie T., Eisen M.B., van de Rijn M., Jeffrey S.S., Rees C.A., Pollack J.R., Ross D.T., Johnsen H., Akslen L.A., Fluge O., Pergamenschikov A., Williams C., Zhu S.X., Lonning P.E., Borresen-Dale A.L., Brown P.O., and Botstein D. 2000. Molecular portraits of human breast tumours. *Nature* **406**: 747–752.

Pomeroy S.L., Tamayo P., Gaasenbeek M., Sturla L.M., Angelo M., McLaughlin M.E., Kim J.Y., Goumnerova L.C., Black P.M., Lau C., Allen J.C., Zagzag D., Olson J.M., Curran T., Wetmore C., Biegel J.A., Poggio T., Mukherjee S., Rifkin R., Califano A., Stolovitzky G., Louis D.N., Mesirov J.P., Lander E.S., and Golub T.R. 2002. Prediction of central nervous system embryonal tumour outcome based on gene expression. *Nature* **415**: 436–442.

Pruitt K.D. and Maglott D.R. 2001. RefSeq and LocusLink: NCBI gene-centered resources. *Nucleic Acids Res.* **29**: 137–140.

Rebhan M., Chalifa-Caspi V., Prilusky J., and Lancet D. 1998. GeneCards: A novel functional genomics compendium with automated data mining and query reformulation support. *Bioinformatics* **14**: 656–664.

Rodriguez-Tome P. and Lijnzaad P. 2001. RHdb: The Radiation Hybrid database. *Nucleic Acids Res.* **29**: 165–166.

Schadt E., Li C., Ellis B., and Wong W.H. 2001. Feature extraction and normalization algorithms for high-density oligonucleotide gene expression array data (see http://preprints.stat.ucla.edu/303/). *J. Cell. Biochem.* (suppl.) **37**: 120–125.

Schena M., Shalon D., Davis R.W., and Brown P.O. 1995. Quantitative monitoring of gene expression patterns with a complementary DNA microarray (comments) *Science* **270**: 467–470.

Schena M., Shalon D., Heller R., Chai A., Brown P.O., and Davis R.W. 1996. Parallel human genome analysis: Microarray-based expression monitoring of 1000 genes. *Proc. Natl. Acad. Sci.* **93**: 10614–10619.

Schiffman S.S., Reynolds M.L., and Young F.W. 1981. *Introduction to multidimensional scaling: Theory, method and applications.* Academic Press, New York.

Sherlock G., Hernandez-Boussard T., Kasarskis A., Binkley G., Matese J.C., Dwight S.S., Kaloper M., Weng

S., Jin H., Ball C.A., Eisen M.B., Spellman P.T., Brown P.O., Botstein D., and Cherry J.M. 2001. The Stanford Microarray Database. *Nucleic Acids Res.* **29:** 152–155.

Soille P. 1999. *Morphological image analysis: Principles and applications.* Springer, Berlin.

Spellman P.T., Sherlock G., Zhang M.Q., Iyer V.R., Anders K., Eisen M.B., Brown P.O., Botstein D., and Futcher B. 1998. Comprehensive identification of cell cycle-regulated genes of the yeast *Saccharomyces cerevisiae* by microarray hybridization. *Mol. Biol. Cell* **9:** 3273–3297.

Stein L., Sternberg P., Durbin R., Thierry-Mieg J., and Spieth J. 2001. WormBase: Network access to the genome and biology of *Caenorhabditis elegans. Nucleic Acids Res.* **29:** 826.

Tamayo P., Slonim D., Mesirov J., Zhu Q., Kitareewan S., Dmitrovsky E., Lander E.S., and Golub T.R. 1999. Interpreting patterns of gene expression with self-organizing maps: Methods and application to hematopoietic differentiation. *Proc. Natl. Acad. Sci.* **96:** 2907–2912.

Tavazoie S., Hughes J.D., Campbell M.J., Cho R.J., and Church G.M. 1999. Systematic determination of genetic network architecture. *Nat. Genet* **22:** 281–285.

Toronen P., Kolehmainen M., Wong G., and Castren E. 1999. Analysis of gene expression data using self-organizing maps. *FEBS Lett.* **451:** 142–146.

Troyanskaya O., Cantor M., Sherlock G., Brown P., Hastie T., Tibshirani R., Botstein D., and Altman R.B. 2001. Missing value estimation methods for DNA microarrays. *Bioinformatics* **17:** 520–525.

Tseng G.C., Oh M.K., Rohlin L., Liao J.C., and Wong W.H. 2001. Issues in cDNA microarray analysis: Quality filtering, channel normalization, models of variations and assessment of gene effects. *Nucleic Acids Res.* **29:** 2549–2557.

Tukey J.W. 1977. *Exploratory data analysis.* Addison-Wesley, Boston, Massachusetts.

Velculescu V.E., Zhang L., Zhou W., Vogelstein J., Basrai M.A., Bassett Jr., D.E., Hieter P., Vogelstein B., and Kinzler K.W. 1997. Characterization of the yeast transcriptome. *Cell* **88:** 243–251.

Vesanto J., Himberg J., Alhoniemi E., and Parhankangas J. 1999. Self-organizing map in Matlab: The SOM Toolbox, pp. 35–40. In *Proceedings of the Matlab DSP Conference*, November, Espoo, Finland (http://www.cis.hut.fi/projects/somtoolbox/documentation/).

Vincent L. and Soille P. 1991. Watersheds in digital spaces: An efficient algorithm based on immersion simulations. *IEEE Trans. Pattern Anal. Machine Intell.* **13:** 583–598.

Wang X., Ghosh S., and Guo S.W. 2001. Quantitative quality control in microarray image processing and data acquisition. *Nucleic Acids Res.* **29:** E75.

Wodicka L., Dong H., Mittmann M., Ho M.H., and Lockhart D.J. 1997. Genome-wide expression monitoring in *Saccharomyces cerevisiae. Nat. Biotechnol.* **15:** 1359–1367.

Wolfinger R.D., Gibson G., Wolfinger E.D., Bennett L., Hamadeh H., Bushel P., Afshari C., and Paules R.S. 2001. Assessing gene significance from cDNA microarray expression data via mixed models. *J. Comput. Biol.* **8:** 625–637.

Yang Y.H., Buckley M.J., and Speed T.P. 2001a. Analysis of cDNA microarray images. *Brief. Bioinformatics* **2:** 341–349.

Yang Y.H., Buckley M.J., Dudoit S., and Speed T.P. 2000. Comparison of methods for image analysis on cDNA microarray data. Department of Statistics, University of California Tech. Rep 584 (http://www.stat.berkeley.edu/tech-reports/index.html).

———. 2002a. Comparison of methods for image anlaysis of cDNA microarrays. *J. Computat. Graph. Stat.* **11:** 108–136.

Yang Y.H., Dudoit S., Luu P., and Speed T.P. 2001b. Normalization for cDNA microarray. Microarrays: Optical technologies and informatics. *SPIE* (The International Society for Optical Engineering) **4266:** 141–152.

Yang Y.H., Dudoit S., Luu P., Lin D., Peng V., Ngai J., and Speed T.P. 2002b. Normalization for cDNA microarray: A robust composite method addressing single and multiple slide systematic variation. *Nucleic Acids Res.* **30:** e15.

Yates F. 1937. The design and analysis of factorial experiments. Imperial Bureau of Soil Science, Tech. commun. no. 35, Harpenden, England.

Young F.W. 1987. *Multidimensional scaling: History, theory and applications* (ed. R.M. Hamer). Lawrence Erlbaum Assoc., Hillsdale, New Jersey.

WWW RESOURCES

For additional WWW addresses, see also Table 7-4 in Part 2 (Image Analysis) and Table 7-10 in the information panel on **GENE ANNOTATION**

http://bioinformatics.weizmann.ac.il/cards/ Genecards$^{(TM)}$ database of human genes, their products and their involvement in diseases, Weizmann Institute of Science.

http://cm.bell-labs.com/cm/ms/departments/sia/wsc/smoothsoft.html Local Regression Software, Bell Labs Innovations, Lucent Technologies.

http://genex.sourceforge.net/ GeneX open source gene expression database.

http://genome-www.stanford.edu/genecards/ Genecards$^{(TM)}$ database of human genes, their products and their involvement in diseases.

http://genome-www.stanford.edu/microarray The Stanford Microarray Database.

http://genome-www.stanford.edu/source The Stanford Online Universal Resource for Clones and ESTs (SOURCE).

http://microarrays.org/software.html The microarrays.org software page.

http://pevsnerlab.kennedykrieger.org/snomad.htm SNOMAD: (Standardization and NOrmalization of MicroArray Data) program.

http://rana.lbl.gov Lawrence Berkeley National Laboratory, University of California at Berkeley, Michael Eisen lab home page.

http://rana.lbl.gov/EisenSoftware.htm ScanAlyze. Michael Eisen lab software.

http://rana.lbl.gov/manuals/ClusterTreeView.pdf Cluster and TreeView Manual written by Michael Eisen.

http://www.axon.com/GN_GenePixSoftware.html Axon Instruments, Inc GenePix Pro 4.0 software.

http://www.cis.hut.fi/projects/somtoolbox/documentation/ SOM Toolbox for Matlab.

http://www.cis.hut.fi/research/ The Helsinki University of Technology Laboratory of Computer and Information Science Neural Networks Research Centre.

http://www.cmis.csiro.au/iap/Spot/spotmanual.htm Buckley M.J. 2000. The Spot user's guide—Software package for the analysis of microarray images. CSIRO Mathematical and Information Sciences, Australia.

http://www.ebi.ac.uk/arrayexpress/ ArrayExpress public database for microarray based gene expression data.

http://www.expasy.ch/sprot/ SWISS-PROT curated protein sequence database.

http://www.fruitfly.org/expression/immunity Genome-wide gene expression of *Drosophila* in response to immune challenge, web supplement to De Gregorio et al. 2001.

http://www.informatics.jax.org/mgihome/GXD/aboutGXD.shtml The Gene Expression Database community resource for gene expression information from the laboratory mouse.

http://www.mathworks.com/products/matlab/ The Mathworks introduction to MATLAB 6.1.

http://www.mathworks.com/products/statistics/ .The Mathworks Statistics Toolbox 3.

http://www.mged.org/ The Microarray Gene Expression Data Group home page.

http://www.mged.org/Annotations-wg/index.html Home page for the microarray annotations working group.

http://www.ncbi.nlm.nih.gov/dbEST/index.html Expressed Sequence Tags database.

http://www.ncbi.nlm.nih.gov/geo/ The NCBI Gene Expression Omnibus gene expression and hybridization array data repository.

http://www.ncbi.nlm.nih.gov/UniGene/ The UniGene experimental system for automatically partitioning GenBank sequences into a nonredundant set of gene-oriented clusters.

http://www.ncgr.org/genex The National Center for Genome Resources (NCGR) GeneX$^{(TM)}$ home page.

http://www.r-project.org/ The R Project for Statistical Computing.

http://www2.stratagene.com/gc/ Stratagene's GeneConnection web portal.

8 | Tissue Microarrays

Juha Kononen,* Galen Hostetter,* Guido Sauter,[†]
and Olli-P. Kallioniemi*

*Cancer Genetics Branch, National Human Genome Research Institute,
National Institutes of Health, Bethesda, Maryland 20892-4470; [†]Institute of Pathology,
University of Basel, Switzerland

Karl Brand and Melanie Trivett

Peter MacCallum Cancer Institute, East Melbourne, Victoria 3002, Australia

INTRODUCTION

Tissue microarray technology is based on the same principles as other microarray technologies, i.e., construction of small array elements (in this case, tissues) at a high density (100–1000 specimens) in a small area (one microscope glass slide). Tissue microarrays (TMAs) are constructed by removing small cylindrical samples (core biopsies) from archival tissue specimens and arraying hundreds of the biopsies at high density into a recipient paraffin block (Figure 8-1). A typical TMA might consist of several hundred core biopsies of a particular type of cancer, of a particular tissue, or of a particular stage of embryonic development. More highly tailored TMAs can be constructed, for example, from pathological specimens that display the different steps of progression of one type of tumor, from samples with specific sets of clinical information (e.g., prognosis or response to treatment), or from paired samples of primary tumors and metastases.

603

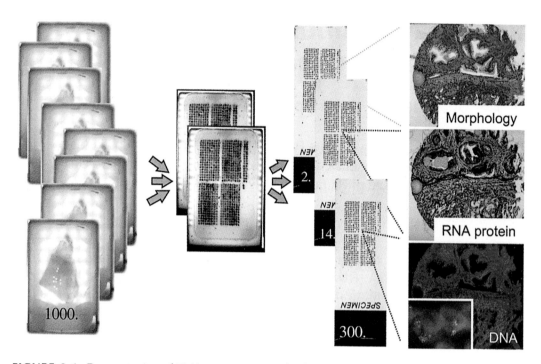

FIGURE 8-1. Demonstration of TMA construction and subsequent analysis. Tissue cores from formalin-fixed, paraffin-embedded tissue blocks are transferred to the TMA block. Multiple TMA blocks can be generated at the same time, and each TMA block can be sectioned ~200 times. All the resulting slides have the same tissues in the same coordinate positions. The individual slides can be used for a variety of molecular analyses, including hematoxylin and eosin staining to assess tissue morphology, mRNA in situ hybridization (ISH), protein immunohistochemistry (IHC), and analysis of genetic alteration using fluorescence in situ hybridization (FISH). (Reprinted, with permission, from Kallioniemi et al. 2001 [© Oxford University Press].)

A major advantage of tissue microarray technology is that a single experiment carried out on a single TMA section yields information on the molecular characteristics of up to 1000 donor specimens. By contrast, in conventional methods of molecular pathology, each slide typically contains a section of a single specimen. With conventional techniques, the analysis of, for example, 500 tumors would require staining 500 individual slides.

Approximately 200 serial sections may be cut from a single TMA block. Many replicate TMAs may be generated by multiple sampling of each donor specimen and positioning the resulting core biopsies at identical *x-y* coordinates in a series of recipient TMA blocks. Deposition of the samples in a precise, predefined format facilitates the development of automated image analysis strategies for the arrayed donor samples. Replication significantly increases the number of experiments that can be performed on one set of samples. More than 1000 identical sections can be generated from five replicate TMA blocks containing the same set of original specimens.

The core biopsies used to construct TMAs must be representative of the cellular composition and architecture of the original pathological specimens. If adequate representation is not achieved, TMAs may yield lower estimates of, for example, the frequency of a particular change in gene expression than would be obtained if the original specimen was analyzed. Increasing the size and number of core biopsies taken from each specimen will improve representation and hence the statistical power of TMAs. However, pathological specimens are precious resources that must be guarded carefully and used economically. Every effort should therefore be made to keep the number and sizes of core biopsies taken from fresh or archival tissues to a minimum. Such tissues are stored in pathology archives, where they are potentially accessible to investigators. Many institutions require investigators to obtain ethical approval for access to archival pathological material for research purposes.

Needles used for core biopsies are commercially available in diameters of 0.6, 1.0, 1.5, 2.0, and 3.0 mm. Core biopsies smaller than 0.6 mm in diameter are less likely to provide adequate representation of anything but the most homogeneous of tissues, whereas biopsy sizes larger than 3.0 mm increasingly negate the purpose of array creation. Using 0.6-mm-diameter core biopsies keeps wastage of the original sample to a minimum, thereby conserving unique and precious research resources while retaining morphological information. Obviously, the aim should be to use the minimal number of core biopsies of the smallest size required to achieve acceptable concordance with the original specimen. Thus, tissues with uniform histopathology, such as liver, can be accurately represented in a single 0.6-mm biopsy. By contrast, a heterogeneous tissue containing a number of different cell types and architectures would be better represented by several 0.6-mm biopsies than by one 2.0-mm biopsy (Camp et al. 2000; Gillett et al. 2000; Sallinen et al. 2000; Hoos et al. 2001; Nocito et al. 2001; Rimm et al. 2001). For tissues of moderate complexity, we recommend using two to three core biopsies taken from distant parts of the specimen.

The acquisition of core biopsy samples and their subsequent deposition for construction of tissue arrays may be undertaken with or without the assistance of an instrument. The use of precision instruments to construct arrays improves array quality and also enables automated array construction and image analysis. Several companies such as Beecher Instruments (Silver Spring, Maryland) and Chemicon International (Termecula, California) sell precision instruments for construction of TMAs. For arrays of <150 biopsies, unassisted tissue array construction using an inexpensive biopsy coring instrument makes it possible for any standard pathology laboratory to adopt this technique.

TMAs represent the only high-throughput technology available for the study of formalin-fixed, archival tissue materials, and they are typically used to validate the expression patterns of candidate genes identified by conventional cDNA microarrays or other genomic and proteomic screening approaches (please see Figure 8-2) (Bubendorf et al. 1999; Barlund et al. 2000; Moch et al. 2001). Almost all techniques performed on conventional "whole-mount" pathological specimens may be performed on TMAs with minimal modification. Techniques that can be used to screen TMAs for specific molecular alterations include molecular and histological analyses such as fluorescence in situ hybridization (FISH) for DNA targets, RNA in situ hybridization (ISH) (please see Protocol 2), polymerase chain reaction (PCR) in situ hybridization, and immunocytochemistry and immunohistochemistry (please see Protocol 3). Although the quality of nucleic acids in routine archival formalin-fixed tissue specimens may vary, these tissue samples represent a powerful research resource to obtain the clinical and follow-up information often available from archived tissue blocks. Archival blocks dating back 20–50 years have been shown to retain their immunoreactivities when fixed with buffered 10% formalin. We therefore recommend the use of 10% buffered formalin for preserving immunoreactivity in tissue specimens after long-term storage. The process of sampling and arraying the specimens is only a fraction of the amount of work required for creating a TMA. Most of the effort is spent in organizing, selecting, and handling the original tissue blocks to be included in the array (Protocol 1).

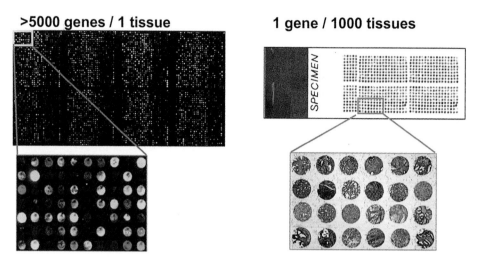

>5000 genes / 1 tissue

1 gene / 1000 tissues

SPECIMEN

FIGURE 8-2. Tissue microarrays are powerful for validation, prioritization, and extension of findings obtained from genomic surveys, such as cDNA microarrays. cDNA microarrays enable up 5,000 or 50,000 genes to be analyzed, in one specimen at a time. By contrast, TMAs are applicable to the analysis of one target at a time, but in up to 1,000 tissues on each slide. (Reprinted, with permission, from Kallioniemi et al. 2001 [© Oxford University Press].)

Using one or more of these techniques, the results obtained on a small number of freshly acquired samples, for example, by expression profiling, can rapidly be extended to a large number of archival samples and simultaneously confirmed in the context of tissue architecture (e.g., please see Kononen et al. 1998; Bubendorf et al. 1999; Hedenfalk et al. 2001). Data from different markers can then be combined to evaluate the power of multi-parametric molecular profiling, perhaps based on dozens or hundreds of parameters. A growing number of published studies have validated the approach and testify to the value of TMA technology in molecular pathology and translational cancer research.

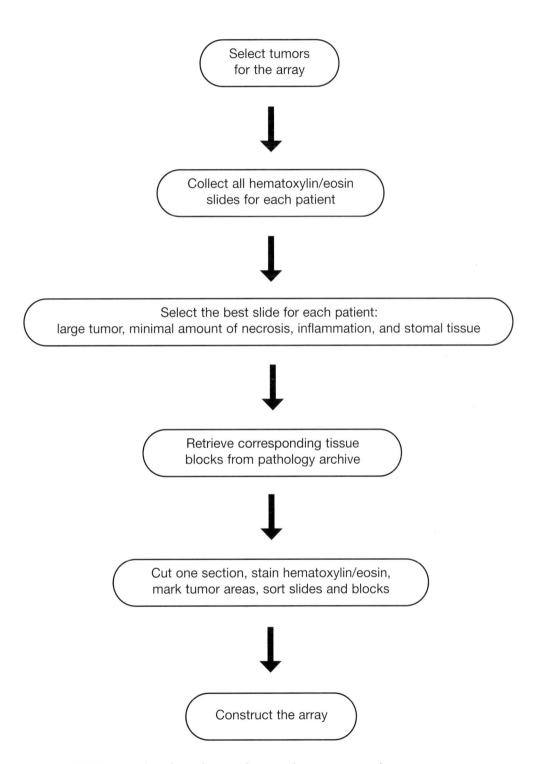

FIGURE 8-3. Flow chart of a typical process for construction of tissue microarrays.

Construction of Tissue Microarrays

Juha Kononen,* Galen Hostetter,* Guido Sauter,†
and Olli-P. Kallioniemi*

*Cancer Genetics Branch, National Human Genome Research Institute,
National Institutes of Health, Bethesda, Maryland 20892-4470; †Institute of Pathology,
University of Basel, Switzerland

This protocol describes the construction of tissue microarrays (TMAs) and provides troubleshooting recommendations. A flow chart of the process is given in Figure 8-3.

MATERIALS

IMPORTANT: Prepare all reagents used in this protocol with DEPC-treated H_2O (please see the information panel on **SPECIAL CONSIDERATIONS FOR WORKING WITH RNA** in Section 3).

Tissue Samples

Control tissues

Include tissues with known phenotypes in every TMA. These tissues may include, for example, a panel of normal tissues (such as liver and kidney skin), cell pellets from well-defined cell lines, or xenograft tumor specimens. Tissues with known phenotypes serve as internal controls to validate the specificity and sensitivity of subsequent molecular and immunohistochemical assays.

Tissue samples

Described here is the use of archival formalin-fixed tissues for construction of arrays. These tissues may have been fixed under different conditions and for variable lengths of time, which may limit their application in some molecular assays. For example, tissues fixed in unbuffered formalin—a common practice until a few years ago—may yield a highly attenuated signal when assayed by RNA in situ hybridization (ISH) or immunohistochemistry (IHC). RNA also tends to become degraded in ethanol-fixed tissues after long-term storage. Fresh or frozen tissues may be used to construct TMAs after fixation using a standardized protocol that preserves the nucleic acids (e.g., buffered formalin) and embedding in paraffin wax.

Reference tissue sections, mounted on slides, and stained with hematoxylin and eosin (H&E)

Sections cut from the donor block (Step 2) may be stained to provide a reference sample.

Special Equipment

Adhesive-coated tape sectioning system (Instrumedics Inc., Hackensack, New Jersey)
Binocular stereomicroscope
Embedding paraffin pellets (Polysciences)
Microtome
Paraffin (ParaPlast+)
Paraffin embedding station
Superfrost Plus slides (Fisher Scientific or Menzel Glaser)
Tissue arrayer instrumentation (e.g., Beecher Instruments, Silver Springs, Maryland, and Chemicon International, Temecula, California)

Additional Reagents and Equipment

Step 2 of this protocol may require reagents for staining tissue sections, including hematoxylin (Sigma) and eosin staining solution (Eosin Y, 1% aqueous solution, EM Diagnostic Systems) and for paraffin embedding of tissue samples. For details, please see Spector and Goldman (1998, Chapter 98) or Bancroft and Stevens (1996).

METHOD

Preparation or Selection of Tissue Specimens

1. Select "donor" blocks, choosing blocks containing specimens that are approximately equal in thickness.

   Donor specimens for TMAs should be at least 1 mm thick to be suitable for constructing tissue arrays. Tissues 3–4 mm in thickness are preferred because they allow increased numbers of sections to be cut from the array block.

2. Prepare or obtain from each donor block a reference section (~3 μm) freshly stained with hematoxylin and eosin (H&E-stained slide).

   Reference sections are used to identify appropriate areas to sample for arraying. Any other recently stained sections (such as immunostained slides) may also be used for this purpose. Do not take additional sections from the donor block before recovering core biopsies, because doing so reduces the representativity of the original reference sections and may result in sampling errors.

3. Review the stained slides prepared from the donor tissue, and decide which of the blocks contain representative areas for sampling.

4. Within the reference section, mark as many of these areas as necessaryy.

5. Prepare a blank paraffin block for use as a recipient for the tissue samples.

6. Melt standard embedding paraffin (melting temperature 55–58ºC) and pour it into an embedding mold.

   Make sure that the mold is free of wax or any other residue. Large (30 x 45 x 10 mm) recipient blocks are easier to handle than the standard 25 x 35 x 5-mm blocks often used in pathology laboratories.

7. Place a plastic block holder on top of the melted paraffin.

8. Allow the complex to cool, and then separate the mold from the solidified donor block.

   Make sure that no air bubbles are trapped in the paraffin.

9. Design the layout of the TMA to accommodate the number of donor tissues to be arrayed in the TMA. To facilitate microscopic analysis of the TMAs, arrange the core biopsies in subsections, each containing 100–200 samples. Leave enough space (2.5–3 mm) at the corners of the array block to avoid cracking of the paraffin.

   The maximum number of samples that can be arrayed in a block 30 x 45 mm is ~1200. However, constructing blocks with >700 samples requires close-packed sample density and places a premium on fidelity of placement. Blocks with 400–500 samples are easier to assemble. Spacing between the centers of two adjacent specimens on the array may range from 0.65 mm to 1 mm (routinely 0.8 mm), when a biopsy needle of 0.6 mm in diameter is used.

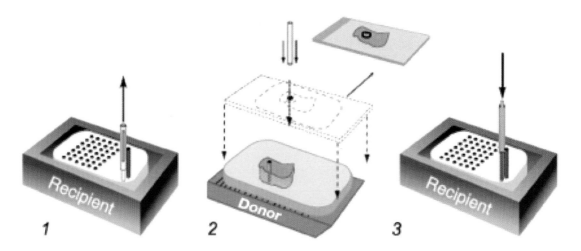

FIGURE 8-4. Tissue microarray construction. (1) Creating a hole for a new specimen in the growing array; (2) sampling donor tissue blocks from morphologically representative sites; (3) depositing the tissue cores to their respective holes in the recipient (array) block.

Construction of a TMA Block Using the Beecher Tissue Arrayer Instrument

To achieve the accuracy required for large arrays containing >500 samples, the use of a precision instrument is necessary. The following manipulations rely upon a device with a design similar to those of instruments used for construction of cDNAs (please see Figure 8-4).

10. Identify and select the region of tissue:

   a. Use the reference section stained with H&E as a guide to ensure that the tissue biopsies are retrieved from the areas previously identified for analysis (Step 4). Occasionally, the areas to be punched can be distinguished and marked directly on the "donor" block surface. However, more accurate selection of the site of the punch is generally required. Use a binocular stereomicroscope to accurately select or view the premarked sampling region on the H&E-stained slide.

   b. Once the desired region is identified, remove the H&E-stained slide and retrieve the sample as described below.

11. Retrieve the tissue cores using the arraying instrument:

   a. Make a hole in the recipient block (Figure 8-4, part 1).

   b. Acquire a sample of tissue from the donor block (Figure 8-4, part 2).

   > The arrayer has two needles with different sizes which are used to retrieve paraffin and tissue cores from the donor blocks. The *smaller* needle is used to make holes in the recipient block. The outer diameter of the smaller needle is only slightly smaller than the inner diameter of the larger needle. Therefore, each tissue core retrieved with the sampling (large) needle fits tightly into the hole of the recipient block.

   c. Deposit this sample into its corresponding hole in the recipient block. Position the samples carefully in the *z*-axis configuration of the recipient block (Figure 8-4, part 3).

   > It is important that all of the samples be deposited at the *same depth* to ensure that a greater number of sections containing representative tissue from all specimens can be cut. If a sample is not pushed deeply enough into the recipient block, a fraction of tis-

sue will be lost during the trimming of the block before sectioning. If a sample is pushed too deep, it will not be present in the first sections cut from the array.

The arraying instrument holds one recipient block at a time, locked accurately in a fixed position by magnets located on the bottom of the block holder. Switching among multiple recipient blocks attached to their holders allows arraying of replicate blocks.

12. Repeat Steps 10 and 11 until the transfer of specimens to the array block is complete.

13. Place the array blocks on a level surface, in preparation for sectioning. To achieve the best possible leveling of the specimens:

    a. Heat the array block by placing it in an incubator for 15 minutes at 37°C.

    b. After heating, place a glass microscope slide on top of the array block, and apply even pressure to push all tissue cores on the array to the same level.

    c. Cool the array block to room temperature. The array block is now ready for sectioning.

14. Section the array block by cutting 5-μm sections to generate multiple TMAs. Cool the block to between −10°C and +10°C, depending on the type of tissue embedded in the block. Float the sections onto sterile, distilled H_2O (for use in IHC) or DEPC-treated sterile distilled H_2O (for use in ISH and IHC) and transfer the sections to Superfrost Plus slides.

    If a small number of tissues have been arrayed (<200), a standard microtome can be used to section the array block. For larger arrays, an adhesive-coated tape sectioning aid facilitates collection of sequential sections and positioning of the sections precisely on the microscope slide. Because tissue sections differ from one another in their adhesion properties, entire sections or individual samples within a section may detach during subsequent processing—in particular during permeabilization (ISH, Protocol 2) or antigen retrieval (Immunocytochemistry, Protocol 3). Adhesive-coated slides used in the tape-sectioning system greatly improve the adhesion properties of TMAs (please see Figure 8-5).

    A section thickness of 5 μm improves the adherence of sections, especially for processes involving extended or harsh washing, such as ISH or fluorescence in situ hybridization (FISH).

15. Bake the TMAs for 30 minutes (for IHC) to 2 hours (for FISH, ISH) at 60°C to remove excess paraffin and moisture and to promote adherence of the TMA to the microscope slide. TMAs may be stored for at least 12 months in a moisture-free environment, for example, a desiccator, at 4°C.

    Slides to be used for ISH are best handled with gloved hands since contact with bare skin may result in contamination with RNase and the consequent possibility of degradation of the target RNA in the TMAs.

QUALITY CONTROL

Examine each array to determine the percentage of missing spots, the percentage of nonrepresentative spots, and the percentage of distorted or otherwise damaged spots. There are no set guidelines as to how a high percentage of success can be achieved. However, to reduce the possibility of sampling bias, the percent of successful spots should be >90%, a goal that can be achieved by careful arraying. Other desirable attributes of TMAs are high precision of x and y coordinates, good staining properties, and high ratios of signal to noise in ISH (Protocol 2) and FISH.

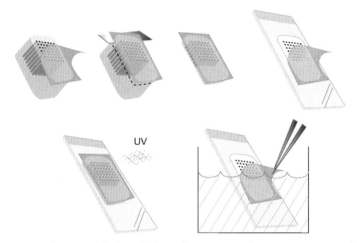

FIGURE 8-5. Sectioning the array block with the adhesive-coated tape sectioning technique. A piece of tape is carefully positioned on top of the block. The microtome knife cuts beneath the tape, and the tape containing a 5-μm section is then transferred to the adhesive-coated slide. After brief UV illumination to polymerize the adhesive on the slide, the tape is removed under solvent solution.

TABLE 8-1. Troubleshooting Guide for Tissue Microarray Construction

Problem	Possible cause	Solution
Some specimens on the array are missing.	Specimens were pushed too deep into the array. Some tissue cores were too short.	Re-array the specimens paying attention to the *z*-axis position of the cores. Make sure that tissue blocks used for generating arrays are of roughly equal thickness and as thick as possible.
	Specimens detached during sectioning with the tape technique.	Make sure that the tape and the adhesive-coated slide are of high-quality. Remove any air bubbles before UV polymerization.
	Specimens detached during staining/ hybridization procedure.	Use adhesive-coated tape technique for sectioning.
Specimens on the array are not representative.	Inaccurate sampling or morphology changes as more sections were cut from the array.	Use a microscope to identify the correct region from the block. Sample from multiple regions.
Distortion in the array.	Arraying needles were bent.	Change the needles.
The middle portion of the array protrudes upward.		Increase the spacing between adjacent array samples and/or make the holes in the array block deeper. After the array is ready, level the block as described.
Paraffin on the array block cracks.	Specimens were placed too close to the edges of the array block.	Leave 2.5–3-mm margins for edges. Use larger recipient array blocks.
Glue residue interferes with molecular analyses.	Too short UV treatment used to polymerize the glue.	Tape sectioning not required for small arrays. Use a longer UV *trans*-illumination time.

ADDITIONAL PROTOCOL: MANUAL CONSTRUCTION OF TISSUE ARRAYS

Karl Brand*

Peter MacCallum Cancer Institute, East Melbourne, Victoria 3002, Australia

Tissue arrays are constructed by retrieving core biopsies from donor blocks and re-embedding them in paraffin in a closely spaced grid for subsequent sectioning and placement on a microscope slide. This process can be carried out with the assistance of a specially designed instrument (Kononen et al. 1998) (please see Protocol 1) or, as described below, by manual transfer of biopsies from donor to recipient blocks. Manual transfer allows up to 200 samples to be arrayed onto a slide, creating TMAs that are valuable for applications involving few specimens, large samples, or specimens that have complex anatomic structures, for example, sections through the central nervous system or mammalian embryos.

Manual construction of a tissue array requires no more dexterity than is used in routine paraffin microtomy. As with any manual technique, there is a learning curve. With diligent practice, a publication-quality array can be constructed using the methodology detailed in this protocol by the fourth array construction, i.e., with ~5 hours of practice. First attempts at array construction can be undertaken with 2.0-mm or preferably 3.0-mm diameter biopsies and with biopsies of <50 per array, before progressing to smaller biopsies with diameters of 1.0 mm or less, which are more difficult to manage.

Additional Materials

Adhesive-coated tape tissue sectioning aid (Instrumedics, Hackensack, New Jersey) (optional)
Control tissue, experimental material, donor blocks, and reference samples (see main Materials list)
Core biopsy instruments (Stiefel Laboratories Inc., Coral Gables, Florida or KaiIndustries Co., Ltd. Oyana, Gifu, Japan)
Section floating water bath
Stylus (custom built or a paperclip is sufficient)
96-U-well plates (Greiner)

Method

Preparation

1. Plan the format and content of the tissue array(s).

2. Obtain stained slides of the donor blocks or cut 3-μm reference sections and stain the sections with H&E.

3. Outline the desired sampling areas with an indelible marker.

Acquisition of Core Biopsies

4. Place the donor block, sectioned surface facing upward, on a flat, vibration-free surface such as a bench top.

5. Align the specimen block with the H&E reference slide, and place the biopsy coring instrument over the selected sampling area.

6. Without disturbing the position of the coring instrument relative to the donor block, remove the H&E-stained slide.

7. Without delay, insert the coring instrument into the donor block until it "bottoms out" on the base of the supporting cassette.

   Apply force in a vertical direction to ensure that the coring instrument drives straight down through the block. Excessive force may cause unnecessary damage to the donor block and/or sample biopsy. The direction of force may need to be altered (from the vertical plane) slightly when sampling an area of variable density or when sampling immediately adjacent to a hole created by previous removal of a biopsy. Any alteration in direction should be away from the site of the previous biopsy.

8. Gently withdraw the coring instrument from the donor block, using a twisting motion to overcome resistance.

9. Use the ejection stylus to eject the biopsy core into predetermined position of a 96-U-well plate.

   The 96-U-well plates are excellent holding pens for core biopsies because they are of the appropriate grid format and size (7 columns x 8 rows). Biopsies are easier to retrieve from 96-U-well plates than from flat-bottomed plates.

Present address: Erasmus University, 3015 GE, Rotterdam, The Netherlands.

Take care when ejecting the biopsy. The stylus presses against the biopsy surface that will subsequently be sectioned. Excessive force will damage the tissue embedded in the block.

Use one 96-U-well plate for each tissue array. Duplicate arrays may be constructed simultaneously by depositing biopsies of the same donor block into separate 96-U-well plates.

Arraying of Core Biopsies

10. Prepare an embedding mold of sufficient length (at least 25 mm), width (at least 30 mm), and depth (at least 4 mm) to accommodate the biopsy samples.

    a. Cover the base of the mold (which subsequently forms the cutting surface of the tissue array) with double-sided tape. Ensure that the tape is aligned with either the *x* or *y* axis of the mold. The tape serves as a guide when positioning the biopsies.

    b. Use an indelible marker to mark the center position of the embedding mold. This assists in correctly aligning core biopsies during arraying (please see notes to Step 11).

       Avoid excessive handling of either side of the double-sided tape. If possible, use double-sided tape with one side covered by protective paper. Stick the uncovered surface of the tape to the base of the mold and remove the protective covering prior to arraying the core biopsies.

11. Use a pair of fine tweezers to recover a biopsy from the 96-U-well plate, dip the sectioned surface of the biopsy into molten paraffin, and immediately deposit the biopsy onto the double-sided tape in the appropriate position of the embedding mold. Repeat the process for each biopsy. The aim is to construct rows and columns of biopsies in the embedding mold that correspond to the rows and columns of the U-well plate

    Do not deposit the first biopsy in position "A1," which is left empty for orientation purposes. Instead, deposit the biopsy in the center position of the top row of the array (e.g., position A4 in an array with seven columns). The center position of the embedding mold was premarked during preparation in the previous step. For the first row only (row A), progressively backfill from this "top-center" position. Row A now serves as an accurate guide template for deposition of the remainder of the biopsies.

    Dipping the core biopsy into molten paraffin aids in the attachment of the biopsy to the double-sided tape.

    If the paraffin cools too quickly, or the biopsy is positioned incorrectly, carefully remove the cooled and hardened dipping wax from the biopsy and repeat the procedure.

    Ensure that the lengths of the biopsies do not exceed the depth of the embedding mold. Biopsies that are oversized may be knocked over during embedding. If necessary, check the biopsy length by overlaying the embedding mold with the cassette base. Carefully remove any biopsies in contact with the cassette and trim excess paraffin. Trim from the opposite end to the sectioned surface. Redeposit the biopsy and check its length for clearance against the cassette.

    WARNING: Some types of paraffin contain dimethylsulfoxide (DMSO). Wear gloves when handling molten paraffin.

Embedding

12. Warm the embedding mold containing the deposited/arrayed biopsies for 20 minutes to 42°C.

    Warming reduces the incidence of air bubbles by slowing the cooling and setting of molten paraffin as it makes contact with the biopsies (Step 13).

    IMPORTANT: Take great care not to disturb the deposited/arrayed biopsies at this time. Disturbance can be disastrous for subsequent identification of biopsies.

13. Gently pour molten paraffin into the embedding mold containing the arrayed biopsies. Take great care not to disturb the biopsies. Continue pouring molten paraffin until the mold is full.

    Direct the stream of molten paraffin onto a corner as far from the deposited/arrayed biopsies as is possible. Pouring molten paraffin directly onto biopsies increases the likelihood of disturbing the deposited/arrayed biopsies.

14. Place a cassette over the embedding mold (as for routine embedding) and immediately top the embedding mold/cassette with additional paraffin.

    Insufficient filling of the mold results in cavity formation within the paraffin block and leads to problems when sectioning.

15. Place the embedding mold/cassette on ice for 30 minutes to allow the paraffin to harden.

    Do not subject the mold to temperatures of less than 0°C. Exposure to low temperatures causes cracks to form in the wax as it hardens.

16. Separate the embedding mold from the cassette by gentle leverage with a screwdriver or other blunt-bladed instrument. Trim off any excess wax.

17. Section and bake the samples as described in Steps 14 and 15 of the main protocol.

TROUBLESHOOTING PANEL

• *Air Bubbles.* When embedding biopsies into molten wax, bubbles often form within the wax. One or two air bubbles are acceptable and should not cause difficulty in sectioning. Excessive bubble formation can be minimized by filling the cavities during sectioning. This is done by warming the tissue array to 50°C and then pouring molten paraffin directly into the cavity. Press the paraffin gently into the cavity by hand. Allow the block to cool at room temperature before sectioning.

    Formation of air bubbles is minimized by prewarming tissue arrays to 42°C before embedding the biopsies in molten paraffin. Increasing the temperature of prewarming to 46°C may further reduce the incidence of bubbles. The temperature of prewarming should not be >46°C. At higher temperatures, the adhesive properties of the paraffin used to secure the biopsies to the double-sided tape decreases, causing the biopsies to lift from their moorings in the embedding mold during application of molten paraffin. The temperatures recommended here are suitable for paraffin whose melting temperature is 55–56°C (e.g., ParaPlast+).

• *Fracture of the Donor Block Tissue.* Fracture can result from poorly fixed tissue and/or excessive numbers of biopsy apertures in the donor block. Ensure that tissue prospectively collected for array construction is fixed for a sufficient period of time to avoid fracturing of the biopsy. Repair of fractured donor blocks and filling of apertures can be performed as follows:

1. Prewarm the specimen donor block to 50°C. This helps to "mix" softened donor block with molten paraffin.

2. Pour molten paraffin directly onto the biopsy aperture. Press the paraffin gently into the tissue fractures/aperture(s) by hand to maximize penetration and re-embedding of the tissue specimen.

3. Allow the block to cool to room temperature before sectioning.

• *Adhesion/Tissue Loss.* Biopsies, because of their small size, are easily detached from sections of tissue arrays. To reduce problems, use Superfrost Plus slides and ensure that the tissue has been baked for at least 2 hours prior to dewaxing. Further steps to prevent the loss of biopsies include the following:

1. During the incubation steps, use coverslips that are raised from the surface of the tissue (e.g., Lifter Slips, Erie Scientific Company Portsmouth, New Hampshire).

2. Use plastic strips instead of coverslips. Plastic used to retain nylon membranes (for Southern and northern blots) are for ideal for this purpose. The strips must be completely free of dust and contaminants.

3. Bake the slides for two periods of 2 hours at 60°C. After the first period of baking, allow the slides to cool to room temperature for 1 hour before baking for the second time. Note that prolonged baking can result in morphological degradation and may adversely effect RNA integrity. Extended baking should only be used after all other methods of tissue adhesion have been exhausted.

4. Use other tissue adhesives (e.g., silanized and gelatin-coated slides, adhesive-coated tape, and tissue sectioning aid available from Instrumedics, Hackensack, New Jersey).

In Situ Hybridization Using Tissue Arrays

Karl Brand*

Peter MacCallum Cancer Institute, East Melbourne 3002, Australia

In situ hybridization (ISH) is used to visualize nucleic acids within histological sections of tissue (John et al. 1969; Pardue and Gall 1969). This protocol describes a nonradioactive method using digoxygenin (DIG)-labeled probes to detect mRNAs in tissue arrays. The technique is based on methods developed in the early 1990s (Heiles et al. 1988; Holtke and Kessler 1990; Kessler et al. 1990; Muhlegger et al. 1990) and commercialized first by Boehringer Mannheim and more recently by Roche Inc. For background information on labeling of nucleic acids with DIG and methods to detect DIG ligands, please see Sambrook and Russell (2001, pages A9.38–9.42).

FIXATION OF TISSUE IN PREPARATION FOR ISH

The type, temperature, and period of fixation all have a significant impact on the subsequent processing of histological samples for ISH. The greater the extent of cross-linkage/precipitation of proteins during fixation, the greater the degree to which nucleic acid targets become masked. This problem is more acute with genomic DNA, which is tightly associated with histones and other proteins, than with RNA, whose association with proteins is more transient and less organized. The recommended procedure for fixation of tissues to be analyzed by ISH for expression of mRNA is to use buffered formalin (pH 7.5) for 16–26 hours at room temperature, depending on the size of the specimen (Bancroft and Stevens 1996).

The ISH protocol presented here has been optimized for formalin-fixed, paraffin-embedded tissue. The protocol can be adapted to tissues that have been fixed using other methods, but problems may arise when tissues fixed by different methods are incorporated into the same array. In this case, a different experimental approach may be required for each of a series of sections cut from the same tissue array (please see Unmasking Target mRNA by Treatment with Proteinase K, below). Obviously, this creates the possibility of a systematic bias in the efficiency of detection of target RNAs in various sections cut from the same array. To avoid problems, it is desirable that all biopsy cores within a single array be fixed using the same fixation protocol.

Present address: Erasmus University, 3015 GE, Rotterdam, The Netherlands.

UNMASKING TARGET MRNA BY TREATMENT WITH PROTEINASE K

A critical step in tissue preparation is the removal of cross-links from chemically fixed proteins that are associated with mRNA. Cross-links formed during the fixation process must be sufficiently reduced in number to allow access of the labeled probe, while maintaining enough cellular structure to retain the target RNA in its natural position throughout the ISH procedure. These goals are best achieved by treating tissue sections with a protease such as proteinase K, which has a broad substrate specificity and the added benefit of inactivating nucleases present in the tissue sections.

Optimization of the unmasking process for ISH consists of altering the extent of proteolytic digestion by varying the concentration of proteinase K in the reaction mixture. Optimal digestion conditions must be determined empirically for each probe and tissue array. For formalin-fixed tissues, 1 µg/ml of proteinase K (incubated for 30 minutes at 37°C) is the suggested starting point. However, enzyme concentrations up to 15 µg/ml may be required for dense tissue, for example, uterine tissue. As discussed above, arrays consisting of differently fixed tissues and/or more than one type of tissue may require digestion under a variety of conditions. For example, arrays containing breast, muscle, and cartilagenous tissue may require a series of individual digests containing increasing amounts of proteinase K (1–5 µg/ml) to obtain optimal unmasking of RNA in all three tissue types.

PROBE DESIGN

A well-designed antisense RNA probe is critical for specific and efficient hybridization to the target mRNA of interest. The least conserved region between related gene families is typically found in the 3′-untranslated region of mRNAs (Lipshutz et al. 1999), and probes are typically directed to this segment of the target mRNA. DIG-labeled transcripts may vary in length between 25 nucleotides for oligoribonucleotide probes, which work well in cocktails containing eight or more probes (Komminoth 1992; Komminoth et al. 1992), and 400 nucleotides. As the size of the probe increases beyond 400 nucleotides, penetration of fixed tissue to target mRNA becomes increasingly limited, with a proportionate reduction in signal strength. Larger fragments of RNA must be reduced in size by limited alkaline hydrolysis (Cox et al. 1984; Angerer et al. 1987; Bales et al. 1993)

Antisense RNA probes for ISH to mRNA are synthesized in an in vitro reaction catalyzed by bacteriophage T7 DNA-dependent RNA polymerase, using a DIG-labeled nucleotide to partially substitute for the standard rNTP (Höltke and Kessler 1990; Komminoth 1992; Komminoth et al. 1992). For a discussion of this reaction and of other methods to synthesize and purify DIG-labeled antisense probes, please see Sambrook and Russell (2001). The modified nucleotide is used at a low concentration in the reaction to ensure that only a few labeled molecules are incorporated per molecule of probe (~1 labeled nucleotide for every 20–25 nucleotides polymerized). Greater incorporation of the modified nucleotide can decrease the efficiency of hybridization of the probe to the target mRNA. The posthybridization recognition of DIG-substituted RNA by antibodies is most efficient when only a few bases are replaced by their labeled counterparts.

CONTROLS

Negative Controls

Negative control probes (NCPs) are essential to determine whether an observed signal is due to specific binding of the experimental probe to its target sequence or due to nonspecific binding. NCPs should have the same length and the same GC content as the antisense experimental probe. Two types of NCPs are in common use: sense negative controls and interphylum negative controls.

- *A sense negative control probe* (SNCP) is derived from the sense strand, i.e., the RNA strand that is exactly complementary in sequence to the antisense probe. The probe sequence is typically subcloned into a vector carrying T3 and T7 transcription sites flanking the insert. Ideally, an SNCP should not bind to any other transcripts in the cell. However, in practice, ~10% of all SNCPs show modest levels of staining, which can often appear highly specific. To minimize this problem, the antisense and sense probes should be carefully designed to avoid homology with other RNAs likely to be present in the tissue arrays. This is best achieved by diligent searching of appropriate databases for the presence of sequences complementary to the antisense probe and its sense partner.

- *Interphylum negative control probes* (INCPs) directed against specific targets from unrelated phyla provide a way to overcome the caveats associated with SNCPs. Probes directed against viral or plant sequences have a low probability of hybridizing to a significant extent to mammalian sequences. When designing INCPs, database searches should be used to identify and minimize and potential cross-hybridizing sequences between INCPs and mRNA transcripts likely to be present in the tissue arrays.

Positive Controls

Postive control probes (PCPs) are used to detect technical problems that may arise during the course of an ISH experiment and also to estimate the degree of variation between ISH experiments. When used in combination with positive control tissues, PCPs can also provide a measure of the efficiency of the ISH protocol. Any ubiquitously expressed housekeeping gene expressed at a reasonable level may be used as a positive control, for example, genes encoding cytokeratins.

Labeling Controls

Labeling control probes (LCPs) are used to check for variation in labeling efficiency between transcription reactions. Using the PCR sequence as the LCP allows measurement of inter-variation between ISH experiments. The PCPs and LCPs are labeled in different transcription reactions: PCP during the establishment of the ISH technique and LCP whenever a new test probe is being labeled. Differences in labeling efficiencies are measured by comparing the intensity and distribution of staining by the PCP with that of the LCP in positive control tissue (please see below).

Tissue Controls

Two types of tissue controls are in use: positive control tissue and postive control tissue for verification of NCP.

- *Positive control tissue* (PCT). This tissue is believed to, or has previously been shown to, express levels of mRNA easily detected by the probe used as the PCP. A PCT can be used to document the staining pattern of each PCP.

- *Positive control tissue for verification of NCP.* This tissue is used to verify the specificity and functionality of the NCP. A control of this type is necessary to ensure that the absence of staining in the target tissue is not the result of poor labeling or inefficient detection of the probe. It is not always possible to obtain tissue that is believed or known to express mRNA complementary to the NCP, especially for sense NCPs. A reasonable alternative is to use a line of cells expressing the NCP sequence after transfection with an appropriate plasmid.

HYBRIDIZATION CONDITIONS

Hybridization conditions for ISH are established by a blend of theory and empirical experimentation. The three major variables are hybridization temperature, solvent, and probe concentration.

- *Hybridization temperature.* The temperature should be determined empirically for each probe on a series of tissue arrays. When using, or "optimizing" a probe for the first time, hybridization should be performed at temperatures between 42°C and 60°C.

- *Solvent.* In the protocol presented here, the hybridization mixture applied to the array contains 60% formamide, and the incubation chamber is humidified with a solution containing 40% formamide. During the 16-hour incubation, the formamide concentration in the hybridization buffer will slowly reduce. This 60/40 buffer/chamber formamide gradient, from experience, gives optimal results with most probes. This situation is analogous, in principle, to "hot start" and "touch down" polymerase chain reaction (PCR), whereby annealing of the probe and target commences under highly stringent conditions, which become progressively less so during hybridization. Some probes, however, benefit from employing a 40/60 buffer/chamber gradient, which causes the concentration of formamide in the hybridization buffer to increase during hybridization.

- *Probe concentration.* Annealing of the probe to the target sequence is a quasi-second-order reaction. Thus, the greater the initial probe concentration, the greater the rate at which the probe anneals to its target (Wetmur and Davidson 1968; Wetmur 1991). Because the concentration of the probe required to saturate an abundant target mRNA is ~300 ng/ml hybridization buffer per kilobase of probe sequence (Wilkinson 1992), applying the probe at concentrations >300 ng/ml/kb will not increase the target signal, but will increase nonspecific background. When the target mRNA is present only in low copy number, lower concentrations of probe may be used. In all cases, the optimum concentration of each probe should be determined empirically.

POSTHYBRIDIZATION TREATMENT

RNase A

Posthybridization treatment of tissue with RNase A removes unhybridized single-stranded RNA. Hybrids between the probe and its target mRNA are resistant to digestion and remain intact. If all works well, treatment with RNase should result in the elimination of nonspecific background without reducing the strength the specific signal. In practice, however, both the specific signal and the nonspecific background are reduced—often by a significant amount (Yang et al. 1999). The net gain in the signal-to-noise ratio is generally small. RNase A should therefore be used only when nonspecific background is unavoidably high and when the signal is sufficiently strong to compensate for signal loss.

Signal Amplification

Amplification of the signal becomes possible when immunological methods are used to detect DIG-labeled probes (Bobrow et al. 1992). A commonly used amplification procedure utilizes the horseradish peroxidase (HRP)-catalyzed conversion of tyramide-biotinyl to dinitrophenyl (DNP). A precipitate of DNP is deposited at the site of the labeled probe and is detected with alkaline-phosphatase-conjugated anti-DNP antibody (anti-DNP-AP). Signal amplification will rarely be required when using an optimized ISH protocol. However, when the target mRNA species is present at very low abundance, when fixation is subnormal, or when the unmasking of the target mRNA is incomplete, signal amplification may intensify the signal and improve the ratio of signal to noise. We, however, recommend signal amplification be used routinely only after the unamplified ISH method has been fully optimized and after the increase in signal to noise gained during signal amplification has been verified and measured. Signal amplification involves the following steps in addition to the standard ISH protocol:

- Quenching endogenous peroxidase activity during pretreatment of tissue.
- Using the probe at one quarter of the usual concentration.
- Amplifying the signal by HRP-catalyzed deposition of DNP.
- Thorough washing following signal amplification.

The amplification steps described in this chapter are based on the technique developed by New England Nuclear (TSA Plus DNP [AP] System).

GENERAL STRATEGY FOR OPTIMIZATION OF ISH

Table 8-2 lists the parameters that (1) should be optimized when setting up ISH and (2) re-optimized whenever a new probe or type of tissue is used. Please note that the suggested range of conditions given for each step are designed for use with formalin-fixed, paraffin-embedded tissues and may not be appropriate for tissues fixed by different procedures.

TABLE 8-2. Optimization of DIG-ISH

Parameter	Reason to vary	Suggested range of optimizing[a]
PREHYBRIDIZATION		
Unmasking mRNA by digestion with proteinase K	different tissue; different fixation method; insufficient probe staining	1 μg/ml, 5 μg/ml, and 10 μg/ml (1 μg/ml)
Probe concentration	different/new probe	100 ng/ml and 200 ng/ml (200 ng/ml) 25–100 ng/ml (amplified ISH) (50 ng/ml, amplified ISH)
Hybridization temperature	different/new probe; different tissue; different fixation method	42°C, 50°C, and 60°C
POSTHYBRIDIZATION		
RNase treatment	only when excessively high background cannot be eliminated	RNase treatment at 20 μg/ml (not performed)
Anti-DIG-AP antibody incubation	insufficient probe signal; excessive background staining	1:500–1:1500 (1:1000)
Anti-DIG-HRP (amplified ISH)	optimizing amplification parameters	1:50–1:500 (1:100)
Anti-DNP-AP (amplified ISH)	optimizing amplification parameters	1:25–1:500 (1:50)
DNP amplification substrate	optimizing amplification parameters	5–30 minutes (10 minutes)

[a]Parentheses indicate suggested starting point.

WORKING WITH RNA

DIG-labeled RNA is rapidly degraded by RNases that are very difficult to inactivate and are virtually ubiquitous in the laboratory. Total elimination of RNases is neither possible nor necessary. Minimizing RNase activity, however, during the preparation of tissue for hybridization and during the hybridization procedure is recommended to prevent attenuation of the hybridization signal. For a detailed discussion of methods to minimize RNase activity during experimental procedures, please refer to the information panel on **SPECIAL CONSIDERATIONS FOR WORKING WITH RNA** in Section 3 of this volume and to Sambrook and Russell (2001, Chapter 7). In brief, the following precautions should be taken to reduce RNase activity to levels acceptable for DIG-ISH:

- Wear latex gloves whenever handling materials that will come into direct contact with the probe; for example, slides, slide racks, coverslips, microfuge tubes, and vessels used for prehybridization and hybridization.

- Use DEPC-treated H_2O and reagents.

- Bake all glassware for 60 minutes at 180°C before use.

- Set aside a special batch of labware to be used only for preparing and handling prehybridization and hybridization solutions.

MATERIALS

CAUTION: Please see Appendix 3 for appropriate handling of materials marked with <!>.

Buffers and Solutions

Please see Appendix 2 for components of stock solutions, buffers, and reagents.
Dilute stock solutions to the appropriate concentrations.

Acetic anhydride (0.25%) <!>
Blocking solution (Roche)
50x Denhardt's solution
10x DIG RNA labeling mix (1 277 073, Roche)
Dithiothreitol (DTT) (250 mM) <!>
EDTA (250 mM, pH 8.0)
Ethanol (absolute crude and analytical grade)
Ethidium bromide <!>
Formamide (deionized) <!>
HCl (0.2 M) <!>
Histolene (Pathtech Diagnostic)
Lithium chloride (LiCl) (4 M)
Maleic acid buffer (pH 7.5)
    100 mM maleic acid <!>
    150 mM NaCl
$MgCl_2 \cdot 6H_2O$
Mounting agents
    Please see Step 38.
    Clearmount (Zymed), Histomount (Zymed), and Kaisers glycerol gelatin (Merck) are convenient water-soluble mountants.
NBT/BCIP buffer (nitroblue tetrazolium/5-bromo-4-chloro-3-indolylphosphate)
    100 mM Tris (pH 9.5)
    50 mM $MgCl_2$
    100 mM NaCl
NBT/BCIP color substrate (1 681 451, Roche) <!>
    10 µl of NBT/BCIP buffer
    200 µl of NBT/BCIP solution
10x Phosphate-buffered saline (PBS)
Prehybridization/Hybridization buffer

formamide (deionized) <!>	23.8 ml
1 M Tris (pH 7.4)	0.95 ml
250 mM EDTA (pH 8)	0.19 ml
5 M NaCl	3.00 ml
dextran sulfate	4.80 g
50x Denhardt's solution	0.95 ml
H₂O (DEPC-treated, sterile, distilled)	6.35 ml
Total volume	40.0 ml

This buffer is best prepared just before use. Alternatively, the buffer can be made and stored in small volumes for up to 3 months at −20ºC with satisfactory results. Do not refreeze the buffer once it has thawed.

Ribonucleic acid solution

herring sperm DNA (10 mg/ml)	1 ml
tRNA (25 mg/ml)	1 ml
yeast total RNA (25 mg/ml)	1.25 ml
H$_2$O (DEPC-treated, sterile, distilled)	748 µl
Total volume	4 ml

  Prepare solution in 500-µl aliquots.

RNase inhibitor (Roche kit 1 175 025 or individually 799 025)

Sodium chloride (5 M)

Triethanolamine (0.1 M) <!>

Tris (1 M, pH 7.4, pH 8.0, and pH 9.5) <!>

Sodium thiosulfate (10%)

20x SSC

Enzymes and Enzyme Buffers

Proteinase K (10 mg/ml) (745 723, Roche)

10x Proteinase K stop solution

  2% glycine in PBS

1x Proteinase K digest buffer

  100 mM Tris (pH 8)

  50 mM EDTA (pH 8)

    Make up to 1 liter and autoclave.

RNase A (109 169, Roche)

T3 RNA polymerase (20 units/µl) (1 031 171, Roche)

T7 RNA polymerase (20 units/µl) (Roche kit 1 175 025 or individually 881 775)

10x Transcription buffer (Roche kit 1 175 025 or supplied with bacteriophage-encoded RNA polymerases)

Antibodies

Anti-DIG-AP Fab´ fragments (1 093 274, Roche)

Anti-DIG-HRP (1207 733, Roche)

Nucleic Acids and Oligonucleotides

Control DIG-labeled RNA (1 585 746, Roche)

Herring sperm DNA (10 mg/ml) (1 467 140, Roche)

Template DNA

  Please see Step 1.

tRNA (25 mg/ml) (109 525, Roche)

Yeast total RNA (25 mg/ml) (109 223, Roche)

Special Equipment

Coverslips (24 x 50 mm/60 mm, Biolab Scientific)

Glass slides (Superfrost Plus, Lomb Scientific)

Hybond N+ filters (Amersham)

Hybridization oven

  The ovens must be large enough to accommodate hybridization devices. Temperatures must be between 40ºC and 60ºC with ±1ºC accuracy. Three ovens allow for simultaneous ISH at three different hybridization temperatures.

Hybridization supports

These supports allow the slides to sit in an orderly pattern in an air-tight chamber above the reservoir of formamide-containing buffer used to humidify the hybridization chamber. Sealing the hybridization support devices in plastic wrap is sufficient when air-tight chambers are not available.

Microtome and tissue-section floating water bath

The microtome is required for accurately sectioning tissues and arrays at 5 μm. The water bath should have ±1°C accuracy within temperatures of 20°C to 50°C.

PAP pen (DAKO S2002) for circling tissue array

Secureline Linemarker Pen II (solvent resistant; Lomb Scientific 1451 Precision Dynamics Corporation San Fernando, California) for labeling details on slide

Shaking water bath

The bath should be large enough to accommodate troughs used to stain slides after hybridization and have a temperature range of 37°C to 60°C ±1°C.

Slide staining troughs and transferable staining racks

All containers used to hold slides leading up to and during hybridization must be cleaned thoroughly by washing in 3% HCl/70% ethanol followed by two rinses in sterile, distilled, DEPC-treated H_2O prior to use. Choose appropriate containers according to the number of slides being processed. Up to 60 slides can be routinely processed using the ISH procedure described here.

Five sets are required for dewaxing and rehydration of slides; five sets are required for tissue pretreatment and seven for posthybridization washing. Coplin jars may be used when <15 slides are being processed.

TSA-Plus DNP (AP) system (NEL746A, New England Nuclear)

U-well microtiter plates

Additional Reagents

Step 15 of this protocol requires the reagents listed in Protocol 1.

METHOD

Labeling DNA with DIG

1. Design, generate, and purify a DNA template for synthesis of an RNA probe by in vitro transcription in a reaction catalyzed by bacteriophage T7 DNA-dependent RNA polymerase.

   Traces of ethanol or other impurities reduce labeling efficiency, as does insufficient quantities of template. Therefore, ensure that the DNA template has been purified correctly and precisely quantitated.

2. Make up a master mix by combining the following reagents and template DNAs in a sterile 1.5-ml microfuge tube. Multiply the volumes shown by ($N + 1$), where N = the desired number of transcription reactions. Include a reaction containing a positive control DNA template to generate a labeling control probe (LCP; please see introduction to this protocol).

10x transcription buffer	2 μl
10x DIG labeling mix	2 μl
RNase inhibitor (20 units/μl)	1 μl
RNA polymerase	2 μl
linearized DNA template	1 μg
H_2O sterile, distilled, RNase-free	to 18 μl
T7 RNA polymerase (20 units/μl)	2 μl
Total	20 μl

Mix the reagents by gently tapping the outside of the tube. Centrifuge the tube for 1–2 seconds to transfer all of the liquid to the bottom. Incubate the reactions in a water bath for 2 hours at 37ºC.

> If the efficiency of labeling is a problem, consider repurifying the DNA template, scaling up the reaction, and/or incubating the reaction for a longer period of time (up to 16 hours). The last two measures are the only available options when information about the sequence of the template is limited, as is often the case when probes have been generated from expressed sequence tags (ESTs).

> Take care when using a linearized DNA prepared from a plasmid that carries different promoters. pBluescript, for example, has bacteriophage T3 and T7 promoters at either end of the multiple cloning site. Much time and labor can be wasted by using the wrong RNA polymerase.

3. Stop the transcription reaction and precipitate the DIG-labeled transcript by adding the following reagents to the reaction mixture:

250 mM EDTA (pH 8.0)	2.0 μl
4 M LiCl	2.5 μl
absolute ethanol (prechilled to –20ºC)	75 μl

> RNA is precipitated efficiently from solutions containing LiCl. The DNA template remains in solution and is discarded during Step 4.

> The probe can be stored for up to 12 months at –70ºC at this stage.

4. Store the ethanolic mixture for 30 minutes at –70ºC and then collect the precipitated nucleic acids by centrifugation in a microfuge at maximum speed for 15 minutes at 4ºC. Discard the supernatant and wash the pellet of RNA with 75 μl of 70% ethanol, prechilled to –20ºC.

> Care must be taken not to lose the pellet. The pellet of RNA pellet is easily dislodged and discarded with the supernatant.

> Handling of the RNA probe from this point on should always be undertaken on ice at the bench and at –70ºC for storage.

5. Dry the pellet briefly under vacuum until the last visible traces of supernatant have just disappeared. Resuspend the pellet of RNA in 100 μl of DEPC-treated H_2O by gentle vortexing. Add 150 units of placental RNase inhibitor to the resuspended probe to prolong shelf life.

> The ISH method described in this protocol uses a hybridization buffer containing dextran sulfate, which is strongly hydrated in solution and hence decreases the amount of solvation available to other molecules contained in the mixture. This has the effect of increasing the apparent probe concentration. However, traces of ethanol remaining with the probe can cause the probe to precipitate, which significantly increases background staining. It is therefore important to ensure that all traces of ethanol are removed from the labeled probe. The cRNA pellet will be virtually invisible to the naked eye after all ethanol has been removed.

Measuring the Concentration of DIG-labeled Transcript

6. Estimate the concentration of the DIG-labeled probe by comparing it to a standard (commercially available) of known concentration.

   a. Pipette 18 μl of distilled H_2O and 2 μl of the probe preparation into a 0.5-ml PCR tube. Mix the contents of the tube thoroughly.

TABLE 8-3. Summary of Serial Dilutions

Tube	Dilution	Volume to add	Control RNA (100 ng/µl) (final concentration [ng/µl])
1	1/10	2 µl (probe) + 18 µl of H_2O	10
2	1/20	10 µl from Tube 1 + 10 µl of H_2O	5
3	1/40	10 µl from Tube 2 + 10 µl of H_2O	2.5
4	1/80	10 µl from Tube 3 + 10 µl of H_2O	1.25
5	1/160	10 µl from Tube 4 + 10 µl of H_2O	6.25
6	1/320	10 µl from Tube 5 + 10 µl of H_2O	3.11
7	1/640	10 µl from Tube 6 + 10 µl of H_2O	1.56
8	1/1280	10 µl from Tube 7 + 10 µl of H_2O	0.78
9	1/2560	10 µl from Tube 8 + 10 µl of H_2O	0.39
10	1/5120	10 µl from Tube 9 + 10 µl of H_2O	0.19
11	1/10240	10 µl from Tube 10 + 10 µl of H_2O	0.10

b. Pipette 10 µl of distilled H_2O into each of ten 0.5-ml PCR tubes. These will become the 1:20, 1:40, and so on, dilutions.

c. Transfer 10 µl of the diluted probe into the first of the tubes containing 10 µl of H_2O and mix thoroughly. Repeat this procedure to obtain 11 serial twofold dilutions of both the probe and the commercial DIG-labeled RNA (100 ng/µl) used as a standard. Please refer to the serial dilution summary in Table 8-3.

   This procedure is also easily performed using a 96-well microtiter plate, especially when several samples are quantified.

7. Spot 1 µl of each dilution onto a nylon membrane in a grid that allows the dilution of each sample to be easily compared to the corresponding dilution of the commercial standard. Bind the RNAs to the membrane by irradiation (800 W) for 2 minutes in a microwave oven or by UV irradiation (1.4 J/cm^2) for 100 seconds at 254 nm.

8. Rinse the membrane in maleic acid buffer (pH 7.5) for 30 seconds.

9. Block unoccupied sites by agitating the membrane for 10 minutes at room temperature in a minimum volume of blocking solution. Then add anti-DIG antibody conjugated to alkaline phosphatase to a final dilution of 1:1000. Incubate the solution for 30 minutes at room temperature with gentle agitation.

10. Rinse the membrane in maleic acid buffer (pH 7.5) for 5 minutes at room temperature with gentle agitation. Repeat this step twice more and then drain the membrane.

11. Add sufficient NBT/BCIP color substrate to cover the membrane and allow the color to develop in the dark, without shaking. Continue developing for 30–45 minutes until dilutions of the standard and sample DIG-labeled RNA are clearly visible to the naked eye. Rinse the membrane twice in H_2O for 5 minutes and dry in the air.

   Steps 8 through 11 inclusive are easily performed in a plastic weighing boat. Use the smallest size boat that allows the membrane to lie completely flat. Ensure that sufficient quantities of blocking/antibody/color substrate solutions are added to completely cover the membrane.

   WARNING: NBT/BCIP contains DMSO.

12. To calculate the amount of probe present in the test samples, use the following calculation:

    (ng amount in *control* x dilution factor of *test* row)/10 = probe concentration (ng/µl) i.e., by using Table 8-3, if the intensity of probe dilution 8 is equivalent to the intensity of the standard dilution 10, the concentration is calculated thus (0.19 ng × 1280)/10 = 24 ng/μl.

13. Store unused probe (from Step 5) at –70°C.

    Repeated freezing/thawing of a probe decreases its shelf life. This can be avoided by distributing the probe into small aliquots according to the anticipated usage. When stored at –70ºC, the probe will retain full activity activity for at least 18 months.

    When 100 μl of probe/hybridization solution is applied to a tissue array at the recommended concentration of 200 ng/ml, 200 ng of probe is sufficient for up to nine slides.

14. Confirm the length and yield of the labeled cRNA transcript by agarose gel electrophoresis. Load 1 μg of linearized template DNA in a lane adjacent to the DIG-labeled RNA. Include RNA and DNA size markers. Stain the gel with ethidium bromide to visualize the template and labeled nucleic acids.

Tissue Preparation and Hybridization

15. Fix, embed, and array tissues as described Protocol 1.

16. Mount 5-μm tissue array sections on Superfrost Plus slides and bake them for 2 hours at 60ºC.

    Use DEPC-treated H_2O to float the sections onto slides.

    Previously cut sections may be used, provided they have been stored at 4ºC in a desiccator. To minimize degradation of labeled probe prior to and during hybridization, observe the precautions outlined in Special Considerations for Working with RNA in Section 3 of this volume.

17. Dewax and rehydrate the sections by passing the slides through the following series of freshly prepared solutions at room temperature. Thoroughly drain the slides before transferring them to the next solution.

Histolene	10 minutes
Histolene	10 minutes
absolute ethanol	5 minutes
90% ethanol	5 minutes
70% ethanol	5 minutes

18. Wash the slides in 0.2 M HCl for 20 minutes with shaking.

19. For unamplified ISH, proceed to Step 20. For amplified ISH, quench any endogenous peroxidase activity by washing slides in 3% H_2O_2 for 10 minutes with shaking. Rinse the slides in PBS for 5 minutes at room temperature with gentle agitation.

20. Rinse the slides twice in DEPC-treated sterile H_2O for 5 minutes with gentle agitation.

21. Unmask the target mRNA by digesting the array with proteinase K, usually at a final concentration of 1 μg/ml. Equilibrate the slides in prewarmed proteinase K buffer (37ºC) for 5 minutes. Add the appropriate amount of proteinase K and mix the solution by immersing and withdrawing the slides several times. Incubate the slides for 30 minutes at 37ºC without shaking.

    Please refer to "Unmasking Target mRNA" in the introduction to this protocol and also see the suggested optimization scheme in Table 8-2.

22. Stop the protein digestion by immersing the slides in 0.2% glycine/PBS (prechilled to 4ºC) for 10 minutes with gentle shaking.

23. Acetylate the tissue arrays by immersing the slides in 0.1 M triethanolamine and immediately adding 100% acetic anhydride to a final concentration of 0.25%. Withdraw and reimmerse the slides several times to ensure efficient acetylation. Incubate the slides for 5 minutes at room temperature with shaking.

   > Acetic anhydride is degraded rapidly and should be added directly from the manufacturer's container; 0.1 M triethanolamine should be freshly made immediately before use. Make sure to accurately measure the highly viscous triethanolamine during preparation of the 0.1 M solution.
   >
   > **WARNING:** Triethanolamine is a skin and mucous membrane irritant. Perform this step in an appropriately exhausted chemical fume hood.

24. Rinse the slides twice in DEPC-treated sterile H_2O for 5 minutes with shaking.

25. Add 40 µl of ribonucleic acid solution to 1 ml of prehybridization buffer and spot 100 µl onto a coverslip. Gently lower a slide containing the tissue array onto the spot of prehybridization buffer until the coverslip has adhered to the slide. Prehybridize the slides for 2 hours at the appropriate hybridization temperature in a hybridization chamber humidified with generous quantities of 40% formamide.

   > Please refer to the discussion "Temperature Conditions" in the Introduction to this section to determine hybridization temperature.

26. Dilute 200 ng (50 ng for amplified ISH) of DIG-labeled probe to 80 µl with DEPC-treated H_2O. Add 40 µl of ribonucleic acid solution and incubate the mixture for 5 minutes at 65°C to denature the labeled RNA. Immediately transfer the tube to ice.

   > Please refer to the discussion of probe concentration and Table 8-2 in the Introduction to this protocol.

Probe Preparation and Hybridization

27. To 1 ml of prehybridization buffer add:

   > 1 µl of 100 mM dithiothreitol
   > 10 µl of 10% sodium thiosulfate
   > 10 µl of 10% SDS

   Mix the solution by inverting the closed tube rapidly and energetically several times.
   > Keep the hybridization buffer chilled on ice at all times.

28. Combine the probe, as prepared in Step 26, with 880 µl of hybridization solution, prepared in Step 27. Mix the solution thoroughly and transfer it immediately to ice.

   > Vortexing is generally not sufficient to mix the highly viscous solution adequately. Run the tube quickly and firmly against the rungs of a plastic rack. The presence of air bubbles in the solution is confirmation of sufficient mixing. Centrifuge the solution briefly in a microfuge at maximum speed at 4°C to remove these bubbles.
   >
   > 1 ml of hybridization buffer/probe mix is sufficient for performing ISH on nine slides.

29. Use forceps to gently slide the coverslips from the prehybridized tissue array. Remove excess prehybridization buffer by tapping the side of the slide two to three times against a sterile absorbent towel. Do not attempt to remove all prehybridization buffer. Add 100 µl of bubble-free probe solution (Step 28) and a clean coverslip. Incubate the slide for 16 hours at the appropriate hybridization temperature in a sealed chamber humidified with generous quantities of 40% formamide.

To minimize loss of tissue from slides, please see the discussion in Table 8-6 at the end of Protocol 3.

Bubbles cause false negatives. Removing air bubbles by pressure on the coverslip has the undesired effect of reducing the available space for the probe to circulate between slide and coverslip. The best way to manage bubbles is to avoid their creation in the first place by carefully applying the probe to the coverslip and then the slide to the coverslip.

The highly viscous hybridization buffer/probe solution will spread across all glass surfaces that it contacts. Ensure that slides containing different probes, and especially negative controls, are well separated from each other in the incubation chamber.

To avoid artifactual staining, make sure that the coverslips are free of any dust particles.

Minimize the period of time between removing the slides from the incubation chambers/ovens and reincubation in the chambers/ovens in order to maintain the temperature of the slide and, hence, the stringency of the reaction hybridization.

Washing and Probe Visualization

30. Gently remove the coverslips from the slides by agitating in 2x SSC for 5 minutes. Perform the following series of washes in shaking water baths:

SSC concentration	Time	Temperature
2x SSC	15 minutes	room temperature
2x SSC	15 minutes	hybridization temperature
1x SSC	15 minutes	hybridization temperature
0.1x SSC	15 minutes	hybridization temperature

Agitation of the slides in 2x SSC before washing is not necessary if the coverslips detach from the slides under their own weight.

31. (*Optional*) If treatment with RNase A is required, wash the slides three times for 5 minutes each time at 37°C in RNase digestion buffer, with shaking. Otherwise proceed to Step 33. Digest unbound probe by adding RNase A to RNase digestion buffer to a final concentration of 20 μg/ml. Incubate the slides for 60 minutes at 37°C with shaking.

Digest with RNase A only when background staining is unacceptably high. Please see the section on RNase A digestion in the introduction to this protocol.

32. Stop the digestion with RNase A by agitating the slides twice for 5 minutes in PBS prechilled to 4°C.

33. Agitate the slides in maleic acid buffer for 5 minutes.

34. Block nonspecific binding of anti-DIG antibody by applying 100 μl of blocking solution to the slides. Perform this step in a humidified chamber or use coverslips to prevent evaporation of the blocking solution. Incubate the slides for 30 minutes at room temperature.

When more than 20 slides are being processed, it is convenient to perform this step by completely immersing slides in a suitable volume (e.g., 150 ml) of blocking solution in a slide box.

35. For unamplified ISH, apply 100 μl of anti-DIG-AP antibody, diluted 1:1000 in blocking solution, to each slide. Incubate the slides for 60 minutes at room temperature. For amplified ISH, apply 100 μl of anti-DIG-HRP antibody, diluted 1:100 in blocking solution, to each slide and incubate the slides for 60 minutes at room temperature.

For suggested concentrations of anti-DIG-HRP antibody, please refer to Table 8-2.

36. Wash the slides three times in maleic acid buffer (pH 7.5) for 10 minutes at room temperature with shaking.

For unamplified ISH: Proceed to Step 37.

For amplified ISH only:

    a. Apply 100 μl of DNP amplification substrate to each slide. Incubate the slides for 10 minutes at room temperature in an enclosed chamber humidified with distilled H_2O.

       For suggested incubation times, please refer to Table 8-2.

    b. Wash the slides for 10 minutes in maleic acid buffer (pH 7.5) three times at room temperature with shaking.

    c. Apply 100 μl of anti-DNP-AP antibody, diluted 1:50 in blocking solution, to each slide. Incubate the slides at room temperature for 30 minutes.

    d. Wash the slides three times in maleic acid buffer (pH 7.5) for 10 minutes at room temperature with shaking.

       For suggested concentrations of anti-DNP-AP antibody, please refer to Table 8-2.

37. Carefully wipe the slides dry, avoiding the tissue sections. Circle the sections with a hydrophobic pen.

38. Add enough freshly prepared NBT/BCIP color development reagent to cover the tissue array. Incubate the slides in the dark. Monitor the color development with a microscope until the desired stain intensity is attained (typically 1–24 hours). Reapply fresh NBT/BCIP chromogen every 6 hours.

39. Rinse the slides in distilled H_2O, counterstain with a water-soluble stain (see note below), and mount the coverslips with an appropriate mounting medium.

    WARNING: Alcohols can dissolve and leach out the products of the chromogenic reaction. Avoid contact of developed slides with histolene and ethanol when counterstaining and mounting.

    Water-soluble mounts such as Kaisers glycerol gelatin, Histomount, or Clearmount are convenient to use.

    The selection of a counterstain to provide contrast with the probe signal (a deep purple/blue hue) and reveal tissue morphology will depend on personal preference. Methyl Green, nuclear Fast Red, or eosin are recommended. Immerse the slides in the counterstain solution until the desired extent of counterstain is achieved.

TABLE 8-4. Troubleshooting Guide for In Situ Hybridization

Symptom	Diagnosis	Potential remedy
Faint or absent signal	Hybridization stringency too high.	Use lower hybridization temperature.
	Overdigestion of tissue arrays with proteinase K (causes mRNA to float from the section).	Reoptimize digestion with proteinase K.
	Underdigestion of tissue arrays with proteinase K (inefficient unmasking of RNA).	Reoptimize digestion with proteinase K.
Nuclear signal	Contaminated or outdated reagents.	Prepare a fresh set of solutions.
Strong nonspecific signal when using SNCP or sense probes	Usually a result of low hybridization stringency.	Increase hybridization stringency; treat samples after hybridization with RNase A.
Tissue loss during hybridization or posthybridization processing	Insecure attachment of tissues to slide.	Use Superfrost Plus slides and ensure that tissue is baked for at least 2 hours before dewaxing. If problem persists, try baking the tissues twice (2 hours each time). Allow the slides to cool to room temperature between the two bakings.
		Use coverslips that are raised off the surface of the tissue, e.g., Lifter Slips.
		Replace coverslips with dust-free plastic strips.
Intra-array variation	Individual elements in the tissue arrays were fixed by different methods.	Select tissues for arraying that have been fixed by the same methods or optimize ISH parameters for each tissue and fixation method (please see Table 8-2).

Immunohistochemistry on Tissue Arrays

Melanie Trivett

Peter MacCallum Cancer Institute, Immunohistochemistry Laboratory
East Melbourne, Victoria 3002, Australia

Immunohistochemistry (IHC) identifies cellular or tissue antigens by means of an antibody-antigen interaction (Miller 1996). The sites of antibody binding are detected by direct labeling of the primary antibody or secondary labeling of the bound primary antibody. The immunohistochemical method described here is made up of three steps, using labeled streptavidin-biotin (LSAB). The tissue section is incubated first with an appropriately characterized primary antibody directed against the antigen of interest and then with a biotinylated link reagent (a secondary antibody) that binds to the primary antibody. Finally, a horseradish peroxidase (HRP)–streptavidin conjugate is used to reveal the location of the biotinylated antibody. Peroxidase activity is visualized using a chromogenic substrate that generates an insoluble precipitate at the target antigen site in the presence of hydrogen peroxide (Miller 1996). For details of the interaction between streptavidin and biotin and of the chromogenic reactions catalyzed by HRP, please see Sambrook and Russell (2001, pages A9.35–A9.37 and A9.45). Counterstaining the sections allows visualization of the tissue morphology against the sites of antibody localization by light microscopy. IHC has been successfully applied to tissue arrays using methodologies established for routine analysis of tissue sections.

TISSUE FIXATION

Hopwood (1996) provides an excellent discussion on fixation and fixatives for histology. Ideally, fixation maintains the tissue in as natural state as possible. Although no one fixative is optimal for all antigens, 10% neutral (pH 7.5) buffered formalin (NBF) is used widely in histopathology because of its ease of use, ready application to a wide range of tissues, and faithful retention of cellular morphology (Hopwood 1996; Miller et al. 2000). However, when using tissue arrays constructed from archival tissue blocks, the investigator may have little control over the fixative used or the duration of fixation (Moch et al. 2000).

A potential problem of formalin fixation is the masking of epitopes in the tissue. An epitope is the part of an antigen that reacts with the primary antibody. Masking may result from conformational changes brought about by the reaction of the fixative with amino acids adjacent to epitopes or by reaction with the epitopes themselves. In most cases, antigens may be unmasked by treatment with proteolytic enzymes or by antigen retrieval (for reviews, please see Miller 1996; Taylor et al. 1996; Miller et al. 2000) of formalin-fixed paraffin-embedded (FFPE) tissue sections. Many commercially available antibodies are tested on FFPE sections and supplied with some form of antigen unmasking suggested in the antibody specification sheet.

PROTEOLYTIC DIGESTION

A variety of proteolytic enzymes including trypsin, pepsin, and proteinase K may be used to unmask antigens in tissue sections (Miller 1996). The success of enzymatic digestion is affected by the duration of formalin fixation (Miller 1996) and depends on finding appropriate conditions to avoid over- or underdigestion. Although a wide variety of antigens can be unmasked by antigen retrieval (see below), proteolytic digestion will remain the optimal method of unmasking for some antigens. The optimal method of unmasking or retrieval must be determined for each antigen by each laboratory (Miller 1996).

ANTIGEN RETRIEVAL

In antigen retrieval, also known as heat-induced epitope retrieval (HIER), heating to high temperature is used to reveal antigens in formalin-fixed tissue sections, to increase the sensitivity of immunohistochemical staining of a wide range of antibodies, and to reduce background staining (Taylor et al. 1996; Shi et al. 1997; Miller et al. 2000). The different sources of heat that may be used include the microwave, pressure cooker, a pressure cooker inside a microwave, vegetable steamers, autoclaves, and water baths. Optimal results are related to the product of temperature and the time of heating rather than the mode of heating (Taylor et al. 1996; Miller et al. 2000; for review, please see Shi et al. 1997). Antigen retrieval may "equalize" the immunoreactivity in a variety of archival paraffin tissue sections that were fixed in formalin for various periods of time (Shi et al. 1997). However, the pH and chemical composition of the retrieval solution influence the efficiency with which particular epitopes are unmasked. Optimal conditions for antigen retrieval must therefore be established empirically for each antibody in each laboratory (Shi et al. 1995; Pileri et al. 1997).

STORAGE OF SECTIONS FOR IHC

Both the intensity and extent of immunostaining may decrease during prolonged storage of cut paraffin sections due to antigen loss or masking during storage (Wester et al. 2000). The mechanism(s) by which antigenicity is lost is not known. The extent of loss varies between antigens and appears to be affected by temperature (Wester et al. 2000). These considerations should be kept in mind when cutting and storing tissue array sections for IHC. It may be useful to compare freshly cut sections with stored sections when optimizing new antibodies for use on tissue arrays. If possible, try to avoid using sections that are heterogeneous with respect to the method of fixation, storage time, and temperature (Wester et al. 2000).

OPTIMIZING IHC PROTOCOLS

Primary Antibodies

Two types of antibodies are used for IHC: monoclonal or polyclonal. Monoclonal antibodies recognize a single local epitope on the antigen target, whereas polyclonal antibodies almost always recognize multiple epitopes (for a discussion, please see Miller 1996). One advantage of a monoclonal antibody is that it provides a constant supply of a single pure reagent with known specificity (Miller 1996). However, polyclonal antisera may be less susceptible to the masking effects of fixation since they recognize a variety of epitopes with a varying capacity to be masked by fixation or to be revealed by unmasking (McNicol and Richmond 1998).

Controls

Tissues known to contain the antigen in question (positive tissue control) are used to eliminate potential false-negative results during antibody/IHC optimization. Tissues known not to produce the antigen in question (negative tissue control) are used to validate the specificity of immunohistochemical staining. Once an antibody has been optimized, other controls such as substitution of nonimmune serum (for polyclonal antisera) or isotype-matched immunoglobulin (for monoclonal antibodies) should be used to validate the immunohistochemical staining (for discussion, please see Miller 1996).

Titration of Antibodies

A broad dilution series should be used when testing new primary antibodies to ensure that false-negative results do not occur (Miller 1996). Starting points for the dilution of the primary antibody may usually be found in the literature if the antibody has been used previously for immunohistochemistry. Specification sheets supplied with commercially available antibodies may also suggest appropriate dilution ranges.

Antigen Unmasking

The efficiency of antigen unmasking varies between antigens and is affected by the mode of fixation (Shi et al. 1995; Taylor et al. 1996; McNichol and Richmond 1998; Frost et al. 2000; Miller et al. 2000). Specification sheets provided with commercial antibodies often suggest methods for antigen unmasking. A range of unmasking protocols (including no treatment, enzyme digestion, and antigen retrieval) should be tried if the primary antibody has not been previously used for IHC. Different fixatives may yield different results with the same antibody, but in the case of tissue arrays, the mode of fixation may be outside the investigator's control if the arrays are constructed from archival paraffin blocks.

A test battery approach (please see Table 8-5; also Shi et al. 1995, 1998; Taylor et al. 1996; McNicol and Richmond 1998) has been recommended for establishing optimal antigen

TABLE 8-5. General "Test Battery" for Development of Optimal Protocols

Citrate Buffer	pH 1–2	pH 6	pH 10–11
Tris-HCl Buffer	pH 1–2	pH 7–8	pH 10–11
Autoclave/pressure cooker[a]			
10 minutes at 120°C	Slide 1	Slide 2	Slide 3
Microwave			
10 minutes at 100°C	Slide 4	Slide 5	Slide 6
Microwave or water bath			
10 minutes at 90°C	Slide 7	Slide 8	Slide 9

Reproduced, with permission, from McNicol and Richmond (1998).
[a]If not available, microwave for 20 minutes.

retrieval conditions for any new primary antibody. We suggest that one slide be left untreated as a control.

The author's laboratory routinely uses citrate buffer (pH 6.0) in a pressure cooker for 2 minutes for antigen retrieval and achieves good immunohistochemical staining with a wide range of antibodies. Antigen retrieval buffers of different compositions and pH values are commercially available. However, the optimal antigen retrieval protocol varies not only for specific antigens, but also among different laboratories analyzing the same antigens. Antigen retrieval should therefore be regarded as a mixture of witchcraft and cookery.

Detection Systems

Ready-to-use detection kits are available for IHC. Our laboratory routinely uses the LSAB 2 kit (DAKO) or the more sensitive LSAB + kit (DAKO) for peroxidase-mediated detection of the primary antibody on human tissues. These kits, which come as ready-to-use secondary antibody and label, detect monoclonal and polyclonal antisera. Detection kits with an alkaline phosphatase detection system are also available. Many commercially available detection kits may not be suitable for use on nonhuman tissue because of the cross-reactivity with the mixture of secondary antibodies provided in the kit. There are a number of commercially available kits for the detection of mouse monoclonal antibodies on mouse tissues.

Some antibodies may require more sensitive detection systems, such as amplification of signal by biotinylated tyramine (please see King et al. 1997). Signal amplification kits for immunohistochemistry are commercially available.

MATERIALS

CAUTION: Please see Appendix 3 for appropriate handling of materials marked with <!>.

IMPORTANT: Store reagents at room temperature unless otherwise specified.

Buffers and Solutions

Please see Appendix 2 for components of stock solutions, buffers, and reagents.
Dilute stock solutions to the appropriate concentrations.

Calcium chloride (1%) <!>
    calcium chloride (dihydrate, m.w. 147.02)   5 g
    distilled H_2O 500 ml
        Mix H_2O and calcium chloride. Store at 4ºC as a stock solution.
Calcium chloride (0.1%)
    1% calcium chloride (see above)   50 ml
    distilled H_2O 450 ml
        Prepare from the above stock solution. Store at 4ºC and use as required for enzyme digestion.
Ethanol (70% and absolute)
Fetal bovine serum (FBS) (10% v/v)
    FBS   1 ml
    50 mM Tris-HCl (pH 7.6)/0.05% Tween-20   9 ml
        Store 1-ml aliquots of FBS at –70ºC. Prepare 10% FBS fresh for each immunohistochemical run.
        Any remaining 10% FBS may be stored at 4ºC for use the following day.
Hydrogen peroxide (3%) <!>
    30% hydrogen peroxide (100 volumes)   5 ml
    distilled H_2O 45 ml
    Prepare 3% hydrogen peroxide fresh just before use.

Instant hematoxylin (available from Shandon)

instant hematoxylin	2x Part A
instant hematoxylin	2x Part B
distilled H_2O	2 liters

Wear gloves. Dissolve Parts A and B instant hematoxylin in 2 liters of distilled H_2O. Mix the solution well and store it in the dark. Filter the solution before use. Filtered hematoxylin in a staining dish will keep for ~2 weeks.

Protein-blocking agent

distilled H_2O	25 ml
protein-blocking agent (2x)	25 ml

Protein-blocking agent (2x) is available from Lipshaw Immunon. Store at 4ºC.

Scotts Tap Water

sodium bicarbonate (m.w. 84.01)	7 g
$MgSO_4 \cdot 7H_2O$ (m.w. 246.48)	20 g
tap water	to 2000 ml

Dissolve the components in tap water.

Sodium citrate (1 M, pH 6.0)

citric acid, trisodium salt (m.w. 294.1) <!>	294.1 g
distilled H_2O	to 1000 ml

Dissolve citric acid (trisodium salt) in distilled H_2O to 1000 ml. Adjust pH to 6.0 using concentrated hydrochloric acid <!>. Store at 4ºC as a stock solution.

Sodium citrate (10 M, pH 6.0)

1 M sodium citrate (pH 6.0) (see above)	20 ml
distilled H_2O	1980 ml

Prepare fresh, from the above stock, for each immunohistochemical run requiring antigen retrieval.

Sodium hydroxide (1 M) <!>

sodium hydroxide (m.w. 40)	4 g
distilled H_2O	to 100 ml

Use as stock solution. Store in a tightly sealed plastic container.

Sodium hydroxide (50 mM)

1 M sodium hydroxide (see above)	5 ml
distilled H_2O	to 95 ml

This concentration is used to adjust the pH of trypsin/calcium chloride solution for proteolytic digestion of tissue sections. Prepare from the above 1 M stock solution of sodium hydroxide.

Tris-Cl (1 M, pH 7.6)/1% Tween-20 (monolaurate)

Tris base (m.w. 121.14)	242.28 g
distilled H_2O	1600 ml
concentrated HCl	120 ml
Tween-20	20 ml

This is used as a stock buffer. Dissolve Tris base in 1600 ml of distilled H_2O. Stir until dissolved and then add 20 ml of Tween-20. Carefully add 120 ml of concentrated HCl and allow the buffer to cool to room temperature. Adjust pH to 7.6 with concentrated HCl. Allow the pH to stabilize overnight at room temperature, and adjust the pH as necessary the following morning. Adjust volume to 2000 ml with distilled H_2O. Recheck pH and adjust if necessary. Prepare the buffer in 500-ml aliquots and store at 4ºC.

Tris-Cl (50 mM, pH 7.6)/0.05% Tween-20

1 M Tris-HCl/1% Tween-20 (see above)	500 ml
distilled H_2O	9500 ml

This is the working buffer for immunohistochemical staining; prepare from the stock of 1 M Tris-Cl above.

Tap water/0.05% Tween-20
    Tween-20   5 ml
    tap water   10 liters
Xylene or a xylene substitute such as histolene <!>

Enzymes and Buffers

Trypsin (10%) <!>
    trypsin (Type IIs)   10 g
    50 mM Tris-HCl (pH 7.6)/0.05% Tween-20   100 ml

        Trypsin is available from Sigma (T 7409). Prepare 10% trypsin in a chemical fume hood. Add 50 mM Tris-HCl (pH 7.6)/0.05% Tween-20 to the trypsin container and mix to dissolve the trypsin. Decant the solution to a 100-ml Schott bottle and add the remaining 50 mM Tris-Cl (pH 7.6)/0.05% Tween-20 and mix. Prepare 0.5-ml aliquots in microfuge tubes. Store the aliquots at –20ºC.

Cells and Tissues

Tissue array block
    Prepare as described in Protocol 1.

Special Equipment

Antigen unmasking
    glass Coplin jars
    pH meter
    stainless steel pressure cooker and electric hot plate
    water bath
Sectioning
    dry-heat fan oven
    flotation bath
    glass slides (Superfrost Plus, Fisher Scientific)
    microtome
    slide warming hot plate
Immunohistochemical staining
    AEC+ (DAKO) or DAB+ (DAKO) chromogens <!>
        Several chromogens are available for peroxidase labeling. A red end-product is obtained with 3-amino-9-ethylcarbozole (AEC), whereas a brown product is obtained with 3′,3′-diaminobenzidene (DAB). The AEC product is alcohol-soluble and so must be mounted in an aqueous mounting medium at the end of the staining procedure. Commercial prediluted preparations of these and other chromogens are available (Miller 1996).
    LSAB 2 (DAKO) and LSAB+ (DAKO) detection kits
    slide incubation boxes (e.g., a plastic or perspex box)
    staining dishes for dewaxing (5)
    staining dishes for washing
    staining racks (heat proof)
Slide mounting
    aqueous mounting media (Crystal Mount from Biomedia or Ultramount from DAKO)
    glass coverslips
    resinous mounting media (DPX)
    staining dishes for dehydration (5)

METHOD

This method can be used with paraffin-embedded tissue arrays. Unless otherwise stated, all steps are performed at room temperature. The optimal conditions (unmasking, primary antibody titration, detection kit) must be determined by each laboratory.

Preparation of Tissue Sections

1. Cut 3-μm sections from a tissue array on a microtome.

   Cut enough sections to try each unmasking method. Remember to include a negative control for each tissue array block for *EACH* unmasking method to be tried.

2. Float the sections out on a flotation bath filled with distilled H_2O.

   Set the temperature of the bath at ~5°C lower than the melting point of the paraffin wax.

3. Mount the sections onto charged slides, such as Superfrost Plus, for greater tissue adhesion.

   The addition of tissue adhesives to the floatation bath may interfere with the bonding of the tissue section to the charged slide.

   Use of tap water in the floatation bath may interfere with bonding between the tissue section and slide. Tap water may be substituted for distilled water in the flotation bath if tissue adhesion to the slide is not compromised.

   If using an automated stainer for the IHC staining, make sure that the sections are mounted on the slides in a position appropriate for dispensing reagents.

4. Dry the slides over a hot plate (set to ~45°C), for at least 30 minutes.

   Before proceeding, make sure that all of the water has evaporated from beneath the tissue array section.

5. Bake the slides in a fan oven for 30 minutes at 56–60°C.

   Slides may be baked for up to 2 hours if tissue adhesion to the slide is poor.

6. Store the cut sections bound together in a slide box to exclude air and moisture. Place a blank slide on top of the uppermost section, put a rubber band around the bundle, and store slides at room temperature in the dark.

   For some antigens, storing cut sections at 4°C (for discussion, please see Wester et al. 2000) may reduce loss of antigenicity.

7. Record the date on the slides to account for problems associated with storage of sections.

Dewax and Rehydrate Sections

Before starting the immunohistochemical staining, make sure that the paraffin wax is dissolved from the tissue array sections and the sections are rehydrated. Slides may be heated briefly in the dry-heat fan oven and then immediately dewaxed (sections will dewax quicker when the wax is molten). The dewaxing series consists of two changes of xylene (or xylene substitute), two changes of absolute ethanol, and one change of 70% ethanol. Use a heat-proof rack so that the slides can be placed into hot buffer for antigen retrieval (if required). It is critical that the sections not dry out at any time once dewaxed and rehydrated. Perform dewaxing in a chemical fume hood at room temperature.

8. Place the slides into xylene, or a xylene substitute such as histolene, for 5 minutes.

9. Transfer the slides to the next batch of xylene/histolene for 5 minutes.

10. Transfer the slides to absolute ethanol for 60 seconds.

11. Transfer the slides to the next dish of absolute ethanol for 60 seconds.

12. Transfer the slides to 70% ethanol for 60 seconds.

13. Transfer the slides to tap water.

> For consistent results, change the dewaxing series regularly, e.g., after every 48 slides if using staining dishes with a 200-ml capacity. While the slides are dewaxing, set up the required solutions for antigen unmasking. If unmasking antigens by digestion with trypsin, prewarm the buffers; heat the buffer for antigen retrieval.

Antigen Unmasking Methods

14. Proceed with antigen unmasking (if required).

> For methods of antigen retrieval and for enzyme digestion, please see the panel on **ALTERNATIVE PROTOCOLS: ANTIGEN UNMASKING AND TRYPSIN DIGESTION** at the end of this protocol. Negative controls should receive the same treatment as the test section(s).

Immunohistochemical Staining

This method uses horseradish peroxidase detection via a biotinylated secondary antibody and streptavidin. Sections must be treated with hydrogen peroxide at the start of the immunohistochemical procedure to block endogenous peroxidase activity within the sections. Our laboratory routinely uses the LSAB 2 (DAKO) and LSAB+ (DAKO) kits, according to the manufacturer's instructions, for detection. Perform all steps at room temperature unless otherwise specified.

15. Place the slides in a dish of freshly prepared 3% (v/v) hydrogen peroxide for 10 minutes (to block endogenous peroxidase).

16. Wash the slides in running tap water for 3 minutes.

17. Place the slides in a dish containing protein-blocking solution for 20 minutes.

> The volume of protein-blocking agent may be minimized by placing the slides flat in a moist incubation chamber and applying the protein-blocking agent onto each section. It is important to cover the entire section.
>
> Some antibodies may not require a protein-blocking step. This should be determined empirically.

18. Prepare the primary antibodies and an appropriate negative control reagent during the protein-blocking step. Dilute the required amount of primary antibody with 10% FBS/50 mM Tris-HCl (pH 7.6)/0.05% Tween-20.

> To prepare negative control reagents: For mouse monoclonal antibodies, the immunoglobulin control should be made up to the same final immunoglobulin concentration as the diluted primary antibody. Similarly for polyclonal antibodies, the final protein concentration of the nonimmune serum should be the same as the protein concentration of the diluted primary antibody.

19. Tip the protein-blocking solution from the sections. Do not rinse the sections.

20. Wipe around the sections with a paper tissue to remove excess blocking reagent.

21. Place the slides in a moist incubation chamber and apply the appropriate diluted primary antiserum to each slide, ensuring that all spots in the array section are covered. Apply negative control reagent to negative controls.

22. Incubate the slides for 30 minutes at room temperature.

    Optimal results may require incubating the primary antibody for 1–2 hours at room temperature or overnight at 4°C. This should be determined empirically.

23. Rinse the primary antibody from the slides with a stream of 50 mM Tris-HCl (pH 7.6)/0.05% Tween-20.

24. Place the slides in a bath of 50 mM Tris-HCl (pH 7.6)/0.05% Tween-20 and wash the sections for 5 minutes.

    Gentle agitation on a rocking platform is preferable for washing steps. Extend the washing time to 10 minutes if agitation is not available.

25. Drain the slides and wipe around the sections with a paper tissue to remove excess buffer.

26. Apply the secondary antibody and place the slides in a moist incubation chamber.

27. Incubate the slides according to the instructions supplied by the manufacturer of the secondary antibody.

28. Wash the slides with a stream of 50 mM Tris-HCl (pH 7.6)/0.05% Tween-20.

29. Place the slides in a rack and wash them in a bath of 50 mM Tris-HCl (pH 7.6)/0.05% Tween-20 for 5 minutes.

    Sections may be left in buffer for up to 30 minutes at this stage if required.

30. Drain slides and wipe around sections with a paper tissue.

31. Apply streptavidin peroxidase, and place the slides in a moist incubation chamber.

32. Incubate the slides according to the manufacturer's instructions.

33. Rinse the slides with a stream of 50 mM Tris-HCl (pH 7.6)/0.05% Tween-20 and place the slides in a slide rack.

34. Wash the slides in 50 mM Tris-HCl (pH 7.6)/0.05% Tween-20 for 5 minutes.

End-product Reaction

35. Wipe around the sections with a paper tissue to remove excess buffer.

36. Apply chromogen (AEC or DAB) to each slide.

    WARNING: Read the manufacturer's safety instructions for chromogens, as many are suspected carcinogens and should be handled with care.

37. Incubate the slides according to the manufacturer's instructions (usually between 5 and 10 minutes).

38. Tip the chromogen off the slides.

    Collect the chromogen into a waste container and dispose of according to local regulations.

39. Wash the slides in running tap water.

Counterstaining

40. Remove any build up from the surface of the hematoxylin solution with a tissue before counterstaining the sections.

41. Place slides in hematoxylin for ~5 seconds to stain nuclei.

    The time required to stain the nuclei will depend on the freshness of the hematoxylin. Ideally, the counterstain should generate blue nuclei with little or no staining of the cytoplasm.

42. Remove the slides from the hematoxylin and wash them in running tap water.

43. Place the slides in Scott's Tap Water for 30 seconds to blue the hematoxylin.

44. Wash the slides in running tap water.

45. Transfer the slides to a dish containing 0.05% Tween-20/tap water.

Aqueous Mounting and Coverslipping

46. Process the slides for coverslipping. Follow one of the methods below depending on the chromogen used in the immunohistochemical staining.

    For alcohol-soluble chromogens: Before placing coverslips on the slides with a resinous mountant, such as DPX, and xylene (or xylene substitute), the slides must be mounted in an aqueous medium if using an alcohol-soluble chromogen, such as AEC. Alcohol-insoluble chromogens can also be treated by this method if a mixture of chromogens was used during the staining procedure.

    a. Drain a few slides at a time and wipe around the sections with a paper tissue to remove excess fluid.

    b. Apply enough aqueous mountant to cover the section.

    c. Create a thin film by holding each slide horizontally and carefully spreading the mountant over the slide.

    d. Remove any bubbles from the slide.

    e. To harden the mountant, place the slides on a hot plate set at 60ºC.

    f. Cool the slides to room temperature before placing coverslips on them.

    g. Place coverslips on the slides using DPX and xylene or xylene substitute.

    h. Remove any air bubbles from beneath the coverslip.

    For alcohol-insoluble chromogens: Aqueous mounting is not required for alcohol-insoluble chromogens, such as DAB. Instead, sections are dehydrated before placing the coverslips on them. This method is *NOT* suitable for alcohol-soluble chromogens.

    a. Place the slides in 70% ethanol for 2 minutes.

    b. Transfer the slides to absolute ethanol for 30 seconds.

    c. Transfer the slides to fresh absolute ethanol for 30 seconds.

    d. Transfer the slides to xylene (or xylene substitute) for 2 minutes.

    e. Transfer the slides to fresh xylene.

    Use a separate dehydrating series for the above steps so as to not contaminate the dewaxing series.

    f. Place glass coverslips on the slides using DPX.

TABLE 8-6. Troubleshooting Guide for Immunohistochemistry

Problem	Possible solution
Loss of tissue sections during antigen retrieval steps	• Use coated slides. • Do not add adhesives to water bath. • Use distilled H_2O in water bath. • Bake the slides longer in a dry-heat oven.
No immunoreactivity seen in positive control	• Check positive control tissue for staining. • Check pH of all buffers used. • Check that the primary antibody, secondary antibody, and label were applied in the correct order. • Review primary antibody dilutions. • Increase incubation time in primary antibody. • Review antigen retrieval protocols (try a different antigen retrieval buffer or different enzyme for digestion). • Try a more sensitive detection system; some antigens may only be detected with amplification systems such as biotinylated tyramine (King et al. 1997). Commercial kits are available. • Cut fresh sections to eliminate possibility of loss.
Variability in staining between IHC runs	• Check storage conditions of slides. • Check freshly cut sections against stored sections to determine if loss of antigenicity has occurred. • Check that the antigen retrieval protocols have been followed consistently. • Keep cool-down times consistent after antigen retrieval (if used), e.g., 20 minutes. • Check pH of enzyme digestion buffers and antigen retrieval buffers.
Staining in negative controls	• Check peroxidase-blocking step. Use fresh 30% hydrogen peroxide for preparation of the 3% solution. • Check for endogenous biotin activity (EBA) as follows: dehydrate a section, unmask antigen (if unmasking was used), block endogenous peroxidase activity, and then apply the streptavidin label, followed by chromogen. The presence of color in the section indicates EBA. Commercial kits are available to block EBA and many homemade recipes may appear on histology or IHC discussion pages. EBA is increased with antigen retrieval in some tissues (Naish 1989). Perform EBA blocking steps after any antigen unmasking/retrieval steps. • Check pH of all buffers used and, if necessary, accuracy of all pH meters used.
Nonspecific immunostaining of sections	• Overstaining; retitrate primary antibody (staining should decrease in intensity with increasing dilution factor). • Try increasing washing times and the number of washes between the antibody (primary and secondary) incubations to remove unbound antibody. • Try a different antibody diluent (commercial preparations to reduce background staining are available). • Include a protein-blocking step if one was not used. Note that the effectiveness of blocking may vary with the blocker used. • Artifactual staining may occur with some unmasking protocols, such as background nuclear staining (Miller 1996; Taylor et al. 1996; Miller et al. 2000). Try re-optimizing the antigen unmasking protocol.
Patchy staining in all slides	• Change dewaxing reagents.
Fading of chromogens	• Use xylene for final dehydration step. • Try another xylene substitute. • Check compatibility of aqueous mountant (if used) with chromogen.

IHC and general histology discussion groups can be found on the Internet. The histonet archives (http://www.histosearch.com/histonet), the IHC homepage (http://immuno.hypermart.net), histology listserver page (http://www.histology.to/listservers.html), and the histonet listserver (http://www.histosearch.com/listserver.html) provide valuable information for trouble shooting, in addition to tricks of the trade and recommendations for reagents. Antibody suppliers produce booklets for IHC procedures that include detailed troubleshooting sections (Naish 1989; Chemicon International 1998).

ALTERNATIVE PROTOCOLS: ANTIGEN UNMASKING AND TRYPSIN DIGESTION

Two methods are presented below for unmasking antigens: heating slides in a pressure cooker or treating them with trypsin.

Pressure Cooker Method for Antigen Retrieval

This method employs heating slides in a citrate buffer (10 mM, pH 6.0) inside a stainless steel pressure cooker heated over an electric hotplate. The volume of buffer used will vary with the size of the pressure cooker. Make sure that enough buffer is used to cover all tissue sections. Treat a maximum of 48 slides for each round of antigen retrieval to help achieve consistency between immunohistochemical runs. Citrate buffer (pH 6.0) works well as an antigen retrieval buffer for a range of antibodies in our laboratory.

This pressure cooker method can be used with other antigen retrieval buffers, such as EDTA and Tris-HCl, in place of the citrate buffer to determine an optimal antigen retrieval method for each antibody used (Table 8-4) (Shi et al. 1995; Pileri et al. 1997; McNichol and Richmond 1998).

Additional Materials

Sodium citrate (10 mm, pH 6.0)
Pressure cooker

Method

1. Place 2 liters of 10 mM sodium citrate (pH 6.0) in the pressure cooker with the lid resting on the top.

    Depending on the size of the pressure cooker used, the volume of 10 mM sodium citrate may need to be varied. Make sure that the antigen retrieval buffer covers the entire tissue array section.

2. Heat the buffer on the highest setting on the electric hot plate until the buffer boils.

3. Immerse slides (dewaxed and rehydrated) into the boiling buffer inside the pressure cooker.

4. Replace the lid and close the pressure cooker.

5. Bring the pressure cooker to the appropriate pressure according to the manufacturer's instructions.

6. Begin timing for 2 minutes when the cooker has reached full pressure.

    Optimal staining for some antibodies or tissue array samples may require extension of the antigen retrieval time. This should be examined empirically.

7. Carefully release the pressure from the pressure cooker, according the manufacturer's instructions, at the end of the 2-minute incubation.

8. Remove the lid and transfer the slides to a dish of tap water.

9. Allow the slides to cool for 20 minutes and then continue with the immunohistochemical staining.

Trypsin Digestion

A solution of 0.1% calcium chloride with 0.1% trypsin is used to digest protein cross-links, formed during fixation, in tissue sections. Enzyme digestion is carried out at 37°C.

Method

1. Place one Coplin jar containing 50 ml of distilled H_2O and one Coplin jar containing 50 ml of 0.1% (w/v) calcium chloride into a water bath at 37°C.

2. Use a thermometer to check that the temperature of the two solutions is 37°C.

3. Place the slides in the warmed distilled H_2O for 10 minutes.

4. Add 0.5 ml of thawed 10% trypsin to the Coplin jar of warmed 0.1% calcium chloride.

5. Adjust the pH (monitor with a pH meter) of the warmed calcium chloride/trypsin to pH 7.8 with 50 mM of sodium hydroxide.

6. Return the calcium chloride/trypsin to 37°C.

7. Place the slides into the calcium chloride/trypsin solution for 10 minutes.

8. Wash the slides in running tap water for 3 minutes after completion of digestion.

9. Continue with the immunohistochemical procedure.

REFERENCES

Angerer L.M., Cox K.H., and Angerer R.C. 1987. Demonstration of tissue-specific gene expression by in situ hybridization. *Methods Enzymol.* **152:** 649–661.

Bales K.R., Hannon K., Smith C.K., 2nd, and Santerre R.F. 1993. Single-stranded RNA probes generated from PCR-derived DNA templates. *Mol. Cell Probes* **7:** 269–275.

Bancroft J.D. and Stevens A.S. 1996. *Theory and practice of histological techniques*, Churchill Livingstone, London.

Barlund M., Monni O., Kononen J., Cornelison R., Torhorst J., Sauter G., Kallioniemi O.-P., and Kallioniemi A. 2000. Multiple genes at 17q23 undergo amplification and overexpression in breast cancer. *Cancer Res.* **60:** 5340–5344.

Bobrow M.N., Litt G.J., Shaughnessy K.J., Mayer P.C., and Conlon J. 1992. The use of catalyzed reporter deposition as a means of signal amplification in a variety of formats. *J. Immunol. Methods* **150:** 145–149.

Bubendorf L., Kononen J., Koivisto P., Schraml P., Moch H., Gasser T.C., Willi N., Mihatsch M.J., Sauter G., and Kallioniemi O.P. 1999. Survey of gene amplifications during prostate cancer progression by high-throughput fluorescence in situ hybridization on tissue microarrays. *Cancer Res.* **59:** 803–806.

Camp R.L., Charette L.A., and Rimm D.L. 2000. Validation of tissue microarray technology in breast carcinoma. *Lab. Invest.* **80:** 1943–1949.

Chemicon International Inc. 1998. *Introduction to antibodies.* Chemicon International, Temecula, California.

Cox K.H., DeLeon D.V., Angerer L.M., and Angerer R.C. 1984. Detection of mRNAs in sea urchin embryos by in situ hybridization using asymmetric RNA probes. *Dev. Biol.* **101:** 485–502.

Frost A.R., Sparks D., and Grizzle W.E. 2000. Methods of antigen recovery vary in their usefulness in unmasking specific antigens in immunohistochemistry. *Appl. Immunohistochem. Mol. Morphol.* **8:** 236–243.

Gillett C.E., Springall R.J., Barnes D.M., and Hanby A.M. 2000. Multiple tissue core arrays in histopathology research: a validation study. *J. Pathol.* **192:** 549–553.

Hedenfalk I., Duggan D., Chen Y., Radmacher M., Bittner M., Simon R., Meltzer P., Gusterson B., Esteller M., Kallioniemi O.P., Wilfond B., Borg A., and Trent J. 2001. Gene-expression profiles in hereditary breast cancer. *N. Engl. J. Med.* **344:** 539–548.

Heiles H.B., Genersch E., Kessler C., Neumann R., and Eggers H.J. 1988. In situ hybridization with digoxigenin-labeled DNA of human papillomaviruses (HPV 16/18) in HeLa and SiHa cells. *BioTechniques* **6:** 978–981.

Holtke H.J. and Kessler C. 1990. Non-radioactive labeling of RNA transcripts in vitro with the hapten digoxigenin (DIG); hybridization and ELISA-based detection. *Nucleic Acids Res.* **18:** 5843–5851.

Hoos A., Urist M.J., Stojadinovic A., Mastorides S., Dudas M.E., Leung D.H., Kuo D., Brennan M.F., Lewis J.J., and Cordon-Cardo C. 2001. Validation of tissue microarrays for immunohistochemical profiling of cancer specimens using the example of human fibroblastic tumors. *Am. J. Pathol.* **158:** 1245–1251.

Hopwood D. 1996. Fixation and fixatives. In *Theory and practice of histological techniques* (ed. J.D. Bancroft and A.S. Stevens), pp. 23–46. Churchill Livingstone, London.

John H.A., Birnstiel M.L., and Jones K.W. 1969. RNA-DNA hybrids at the cytological level. *Nature* **223:** 582–587.

Kallioniemi O.-P., Wagner U., Konenen J., and Sauter G. 2001. Tissue microarray technology for high-throughput molecular profiling of cancer. *Hum. Mol. Genet.* **10:** 657–662.

Kessler C., Holtke H.J., Seibl R., Burg J., and Muhlegger K. 1990. Non-radioactive labeling and detection of nucleic acids. I. A novel DNA labeling and detection system based on digoxigenin: Anti-digoxigenin ELISA principle (digoxigenin system). *Biol. Chem. Hoppe Seyler* **371:** 917–927.

King G., Payne S., Walker F., and Murray G.I. 1997. A highly sensitive detection method for immunohistochemistry using biotinylated tyramine. *J. Pathol.* **183:** 237–241.

Komminoth P. 1992, Digoxigenin as an alternative probe labeling for in situ hybridization. *Diagn. Mol. Pathol.* **1:** 142–150.

Komminoth P., Merk F.B., Leav I., Wolfe H.J., and Roth J. 1992. Comparison of 35S- and digoxigenin-labeled RNA and oligonucleotide probes for in situ hybridization. Expression of mRNA of the seminal vesicle secretion protein II and androgen receptor genes in the rat prostate. *Histochemistry* **98:** 217–228.

Kononen J., Bubendorf L., Kallioniemi A., Barlund M., Schraml P., Leighton S., Torhorst J., Mihatsch M.J., Sauter G., and Kallioniemi O.P. 1998. Tissue microarrays for high-throughput molecular profiling of tumor specimens. *Nat. Med.* **4:** 844–847.

Lipshutz R.J., Fodor S.P., Gingeras T.R., and Lockhart D.J. 1999. High density synthetic oligonucleotide arrays. *Nat. Genet.* (suppl.) **21:** 20–24.

McNicol A.M. and Richmond J.A. 1998. Optimizing immunohistochemistry: Antigen retrieval and signal amplification. *Histopathology* **32:** 97–103.

Miller K. 1996. Immunocytochemical techniques. In *Theory and practice of histological techniques* (ed. J.D. Bancroft, and A. S. Stevens, pp. 435–470. Churchill Livingstone, London.

Miller R.T., Swanson P.E., and Wick M.R. 2000. Fixation and epitope retrieval in diagnostic immunohisto-chemistry: A concise review with practical considerations. *Appl. Immunohistochem. Mol. Morphol.* **8:** 228–235.

Moch H., Kononen T., Kallioniemi O.P., and Sauter G. 2001. Tissue microarrays: What will they bring to molecular and anatomic pathology? *Adv. Anat. Pathol.* **8:** 14–20.

Muhlegger K., Huber E., von der Eltz H., Ruger R., and Kessler C. 1990. Non-radioactive labeling and detection of nucleic acids. IV. Synthesis and properties of digoxigenin-modified 2´-deoxyuridine-5´-triphosphates and a photoactivatable analog of digoxigenin (photodigoxigenin). *Biol. Chem. Hoppe Seyler* **371:** 953–965.

Naish S.J. 1989. *Handbook: Immunochemical staining methods.* Dako Corporation, Carpinteria.

Nocito A., Bubendorf L., Tinner E.A., Suess K., Wagner U., Forster T., Kononen J., Fijan A., Bruderer J., Schmid U., Ackermann D., Maurer R., Alund G., Knonagel H., Rist M., Anabitarte M., Hering F., Hardmeier T., Schoenenberger A.J., Flury R., Jager P., Luc Fehr J., Schraml P., Moch H., Mihatsch M.J., Gasser T., and Sauter G. 2001. Microarrays of bladder cancer tissue are highly representative of proliferation index and histological grade. *J. Pathol.* **194:** 349–357.

Pardue M.L. and Gall J.G. 1969. Molecular hybridization of radioactive DNA to the DNA of cytological preparations. *Proc. Natl. Acad. Sci.* **64:** 600–604.

Pileri S.A., Roncador G., Ceccarelli C., Piccioli M., Briskomatis A., Sabattini E., Ascani S., Santini D., Piccaluga P.P., Leone O., Damiani S., Ercolessi C., Sandri F., Pieri F., Leoncini L., and Falini B. 1997. Antigen retrieval techniques in immunohistochemistry: Comparison of different methods. *J. Pathol.* **183:** 116–123.

Rimm D.L., Camp R.L., Charette L.A., Costa J., Olsen D.A., and Reiss M. 2001. Tissue microarray: A new technology for amplification of tissue resources. *Cancer J.* **7:** 24–31.

Sallinen S.L., Sallinen P.K., Haapasalo H.K., Helin H.J., Helen P.T., Schraml P., Kallioniemi O.P., and Kononen J. 2000. Identification of differentially expressed genes in human gliomas by DNA microarray and tissue chip techniques. *Cancer Res.* **60:** 6617–6622.

Sambrook J. and Russell D. 2001. *Molecular cloning: A laboratory manual,* 3rd edition. Cold Spring Harbor Laboratory Press, Cold Spring Harbor, New York.

Shi S.-R., Cote R.J., Chaiwun B., Young L.L., Shi Y., Hawes D., Chen T., and Taylor C.R. 1998. Standardization of immunohistochemistry based on antigen retrieval technique for antigen retrieval technique for routine formalin-fixed tissue sections. *Appl. Immunohistochem.* **6:** 89–96.

Shi S.R., Cote R.J., and Taylor C.R. 1997. Antigen retrieval immunohistochemistry: Past, present, and future. *J. Histochem. Cytochem.* **45:** 327–343.

Shi S.R., Imam S.A., Young L., Cote R.J., and Taylor C.R. 1995. Antigen retrieval immunohistochemistry under the influence of pH using monoclonal antibodies. *J. Histochem. Cytochem.* **43:** 193–201.

Taylor C.R., Shi S.-R., and Cote R.J. 1996. Antigen retrieval for immunohistochemistry. *Appl. Immunohistochem.* **4:** 144–166.

Wester K., Wahlund E., Sundstrom C., Ranefall P., Bengtsson E., Russell P.J., Ow K.T., Malmstrom P.U., and Busch C. 2000. Paraffin section storage and immunohistochemistry. Effects of time, temperature, fixation, and retrieval protocol with emphasis on p53 protein and MIB1 antigen. *Appl. Immunohistochem. Mol. Morphol.* **8:** 61–70.

Wetmur J.G. 1991. DNA probes: Applications of the principles of nucleic acid hybridization. *Crit. Rev. Biochem. Mol. Biol.* **26:** 227–259.

Wetmur J.G. and Davidson N. 1968. Kinetics of renaturation of DNA. *J. Mol. Biol.* **31:** 349–370.

Wilkinson D.G. 1992. Theory and practice of in situ hybridization. In *In situ hybridization: A practical approach* (ed. D.G. Wilkinson). IRL Press, Oxford, United Kingdom.

Yang H., Wanner I.B., Roper S.D., and Chaudhari N. 1999. An optimized method for in situ hybridization with signal amplification that allows the detection of rare mRNAs. *J. Histochem. Cytochem.* **47:** 431–446.

WWW RESOURCES

http://www.histosearch.com/histonet The Histonet Archives.

http://immuno.hypermart.net The Immunohistochemistry homepage: A comprehensive list of immunohistochemistry resources on the Internet.

http://www.histology.to/listservers.html Histology Listservers and Newsgroups.

http://www.histosearch.com/listserver.html The Histonet Listserver.

Generation of Full-length Libraries

Piero Carninci

Genome Science Laboratory, Riken Main Campus
Wako, Saitama, Japan

Representative libraries containing a high proportion of full-length cDNAs are difficult to prepare but rewarding to use. Such libraries are particularly valuable for large-scale gene discovery projects involving single-pass sequencing of ESTs. Downstream analysis involving protein expression, bioinformatics, and functional assignment is greatly simplified when the relevant cDNA clones in the library contain the complete coding sequence as well as the untranslated 3′ and 5′ regions. However, several problems have traditionally hampered production of full-length cDNAs and of libraries in which all cDNAs are represented at equal frequency. These include:

- The inefficiency with which reverse transcriptase copies sequences in the 5′regions of mammalian cDNAs. Stable secondary structures cause early termination and detachment of the enzyme from a large fraction of mRNA templates, resulting in cDNA clones that lack sequences corresponding to the 5′ region of the mRNAs. This problem is particularly severe when first-strand synthesis is primed by oligo(dT).

- The lack of effective methods to selectively remove truncated cDNAs from the products of first-strand cDNA synthesis.

- The failure to develop and exploit vectors that can accept and propagate cDNAs of a variety of lengths with equal efficiency. Most vectors in current use propagate shorter inserts more efficiently, with consequent selection against longer cDNAs.

- The difficulty of generating normalized cDNA libraries, in which every species of mRNA is present at equal frequency. Creating representative libraries requires that the large differences in abundance of individual mRNAs in the initial population be corrected and that no additional bias be introduced during cloning and propagation of the library, for example, during amplification of cDNA sequences by PCR or during growth of plasmid-based libraries.

During the past few years, we have developed a protocol that overcomes many of these problems:

1. Selection of full-length cDNAs is achieved by cap-trapping (Carninci and Hayashizaki 1999). A biotin residue is chemically linked to the diol group of the cap

This appendix was prepared by Siân Curtis from material contributed by Piero Carninci. When the methods are standard, or close to it, the reader is simply referred to published sources. When important modifications/improvements have been made, alternative protocols are outlined following the table.

647

structure located at the 5′ ends of mammalian mRNAs. RNase I is used to eliminate the biotinylated cap from incompletely synthesized cDNA-mRNA hybrids. Full-length cDNA-mRNA hybrids are recovered by binding to streptavidin-coated magnetic beads.

2. Trehalose is used to stabilize reverse transcriptase during synthesis of first-strand cDNA (Carninci et al. 1998; Carninci and Hayashizaki 1999).

3. When preparing representative full-length cDNA libraries, it is essential to use cloning vectors that can efficiently accommodate and propagate long cDNAs. Otherwise, cDNAs of this class will be severely underrepresented in the library or, in the worst case, absent from it. To obviate discrimination on the basis of size, cDNAs should be cloned in a large-capacity bacteriophage vector that accommodates and efficiently propagates long cDNAs (>15 kb). In addition to large capacity, the vector should be equipped with sequences to allow bulk-excision of inserts from the cDNA library in the form of plasmids. The vectors with the best combination of properties for propagation and excision of full-length cDNA libraries are those of the λ-FLC family, which contain (1) "size balancers" to accommodate a broad range of sizes of eukaryotic DNA; (2) two excision systems (Cre-*loxP* and Gateway) that are used for direct bulk excision of plasmids; and (3) restriction sites that allow transfer of cDNAs into specialized functional vectors (Carninci et al. 2001).

4. Many of the problems in discovering new genes stem from the differences in expression levels between mRNAs in mammalian cells. The population of mammalian mRNAs comprises three or more kinetic classes that differ in abundance. The most prevalent transcripts contribute 30–90% of the mass of mRNA, but only 0.1% of its sequence complexity. Moderately abundant mRNAs account for ~50–60% of the mass of the mRNA and 2–5% of it sequence complexity. Rare mRNAs make a negligible contribution by mass but provide >95% of the sequence complexity of the polysomal RNA. Because of these differences in abundance, single-pass sequencing of cDNAs selected at random from conventional cDNA libraries is a highly inefficient method to isolate weakly expressed genes.

The efficiency of single-pass sequencing can be improved by reducing the prevalence of superabundant and intermediately expressed cDNAs and bringing all the species of cDNAs to similar frequency. Further improvement can be achieved by subtracting unwanted cDNAs from the final library. In this protocol, both normalization and subtraction are accomplished by carefully controlled hybridization of first-strand cDNA to RNA drivers. For normalization, the driver is a biotinylated aliquot of the RNA used initially as template for cDNA synthesis; for subtraction, the driver is a biotinylated RNA population prepared by in vitro transcription of well-characterized sets of cDNA clones. Hybrids formed between the abundant and unwanted cDNAs and the drivers are removed by absorption to streptavidin-coated magnetic beads, leaving a population of single-stranded normalized and subtracted cDNA.

Organization of the Protocol

The protocol is organized into 17 stages (I–XVII), beginning with extraction and purification of template mRNA and ending with evaluation of the cDNA library (please see Figure A1-1 on page 660). The stages and methods are summarized in the following pages, allowing the reader to judge the range of techniques and the scale of the effort required to generate a full-length cDNA library. However, this summary is not meant to be a detailed guide for use at the laboratory bench. Readers who are interested in generating full-length cDNA libraries should follow the complete step-by-step description available at the DNA Microarrays Companion Web Site at www.dna-microarrays.com.

TABLE A1-1. Construction of Full-length cDNA Libraries

Stage	Method	Modifications/Comments
Stage I: RNA preparation	Extraction and purification	Please see Sambrook and Russell (2001, Chapter 7), Carninci and Hayashizaki (1999), and Carninci et al. (2002).
	Extraction with guanidinium isothiocyanate	Following extraction, CTAB precipitation is used to remove polysaccharides (include after Step 10 in Chapter 7, Protocol 1 in Sambrook and Russell [2001]). Note that hnRNA is present (to ~5%) in the final product (Sambrook and Russell 2001, Chapter 7, Protocol 1) (please see Additional Protocols following this table).
	Lysis with NP-40 and precipitation with CTAB-urea	Cytoplasmic RNA is recovered from cells lysed with NP-40 in a buffer containing vanadyl ribonuclease complexes. No hnRNA is present in final product (please see Additional Protocols for method).
Stage II: mRNA purification	Selection of poly(A)+ mRNA	mRNA is purified with commercial kits based on the use oligo(dT)-cellulose chromatography (Sambrook and Russell 2001, Chapter 7, Protocol 3; see also commercial suppliers' manuals).
Stage III: Design and preparation of the primers	Design considerations and methods used to purify synthetic oligonuleotides	The recommended primers include recognition sites for methylation-sensitive restriction enzymes, to facilitate subsequent selective cleavage at the ends of the full-length molecules for cloning. Oligo-nucleotide primers are synthesized and purified according to standard procedures. Final purification of primers is achieved by denaturing polyacrylamide gel electrophoresis (Sambrook and Russell 2001, Chapter 10, introduction and Protocol 1; see also "Methods to Purify Synthetic Oligos," page 10.48).
Stage IV: First-strand synthesis	Synthesis of full-length cDNA in the presence of trehalose and sorbitol	First-strand synthesis is carried out using SUPERSCRIPT II reverse transcriptase (Life Technologies/Invitrogen) essentially as described by Sambrook and Russell (2001, Chapter 11, Protocol 1).

Modifications to the synthesis first-strand reaction include:

1. The incorporation of 5-methyl-dCTP, in place of dCTP, to produce a methylated cDNA. Because 5-methyl dCTP is used in the reaction, [α-^{32}P]dGTP, rather than [α-^{32}P]dCTP, is used in a parallel small-scale reaction as radioactive tracer.
2. Trehalose and sorbitol are included in the reaction to stabilize the reverse transcriptase at the high (~56ºC) reaction temperature (Carninci et al. 1998, 2000).
3. A "hot-start" reaction is used to facilitate transcription of knotty secondary structures in mRNA into full-length cDNA. |
| | Synthesis of full-length cDNA in GCI buffer with trehalose and sorbitol | This first-strand synthesis protocol is a variation of that described in Stage IV. The reaction uses GCI buffer (TaKaRa), optimized for long PCR in place of the standard 5x first-strand buffer. |

(Continued on following page.)

TABLE A1-1. Construction of Full-length cDNA Libraries (*continued*)

Stage	Method	Modifications/Comments
Stage V: Measuring the sample yield	Measurement of radioactivity in nucleic acids	The yield of the first-strand reaction is calculated using DE-81 adsorption (Sambrook and Russell 2001, Appendix 8, page A8.26).
		The size of the first-strand cDNA product is visualized on an agarose gel (Sambrook and Russell 2001, Chapter 5, Protocol 8).
Stage VI: Precipitation of first-strand cDNA	CTAB precipitation of product	CTAB precipitation of RNA removes proteins and polysaccharides, which can interfere with the cap-trapping process (please see Additional Protocols for method).
Stage VII: Enrichment for full-length cDNAs	Oxidation and biotinylation of the 5′ cap	The first-strand cDNA product is enriched for full-length cDNAs by modification by biotinylation of the cap structure found at the 5′ end of mRNA (please see Additional Protocols for method; Carninci and Hayashizaki 1999).
Stage VIII: Enrichment for full-length cDNAs	Cap-trapping and release of full-length cDNA	Biotinylation of the 5′ cap allows full-length cDNAs to be selected using streptavidin-coated beads (please see Additional Protocols for method; Carninci and Hayashizaki 1999).
Stage IX: Second-strand synthesis	Adding a 5′-end priming site to the cDNA	A variety of methods can be employed to prime second-strand synthesis (please see Sambrook and Russell 2001, Chapter 11 introduction [pages 11.14–11.20]). Two alternative methods are recommended (the preferred method is 1):
		1. Single-strand linker ligation method (SSLLM) adds a double-stranded DNA linker to the single-stranded cDNA. The linkers have random 6-bp (dN6 or dGN5) 3′ overhangs that can ligate to any cDNA sequence. This method simplifies cDNA sequencing and protein expression from cDNA clones (please see Additional Protocols for SSLLM method).
		2. Homopolymeric tail of dG residues is added to the 3′ end of the cDNA (Deininger 1987). Second-strand synthesis is then primed by an oligo(dC) synthetic primer (Sambrook and Russell 2001, pages 11.17–11.18.).
Stage X: Normalization and subtraction of cDNA libraries		When complex or rare cDNAs are identified by single-pass sequencing, the presence of highly abundant cDNAs greatly reduces the chance of finding a clone of interest. To increase the efficiency of single-pass sequencing, the representation of highly expressed cDNAs can be reduced by using a technique based on the kinetics of nucleic acid hybridization. "Normalization" results in the equalization of high- and low-abundance species represented in the cDNA library. For detailed information on normalization and subtraction, please see Carninci et al. (2000) and Hames and Higgins (1985).
		In addition to normalizing the library, it may be useful to eliminate unwanted cDNAs. This can be achieved by hybridizing single-stranded cDNA, prepared from mRNA extracted from the tissue of interest, to an excess of DNA or RNA (driver), prepared from another source that does not express the gene of interest. Previously identified clones can also be used as subtraction drivers, to reduce the chance of identifying the same clone twice (Sambrook and Russell 2001, Chapter 11 introduction, page 11.29).

Stage XI: Second-strand cDNA synthesis	First-strand cDNA, treated with SSLLM and/or normalized-subtracted, is used as substrate for second-strand cDNA synthesis. The second strand is made by primer extension using mixtures of long-range thermostable polymerases to facilitate efficient synthesis of long second-strand cDNAs (please see Additional Protocols for long PCR method [Cheng et al. 1994]; see also Sambrook and Russell 2001, Chapter 8, Protocol 13).
Stage XII: Cleaving the cDNA	Because methyl-dCTP was incorporated into the first-strand cDNA, the double-stranded cDNA is hemimethylated. However, the adapter primers that flank the cDNA are not. This provides an easy means by which to digest the flanking sequences to completion without the risk of cleaving cDNA sequences. This protocol uses primers containing *XhoI* and *BamHI* sites. Proceed as follows: 1. *Restriction digestion:* To ensure complete digestion, carry out two separate reactions, one for each enzyme (in this example, *BamHI* and *XhoI*), using an excess of enzyme (25–50 units/μg cDNA). Process the sample by digestion with proteinase K, phenol:chloroform <!> extraction, and ethanol precipitation after each reaction (Sambrook and Russell 2001, Appendix 8). 2. *Dephosphorylation:* To avoid cloning multiple inserts, it is advisable to dephosphorylate the cDNAs (Sambrook and Russell 2001, Chapter 9, Protocol 13). If the vector has been dephosphorylated, cDNAs must *not* be dephosphorylated.
Stage XIII: Size fractionation of double-stranded cDNA	To remove any primer adaptors or short cDNAs, it is advisable to size-fractionate the cDNAs prior to cloning. The use of CL-4B spin columns or agarose gels is recommended (Sambrook and Russell 2001, Chapter 11, Protocol 1, Stage 5, or Chapter 5, Protocol 1).
Fractionation by CL-4B or agarose gel electrophoresis	
Stage XIII: Agarose gel fractionation (alternative to CL-4B)	
Stages XIV and XV: Preparation and use of cloning vectors	Many vectors are suitable for cloning cDNA. The λ-FLC family of vectors (Carninci et al. 2001) is recommended as it can accommodate cDNAs exceeding 15 kb, and it does not show a preference for smaller fragments. For a description of λ-FLC, see Carninci et al. (2001). Vector preparation, testing, and ligation are carried out as described by Sambrook and Russell (2001, Chapter 11, Protocol 1, Stage 6).
Stage XVI: Bulk excision of inserts	Excision mechanisms for cloning vectors, in particular, the λZap and λZipLox series are discussed in Sambrook and Russell (2001, Chapter 11 introduction, page 11.34). The use of λ-FLC vectors (Carninci et al. 2001) is described with detailed instructions provided in the Web supplement.
In vivo, solid-phase excision, and λ-FLC-mediated bulk-excision	
Stage XVII: Evaluation of cDNA libraries	Methods for validation of cDNA clones can be found in Sambrook and Russell (2001, Chapter 11 introduction, page 11.34). The size of inserts in a cDNA library can be assessed by picking 20–30 clones and carrying out long PCR on lysates or preparing a DNA minipreparation for each clone and digesting with restriction endonucleases. The results are analyzed using gel electrophoresis. Full-length cDNA rate may be evaluated by end-sequencing and comparison with known genes in public databases.

Additional Protocols

STAGE I: RNA PREPARATION

EXTRACTION OF RNA FROM CELLS WITH GUANIDINIUM ISOTHIOCYANATE

A CTAB precipitation step is recommended for DNA array applications to remove polysaccharides (include after Step 10 in Chapter 7, Protocol 1 [Sambrook and Russell 2001]). This method is quick; however, heterogeneous nuclear RNA (hnRNA) is present (to ~5%) in the final product. For RNA quality control, see Sambrook and Russell (2001, Chapter 7 information panels).

METHOD

1. Follow Chapter 7, Protocol 1 in Sambrook and Russell (2001) through Step 10.

2. Precipitate the sample with 2 volumes of CTAB/urea solution (1% CTAB, 4 M urea, 50 mM Tris-HCl at pH 7.0, 1 mM EDTA at pH 8.0).

3. Recover the RNA by centrifugation at 9500g for 15 minutes at 4ºC.

4. Dissolve the precipitate in 4 ml of 7 M guanidinium chloride.

5. Precipitate the sample by isopropanol precipitation, and resuspend the pellet in 500–1000 μl of H_2O.

EXTRACTION OF RNA FROM CELLS WITH NP-40 BUFFER

Alternatively, cells may be treated with buffer containing NP-40, followed by precipitation with CTAB/urea. In this approach, no hnRNA is present in the final product. For RNA quality control, see Sambrook and Russell (2001, Chapter 7 information panels).

METHOD

CAUTION: Please see Appendix 3 for appropriate handling of materials marked with <!>.

1. Collect the cells and resuspend them in 2 ml of Ca^{2+}- and Mg^{2+}-free phosphate-buffered saline (PBS).

2. To lyse the cells, add 5 ml of lysis buffer (100 mM NaCl, 5 mM $MgCl_2$, 50 mM Tris-HCl at pH 7.5, 0.5% NP-40) containing 20 mM vanadyl ribonuclease complex.

3. Mix the solution well and incubate for 3 minutes on ice.

4. Centrifuge the solution at 9500g for 1–3 minutes at 4ºC. The nuclei containing the DNA and hnRNA will pellet from solution, leaving the remaining cytoplasmic RNA in the supernatant.

5. Transfer the supernatant to a tube containing 2 volumes of CTAB/urea solution (1% CTAB, 4 M urea, 50 mM Tris-HCl at pH 7.0, 1 mM EDTA at pH 8.0).

6. Recover the RNA by centrifugation at 9500*g* for 10 minutes at 4°C.

7. Dissolve the pellet in 4 ml of 7 M guanidinium chloride.

8. Purify the sample by phenol:chloroform <!> extraction and isopropanol precipitation, and resuspend the pellet in 100–500 μl of H_2O.

STAGE VI: CTAB PRECIPITATION OF FIRST-STRAND cDNA

CTAB precipitation, enhanced by proteinase K digestion, serves to purify the sample of protein and polysaccharide contamination, which would interfere with the cap-trapping enrichment procedure in Stages VII and VIII.

METHOD

CAUTION: Please see Appendix 3 for appropriate handling of materials marked with <!>.

WARNING: A highly radioactive sample will be handled at this stage. Until the unincorporated dNTPs have been removed, extreme caution should be used.

1. Mix the large-scale first-strand cDNA reaction with the small-scale pilot reaction containing [α-^{32}P]dGTP <!>.

2. Add 3 μl of EDTA (0.5 M, final concentration of 10 mM) and 2 μl of proteinase K (10 μg/μl). Incubate for 15 minutes to 1 hour at 45–50°C in a final volume of 150 μl.

3. After incubation, add 32 μl of sodium chloride (5 M, RNase-free), 320 μl of CTAB/urea solution (1% CTAB, 4 M urea, 50 mM Tris-HCl at pH 7.0, 1 μM EDTA [0.5 M at pH 8.0]). Incubate for a further 10 minutes at room temperature.

4. Centrifuge at 15,000*g* (or at maximum speed in a microfuge) for 10 minutes and carefully remove the supernatant, which contains most of the free dNTPs and will be radioactive <!>.

5. Carefully dissolve the pellet in 100 μl of guanidinium chloride (7 M), add 250 μl of ethanol, and place on ice (or at –20/–80°C) for 30–60 minutes (or longer for a small quantity of cDNA) .

6. Centrifuge at 15,000*g* (or at maximum speed in a microfuge) for 10 minutes and remove the supernatant. Wash the pellet twice, very gently, with 800 μl of 80% ethanol. Centrifuge again at 15,000*g* for 3 minutes.

7. Dissolve the cDNA in 46 μl of H_2O (not TE) and proceed to the enrichment protocols in Stages VII and VIII.

   The volumes given here are proportional to the first-strand cDNA reaction volume. In case of different starting volumes, scale up or down appropriately.

   Make sure that the pellets have been completely resuspended by checking the counts in the tube and in the solution using a hand-held monitor. When resuspension is complete, less than 5% of the total counts will remain on the tube wall.

   In the case of very small-scale cDNA synthesis (<2 μg starting mRNA), a carrier can be added to enhance precipitation efficiency. Do not use glycogen.

STAGE VII: ENRICHMENT FOR FULL-LENGTH cDNAs: OXIDATION AND BIOTINYLATION OF THE 5′ CAP

After first-strand cDNA synthesis, the product is enriched for full-length cDNAs by modification of the cap structure found at the 5′ end of mRNA. Biotinylation of the cap structures allows full-length cDNAs to be isolated using streptavidin-coated beads as described in Stage VIII (Carninci and Hayashizaki 1999). In this protocol, the diol groups of mRNA are oxidized in the presence of sodium iodate and subsequently biotinylated.

METHOD

CAUTION: Please see Appendix 3 for appropriate handling of materials marked with <!>.

IMPORTANT: All solutions must be RNase-free. Use tested reagents and sterile H_2O to prepare them with RNase-free glassware and plasticware. Acetate and citrate buffers can be autoclaved.

Oxidation of the Diol Groups of mRNA

1. Add the following reagents directly to the 46 μl of CTAB-precipitated first-strand reaction obtained in Stage VI.

   3.3 μl of 1 M sodium acetate (pH 4.5)
   100 mM $NaIO_4$ (freshly prepared) to a final concentration of 10 mM

   Incubate for 45 minutes on ice in the dark. Stop the reaction by adding 1 μl of 80% glycerol and vortexing.

2. Recover the nucleic acids by precipitation with 61 μl of isopropanol, 0.5 μl of 10% SDS <!>, and 11 μl of 5 M NaCl. Incubate for 30 minutes at –20/–80°C in the dark and centrifuge at 15,000g for 15 minutes. Carefully discard the supernatant.

   From this point on, most of the counts should be in the alcohol precipitate. If counts remain in the supernatant, the precipitation is incomplete.

3. Wash the pellet in 500 μl of 80% ethanol and centrifuge at 15,000g for 2–3 minutes. Carefully discard the supernatant.

4. Centrifuge again briefly and remove any remaining ethanol. Dissolve the nucleic acids in 50 μl of H_2O.

Derivatization of the Oxidized Diol Groups

5. Prepare a 10 mM solution of biotin hydrazide (long-arm variant) by dissolving 0.56 g of biotin hydrazide in 160 μl of fresh biotinylation buffer (33 mM Na-citrate at pH 6.0 [from 1 M stock], 0.33% SDS [from 10% w/v stock]).

6. Add 160 μl of buffer to the first-strand cDNA (50 μl) obtained in Step 4, and mix gently. Incubate overnight (10–16 hours) at room temperature or for 3–4 hours at 37°C.

   Some batches of biotin hydrazide can cause DNA degradation at 37°C.

7. At the end of the incubation, precipitate the biotinylated cDNA-mRNA hybrid by adding:

1 M Na-citrate (pH 6.1)	75 μl
5 M NaCl	5 μl
ethanol	750 μl

Mix gently and incubate on ice for 1 hour or for 30 minutes at –80/–20ºC.

8. Centrifuge the sample at 15,000*g* for 10 minutes. Discard the supernatant and remove any free biotin hydrazide from the pellet by washing three times with 80% ethanol, centrifuging after each wash.

9. Dissolve the final pellet in 75 μl of TE. Monitor for complete resuspension using a hand-held monitor and visual inspection.

STAGE VIII: ENRICHMENT FOR FULL-LENGTH cDNAS: CAP-TRAPPING AND RELEASE OF FULL-LENGTH cDNA

After carrying out the biotinylation reaction described in Stage VII, the sample is treated with RNase I, which specifically degrades single-stranded RNA. This reaction severs the 5′ cap from incomplete heteroduplexes and removes the single-stranded portion of the 3′ poly(A) tail. Biotinylated molecules are then trapped on streptavidin-coated beads and washed under conditions that favor retention of small molecules and release of long cDNAs (Kotsopoulos and Shuber 1996). Streptavidin-coated magnetic porous glass (MPG) beads (CPG Inc., New Jersey) are recommended for this protocol. To minimize nonspecific binding of nucleic acids, in particular, the binding of non-full-length cDNAs, the beads are preincubated with an excess of DNA-free tRNA.

METHOD

CAUTION: Please see Appendix 3 for appropriate handling of materials marked with <!>.

1. To the cDNA sample obtained in Step 9 above (75 μl) add:

RNase I buffer (Promega)	20 μl
RNase I (5 or 10 μl/μl,	1 μl/μg starting mRNA
RNase ONE, Promega)	or total RNA

Incubate for 30 minutes at 37ºC.

2. Stop the RNase I reaction by placing the sample on ice and adding 4 μl of SDS <!> (10%) and 3 μl of proteinase K (10 μg/μl). Incubate for 15 minutes at 45ºC.

3. Stop the proteinase K reaction by phenol <!> extraction. Transfer the supernatant to a clean tube and back-extract the spent phenol with H$_2$O. Pool the aqueous phases and filter using a Microcon YM-100 microconcentrator.

   Alternatively, after proteinase K treatment, extract with phenol:chloroform <!> and then with chloroform. Back-extract and precipitate the nucleic acids using isopropanol and 20 μg of tRNA as carrier.

4. Dissolve the pellet in 20 μl of 0.1x TE.

Pretreatment of Magnetic Beads

5. For each library, pretreat MPG beads (CPG Inc., New Jersey) (500 µl per 25 µg of starting mRNA) with 100 µg of DNA-free tRNA. Incubate for 30 minutes on ice with occasional mixing.

6. Separate the beads by standing the tube in a magnetic rack (supplied by the bead manufacturer) for 3 minutes. Carefully remove the supernatant and wash three times with binding buffer (4.5 M NaCl, 50 mM EDTA at pH 8.0, 500 µl per wash).

Capture of Full-length cDNA

7. Resuspend the tRNA-treated MPG beads in 500 µl of wash/binding buffer and transfer 350 µl of the suspension to a fresh tube containing the biotinylated first-strand cDNA obtained in Step 4 (20 µl of cDNA in 0.1× TE). After mixing gently, incubate the reaction for 10 minutes at 50°C, with end-over-end rotation.

8. At the end of this incubation, transfer the remaining 150 µl of beads to the reaction tube and continue the incubation for a further 20 minutes at 50°C.

9. Separate the beads by standing the tube in a magnetic rack for 3 minutes.

10. Carefully remove the supernatant and wash the beads as follows (wash volume is 0.5 ml):

    2× with washing/binding solution (4.5 M NaCl, 50 mM EDTA at pH 8.0)
    1× with 0.3 M NaCl, 1 mM EDTA
    2× with 0.4% SDS, 0.5 M NaOAc, 20 mM Tris-HCl (pH 8.5), 1 mM EDTA
    2× with 0.5 M NaOAc, 10 mM Tris-HCl (pH 8.5), 1 mM EDTA

11. (*Optional control*) Remove a 50-µl aliquot of the noncaptured fraction (supernatant from Step 9) and dilute in 9 volumes of H_2O. Precipitate the nucleic acids in 0.6 volume of isopropanol and 2 µg of glycogen, and set aside for later comparison with captured fraction (see Step 16).

12. After the final wash, elute the cDNA by adding 100 µl of 50 mM NaOH, 5 mM EDTA. Stir briefly and incubate for 5 minutes at room temperature, mixing occasionally.

13. Separate the magnetic beads and transfer the supernatant (containing the eluted cDNA) to a fresh tube. Store the cDNA on ice.

14. Repeat the elution twice more using 100 µl of 50 mM NaOH, 5 mM EDTA. Check that the elution is complete (80–90%) by monitoring the counts present in the eluate and on the beads.

15. Pool the eluates and store on ice especially after Tris neutralization to prevent any hybridization between cDNAs and any contaminating RNAs that might be present. This is important for the normalization procedure.

16. Remove a 10-µl aliquot of the eluate and analyze on an alkaline agarose gel, alongside the uncaptured aliquot taken at Step 10 above. The unbound fraction should be slightly shorter than the captured fraction.

17. Keep the cDNA on ice and proceed to the addition of a 5′-end priming site (Stage IX).

STAGE IX: ADDING A 5′-END PRIMING SITE TO THE cDNA

Alternative Protocol: Single-stranded Linker Ligation Method (SSLM)

Creating a site for priming second-strand synthesis can be accomplished in a number of ways (for a complete discussion, please see the introduction to Chapter 11 in Sambrook and Russell 2001). Addition of a double-stranded DNA linker to the end of the single-stranded cDNA product to prime second-strand synthesis provides an alternative to conventional tailing (addition of a single-stranded primer). This protocol describes the ligation of a DNA linker to the 5′ end of the cDNA (Shibata et al. 2001).

MATERIALS

CAUTION: Please see Appendix 3 for appropriate handling of materials marked with <!>.

Oligonucleotide primers

Prepare the following oligonucleotides, each containing an *Xho*I restriction site:

- Oligonucleotide GN5:
  5′-AGAGAGAGAGCTCGAGCTCTATTTAGGTGACACTATAGAACCAGNNNNN-3′

- Oligonucleotide N6:
  5′-AGAGAGAGAGCTCGAGCTCTATTTAGGTGACACTATAGAACCANNNNNN-3′

- Oligonucleotide "down":
  5′P-TGGTTCTATAGTGTCACCTAAATAGAGCTCGAGCTCTCTCTCT-NH$_2$ 3′

P indicates that the oligonucleotide must be 5′-phosphorylated, and N indicates that an amino link is added to avoid nonspecific ligation and possible hairpin priming. Purify oligonucleotides by acrylamide gel electrophoresis (Sambrook and Russell 2001) and extract with phenol:chloroform <!> and then chloroform.

TaKaRa DNA Ligation Kit II (TaKaRa)

METHOD

1. Maintain the tube of the eluate pool of first-strand product (Stage X, Step 15) on ice, and add 50 μl of 1 M Tris-HCl (pH 7.0) and 1 μl of RNase I (10 μl/μl RNase ONE, Promega). Mix quickly and incubate for 10 minutes at 37ºC.

2. Stop the RNase I reaction with proteinase K treatment, followed by phenol:chloroform extraction and one back extraction.

3. Add 3 μg of glycogen and filter the sample using a Microcon YM-100 microconcentrator.

4. Remove traces of first-strand primer by fractionating the cDNA on an S400 spun column (Amersham Biosciences) or equivalent, according to manufacturer's instructions. Load the cDNA onto the column, and then load 80 μl of H$_2$O.

5. Continue according to the manufacturer's instructions and concentrate the final sample using a Centricon YM-100 microconcentrator or by isopropanol precipitation.

6. Dissolve the final sample in 10 μl of 0.1x TE.

7. Precipitate each of the three oligonucleotides in 2.5 volumes of ethanol, wash in 80% ethanol, and finally dissolve each in H_2O at 2 μg/μl.

8. Check the OD_{260} of the oligonucleotide primer solutions, and mix GN5, N6, and the "down" oligonucleotides in the ratio 4:1:5, respectively.

9. Add NaCl to a final concentration of 100 mM and anneal by heating the mixture for 5 minutes at 65°C, 5 minutes at 45°C, 10 minutes at 37°C, and 10 minutes at 25°C. The annealed linker mixture can be stored at –20°C indefinitely.

Ligation of the First-strand cDNA

10. Incubate the cDNA for 5 minutes at 65°C, to denature any secondary structure in the single-stranded cDNA, and transfer the tube to ice.

11. Set up the linker:cDNA ligation reaction using the TaKaRa DNA Ligation Kit II. Use 2 μg of linker mixture for up to 1 μg of single-stranded cDNA. For larger quantities of cDNA, scale up the linker mixture.

12. Mix the annealed linker mixture and cDNA in a final volume of 5 μl.

13. Add 5 μl of Solution II from the TaKaRa DNA Ligation Kit and then add 10 μl of Solution I.

14. Incubate at the reaction overnight (at least 10 hours) at 10°C.

15. Stop the ligation reaction by adding the following:

0.5 M EDTA	1 μl
10% SDS	1 μl
10 mg/ml proteinase K	1 μl
H_2O	10 μl

    Incubate the reaction at for 15 minutes at 45°C.

16. Stop the proteinase K reaction by extracting with phenol:chloroform <!> and chloroform. Perform a back extraction with 60 μl of column buffer (10 mM Tris at pH 8.0, 1 mM EDTA, 0.1% SDS, 100 mM NaCl).

17. After the ligation, remove excess linker by purification using an S300 spun column.

    a. Set up the column according to the manufacturer's instructions and apply 2 ml of column buffer. Allow the column to drain by gravity and repeat this step.

    b. Apply 100 μl of buffer to the column and centrifuge. Check that the eluted volume is 100 μl. Apply the sample (Step 16) to the column and centrifuge at 400*g* for 2 minutes.
       If the eluted volume is not 100 μl, reequilibrate the column as per Step a.

    c. Elute the sample, collecting separate 50-μl fractions of the filtrates.

18. Count the collected fractions by scintillation (see Sambrook and Russell 2001, Appendix 8). Pool the first two or three fractions, or those containing 80% of the counts.

19. Concentrate the sample either by isopropanol precipitation (in the presence of 0.2 M NaCl) or using a Microcon YM-100 microconcentrator.

STAGE XI: SECOND-STRAND cDNA SYNTHESIS FOR SSLLM cDNA

First-strand cDNA, treated with SSLLM and/or normalized-subtracted, is used as substrate for second-strand cDNA synthesis. The second strand is made by primer extension by using mixtures of long-range thermostable polymerases (Cheng et al. 1994), which allow efficient synthesis of long second-strand cDNAs. The Elongase mix available from Invitrogen is recommended.

As was the case for the first-strand cDNA, the primer-adaptor for the second-strand cDNA should contain the annealing site and a restriction site, such as *Xho*I. An aliquot of the reaction is radiolabeled to monitor the yield and size. Note that mixing should be performed very quickly due to the high polymerization speed of the *Taq* polymerase cocktail.

METHOD

1. Synthesize the appropriate second-strand primer. For cDNAs treated as described in Stage IX, use the following primer:

   5′-AGAGAGAGAGCTCGAGCTCTATTTAGGTGACACTATAGAACCA-3′

   This primer contains a *Xho*I site and a $(GA)_7$ repeat to ensure efficient restriction digestion.

2. Prepare Tubes A and B containing the following reagents:

   Tube A:

first-strand cDNA	
100 ng/μl second-strand primer adaptor	6 μl
5x eLONGase A buffer (Invitrogen)	5.2 μl
5x eLONGase B buffer (Invitrogen)	4.8 μl
2.5 mM (each) dNTPs	`6 μl

   Adjust the volume to 45 μl with H_2O.

   Tube B:

$[\alpha\text{-}^{32}P]$dGTP	0.5 μl

3. Program the thermal cycler for second-strand synthesis as follows:

   Step 1:   5 minutes at 65°C
   Step 2:   30 minutes at 68°C
   Step 3:   10 minutes at 72°C
   Step 4:   +4°C

4. Transfer Tubes A and B into the thermal cycler, and start the second-strand program. When the block reaches 65°C, add 1.5 μl of eLONGase mixture (1 unit/μl) to Tube A.

5. Mix the contents of the tube quickly but thoroughly, and immediately transfer a 3–5-μl aliquot to Tube B.

6. Allow the program to continue, and then transfer the tubes onto ice.

7. Quantify the yield of the second-strand reaction using DE-81 adsorption (please see Sambrook and Russell 2001, Appendix 8).

   Yields vary greatly depending on the protocol used; however, yields as low as 20–30 ng of normalized cDNA at this stage may be sufficient to produce a representative cDNA library, provided the cDNA is of high quality.

8. Treat the second-strand cDNA product with proteinase K, extract with phenol:chloroform, back-extract, and precipitate with ethanol or isopropanol.

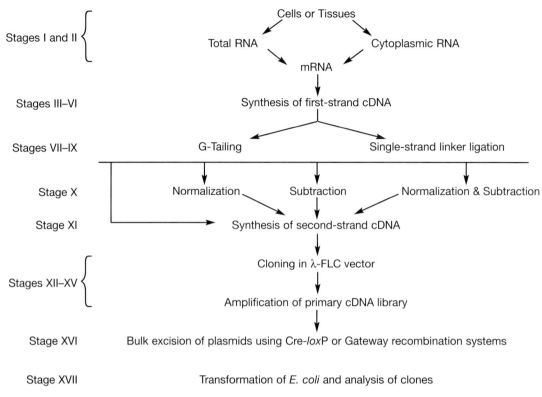

FIGURE A1-1. Flow chart of the stages in construction of a normalized full-length cDNA library.

REFERENCES

Carninci P. and Hayashizaki Y. 1999. High efficiency full-length cDNA cloning. *Methods Ezymol.* **303:** 19–44.

Carninci P., Nakamura M., Sato K., Hayashizaki K., and Brownstein M.J. 2002. Cytoplasmic RNA extraction from fresh and frozen mammalian tissues. *BioTechniques* **33:** 306–309.

Carninci P., Nishiyama Y., Westover A., Itoh M., Nagaoka S., Sasaki N., Okazaki Y., Muramatsu M., and Hayashizaki Y. 1998. Thermostabilization and thermoactivation of thermolabile enzymes by trehalose and its application for the synthesis of full length cDNA. *Proc. Natl. Acad. Sci.* **95:** 520–524.

Carninci P., Shibata Y., Hayatsu N., Sugahara Y., Shibata K., Itoh M., Konno H., Okazaki Y., Muramatsu M., and Hayashizaki Y. 2000. Normalization and subtraction of cap-trapper-selected cDNAs to prepare full-length cDNA libraries for rapid discovery of new genes. *Genome Res.* **10:** 1617–1630.

Carninci P., Shibata Y., Hayatsu N., Itoh M., Shiraki T., Hirozane T., Watahiki A., Shibata K., Konno H., Muramatsu M., and Hayashizaki Y. 2001. Balanced-size and long-size cloning of full-length, cap-trapped cDNAs into vectors of the novel λ-FLC family allows enhanced gene discovery rate and functional analysis. *Genomics* **77:** 79–90.

Cheng S., Fockler C., Barnes W.M., and Higuchi R. 1994. Effective amplification of long targets from cloned inserts and human genomic DNA. *Proc. Natl. Acad. Sci.* **91:** 5695–5699.

Deininger P.L. 1987. Full-length cDNA clones: Vector-primed cDNA synthesis. *Methods Enzymol.* **152:** 371–389.

Hames B.D. and Higgins S.J., eds. 1985. *Nucleic acid hybridization: A practical approach.* IRL Press, Oxford, United Kingdom.

Kotsopoulos S.T. and Shuber A.P. 1996. Isolation of 3.5-kb fragments on magnetic solid supports. *BioTechniques* **20:** 198–200.

Sambrook J. and Russel D.W. 2001. *Molecular cloning: A laboratory manual,* 3rd edition. Cold Spring Harbor Laboratory Press, Cold Spring Harbor, New York.

Shibata Y., Carninci P., Watahiki A., Shiraki T., Konno H., Muramatsu M., and Hayashizaki Y. 2001. Cloning full-length, cap-trapper-selected cDNAs by using the single-strand linker ligation method. *BioTechniques* **30:** 1250–1253.

Reagents, Buffers, and Media

BUFFERS AND STOCK SOLUTIONS FOR USE IN MOLECULAR BIOLOGY

CAUTION: Please see Appendix 3 for appropriate handling of materials marked with <!>.

pH Buffers

Phosphate-buffered Saline (PBS)

137 mM NaCl
2.7 mM KCl
10 mM Na_2HPO_4
2 mM KH_2PO_4

Dissolve 8 g of NaCl, 0.2 g of KCl, 1.44 g of Na_2HPO_4, and 0.24 g of KH_2PO_4 in 800 ml of distilled H_2O. Adjust the pH to 7.4 with HCl. Add H_2O to 1 liter. Dispense the solution into aliquots and sterilize them by autoclaving for 20 minutes at 15 psi (1.05 kg/cm²) on liquid cycle or by filter sterilization. Store the buffer at room temperature.

> PBS is a commonly used reagent that has been adapted for different applications. Note that the recipe presented here lacks divalent cations. If necessary, PBS may be supplemented with 1 mM $CaCl_2$ and 0.5 mM $MgCl_2$.

10x Tris EDTA (TE)

pH 7.4
100 mM Tris-Cl (pH 7.4)
10 mM EDTA (pH 8.0)

pH 7.6
100 mM Tris-Cl (pH 7.6)
10 mM EDTA (pH 8.0)

pH 8.0
100 mM Tris-Cl (pH 8.0)
10 mM EDTA (pH 8.0)

Sterilize solutions by autoclaving for 20 minutes at 15 psi (1.05 kg/cm²) on liquid cycle. Store the buffer at room temperature.

Tris-Cl (1 M)

Dissolve 121.1 g of Tris base in 800 ml of H_2O. Adjust the pH to the desired value by adding concentrated HCl <!>.

pH	HCl
7.4	70 ml
7.6	60 ml
8.0	42 ml

Allow the solution to cool to room temperature before making final adjustments to the pH. Adjust the volume of the solution to 1 liter with H_2O. Dispense into aliquots and sterilize by autoclaving.

If the 1 M solution has a yellow color, discard it and obtain Tris of better quality. The pH of Tris solutions is temperature-dependent and decreases ~0.03 pH units for each 1°C increase in temperature. For example, a 0.05 M solution has pH values of 9.5, 8.9, and 8.6 at 5°C, 25°C, and 37°C, respectively.

Tris Magnesium Buffer (TM)
 50 mM Tris-Cl (pH 7.8)
 10 mM $MgSO_4$

Tris-buffered Saline (TBS)
 Dissolve 8 g of NaCl, 0.2 g of KCl, and 3 g of Tris base in 800 ml of distilled H_2O. Add 0.015 g of phenol red and adjust the pH to 7.4 with HCl. Add distilled H_2O to 1 liter. Dispense the solution into aliquots and sterilize them by autoclaving for 20 minutes at 15 psi (1.05 kg/cm^2) on liquid cycle. Store the buffer at room temperature.

Enzyme Stocks and Buffers

Enzyme Stocks

Lysozyme (10 mg/ml)
 Dissolve solid lysozyme at a concentration of 10 mg/ml in 10 mM Tris-Cl (pH 8.0) immediately before use. Make sure that the pH of the Tris solution is 8.0 before dissolving the protein. Lysozyme will not work efficiently if the pH of the solution is less than 8.0.

Pancreatic DNase I (1 mg/ml)
 Dissolve 2 mg of crude pancreatic DNase I (Sigma or equivalent) in 1 ml of

 10 mM Tris-Cl (pH 7.5)
 150 mM NaCl
 1 mM $MgCl_2$

 When the DNase I is dissolved, add 1 ml of glycerol to the solution and mix by gently inverting the closed tube several times. Take care to avoid creating bubbles and foam. Store the solution in aliquots of –20°C.

Pancreatic RNase (1 mg/ml)
 Dissolve 2 mg of crude pancreatic RNase I (Sigma or equivalent) in 2 ml of TE (pH 7.6).

Proteinase K (20 mg/ml)
 Purchase as a lyophilized powder and dissolve at a concentration of 20 mg/ml in sterile 50 mM Tris (pH 8.0), 1.5 mM calcium acetate. Divide the stock solution into small aliquots and store at –20ºC. Each aliquot can be thawed and refrozen several times but should then be discarded. Unlike much cruder preparations of protease (e.g., pronase), proteinase K need not be self-digested before use.

Trypsin
 Prepare bovine trypsin <!> at a concentration of 250 µg/ml in 200 mM ammonium bicarbonate (pH 8.9) (Sequencer grade; Boehringer Mannheim). Store the solution in aliquots at –20°C.

Enzyme Reaction Buffers

IMPORTANT: Wherever possible, use the 10x reaction buffer supplied by the manufacturer of the enzyme used. Otherwise, use the recipes given here.

10x Amplification Buffer
500 mM KCl
100 mM Tris-Cl (pH 8.3 at room temperature)
15 mM $MgCl_2$

Autoclave the 10x buffer for 10 minutes at 15 psi (1.05 kg/cm^2) on liquid cycle. Divide the sterile buffer into aliquots and store them at –20ºC.

10x Bacteriophage T4 DNA Ligase Buffer
200 mM Tris-Cl (pH 7.6)
50 mM $MgCl_2$
50 mM dithiothreitol <!>
0.5 mg/ml bovine serum albumin (Fraction V; Sigma) (*optional*)

Divide the buffer in small aliquots and store at –20ºC. Add ATP when setting up the reaction. Add ATP to the reaction to an appropriate concentation (e.g., 1 mM).

10x Bacteriophage T4 DNA Polymerase Buffer
330 mM Tris-acetate (pH 8.0)
660 mM potassium acetate
100 mM magnesium acetate
5 mM dithiothreitol <!>
1 mg/ml bovine serum albumin (Fraction V; Sigma)

Divide the 10x stock into small aliquots and store frozen at –20ºC.

10x Bacteriophage T4 Polynucleotide Kinase Buffer
700 mM Tris-Cl (pH 7.6)
100 mM $MgCl_2$
50 mM dithiothreitol <!>

Divide the 10x stock into small aliquots and store frozen at –20ºC.

10x Dephosphorylation Buffer (for Use with CIP)
100 mM Tris-Cl (pH 8.3)
10 mM $MgCl_2$
10 mM $ZnCl_2$

10x Dephosphorylation Buffer (for Use with SAP)
200 mM Tris-Cl (pH 8.8)
100 mM $MgCl_2$
10 mM $ZnCl_2$

10x Exonuclease III Buffer

660 mM Tris-Cl (pH 8.0)
66 mM $MgCl_2$
100 mM β-mercaptoethanol <!>

Add β-mercaptoethanol just before use.

10x Klenow Buffer

0.4 M potassium phosphate (pH 7.5)
66 mM $MgCl_2$
10 mM β-mercaptoethanol <!>

10x Linker Kinase Buffer

600 mM Tris-Cl (pH 7.6)
100 mM $MgCl_2$
100 mM dithiothreitol <!>
2 mg/ml bovine serum albumin

Prepare the buffer fresh just before use.

10x Proteinase K Buffer

100 mM Tris-Cl (pH 8.0)
50 mM EDTA (pH 8.0)
500 mM NaCl

10x Reverse Transcriptase Buffer

500 mM Tris-Cl (pH 8.3)
750 mM KCl
30 mM $MgCl_2$

RNase H Buffer

20 mM Tris-Cl (pH 7.6)
20 mM KCl
0.1 mM EDTA (pH 8.0)
0.1 mM dithiothreitol <!>

Prepare the buffer fresh just before use.

5x Terminal Transferase Buffer

Most manufacturers supply a 5x reaction buffer, which typically contains:

500 mM potassium cacodylate (pH 7.2) <!>
10 mM $CoCl_2·6H_2O$
1 mM dithiothreitol <!>

5x terminal transferase (or tailing) buffer may be prepared according to the following method (Eschenfeldt et al. 1987):

1. Equilibrate 5 g of Chelex 100 (Bio-Rad) with 10 ml of 3 M potassium acetate at room temperature.
2. After 5 minutes, remove excess liquid by vacuum suction. Wash the Chelex three times with 10 ml of deionized H_2O.
3. Prepare a 1 M solution of potassium cacodylate. Equilibrate the cacodylate solution with the treated Chelex resin.
4. Recover the cacodylate solution by passing it through a Buchner funnel fitted with Whatman No. 1 filter paper.
5. To the recovered cacodylate add in order: H_2O, dithiothreitol, and cobalt chloride to make the final concentrations of 500 mM potassium cacodylate, 1 mM dithiothreitol, and 20 mM $CoCl_2$.

Store the buffer in aliquots at –20ºC.

10x Universal KGB (Restriction Endonuclease) Buffer
1 M potassium acetate
250 mM Tris-acetate (pH 7.6)
100 mM magnesium acetate tetrahydrate
5 mM β-mercaptoethanol <!>
0.1 mg/ml bovine serum albumin

Store the 10x buffer in aliquots at –20ºC.

Hybridization Buffers

HCl (2.5 N)
Add 25 ml of concentrated HCl <!> (11.6 N) to 91 ml of sterile H_2O. Store the diluted solution at room temperature.

Hybridization Buffer with Formamide (for RNA)
40 mM PIPES (pH 6.8)
1 mM EDTA (pH 8.0)
0.4 M NaCl
80% (v/v) deionized formamide <!>

Use disodium salt of PIPES to prepare the buffer, and adjust the pH to 6.4 with 1 N HCl.

Hybridization Buffer without Formamide (for RNA)
40 mM PIPES (pH 6.4)
0.1 mM EDTA (pH 8.0)
0.4 M NaCl

Use disodium salt of PIPES to prepare the buffer, and adjust the pH to 6.4 with 1 N HCl.

Prehybridization and Hybridization Solutions

Prehybridization/Hybridization Solution (for Hybridization in Aqueous Buffer)

6x SSC (or 6x SSPE)
5x Denhardt's reagent
0.5% (w/v) SDS <!>
1 µg/ml poly(A)
100 µg/ml salmon sperm DNA

Prehybridization/Hybridization Solution (for Hybridization in Formamide Buffers)

6x SSC (or 6x SSPE)
5x Denhardt's reagent
0.5% (w/v) SDS <!>
1 µg/ml poly(A)
100 µg/ml salmon sperm DNA
50% (v/v) formamide <!>

After a thorough mixing, filter the solution through a 0.45-µm disposable cellulose acetate membrane (Schleicher & Schuell Uniflow syringe membrane or equivalent). To decrease background when hybridizing under conditions of reduced stringency (e.g., 20–30% formamide), it is important to use formamide that is as pure as possible.

Prehybridization/Hybridization Solution (for Hybridization in Phosphate-SDS Buffer)

0.5 M phosphate buffer (pH 7.2)*
1 mM EDTA (pH 8.0)
7% (w/v) SDS <!>
1% (w/v) bovine serum albumin

Use an electrophoresis grade of bovine serum albumin. No blocking agents or hybridization rate enhancers are required with this particular prehybridization/ hybridization solution.
*0.5 M phosphate buffer is 134 g of $Na_2HPO_4 \cdot 7H_2O$, 4 ml of 85% H_3PO_4 <!> (concentrated phosphoric acid), H_2O to 1 liter.

20x SSC

Dissolve 175.3 g of NaCl and 88.2 g of sodium citrate in 800 ml of H_2O. Adjust the pH to 7.0 with a few drops of a 14 N solution of HCl <!>. Adjust the volume to 1 liter with H_2O. Dispense into aliquots. Sterilize by autoclaving. The final concentrations of the ingredients are 3.0 M NaCl and 0.3 M sodium citrate.

20x SSPE

Dissolve 175.3 g of NaCl, 27.6 g of $NaH_2PO_4 \cdot H_2O$, and 7.4 g of EDTA in 800 ml of H_2O. Adjust the pH to 7.4 with NaOH <!> (~6.5 ml of a 10 N solution). Adjust the volume to 1 liter with H_2O. Dispense into aliquots. Sterilize by autoclaving. The final concentrations of the ingredients are 3.0 M NaCl, 0.2 M NaH_2PO_4, and 0.02 M EDTA.

Gel-loading Buffers

TABLE A2-1. 6x Gel-loading Buffers

Buffer type	6x Buffer	Storage temperature
I	0.25% (w/v) bromophenol blue <!> 0.25% (w/v) xylene cyanol FF <!> 40% (w/v) sucrose in H_2O	4°C
II	0.25% (w/v) bromophenol blue 0.25% (w/v) xylene cyanol FF 15% (w/v) Ficoll (Type 400; Pharmacia) in H_2O	room temperature
III	0.25% (w/v) bromophenol blue 0.25% (w/v) xylene cyanol FF 30% (v/v) glycerol in H_2O	4°C
IV	0.25% (w/v) bromophenol blue 40% (w/v) sucrose in H_2O	4°C

Special Buffers and Solutions

STE

10 mM Tris-Cl (pH 8.0)
0.1 M NaCl
1 mM EDTA (pH 8.0)

Sterilize by autoclaving for 15 minutes at 15 psi (1.05 kg/cm^2) on liquid cycle. Store the sterile solution at 4°C.

STET

10 mM Tris-Cl (pH 8.0)
0.1 M NaCl
1 mM EDTA (pH 8.0)
5% (v/v) Triton X-100

Make sure that the pH of STET is 8.0 after all ingredients are added. There is no need to sterilize STET before use.

10x TEN Buffer

0.1 M Tris-Cl (pH 8.0)
0.01 M EDTA (pH 8.0)
1 M NaCl

TES

10 mM Tris-Cl (pH 7.5)
1 mM EDTA (pH 7.5)
0.1% (w/v) SDS <!>

Triton/SDS Solution

10 mM Tris-Cl (pH 8.0)
2% (v/v) Triton X-100
1% (w/v) SDS <!>
100 mM NaCl
1 mM EDTA (pH 8.0)

Sterilize the solution by passing it through a 0.22-μm filter, and store it at room temperature.

Tris-Sucrose

50 mM Tris-Cl (pH 8.0)
10% (w/v) sucrose

Sterilize the solution by passing it through a 0.22-μm filter, and store it at room temperature. Solutions containing sucrose should not be autoclaved since the sugar tends to carbonize at high temperatures.

Wash Buffer (QIAGEN)

50 mM MOPS-KOH <!> (pH 7.5–7.6)
0.75 M NaCl
15% (v/v) ethanol

When making this buffer, adjust the pH of a MOPS/NaCl solution before adding the ethanol.

PREPARATION OF ORGANIC REAGENTS

CAUTION: Please see Appendix 3 for appropriate handling of materials marked with <!>.

Phenol

Most batches of commercial liquefied phenol <!> are clear and colorless and can be used in molecular cloning without redistillation. Occasionally, batches of liquefied phenol are pink or yellow, and these should be rejected and returned to the manufacturer. Crystalline phenol is not recommended because it must be redistilled at 160ºC to remove oxidation products, such as quinones, that cause the breakdown of phosphodiester bonds or cause cross-linking of RNA and DNA.

Equilibration of Phenol

Before use, phenol must be equilibrated to a pH of >7.8 because the DNA partitions into the organic phase at acid pH. Wear gloves, full face protection, and a lab coat when carrying out this procedure.

1. Store liquefied phenol at –20ºC. As needed, remove the phenol from the freezer, allow it to warm to room temperature, and then melt it at 68ºC. Add hydroxyquinoline to a final concentration of 0.1%. This compound is an antioxidant, a partial inhibitor of

RNase, and a weak chelator of metal ions (Kirby 1956). In addition, its yellow color provides a convenient way to identify the organic phase.

2. To the melted phenol, add an equal volume of buffer (usually 0.5 M Tris-Cl [pH 8.0] at room temperature). Stir the mixture on a magnetic stirrer for 15 minutes. Turn off the stirrer, and when the two phases have separated, aspirate as much as possible of the upper (aqueous) phase using a glass pipette attached to a vacuum line equipped with appropriate traps.

3. Add an equal volume of 0. 1 M Tris-Cl (pH 8.0) to the phenol. Stir the mixture on a magnetic stirrer for 15 minutes. Turn off the stirrer and remove the upper aqueous phase as described in Step 2. Repeat the extractions until the pH of the phenolic phase is >7.8 (as measured with pH paper).

4. After the phenol is equilibrated and the final aqueous phase has been removed, add 0.1 volume of 0.1 M Tris-Cl (pH 8.0) containing 0.2% β-mercaptoethanol <!>. The phenol solution may be stored in this form under 100 mM Tris-Cl (pH 8.0) in a light-tight bottle at 4°C for periods of up to 1 month.

Phenol:Chloroform:Isoamyl Alcohol (25:24:1)

A mixture consisting of equal parts of equilibrated phenol and chloroform:isoamyl alcohol <!> (24:1) is frequently used to remove proteins from preparations of nucleic acids. The chloroform denatures proteins and facilitates the separation of the aqueous and organic phases, and the isoamyl alcohol reduces foaming during extraction. Neither chloroform nor isoamyl alcohol requires treatment before use. The phenol:chloroform:isoamyl alcohol mixture may be stored under 100 mM Tris-Cl (pH 8.0) in a light-tight bottle at 4°C for periods of up to 1 month.

Deionization of Formamide

Many batches of reagent-grade formamide <!> are sufficiently pure to be used without further treatment. However, if any yellow color is present, deionize the formamide by stirring on a magnetic stirrer with Dowex XG8 mixed bed resin for 1 hour and filtering it twice through Whatman No. 1 paper. Store deionized formamide in small aliquots under nitrogen at −70°C.

CHEMICAL STOCK SOLUTIONS

CAUTION: Please see Appendix 3 for appropriate handling of materials marked with <!>.

Acrylamide Solution (45% w/v)

acrylamide (DNA-sequencing grade) <!>	434 g
N,N'-methylenebisacrylamide <!>	16 g
H_2O	to 600 ml

Heat the solution to 37°C to dissolve the chemicals. Adjust the volume to 1 liter with distilled H_2O. Filter the solution through a nitrocellulose filter (e.g., Nalge, 0.45-μm pore size), and store the filtered solution in dark bottles at room temperature.

Ammonium Acetate (10 M)

To prepare a 1-liter solution, dissolve 770 g of ammonium acetate in 800 ml of H_2O. Adjust volume to 1 liter with H_2O. Sterilize by filtration. Alternatively, to prepare a 100-ml solution, dissolve 77 g of ammonium acetate in 70 ml of H_2O at room temperature. Adjust the volume to 100 ml with H_2O. Sterilize the solution by passing it through a 0.22-μm filter. Store the solution in tightly sealed bottles at 4°C or at room temperature. Ammonium acetate decomposes in hot H_2O and solutions containing it should not be autoclaved.

Ammonium Persulfate (10% w/v)

| ammonium persulfate <!> | 1 g |
| H_2O | to 10 ml |

Dissolve 1 g of ammonium persulfate in 10 ml of H_2O and store at 4°C. Ammonium persulfate decays slowly in solution, so replace the stock solution every 2–3 weeks. Ammonium persulfate is used as a catalyst for the copolymerization of acrylamide and bisacrylamide gels. The polymerization reaction is driven by free radicals generated by an oxido-reduction reaction in which a diamine (e.g., TEMED) is used as the adjunct catalyst (Chrambach and Rodbard 1972).

ATP (10 mM)

Dissolve an appropriate amount of solid ATP in 25 mM Tris-Cl (pH 8.0). Store the ATP solution in small aliquots at –20°C.

Calcium Chloride (2.5 M)

Dissolve 11 g of $CaCl_2 \cdot 6H_2O$ in a final volume of 20 ml of distilled H_2O. Sterilize the solution by passing it through a 0.22-μm filter. Store in 1-ml aliquots at 4°C.

dNTP solution containing all four dNTPs, each a concentration of 10 mM

Stock solutions are stored at –20°C in small aliquots and may be diluted to generate, for example, samples that contain all four dNTPs at a concentration of 2.5 mM. Use a microbalance to weigh out the required amounts of each deoxynucleotide triphosphate into sterile microfuge tubes. Either use a disposable spatula or clean the spatula well with ethanol between each weighing when making up solutions of different dNTPs. The table below shows the amount of solid, anhydrous dNTP required to make 1 ml of a 10 mM stock solution.

Deoxynucleotide	FW	Amount (in mg) required to make 1 ml of a 10 mM solution
dATP	491.2	4.91
dCTP	467.3	4.67
dTTP	482.2	4.82
dGTP	507.2	5.07

Dissolve the deoxynucleotide triphosphates in a small volume of H_2O and then, using pH paper and an automatic pipetting device, adjust the pH to ~8.0 by adding small amounts of 2 N NaOH until the pH reaches 8.0

Alternatively, the stock solutions may be generated from monosodium salts of the deoxynucleotide triphosphates by dissolving an appropriate amount of the solid in 1.0 ml of TE (pH 8.0). Mix the contents of the tube well and store the stock solution in small aliquots at –20°C.

pH-adjusted solutions of dNTPs are available from many commercial manufacturers.

Dimethylsulfoxide (DMSO)

Purchase a high grade of DMSO <!> (HPLC grade or better). Divide the contents of a fresh bottle into 1-ml aliquots in sterile tubes. Close the tubes tightly and store at –20°C. Use each aliquot only once and then discard.

Dithiothreitol (DTT, 1 M)

Dissolve 3.09 g of dithiothreitol <!> in 20 ml of 0.01 M sodium acetate (pH 5.2) and sterilize by filtration. Dispense into 1-ml aliquots and store at –20°C. Under these conditions, dithiothreitol is stable to oxidation by air.

EDTA (0.5 M, pH 8.0)

Add 186.1 g of disodium EDTA·2H$_2$O to 800 ml of H$_2$O. Stir vigorously on a magnetic stirrer. Adjust the pH to 8.0 with NaOH (~20 g of NaOH pellets <!>). Dispense into aliquots and sterilize by autoclaving. The disodium salt of EDTA will not go into solution until the pH of the solution is adjusted to ~8.0 by the addition of NaOH.

EGTA (0.5 M, pH 8.0)

EGTA is ethylene glycol bis(β-aminoethyl ether) N,N,N',N'-tetraacteic acid. A solution of EGTA is made up essentially as described for EDTA above and sterilized by either autoclaving or filtering. Store the sterile solution at room temperature.

Ethidium Bromide (10 mg/ml)

Add 1 g of ethidium bromide <!> to 100 ml of H$_2$O. Stir on a magnetic stirrer for several hours to ensure that the dye has dissolved. Wrap the container in aluminum foil or transfer the solution to a dark bottle and store at room temperature.

Gelatin (2% w/v)

Add 2 g of gelatin to a total volume of 100 ml of H$_2$O and autoclave the solution for 15 minutes at 15 psi (1.05 kg/cm^2) on liquid cycle.

Glycerol (10% v/v)

Dilute 1 volume of molecular-biology-grade glycerol in 9 volumes of sterile pure H$_2$O. Sterilize the solution by passing it through a prerinsed 0.22-μm filter. Store in 200-ml aliquots at 4°C.

KCl (4 M)

Dissolve an appropriate amount of solid KCl in H$_2$O, autoclave for 20 minutes on liquid cycle, and store at room temperature. Ideally, this solution should be divided into small (~100 μl) aliquots in sterile tubes and each aliquot thereafter used one time.

Linear Polyacrylamide

Linear polyacrylamide is an efficient neutral carrier for precipitating picogram amounts of nucleic acids with ethanol (Gaillard and Strauss 1990). To prepare linear polyacrylamide, prepare a 5% solution of acrylamide (without bis-acrylamide) in 40 mM Tris-Cl (pH 8.3), 20 mM sodium acetate, 1 mM EDTA (pH 8.0). Add 1/100 volumes of fresh 10% ammonium persulfate and 1/1000 volumes of TEMED. When the solution becomes viscous, precipitate the polymer with 2.5 volumes of ethanol. Dissolve the pellet in 20 volumes of H_2O by shaking overnight. The 0.25% solution of linear polyacrylamide is stable for several years at 4°C.

Lithium Chloride (LiCl, 5 M)

Dissolve 21.2 g of LiCl in a final volume of 90 ml of H_2O. Adjust the volume of the solution to 100 ml with H_2O. Sterilize the solution by passing it through a 0.22-μm filter, or by autoclaving for 15 minutes at 15 psi (1.05 kg/cm^2) on liquid cycle. Store the solution at 4°C.

$MgCl_2 \cdot 6H_2O$ (1 M)

Dissolve 203.3 g of $MgCl_2 \cdot 6H_2O$ in 800 ml of H_2O. Adjust the volume to 1 liter with H_2O. Dispense into aliquots and sterilize by autoclaving. $MgCl_2$ is extremely hygroscopic. Buy small bottles (e.g., 100 g) and do not store opened bottles for long periods of time.

$MgSO_4$ (1 M)

Dissolve 12 g of $MgSO_4$ in a final volume of 100 ml of H_2O. Sterilize by autoclaving or filter sterilization. Store at room temperature.

NaOH (10 N)

The preparation of 10 N NaOH <!> involves a highly exothermic reaction, which can cause breakage of glass containers. Prepare this solution with extreme care in plastic beakers. To 800 ml of H_2O, slowly add 400 g of NaOH pellets <!>, stirring continuously. As an added precaution, place the beaker on ice. When the pellets have dissolved completely, adjust the volume to 1 liter with H_2O. Store the solution in a plastic container at room temperature. Sterilization is not necessary.

NaCl (Sodium Chloride, 5 M)

Dissolve 292 g of NaCl in 800 ml of H_2O. Adjust the volume to 1 liter with H_2O. Dispense into aliquots and sterilize by autoclaving. Store the NaCl solution at room temperature.

NTP solution containing all four ribonucleotide triphosphates, each a concentration of 2.5 mM

Stock solutions may be generated from trisodium salts of the ribonucleotide triphosphates by dissolving an appropriate amount of the solid in 1.0 ml of 20 mM Tris-Cl (pH 7.6). Mix the contents of the tube well and store the stock solution in small aliquots at –20°C.

Ribonucleotide	FW	Amount (in mg) required to make 1 ml of a 2.5 mM solution
ATP-3Na	573.1	1.43
CTP-3Na	549.1	1.37
TTP-3Na	589.2	1.47
GTP-3Na	550.1	1.37

pH-adjusted solutions of NTPs are available from commercial manufacturers.

PEG 8000

Working concentrations of PEG <!> range from 13% to 40% (w/v). Prepare the appropriate concentration by dissolving PEG 8000 in sterile H_2O, warming if necessary. Sterilize the solution by passing it through a 0.22-μm filter. Store the solution at room temperature.

Polyethylene glycol (PEG) is a straight-chain polymer of a simple repeating unit $H(OCH_2CH_2)_nOH$. PEG is available in a range of molecular weights whose names reflect the number (n) of repeating units in each molecule. In PEG 400, for example, $n = 8-9$, whereas in PEG 4000, n ranges from 68 to 84. PEG induces macromolecular crowding of solutes in aqueous solution (Zimmerman and Minton 1993) and has a range of uses in molecular cloning, including:

- *Precipitation of DNA molecules according to their size.* The concentration of PEG required for precipitation is in inverse proportion to the size of the DNA frgaments (Lis and Schleif 1975a,b; Ogata and Gilbert 1977; Lis 1980).

- *Precipitation and purification of bacteriophage particles* (Yamamoto et al. 1970).

- *Increasing the efficiency of reassociation of complementary chains* of nucleic acids during hybridization, blunt-end ligation of DNA molecules, and end-labeling of DNA with bacteriophage T4 polynucleotide kinase (Zimmerman and Minton 1993).

- *Fusion of cultured cells with bacterial protoplasts* (Schaffner 1980; Rassoulzadegan et al. 1982).

Potassium Acetate (5 M)

5 M potassium acetate	60 ml
glacial acetic acid <!>	11.5 ml
H_2O	28.5 ml

The resulting solution is 3 M with respect to potassium and 5 M with respect to acetate. Store the buffer at room temperature.

SDS (20% w/v)

Also called sodium lauryl sulfate. Dissolve 200 g of electrophoresis-grade SDS <!> in 900 ml of H_2O. Heat to 68°C and stir with a magnetic stirrer to assist dissolution. If necessary, adjust the pH to 7.2 by adding a few drops of concentrated HCl <!>. Adjust the volume to 1 liter with H_2O. Store at room temperature. Sterilization is not necessary. Do not autoclave.

Sodium Acetate (3 M, pH 5.2 and pH 7.0)

Dissolve 408.3 g of sodium acetate·$3H_2O$ in 800 ml of H_2O. Adjust the pH to 5.2 with glacial acetic acid <!> or adjust the pH to 7.0 with dilute acetic acid. Adjust the volume to 1 liter with H_2O. Dispense into aliquots and sterilize by autoclaving.

Spermidine (1 M)

Dissolve 1.45 g of spermidine (free-base form) in 10 ml of deionized H_2O and sterilize by passing it through a 0.22-μm filter. Store the solution in small aliquots at –20ºC. Make a fresh stock solution of this reagent every month.

Trichloroacetic Acid (TCA; 100% solution)

To a previously unopened bottle containing 500 g of TCA <!>, add 227 ml of H_2O. The resulting solution will contain 100% (w/v) TCA.

LIQUID MEDIA FOR *E. COLI*

IMPORTANT: Use distilled deionized H_2O in all recipes. Unless otherwise stated, sterile media can be stored at room temperature.

GYT Medium (Tung and Chow 1995)

10% (v/v) glycerol
0.125% (w/v) yeast extract
0.25% (w/v) tryptone

Sterilize the medium by passing it through a prerinsed 0.22-μm filter. Store in 2.5-ml aliquots at 4ºC.

LB Medium (Luria-Bertani Medium)

Per liter:
To 950 ml of deionized H_2O, add:

tryptone	10 g
yeast extract	5 g
NaCl	10 g

Shake until the solutes have dissolved. Adjust the pH to 7.0 with 5 N NaOH (~0.2 ml). Adjust the volume of the solution to 1 liter with deionized H_2O. Sterilize by autoclaving for 20 minutes at 15 psi (1.05 kg/cm^2) on liquid cycle.

M9 Minimal Medium

Per liter:
To 750 ml of sterile H_2O (cooled to 50ºC or less), add:

5x M9 salts*	200 ml
1 M $MgSO_4$	2 ml
20% solution of the appropriate carbon source (e.g., 20% glucose)	20 ml
1 M $CaCl_2$	0.1 ml
sterile deionized H_2O	to 980 ml

If necessary, supplement the M9 medium with stock solutions of the appropriate amino acids and vitamins.

*5x M9 salts is made by dissolving the following salts in deionized H_2O to a final volume of 1 liter:

$Na_2HPO_4 \cdot 7H_2O$	64 g
KH_2PO_4	15 g
NaCl	2.5 g
NH_4Cl	5.0 g

Divide the salt solution into 200-ml aliquots and sterilize by autoclaving for 15 minutes at 15 psi (1.05 kg/cm^2) on liquid cycle.

Prepare the $MgSO_4$ and $CaCl_2$ solutions separately, sterilize by autoclaving, and add the solutions after diluting the 5x M9 salts to 980 ml with sterile H_2O. Sterilize the glucose by passing it through a 0.22-μm filter before it is added to the diluted M9 salts.

When using *E. coli* strains that carry a deletion of the proline biosynthetic operon [Δ(*lac-proAB*)] in the bacterial chromosome and the complementing *proAB* genes on the F′ plasmid, supplement the M9 minimal medium with the following:

0.4% (w/v) glucose (dextrose)

5 mM $MgSO_4 \cdot 7H_2O$

0.01% thiamine

NZCYM Medium

Per liter:

To 950 ml of deionized H_2O, add:

NZ amine	10 g
NaCl	5 g
yeast extract	5 g
casamino acids	1 g
$MgSO_4 \cdot 7H_2O$	2 g

Shake until the solutes have dissolved. Adjust the pH to 7.0 with 5 N NaOH (~0.2 ml). Adjust the volume of the solution to 1 liter with deionized H_2O. Sterilize by autoclaving for 20 minutes at 15 psi (1.05 kg/cm^2) on liquid cycle.

NZ amine: Casein hydrolysate enzymatic (ICN Biochemicals). NZCYM, NZYM, and NZM are also available as dehydrated media from BD Biosciences.

SOB Medium

Per liter:

To 950 ml of deionized H_2O, add:

tryptone	20 g
yeast extract	5 g
NaCl	0.5 g

Shake until the solutes have dissolved. Add 10 ml of a 250 mM solution of KCl. (This solution is made by dissolving 1.86 g of KCl in 100 ml of deionized H_2O.) Adjust the pH of the medium to 7.0 with 5 N NaOH <!> (~0.2 ml). Adjust the volume of the solution to 1 liter with deionized H_2O. Sterilize by autoclaving for 20 minutes at 15 psi (1.05 kg/cm^2) on liquid cycle. Just before use, add 5 ml of a sterile solution of 2 M $MgCl_2$. (This solution is made by dissolving 19 g of $MgCl_2$ in 90 ml of deionized H_2O. Adjust the volume of the solution to 100 ml with deionized H_2O and sterilize by autoclaving for 20 minutes at 15 psi [1.05 kg/cm^2] on liquid cycle.)

Terrific Broth (also known as TB; Tartof and Hobbs 1987)

Per liter:

To 900 ml of deionized H_2O, add:

tryptone	12 g
yeast extract	24 g
glycerol	4 ml

Shake until the solutes have dissolved and then sterilize by autoclaving for 20 minutes at 15 psi (1.05 kg/cm^2) on liquid cycle. Allow the solution to cool to 60°C or less, and then add 100 ml of a sterile solution of 0.17 M KH_2PO_4, 0.72 M K_2HPO_4. (This solution is made by dissolving 2.31 g of KH_2PO_4 and 12.54 g of K_2HPO_4 in 90 ml of deionized H_2O. After the salts have dissolved, adjust the volume of the solution to 100 ml with deionized H_2O and sterilize by autoclaving for 20 minutes at 15 psi [1.05 kg/cm^2] on liquid cycle.)

2× YT Medium

Per liter:

To 900 ml of deionized H_2O, add:

tryptone	16 g
yeast extract	10 g
NaCl	5 g

Shake until the solutes have dissolved. Adjust the pH to 7.0 with 5 N NaOH <!>. Adjust the volume of the solution to 1 liter with deionized H_2O. Sterilize by autoclaving for 20 minutes at 15 psi (1.05 kg/cm^2) on liquid cycle.

MEDIA CONTAINING AGAR OR AGAROSE

IMPORTANT: Use distilled deionized H_2O in all recipes.

Prepare liquid media according to the recipes given above. Just before autoclaving, add one of the following:

Bacto Agar (for plates)	15 g/liter
Bacto Agar (for top agar)	7 g/liter
agarose (for plates)	15 g/liter
agarose (for top agarose)	7 g/liter

Sterilize by autoclaving for 20 minutes at 15 psi (1.05 kg/cm^2) on liquid cycle. When the medium is removed from the autoclave, swirl it gently to distribute the melted agar or agarose evenly throughout the solution. *Be careful!* The fluid may be superheated and may boil over when swirled. Allow the medium to cool to 50–60°C before adding thermolabile substances (e.g., antibiotics). To avoid producing air bubbles, mix the medium by swirling. Plates can then be poured directly from the flask; allow ~30–35 ml of medium per 90-mm plate. To remove bubbles from medium in the plate, flame the surface of the medium with a Bunsen burner before the agar or agarose hardens. Set up a color code (e.g., two red stripes for LB-ampicillin plates; one black stripe for LB plates, etc.) and mark the edges of the plates with the appropriate colored markers.

When the medium has hardened completely, invert the plates and store them at 4ºC until needed. The plates should be removed from storage 1–2 hours before they are used. If the plates are fresh, they will "sweat" when incubated at 37ºC. When this condensation drops on the agar/agarose surface, it allows bacterial colonies or bacteriophage plaques to spread and increases the chances of cross-contamination. This problem can be avoided by wiping off the condensation from the lids of the plates and then incubating the plates for several hours at 37ºC in an inverted position before they are used. Alternatively, remove the liquid by shaking the lid with a single, quick motion. To minimize the possibility of contamination, hold the open plate in an inverted position while removing the liquid from the lid.

ANTIBIOTICS

TABLE A2-2. Commonly Used Antibiotic Solutions

| | Stock solution[a] | | Working concentration | |
	Concentration	storage	Stringent plasmids	Relaxed plasmids
Ampicillin	50 mg/ml in H_2O	–20ºC	20 µg/ml	50 µg/ml
Carbenicillin	50 mg/ml in H_2O	–20ºC	20 µg/ml	60 µg/ml
Chloramphenicol	34 mg/ml in ethanol	–20ºC	25 µg/ml	170 µg/ml
Kanamycin	10 mg/ml in H_2O	–20ºC	10 µg/ml	50 µg/ml
Streptomycin	10 mg/ml in H_2O	–20ºC	10 µg/ml	50 µg/ml
Tetracycline[b]	5 mg/ml in ethanol	–20ºC	10 µg/ml	50 µg/ml

Magnesium ions are antagonists of tetracycline. Use media without magnesium salts (e.g., LB medium) for selection of bacteria resistant to tetracycline.
[a]Sterilize stock solutions of antibiotics dissolved in H_2O by filtration through a 0.22-µm filter.
[b]Antibiotics dissolved in ethanol need not be sterilized. Store solutions in light-tight containers.

MEDIA FOR THE PROPAGATION AND SELECTION OF YEAST*

CAUTION: Please see Appendix 3 for appropriate handling of materials marked with <!>.

IMPORTANT: Use distilled deionized H_2O in all recipes. Unless otherwise stated, media and solutions are sterilized by autoclaving at 15 psi (1.05 kg/cm²) for 15–20 minutes.

Complete Minimal (CM) or Synthetic Complete (SC) and Drop-out Media

To test the growth requirements of strains, it is useful to have media in which each of the commonly encountered auxotrophies is supplemented except the one of interest (drop-out media). Dry growth supplements are stored premixed. CM (or SC) is a medium in which the drop-out mix contains all possible supplements (i.e., nothing is "dropped out").

yeast nitrogen base without amino acids*	6.7 g
glucose	20 g
Bacto Agar	20 g
drop-out mix	2 g
H_2O	to 1000 ml

*Yeast nitrogen base without amino acids (YNB) is sold either with or without ammonium sulfate. This recipe is for YNB with ammonium sulfate. If the bottle of YNB is lacking ammonium sulfate, add 5 g of ammonium sulfate and only 1.7 g of YNB.

Drop-out Mix

Combine the appropriate ingredients, minus the relevant supplements, and mix in a sealed container. Turn the container end-over-end for at least 15 minutes; add a few clean marbles to help mix the solids.

Adenine	0.5 g
Alanine	2.0 g
Arginine	2.0 g
Asparagine	2.0 g
Aspartic acid	2.0 g
Cysteine	2.0 g
Glutamine	2.0 g
Glutamic acid	2.0 g
Glycine	2.0 g
Histidine	2.0 g
Inositol	2.0 g
Isoleucine	2.0 g
Leucine	10.0 g
Lysine	2.0 g
Methionine	2.0 g
para-Aminobenzoic acid	0.2 g
Phenylalanine	2.0 g
Proline	2.0 g
Serine	2.0 g
Threonine	2.0 g
Tryptophan	2.0 g
Tyrosine	2.0 g
Uracil	2.0 g
Valine	2.0 g

TABLE A2-3. Components of Supplemented Minimal Media

Constituent	Stock concentration (g/100 ml)	Volume for 1 liter of stock of medium (ml)	Final concentration in medium (mg/liter)	Volume of stock to spread on plate (ml)
Adenine sulfate	0.2[a]	10	20	0.2
Uracil	0.2[a]	10	20	0.2
L-Tryptophan	1	2	20	0.1
L-Histidine HCl	1	2	20	0.1
L-Arginine LiCl	1	2	20	0.1
L-Methionine	1	2	20	0.1
L-Tyrosine	0.2	15	30	0.2
L-Leucine	1	10	100	0.1
L-Isoleucine	1	3	30	0.1
L-Lysine HCl	1	3	30	0.1
L-Phenylalanine	1[a]	5	50	0.1
L-Glutamic acid	1[a]	10	100	0.2
L-Aspartic acid	1[a,b]	10	100	0.2
L-Valine	3	5	150	0.1
L-Threonine	4[a,b]	5	200	0.1
L-Serine	8	5	400	0.1

[a]Store at room temperature.
[b]Add after autoclaving the medium.

Supplemented Minimal Medium (SMM)

SMM is synthetic dextrose minimal medium (SD) to which various growth supplements have been added. These solutions can be stored for extended periods. Some should be stored at room temperature, in order to prevent precipitation, whereas the other solutions may be refrigerated. Wherever applicable, HCl salts of amino acids are preferred.

Prepare the medium by adding the appropriate volumes of the stock solutions to the ingredients of SD medium and then adjusting the total volume to 1 liter with distilled H_2O. Add threonine and aspartic acid solutions separately to the medium after it is autoclaved.

Alternatively, it is often more convenient to prepare the medium by spreading a small quantity of the supplement(s) on the surface of an SD plate. Allow the solution(s) to then dry thoroughly onto the plate before inoculating it with yeast strains.

Table A2-3 provides the concentrations of the stock solutions, the volume of stock solution necessary for mixing 1 liter of medium, the volume of stock solution to spread on SD plates, and the final concentration of each constituent in SMM.

Synthetic Dextrose Minimal Medium (SD)

SD is a synthetic minimal medium containing salts, trace elements, vitamins, a nitrogen source (yeast nitrogen base without amino acids), and glucose.

yeast nitrogen base without amino acids*	6.7 g
glucose	20 g
Bacto Agar	20 g
H_2O	1000 ml

*Please see note to recipe for CM above.

YPD (YEPD) Medium

YPD is a complex medium for routine growth of yeast.

yeast extract	10 g
peptone	20 g
glucose	20 g
H_2O	to 1000 ml

To prepare plates, add 20 g of Bacto Agar (2%) before autoclaving.

REFERENCES

Chrambach A. and Rodbard D. 1972. Polymerization of polyacrylamide gels: Efficiency and reproducibility as a function of catalyst concentrations. *Sep. Sci.* **7:** 663–703.

Gaillard C. and Strauss F. 1990. Ethanol precipitation of DNA with linear acrylamide as a carrier. *Nucleic Acids Res.* **18:** 378.

Kirby K.S. 1956. A new method for the isolation of ribonucleic acids from mammalian tissues. *Biochem. J.* **64:** 405.

Lis J.T. 1980. Fractionation of DNA fragments by polyethylene glycol induced precipitation. *Methods Enzymol.* **65:** 347–353.

Lis J.T. and Schleif R. 1975a. Size fractionation of double-stranded DNA by precipitation with polyethylene glycol. *Nucleic Acids Res.* **2:** 383–389.

———. 1975b. The regulatory region of the L-arabinose operon: Its isolation on a 1000 base-pair fragment with DNA heteroduplexes. *J. Mol. Biol.* **95:** 409–416.

Ogata R. and Gilbert W. 1977. Contacts between the *lac* repressor and the thymines in the *lac* operator. *Proc. Natl. Acad. Sci.* **74:** 4973–4976.

Rassoulzadegan M., Binetruy B., and Cuzin F. 1982. High frequency of gene transfer after fusion between bacteria and eukaryotic cells. *Nature* **295:** 257–259.

Schaffner W. 1980. Direct transfer of cloned genes from bacteria to mammalian cells. *Proc. Natl. Acad. Sci.* **77:** 2163–2167.

Tartof K.D. and Hobbs C.A. 1987. Improved media for growing plasmid and cosmid clones. *Focus* (Life Technologies) **9:** 12.

Tung W.L. and Chow K.C. 1995. A modified medium for efficient electrotransformation of *E. coli. Trends Genet.* **1:** 128–129.

Yamamoto K.R., Alberts B.M., Benzinger R., Lawhorne L., and Treiber G. 1970. Rapid bacteriophage sedimentation in the presence of polyethylene glycol and its application to large-scale virus purification. *Virology* **40:** 734–744.

Zimmerman S.B. and Minton A.P. 1993. Macromolecular crowding: Biochemical, biophysical, and physiological consequences. *Annu. Rev. Biophys. Biomol. Struct.* **22:** 27–65.

3 | Cautions

GENERAL CAUTIONS

The following general cautions should always be observed.

- **Become completely familiar with the properties of substances used before** beginning the procedure.

- **The absence of a warning** does not necessarily mean that the material is safe, since information may not always be complete or available.

- **If exposed to toxic substances,** contact your local safety office immediately for instructions.

- **Use proper disposal procedures** for all chemical, biological, and radioactive waste.

- **For specific guidelines on appropriate gloves,** consult your local safety office.

- **Handle concentrated acids and bases** with great care. Wear goggles and appropriate gloves. Wear a face shield when handling large quantities.

    Do not mix strong acids with organic solvents as they may react. Sulfuric acid and nitric acid especially may react highly exothermically and cause fires and explosions.

    Do not mix strong bases with halogenated solvent as they may form reactive carbenes which can lead to explosions.

- **Never pipette** solutions using mouth suction. This method is not sterile and can be dangerous. Always use a pipette aid or bulb.

- **Keep halogenated and nonhalogenated solvents separately** (e.g., mixing chloroform and acetone can cause unexpected reactions in the presence of bases). Halogenated solvents are organic solvents such as chloroform, dichloromethane, trichlorotrifluoroethane, and dichloroethane. Some nonhalogenated solvents are pentane, heptane, ethanol, methanol, benzene, toluene, N,N-dimethylformamide (DMF), dimethylsulfoxide (DMSO), and acetonitrile.

- **Laser radiation,** visible or invisible, can cause severe damage to the eyes and skin. Take proper precautions to prevent exposure to direct and reflected beams. Always follow manufacturers safety guidelines and consult your local safety office. See caution below for more detailed information.

- **Flash lamps,** due to their light intensity, can be harmful to the eyes. They also may explode on occasion. Wear appropriate eye protection and follow the manufacturer's guidelines.

- **Photographic fixatives and developers** also contain chemicals that can be harmful. Handle them with care and follow manufacturer's directions.

- **Power supplies and electrophoresis equipment** pose serious fire hazard and electrical shock hazards if not used properly.

- **Microwave ovens and autoclaves in the lab require certain precautions.** Accidents have occurred involving their use (e.g., to melt agar or bacto-agar stored in bottles or to sterilize). If the screw top is not completely removed and there is not enough space for the steam to vent, the bottles can explode and cause severe injury when the containers are removed from the microwave or autoclave. Always completely remove bottle caps before microwaving or autoclaving. An alternative method for routine agarose gels that do not require sterile agar is to weigh out the agar and place the solution in a flask.

- **Use extreme caution when handling cutting devices** such as microtome blades scalpels, razor blades, or needles. Microtome blades are extremely sharp! Use care when sectioning. If unfamiliar with their use, have someone demonstrate proper procedures. For proper disposal, use the "sharps" disposal container in the lab. Discard used needles *unshielded*, with the syringe still attached. This prevents injuries (and possible infections; see Biological Safety) while manipulating used needles since many accidents occur while trying to replace the needle shield. Injuries may also be caused by broken Pasteur pipettes, coverslips, or slides.

GENERAL PROPERTIES OF COMMON CHEMICALS

The hazardous materials list can be summarized in the following categories:

- Inorganic acids, such as hydrochloric, sulfuric, nitric, or phosphoric, are colorless liquids with stinging vapors. Avoid spills on skin or clothing. Spills should be diluted with large amounts of water. The concentrated forms of these acids can destroy paper, textiles, and skin as well as cause serious injury to the eyes.

- Inorganic bases such as sodium hydroxide are white solids which dissolve in water and under heat development. Concentrated solutions will slowly dissolve skin and even fingernails.

- Salts of heavy metals are usually colored powdered solids which dissolve in water. Many of them are potent enzyme inhibitors and therefore toxic to humans and to the environment (e.g., fish and algae).

- Most organic solvents are flammable volatile liquids. Avoid breathing the vapors which can cause nausea or dizziness. Also avoid skin contact.

- Other organic compounds, including organosulphur compounds such as mercaptoethanol or organic amines, can have very unpleasant odors. Others are highly reactive and should be handled with appropriate care.

- If improperly handled, dyes and their solutions can stain not only the sample, but also skin and clothing. Some of them are also mutagenic (e.g., ethidium bromide), carcinogenic, and toxic.

- All names ending with "ase" (e.g., catalase, β-glucuronidase, or zymolase) refer to enzymes. There are also other enzymes with nonsystematic names like pepsin. Many of them are provided by manufacturers in preparations containing buffering substances, etc. Be aware of the individual properties of materials contained in these substances.

- Toxic compounds are often used to manipulate cells. They can be dangerous and should be handled appropriately.

- Be aware that several of the compounds listed have not been thoroughly studied with respect to their toxicological properties. Handle each chemical with the appropriate respect. Although the toxic effects of a compound can be quantified (e.g., LD_{50} values), this is not possible for carcinogens or mutagens where one single exposure can have an effect. Also realize that dangers related to a given compound may also depend on its physical state (fine powder vs. large crystals/diethylether vs. glycerol/dry ice vs. carbon dioxide under pressure in a gas bomb). Anticipate under which circumstances during an experiment exposure is most likely to occur and how best to protect yourself and your environment.

HAZARDOUS MATERIALS

[α-^{32}P]CTP, *see* **Radioactive substances**

Acetic acid (concentrated) is highly corrosive and must be handled with great care. Liquid and mist cause severe burns to all body tissues. It may be harmful by inhalation, ingestion, or skin absorption. Wear appropriate gloves and goggles and use in a chemical fume hood. Keep away from heat, sparks, and open flame.

Acetic anhydride is extremely destructive to the skin, eyes, mucous membranes, and upper respiratory tract. It may be harmful by inhalation, ingestion, or skin absorption. Wear appropriate gloves and safety glasses. and use in a chemical fume hood.

Acetonitrile (Methyl cyanide) is very volatile and extremely flammable. It is an irritant and a chemical asphyxiant that can exert its effects by inhalation, ingestion, or skin absorption. Treat cases of severe exposure as cyanide poisoning. Wear appropriate gloves and safety glasses and use only in a chemical fume hood. Keep away from heat, sparks, and open flame.

Acrylamide (unpolymerized) is a potent neurotoxin and is absorbed through the skin (the effects are cumulative). Avoid breathing the dust. Wear appropriate gloves and a face mask when weighing powdered acrylamide and methylene-bisacrylamide. Use in a chemical fume hood. Polyacrylamide is considered to be nontoxic, but it should be handled with care because it might contain small quantities of unpolymerized acrylamide.

S-**Adenosyl methionine (SAM)** is toxic and may be harmful by inhalation, ingestion, or skin absorption. Wear appropriate gloves and safety glasses and use in a chemical fume hood. Do not breathe the dust.

Ammonium acetate, $H_3CCOONH_4$, may be harmful by inhalation, ingestion, or skin absorption. Wear appropriate gloves and safety glasses and use in a chemical fume hood.

Ammonium persulfate, $(NH_4)_2S_2O_8$, is extremely destructive to tissue of the mucous membranes and upper respiratory tract, eyes, and skin. Inhalation may be fatal. Wear appropriate gloves, safety glasses, and protective clothing and use only in a chemical fume hood. Wash thoroughly after handling.

Bromophenol blue may be harmful by inhalation, ingestion, or skin absorption. Wear appropriate gloves and safety glasses and use in a chemical fume hood.

Cacodylate contains arsenic, is highly toxic, and may be fatal if inhaled, ingested, or absorbed through the skin. Wear appropriate gloves and safety glasses and use in a chemical fume hood.

Chloroform, $CHCl_3$, is irritating to the skin, eyes, mucous membranes, and respiratory tract. It is a carcinogen and may damage the liver and kidneys. It is also volatile. Avoid breathing the vapors. Wear appropriate gloves and safety glasses and always use in a chemical fume hood.

Citric acid is an irritant and may be harmful by inhalation, ingestion, or skin absorption. It poses a risk of serious damage to the eyes. Wear appropriate gloves and safety goggles. Do not breathe the dust.

Cycloheximide may be fatal if inhaled, ingested, or absorbed through the skin. Wear appropriate gloves and safety glasses and use in a chemical fume hood.

DAB, *see* **3,3′-Diaminobenzidine tetrahydrochloride**

DEPC, *see* **Diethyl pyrocarbonate**

3,3′-Diaminobenzidine tetrahydrochloride (DAB) is a carcinogen. Handle with extreme care. Avoid breathing vapors. Wear appropriate gloves and safety glasses and use in a chemical fume hood.

Diethyl pyrocarbonate (DEPC) is a potent protein denaturant and is a suspected carcinogen. Aim bottle away from you when opening it; internal pressure can lead to splattering. Wear appropriate gloves, safety goggles, and lab coat and use in a chemical fume hood.

N,N-Dimethylformamide (DMF), $HCON(CH_3)_2$, is a possible carcinogen and is irrating to the eyes, skin, and mucous membranes. It can exert its toxic effects through inhalation, ingestion, or skin absorption. Chronic inhalation can cause liver and kidney damage. Wear appropriate gloves and safety glasses and use in a chemical fume hood.

Dimethyl sulfoxide (DMSO) may be harmful by inhalation or skin absorption. Wear appropriate gloves and safety glasses and use in a chemical fume hood. DMSO is also combustible. Store in a tightly closed container. Keep away from heat, sparks, and open flame.

Dithiothreitol (DTT) is a strong reducing agent that emits a foul odor. It may be harmful by inhalation, ingestion, or skin absorption. When working with the solid form or highly concentrated stocks, wear appropriate gloves and safety glasses and use in a chemical fume hood.

DMF, *see* **N,N-Dimethylformamide**

DMSO, *see* **Dimethyl sulfoxide**

DTT, *see* **Dithiothreitol**

Ethidium bromide is a powerful mutagen and is toxic. Consult the local institutional safety officer for specific handling and disposal procedures. Avoid breathing the dust. Wear appropriate gloves when working with solutions that contain this dye.

Formaldehyde, HCHO, is highly toxic and volatile. It is also a carcinogen. It is readily absorbed through the skin and is irritating or destructive to the skin, eyes, mucous membranes, and upper respiratory tract. Avoid breathing the vapors. Wear appropriate gloves and safety glasses and always use in a chemical fume hood. Keep away from heat, sparks, and open flame.

Formamide is teratogenic. The vapor is irritating to the eyes, skin, mucous membranes, and upper respiratory tract. It may be harmful by inhalation, ingestion, or skin absorption. Wear appropriate gloves and safety glasses and always use a chemical fume hood when working with concentrated solutions of formamide. Keep working solutions covered as much as possible.

HCl, *see* **Hydrochloric acid**

HCHO, *see* **Formaldehyde**

H_3COH, *see* **Methanol**

H_2O_2, *see* **Hydrogen peroxide**

$HOCH_2CH_2SH$, *see* **β-Mercaptoethanol**

Hydrochloric acid, HCl, is volatile and may be fatal if inhaled, ingested, or absorbed through the skin. It is extremely destructive to mucous membranes, upper respiratory tract, eyes, and skin. Wear appropriate gloves and safety glasses and use with great care in a chemical fume hood. Wear goggles when handling large quantities.

Hydrogen peroxide, H_2O_2, is corrosive, toxic, and extremely damaging to the skin. It may be harmful by inhalation, ingestion, and skin absorption. Wear appropriate gloves and safety glasses and use only in a chemical fume hood.

Isopropanol is flammable and irritating. It may be harmful by inhalation, ingestion, or skin absorption. Wear appropriate gloves and safety glasses. Do not breathe the vapor. Keep away from heat, sparks, and open flame.

KOH, *see* **Potassium hydroxide**

Laser radiation, both visible and invisible, can be seriously harmful to the eyes and skin and may generate airborne contaminants, depending on the class of laser used. High-power lasers cause permanent eye damage and can burn exposed skin, ignite flammable materials, and activate toxic chemicals that release hazardous by-products. Avoid eye or skin exposure to direct or scattered radiation. Do not stare at the laser and do not point the laser at anyone. Wear appropriate eye protection and use suitable shields that are designed to offer protection for the specific type of wavelength, mode of operation (continuous wave or pulsed), and power output (watts) of the laser being used. Avoid wearing jewelry or other objects that may reflect or scatter the beam. Some non-beam hazards include electrocution, fire, and asphyxiation. Entry to the area in which the laser is being used must be controlled and posted with warning signs that indicate when the laser is in use. Always follow suggested safety guidelines that accompany the equipment and contact your local safety office for further information.

- **Ion lasers** present a hazard due to high-voltage high-current power supplies. Always follow manufacturer's suggested safety guidelines.
- **Ultraviolet lasers** present a hazard due to invisible beam, high-energy-radiation. Always use beam traps, scattered light shields, and fluorescent beamfinder cards.
- **Blue-green lasers** present a hazard due to photothermal coagulation. Blue and green wavelengths are readily absorbed by blood hemoglobin.

Liquid nitrogen can cause severe damage due to extreme temperature. Handle frozen samples with extreme caution. Do not breathe the vapors. Seepage of liquid nitrogen into frozen vials can result in an exploding tube upon removal from liquid nitrogen. Use vials with O-rings when possible. Wear cryo-mitts and a face mask.

Maleic acid is toxic and harmful by inhalation, ingestion, or skin absorption. Reaction with water or moist air can release toxic, corrosive, or flammable gases. Do not breathe the vapors or dust. Wear appropriate gloves and safety glasses.

MeOH or H₃COH, *see* **Methanol**

β-Mercaptoethanol (2-Mercaptoethanol), HOCH₂CH₂SH, may be fatal if inhaled or absorbed through the skin and is harmful if ingested. High concentrations are extremely destructive to the mucous membranes, upper respiratory tract, skin, and eyes. β-Mercaptoethanol has a very foul odor. Wear appropriate gloves and safety glasses and always use in a chemical fume hood.

Methanol, MeOH or H₃COH, is poisonous and can cause blindness. It may be harmful by inhalation, ingestion, or skin absorption. Adequate ventilation is necessary to limit exposure to vapors. Avoid inhaling these vapors. Wear appropriate gloves and goggles and use only in a chemical fume hood.

***N,N′*-Methylenebisacrylamide** is a poison and may effect the central nervous system. It may be harmful by inhalation, ingestion, or skin absorption. Wear appropriate gloves and safety glasses. Do not breathe the dust.

***N*-Methyl-2-pyrrolidinone (2-methyl-2-pyrrolidinone)** may be harmful by inhalation, ingestion, or skin absorption. Wear appropriate gloves and safety glasses and use in a chemical fume hood. Do not breathe the vapors. Keep away from heat, sparks, and open flame.

3-(*N*-Morpholino)-propanesulfonic acid (MOPS) may be harmful by inhalation, ingestion, or skin absorption. It is irritating to mucous membranes and upper respiratory tract. Wear appropriate gloves and safety glasses and use in a chemical fume hood.

MOPS, *see* **3-(*N*-Morpholino)-propanesulfonic acid**

NaBH₄, *see* **Sodium borohydride**

NaOH, *see* **Sodium hydroxide**

PEG, *see* **Polyethyleneglycol**

Phenol is extremely toxic, highly corrosive, and can cause severe burns. It may be harmful by inhalation, ingestion, or skin absorption. Wear appropriate gloves, goggles, protective clothing, and always use in a chemical fume hood. Rinse any areas of skin that come in contact with phenol with a large volume of water and wash with soap and water; do not use ethanol!

Phenyl-methyl-sulfonyl fluoride (PMSF), C₇H₇FO₂S or C₆H₅CH₂SO₂F, is a highly toxic cholinesterase inhibitor. It is extremely destructive to the mucous membranes of the respiratory tract, eyes, and skin. It may be fatal by inhalation, ingestion, or skin absorption. Wear appropriate gloves and safety glasses and always use in a chemical fume hood. In case of contact, immediately flush eyes or skin with copious amounts of water and discard contaminated clothing.

PMSF, *see* **Phenyl-methyl-sulfonyl fluoride**

Polyethyleneglycol (PEG) may be harmful by inhalation, ingestion, or skin absorption. Avoid inhalation of powder. Wear appropriate gloves and safety glasses.

Potassium cacodylate, *see* **Cacodylate**

Potassium hydroxide, KOH and KOH/methanol, is highly toxic and may be fatal if swallowed. It may be harmful by inhalation, ingestion, or skin absorption. Solutions are corrosive and can cause severe burns. It should be handled with great care. Wear appropriate gloves and safety goggles.

Radioactive substances: When planning an experiment that involves the use of radioactivity, include the physicochemical properties of the isotope (half-life, emission type, and energy), the chemical form of the radioactivity, its radioactive concentration (specific activity), total amount, and its chemical concentration. Order and use only as much as really needed. Always wear appropriate gloves, lab coat, and safety goggles when handling radioactive material. **X-rays** and **gamma** rays are electromagnetic waves of very short wavelengths either generated by technical devices or emitted by radioactive materials. They may be emitted isotropically from the source or may be focused into a beam. Their potential dangers depend on the time period of exposure, the intensity experienced, and the wavelengths used. Be aware that appropriate shielding is usually of lead or other similar material. The thickness of the shielding is determined by the energy(s) of the X-rays or gamma rays. Consult the local safety office for further guidance in the appropriate use and disposal of radioactive materials. Always monitor thoroughly after using radioisotopes. A convenient calculator to perform routine radioactivity calculations can be found at:

http://www.graphpad.com/calculators/radcalc.cfm

SAM, *see* **S-Adenosyl methionine**

SDS, *see* **Sodium dodecyl sulfate**

Sodium borohydride, NaBH₄, is corrosive and causes burns. It may be harmful by inhalation, ingestion, or skin absorption. Wear appropriate gloves and safety goggles and use in a chemical fume hood.

Sodium dodecyl sulfate (SDS) is toxic, an irritant, and poses a risk of severe damage to the eyes. It may be harmful by inhalation, ingestion, or skin absorption. Wear appropriate gloves and safety goggles. Do not breathe the dust.

Sodium hydroxide, NaOH, and solutions containing NaOH are highly toxic and caustic and should be handled with great care. Wear appropriate gloves and a face mask. All other concentrated bases should be handled in a similar manner.

Succinic anhydride is a possible mutagen and is a severe eye irritant. It may be harmful by inhalation, ingestion, or skin absorption. Wear appropriate gloves and safety glasses and use only in a chemical fume hood. Do not breathe the dust.

TCA, *see* **Trichloroacetic acid**

Trichloroacetic acid (TCA) is highly caustic. Wear appropriate gloves and safety goggles.

Trypsin may cause an allergic respiratory reaction. It may be harmful by inhalation, ingestion, or skin absorption. Do not breathe the dust. Wear appropriate gloves and safety goggles. Use with adequate ventilation.

UV light and/or UV radiation is dangerous and can damage the retina. Never look at an unshielded UV light source with naked eyes. Examples of UV light sources that are common in the laboratory include hand-held lamps and transilluminators. View only through a filter or safety glasses that absorb harmful wavelengths. UV radiation is also mutagenic and carcinogenic. To minimize exposure, make sure that the UV light source is adequately shielded. Wear protective appropriate gloves when holding materials under the UV light source.

Xylene is flammable and may be narcotic at high concentrations. It may be harmful by inhalation, ingestion, or skin absorption. Wear appropriate gloves and safety glasses and use only in a chemical fume hood. Keep away from heat, sparks, and open flame.

Xylene cyanol, *see* **Xylene**

Suppliers

With the exception of those suppliers listed in the text with their addresses, all suppliers mentioned in this manual can be found in the BioSupplyNet Source Book and on the Web Site at

http://www.biosupplynet.com

If a copy of the BioSupplyNet Source Book was not included with this manual, a free copy can be ordered by any of the following methods:

- Complete the Free Source Book Request Form found at the Web Site at http://www.biosupplynet.com
- E-mail a request to info@biosupplynet.com
- Fax a request to 1-919-659-2199

Index